TEACHER'S EDITION

Introductory
ALGEBRA 2

Fourth Edition / Russell F. Jacobs

Harcourt Brace Jovanovich, Publishers

New York Chicago San Francisco Atlanta Dallas *and* London

We do not include a Teacher's Edition automatically with each shipment of a classroom set of textbooks. We prefer to send a Teacher's Edition only when it is requested by the teacher or administrator concerned or by one·of our representatives. A Teacher's Edition can easily be mislaid when it arrives as part of a shipment delivered to a school stockroom and since it contains answer materials, we want to be sure that it is sent directly to the person who will use it or to someone concerned with the use or selection of textbooks.

If your class assignment changes and you no longer are using or examining this Teacher's Edition, you may wish to pass it on to a teacher who has use for it.

A "Teacher's Resource Book" is available for "Introductory Algebra 2," Fourth Edition. For information, please call your sales representative.

CONTENTS

INTRODUCTION	M-1
THE LESSON	M-2
PROBLEM SOLVING LESSONS	M-3
OPTIONAL FEATURES	M-4
REVIEW AND TESTING	M-6
TEACHER'S RESOURCE BOOK	M-7
ADMINISTRATIVE CONCERNS	M-8
LESSON PLAN GUIDE	M-9
SUGGESTED TIMETABLE	M-46
ANNOTATED STUDENT TEXTBOOK	Following M-46

Printed in the United States of America
ISBN 0-15-357873-4

INTRODUCTION

Overview *Introductory Algebra 1* and *Introductory Algebra 2* represent a comprehensive program in first-year algebra that is designed to be studied over a two-year period. It has been developed for college-bound students who are not mathematically oriented. Even within this definition there is a wide range of student abilities and interests. With this, each textbook has been structured to accommodate three levels of ability. (See page M-9 regarding Levels 1, 2, and 3.)

The author has paid special attention to the readability level. The amount of reading has been kept to a minimum. The book utilizes short words and short sentences. An effort has been made to keep the vocabulary simple with familiar terms selected whenever possible. However, this has not been done at the expense of mathematical content.

Features Pages M-2 through M-7 describe the numerous features of the program both verbally and pictorially.

TEACHER'S RESOURCE BOOK

In addition to receiving a copy of the Teacher's Edition, upon request, each teacher will also receive a copy of the *Teacher's Resource Book*, upon request. This paperback publication consists of copying masters that are perforated and pre-holed. This title has the following components.

Tests It contains two forms of each chapter test and three cumulative tests. The *Teacher's Resource Book* that accompanies *Introductory Algebra 1* also contains a placement test.

Practice There is a 112-page *Skills Practice* section that contains additional examples and exercises for each section of the student textbook.

Warm-Ups This section contains Warm-Up exercises for each section of the textbook. Each set of Warm-Up exercises is designed to be used prior to beginning the related section. Each is a pre-lesson activity of about 10 minutes in length.

Answers The answers for the Tests and Skills Practice exercises are included in the back of the *Teacher's Resource Book*.

The Lesson

Examples
The Examples contain the procedure in clearly spelled-out steps.

At key points within each section, **pivotal exercises** (P-1, P-2, etc.) give students the opportunity to practice the skill just presented.

Classroom Exercises
Each set of exercises is referenced to steps in an **Example**, to **Example(s)**, to tables, to **Checks**, or to **pivotal exercises.**

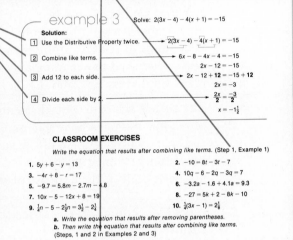

example 3   Solve: $2(3x - 4) - 4(x + 1) = -15$

Solution:
1. Use the Distributive Property twice. — $2(3x - 4) - 4(x + 1) = -15$
2. Combine like terms. — $6x - 8 - 4x - 4 = -15$
   $2x - 12 = -15$
3. Add 12 to each side. — $2x - 12 + 12 = -15 + 12$
   $2x = -3$
4. Divide each side by 2. — $\frac{2x}{2} = \frac{-3}{2}$
   $x = -1\frac{1}{2}$

3.4 Like Terms in Equations

In solving some equations, you should combine like ter

example 1   Solve and check: $5x - 7 - 3x = -1$

Solution: $5x - 7 - 3x = -19$ **Check:** $5x$
1. Combine like terms. $5x - 7 - 3x = -19$ $5(-6) - 7$
   $2x - 7 = -19$ -30
2. Add 7 to each side. $2x - 7 + 7 = -19 + 7$
   $2x = -12$
3. Divide each side by 2. — $\frac{2x}{2} = \frac{-12}{2}$
   $x = -6$

P-1 Solve.
a. $7m - 3 + 4m = 30$ b. $9k + 6 - 3k = -36$

In solving some equations, you have to use the Distribu first to remove parentheses. The check in the following left for you to do.

example 2   Solve and check: $26 = 5 - 3(2t + $

Solution: 1. Use the Distributive Property. — $26 = 5 - 3(2$
2. Simplify. — $26 = 5 - 6t$
   $26 = -4 - 6$
3. Add 4 to each side. — $26 + 4 = -4 - 6$
   $30 = -6t$
4. Divide each side by -6. — $\frac{30}{-6} = \frac{-6t}{-6}$
   $-5 = t$

P-2 Solve.
a. $24 = 8 - 4(3y - 1)$ b. $17 = 12 + 5(r - 4)$

62 / Chapter 3

CLASSROOM EXERCISES

Write the equation that results after combining like terms. (Step 1, Example 1)

1. $5y + 6 - y = 13$
2. $-10 = 8t - 3t - 7$
3. $-4r + 8 - r = 17$
4. $10q - 6 - 2q - 3q = 7$
5. $-9.7 = 5.8m - 2.7m - 4.8$
6. $-3.2a - 1.6 + 4.1a = 9.3$
7. $10x - 5 - 12x + 8 = 19$
8. $-27 = 5k + 2 - 8k - 10$
9. $\frac{1}{2}n - 5 - 2\frac{1}{2}n = 3\frac{1}{2} - 2\frac{1}{4}$
10. $\frac{1}{4}(3x - 1) = 2\frac{1}{8}$

a. *Write the equation that results after removing parentheses.*
b. *Then write the equation that results after combining like terms.*
(Steps, 1 and 2 in Examples 2 and 3)

WRITTEN EXERCISES

Goal: To solve equations having like terms
Sample Problem: $-5(2x + 1) - 7x = 29$
Answer: $x = -2$

Solve. Check each answer. (Examples 1, 2, and 3)

1. $3x + 5 + x = 33$
2. $2y - 8 - 5y = -47$
3. $-z + 1.2 - 3z = 2.8$
4. $4.6a - 5.8a - 30 = -12$
5. $37 = 8x - 19 - 15x$
6. $-26 = 22 - c - 5c$
7. $\frac{1}{4}(b + 3) = 2\frac{1}{2}$
8. $15 = 3(\frac{5}{3}d - \frac{1}{3})$
9. $-2(x + 1) - 7 = 15$
10. $-3(4n + 1) + 8n = -35$
11. $-32 = -5(f - 2) + 2f$
12. $15 - 4(2g - 3) + 4g = 39$
13. $(4k - 3) - (7k + 8) = 6\frac{1}{2}$
14. $17\frac{1}{2} = \frac{1}{3}(y + 1) - (2y - \frac{1}{3})$
15. $92 = (m + 4) - (3m - 12)$
16. $2(3 - 2x) - 4(x + 4) = -118$
17. $-0.5(3n + 3) - 2(n + 0.6) = 0.8$
18. $-7 = 6(4 + 0.3) + 0.5(2r - 5)$

Solve each equation. (Examples 1–3)

19. $\frac{1}{2}x + 6 + 4x = 5\frac{1}{2}$
20. $7(n + 1) = 21$
21. $-12 + 2(5 - h) - 3h = -57$
22. $-3.6b + 26 - 0.8b = -84$
23. $19.2 - 23.8 = 5d - 14.8 - 7d$
24. $-2(5 - x) - 6(x + 3) = -102$
25. $0.9 - 5.7 = 10.4 - e - 3e$
26. $16 = 2r - 4(r - 6) + 6r$
27. $-85 = 5t - 9t - (14 - 2t)$
28. $4z + 6z - (20 - 8z) = 25$
29. $2\frac{1}{2}y - 3(y + \frac{1}{4}) + 6y = 13$
30. $70 = 6(2t - 1) - 3(2t + 1)$

MORE CHALLENGING EXERCISES

Solve each equation.

31. $z + 5 = 2z - 4$
32. $3y - 12 = 4y + 7$
33. $4 - 6y = 12 - 4y$

REVIEW CAPSULE FOR SECTION 3.5

For Exercises 1–6, evaluate both expressions for the given value of the variable. (Section 1.7)

1. $\left.\begin{array}{c} \frac{5x + 3}{4x - 9} \end{array}\right\}$ $x = 6$
2. $\left.\begin{array}{c} \frac{20 - 2y}{56 - 5y} \end{array}\right\}$ $y = 12$
3. $\left.\begin{array}{c} \frac{4 - 3z}{z + 22} \end{array}\right\}$ $z = -4\frac{1}{2}$
4. $\left.\begin{array}{c} \frac{21 + m}{-19 - 7m} \end{array}\right\}$ $m = -5$
5. $\left.\begin{array}{c} \frac{5r + 2(r - 1)}{3(r + 1)} \end{array}\right\}$ $r = 1\frac{1}{4}$
6. $\left.\begin{array}{c} \frac{8p - 2(2p - 1)}{6(p + 2)} \end{array}\right\}$ $p = -5$

64 / Chapter 3

Written Exercises
Each set of exercises is referenced to the related **Example(s)** or **pivotal exercises.**

The exercises in the **Review Capsules** are referenced to the appropriate help.

Problem Solving Lessons

Each problem-solving lesson is clearly indicated in the Table of Contents. The applications included in these sections cover a wide range of practical and mathematical topics.

Word Rule/Formula
Formulas are introduced first with words, then with symbols.

Tables are used to organize information. Certain exercises are set up in tabular form.

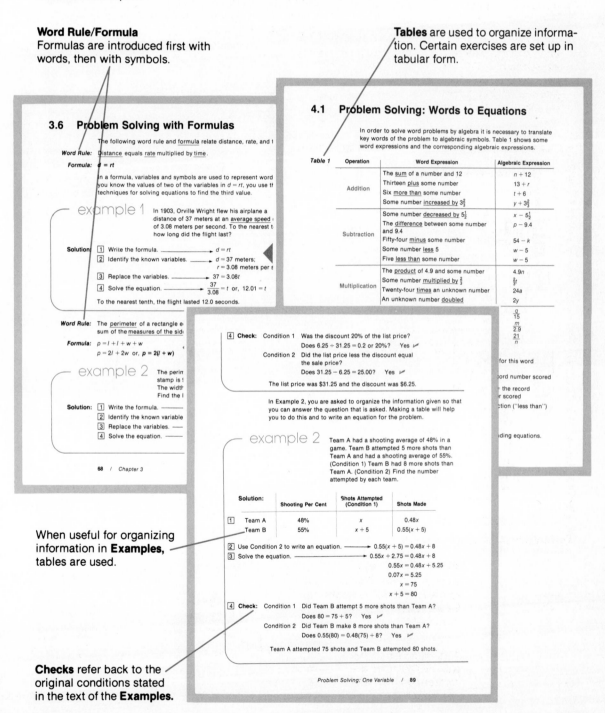

3.6 Problem Solving with Formulas

The following word rule and formula relate distance, rate, and t

Word Rule: Distance equals rate multiplied by time.

Formula: d = rt

In a formula, variables and symbols are used to represent word you know the values of two of the variables in $d = rt$, you use th techniques for solving equations to find the third value.

example 1

In 1903, Orville Wright flew his airplane a distance of 37 meters at an average speed of 3.08 meters per second. To the nearest t how long did the flight last?

Solution:
1. Write the formula. —— $d = rt$
2. Identify the known variables. —— $d = 37$ meters; $r = 3.08$ meters per s
3. Replace the variables. —— $37 = 3.08t$
4. Solve the equation. —— $\frac{37}{3.08} = t$ or, $12.01 = t$

To the nearest tenth, the flight lasted 12.0 seconds.

Word Rule: The perimeter of a rectangle e sum of the measures of the side

Formula: $p = l + l + w + w$
$p = 2l + 2w$ or, $p = 2(l + w)$

example 2

The perim
stamp is
The width
Find the l

Solution:
1. Write the formula. ——
2. Identify the known variable
3. Replace the variables. ——
4. Solve the equation. ——

68 / Chapter 3

4.1 Problem Solving: Words to Equations

In order to solve word problems by algebra it is necessary to translate key words of the problem to algebraic symbols. Table 1 shows some word expressions and the corresponding algebraic expressions.

Table 1

Operation	Word Expression	Algebraic Expression
Addition	The sum of a number and 12	$n + 12$
	Thirteen plus some number	$13 + r$
	Six more than some number	$t + 6$
	Some number increased by $3\frac{2}{3}$	$y + 3\frac{2}{3}$
Subtraction	Some number decreased by $5\frac{1}{2}$	$x - 5\frac{1}{2}$
	The difference between some number and 9.4	$p - 9.4$
	Fifty-four minus some number	$54 - k$
	Some number less 5	$w - 5$
	Five less than some number	$w - 5$
Multiplication	The product of 4.9 and some number	$4.9n$
	Some number multiplied by $\frac{2}{3}$	$\frac{2}{3}t$
	Twenty-four times an unknown number	$24a$
	An unknown number doubled	$2y$
		$\frac{q}{15}$
		$\frac{m}{2.9}$
		$\frac{21}{n}$

for this word

ord number scored

the record
scored

ction ("less than")

ding equations.

4. **Check:** Condition 1 Was the discount 20% of the list price?
Does $6.25 \div 31.25 = 0.2$ or 20%? Yes ✓
Condition 2 Did the list price less the discount equal the sale price?
Does $31.25 - 6.25 = 25.00$? Yes ✓

The list price was $31.25 and the discount was $6.25.

In Example 2, you are asked to organize the information given so that you can answer the question that is asked. Making a table will help you to do this and to write an equation for the problem.

example 2

Team A had a shooting average of 48% in a game. Team B attempted 5 more shots than Team A and had a shooting average of 55%. (Condition 1) Team B had 8 more shots than Team A. (Condition 2) Find the number attempted by each team.

When useful for organizing information in **Examples,** tables are used.

Solution:

	Shooting Per Cent	Shots Attempted (Condition 1)	Shots Made
1 Team A	48%	x	$0.48x$
Team B	55%	$x + 5$	$0.55(x + 5)$

2. Use Condition 2 to write an equation. —— $0.55(x + 5) = 0.48x + 8$
3. Solve the equation. —— $0.55x + 2.75 = 0.48x + 8$
$0.55x = 0.48x + 5.25$
$0.07x = 5.25$
$x = 75$
$x + 5 = 80$

4. **Check:** Condition 1 Did Team B attempt 5 more shots than Team A?
Does $80 = 75 + 5$? Yes ✓
Condition 2 Did Team B make 8 more shots than Team A?
Does $0.55(80) = 0.48(75) + 8$? Yes ✓

Team A attempted 75 shots and Team B attempted 80 shots.

Checks refer back to the original conditions stated in the text of the **Examples.**

Problem Solving: One Variable / **89**

Optional Features

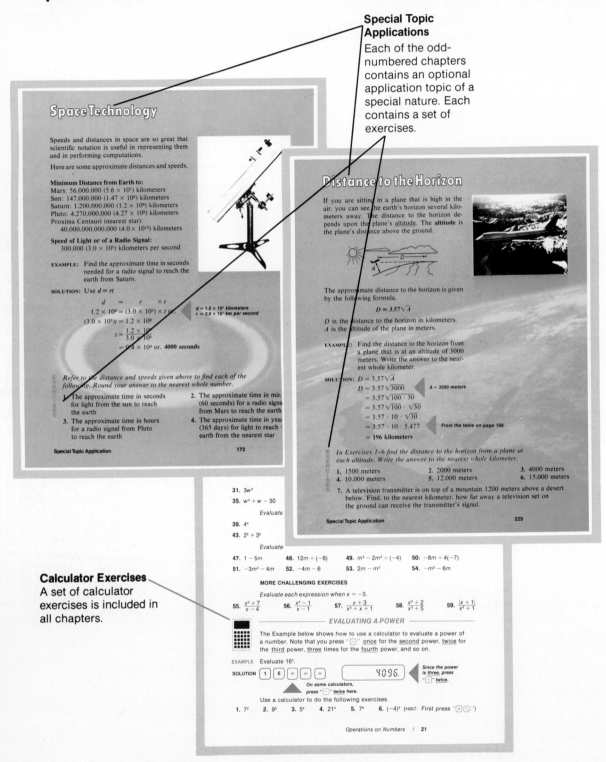

Special Topic Applications
Each of the odd-numbered chapters contains an optional application topic of a special nature. Each contains a set of exercises.

Space Technology

Speeds and distances in space are so great that scientific notation is useful in representing them and in performing computations.

Here are some approximate distances and speeds.

Minimum Distance from Earth to:
Mars: 56,000,000 (5.6×10^7) kilometers
Sun: 147,000,000 (1.47×10^8) kilometers
Saturn: 1,200,000,000 (1.2×10^9) kilometers
Pluto: 4,270,000,000 (4.27×10^9) kilometers
Proxima Centauri (nearest star):
    40,000,000,000,000 (4.0×10^{13}) kilometers

Speed of Light or of a Radio Signal:
300,000 (3.0×10^5) kilometers per second

EXAMPLE: Find the approximate time in seconds needed for a radio signal to reach the earth from Saturn.

SOLUTION: Use $d = rt$

$$d = r \times t$$
$$1.2 \times 10^9 = (3.0 \times 10^5) \times t \text{ or,}$$
$$(3.0 \times 10^5)t = 1.2 \times 10^9$$
$$t = \frac{1.2 \times 10^9}{3.0 \times 10^5}$$
$$= 0.4 \times 10^4 \text{ or, } 4000 \text{ seconds}$$

$d = 1.2 \times 10^9$ kilometers
$r = 3.0 \times 10^5$ km per second

Refer to the distance and speeds given above to find each of the following. Round your answer to the nearest whole number.

1. The approximate time in seconds for light from the sun to reach the earth
2. The approximate time in min. (60 seconds) for a radio signal from Mars to reach the earth
3. The approximate time in hours for a radio signal from Pluto to reach the earth
4. The approximate time in year (365 days) for light to reach earth from the nearest star

Special Topic Application   173

Distance to the Horizon

If you are sitting in a plane that is high in the air, you can see the earth's horizon several kilometers away. The distance to the horizon depends upon the plane's altitude. The **altitude** is the plane's distance above the ground.

The approximate distance to the horizon is given by the following formula.

$$D = 3.57\sqrt{A}$$

D is the distance to the horizon in kilometers. A is the altitude of the plane in meters.

EXAMPLE: Find the distance to the horizon from a plane that is at an altitude of 3000 meters. Write the answer to the nearest whole kilometer.

SOLUTION: $D = 3.57\sqrt{A}$
$$D = 3.57\sqrt{3000}$$
$$= 3.57\sqrt{100 \cdot 30}$$
$$= 3.57\sqrt{100} \cdot \sqrt{30}$$
$$= 3.57 \cdot 10 \cdot \sqrt{30}$$
$$= 3.57 \cdot 10 \cdot 5.477$$
$$= 196 \text{ kilometers}$$

$A = 3000$ meters

From the table on page 198

In Exercises 1–6 find the distance to the horizon from a plane at each altitude. Write the answer to the nearest whole kilometer.

1. 1500 meters   2. 2000 meters   3. 4000 meters
4. 10,000 meters   5. 12,000 meters   6. 15,000 meters

7. A television transmitter is on top of a mountain 1200 meters above a desert below. Find, to the nearest kilometer, how far away a television set on the ground can receive the transmitter's signal.

Special Topic Application   229

Calculator Exercises
A set of calculator exercises is included in all chapters.

31. $3w^2$

35. $w^2 + w - 30$

Evaluate

39. 4^4

43. $2^2 + 3^2$

Evaluate

47. $1 - 5m$ 48. $12m \div (-8)$ 49. $m^3 - 2m^2 \div (-4)$ 50. $-8m \div 4(-7)$
51. $-3m^2 - 4m$ 52. $-4m - 6$ 53. $2m - m^2$ 54. $-m^2 - 6m$

MORE CHALLENGING EXERCISES

Evaluate each expression when $x = -3$.

55. $\frac{x^2 + 7}{x - 4}$ 56. $\frac{x^2 - 1}{x - 1}$ 57. $\frac{x + 3}{x^2 + x + 1}$ 58. $\frac{x^2 + 2}{x^3 + 5}$ 59. $\frac{|x + 1|}{x^2 + 1}$

— EVALUATING A POWER —

The Example below shows how to use a calculator to evaluate a power of a number. Note that you press "$\boxed{\times}$" <u>once</u> for the <u>second</u> power, <u>twice</u> for the <u>third</u> power, three times for the <u>fourth</u> power, and so on.

EXAMPLE Evaluate 16^3.

SOLUTION $\boxed{1}\ \boxed{6}\ \boxed{\times}\ \boxed{=}\ \boxed{=}$ |4096.|

Since the power is three, press "$\boxed{=}$" twice.

On some calculators, press "$\boxed{\times}$" twice here.

Use a calculator to do the following exercises.

1. 7^2 2. 9^3 3. 5^4 4. 21^4 5. 7^6 6. $(-4)^3$ (HINT: First press "$\boxed{\times}\boxed{+/-}$")

Operations on Numbers / 21

Optional Features

Computer Programming

An **Appendix** on BASIC programming follows Chapter 18. Each lesson can be taught with the related chapter, or the **Appendix** can be taught as a chapter.

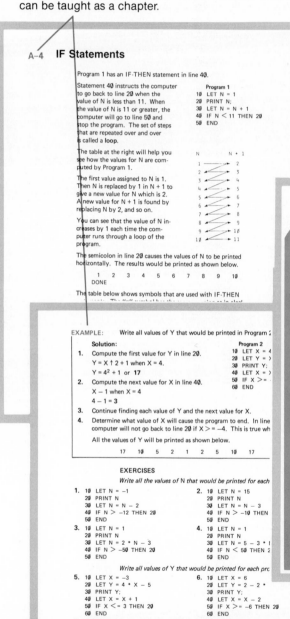

A-4 IF Statements

Program 1 has an IF-THEN statement in line 40.

Statement 40 instructs the computer to go back to line 20 when the value of N is less than 11. When the value of N is 11 or greater, the computer will go to line 50 and stop the program. The set of steps that are repeated over and over is called a loop.

```
Program 1
10  LET N = 1
20  PRINT N;
30  LET N = N + 1
40  IF N < 11 THEN 20
50  END
```

The table at the right will help you see how the values for N are computed by Program 1.

The first value assigned to N is 1. Then N is replaced by 1 in N + 1 to give a new value for N which is 2. A new value for N + 1 is found by replacing N by 2, and so on.

You can see that the value of N increases by 1 each time the computer runs through a loop of the program.

The semicolon in line 20 causes the values of N to be printed horizontally. The results would be printed as shown below.

```
1   2   3   4   5   6   7   8   9   10
DONE
```

The table below shows symbols that are used with IF-THEN

EXAMPLE: Write all values of Y that would be printed in Program 2.

Solution:

```
Program 2
10  LET X = 4
20  LET Y =
30  PRINT Y;
40  LET X =
50  IF X >=
60  END
```

1. Compute the first value for Y in line 20.
   $Y = X \uparrow 2 + 1$ when X = 4.
   $Y = 4^2 + 1$ or **17**

2. Compute the next value for X in line 40.
   X − 1 when X = 4
   4 − 1 = 3

3. Continue finding each value of Y and the next value for X.

4. Determine what value of X will cause the program to end. In line computer will not go back to line 20 if X > = −4. This is true wh

All the values of Y will be printed as shown below.

```
17   10   5   2   1   2   5   10   17
```

EXERCISES

Write all the values of N that would be printed for each

```
1. 10  LET N = -1
   20  PRINT N
   30  LET N = N - 2
   40  IF N > -12 THEN 20
   50  END
```

```
2. 10  LET N = 15
   20  PRINT N
   30  LET N = N - 3
   40  IF N > -10 THEN
   50  END
```

```
3. 10  LET N = 1
   20  PRINT N
   30  LET N = 2 * N - 3
   40  IF N > -50 THEN 20
   50  END
```

```
4. 10  LET N = 1
   20  PRINT N
   30  LET N = 5 - 3 *
   40  IF N < 50 THEN
   50  END
```

Write all values of Y that would be printed for each pro

```
5. 10  LET X = -3
   20  LET Y = 4 * X - 5
   30  PRINT Y;
   40  LET X = X + 1
   50  IF X <= 3 THEN 20
   60  END
```

```
6. 10  LET X = 6
   20  LET Y = 2 - 2 *
   30  PRINT Y;
   40  LET X = X - 2
   50  IF X >= -6 THEN 20
   60  END
```

```
7. 10  READ X
   20  DATA -3, 0, 2, -1
   30  LET Y = 1 - X ↑ 2
   40  IF Y <= 0 THEN 10
   50  PRINT Y;
   60  GO TO 10
   70  END
```

```
8. 10  READ X
   20  DATA -2, 4, 0, -3
   30  LET Y = X ↑ 2 - 10
   40  IF Y >= 0 THEN 10
   50  PRINT Y
   60  GO TO 10
   70  END
```

BASIC Programming / **487**

Career Applications

Each of the even-numbered chapters contains an optional application topic related to a specific career area. Each contains a set of exercises.

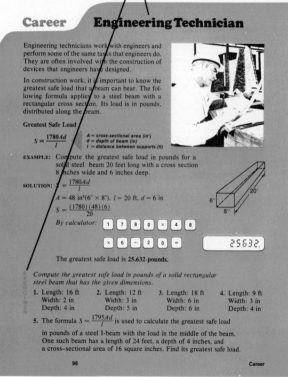

Career   Engineering Technician

Engineering technicians work with engineers and perform some of the same tasks that engineers do. They are often involved with the construction of devices that engineers have designed.

In construction work, it is important to know the greatest safe load that a beam can bear. The following formula applies to a steel beam with a rectangular cross section. Its load is in pounds, distributed along the beam.

Greatest Safe Load

$$S = \frac{1780Ad}{l}$$

A = cross-sectional area (in²)
d = depth of beam (in)
l = distance between supports (ft)

EXAMPLE: Compute the greatest safe load in pounds for a solid steel beam 20 feet long with a cross section 8 inches wide and 6 inches deep.

SOLUTION: $S = \frac{1780Ad}{l}$

$A = 48$ in²(6" × 8"), $l = 20$ ft, $d = 6$ in

$$S = \frac{(1780)(48)(6)}{20}$$

By calculator:

```
1 7 8 0 × 4 8
× 6 ÷ 2 0 =      25632.
```

The greatest safe load is **25,632 pounds.**

Compute the greatest safe load in pounds of a solid rectangular steel beam that has the given dimensions.

1. Length: 16 ft
   Width: 2 in
   Depth: 4 in

2. Length: 12 ft
   Width: 3 in
   Depth: 5 in

3. Length: 18 ft
   Width: 6 in
   Depth: 6 in

4. Length: 9 ft
   Width: 3 in
   Depth: 4 in

5. The formula $S = \frac{1795Ad}{l}$ is used to calculate the greatest safe load

in pounds of a steel I-beam with the load in the middle of the beam. One such beam has a length of 24 feet, a depth of 4 inches, and a cross-sectional area of 16 square inches. Find its greatest safe load.

96   Career

Review and Testing

Mid-Chapter Review

This item appears after the first three or four sections of each chapter. Each set of exercises is referenced to the related section.

MID-CHAPTER REVIEW

Choose a variable and write an equation for each word sentence. Then solve the equation. (Section 4.1)

1. The number of visitors to the park this past year, 356,000, was 45,000 more than the number of visitors the previous year.

2. The difference between the number of persons playing tennis at a club last month and 512, the number playing racquetball, was 74.

3. One month's phone bill of $38.50 for long distance calls was exactly twice the charge for local calls.

4. A company sells one product for $11.25 which is 1.8 times the cost of the product.

In Exercises 5–10 use Condition 1 to represent unknowns. Use Condition 2 to write an equation for the problem. Solve the problem. (Section 4.2)

5. A tumbling class for 5–5 year olds at the Y had seven more girls than boys. The total number enrolled for the class was 45. Find the number of girls and the number of boys.

6. Joel bought a sports coat for $15 less than five times the cost of a pair of slacks. The total cost of the coat and slacks was $273. Find the cost of each item.

7. A traffic count between 6:00 a.m. and 8:00 a.m. on a highway showed 2900 fewer cars the first hour than the second hour. The total number of cars for the two-hour period was 24,500. Find the number for each hour.

8. A school club's receipts from special projects was $5.00 more than three times the receipts from dues. The amount of total receipts was $485. Find the amounts received from dues and special projects.

(Section 4.3)

9. A rectangular parking lot has a length that is 6.2 meters greater than twice its width. The perimeter is 106.6 meters. Find the length and width.

10. An Olympic-size swimm a length and width in th 25:12. The pool's perime meters. Find the length

REVIEW CAPSULE FOR SECTION 4.4

Compute.

EXAMPLE: 8.5% of 350   **ANSWER:** 8.5% = 0.085; 0.085 · 350 = 29.7

1. 12% of $960
2. 8% of $87.50
3. 5% of 2780
4. 40
5. 75% of 56
6. 17% of 250
7. 4.5% of $750
8. 33

Problem Solving: One Variable / 87

Cumulative Review

This item appears after Chapters 6, 12, and 18. Each set of exercises is referenced to the related section.

CUMULATIVE REVIEW: CHAPTERS 7–12

Write each product or quotient as one power. (Sections 7.1–7.3)

1. $8^2 \cdot 8^3$
2. $(-13)^4(-13)^5$
3. $r^3 \cdot r^3 \cdot r^2$
4. $5^x \cdot 5^3$
5. $\frac{(13)^8}{(13)^4}$

6. $\frac{(-2.6)^9}{(-2.6)^3}$
7. $(3^{-1})(3^{-4})(3^2)$
8. $(t^3)(t^{-7})$
9. $\frac{p^4 \cdot p^{-6}}{p^5}$
10. $\frac{r^2}{r^5}$

Simplify. (Sections 7.4 and 7.5)

11. $(-7t)^2$
12. $(-2r)^3$
13. $\left(\frac{-3}{x}\right)^3$
14. $\left(\frac{4p}{5q}\right)^2$

15. $(2t^{-2})^3$
16. $(-5n^3)^{-2}$
17. $\left(\frac{-2ab^3}{c^2}\right)^4$
18. $\left(\frac{3p^2}{-q}\right)^3$

Write the decimal form of each number. (Section 7.6)

19. 5.8×10^4
20. 7.34×10^{-2}
21. 4.005×10^{-1}
22. 8.08×10^3

Simplify. (Sections 8.1–8.4)

23. $-\sqrt{169}$
24. $\sqrt{324}$
25. $\sqrt{2 \cdot 5 \cdot 2 \cdot 5 \cdot 2}$
26. $-\sqrt{2^2 \cdot 5^2 \cdot 11^4}$
27. $(-\sqrt{5})(\sqrt{3})$
28. $(-\sqrt{10})(-\sqrt{7})$
29. $\sqrt{5} \cdot \sqrt{7} \cdot \sqrt{35}$
30. $\sqrt{2} \cdot \sqrt{10} \cdot \sqrt{5}$
31. $\sqrt{56}$
32. $\sqrt{63}$
33. $\sqrt[3]{32}$
34. $\sqrt[3]{56}$
35. $\sqrt{20r^3}$
36. $\sqrt{45r^2s^3}$
37. $\sqrt[3]{y^{15}}$
38. $\sqrt[3]{n^{21}}$

Add or subtract. Simplify where necessary. (Section 8.5)

39. $5\sqrt{7} + \sqrt{7}$
40. $3\sqrt{14} - 8\sqrt{14}$
41. $\sqrt{50} - 7\sqrt{2}$
42. $3\sqrt{80} + 2\sqrt{5}$

Rationalize each denominator. Then simplify. (Section 8.6)

43. $\frac{\sqrt{9a}}{\sqrt{a^3}}$
44. $\frac{\sqrt{48a^5}}{\sqrt{3a}}$
45. $\frac{\sqrt{2}}{\sqrt{3}}$
46. $\frac{\sqrt{10}}{\sqrt{7}}$

Approximate the value of each square root to three decimal places. Use the

Chapter Summary

This item appears at the end of each chapter. It lists important terms and ideas covered in the chapter.

CHAPTER SUMMARY

IMPORTANT TERMS

Equation (p. 52)   Root (p. 52)
Solution (p. 52)   Equivalent equations (p. 52)

IMPORTANT IDEAS

1. *Addition Property for Equations:* Adding the same real number to each side of an equation forms an equivalent equation.

2. *Subtraction Property for Equations:* Subtracting the same real number from each side of an equation forms an equivalent equation.

3. *Multiplication Property for Equations:* Multiplying each side of an equation by the same nonzero real number forms an equivalent equation.

4. *Division Property for Equations:* Dividing each side of an equation by the same nonzero real number forms an equivalent equation.

5. To solve an equation that involves more than one operation, the Addition or Subtraction Property for Equations is generally used before the Multiplication or Division Property.

6. In equations that contain parentheses, use the Distributive Property first.

Chapter Review

Each Chapter Review prepares the student for the formal chapter test. Two forms are included for each chapter test in the **Teacher's Resource Book.**

CHAPTER REVIEW

In Exercises 1–40, solve each equation. Check each answer.

SECTION 3.1

1. $x + 23 = 16$
2. $y + 29 = -18$
3. $b - 47 = -28$
4. $d - 37 = 49$
5. $-28 = 14 + f$
6. $76 = -32 + g$
7. $5.6 = t - 24.7$
8. $-12.3 = x + 19.8$

SECTION 3.2

9. $-7k = 63$
10. $-96 = 12n$
11. $-8 = \frac{m}{14}$
12. $\frac{x}{-8} = 19$
13. $-\frac{3}{4}t = -27$
14. $60 = -\frac{12}{4}z$
15. $12y = -99.6$
16. $131.4 = -9r$

SECTION 3.3

17. $4z - 3 = 42$
18. $6t - 14 = 38$
19. $-68 = 8m + 12$
20. $-54 = 18 + 12p$
21. $78 - 6x = 34$
22. $69 = 102 - 8n$
23. $-22 + \frac{v}{2.4} = -46$
24. $-9 = \frac{w}{1.9} + 48$

Equations / 71

Teacher's Resource Book

This paperback consists of perforated and pre-holed copying masters. You are given permission to reproduce these pages.
It consists of a

1. Testing program
2. Skills Practice section
3. Warm-up exercises
4. Answer section

Skills Practice Section

There is a supplement for each lesson in the Skills Practice Section.

The Testing Program

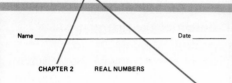

2.5 MULTIPLYING AND FACTORING EXPRESSIONS

Multiply and simplify.

Example: $-4y(6y + 2)$ Solution: $-4y(6y + 2) = (-4y)(6y) + (-4y)(2)$
$$= -24y^2 + (-8y) = -24y^2 - 8y$$

1. $5(p + q)$ _____
2. $-4(b + 5)$ _____
3. $\frac{1}{2}(x - 4)$ _____
4. $-7(z - 8)$ _____
5. $(m^2 + 3m)(4)$ _____
6. $(-2x + y)(-10)$ _____
7. $-3c(2c + 5)$ _____
8. $(n - 4p)(-8p)$ _____

Name _____ Date _____

CHAPTER 2   REAL NUMBERS

Write each number as a quotient of two integers.

(2.1) 1. $-3\frac{2}{5}$

2. 0.25

Write each number as a decimal.

3. $\frac{4}{5}$

4. $\frac{2}{11}$

Write the members of set B named in the following.

$B = \left\{-2, \frac{1}{2}, -2.2, \sqrt{22}, 0.\overline{2}, 0.\sqrt{4}\right\}$

5. Irrational numbers

6. Rational numbers

7. Integers

Write the number that makes the equation true.

(2.2) 8. $m + 3 = 3 + 7.2$

9. $-17 + x = 0$

(2.3) 10. $(25)(3.1) = (3.1)(m)$

Simplify.

(2.2) 11. $15 + q - 2 + 8$

(2.3) 12. $(-4)(12)(-\frac{1}{3})$

FORM A

There are two forms of each chapter test. Plus 3 cumulative tests.

Name _____ Date _____ Score _____

CHAPTER 2   REAL NUMBERS

Write each number as a quotient of two integers.

(2.1) 1. $-5\frac{1}{3}$

2. 0.8

Write each number as a decimal.

3. $-\frac{3}{4}$

4. $\frac{1}{6}$

Write the members of set B named in the following.

$B = \left\{\frac{1}{3}, \sqrt{9}, -0.\overline{3}, \sqrt{33}, 0, -3, 3.3\right\}$

5. Irrational numbers

6. Rational numbers

7. Whole numbers

Write the number that makes the equation true.

(2.2) 8. $7 + (-11) = (-11) + n$

(2.3) 9. $(t)(\frac{15}{2}) = -\frac{15}{2}$

(2.2) 10. $x + 16 = 0$

Simplify.

(2.2) 11. $x - 10 + 3 - 4$

(2.3) 12. $(-3)(15)(-\frac{1}{5})$

1. _____
2. _____
3. _____
4. _____
5. _____
6. _____
7. _____
8. _____
9. _____
10. _____
11. _____
12. _____

FORM B   CHAPTER 2   39

ADMINISTRATIVE CONCERNS

Overview One of the first questions that arises in offering first-year algebra as a course to be studied over a period of two years is related to the matter of credit. Should students be given credit for two years of high school mathematics, or should they be given credit for just one year, since they have not progressed beyond the usual content of the first-year course? Another question is how to label this credit on students' permanent records; that is, what names should be given to these courses? Some school officials, when considering the implementation of a two-year algebra program, are concerned that *Introductory Algebra 2* may be confused with the second college preparatory algebra course, often called *Second Year Algebra* or *Algebra Two*.

Solutions Years of experience by personnel in many schools and school districts across the country with the *Introductory Algebra* courses have provided answers to these administrative problems. Almost without exception, schools <u>do</u> give students credit toward graduation for two years of mathematics upon successful completion of both years of the *Introductory Algebra* courses. The first course is usually offered in the ninth grade and the second course in the tenth grade. However, some schools offer the two courses in the eighth and ninth grades. The rationale for awarding two years of credit is based upon what typically happened to this type of student prior to the advent of this program. Many of these students traditionally enrolled in a general mathematics course in the ninth grade and the regular one-year algebra course in the tenth grade. Those students who completed the two years of work successfully received two years of credit.

Course Titles Most schools have chosen to adopt new course titles when they have inaugurated the two-year program in first-year algebra. The most popular course titles have been *Introductory Algebra 1* and *Introductory Algebra 2*. Some school personnel have chosen to call the first year of the course *Pre-Algebra* and the second year of the course *Algebra One*. Most school personnel do not want to label the first year of the course General Mathmatics. This title has the stigma that is often associated with a general mathematics course. Students take pride in being enrolled in a course that is called algebra.

LESSON PLAN GUIDE

Overview On the following pages, M-10 through M-45, you will find a two-page *Lesson Plan Guide* for each chapter. Each consists of an *Overview*, brief commentary for each section, two quizzes, and a *Suggested Timetable of Assignments* for three levels identified as Level 1, Level 2, and Level 3. A *Suggested Timetable* that covers the year's work appears on page M-46.

Level 1 This represents the minimum course — Chapters 1-15 less sections 12.6, 12.7, and 15.7.

Level 2 This represents the average course — Chapters 1 through 16. The *Suggested Timetable of Assignments* for each of these chapters provides one day for enrichment topics — a *Special Topic Application*, a *Career*, or *Calculator Exercises*. Although the *Appendix* on computer programming in the BASIC language is intended primarily for Level 3, the content of the *Appendix* is within the ability level of these students.

Level 3 This represents the maximum course — Chapters 1 through 18. Students at this level should be able to handle all of the enrichment topics (described in Level 2 above) plus the *More Challenging Exercises*. The *Appendix* on computer programming in the BASIC language is intended primarily for these students.

Objectives The objectives for each section appear as annotations on the student pages. They are appropriately positioned near the title of the related section.

CHAPTER 1:   OPERATIONS ON NUMBERS

Overview   The first chapter is devoted to a review of important concepts that were introduced in *Introductory Algebra 1*. The material is presented at a more sophisticated level than when introduced earlier.

Section 1.1   The purpose of this introductory section is to defined absolute value in terms of the opposite of a number.

Section 1.2   This section reviews addition of positive and negative real numbers as integers, common fractions, or decimal fractions. It is not necessary to require the students to parrot the formal rules. However, they should have a working knowledge of them.

Section 1.3   Subtracting a number is defined as adding its opposite. This is the best approach to teaching subtraction of real numbers because students do not have to learn two sets of rules.

Section 1.4   The multiplication rules are developed by the use of patterns of products of numbers. This method seems to be convincing to most students.

Section 1.5   In this section division is defined in terms of multiplication. This is a good opportunity to emphasize that zero cannot be a divisor. This concept is an easy one for students to forget.

Section 1.6   The rules for the order of operations in an expression are reviewed.

Section 1.7   The important terms *base*, *exponent*, and *power* are reviewed in this section. Then emphasis is given to practicing the evaluation of expressions containing powers.

Quiz for Sections 1.1–1.4

Simplify.

1. $|-7.9|$ Ans: 7.9

2. $|3\frac{1}{4}|$ Ans: $3\frac{1}{4}$

3. $-|-83|$ Ans: -83

4. $|-(-0.9)|$ Ans: 0.9

Add.

5. $-253 + 198$ Ans: -55

6. $(-8.7) + (-5.6)$ Ans: -14.3

7. $4\frac{1}{8} + (-3\frac{3}{4})$ Ans: $\frac{3}{8}$

8. $0.7 + (-1.3)$ Ans: -0.6

Subtract.

9. $13 - 27$ Ans: -14

10. $(-14.2) - (-4.7)$ Ans: -9.5

11. $0 - 5\frac{3}{8}$ Ans: $-5\frac{3}{8}$

12. $-59 - 38$ Ans: -97

Multiply.

13. $(-12)(-9)$ Ans: 108

14. $(-\frac{3}{4})(32)$ Ans: -24

15. $(\frac{5}{6})(-\frac{3}{8})$ Ans: $-\frac{5}{16}$

16. $(-19.6)(-4)$ Ans: 78.4

Quiz for Sections 1.5–1.7

Divide.

1. $(-288) \div 8$ Ans: -36

2. $(-28) \div (-\frac{2}{3})$ Ans: 42

3. $34.8 \div (-6)$ Ans: -5.8

4. $0 \div -15$ Ans: 0

5. $\frac{-216}{-9}$ Ans: 24

6. $\frac{-4.8}{0.2}$ Ans: -24

Evaluate.

7. $24 + 18 \div (-3)$ Ans: 18

8. $16 - 24(-2)$ Ans: 64

9. $-8(7) - (-3)(-18)$ Ans: -110

10. $22 - 38 - 14 + 9$ Ans: -21

Evaluate each expression when $t = -3$.

11. $t^2 - 3$ Ans: 6

12. $-2t^2 - t + 1$ Ans: -14

13. $t^3 - t^2 - t$ Ans: -33

14. $(-5)(-6)(-8t^2)$ Ans: -2160

SUGGESTED TIMETABLE OF ASSIGNMENTS

Section	Page(s)	Level One	Level Two	Level Three
1.1	3	Odds 1-33	Odds 1-33	Odds 1-33
1.2	7	Odds 1-35	Odds 1-39	Odds 1-45
1.3	9	1st Day: Odds 1-39 2nd Day: Evens 2-40	Odds 1-43	Odds 1-46
1.4	12	Odds 1-39	Odds 1-43	Odds 1-51
1.5	16	Odds 1-39	Odds 1-45	Odds 1-45
1.6	18	Odds 1-35	Odds 1-35	Odds 1-35
1.7	20-21	1st Day: Odds 1-21 2nd Day: Odds 23-53	Odds 1-53	Odds 1-59
Review and Testing		3 days	3 days	2 days
Enrichment Topics		–	1 day	1 day
Total Days		12	11	10

CHAPTER 2:   REAL NUMBERS

Overview   The chapter opens with a review of the subsets of the set of real numbers: counting numbers, whole numbers, integers, rational numbers, and irrational numbers. The Addition and Multiplication Properties of Real Numbers are presented as are special properties of real numbers and the Distributive Property. In Section 2.6 the properties of real numbers are applied to combining like terms.

Section 2.1   Starting with the set of counting numbers, you can show students how to define larger number sets. The set of whole numbers consists of the set of counting numbers and 0. The set of integers consists of the set of whole numbers and their opposites. The set of rational numbers consists of quotients of integers in which no divisor equals zero. Finally, the set of real numbers is composed of the sets of rational and irrational numbers.

Section 2.2   Students tend to accept the Commutative Property of Addition as an obvious fact. You can show them that subtraction, for example, is not a commutative operation.

Section 2.3   It would be appropriate at this time to point out the similarities between the Addition and Multiplications Properties. Both include Commutative and Associative Properties.

Section 2.4   Several concepts that often cause difficulty for students are stated as special properties in this section. Perhaps the most troublesome concept is covered by the special property which shows that $a - (b + c)$ and $a - b - c$ are equivalent expressions.

Section 2.5   Factoring is introduced in this section. This topic is covered more thoroughly in Chapter 10.

Section 2.6   Point out that the sum of like terms can always be expressed as a product. However, the sum of unlike terms cannot always be expressed as a product.

Quiz for Sections 2.1–2.3

Write Rational or Irrational to describe each number.

1. $-3\frac{1}{8}$ **Ans: Rational**

2. $\sqrt{10}$ **Ans: Irrational**

3. $-5.232232223\cdots$ **Ans: Irrational**

4. $0.373737\cdots$ **Ans: Rational**

Simplify.

5. $16.5 - t - 19.3 + w$ Ans: $-2.8 - t + w$
6. $2\frac{5}{6} - 5\frac{3}{8} + 4\frac{1}{6} - 1\frac{5}{8}$ Ans: 0
7. $-43 + 78 - 29 - 17$ Ans: -11
8. $-0.8 + m - 0.9 - n$
   Ans: $-1.7 + m - n$

Multiply.

9. $(-28)(-\frac{3}{4})(-\frac{3}{7})$ Ans: -9
10. $(-12)(-r)(-s)(-4)$ Ans: $48rs$
11. $(4.2)(-p)(25)(-q)$ Ans: $105pq$
12. $(32)(\frac{7}{8})(-a)(b)$ Ans: $-28ab$

Quiz for Sections 2.4–2.6

Simplify.

1. $(-7mn)(4n)$ Ans: $-28mn^2$
2. $(-r)(-3s)(-2rt)$ Ans: $-6r^2st$
3. $(2x - 3)(-1)$ Ans: $-2x + 3$
4. $\frac{4(5t - 3)}{-(3 - 5t)}$ Ans: 4
5. $-3(4a - 5)$ Ans: $-12a + 15$
6. $(4t - s)(\frac{3}{4}s)$ Ans: $3st - \frac{3}{4}s^2$

Factor.

7. $4x - 10x^2$ Ans: $2x(2 - 5x)$
8. $-15n^2 + 5n$ Ans: $5n(-3n + 1)$

Simplify.

9. $-1.3qt - qt$ Ans: $-2.3qt$
10. $2w - 19 - 5w + 27$ Ans: $-3w + 8$
11. $-r^2 + 3r - 2 - r + 5r^2$
    Ans: $4r^2 + 2r - 2$
12. $1.2mn^2 - 0.8mn^2 - mn^2$
    Ans: $-0.6mn^2$

SUGGESTED TIMETABLE OF ASSIGNMENTS

Section	Page(s)	Level One	Level Two	Level Three
2.1	28-29	1st Day: Odds 1-45 2nd Day: Evens 2-46	All 1-45	All 1-45
2.2	32-33	Odds 1-41	Odds 1-47	Odds 1-51
2.3	36	Odds 1-23	Odds 1-29	Odds 1-29
2.4	40-41	Odds 1-45	Odds 1-45	Odds 1-51
2.5	44	1st Day: 1-16 2nd Day: Odds 17-39	Odds 1-39	Odds 1-51
2.6	46	Odds 1-35	Odds 1-35	Odds 1-35
Review and Testing		3 days	3 days	2 days
Enrichment Topics		–	1 day	1 day
Total Days		11	10	9

CHAPTER 3:   EQUATIONS

Overview   In this chapter, solutions of equations using one operation are studied first. This is expanded to solutions by two or more operations. More complicated equations involving like terms and having the variable on both sides of the equal sign are then introduced. In Section 3.6, students are given an opportunity to apply the abstract principles they have been learning to solving word problems.

Section 3.1   The concept of equivalent equations is introduced in this section. This is needed in order to present the Addition Property of Equations. Students should be required to give detailed steps in their work until they show a good knowledge of equation solving. Remind students that the check is for the purpose of discovering any computational errors.

Section 3.2   The Multiplication and Division Properties of Equations are presented in this section. Students should still be required to give detailed steps in solutions of equations.

Section 3.3   Two or more operations are used to solve the equations in this section.

Section 3.4   More complex equations are introduced in this section. Students are taught to identify and combine like terms before proceeding.

Section 3.5   In this section the equations to be solved have the variable on both sides of the equal sign. Solutions by both the Addition and Subtraction Properties of Equations are shown. The example in the text illustrates that the variable can end on either side of the equality symbol.

Section 3.6   The word problems in this section involve two important applications. One is the distance-rate-time formula, $d = rt$, and the problems involve finding values for r or t. The other is the formula for the perimeter of a rectangle, $p = 2(\ell + w)$, and the problems involve finding values for ℓ or w.

Quiz for Sections 3.1–3.3

Solve and check.

1. $34 = t + 45$ **Ans: t = −11**
2. $r - 19.8 = -14.9$ **Ans: r = 4.9**
3. $n + 2\frac{3}{4} = -5\frac{3}{4}$ **Ans: n = $-8\frac{1}{2}$**
4. $10.6 + w = 12.3$ **Ans: w = 1.7**
5. $\frac{q}{9} = -4\frac{2}{3}$ **Ans: q = −42**
6. $-3.5k = 49$ **Ans: k = −14**
7. $-\frac{2}{3}a = -38$ **Ans: a = 57**
8. $-25 = \frac{y}{-1.4}$ **Ans: y = 35**

9. $4t - 3 = -19$ Ans: $t = -4$

10. $-14 = \frac{n}{9} - 6$ Ans: $n = -72$

11. $6r + 9.8 = -7.6$ Ans: $r = -2.9$

12. $-24 = \frac{3}{8}x - 3$ Ans: $x = -56$

Quiz for Sections 3.4—3.6

Solve and check.

1. $3m - 17 - 7m = -43$ Ans: $m = 6\frac{1}{2}$

2. $13 = -7t + 27 - t$ Ans: $t = 1\frac{3}{4}$

3. $4(-3d + 2) + 9d = 20$
   Ans: $d = -4$

4. $-27 = -\frac{3}{4}(8y - 12) + 10y$
   Ans: $y = -9$

5. $6n - 13 = 9n + 35$ Ans: $n = -16$

6. $\frac{13}{4} - \frac{7}{4}p = \frac{9}{4}p - \frac{27}{4}$ Ans: $p = 2\frac{1}{2}$

7. $8 - 3x = 3(5 - 2x) + x$
   Ans: $x = 3\frac{1}{2}$

8. $\frac{2}{3}(\frac{1}{2} - 6w) + w = -2w + \frac{4}{3}$
   Ans: $w = -1$

Find the rate, r, or the time, t.

9. A plane made a flight of 3150 miles at an average speed of 450 miles per hour. How many hours did it take for the flight?
   Ans: **7 hours**

10. A family made a trip by auto which took $7\frac{1}{2}$ hours. The entire distance was 572 kilometers. Find the average speed for the trip, rounded to the nearest tenth.   Ans: **76.3 km/hr**

Find the width, w, or the length, l.

11. The perimeter of a poster is 127.6 centimeters. The length is 35.6 centimeters. Find the width.
    Ans: **28.2 cm**

12. The perimeter of a window is 4.12 meters. The width is 0.58 meter. Find the length.
    Ans: **1.48 m**

SUGGESTED TIMETABLE OF ASSIGNMENTS

Section	Page(s)	Level One	Level Two	Level Three
3.1	54	Odds 1-41	Odds 1-41	Odds 1-41
3.2	57	Odds 1-39	Odds 1-39	Odds 1-43
3.3	60	1st Day: Odds 1-21 2nd Day: Odds 23-41	Odds 1-41	Odds 1-51
3.4	64	1st Day: Odds 1-17 2nd Day: All 19-30	Odds 1-29	Odds 1-33
3.5	67	1st Day: Odds 1-15 2nd Day: Odds 17-35	1st Day: Odds 1-23 2nd Day: All 25-36	Odds 1-39
3.6	69	All 1-6	All 1-6	All 1-6
Review and Testing		3 days	3 days	2 days
Enrichment Topics		—	1 day	1 day
Total Days		12	11	9

CHAPTER 4: PROBLEM SOLVING: ONE VARIABLE

Overview   This chapter parallels somewhat the development of problem-solving skills as presented in *Introductory Algebra 1*. The chapter opens with a review of the important process of translating word expressions to algebraic expressions and word sentences to equations. Then the important steps of identifying the conditions in a problem and using these conditions to represent the unknowns and to write an equation are presented. The next section covers problem solving applications involving perimeters of rectangles and triangles. Then applications of per cent are covered in Section 4.4 concluding with applications involving formulas in Section 4.5. In all of the problem solving applications, emphasis is given to identifying the two conditions in each problem and using these conditions to solve the problem.

Section 4.1   It is important that students have confidence in accurately translating word expressions to algebraic expressions.

Section 4.2   This section contains a wide variety of word problems that involve two conditions. The use of these conditions in solving the problem and in checking the solution is highlighted.

Section 4.3   Problems involving the perimeter formulas for rectangles and triangles are covered in this section.

Section 4.4   Per cent problems based on the formula $d = rp$ involving discount, rate of discount, and list price are studied in this section. Also included are some miscellaneous per cent problems involving sports statistics.

Section 4.5   Problems involving two types of rate formulas are presented in this section. One is the familiar distance/rate/time formula $d = rt$. The other involves cruising range, automobile mileage, and fuel capacity.

Quiz for Sections 4.1–4.3

Choose a variable and write an equation for each word sentence. Then solve the equation.

1. The travel cost per member on a ski club trip equals the total cost of a bus, $1495, divided by the number of members, 23.
   Ans: Cost per member = $65

2. There were 136 hot-air balloons in the race last year which was 27 less than this year's number.
   Ans: 163 balloons this year

Solve each problem.

3. A golfer's total score the first two days of a tourney was 136. Find her second day's score if it was 4 strokes less than her first day's score.   **Ans: 66**

4. The width of a computer form is $2\frac{3}{8}$ inches less than the length. The perimeter is $43\frac{1}{4}$ inches. Find the length and width.   **Ans: 12 in and $9\frac{5}{8}$ in**

5. A sailboat race course is in the shape of a triangle with the three lengths in the ratio 3:5:6. Find each length if the perimeter of the triangle is 154 kilometers.   **Ans: 33 km, 55 km, 66 km**

Quiz for Sections 4.4—4.5

Solve each problem.

1. Some hikers took 3 hours to hike into a canyon. The return trip took 5 hours. The average rate returning was 2.4 kilometers per hour less than the average rate going. Find the distance one way.   **Ans: 18 km**

2. A car averages 27 miles per gallon of fuel for city driving and 32 miles per gallon on the highway. The car's cruising range in the city is 60 miles less than on the highway. Find the car's fuel tank capacity.   **Ans: 12 gal**

3. A basketball season ticket costs $338.40 at a 6% discount with cash payment. What is the regular price of a ticket without the discount?   **Ans: $360**

SUGGESTED TIMETABLE OF ASSIGNMENTS

Section	Page(s)	Level One	Level Two	Level Three
4.1	76-77	Odds 1-25	Odds 1-25	Odds 1-25
4.2	80-82	1st Day: Odds 1-17 2nd Day: Evens 2-18	1st Day: Odds 1-17 2nd Day: Evens 2-18	Odds 1-17
4.3	85-86	1st Day: Odds 1-13 2nd Day: Evens 2-14	Odds 1-13	Odds 1-13
4.4	91	All 1-7	All 1-7	All 1-7
4.5	95	Odds 1-7	All 1-7	All 1-7
Review and Testing		3 days	3 days	2 days
Enrichment Topics		—	1 day	1 day
Total Days		10	10	8

CHAPTER 5: PROPERTIES OF ORDER

Overview   This chapter presents the various properties of order and shows their application to finding solution sets of inequalities. Since solving inequalities is so closely related to solving equations, it will give students further review of the necessary skills. The Addition, Subtraction, Multiplication, and Division Properties for Inequalities are the main working tools for this chapter. The work proceeds from inequalities with the variable on one side and involving one operation to inequalities with the variable on both sides and involving two or more operations.

Section 5.1   Graphs of various inequalities including $<, >, \leq,$ and $\geq$ are covered in this section. In this text, "etc." is used with graphs only when the solution set is an infinite subset of {integers}.

Section 5.2   In this section the Comparison Property, the Order Property of Opposites, and the Transitive Property of Order are studied. Students should be cautioned about applying the Order Property of Opposites.

Section 5.3   The Addition and Subtraction Properties for Inequalities are introduced in this section. A graph is used to show that the Addition Property is reasonable. The concept of equivalent inequalities is used in stating both properties and again in finding the solution sets in the Examples.

Section 5.4   Two important kinds of inequalities are considered. One has an empty solution set and the other has the entire domain as its solution set.

Section 5.5   The Multiplication and Division Properties of Inequalities are developed in this section and are used in solving simple inequalities requiring two steps.

Section 5.6   This section will provide additional practice in solving inequalities with several steps. The section also provides some applications of inequalities to solving some number problems.

Quiz for Sections 5.1–5.3

Draw a graph of each inequality.

1. $x < -\frac{1}{2}$; Domain = {integers}

Ans: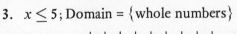

2. $x \geq -2\frac{3}{4}$; Domain = {real numbers}

Ans: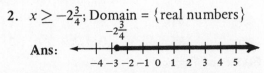

3. $x \leq 5$; Domain = {whole numbers}

Ans: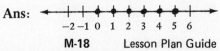

4. $x > -1.8$; Domain = {counting numbers}

Ans: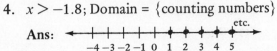

Write an inequality for r and s. Use <.

5. $r = -1.03; s = -1.04$ **Ans: s $<$ r**

6. $-s > -r$ **Ans: s $<$ r**

7. $r > 3$ and $-s > -3$ **Ans: s $<$ r**

8. $-r > 1.4$ and $s > -1.4$ **Ans: r $<$ s**

Solve.

9. $5.6 < t - 2.9$ **Ans: $\{t : t > 8.5\}$**

10. $w + 1\frac{3}{8} > -2\frac{1}{4}$ **Ans: $\{w : w > -3\frac{5}{8}\}$**

Quiz for Sections 5.4–5.6

Solve.

1. $-12 > 2t - 5 - t$
    Ans: $\{t : t < -7\}$

2. $3.4 + 2.9k < 1.7k + 2.2k$
    Ans: $\{k : k > 3.4\}$

3. $m - 2(m + 3) < 24 - 2m$
    Ans: $\{m : m < 30\}$

4. $\frac{1}{4}(8q - 20) < 4(q - 3) - q$
    Ans: $\{q : q > 7\}$

5. $-4r > 14$ **Ans: $\{r : r < -3\frac{1}{2}\}$**

6. $-28 < \frac{4}{3}w$ **Ans: $\{w : w > -21\}$**

7. $-\frac{1}{2}b < -16.3$ **Ans: $\{b : b > 32.6\}$**

8. $-29.4 > -4.9y$ **Ans: $\{y : y > 6\}$**

9. $4x - 8 < 2x + 5$
    Ans: $\{x : x < 6\frac{1}{2}\}$

10. $-3(x - 2) > 7x - 8 - 6x$
    Ans: $\{x : x < 3\frac{1}{2}\}$

11. Three times a number decreased by 5 is less than 15.1. For what numbers is this statement true?
     Ans: $\{x : x < 6.7\}$

12. The sum of two consecutive integers is less than -36. What is the greatest value the lesser of the two integers can have?   **Ans: -19**

SUGGESTED TIMETABLE OF ASSIGNMENTS

Section	Page(s)	Level One	Level Two	Level Three
5.1	102-103	All 1-18	Odds 1-31	Odds 1-31
5.2	106	Odds 1-31	Odds 1-31	Odds 1-31
5.3	109	Odds 1-21	Odds 1-27	Odds 1-33
5.4	112	1st Day: Odds 1-11 2nd Day: All 13-21	1st Day: All 1-10 2nd Day: All 11-21	Odds 1-21
5.5	115	Odds 1-19	Odds 1-19	Odds 1-19
5.6	118	1st Day: Odds 1-17 2nd Day: All 18-24	Odds 1-23	Odds 1-23
Review and Testing		3 days	3 days	2 days
Enrichment Topics		–	1 day	1 day
Total Days		**11**	**11**	**9**

CHAPTER 6:   RELATIONS AND FUNCTIONS

Overview   This chapter introduces graphing in a coordinate plane. Graphing will be utilized as a vehicle for presenting a number of mathematical topics including relations, functions, linear and quadratic functions, systems of linear equations and inequalities, and truth sets of quadratic equations.

Section 6.1   This section includes the mechanics of locating points that are graphs of ordered pairs of numbers.

Section 6.2   This section develops the concept of one-to-one correspondence between the set of points of a coordinate plane and ordered pairs of real numbers.

Section 6.3   Emphasis should be given to the fact that the elements of a set that is a relation are the ordered pairs of numbers and not the single numbers that make up the pairs.

Section 6.4   The vertical line test of a function is shown in this section.

Section 6.5   The purpose of this section is to show students how to make graphs of functions when the domain is given and the rule is given by an algebraic formula.

Section 6.6   Several illustrations of the use of functions are presented in this section.

Quiz for Sections 6.1–6.3

Graph these points in the same coordinate plane.

1. $A(4, -2)$
2. $B(-3\frac{1}{2}, 0)$ **Ans:**
3. $C(2\frac{1}{2}, 3\frac{1}{2})$
4. $D(0, -5)$
5. $E(1.4, -3.7)$
6. $F(4\frac{3}{4}, 0)$
7. $G(-2, -3)$
8. $H(-2\frac{1}{2}, 3\frac{1}{2})$

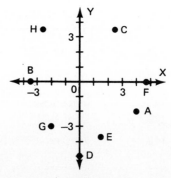

Write each relation in roster form. Then draw its graph.
The x values are $-3, -\frac{1}{2}, 0, 2$.

9. $(x, y) : y = -2x + 1$
   Ans: $\{(-3, 7), (-\frac{1}{2}, 2), (0, 1), (2, -3)\}$

10. $(x, y) : y = 4x^2 - x$
   Ans: $\{(-3, 39), (-\frac{1}{2}, 1\frac{1}{2}), (0, 0), (2, 14)\}$

11. $(x, y) : y = |2x - 1|$
   Ans: $\{(-3, 7), (-\frac{1}{2}, 2), (0, 1), (2, 3)\}$

12. $(x, y) : y = \sqrt{x^2}$
   Ans: $\{(-3, 3), (-\frac{1}{2}, \frac{1}{2}), (0, 0), (2, 2)\}$

Quiz for Sections 6.4—6.6

Write Yes or No to show whether each relation is a function.

1.

x	-1	4	0	$\frac{1}{2}$	-5	-1.3
y	4	-1	$\frac{1}{2}$	-2	$\frac{1}{2}$	10

Ans: **Yes**

2.

x	1.8	-3	$2\frac{1}{2}$	-3	0
y	2	4	6	8	10

Ans: **No**

3. 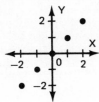   Ans: **Yes**

4. 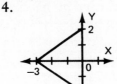   Ans: **No**

5. $(0, -3)$, $(\frac{1}{2}, -1)$, $(8, 2)$, $(0.5, 0.7)$
Ans: **No**

6. $(2, 6)$, $(\sqrt{2}, -1)$, $(\pi, 3)$, $(\frac{22}{7}, -1)$
Ans: **Yes**

Draw a graph of each function with {real numbers} as the domain.
First graph the ordered pairs with x values $-4, -2, 0, 2, 4$.

7. $(x, y) : y = -\frac{1}{2}x + 2$
Ans: **The graph contains: $(-4, 4)$,**
$(-2, 3)$, $(0, 2)$, $(2, 1)$, $(4, 0)$

8. $(x, y) : y = |x + 1| - 1$
Ans: **The graph contains: $(-4, 2)$,**
$(-2, 0)$, $(0, 0)$, $(2, 2)$, $(4, 4)$

The formula $y = 0.425x$ relates the number of miles per gallon,
x, to the approximate number of kilometers per liter, y.

9.   Find the number of kilometers per liter corresponding to 25 miles per gallon. Ans: **Approx. 10.6 km/L**

10.   Find the number of kilometers per liter corresponding to 32 miles per gallon. Ans: **Approx. 13.6 km/L**

SUGGESTED TIMETABLE OF ASSIGNMENTS

Section	Page(s)	Level One	Level Two	Level Three
6.1	126	All 1-24	All 1-24	All 1-24
6.2	129	All 1-22	All 1-22	All 1-22
6.3	132	Odds 1-25	Odds 1-25	Odds 1-25
6.4	136-137	Odds 1-25	Odds 1-25	Odds 1-25
6.5	140	Odds 1-11	Odds 1-15	Odds 1-15
6.6	143	Odds 1-15	Odds 1-15	Odds 1-15
Review and Testing		3 days	3 days	2 days
Enrichment Topics		—	1 day	1 day
Total Days		9	10	9

CHAPTER 7: POWERS

Overview   This chapter covers various properties of powers including products, quotients, powers of products and quotients, and powers of powers. In the Examples and Exercises, variables as well as numbers are used for the various bases and exponents that occur. In this course, exponents are restricted to integers, but powers involving both negative and zero exponents are used in this chapter and elsewhere in the text.

Section 7.1   The Product Property of Powers is introduced inductively by use of several Examples. Although these examples involve positive integral exponents, the property is stated for zero or negative exponents as well.

Section 7.2   Two important concepts are covered in this section — the Quotient Property of Powers and the Property of a Zero Exponent. Both properties are developed in an inductive fashion.

Section 7.3   The Examples and Exercises apply the Product and Quotient Properties of Powers to both positive and negative exponents.

Section 7.4   In this section students learn to apply the properties that involve raising a product or a quotient to a power. Students should learn to distinguish between expressions such as $(5y)^2$ and $(5y^2)$.

Section 7.5   The inductive method is used in this section to introduce the Property of the Power of a Power. Care should be taken with $(x^a)(x^b)$ and $(x^a)^b$, as these expressions are easily confused.

Section 7.6   Remind students to check their results after converting decimals to scientific notation.

Quiz for Sections 7.1–7.3

Write each product as one power.

1. $(-8)^5 \cdot (-8)^3$ **Ans: $(-8)^8$**

2. $w^4 \cdot w^2 \cdot w^3$ **Ans: w^9**

Multiply and simplify.

3. $m^3(m^2 - m^4)$ **Ans: $m^5 - m^7$**

4. $7^5(7^4 + 7^2)$ **Ans: $7^9 + 7^7$**

Write each quotient as one power.

5. $\dfrac{(2.9)^{12}}{(2.9)^3}$ **Ans: $(2.9)^9$**

6. $\dfrac{p^8}{p^4}$ **Ans: p^4**

Simplify.

7. $2^0 + (1.5)^0 - x^0$ **Ans: 1**

8. $-3r^0 + 5t^0$ **Ans: 2**

Write each product or quotient as one power.

9. $q^{-2} \cdot q^0 \cdot q^{-1}$ **Ans: q^{-3}**

10. $\dfrac{s^4 \cdot s^{-1}}{s^{-2}}$ **Ans: s^5**

Quiz for Sections 7.4–7.6

Simplify.

1. $(2m)^5$ **Ans: $32m^5$**

2. $(s^3)^4$ **Ans: s^{12}**

3. $(5t)^{-2}$ **Ans: $\dfrac{1}{25t^2}$**

4. $(\tfrac{2}{3})^{-3}$ **Ans: $\dfrac{27}{8}$**

5. $(\tfrac{4}{c})^3$ **Ans: $\dfrac{64}{c^3}$**

6. $(\dfrac{3ab^2}{c^3})^4$ **Ans: $\dfrac{81a^4b^8}{c^{12}}$**

7. $(5m^{-1}n^{-3}p^2)^{-2}$ **Ans: $\dfrac{m^2n^6}{25p^4}$**

8. $(\dfrac{2r^3s^{-2}}{t^{-1}})^4$ **Ans: $\dfrac{16r^{12}t^4}{s^8}$**

Write the decimal form.

9. 2.156×10^{-2} **Ans: 0.02156**

10. 4.0238×10^6 **Ans: 4,023,800.**

Write in scientific notation.

11. 53,806,400.   **Ans: 5.38064×10^7**

12. 0.0000186   **Ans: 1.86×10^{-5}**

SUGGESTED TIMETABLE OF ASSIGNMENTS

Section	Page(s)	Level One	Level Two	Level Three
7.1	154	Odds 1-35	Odds 1-35	Odds 1-35
7.2	157-158	Odds 1-45	Odds 1-45	Odds 1-45
7.3	161	Odds 1-33	Odds 1-33	Odds 1-33
7.4	165	Odds 1-29	Odds 1-29	Odds 1-29
7.5	169	Odds 1-29	Odds 1-33	Odds 1-39
7.6	172	Odds 1-25	Odds 1-27	Odds 1-27
Review and Testing		3 days	2 days	2 days
Enrichment Topics		–	1 day	1 day
Total Days		9	9	9

CHAPTER 8: ROOTS

Overview This chapter includes simplification of numbers expressed in radical form and the various operations with radicals. Emphasis is given to radicals that represent *square* roots, but cube and fourth roots are introduced in Section 8.3. The opening sections concentrate on square roots of counting numbers as basic concepts of radicals are presented. Radicals involving variables and algebraic expressions are introduced in Section 8.4. The chapter concludes with quotients of radicals including rationalizing denominators and computing approximations.

Section 8.1 Students need a clear understanding of the meaning of a square root. They often think of *the* square root of a number — forgetting the negative root.

Section 8.2 Students usually have no problem in understanding the general Product Property of Radicals. However, they sometimes get confused with a special product such as $\sqrt{2} \cdot \sqrt{2}$.

Section 8.3 Square root radicals are simplified by expressing the prime factorization of the radicands and applying the Product Property of Radicals. This method is then extended to cube roots and fourth roots.

Section 8.4 Radicands expressed as variables or algebraic expressions are introduced in this section.

Section 8.5 The Distributive Property should be used as the basis for explaining how to simplify the sum of two "like" radicals. Students will quickly see the analogy between "combining like terms" and "combining like radicals."

Section 8.6 Rationalizing the denominator is included in this section.

Section 8.7 This section is devoted to finding approximations of square roots by means of a simple table.

Quiz for Sections 8.1—8.4

Simplify.

1. $\sqrt{1089}$ Ans: 33

2. $\sqrt{4225}$ Ans: 65

3. $\sqrt{37} \cdot \sqrt{37}$ Ans: 37

4. $\sqrt{2} \cdot \sqrt{18}$ Ans: 6

5. $-\sqrt{19} \cdot \sqrt{3}$ Ans: $-\sqrt{57}$

6. $\sqrt{3} \cdot \sqrt{11} \cdot \sqrt{2}$ Ans: $\sqrt{66}$

7. $(-\sqrt{2})(-\sqrt{3})(-\sqrt{6})$ Ans: -6

8. $\sqrt{5^2 \cdot 7^2} \cdot \sqrt{14}$ Ans: $35\sqrt{14}$

9. $-\sqrt{75}$ Ans: $-5\sqrt{3}$

10. $\sqrt{152}$ Ans: $2\sqrt{38}$

11. $\sqrt{48a^2b^3}$ Ans: $4ab\sqrt{3b}$ 12. $\sqrt[3]{40r^3s^4}$ Ans: $2rs\sqrt[3]{5s}$

Quiz for Sections 8.5–8.7

Add or subtract. Simplify where necessary.

1. $7\sqrt{3} - \sqrt{3}$ Ans: $6\sqrt{3}$ 2. $-8\sqrt{2w} - 3\sqrt{2w}$ Ans: $-11\sqrt{2w}$

3. $\sqrt{12} + 5\sqrt{3}$ Ans: $7\sqrt{3}$ 4. $3\sqrt{8} + \sqrt{18}$ Ans: $9\sqrt{2}$

Simplify.

5. $\dfrac{\sqrt{63}}{\sqrt{7}}$ Ans: 3 6. $\sqrt{\dfrac{40}{2y^2}}$ Ans: $\dfrac{2}{y}\sqrt{5}$

Rationalize each denominator.

7. $\dfrac{\sqrt{2}}{\sqrt{3}}$ Ans: $\dfrac{\sqrt{6}}{3}$ 8. $\dfrac{\sqrt{3s}}{\sqrt{8r}}$ Ans: $\dfrac{\sqrt{6rs}}{4r}$

Approximate each square root to two decimal places based on:
$$\sqrt{2} \approx 1.414 \quad \sqrt{3} \approx 1.732 \quad \sqrt{5} \approx 2.236 \quad \sqrt{7} \approx 2.646$$

9. $\sqrt{27}$ Ans: 5.20 10. $\sqrt{35}$ Ans: 5.92

SUGGESTED TIMETABLE OF ASSIGNMENTS

Section	Page(s)	Level One	Level Two	Level Three
8.1	180	Odds 1-41	Odds 1-41	Odds 1-41
8.2	183	Odds 1-25	Odds 1-29	Odds 1-33
8.3	186	1st Day: Odds 1-21 2nd Day: Odds 23-45	Odds 1-45	Odds 1-45
8.4	189	1st Day: Odds 1-19 2nd Day: Odds 21-35	Odds 1-35	Odds 1-47
8.5	193	1st Day: Odds 1-21 2nd Day: Odds 23-41	1st Day: Odds 1-21 2nd Day: Odds 23-41	Odds 1-41
8.6	196	1st Day: Odds 1-19 2nd Day: Odds 21-35	Odds 1-35	Odds 1-35
8.7	200	Odds 1-27	Odds 1-27	Odds 1-31
Review and Testing		3 days	2 days	2 days
Enrichment Topics		–	1 day	1 day
Total Days		14	11	10

CHAPTER 9:   POLYNOMIALS

Overview   This chapter covers the operations with polynomials. The first two sections are on monomials. Section 9.3 is concerned with simplifying and evaluating polynomials. The operations with polynomials are developed in the remaining sections with the two final sections covering division.

Section 9.1   It is important to emphasize that an expression such as $\frac{5}{x}$ is not a monomial even though it has a value when x is replaced by a nonzero number. When this expression is written in a monomial form, it becomes $5x^{-1}$ and a negative exponent is not acceptable in a monomial.

Section 9.2   The Product of Powers and the Commutative and Associative Properties of Multiplication provide a method for multiplying monomials. Likewise, the Quotient Property of Powers and the Product Rule for Fractions explain the procedure for dividing monomials.

Section 9.3   Polynomials are defined in this section.

Section 9.4   Both horizontal and vertical addition and subtraction are included. Subtraction of polynomials is based on the meaning of subtraction.

Section 9.5   Both horizontal and vertical multiplication are included.

Section 9.6   Division of polynomials serves an indirect purpose, many of the basic concepts and skills of algebra are reviewed when using this algorithm.

Section 9.7   Division involving non-zero remainders is included in this section. Compare the method of expressing the answer in Example 1 with a mixed numeral in arithmetic.

Quiz for Sections 9.1—9.3

Evaluate.

1. $2n^5$ when $n = -1$ Ans: -2

2. $-\frac{2}{3}y^4$ when $y = 3$ Ans: -54

Multiply or divide.

3. $(-5t^2)(7t^3)$ Ans: $-35t^5$

4. $(-1.2pq^2)(-8p^2qr)$ Ans: $9.6p^3q^3r$

5. $\frac{14.4w^5}{-4w^2}$ Ans: $-3.6w^3$

6. $\frac{-15m^8n^5}{-8m^2n}$ Ans: $1\frac{7}{8}m^6n^4$

Simplify.

7. $2x - 5x^2 + 3x - 5 - x^2$
   Ans: $-6x^2 + 5x - 5$

8. $0.5rs - 1.2r^2s - 0.9rs + rs^2$
   Ans: $-1.2r^2s - 0.4rs + rs^2$

Evaluate.

9. $y^3 - y - 2; y = -1$ Ans: -2

10. $x^3 - x^2 + x - 1; x = -2$ Ans: -15

Quiz for Sections 9.4–9.7

Add or subtract.

1. $\quad\quad 1.9n^2 - 3.8n - 5.7$
   $\underline{(+) -2.3n^2 - 5.9n + 8.3}$
   Ans: $-0.4n^2 - 9.7n + 2.6$

2. $\quad\quad 3x^3 \quad\quad - x \quad + 19$
   $\underline{(-) -7x^3 + x^2 - 12x + 13}$
   Ans: $10x^3 - x^2 + 11x + 6$

3. $(\frac{3}{4}t^2 - \frac{1}{2} + \frac{1}{8}t) + (\frac{3}{4} - \frac{1}{4}t + t^2)$
   Ans: $\frac{7}{4}t^2 - \frac{1}{8}t + \frac{1}{4}$

4. $(4y - y^3 + 7) - (2y^2 - y + 16)$
   Ans: $-y^3 - 2y^2 + 5y - 9$

Multiply or divide.

5. $(x - 12)(x + 7)$ Ans: $x^2 - 5x - 84$

6. $(2x - 5)(3x + 1)$ Ans: $6x^2 - 13x - 5$

7. $\quad 2.1x^3 - 0.8x^2 \quad\quad + 1.4$
   $\quad\quad\quad\quad\quad \underline{2x - \quad 5}$
   Ans: $4.2x^4 - 12.1x^3 + 4x^2 + 2.8x - 7$

8. $3x - 4 \overline{)12x^2 - 37x + 15}$
   Ans: $4x - 7 - \dfrac{13}{3x - 4}$

SUGGESTED TIMETABLE OF ASSIGNMENTS

Section	Page(s)	Level One	Level Two	Level Three
9.1	207	Odds 1-33	Odds 1-33	Odds 1-33
9.2	210	Odds 1-27	Odds 1-27	Odds 1-27
9.3	213	Odds 1-29	Odds 1-33	Odds 1-33
9.4	217	Odds 1-17	Odds 1-17	Odds 1-17
9.5	220-221	1st Day: All 1-16 2nd Day: All 17-31	Odds 1-31	Odds 1-37
9.6	224	Odds 1-23	Odds 1-23	Odds 1-23
9.7	227-228	1st Day: Odds 1-17 2nd Day: Evens 2-18	1st Day: Odds 1-17 2nd Day: Odds 19-37	Odds 1-37
Review and Testing		3 days	2 days	2 days
Enrichment Topics		–	1 day	1 day
Total Days		12	11	10

CHAPTER 10: FACTORING POLYNOMIALS

Overview   This chapter expands on the definition of factoring given in Section 2.5. At that point, factoring was defined as the process of expressing a sum as a product. The concepts of *prime polynomial* and *greatest common factor* are introduced in order to define factoring of polynomials. The first six sections cover common monomial factoring, factoring the difference of two squares, factoring quadratic trinomials, and factoring trinomial squares. Section 10.7 combines more than one type of factoring in one polynomial.

Section 10.1   The concept of prime polynomial is introduced in this section. Emphasize that in common monomial factoring it is usually not necessary to express integral factors in terms of their prime factors.

Section 10.2   This section expresses factorable polynomials like $x^2 + bx + c$ in the form $x^2 + rx + sx + rs$. This leads to the factoring of quadratic trinomials like $ax^2 + bx + c$ in later sections.

Section 10.3   Students are taught to write a factorable quadratic trinomial in the form $x^2 + rx + sx + rs$ and then proceed as in Section 10.2. To do this they must find two integers, r and s, such that $r + s = b$ and $r \cdot s = c$.

Section 10.4   An example is used to show that the factoring of a trinomial such as $ax^2 + bx + c$ is the reverse of multiplying two binomials. The first step is to find two integers r and s such that $r + s = b$ and $r \cdot s = ac$ in order to write the trinomial as $ax^2 + rx + sx + c$.

Section 10.5   Development of a rule for factoring the difference of two squares is accomplished by first considering the nature of the general product of two binomials. One represents the difference of two numbers and the other represents the sum of the same numbers.

Section 10.6   In this section the conditions necessary for a trinomial of the form $ax^2 + bx + c$ to be a trinomial square are presented.

Section 10.7   Students of low-average ability often experience difficulty in applying one or more of the methods learned in the preceding sections. They must first identify the method of factoring to use. Several steps are often involved with factoring a general polynomial, and a student may "lose" some of the factors in the process. Emphasis should be given to the importance of applying common monomial factoring first.

Quiz for Sections 10.1–10.4

Factor.

1. $3x - 6y$ Ans: $3(x - 2y)$
2. $-8x^4 - 12x^3 + 16x$ Ans: $4x(-2x^3 - 3x^2 + 4)$
3. $x^2 + 12x + 27$ Ans: $(x + 3)(x + 9)$
4. $x^2 - 5x - 14$ Ans: $(x - 7)(x + 2)$
5. $3x^2 + 4x - 15$ Ans: $(3x - 5)(x + 3)$
6. $4x^2 - 12x + 5$ Ans: $(2x - 1)(2x - 5)$

Quiz for Sections 10.5–10.7

Multiply.

1. $(7r - 5)(7r + 5)$ Ans: $49r^2 - 25$
2. $(3mn - 4)(3mn + 4)$ Ans: $9m^2n^2 - 16$

Factor.

3. $16t^2 - 81$ Ans: $(4t - 9)(4t + 9)$
4. $25x^2y^2 - 20xy + 4$ Ans: $(5xy - 2)(5xy - 2)$
5. $2x^2 - 72$ Ans: $2(x - 6)(x + 6)$
6. $6x^2 - 3x - 9$ Ans: $3(2x - 3)(x + 1)$

SUGGESTED TIMETABLE OF ASSIGNMENTS

Section	Page(s)	Level One	Level Two	Level Three
10.1	236	Odds 1-23	Odds 1-23	Odds 1-23
10.2	239	Odds 1-21	Odds 1-25	Odds 1-27
10.3	243	1st Day: 1,5,9,···,59 2nd Day: 3,7,11,···,57	1st Day: 1,5,9,···,59 2nd Day: 3,7,11,···,57	Odds 1-59
10.4	246	1st Day: 1,5,9,···,33 2nd Day: 3,7,11,···,31	1st Day: 1,5,9,···,33 2nd Day: 3,7,11,···,31	Odds 1-33
10.5	250	Odds 1-35	Odds 1-41	Odds 1-47
10.6	253	1st Day: 1,5,9,···,41 2nd Day: 3,7,11,···,39	Odds 1-41	Odds 1-41
10.7	256	1, 5, 9, ···, 33	1, 5, 9, ···, 37	1, 5, 9, ···, 41
Review and Testing		3 days	2 days	2 days
Enrichment Topics		–	1 day	1 day
Total Days		13	12	10

CHAPTER 11: LINEAR EQUATIONS

Overview
The concept of function was introduced and defined in Chapter 6. This chapter treats the linear function in a somewhat more detailed fashion. Such concepts as slope, parallel lines, and intercepts are covered. Some applications of the linear function are shown in Section 11.7.

Section 11.1
The techniques taught in Section 6.6 are now applied to the linear function.

Section 11.2
The y value of the point of intersection of the line and the Y axis is defined to be the Y intercept. However, the point itself is referred to as the intercept on occasion.

Section 11.3
In this section, *slope* is defined as a in the linear function $y = ax + b$.

Section 11.4
A common error in using the slope formula is for students to express the ratio incorrectly, interchanging the subscripts, for example.

Section 11.5
The main idea of this section is that wo lines in a coordinate plane are parallel if they have the same slope.

Section 11.6
The X intercept is defined in this lesson. A technique for graphing a linear function using only the X and Y intercepts is demonstrated.

Section 11.7
In this section, some practical applications of linear functions are presented.

Quiz for Sections 11.1—11.4

Graph at least four ordered pairs of each function.
Then draw the graph. The domain is the set of real numbers.

1. $(x, y) : y = x - 2$
   Ans: The graph intersects the axes at $(0, -2)$ and $(2, 0)$.

2. $(x, y) : y = -\frac{1}{2}x - 1$
   Ans: The graph intersects the axes at $(0, -1)$ and $(-2, 0)$.

Write each Y intercept.

3. $y = \frac{3}{4}x - \frac{1}{2}$ **Ans:** $-\frac{1}{2}$

4. $y = -0.6x + 1.5$ **Ans:** 1.5

Write the slope of the graph of each function.

5. $y = 3x - 5$ **Ans:** 3

6. $y = 4 - \frac{2}{3}x$ **Ans:** $-\frac{2}{3}$

Write the slope of the line that contains the two points.

7. $(-1, 5); (4, -2)$ Ans: $-\frac{7}{5}$

8. $(0, -6); (1, 2)$ Ans: 8

Quiz for Sections 11.5—11.7

Graph each pair of functions in the same plane.
Write Yes or No to tell whether the two lines are parallel.

1. $y = -\frac{3}{4}x + 1$ Ans: No
   $y = \frac{4}{3}x - 2$

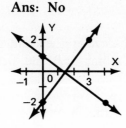

2. $y = -\frac{1}{2}(x + 2)$ Ans: Yes
   $y = 4 - \frac{1}{2}x$

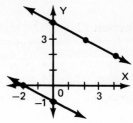

Write each X intercept.

3. $y = 4x - 8$ Ans: 2

4. $y = -\frac{1}{2}x + 3$ Ans: 6

Graph each linear relation.

5. $x = -1$ Ans: **The line contains**
   $(-1, 0)$ and is parallel to the y axis.

6. $x = 3\frac{1}{2}$ Ans: **The line contains**
   $(3\frac{1}{2}, 0)$ and is parallel to the y axis.

The formula $C = \frac{5}{9}(F - 32)$ shows Celsius temperature (C) as a
function of Fahrenheit temperature (F).

7. Find the value of C corresponding
   to 113°F.   Ans: **45°**

8. Find the value of C corresponding to
   14°F.   Ans: **−10°**

SUGGESTED TIMETABLE OF ASSIGNMENTS

Section	Page(s)	Level One	Level Two	Level Three
11.1	264	Odds 1-19	Odds 1-19	Odds 1-19
11.2	267	Odds 1-21	Odds 1-21	Odds 1-21
11.3	270	Odds 1-29	Odds 1-29	Odds 1-29
11.4	273-274	Odds 1-27	Odds 1-31	Odds 1-33
11.5	278	Odds 1-13	Odds 1-13	Odds 1-15
11.6	281	Odds 1-23	Odds 1-23	Odds 1-23
11.7	284	Odds 1-17	Odds 1-17	Odds 1-17
Review and Testing		3 days	2 days	2 days
Enrichment Topics		—	1 day	1 day
Total Days		10	10	10

CHAPTER 12:   SYSTEMS OF LINEAR EQUATIONS

Overview   This chapter covers a variety of methods for finding solution sets of systems of linear equations. Included are the graphical, substitution, multiplication/addition, and determinant methods. The introduction of the determinant method for solving linear systems is a unique feature of the chapter. Sections 12.6 and 12.7 are considered optional for Level One students.

Section 12.1   The main purpose of this lesson is to develop the standard form of the linear equation, $Ax + By + C = 0$, in which A, B, and C are integers.

Section 12.2   In this section, attention is directed to the graph of the solution set of a linear equation in two variables.

Section 12.3   In this section, the graphical method of finding solution sets is presented.

Section 12.4   The substitution method is introduced as it is the most useful method for working with applications of systems of equations.

Section 12.5   The three Examples of this section have been carefully paced to help students learn the Multiplication/Addition method.

Section 12.6   The purpose of this section is to teach the student what a 2 × 2 determinant is and how to find its value.

Section 12.7   The method of determinants for solving systems of equation in two variables is presented.

Quiz for Sections 12.1–12.4

Write each equation in standard form.

1. $2y - 5 = 3x$
    Ans: $3x - 2y + 5 = 0$

2. $3(x - 2) = 5(y + 4)$
    Ans: $3x - 5y - 26 = 0$

Graph each equation.

3. $x - 2y - 4 = 0$
    Ans: Some points are:
    $(0, -2), (2, -1, (4, 0)$

4. $3x + 2y - 1 = 0$
    Ans: Some points are:
    $(0, \frac{1}{2}), (1, -1), (3, -4)$

Solve each system by graphing.

5. $\begin{cases} x - y - 2 = 0 \\ 2x + y - 4 = 0 \end{cases}$ Ans: $x = 2, y = 0$

6. $\begin{cases} 3x - y + 4 = 0 \\ -3x + 2y - 2 = 0 \end{cases}$ Ans: $x = -2, y = -2$

Solve by the substitution method.

7. $\begin{cases} x + 2y = 4 \\ x = 3y - 1 \end{cases}$ Ans: $x = 2, y = 1$

8. $\begin{cases} x - 2y + 3 = 0 \\ 2x - y - 3 = 0 \end{cases}$ Ans: $x = 3, y = 3$

Quiz for Sections 12.5–12.7

Solve by the multiplication/addition method.

1. $\begin{cases} 3x - y = 4 \\ 2x + y = 6 \end{cases}$ Ans: $x = 2, y = 2$

2. $\begin{cases} 4x - 2y = -1 \\ -x + y = 4 \end{cases}$ Ans: $x = 3\frac{1}{2}, y = 7\frac{1}{2}$

Compute the value of each determinant.

3. $\begin{vmatrix} -4 & -5 \\ 2 & 1 \end{vmatrix}$ Ans: 6

4. $\begin{vmatrix} -\frac{1}{3} & 5 \\ \frac{1}{2} & -6 \end{vmatrix}$ Ans: $-\frac{1}{2}$

Write the determinant of each system.

5. $\begin{cases} 3x - 2y = 4 \\ x - y = -2 \end{cases}$ Ans: $\begin{vmatrix} 3 & -2 \\ 1 & -1 \end{vmatrix}$

6. $\begin{cases} 4y - 1 = x \\ 6 + x = -y \end{cases}$ Ans: $\begin{vmatrix} -1 & 4 \\ 1 & 1 \end{vmatrix}$

Solve by the method of determinants.

7. $\begin{cases} 2x - y = 1 \\ 3x + 2y = -3 \end{cases}$ Ans: $x = -\frac{1}{7},$ $y = -1\frac{2}{7}$

8. $\begin{cases} \frac{1}{2}x - y = -1 \\ \frac{3}{4}x + y = 2 \end{cases}$ Ans: $x = \frac{4}{5},$ $y = 1\frac{2}{5}$

SUGGESTED TIMETABLE OF ASSIGNMENTS

Section	Page(s)	Level One	Level Two	Level Three
12.1	292	Odds 1-35	Odds 1-39	Odds 1-41
12.2	295	Odds 1-17	Odds 1-17	Odds 1-17
12.3	299	Odds 1-17	Odds 1-17	Odds 1-21
12.4	302	1st Day: Odds 1-11 2nd Day: Evens 2-12	Odds 1-11	Odds 1-11
12.5	306	1st Day: Odds 1-17 2nd Day: Evens 2-18	Odds 1-17	Odds 1-17
12.6	309	Optional	Odds 1-21	Odds 1-21
12.7	312	Optional	Odds 1-15	Odds 1-15
Review and Testing		3 days	2 days	2 days
Enrichment Topics		—	1 day	1 day
Total Days		10	10	10

CHAPTER 13:   PROBLEM SOLVING: TWO VARIABLES

Overview   Problem solving was encountered first in Section 3.6 and in Chapter 4 when the properties of equations were applied to one equation with one variable in order to solve word problems. Some problems, such as the ones in this chapter, seem more naturally suited to a solution by a system of equations. Students will have an opportunity to apply the techniques they learned in Chapter 12 as they solve problems in this chapter.

Section 13.1   A variety of word problems involving two unknown numbers is included in this lesson.

Section 13.2   The problems in this section deal exclusively with costs.

Section 13.3   The two-variable representation of two-digit numbers is explained.

Section 13.4   The basic formula for distance, $d = rt$, is used in this lesson. The use of tables to represent quantities in the problems may help students in this rather challenging type of word problem.

Section 13.5   The main purpose of this lesson is for students to learn to solve mixture problems by systems of linear equations.

Quiz for Sections 13.1–13.3

Solve each problem.

1. The sum of two numbers is 19. The difference of the two numbers is 6. Find the two numbers.
    Ans: $6\frac{1}{2}$ and $12\frac{1}{2}$

2. The sum of two numbers is -11. One number exceeds the other by 37. Find the two numbers.
    Ans: 13 and -24

3. Dave and Lisa sold a total of 26 magazine subscriptions for $1222. One subscription plan cost $55 and the other cost $42. Find the number of each they sold.
    Ans: 10 at $55; 16 at $42

4. A store sold shirts for $18.75 each and ties for $9.50 each. The total receipts were $2803.50. It sold 32 more shirts than ties. Find the number of each item that were sold.
    Ans: 110 shirts; 78 ties

5. The ten's digit of a two-digit number is 3 more than the one's digit. The sum of the digits is 15. Write the two-digit number.
    Ans: 96

6. The one's digit of a two-digit number is four times the ten's digit. The number is 4 more than 3 times the one's digit. Write the two-digit number.
    Ans: 28

Quiz for Sections 13.4—13.5

Solve each problem.

1. A small plane takes one hour to fly 150 miles with a tailwind. Returning against a headwind the same distance takes $1\frac{1}{2}$ hours. Find the plane's speed, x, in still air and the speed of the wind, y. **Ans: x = 125 mph; y = 25 mph**

	Time	Speed	Distance
With the wind	1 hr	x + y	?
Against the wind	?	x − y	?

2. To reach work, a person walks at 6 miles per hour to catch a bus. She then rides the bus for the rest of the distance at 30 miles per hour. The total distance is 13.2 miles and the total time needed is 0.6 hour. Find the time spent in walking and the time spent on the bus. **Ans: Walking: 0.2 hr(12 min); Riding: 0.4 hr(24 min)**

	Distance	Rate	Time
Walking	?	6 mph	x hr
Riding	?	30 mph	y hr
Total	13.2 mi		0.6 hr

3. A 6% acid solution is mixed with a 10% acid solution. How many grams of each solution are needed to form 500 grams of an 8% solution?
   Ans: 6% solution: 250 g;
          10% solution: 250 g

	Grams of Solution	Grams of Pure Acid
6% solution	x	0.06x
10% solution	y	?
8% solution	?	?

SUGGESTED TIMETABLE OF ASSIGNMENTS

Section	Page(s)	Level One	Level Two	Level Three
13.1	322	Odds 1-9	Odds 1-9	Odds 1-9
13.2	326	1st Day: Odds 1-7 2nd Day: Evens 2-8	All 1-8	All 1-8
13.3	330	1st Day: Odds 1-9 2nd Day: Evens 2-10	Odds 1-11	Odds 1-11
13.4	335-336	1st Day: Odds 1-5 2nd Day: Evens 2-6	1st Day: Odds 1-5 2nd Day: Evens 2-6	All 1-6
13.5	339-340	1st Day: Odds 1-11 2nd Day: Evens 2-12	1st Day: Odds 1-11 2nd Day: Evens 2-12	Odds 1-7; All 9-12
Review and Testing		3 days	2 days	2 days
Enrichment Topics		—	1 day	1 day
Total Days		12	10	8

CHAPTER 14:   PRODUCTS AND QUOTIENTS OF RATIONAL EXPRESSIONS

Overview   The chapter begins with the definition of a rational expression. The opening section also includes evaluating rational expressions and examining restrictions on the domain of the variable(s). The work extends to simplifying (reducing) rational expressions in preparation for the operations of multiplication and division. Note that addition and subtraction of rational expressions follow in Chapter 15. All of the work with rational expressions includes polynomials that are relatively easy to factor. Factoring of polynomials seems to be a difficult skill for low-average ability students to develop and maintain.

Section 14.1   In this section *rational expression* is defined. The polynomials used to form rational expressions will be polynomials over {rational numbers}. This lesson asks students to find restrictions on the domain of each variable. In doing this they review solving simple equations and also get some practice in evaluating expressions.

Section 14.2   In helping students to find the simplest name for a rational expression, you will want to emphasize the Multiplication Property of One.

Section 14.3   The Examples and Exercises of this section involve only rational expressions with numerators and denominators represented by monomials. Several steps may be combined in order to work problems of this type more expeditiously.

Section 14.4   In this section rational expressions with binomial numerators and denominators are used in the Examples and Exercises. The work is restricted to types that involve no factoring.

Section 14.5   A brief review of three types of factoring is included in this section. It is usually desirable to have students leave numerators and denominators in factored form.

Section 14.6   The Quotient Rule is postulated for rational expressions.

Section 14.7   In this lesson the Quotient Rule is applied to problems in which factoring of polynomials is also an essential step. Each quotient must first be expressed as a product, after which the techniques of Section 14.5 can be used.

Quiz for Sections 14.1–14.4

Evaluate each rational expression if x equals −3.

1. $\dfrac{x+2}{x^2-5}$ Ans: $-\dfrac{1}{4}$

2. $\dfrac{x^2-2x+3}{-2x^2+x-5}$ Ans: $-\dfrac{9}{13}$

Simplify. No divisor equals 0.

3. $\dfrac{x-2}{x^2-4}$ Ans: $\dfrac{1}{x+2}$

4. $\dfrac{3x^2-15x}{x^2-4x-5}$ Ans: $\dfrac{3x}{x+1}$

Multiply. Simplify where necessary.

5. $\dfrac{3x^2y}{5}\cdot\dfrac{10}{9xy}$ Ans: $\dfrac{2x}{3}$

6. $-\dfrac{4rt^2}{15s}\cdot\dfrac{3s^2}{20rt}$ Ans: $-\dfrac{st}{25}$

7. $\dfrac{x+5}{x+2}\cdot\dfrac{x+3}{x+5}$ Ans: $\dfrac{x+3}{x+2}$

8. $\dfrac{4(x+2y)}{x-3}\cdot\dfrac{3}{10(2y+x)}$ Ans: $\dfrac{6}{5(x-3)}$

Quiz for Sections 14.5–14.7

Multiply and simplify.

1. $\dfrac{2x+4}{x+3}\cdot\dfrac{x^2-9}{x+2}$ Ans: $2(x-3)$

2. $\dfrac{x^2+2x-3}{2x^2-2}\cdot\dfrac{6x}{3x+9}$ Ans: $\dfrac{x}{x+1}$

Divide and simplify.

3. $\dfrac{4}{x^3}\div\dfrac{10}{x}$ Ans: $\dfrac{2}{5x^2}$

4. $\dfrac{x^2+2x-3}{2x^2-2}\div\dfrac{x+3}{2x^2}$ Ans: $\dfrac{x^2}{x+1}$

5. $\dfrac{x^2-9}{6}\div\dfrac{x^2-6x+9}{3}$ Ans: $\dfrac{x+3}{2(x-3)}$

6. $\dfrac{x^2-x-6}{3x-9}\div(x^2-2x-8)$

   Ans: $\dfrac{1}{3(x-4)}$

SUGGESTED TIMETABLE OF ASSIGNMENTS

Section	Page(s)	Level One	Level Two	Level Three
14.1	348	Odds 1-31	Odds 1-31	Odds 1-31
14.2	351	Odds 1-31	Odds 1-31	Odds 1-31
14.3	354	Odds 1-23	Odds 1-23	Odds 1-23
14.4	357	Odds 1-21	Odds 1-21	Odds 1-21
14.5	361	Odds 1-11	Odds 1-13	Odds 1-15
14.6	364	Odds 1-19	Odds 1-21	Odds 1-23
14.7	367	1, 5, 9, 13, 17	Odds 1-17	Odds 1-21
Review and Testing		3 days	2 days	1 day
Enrichment Topics		—	1 day	1 day
Total Days		10	10	9

CHAPTER 15: SUMS AND DIFFERENCES OF RATIONAL EXPRESSIONS

Overview   Adding and subtracting with rational expressions may be a difficult skill for some students to develop. Many steps are involved and students must know many previously studied concepts very well in order to perform the steps correctly. As in the preceding chapter, the polynomial factoring is kept relatively simple in the Exercises. The main outcome to be expected of students is a demonstrated understanding of the process for adding and subtracting with rational expressions.

Section 15.1   The fundamental rules for the sum and difference of two rational expressions are stated in this section.

Section 15.2   This section is an extension of Section 15.1. Some of the Examples and Exercises may need to be simplified after the application of the Sum or Difference Rule.

Section 15.3   The goal of this section is for students to learn to find the least common multiple of two or more polynomials. A review of the meaning of the least common multiple of two or more counting numbers is included. For purposes of the work in this chapter it is desirable to express the least common multiple of two or more polynomials in factored form.

Section 15.4   As the title suggests, the work of this lesson will be restricted to expressions having monomial denominators. This approach should allow students to develop some proficiency in the process before the manipulative work gets complicated.

Section 15.5   All the Examples and Exercises of this section require no factoring of polynomial denominators. In each case the least common multiple is the product of the two denominators.

Section 15.6   This section includes addition and subtraction with rational expressions of the most general type. Students should be encouraged to arrange their work in a form that will help them proceed toward a solution in a step-by-step manner.

Section 15.7   It is probably good to have students note restriction on the domain of the variables in an equation before they transform the equation in any way. This will avoid the problem of students forgetting to check for so-called "extraneous" roots.

Quiz for Sections 15.1—15.4

Add or subtract. Simplify where necessary.

1. $\dfrac{x}{x+2} + \dfrac{2x}{x+2}$ Ans: $\dfrac{3x}{x+2}$

2. $\dfrac{4t}{t+5} - \dfrac{7t}{t+5}$ Ans: $-\dfrac{3t}{t+5}$

3. $\dfrac{x+2}{x+3} + \dfrac{x+4}{x+3}$ Ans: 2

4. $\dfrac{x^2+x}{x-5} - \dfrac{25+x}{x-5}$ Ans: $x+5$

Find each LCM.

5. $3x^2y;\ 2xy^2;\ 12x^3y$
   Ans: $12x^3y^2$

6. $x^2 - 2x;\ x^2 - 4;\ 2x^2 + 4x$
   Ans: $2x(x-2)(x+2)$

Add or subtract.

7. $\dfrac{2}{3x} - \dfrac{1}{4x}$ Ans: $\dfrac{5}{12x}$

8. $\dfrac{2a}{3bc} + \dfrac{b}{6ac}$ Ans: $\dfrac{4a^2 + b^2}{6abc}$

Quiz for Sections 15.5—15.7

Add or subtract.

1. $\dfrac{2}{x-4} + \dfrac{3}{x+2}$ Ans: $\dfrac{5x-8}{(x-4)(x+2)}$

2. $\dfrac{x+1}{2x-1} - \dfrac{3}{x-1}$ Ans: $\dfrac{x^2 - 6x + 2}{(2x-1)(x-1)}$

3. $\dfrac{x}{x^2+x-2} + \dfrac{2}{x^2-x-6}$
   Ans: $\dfrac{(x-2)(x+1)}{(x-1)(x+2)(x-3)}$

4. $\dfrac{3}{2x-12} - \dfrac{x-1}{x^2-36}$
   Ans: $\dfrac{x+20}{2(x-6)(x+6)}$

Solve and check each equation.

5. $\dfrac{3}{x} + \dfrac{2}{x-2} = \dfrac{1}{x}$ Ans: $x = 1$

6. $\dfrac{4}{x-1} = \dfrac{3}{x} + \dfrac{2}{x-1}$ Ans: $x = 3$

SUGGESTED TIMETABLE OF ASSIGNMENTS

Section	Page(s)	Level One	Level Two	Level Three
15.1	374	Odds 1-25	Odds 1-25	Odds 1-25
15.2	377	Odds 1-19	Odds 1-21	Odds 1-23
15.3	380	Odds 1-19	Odds 1-23	Odds 1-25
15.4	383	Odds 1-19	Odds 1-23	Odds 1-25
15.5	387	Odds 1-15	Odds 1-17	Odds 1-19
15.6	390-391	Odds 1-17	Odds 1-17	Odds 1-17
15.7	394	Optional	Odds 1-15	Odds 1-19
Review and Testing		3 days	2 days	1 day
Enrichment Topics		–	1 day	1 day
Total Days		9	10	9

CHAPTER 16: SYSTEMS OF INEQUALITIES

Overview   The material of this chapter is included because the study of inequalities has become standard in elementary algebra courses. Also, the work with systems of inequalities is a natural combination of the material studied in Chapters 5 and 12. The approach used in Chapter 16 provides students with an opportunity to learn more about the concepts of relation and the linear function. Furthermore, the manipulative algebra required will help students strengthen their understanding and improve their accuracy in fundamental skills. Finally, the emphasis given to graphs should provide students with increased knowledge and skill in graphical interpretation.

This chapter and those that follow are considered optional for Level One classes.

Section 16.1   Linear inequalities in two variables are introduced in this section. Students will have to be reminded that multiplying each side of an inequality by a negative number reverses the order.

Section 16.2   Students should understand that each linear function separates the co-ordinate plane into three regions. This concept will help students in making graphs of linear inequalities.

Section 16.3   This section parallels Section 16.2.

Section 16.4   In this section, a system of two sentences is studied as an example of a compound <u>and</u> sentence.

Section 16.5   Graphing of systems of linear sentences is extended to systems with three or more sentences.

Quiz for Sections 16.1–16.3

Write the slope-intercept form of each inequality.

1. $x - y + 2 > 0$ Ans: $y < x + 2$

2. $5x + 3y \leq 7$ Ans: $y \leq -\frac{5}{3}x + \frac{7}{3}$

Graph each inequality.

3. $y < -\frac{1}{2}x + 3$ Ans: The graph is the region below the dashed line $y = -\frac{1}{2}x + 3$.

4. $2x - y - 1 < 0$ Ans: The graph is the region to the left of the dashed line $y = 2x - 1$.

5. $y \leq -x + 3$ Ans: The graph is the region below and including the line $y = -x + 3$.

6. $3x - 4y \leq 8$ Ans: The graph is the region above and including the line $y = \frac{3}{4}x - 2$.

Quiz for Sections 16.4–16.5

Write a system of linear sentences for each graph.
The equations of the lines are $y = \frac{1}{2}x$ and $y = -\frac{1}{2}x$.

1.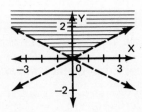

Ans:
$y > \frac{1}{2}x$
$y > -\frac{1}{2}x$

2.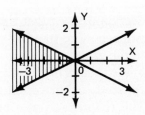

Ans:
$y \leq -\frac{1}{2}x$
$y \geq \frac{1}{2}x$

Graph each linear system.

3. $y \geq \frac{1}{2}x - 1$ Ans:
   $y < -x + \frac{3}{2}$

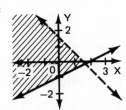

4. $x \leq 2$ Ans:
   $y \geq -2$
   $y \leq x + 2$

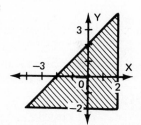

The vertices of a shaded region of a graph are given. Find the maximum and minimum values of k for each expression.

5. Vertices: $(0, 2), (3, -1), (-2, -2),$
   $(-4, 2)$ $k = 3x - 2y$
   Ans: Maximum value: 11, when
   x = 3, y = −1 Minimum value: −16,
   when x = −4, y = 2

6. Vertices: $(-3, 0), (2, 3), (4, -1),$
   $(1, -3)$ $k = 5x + 3y$
   Ans: Maximum value: 19, when
   x = 2, y = 3 Minimum value: −15,
   when x = −3, y = 0

SUGGESTED TIMETABLE OF ASSIGNMENTS

Section	Page(s)	Level One	Level Two	Level Three
16.1	402	Optional	Odds 1-27	Odds 1-27
16.2	405	Optional	Odds 1-17	Odds 1-17
16.3	409	Optional	Odds 1-23	Odds 1-23
16.4	414	Optional	Odds 1-11	Odds 1-11
16.5	416	Optional	Odds 1-11	Odds 1-11
Review and Testing	–		2 days	1 day
Enrichment Topics	–		1 day	1 day
Total Days	–		8	7

CHAPTER 17:   QUADRATIC FUNCTIONS

Overview   The quadratic function is studied in this chapter with emphasis on graphing and graphical interpretation. The graph of a parabola was introduced in Section 6.5. At that time it was presented simply as a function to be graphed. The standard form of the quadratic polynomial and the effects of the values of a, h, and k on the graph are presented. The highest and lowest points of the graph of a parabola are discussed in connection with the study of the vertex and the axis of the parabola.

This chapter and the one that follows are considered optional for Level One and Level Two classes.

Section 17.1   In this section, quadratic trinomials are used to form rules for quadratic functions, namely $y = ax^2 + bx + c$.

Section 17.2   Showing several graphs of parabolas can generate a good discussion about domain and range.

Section 17.3   Several quadratic functions whose rules are of the form $y = ax^2$ are graphed to show the effect of the coefficient a on the graphs.

Section 17.4   The main difficulty that students will have in this section is to identify the correct value for h. For example, there is a natural tendency for students to think that the graph of $y = (x - 2)^2$ is 2 units to the left of the graph of $y = x^2$ rather than to its right.

Section 17.5   In this section, functions defined by rules of the forms $y = ax^2$, $y = a(x - h)^2$, and $h = a(x - h)^2 + k$ are compared by showing their graphs in the same coordinate plane.

Section 17.6   The emphasis in this section is on changing a quadratic polynomial to the standard form, $a(x - h)^2 + k$.

Section 17.7   Students may need help on the idea that a parabola has a highest point if it opens downward and a lowest point if it opens upward.

Quiz for Sections 17.1—17.4

Compute f(−2), f(0), and f(3) for each function.

1. $(x, y) : y = -x^2 + x - 2$
     Ans: $-8, -2, -8$

2. $(x, y) : y = 2x^2 - 3x + 5$
     Ans: $19, 5, 14$

Graph each function.

3. $(x, y) : y = -x^2 + 1$
     Ans: The highest point is $(0, 1)$.
     Other points are: $(1, 0)$,
     $(-1, 0), (2, -3), (-2, -3)$.

4. $(x, y) : y = x^2 - 6x + 7$
     Ans: The lowest point is $(3, -2)$.
     Other points are: $(0, 7), (1, 2)$,
     $(2, -1), (4, -1), (5, 2), (6, 7)$.

Graph each pair of functions in the same coordinate plane.

5. $y = \frac{3}{2}x^2$; $y = -\frac{1}{4}x^2$

Ans: For the first equation, the lowest point is $(0, 0)$. Other points are: $(1, \frac{3}{2})$, $(-1, \frac{3}{2})$, $(2, 6)$, $(-2, 6)$. For the second equation, the highest point is $(0, 0)$. Other points are: $(-2, -1)$, $(2, -1)$, $(-4, -4)$, $(4, -4)$.

6. $y = x^2 - 1$; $y = x^2 + 1$

Ans: For the first equation, the lowest points is $(0, -1)$. Other points are: $(-2, 3)$, $(-1, 0)$, $(1, 0)$, $(2, 3)$. For the second equation, the lowest points is $(0, 1)$. Other points are: $(-2, 5)$, $(-1, 2)$, $(1, 2)$, $(2, 5)$.

Write the number of units and the direction the graph of the first function can be moved to obtain the graph of the second function.

7. $y = \frac{5}{2}x^2$; $y = \frac{5}{2}(x - 6)^2$

Ans: 6 units right

8. $y = -\frac{3}{4}x^2$; $y = -\frac{3}{4}(x + \frac{5}{4})^2$

Ans: $\frac{5}{4}$ units left

Quiz for Sections 17.5–17.7

Write an equation of a function for which the graph is obtained as described in each exercise.

1. The graph of $y = -4x^2$ is moved 5 units to the right.
   Ans: $y = -4(x - 5)^2$

2. The graph of $y = \frac{7}{2}(x - \frac{1}{2})^2$ is moved 2 units downward.
   Ans: $y = \frac{7}{2}(x - \frac{1}{2})^2 - 2$

3. Write $x^2 - 4x + 7$ in the form $a(x - h)^2 + k$. Ans: $(x - 2)^2 + 3$

4. Write $x^2 + 5x - 1$ in the form $a(x - h)^2 + k$. Ans: $(x + \frac{5}{2})^2 - \frac{29}{4}$

5. Write the coordinates of the vertex of the graph of $y = -(x - 6)^2$ Ans: $(6, 0)$

6. Write the coordinates of the vertex of the graph of $y = \frac{1}{2}(x + \frac{3}{2})^2 + \frac{1}{4}$ Ans: $(-\frac{3}{2}, \frac{1}{4})$

SUGGESTED TIMETABLE OF ASSIGNMENTS

Section	Page(s)	Level One	Level Two	Level Three
17.1	424	Optional	Optional	Odds 1-25
17.2	427	Optional	Optional	Odds 1-11
17.3	430-431	Optional	Optional	Odds 1-13
17.4	434	Optional	Optional	Odds 1-17
17.5	439	Optional	Optional	Odds 1-17
17.6	441	Optional	Optional	Odds 1-19
17.7	444	Optional	Optional	Odds 1-21
Review and Testing	—	—	—	1 day
Enrichment Topics	—	—	—	1 day
Total Days	—	—	—	9

CHAPTER 18: QUADRATIC EQUATIONS

Overview   The first section covers the graphical method, and the second section covers the factoring method. Then in the third section, special quadratic equations of the form $(x - a)^2 = k$ are solved by inspection. This section is preparatory material for the method of completing the square that is presented in Section 18.4. The quadratic formula is then presented in Section 18.5

This chapter is considered optional for Level One and Level Two classes.

Section 18.1   You may want to show students graphs of functions such as $y = x^2 - x - 2$ and $y = -x^2 + x + 2$ in the same coordinate plane.

Section 18.2   A common error is for students to say that the solutions of an equation such as $(x + 3)(x + 1) = 0$ are 3 and 1. This can be avoided by having students actually write the equivalent <u>or</u> sentence, $x + 3 = 0$ <u>or</u> $x + 1 = 0$.

Section 18.3   Identification of trinomial squares is reviewed. However, emphasis is given to factoring over the set of rational numbers.

Section 18.4   The work of the section leads to the steps for solving the general quadratic $ax^2 + bx + c = 0$ by the method of completing the square.

Section 18.5   If the material of Sections 18.3 and 18.4 has been developed carefully, students should be able to follow the steps of the development of the quadratic formula.

Section 18.6   You may need several examples to develop the concept that a perfect square discriminant guarantees rational solutions.

Section 18.7   This section includes two kinds of problems that require quadratic equations for their solution: areas of rectangles and squares and products of integers.

Quiz for Sections 18.1–18.3

Graph $y = x^2 + 4x + 2$. Estimate the solutions of each equation.

1. $x^2 + 4x + 2 = 1$
    Ans: (approx.) $-0.3, -3.7$

2. $x^2 + 4x + 2 = 3$
    Ans: (approx.) $0.2, -4.2$

Solve by factoring.

3. $x^2 + 2x - 8 = 0$
    Ans: $x = 2, x = -4$

4. $2x^2 + 5x - 3 = 0$
    Ans: $x = \frac{1}{2}, x = -3$

Solve.

5. $(x + 3)^2 = 36$

   Ans: $x = 3, x = -9$

6. $(x - \frac{3}{4})^2 = \frac{9}{4}$

   Ans: $x = \frac{9}{4}, x = -\frac{3}{4}$

Quiz for Sections 18.4–18.7

Solve by completing the square.

1. $x^2 - 4x + 3 = 0$

   Ans: $x = 3, x = 1$

2. $x^2 - 5x - 4 = 0$

   Ans: $\dfrac{5 + \sqrt{41}}{2}, \dfrac{5 - \sqrt{41}}{2}$

Solve by the quadratic formula.

3. $6x^2 + x - 2 = 0$
   Ans: $x = \frac{1}{2}, x = -\frac{2}{3}$

4. $8x^2 - 2x - 15 = 0$
   Ans: $x = -\frac{5}{4}, x = \frac{3}{2}$

Compute the value of $b^2 - 4ac$ for each equation. Then write
Rational, Irrational, or Not Real for the solutions.

5. $x^2 + 5x - 3 = 0$
   Ans: 37; Irrational

6. $2x^2 - 3x + 4 = 0$
   Ans: -23, Not Real

Solve.

7. The product of two consecutive integers is 72. Find two pairs of such integers.
   Ans: 8 and 9; -8 and -9

SUGGESTED TIMETABLE OF ASSIGNMENTS

Section	Page(s)	Level One	Level Two	Level Three
18.1	452	Optional	Optional	Odds 1-17
18.2	455	Optional	Optional	Odds 1-35
18.3	458	Optional	Optional	Odds 1-35
18.4	462	Optional	Optional	Odds 1-27
18.5	465	Optional	Optional	Odds 1-23
18.6	468	Optional	Optional	Odds 1-27
18.7	471	Optional	Optional	Odds 1-7
Review and Testing	–	–	–	1 day
Enrichment Topics	–	–	–	1 day
Total Days	–	–	–	9

SUGGESTED TIMETABLE

Overview   The following *Suggested Timetable* for three levels of ability (as described on page M-9) is coordinated with the *Suggested Timetables of Assignments* that appear in the *Lesson Plan Guide*. Note that the total number of days for each chapter includes three days per chapter for review and testing for Level 1, two or three days for Level Two, and one or two days for Level Three. The *Suggested Timetable* should be considered as a guideline only.

INTRODUCTORY ALGEBRA 2

Chapter	Level One Sections	Level One Days	Level Two Sections	Level Two Days	Level Three Sections	Level Three Days
1	All	12	All	11	All	10
2	All	11	All	10	All	9
3	All	12	All	11	All	9
4	All	10	All	10	All	8
5	All	11	All	11	All	9
6	All	9	All	10	All	9
7	All	9	All	9	All	9
8	All	14	All	11	All	10
9	All	12	All	11	All	10
10	All	13	All	12	All	10
11	All	10	All	10	All	10
12	12.1–12.5	10	All	10	All	10
13	All	12	All	10	All	8
14	All	10	All	10	All	9
15	15.1–15.6	9	All	10	All	9
16	Omit	0	All	8	All	7
17	Omit	0	Omit	0	All	9
18	Omit	0	Omit	0	All	9
Cumulative Reviews		6		6		6
Total Days		**170**		**170**		**170**

Introductory
ALGEBRA 2

Fourth Edition / Russell F. Jacobs

Harcourt Brace Jovanovich, Publishers

New York Chicago San Francisco Atlanta Dallas *and* London

ABOUT THE AUTHOR

RUSSELL F. JACOBS

*Formerly Mathematics Supervisor for
the Phoenix Union High School System
Phoenix, Arizona*

EDITORIAL ADVISORS

Muriel Altenburg
*Mathematics Teacher
Eleanor Roosevelt High School
Greenbelt, Maryland*

Roy Johnson
*Formerly Project Resource Teacher
San Diego Unified School District
San Diego, California*

Brother Neal Golden
*Chairman, Department of
Mathematics and Computer Science
Brother Martin High School
New Orleans, Louisiana*

Vincent O'Connor
*Curriculum Specialist
Milwaukee Public Schools
Milwaukee, Wisconsin*

John Stewart
*Chairman, Department of Mathematics
North High School
Akron, Ohio*

PICTURE CREDITS

KEY: *t* top; *b* bottom

Cover: Jerome Kresch

p. 47 HBJ Photo; p. 70 Will McIntyre from Photo Researchers; p. 80 UPI; p. 81 Focus on Sports; p. 84 Department of Conservation & Development, Raleigh, N.C.; p. 85 Ira Merritt/Merritt Productions; p. 86 Hewlett-Packard Corp.; p. 91 Ben Schnall from Frederic Lewis; p. 92 TWA; p. 95 Erika Stone from Peter Arnold; p. 96 H. Armstrong Roberts; p. 119 Richard R. Collins from DPI; p. 141 Redwood Empire Association; p. 144 Freda Leinwand from Monkmeyer; p. 173 (*t*) HBJ Photo, (*b*) Mount Wilson and Palomar Observatories; p. 201 UPI; p. 202 L.L.T. Rhodes from Taurus; p. 229 (*t*) Pan American, (*b*) H. Armstrong Roberts; p. 257 Chester Higgens, Jr. from Photo Researchers; p. 258 Grant Heilman; p. 313 Ray Ellis from Photo Researchers; p. 324 American Airlines; p. 326 HBJ Photo; p. 332 (*t*) American Airlines, (*b*) Chevrolet Motor Division; p. 340 HBJ Photo; p. 341 UPI; p. 368 HBJ Photo; p. 395 Ray Ellis from Rapho/Photo Researchers; p. 396 J. Allan Cash from Rapho/Photo Researchers; p. 418 Frederic Lewis; p. 445 Harold Lambert from Frederic Lewis; p. 472 Tom Tracy from Alpha

Printed in the United States of America

ISBN 0-15-357871-8

Contents

Chapter 1:   Operations on Numbers   1
Sections   1.1   Opposites and Absolute Value   2
                   1.2   Addition   4
                   1.3   Subtraction   8
                   1.4   Multiplication   10
                   1.5   Division   14
                   1.6   Order of Operations   17
                   1.7   Powers   19
Features   *Calculator Exercises* 21 ● Saving Energy and Money 22
Review and Testing   *Mid-Chapter Review* 13 ● *Chapter Summary* 23 ● *Chapter Review* 23

Chapter 2:   Real Numbers   25
Sections   2.1   Real Numbers   26
                   2.2   Addition Properties   30
                   2.3   Multiplication Properties   34
                   2.4   Special Properties   38
                   2.5   Multiplying and Factoring   42
                   2.6   Combining Like Terms   45
Features: *Career:* Statistician 47 ● *Calculator Exercises* 47
Review and Testing   *Mid-Chapter Review* 37 ● *Chapter Summary* 48 ● *Chapter Review* 49

Chapter 3:   Equations   51
Sections   3.1   Addition and Subtraction   52
                   3.2   Multiplication and Division   55
                   3.3   Two or More Operations   58
                   3.4   Like Terms in Equations   62
                   3.5   A Variable on Both Sides   65
                   3.6   Problem Solving with Formulas   68
Features   *Calculator Exercises* 61 ● Unit Price 70
Review and Testing   *Mid-Chapter Review* 61 ● *Chapter Summary* 71 ● *Chapter Review* 71

Chapter 4:   Problem Solving: One Variable   73
Sections   4.1   Problem Solving: Words to Equations   74
                   4.2   Problem Solving: Conditions to Equations   78
                   4.3   Problem Solving: Perimeter   83
                   4.4   Problem Solving: Using Per Cent   88
                   4.5   Problem Solving with Formulas   92
Features   *Calculator Exercises* 82 ● *Career:* Engineering Technician 96
Review and Testing   *Mid-Chapter Review* 87 ● *Chapter Summary* 97 ● *Chapter Review* 97

Chapter 5:   Properties of Order   99
Sections   5.1   Graphs of Inequalities   100
                   5.2   Properties of Order   104
                   5.3   Addition and Subtraction   107
                   5.4   Solving Inequalities   111
                   5.5   Multiplication and Division   113
                   5.6   Problem Solving with Inequalities   116

Features   *Calculator Exercises* 110 • *Compound Interest* 119
Review and Testing   *Mid-Chapter Review* 110 • *Chapter Summary* 120 • *Chapter Review* 120

Chapter 6: Relations and Functions   123

Sections   6.1 Graphs of Ordered Pairs   124
        6.2 Points and Ordered Pairs   127
        6.3 Relations   130
        6.4 Functions   134
        6.5 Graphs of Functions   138
        6.6 Problem Solving: Using Functions   141

Features   *Calculator Exercises* 133 • *Career:* Air Conditioning Technician 144
Review and Testing   *Mid-Chapter Review* 133 • *Chapter Summary* 145 • *Chapter Review* 145
        Cumulative Review: Chapters 1-6 147

Chapter 7: Powers   151

Sections   7.1 Products of Powers   152
        7.2 Quotients of Powers and Zero Exponents   155
        7.3 Negative Exponents   159
        7.4 Powers of Products and Quotients   163
        7.5 Powers of Powers   166
        7.6 Scientific Notation   170

Features   *Calculator Exercises* 162 • *Space Technology* 173
Review and Testing   *Mid-Chapter Review* 162 • *Chapter Summary* 174 • *Chapter Review* 174

Chapter 8: Roots   177

Sections   8.1 Numbers in Radical Form   178
        8.2 Products   181
        8.3 Simplifying Radicals   184
        8.4 Simplifying Radical Expressions   187
        8.5 Sums and Differences   191
        8.6 Quotients   194
        8.7 Approximations   197

Features   *Calculator Exercises* 190 • *Career:* Meteorologist 201
Review and Testing   *Mid-Chapter Review* 190 • *Chapter Summary* 203 • *Chapter Review* 203

Chapter 9: Polynomials   205

Sections   9.1 Monomials   206
        9.2 Operations with Monomials   208
        9.3 Polynomials   211
        9.4 Addition and Subtraction   215
        9.5 Multiplication   218
        9.6 Division   222
        9.7 Division with Remainders   225

Features   *Calculator Exercises* 214 • *Distance to the Horizon* 229
Review and Testing   *Mid-Chapter Review* 214 • *Chapter Summary* 230 • *Chapter Review* 230

Chapter 10: Factoring Polynomials   233

Sections   10.1 Common Monomial Factors   234
        10.2 Quadratic Polynomials   237
        10.3 Factoring $x^2 + bx + c$ 240

	10.4	Factoring $ax^2 + bx + c$	244
	10.5	Difference of Two Squares	248
	10.6	Trinomial Squares	251
	10.7	Combined Types of Factoring	254

Features *Calculator Exercises 247 • Career: Life Scientist 257*
Review and Testing *Mid-Chapter Review 247 • Chapter Summary 259 • Chapter Review 259*

Chapter 11: Linear Equations **261**
Sections 11.1 Graphs of Linear Equations 262
      11.2 *Y* Intercept 265
      11.3 Slope of a Line 268
      11.4 Slope Formula 271
      11.5 Parallel Lines 276
      11.6 *X* Intercept 279
      11.7 Problem Solving: Linear Functions 282

Features *Calculator Exercises 275 • Latitude and Longitude 285*
Review and Testing *Mid-Chapter Review 275 • Chapter Summary 286 • Chapter Review 286*

Chapter 12: Systems of Linear Equations **289**
Sections 12.1 Linear Equations 290
      12.2 Graphs 293
      12.3 Systems of Equations 296
      12.4 Substitution Method 300
      12.5 Multiplication/Addition Method 304
      12.6 2×2 Determinants 307
      12.7 Solving Systems by Determinants 310

Features *Calculator Exercises 303 • Career: Pharmacist 313*
Review and Testing *Mid-Chapter Review 303 • Chapter Summary 314 • Chapter Review 314*
      Cumulative Review: Chapters 7-12 316

Chapter 13: Problem Solving: Two Variables **319**
Sections 13.1 Problem Solving: Number Problems 320
      13.2 Problem Solving: Money Problems 323
      13.3 Problem Solving: Digit Problems 327
      13.4 Problem Solving: Distance/Rate/Time 332
      13.5 Problem Solving: Mixture Problems 337

Features *Calculator Exercises 331 • Longitude and Time Zones 341*
Review and Testing *Mid-Chapter Review 331 • Chapter Summary 342 • Chapter Review 342*

Chapter 14: Products and Quotients of Rational Expressions **345**
Sections 14.1 Rational Expressions 346
      14.2 Simplifying Rational Expressions 349
      14.3 Multiplying Rational Expressions 352
      14.4 Binomial Numerators and Denominators 355
      14.5 Trinomial Numerators and Denominators 359
      14.6 Dividing Rational Expressions 362
      14.7 More Quotients 365

Features *Calculator Exercises 358 • Career: Electrician 368*
Review and Testing *Mid-Chapter Review 358 • Chapter Summary 369 • Chapter Review 369*

Chapter 15: Sums and Differences of Rational Expressions 371

Sections
15.1 Sums/Differences: Like Denominators 372
15.2 More Sums and Differences 375
15.3 Least Common Multiple of Polynomials 378
15.4 Unlike Monomial Denominators 381
15.5 Sums/Differences: Unlike Denominators 385
15.6 More Sums and Differences 388
15.7 Equations with Rational Expressions 392

Features *Calculator Exercises 384 • Rate of Work 395*
Review and Testing *Mid-Chapter Review 384 • Chapter Summary 397 • Chapter Review 397*

Chapter 16: Systems of Inequalities 399

Sections
16.1 Inequalities in Two Variables 400
16.2 Graphs of Inequalities with $<$ and $>$ 403
16.3 Graphs of Inequalities with $\leq$ and $\geq$ 406
16.4 Graphs of Systems of Inequalities 411
16.5 Systems of Three or More Inequalities 415

Features *Calculator Exercises 410 • Career: Production Planner 417*
Review and Testing *Mid-Chapter Review 410 • Chapter Summary 419 • Chapter Review 419*

Chapter 17: Quadratic Functions 421

Sections
17.1 Quadratic Functions 422
17.2 Graphs of Quadratic Functions 425
17.3 Functions Defined by $y = ax^2$ 428
17.4 Functions Defined by $y = a(x - h)^2$ 432
17.5 Functions Defined by $y = a(x - h)^2 + k$ 436
17.6 Standard Form of Quadratic Polynomials 440
17.7 Vertex and Axis of a Parabola 442

Features *Calculator Exercises 435 • Gravity 445*
Review and Testing *Mid-Chapter Review 435 • Chapter Summary 446 • Chapter Review 446*

Chapter 18: Quadratic Equations 449

Sections
18.1 Quadratic Equations and Graphs 450
18.2 Solving by Factoring 453
18.3 Special Quadratic Equations 456
18.4 Completing the Square 460
18.5 The Quadratic Formula 463
18.6 The Discriminant 466
18.7 Problem Solving with Quadratic Equations 469

Features *Calculator Exercises 459 • Career: Industrial Production Technician 472*
Review and Testing *Mid-Chapter Review 459 • Chapter Summary 473 • Chapter Review 473*
Cumulative Review: Chapters 13-18 475

Appendix: Basic Programming 479
A-1 Computer Programming Statements 479
A-2 Computer Programming Operations 481
A-3 READ and DATA Statements 484
A-4 IF Statements 486
A-5 FOR and NEXT Statements 488

Glossary 490
Index 493
Answers to Selected Exercises 497

CHAPTER 1

Operations on Numbers

Sections

1.1 Opposites and Absolute Value

1.2 Addition

1.3 Subtraction

1.4 Multiplication

1.5 Division

1.6 Order of Operations

1.7 Powers

Features

Calculator Exercises: Evaluating Powers

Special Topic Application: Saving Energy and Money

Review and Testing

Review Capsules

Mid-Chapter Review

Chapter Summary

Chapter Review

OBJECTIVES: To write the simplest name of the opposite of a number
To simplify a numeral involving the absolute value symbol
To identify which of two numbers has the greater absolute value

1.1 Opposites and Absolute Value

Note on this number line that 3 and −3 (negative 3) are the same distance from 0 <u>and</u> are in opposite directions from 0. Thus, 3 and −3 are **opposites.**

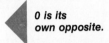

0 is its
own opposite.

The symbol for the opposite of a number is the dash, −.

Table 1	Number	Opposite	Simplest Form of the Opposite
	−5	−(−5)	5
	2	−2	−2
	0	−0	0

The opposite of a negative number is positive. $-(-7) = 7$
The opposite of a positive number is negative. $-7 = -7$
The opposite of 0 is 0. $-0 = 0$

To indicate distance, but <u>not</u> direction, from zero, you use <u>absolute value.</u> Since 3 and −3 are the same distance from 0, they have the same **absolute value.**

The absolute value of 3 is 3.   The absolute value of −3 is 3.

The symbol │ │ is used to represent absolute value.

Table 2	Absolute Value	Meaning	Value
	$|-5|$	Distance of −5 from 0	5
	$|2|$	Distance of 2 from 0	2
	$|0|$	Distance of 0 from 0	0
	$-|-4|$	Opposite of the distance of −4 from 0	−4

The absolute value of a positive number equals the number. The absolute value of a negative number equals the opposite of the number. The absolute value of 0 equals 0.

$|7| = 7$
$|-7| = 7$
$|0| = 0$

▲ $|x| = x$ if $x \geq 0$; $|x| = -x$ if $x < 0$.

Remind students that −x does not necessarily represent a negative number.

example 1

Which number has the greater absolute value?

a. −15 or 9   **b.** −8 or 13

Solutions:

a. $|-15| = 15$; $|9| = 9$ **Answer:** −15

b. $|-8| = 8$; $|13| = 13$ **Answer:** 13

CLASSROOM EXERCISES

Write the opposite of each number in simplest form. (Table 1)

1. −25 25
2. 0 0
3. −0.001 0.001
4. 0.001 −0.001
5. $-\frac{2}{3}$ $\frac{2}{3}$

6. $-4\frac{1}{2}$ $4\frac{1}{2}$
7. $8\frac{7}{8}$ $-8\frac{7}{8}$
8. $-(-1\frac{2}{3})$ $-1\frac{2}{3}$
9. −(−8.5) −8.5
10. −(−12) −12

Simplify. (Table 2)

11. $|9|$ 9
12. $|-13|$ 13
13. $|-0|$ 0
14. $|-2.38|$ 2.38
15. $|\frac{4}{5}|$ $\frac{4}{5}$

16. $|-3\frac{5}{8}|$ $3\frac{5}{8}$
17. $|0.053|$ 0.053
18. $-|-47|$ −47
19. $|-(-\frac{1}{4})|$ $\frac{1}{4}$
20. $|-100|$ 100

21. $-|0.01|$ −0.01
22. $-|8.7|$ −8.7
23. $-|-2.5|$ −2.5
24. $-|-\frac{1}{2}|$ $-\frac{1}{2}$
25. $-|-2\frac{1}{2}|$ $-2\frac{1}{2}$

Which number has the greater absolute value? (Example 1)

26. 42 or −37 42
27. 12 or −3 12
28. 7 or −2 7
29. −5 or 4 −5
30. −3 or −8 −8

WRITTEN EXERCISES

See the Teacher's Manual for the suggested assignments.
Goal: To write the absolute value of a number
Sample Problems: $|8|$; $|-7|$ **Answers:** 8; 7

Write the opposite of each number in simplest form. (Table 1)

1. 23 −23
2. −41 41
3. −0.12 0.12
4. 0.03 −0.03
5. 0 0

6. −1 1
7. $\frac{3}{5}$ $-\frac{3}{5}$
8. $1\frac{3}{8}$ $-1\frac{3}{8}$
9. $-5\frac{6}{7}$ $5\frac{6}{7}$
10. $-\frac{2}{7}$ $\frac{2}{7}$

Simplify. (Table 2)

11. $|-18|$ 18
12. $|-35|$ 35
13. $|227|$ 227
14. $|508|$ 508
15. $|\frac{7}{8}|$ $\frac{7}{8}$

16. $|\frac{2}{3}|$ $\frac{2}{3}$
17. $|-5\frac{1}{8}|$ $5\frac{1}{8}$
18. $|-3\frac{3}{4}|$ $3\frac{3}{4}$
19. $|0.083|$ 0.083
20. $|0.006|$ 0.006

21. $|-2.73|$ 2.73
22. $|-5.18|$ 5.18
23. $|-(-23)|$ 23
24. $|-(-72)|$ 72
25. $-|-6.8|$ −6.8

Which number has the greater absolute value? (Example 1)

26. −23 or 21 −23
27. 12 or 7 12
28. −23 or 6 −23
29. 23 or −6 23

30. −8 or −7 −8
31. −13 or −8 −13
32. 7 or −3 7
33. 13 or −5 13

OBJECTIVES: To add two negative numbers
To add a positive and a negative number
To add 0 and any number

1.2 Addition

You can use this rule for adding on the number line.

Rule for Adding on the Number Line

1. Graph the first addend.
2. From this point draw an arrow for the second addend.
   If this addend is negative, draw the arrow to the left.
   If this addend is positive, draw the arrow to the right.
3. Read the coordinate of the point where the arrow ends.

Table Problems	Solution
1. $-2+(-7)$	$-2+(-7)=-9$
2. $-7+9$ NOTE: $\lvert 9 \rvert > \lvert -7 \rvert$	$-7+9=2$
3. $-8+5$ NOTE: $\lvert -8 \rvert > \lvert 5 \rvert$	$-8+5=-3$
4. $-6+6$ NOTE: $\lvert -6 \rvert = \lvert 6 \rvert$	$-6+6=0$

Problem **1** above shows that <u>the sum of two negative numbers is a negative number</u>. The following rule tells how to find the sum of two negative numbers without using the number line.

Rule for Adding Two Negative Numbers

1. Add the absolute values.
2. Write the opposite of the result.

---

example 1   Add: $-5.6+(-3.2)$

Solution: ① Add the absolute values. ⟶ $\lvert -5.6 \rvert + \lvert -3.2 \rvert = 5.6 + 3.2 = 8.8$

         ② Write the opposite of the result. ⟶ -8.8

P-1 **Add.**

a. $-2+(-7)$ -9 **b.** $-\frac{1}{4}+(-2\frac{1}{4})$ $-2\frac{1}{2}$ **c.** $-4.7+0$ -4.7 ◀ The sum of any number *n* and 0 is *n*.

Problems **2–4** show that <u>the sum of a positive number and a negative number may be a positive number, a negative number, or zero</u>. The following rules tell how to use absolute value to find the sum of a positive and a negative number without using the number line.

> ### Rules for Adding a Negative Number and a Positive Number
>
> 1. Subtract the lesser absolute value from the greater absolute value.
>
> 2. The answer is positive if the positive number has the greater absolute value. $8+(-3)=5$
>
>   The answer is negative if the negative number has the greater absolute value. $5+(-7)=-2$
>
>   The answer is zero if the two absolute values are equal. $9+(-9)=0$

example 2

Add: $-9.7+15.2$ ◀ $|15.2| > |-9.7|$

Solution:

1. Subtract the lesser absolute value from the greater. ⟶ $|15.2|-|-9.7|=15.2-9.7$
   $$=5.5$$

2. The answer is positive because the positive number has the greater absolute value. ⟶ $-9.7+15.2=5.5$ In this case the difference is the answer.

P-2 **Add: a.** $-7+9$ 2 **b.** $5\frac{1}{4}+(-3\frac{3}{4})$ $1\frac{1}{2}$ **c.** $-23.1+(25.7)$ 2.6

example 3

Add: $-13.3+8.6$ ◀ $|-13.3| > |8.6|$

Solution:

1. Subtract the lesser absolute value from the greater. ⟶ $|-13.3|-|8.6|=13.3-8.6$
   $$=4.7$$

2. The answer is negative because the negative number has the greater absolute value. ⟶ $-13.3+8.6=-4.7$
   In this case the opposite of the difference is the answer.

P-3 **Add.**

a. $-11 + 8$ –3 **b.** $-6\frac{1}{3} + 5\frac{2}{3}$ $-\frac{2}{3}$ **c.** $-8.5 + 1.1$ –7.4

Since the absolute values of opposites are equal,

<u>the sum of opposites is 0</u>.

$$(-3) + (3) = |-3| - |3|$$
$$= 3 - 3$$
$$= 0$$

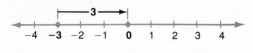

CLASSROOM EXERCISES

Match each of Exercises 1–4 with one of the graphs **a–d.** (Table)

1. $1 + (-6)$ b   **2.** $-7 + 11$ c   **3.** $4 + (-7)$ d   **4.** $-5 + 6$ a

a.

b.

c.

d.

Add. (Example 1)

5. $-28 + (-12)$ –40   **6.** $-4.3 + (-1.5)$ –5.8   **7.** $-3\frac{1}{2} + (-2\frac{1}{2})$ –6

8. $-19 + (-13)$ –32   **9.** $-0.5 + (-0.2)$ –0.7   **10.** $-0.05 + (-0.09)$
                                                                                    –0.14

(Example 2)

11. $28 + (-12)$ 16   **12.** $-16 + 32$ 16   **13.** $-2.4 + 5.8$ 3.4

14. $0.28 + (-0.13)$ 0.15   **15.** $-\frac{2}{5} + \frac{3}{5}$ $\frac{1}{5}$ **16.** $-\frac{1}{3} + \frac{2}{3}$ $\frac{1}{3}$

(Example 3)

17. $-36 + 30$ –6   **18.** $52 + (-61)$ –9   –3.3
                                                              19. $22.6 + (-25.9)$

20. $-16.8 + 9.3$ –7.5   **21.** $-12\frac{5}{8} + 5\frac{1}{8}$ $-7\frac{1}{2}$ **22.** $3\frac{3}{4} + (-6\frac{1}{4})$ $-2\frac{1}{2}$

23. $-56 + 56$ 0   **24.** $38\frac{1}{9} + (-38\frac{1}{9})$ 0   **25.** $2.18 + (-2.18)$ 0

WRITTEN EXERCISES

See the Teacher's Manual for the suggested assignments.

Goal: To add positive and negative numbers

Sample Problems: a. $(-49) + (52)$ **b.** $(-32) + (-12)$

Answers: a. 3 **b.** -44

Add. (Example 1)

1. $-23 + (-19)$ $_{-42}$

2. $-38 + (-17)$ $_{-55}$

3. $-47 + (-59)$ $_{-106}$

4. $-66 + (-48)$ $_{-114}$

5. $0 + (-0.08)$ $_{-0.08}$

6. $-17.8 + (-9.5)$ $_{-27.3}$

(Example 2)

7. $26 + (-18)$ $_8$

8. $-24 + 32$ $_8$

9. $14.4 + (-9.7)$ $_{4.7}$

10. $12.3 + (-7.9)$ $_{4.4}$

11. $-0.12 + 0.25$ $_{0.13}$

12. $-2.3 + 8.6$ $_{6.3}$

(Example 3)

13. $-39 + 14$ $_{-25}$

14. $-24 + 15$ $_{-9}$

15. $23 + (-55)$ $_{-32}$

16. $25 + (-44)$ $_{-19}$

17. $-28.7 + 19.8$ $_{-8.9}$

18. $-43.3 + 29.7$ $_{-13.6}$

19. $22 + (-22)$ $_0$

20. $37 + (-37)$ $_0$

21. $-2.16 + 2.16$ $_0$

22. $46.8 + (-46.8)$ $_0$

23. $-4.17 + 4.17$ $_0$

24. $0.98 + (-0.98)$ $_0$

(Examples 1–3)

25. $-24 + 14$ $_{-10}$

26. $-20 + (-38)$ $_{-58}$

27. $-31 + 47$ $_{16}$

28. $3.2 + (-2.1)$ $_{1.1}$

29. $-29.6 + (-15.9)$ $_{-45.5}$

30. $0.38 + (-0.45)$ $_{-0.07}$

31. $4.67 + (-4.67)$ $_0$

32. $-\frac{2}{3} + \frac{5}{3}$ $_1$

33. $-2.13 + (-4.84)$ $_{-6.97}$

34. $-\frac{9}{13} + \frac{7}{13}$ $_{-\frac{2}{13}}$

35. $-81.3 + 81.3$ $_0$

36. $\frac{11}{15} + (-\frac{13}{15})$ $_{-\frac{2}{15}}$

MORE CHALLENGING EXERCISES

37. $24 + (-19 + 7)$ $_{12}$

38. $-16 + (-12 + 8)$ $_{-20}$

39. $(-34 + 17) + (-5)$ $_{-22}$

40. $(-56 + 29) + 16$ $_{-11}$

41. $-58 + (-7 + 18)$ $_{-47}$

42. $27 + (-39 + 12)$ $_0$

43. $(-13.6 + 10.3) + 15.8$ $_{12.5}$

44. $(-3\frac{3}{4} + 5\frac{1}{2}) + (-4\frac{1}{4})$ $_{-2\frac{1}{2}}$

45. $-6\frac{3}{8} + (-4\frac{5}{8} + \frac{1}{8})$ $_{-10\frac{7}{8}}$

REVIEW CAPSULE FOR SECTION 1.3

1.a. 4   b. 4 Both a and b are the same.   2.a. 4 b. 4 Both a and b are the same.   3.a. 7 b. 7 Both a and b are the same.

*Add or subtract as indicated. Compare the answers in **a** and **b**.*

1. a. $8 - 4$ **b.** $8 + (-4)$ See above.
2. a. $12 - 8$ **b.** $12 + (-8)$ See above.
3. a. $16 - 9$ **b.** $16 + (-9)$ See above.

4. a. $21 - 11$ **b.** $21 + (-11)$
5. a. $33 - 12$ **b.** $33 + (-12)$
6. a. $1.5 - 1.5$ **b.** $1.5 + (-1.5)$

4.a. 10 b. 10 Both a and b are the same.   5.a. 21 b. 21 Both a and b are the same.   6.a. 0 b. 0 Both a and b are the same.

1.3   Subtraction

You can think of subtraction as meaning "add the opposite."

Subtraction	Addition	Answer
$5 - 2$	$5 + (-2)$	3
$3 - 8$	$3 + (-8)$	-5
$7 - (-3)$	$7 + 3$	?
$-2.7 - (-3.5)$	$-2.7 + 3.5$	?
$0 - 37$	$0 + (-37)$	?
$-10.8 - (-10.8)$	$-10.8 + 10.8$	?

P-1   **Find the missing answers in the table above.** 10, 0.8, −37, 0

To subtact b
from a, add
the opposite of
b to a.

> To subtract a number, add its opposite. $7 - 5 = 7 + (-5)$
>
> ▲ $a - b = a + (-b)$ $-8 - (-3) = -8 + 3$

example 1   Subtract: $12 - 25$

Solution: ① Write a sum for the difference. ──────► $12 - 25 = 12 + (-25)$

② Add. ──────────────────────────► $= -13$

example 2   Subtract: $-13.1 - (-9.4)$

Solution: ① Write a sum for the difference. ──► $-13.1 - (-9.4) = -13.1 + 9.4$

② Add. ──────────────────────────► $= -3.7$

P-2   **Subtract.**

a. $30 - 12$ 18   b. $12 - (-8)$ 20   c. $-18 - 7$ −25   d. $-5.6 - (-9.8)$ 4.2

CLASSROOM EXERCISES

Write a sum for each difference. (Step 1, Examples 1 and 2)

18 + 5

1. $20 - 15$ 20 + (−15)   **2.** $6 - 11$ 6 + (−11)   **3.** $0 - 12$ 0 + (−12)   **4.** $18 - (-5)$

5. $(-12) - 6$ (−12)+(−6) **6.** $18 - (-7)$ 18 + 7   **7.** $-20 - (-18)$ −20 + 18   **8.** $-13 - (-19)$

−13 + 19

9. $5 - (-23)$ 5 + 23   **10.** $7 - 12$ 7 + (−12)   **11.** $-\frac{1}{4} - 8$ $-\frac{1}{4}$ + (−8)   **12.** $-2.6 - 3.4$

−2.6 + (−3.4)

Subtract. (Example 1)

13. $12 - 16$ $_{-4}$ **14.** $0 - 18$ $_{-18}$ **15.** $-15 - 8$ $_{-23}$ **16.** $-15 - 15$ $_{-30}$

17. $-11 - 23$ $_{-34}$ **18.** $-7\frac{1}{2} - 2\frac{1}{4}$ $_{-9\frac{3}{4}}$ **19.** $-7.3 - 2.7$ $_{-10}$ **20.** $-2.7 - 7.3$ $_{-10}$

(Example 2)

21. $6 - (-10)$ $_{16}$ **22.** $18 - (-3)$ $_{21}$ **23.** $-24 - (-10)$ $_{-14}$ **24.** $0 - (-32)$ $_{32}$

WRITTEN EXERCISES

See the Teacher's Manual for the suggested assignments.

Goal: To subtract positive and negative numbers

Sample Problems: a. $-11 - (-11)$ **b.** $-11 - 11$

Answers: a. 0 **b.** -22

Subtract. (Example 1)

1. $9 - 5$ $_4$ **2.** $18 - 6$ $_{12}$ **3.** $24 - 18$ $_6$ **4.** $16 - 9$ $_7$

5. $0 - 5$ $_{-5}$ **6.** $-2\frac{2}{3} - 1\frac{1}{8}$ $_{-3\frac{19}{24}}$ **7.** $14 - 23$ $_{-9}$ **8.** $28 - 35$ $_{-7}$

9. $0 - 22$ $_{-22}$ **10.** $0 - 36$ $_{-36}$ **11.** $-9.3 - 1.5$ $_{-10.8}$ **12.** $-7.6 - 18.1$ $_{-25.7}$

13. $-18.9 - 5.8$ $_{-24.7}$ **14.** $-0.14 - 0.58$ $_{-0.72}$ **15.** $\frac{1}{4} - \frac{7}{8}$ $_{-\frac{5}{8}}$ **16.** $-\frac{5}{6} - \frac{1}{6}$ $_{-1}$

(Example 2)

17. $25 - (-6)$ $_{31}$ **18.** $19 - (-7)$ $_{26}$ **19.** $13 - (-19)$ $_{32}$ **20.** $26 - (-11)$ $_{37}$

21. $-16 - (-18)$ $_2$ **22.** $-14 - (-20)$ $_6$ **23.** $0 - (-42)$ $_{42}$ **24.** $0 - (-96)$ $_{96}$

25. $2.7 - (-5.6)$ $_{8.3}$ **26.** $4.3 - (-8.9)$ $_{13.2}$ **27.** $-0.27 - (-0.38)$ $_{0.11}$ **28.** $-10\frac{3}{8} - (-4\frac{3}{8})$ $_{-6}$

(Examples 1 and 2)

29. $11 - 24$ $_{-13}$ **30.** $11 - (-24)$ $_{35}$ **31.** $0 - 18$ $_{-18}$ **32.** $0 - (-18)$ $_{18}$

33. $-4 - (-12)$ $_8$ **34.** $-4 - 12$ $_{-16}$ **35.** $7.8 - 3.4$ $_{4.4}$ **36.** $3.4 - 7.8$ $_{-4.4}$

37. $\frac{5}{7} - \frac{6}{7}$ $_{-\frac{1}{7}}$ **38.** $-0.71 - 0.82$ $_{-1.53}$ **39.** $-3.2 - (-4.5)$ $_{1.3}$ **40.** $-\frac{1}{3} - (-\frac{4}{3})$ $_1$

MORE CHALLENGING EXERCISES

41. $12 - (-10 - 3)$ $_{25}$ **42.** $(2 - 9 - (12 - 15)$ $_{-4}$ **43.** $(14 - 18) - (0 - 12)$ $_8$

44. $(-3 - 8) - (22 - 18)$ $_{-15}$ **45.** $(27 - 23) - (16 - 28)$ $_{16}$ **46.** $(23 - 27) - (28 - 26)$ $_{-6}$

REVIEW CAPSULE FOR SECTION 1.4

Multiply.

1. $(10)(3)$ $_{30}$ **2.** $(4)(1.3)$ $_{5.2}$ **3.** $(\frac{1}{2})(18)$ $_9$ **4.** $(\frac{1}{2})(\frac{2}{3})$ $_{\frac{1}{3}}$

5. $(1.5)(1.5)$ $_{2.25}$ **6.** $(0.8)(0.7)$ $_{0.56}$ **7.** $(0.9)(1.6)$ $_{1.44}$ **8.** $(5)(0)$ $_0$

1.4 Multiplication

OBJECTIVES: To multiply 0 and any number
To multiply a positive number and a negative number
To multiply two negative numbers

In the following multiplication problems, one factor, 8, stays the same. The other factor decreases by 1.

$$8(\ 3 \ ) = \ 24$$
$$8(\ 2 \ ) = \ 16$$
$$8(\ 1 \ ) = \ \ 8$$
$$8(\ 0 \ ) = \ \underline{\ ?\ }$$
$$8(-1) = \ \underline{\ ?\ }$$
$$8(-2) = \ \underline{\ ?\ }$$
$$8(-3) = \ \underline{\ ?\ }$$

Each product is eight *less* than the preceding one.

The product of a positive number and a negative number is a negative number.

P-1 **If the pattern continues, what is the answer to 8(0)?** o

> **Multiplication Property of Zero**
>
> For any number a, $a \cdot 0$ or $0 \cdot a = 0$.
>
> $3 \cdot 0 = 0$
>
> $0 \cdot \frac{1}{2} = 0$

P-2 **If the pattern above continues, what are the other missing numbers?**
−8, −16, −24

The following rule tells how to find the product of a positive and a negative number by using absolute value.

> **Rule for Multiplying a Positive Number and a Negative Number**
>
> 1. Multiply the absolute values.
> 2. Write the opposite of the result.
>
> $(3) \ (-7) = -21$
> $(-8) \ (4) = -32$

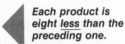 example 1   Multiply: (9) (−7.8)

Solution: ☐1 Multiply the absolute values. ⟶ $(9) \ (-7.8) = 9 \cdot 7.8$
$$= 70.2$$

☐2 Write the opposite of the result. ⟶ − 70.2

P-3 **Multiply.**

a. $(-6) \ (7)$ −42 **b.** $(4) \ (-1.2)$ −4.8 **c.** $\left(-\frac{1}{2}\right) (0)$ o   **d.** $\left(-\frac{3}{4}\right) \left(\frac{4}{3}\right)$ −1

In the following multiplication problem, one factor, −6, stays the same. The other factor decreases by 1.

$$-6(\ 3\ ) = -18$$
$$-6(\ 2\ ) = -12$$
$$-6(\ 1\ ) = -6$$
$$-6(\ 0\ ) =\ \ \ 0$$
$$-6(-1) = \underline{\ \ ?\ \ }$$
$$-6(-2) = \underline{\ \ ?\ \ }$$
$$-6(-3) = \underline{\ \ ?\ \ }$$

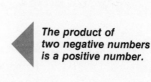

Each product is greater (less negative) than the answer that precedes it. Think of the relative position of −18, −12, −6, and 0 in the number line.

The product of two negative numbers is a positive number.

P-4   **If the pattern continues, what are the missing numbers?**   6, 12, 18

The following rule tells you how to find the product of two negative numbers by using absolute value.

> ### Rule for Multiplying Two Negative Numbers
> 1. Multiply the absolute values.
> 2. Write the result. $(-7)(-6) = 42$

example 2   Multiply: $(-8)(-5.4)$

Solution: ☐1 Multiply the absolute values. ⟶ $(-8)(-5.4) = |-8| \cdot |-5.4|$

$$= 8 \cdot 5.4$$

☐2 Write the result. ⟶ $= 43.2$

P-5   **Multiply.**

a. $(-5)(-9)$ 45 **b.** $\left(-\frac{3}{2}\right)\left(-\frac{4}{5}\right)$ $\frac{6}{5}$ **c.** $(-2)(-0.13)$ 0.26 **d.** $(-6)(-0.5)$ 3

CLASSROOM EXERCISES

Multiply. (Example 1)

1. $(-4)(9)$ −36
2. $(10)(-6)$ −60
3. $(-12)(8)$ −96
4. $\left(-\frac{1}{4}\right)(12)$ −3

5. $\left(-\frac{1}{3}\right)(9)$ −3
6. $(-15)\left(\frac{1}{5}\right)$ −3
7. $\left(-\frac{3}{7}\right)(0)$ 0
8. $(0)(-75)$ 0

9. $\left(-2\frac{1}{2}\right)(10)$ −25
10. $(-2)(1.8)$ −3.6
11. $(-3)(0.7)$ −2.1
12. $(-10)(2.6)$ −26

Multiply. (Example 2)

13. $(-11)(-7)$ 77   **14.** $(-5)(-9)$ 45   **15.** $(-10)(-15)$ 150   **16.** $(-\frac{1}{2})(-26)$ 13

17. $(-9)(-\frac{2}{3})$ 6   **18.** $(-4.3)(-3)$ 12.9   **19.** $(-5)(-1.2)$ 6   **20.** $(-0.7)(-30)$ 21

21. $(-\frac{1}{4})(-4)$ 1   **22.** $(-\frac{3}{8})(-\frac{8}{3})$ 1   **23.** $(-\frac{1}{8})(-8)$ 1   **24.** $(-\frac{2}{5})(-\frac{3}{5})$ $\frac{6}{25}$

WRITTEN EXERCISES

See the Teacher's Manual for the suggested assignments.

Goal: To multiply positive and negative numbers
Sample Problems: a. $(-7)(-8)$ **b.** $(-9)(12)$
Answers: a. 56   **b.** -108

Multiply. (Example 1)

1. $(-14)(5)$ -70 **2.** $(-16)(6)$ -96 **3.** $(0)(-63)$ 0   **4.** $(-0.003)(0)$ 0

5. $(22)(-3)$ -66 **6.** $(18)(-7)$ -126 **7.** $(-\frac{1}{2})(24)$ -12 **8.** $(-\frac{1}{4})(32)$ -8

9. $(15)(-\frac{2}{3})$ -10 **10.** $(20)(-\frac{3}{4})$ -15 **11.** $(\frac{3}{5})(-\frac{4}{9})$ $-\frac{4}{15}$ **12.** $(-\frac{2}{9})(\frac{3}{4})$ $-\frac{1}{6}$

13. $(-12)(1.7)$ -20.4 **14.** $(-9)(3.4)$ -30.6 **15.** $(-1)(8.36)$ -8.36 **16.** $(9.01)(-1)$ -9.01

(Example 2)

17. $(-24)(-3)$ 72   **18.** $(-16)(-8)$ 128   **19.** $(-\frac{4}{5})(-\frac{5}{4})$ 1   **20.** $(-\frac{7}{4})(-\frac{4}{7})$ 1

21. $(-15)(-5.8)$ 87   **22.** $(-24)(-2.7)$ 64.8   **23.** $(-160)(-20)$ 3200   **24.** $(-180)(-99)$ 17820

25. $(-1.6)(-0.625)$ 1   **26.** $(-1.25)(-0.8)$ 1   **27.** $(-1)(-99)$ 99   **28.** $(-8.6)(-1)$ 8.6

(Examples 1 and 2)

29. $(36)(-12)$ -432 **30.** $(-42)(8)$ -336 **31.** $(-18)(-11)$ 198   **32.** $(-23)(-5)$ 115

33. $(-240)(15)$ -3600 **34.** $(0)(-341)$ 0   **35.** $(817)(0)$ 0   **36.** $(-325)(7)$ -2275

37. $(-1.2)(-1.3)$ 1.56   **38.** $(-2.4)(-5.1)$ 12.24   **39.** $(-\frac{2}{3})(\frac{4}{5})$ $-\frac{8}{15}$ **40.** $(-\frac{1}{7})(-\frac{2}{9})$ $\frac{2}{63}$

MORE CHALLENGING EXERCISES

Multiply.

41. $(-5)(2)(-3)$ 30   **42.** $(-12)(-3)(4)$ 144   **43.** $(-3)(-8)(4)$ 96

44. $(-2)(-4)(-3)$ -24 **45.** $(-11)(0)(-86)$ 0   **46.** $(-10)(-7)(9)$ 630

47. $(-8+5)(-2)$ 6   **48.** $(-3)(9-12)$ 9   **49.** $(-6)(-7-3)$ 60

50. $(9-16)(0)$ 0   **51.** $(10)(-11+9)$ -20 **52.** $(8-15)(-6+4)$ 14

Write the opposite of each number in simplest form. (Section 1.1)

1. 17 −17   **2.** 32 −32   **3.** $-\frac{1}{2}$ $\frac{1}{2}$ **4.** $-1\frac{1}{2}$ $1\frac{1}{2}$ **5.** −0.06 0.06

Simplify. (Section 1.1)

6. |20| 20   **7.** |0| 0   **8.** |−3.7| 3.7   **9.** |2.5| 2.5   **10.** $|-1\frac{3}{5}|$ $1\frac{3}{5}$

Which number has the greater absolute value? (Section 1.1)

11. −17 or 12 −17   **12.** −8 or −12 −12   **13.** 10 or −5 10   **14.** 9 or −38 −38

Add. (Section 1.2)

15. −20 + (−13) −33   **16.** −18.1 + 19.1 1   **17.** $8\frac{1}{4} + (-12\frac{3}{4})$ $-4\frac{1}{2}$

18. −6.8 + 6.8 0   **19.** $-12\frac{1}{2} + (-13\frac{1}{2})$ −26   **20.** −0.05 + 1.35 1.30

Write a sum for each difference. (Section 1.3)

21. 11 − 7   **22.** −8.7 − 9.6   **23.** 12.1 − (−7.9)
    11 + (−7)   −8.7 + (−9.6)   12.1 + 7.9

Subtract. (Section 1.3)

24. 13 − 28 −15   **25.** $-6\frac{1}{2} - 6\frac{1}{2}$ −13   **26.** 0 − (−9.25) 9.25

27. −4 − (−12) 8   **28.** $\frac{1}{2} - 7$ $-6\frac{1}{2}$ **29.** 2.6 − (−3.3) 5.9

Multiply. (Section 1.4)

30. (−7)(8) −56   **31.** (−4)(13) −52   **32.** (9)$(-1\frac{1}{3})$ −12   **33.** (12)$(-\frac{1}{4})$ −3

34. (−1)(−1) 1   **35.** (−4.5)(0) 0   **36.** (−4)(−8.4) 33.6   **37.** (−10)(−4.5) 45

REVIEW CAPSULE FOR SECTION 1.5

Write a fraction for each of the following.

1. $1\frac{1}{2}$ $\frac{3}{2}$ **2.** 12 $\frac{12}{1}$ **3.** $1\frac{3}{5}$ $\frac{8}{5}$ **4.** $2\frac{1}{3}$ $\frac{7}{3}$ **5.** $3\frac{1}{7}$ $\frac{22}{7}$

Multiply or divide as indicated.

6. $\frac{7}{2} \times \frac{2}{7}$ 1   **7.** $-\frac{3}{5} \times (-\frac{5}{3})$ 1   **8.** $1\frac{2}{3} \times \frac{3}{5}$ 1   **9.** $(-6) \times (-\frac{1}{6})$ 1

10. 24 ÷ 8 3   **11.** $\frac{24}{8}$ 3   **12.** $24 \times \frac{1}{8}$ 3   **13.** $4\frac{1}{2} \div 6$ $\frac{3}{4}$

OBJECTIVES: To divide two negative numbers
To divide a positive number and a negative number
To divide 0 by any number

1.5 Division

Each of the following products equals 1.

$$\frac{7}{2} \times \frac{2}{7} = 1 \qquad -\frac{3}{5} \times \left(-\frac{5}{3}\right) = 1 \qquad \frac{5}{3} \times \frac{3}{5} = 1$$

> Two numbers are **reciprocals** of each other
> if their product is 1.
>
> $a \cdot \dfrac{1}{a} = 1$ *(a is not zero.)*
>
> $\frac{7}{2}$ and $\frac{2}{7}$
>
> $-\frac{5}{3}$ and $-\frac{3}{5}$

The reciprocal of
any number n,
except 0, can be
expressed as $\dfrac{1}{n}$.

Thus, the reciprocal
of $\dfrac{2}{3}$ is $\dfrac{1}{\frac{2}{3}}$ or $\dfrac{3}{2}$.

P-1 **What is the reciprocal of each number below?**

a. $\frac{3}{10}$ $\quad\frac{10}{3}$ **b.** -3 $\quad-\frac{1}{3}$ **c.** $1\frac{1}{3}$ $\quad\frac{3}{4}$ **d.** 1 $\quad$ 1 **e.** -1 $\quad-1$

The following illustrates that

<u>dividing by a number is the same as multiplying by its reciprocal.</u>

$$36 \div 9 = 4 \qquad\qquad 36 \times \frac{1}{9} = 4$$

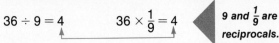 9 and $\frac{1}{9}$ are
reciprocals.

> To divide by a number, multiply
> by its reciprocal.
>
> $a \div b = a \cdot \dfrac{1}{b}, \; b \neq 0$ *(b is not zero.)*
>
> $3\frac{1}{2} \div 1\frac{3}{4} = \frac{7}{2} \times \frac{4}{7}$
> $= \frac{28}{14}$
> $= 2$

Any number <u>except zero</u> can be a divisor. Thus, "$\frac{6}{2}$" is permitted
because "$6 = 3 \cdot 2$" is true. However, "$\frac{6}{0}$" is not permitted because
"$6 = a \cdot 0$" is false no matter what number a represents. $a \cdot 0$ always
equals 0.

example 1 Divide: $(-12) \div \left(-\frac{1}{3}\right)$

Solution: The reciprocal of $-\frac{1}{3}$ is $-\frac{3}{1}$, or -3.

1 Write a product for the quotient. ⟶ $(-12) \div \left(-\frac{1}{3}\right) = (-12) \times (-3)$
2 Multiply. ⟶ $= 36$

P-2 **Divide.**

a. $(-16) \div \left(-\frac{1}{4}\right)$ $\quad$ 64 **b.** $\left(-\frac{5}{9}\right) \div (-5)$ $\quad\frac{1}{9}$ **c.** $0 \div \left(-\frac{1}{8}\right)$ 0 $0 \cdot a = 0$

example 2

Divide: $4\frac{1}{2} \div (-6)$

Solution: The reciprocal of -6 is $-\frac{1}{6}$.

1. Write a product for the quotient. ⟶ $4\frac{1}{2} \div (-6) = \frac{9}{2} \times (-\frac{1}{6})$

2. Multiply. ⟶ $= -\frac{9}{12}$

3. Write the answer in lowest terms. ⟶ $= -\frac{3}{4}$

P-3 **Divide.**

a. $5\frac{1}{9} \div (-3)$ $-1\frac{19}{27}$ **b.** $(-18) \div 1\frac{1}{6}$ $15\frac{3}{7}$ **c.** $\frac{-2.4}{8}$ -0.3

This represents the quotient of -2.4 and 8.

Rules for Division

1. If a positive number is divided by a positive number, the quotient is a positive number.

   $30 \div 3 = 10$

2. If a negative number is divided by a negative number, the quotient is a positive number.

   $-4\frac{1}{2} \div -2\frac{1}{4} = 2$

3. If a negative number is divided by a positive number, the quotient is a negative number.

   $-25 \div 5 = -5$

4. If a positive number is divided by a negative number, the quotient is a negative number.

   $35 \div -7 = -5$

5. If zero is divided by a positive or a negative number, the quotient is zero.

   $0 \div -6 = 0$

6. Zero can never be a divisior.

CLASSROOM EXERCISES

Write a product for each quotient. (Step 1 in Examples 1 and 2)

1. $-8 \div \frac{1}{4}$ -8×4 **2.** $-12 \div 3$ $-12 \times \frac{1}{3}$ **3.** $28 \div (-7)$ $28 \times (-\frac{1}{7})$ **4.** $\frac{-3.2}{4}$ $-3.2 \times \frac{1}{4}$

Divide. (Example 1)

5. $-35 \div (-\frac{1}{5})$ 175 **6.** $-32 \div (-\frac{1}{2})$ 64 **7.** $-30 \div (-10)$ 3 **8.** $\frac{-44}{-11}$ 4

(Example 2)

9. $4\frac{1}{2} \div (-9)$ -0.5 **10.** $3\frac{1}{5} \div (-8)$ -0.4 **11.** $6\frac{2}{3} \div (-10)$ $-\frac{2}{3}$ **12.** $0 \div (-\frac{1}{5})$ 0

13. $-9 \div \frac{1}{4}$ -36 **14.** $-13 \div \frac{1}{2}$ -26 **15.** $\frac{-5.6}{8}$ -0.7 **16.** $\frac{16.9}{-13}$ -1.3

WRITTEN EXERCISES

See the Teacher's Manual for the suggested assignments.

Goal: To divide positive and negative numbers

Sample Problems: **a.** $125 \div (-5)$ **b.** $(-1\frac{1}{2}) \div (-6\frac{1}{4})$

Answers: a. -25 **b.** $\frac{6}{25}$

Divide. (Example 1)

1. $-480 \div (-20)$ _24_   **2.** $(-325) \div (-25)$ _13_   **3.** $\frac{-27}{-9}$ _3_   **4.** $\frac{-132}{-12}$ _11_

5. $-16 \div (-1\frac{1}{2})$ $10\frac{2}{3}$ **6.** $-25 \div (-1\frac{1}{4})$ _20_   **7.** $-1\frac{1}{4} \div (-7\frac{1}{2})$ $\frac{1}{6}$ **8.** $-4\frac{1}{2} \div (-\frac{3}{4})$ _6_

(Example 2)

9. $7.2 \div (-8)$ _−0.9_   **10.** $10 \div (-\frac{1}{3})$ _−30_   **11.** $16 \div (-1\frac{1}{2})$ $-10\frac{2}{3}$ **12.** $2\frac{2}{5} \div (-\frac{2}{5})$ _−6_

13. $\frac{24}{-8}$ _−3_   **14.** $\frac{18}{-9}$ _−2_   **15.** $\frac{108}{-12}$ _−9_   **16.** $176 \div (-16)$ _−11_

17. $0 \div 17$ _0_   **18.** $0 \div (-81)$ _0_   **19.** $-121 \div 11$ _−11_   **20.** $-216 \div 12$ _−18_

21. $-6.3 \div 7$ _−0.9_   **22.** $-18 \div \frac{1}{3}$ _−54_   **23.** $-2\frac{1}{2} \div \frac{1}{4}$ _−10_   **24.** $-13 \div \frac{1}{4}$ _−52_

(Examples 1 and 2)

25. $\frac{36}{-9}$ _−4_   **26.** $\frac{-54}{-6}$ _9_   **27.** $-25 \div 5$ _−5_   **28.** $72 \div (-12)$ _−6_

29. $-13 \div (-\frac{1}{4})$ _52_   **30.** $-18 \div \frac{2}{3}$ _−27_   **31.** $\frac{0}{-3}$ _0_   **32.** $\frac{-39}{13}$ _−3_

33. $20.5 \div (-0.5)$ _−41_   **34.** $\frac{17}{-2}$ $-8\frac{1}{2}$ **35.** $-\frac{7}{9} \div 2\frac{1}{3}$ $-\frac{1}{3}$ **36.** $0 \div (-21.2)$ _0_

37. $\frac{-8.1}{-0.1}$ _81_   **38.** $\frac{-23}{10}$ _−2.3_   **39.** $\frac{110}{-11}$ _−10_   **40.** $-3.6 \div (-1.2)$ _3_

MORE CHALLENGING EXERCISES

Evaluate. First, perform the operation within parentheses or brackets.

41. $(-4 \cdot 5) \div (-2)$ _10_   **42.** $[(-8)(-2)] \div 4$ _4_   **43.** $-11 \cdot (-6 \div 2)$ _33_

44. $-12 \div (-3 \cdot 4)$ _1_   **45.** $(-9 \div 3) \cdot (-13)$ _39_   **46.** $-18 \div [-6 \div (-2)]$ _−6_

REVIEW CAPSULE FOR SECTION 1.6

In each case find the simplest form. Perform the operation in parentheses first.

EXAMPLE 1: $(8 \cdot 3) + 7$ **EXAMPLE 2:** $8 + (3 \cdot 7)$

SOLUTION: $(8 \cdot 3) + 7$ **SOLUTION:** $8 + (3 \cdot 7)$

$\qquad\qquad 24 + 7$ $\qquad\qquad 8 + 21$

$\qquad\qquad\quad 31$ $\qquad\qquad\quad 29$

1. $(16 + 2) - 4$ _14_   **2.** $(10 - 2) - 6$ _2_   **3.** $(56 \div 7) \div 2$ _4_

4. $(8 \cdot 9)(-3)$ _−216_   **5.** $(42 \cdot 3) + (-20)$ _106_   **6.** $-7 + (18 \div 2)$ _2_

1.6   Order of Operations

To evaluate an expression involving addition and multiplication, addition and division, subtraction, and multiplication, or subtraction and division

An **expression,** such as $12 - 18$ or $2 \cdot 5 + 7$, includes at least one of the operations of addition, subtraction, multiplication, or division.

P-1   **Which of the following answers are correct?**

a. $2 \cdot 5 + 7 = 10 + 7$ **Ans. 17** Correct

b. $2 \cdot 5 + 7 = 2 \cdot 12$ **Ans. 24** Incorrect

c. $10 \div 5 - 3 = 2 - 3$ **Ans. -1** Correct

d. $10 \div 5 - 3 = 10 \div 2$ **Ans. 5** Incorrect

Rules are needed so that a given expression has only one value.

> If only addition and subtraction are involved, the operations are performed from left to right.
> $8 - 2 - 1 = 5$
> $1 - 2 + 8 = 7$

example 1

Evaluate: **a.** $12 + 5 - 4$ **b.** $4 - 9 + 3$ ◀ Evaluate means "find the value of."

Solutions: **a.** $12 + 5 - 4 = 17 - 4 = 13$ **b.** $4 - 9 + 3 = -5 + 3 = -2$

> If only multiplication and division are involved, the operations are performed from left to right.
> $8 \times 2 \div 4 = 4$
> $27 \div 9 \div 3 = 1$

example 2

Evaluate: **a.** $28 \div 7(-9)$ **b.** $(-2)(-13) \div (-4)$

Solutions: **a.** $28 \div 7(-9) = 4(-9) = -36$ **b.** $(-2)(-13) \div (-4) = 26 \div (-4) = -6\frac{1}{2}$

> Multiplication or division is performed before addition or subtraction.
> $2 \cdot 5 + 7 = 17$
> $10 \div 5 - 3 = -1$

A common error is for students to perform the operation first that appears first in the expression.

example 3

Evaluate.

a. $2 \cdot 5 + 7$ **b.** $4 + 3 \cdot 6$ **c.** $10 - 6 \cdot 2$ **d.** $10 \div 5 - 3$

Solutions: **a.** $2 \cdot 5 + 7 = 10 + 7 = 17$ **b.** $4 + 3 \cdot 6 = 4 + 18 = 22$

c. $10 - 6 \cdot 2 = 10 - 12 = -2$ **d.** $10 \div 5 - 3 = 2 - 3 = -1$

CLASSROOM EXERCISES

Evaluate. (Example 1)

1. $12 - 3 + 7$ 16   **2.** $14 + 1 - 9$ 6   **3.** $7 - 10 + 3$ 0   **4.** $5 - 8 - 11$ −14

(Example 2)

5. $2 \cdot 15 \div 6$ 5   **6.** $42 \div 7 \cdot 3$ 18   **7.** $-8 \div 2(-3)$ 12   **8.** $-10 \div (-2) \div (-5)$ −1

(Example 3)

9. $3 + 10 \cdot 4$ 43   **10.** $20 - 4 \cdot 2$ 12   **11.** $21 - 27 \div 3$ 12   **12.** $3 + 5(-7)$ −32

13. $(-3)(5) - (-2)(2)$ −11   **14.** $-9 \div 3 - 7$ −10   **15.** $11 \div (-\frac{1}{2}) + 6$ −16   **16.** $-8 + (-4) \div (-1)$ −4

WRITTEN EXERCISES

See the Teacher's Manual for the suggested assignments.

Goal: To evaluate an expression that involves order of operations

Sample Problems: a. Evaluate: $5 + 8 \cdot 3$ **b.** Evaluate: $-2(-3) + 3 \div (-1)$

Answers: a. 29   **b.** 3

Evaluate. (Example 1)

1. $5 - 8 + 12$ 9   **2.** $10 - 14 + 7$ 3   **3.** $5 - 10 - 7$ −12   **4.** $-6 + 7 + 8$ 9

5. $-0.4 + 0.7 - 0.8$ −0.5   **6.** $1.2 - 2.3 + 3.6$ 2.5   **7.** $8 + 9 - 10 + 6$ 13   **8.** $17 - 13 - 2 + 10$ 12

(Example 2)

9. $8 \cdot 2 \div 4$ 4   **10.** $20 \div 5 \cdot 4$ 16   **11.** $-240 \div 8 \cdot 2$ −60   **12.** $9(-8) \div (-12)$ 6

13. $-3 \cdot 12 \div (-4)$ 9   **14.** $-6(-8) \div 3(4)$ 64   **15.** $15 \div \frac{1}{2}(-3)$ −90   **16.** $(-27) \div \frac{1}{3}(-5)$ 405

(Example 3)

17. $6 - 5 \cdot 4$ −14   **18.** $12 - 3 \cdot 9$ −15   **19.** $-17 + (-9)2$ −35   **20.** $-21 + 5(-3)$ −36

21. $12 - 32 \div (-4)$ 20   **22.** $15 - 39 \div (-3)$ 28   **23.** $6.3 + 4.8 \div (-8)$ 5.7   **24.** $1\frac{1}{2} + 2\frac{1}{3} \div (-18)$ $1\frac{10}{27}$

(Examples 1–3)

25. $16 + 14 \div (-2)$ 9   **26.** $9 + 2 - 15$ −4   **27.** $20 - 6 \cdot 7$ −22   **28.** $-3 \cdot 5 - 21$ −36

29. $13 - 8 - 5 + 9$ 9   **30.** $21 \div 7 + 4$ 7   **31.** $7 - 11 + 18$ 14   **32.** $4(3) + 9(8)$ 84

33. $-1(8) - 2(-3)$ −2   **34.** $-5 - 12 \div 6$ −7   **35.** $2.3 - 3.7 + 8.1$ 6.7   **36.** $-200 \div (-2)(-3)$ −300

REVIEW CAPSULE FOR SECTION 1.7

Perform the indicated operations.

1. $2 \times 2 \times 2$ 8   **2.** $0.4 \times 0.4 \times 0.4$ 0.064   **3.** $\frac{2}{3} \times \frac{2}{3} \times \frac{2}{3}$ $\frac{8}{27}$

4. $(-3)(-3)$ 9   **5.** $(-1)(-1)(-1)(-1)(-1)$ −1   **6.** $(-4)(-4)(-4)$ −64

1.7 Powers

An expression such as $(-2)^3$ is called a **power.** The 3 is the **exponent** and the -2 is the **base.** The exponent tells how many times to use the base as a factor.

example 1 Evaluate: $(-2)^3$

Solution: Use -2 as a factor 3 times $\longrightarrow$ $(-2)^3 = (-2)(-2)(-2) = -8$

Powers are evaluated before multiplication and division are performed <u>and</u> before addition and subtraction are performed.

example 2 Evaluate.

a. $2 \cdot 3^2$ b. $-8 \div 4^3$ c. $-6 + 2^3$ d. $(-5)^2 - 6(-2)$

Solutions: a. $2 \cdot 3^2 = 2 \cdot 9 = 18$ b. $-8 \div 4^3 = (-8) \div 64 = \dfrac{-8}{64} = -\dfrac{1}{8}$

c. $-6 + 2^3 = -6 + 8$
$ = 2$

d. $(-5)^2 - 6(-2) = 25 - (-12)$
$ = 25 + 12 = 37$

P-1   **Evaluate:**   a. $3 \cdot 2^2$ 12   b. $(-4)^2 \div 2^3$ 2   c. $-10 - 5(-\frac{1}{2})$ $-7\frac{1}{2}$

A **variable** is a letter such as x that represents one or more numbers. An **algebraic expression** is an expression with one or more variables, such as the following.

$x + 2$ $5n$ $p^2 - 7y$ z^3 A variable represents any number in its replacement set.

To evaluate an algebraic expression, replace each variable with its value. Then perform the operations.

example 3 Evaluate $3n^2 - 4$ when $n = 5$.

Solution: ① Replace n with 5. $\longrightarrow$ $3n^2 - 4 = 3(5)^2 - 4$

② Evaluate the power. Then multiply. $\longrightarrow$ $= 3(25) - 4$

③ Subtract. $\longrightarrow$ $= 75 - 4 = 71$

P-2   Evaluate each expression when $p = 3$.

   a. $p^2 - 5$ 4   **b.** $5 - p^2$ -4 **c.** $4p^2 - p$ 33

example 4   Evaluate $x^2 - 3x$ when $x = -2$.

Solution: $\boxed{1}$ Replace x with -2. $\longrightarrow$ $x^2 - 3x = (-2)^2 - 3(-2)$
            $\boxed{2}$ Evaluate the power. Then multiply. $\longrightarrow$ $= 4 - 3(-2)$
            $\boxed{3}$ Subtract. $\longrightarrow$ $= 4 - (-6) = 10$

CLASSROOM EXERCISES

Evaluate each expression in Exercises 1–14. (Example 1)

1. 6^2 36   **2.** 2^3 8   **3.** 5^3 125   **4.** $(-3)^2$ 9   **5.** $(-4)^3$ -64 **6.** $(-1)^4$ 1

(Example 2)

7. $12 - 4^2$ -4 **8.** $3 \cdot 7^2$ 147   **9.** $2 \cdot 3^2 - 10$ 8   **10.** $4 - 3 \cdot 2^2$ -8

11. $8^2 \div (-4)$ -16 **12.** $-9 \div 3^3$ $-\frac{1}{3}$ **13.** $-10 - 10^2$ -110 **14.** $(-4)^2 - 3(-4)$ 28

Evaluate each expression when $t = 4$ (Example 3)

15. $t^2 - 5$ 11   **16.** $2 - t^2$ -14 **17.** $-4t - 7$ -23 **18.** $-13 + 7t$ 15

Evaluate each expression when $y = -3$. (Example 3)

19. $2y^2$ 18   **20.** $y^3 + 6$ -21 **21.** $-8 - y^2$ -17 **22.** $-2y + 13$ 19

Evaluate each expression when $n = 5$. (Example 4)

23. $n^2 + n$ 30   **24.** $n^3 - 7n$ 90   **25.** $2n^2 - 5n$ 25   **26.** $-2n^2 - 4n + 5$
                                                                        -65

Evaluate each expression when $x = -2$. (Example 4)

27. $3x - x^2$ -10 **28.** $x^3 - 7x$ 6   **29.** $3x^2 + 6x$ 0   **30.** $5x^3 - x^2 - x$ -42

WRITTEN EXERCISES

See the Teacher's Manual for the suggested assignments.

Goal: To evaluate an expression
Sample Problems: Evaluate: **a.** $5 + 9 \cdot 3^2$ **b.** $n^2 - 6$ when $n = 3$
Answers: a. 86   **b.** 3

Evaluate each expression in Exercises 1–14. (Example 1)

1. 11^2 121   **2.** 6^3 216   **3.** 10^3 1000   **4.** $(-5)^2$ 25   **5.** $(-7)^3$ -343 **6.** $(-3)^3$
                                                                                                                -27

(Example 2)

7. $6(-3)^2$ 54   **8.** $-4 \cdot (-1)^3$ 4   **9.** $5 + 2 \cdot 4^2$ 37   **10.** $9 + 3 \cdot 5^2$ 84

11. $4 \cdot 2^3 - 50$ −18   **12.** $(-5)3^2 + 37$ −8   **13.** $5^2 - 4^2 + 3^2$ 18   **14.** $5^2 + 2^2 - 3^2$ 20

Evaluate each expression when n = 3. (Example 3)

15. $n^2 + 4$ 13   **16.** $n^2 - 7$ 2   **17.** $8n^2 - 12$ 60   **18.** $-4n^2 + 9$ −27

Evaluate each expression when r = −1. (Example 3)

19. $7 + r^2$ 8   **20.** $13 - r^3$ 14   **21.** $4r^2 - 6$ −2   **22.** $-5r^2 + 10$ 5

Evaluate each expression when s = 4 or when w = −10. (Example 4)

23. $s^2 - 4s$ 0   **24.** $10s^2 - s$ 156   **25.** $-5s^2 - s$ −84   **26.** $s^2 + s + 1$ 21

27. $3s^2 - 5s + 2$ 30 **28.** $6s^2 + 3s - 5$ 103   **29.** $s^3 + 2s^2 - 3s - 1$ 83 **30.** $3s^3 - 4s^2 + 2s - 5$ 131

31. $3w^2$ 300   **32.** $-4w^2$ −400   **33.** $2w^2 + w$ 190   **34.** $5w - w^2$ −150

35. $w^2 + w - 30$ 60 **36.** $2w^2 - 4w + 20$ 260 **37.** $w^3 + 2w^2 - w$ −790 **38.** $3w^3 - 4w^2 - w + 60$ −3330

Evaluate each expression. (Examples 1 and 2)

39. 4^4 256   **40.** $3 \cdot 2^3$ 24   **41.** $(-6)^3$ −216   **42.** $-2(-4)^2$ −32

43. $2^2 + 3^2$ 13   **44.** $4 \cdot 7 - 5^2$ 3   **45.** $-6 \div 4^2$ $-\frac{3}{8}$ **46.** $(-1)^5 - 4(-3)$ 11

Evaluate each expression when m = −5. (Examples 3 and 4)

47. $1 - 5m$ 26   **48.** $12m \div (-8)$ $7\frac{1}{2}$ **49.** $m^3 - 2m^2 \div (-4)$ $-112\frac{1}{2}$ **50.** $-8m \div 4(-7)$ −70

51. $-3m^2 - 4m$ −55   **52.** $-4m - 6$ 14   **53.** $2m - m^2$ −35   **54.** $-m^2 - 6m$ 5

MORE CHALLENGING EXERCISES

Evaluate each expression when x = −3.

55. $\dfrac{x^2 + 7}{x - 4}$ $-\frac{16}{7}$ **56.** $\dfrac{x^2 - 1}{x - 1}$ −2   **57.** $\dfrac{x + 3}{x^2 + x + 1}$ 0   **58.** $\dfrac{x^2 + 2}{x^3 + 5}$ $-\frac{1}{2}$ **59.** $\dfrac{|x + 1|}{x^2 + 1}$ $\frac{1}{5}$

 ——————— *EVALUATING A POWER* ———————

The Example below shows how to use a calculator to evaluate a power of a number. Note that you press "$=$" <u>once</u> for the <u>second</u> power, <u>twice</u> for the <u>third</u> power, <u>three</u> times for the <u>fourth</u> power, and so on.

EXAMPLE   Evaluate 16^3.

SOLUTION  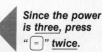   *Since the power is three, press "$=$" twice.*

 On some calculators, press "$\times$" twice here.

Use a calculator to do the following exercises.

1. 7^2 49   **2.** 9^3 729   **3.** 5^4 625   **4.** 21^4 194,481   **5.** 7^6 117,649   **6.** $(-4)^3$ −64   (HINT: First press "4 $+/-$.")

Saving Energy and Money

You can save money on energy costs by keeping your thermostat set at the recommended settings for winter and for summer shown at the right.

The table at the right shows the per cent of increase or decrease in energy costs for several thermostat settings that are at or near the recommended levels. Positive per cents represent energy–cost savings. Negative per cents represent energy–cost losses.

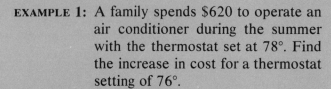

78°F min for COOLING (Summer)   **65°F max** for HEATING (Winter)

Thermostat Settings

EXAMPLE 1: A family spends $620 to operate an air conditioner during the summer with the thermostat set at 78°. Find the increase in cost for a thermostat setting of 76°.

SOLUTION: The cost is 18% more.

$$\$620 \times 0.18 = \textbf{\$111.60 more}$$

EXAMPLE 2: A family spends $1400 to heat its home during the winter with the thermostat set at 65°. Find the decrease in cost for a thermostat setting of 62°.

SOLUTION: The cost is 9% less.

$$\$1400 \times 0.09 = \textbf{\$126 less}$$

Summer		Winter	
Thermostat Setting	Saving or Loss	Thermostat Setting	Saving or Loss
80°F	16%	70°F	−15%
79	8%	69	−12%
78	0	68	−9%
77	−8%	67	−6%
76	−18%	66	−3%
75	−28%	65	0
74	−39%	64	3%
73	−50%	63	6%
72	−63%	62	9%

EXERCISES

A family spends $700 to operate its air conditioner during the summer (thermostat setting: 78°). Find the increase or decrease in cost for each given thermostat setting.

1. 77° $56 more   **2.** 80° $112 less   **3.** 75° $196 more   **4.** 72° $441 more   **5.** 74° $273 more

A family spends $1100 to heat its home in the winter (thermostat setting: 65°). Find the increase or decrease in cost for each given thermostat setting.

6. 70° $165 more   **7.** 68° $99 more   **8.** 64° $33 less   **9.** 67° $66 more   **10.** 63° $66 less

Special Topic Application

CHAPTER SUMMARY

IMPORTANT TERMS	Opposite *(p. 2)* Exponent *(p. 19)* Absolute value *(p. 2)* Base *(p. 19)* Reciprocal *(p. 14)* Variable *(p. 19)* Quotient *(p. 14)* Algebraic expression *(p. 19)* Power *(p. 19)*

IMPORTANT IDEAS

1. The absolute value of a positive number equals that number. The absolute value of a negative number equals the opposite of that number. The absolute value of 0 equals 0.

2. Rules for Adding Positive and Negative Numbers: See pages 4 and 5.

3. To subtract a number, add its opposite.

4. *Multiplication Property of Zero:* $a \cdot 0 = 0 \cdot a = 0$.

5. Rules for Multiplying Positive and Negative Numbers: See pages 10–11.

6. To divide by a number, multiply by its reciprocal.

7. If a is any number, $\frac{a}{0}$ does not represent a number.

8. Rules for Dividing Positive and Negative Numbers: See page 15.

9. Rules for Order of Operations
   a. Multiplication or division is performed before addition or subtraction.
   b. If only addition and subtraction are involved, the operations are performed from left to right.
   c. If only multiplication and division are involved, the operations are performed from left to right.
   d. Powers are evaluated before multiplication and division are performed *and* before addition and subtraction are performed.

CHAPTER REVIEW

NOTE: The Teacher's Resource Book contains two forms of each Chapter Test

SECTION 1.1

Write the opposite of each number in simplest form.

1. -1.5 1.5   **2.** 27 -27 **3.** $-\frac{3}{8}$ $\frac{3}{8}$ **4.** $-2\frac{1}{2}$ $2\frac{1}{2}$ **5.** 0   0

Simplify.

6. $|24|$ 24   **7.** $|-2.6|$ 2.6   **8.** $-|-\frac{3}{8}|$ $-\frac{3}{8}$ **9.** $|-35|$ 35   **10.** $-|-9|$ -9

Which number has the greater absolute value?

11. 0 or -3 -3 **12.** 0 or 1   1   **13.** -2 or 4   4   **14.** -5 or 3 -5

SECTION 1.2
Add.

15. $-13 + 24$ 11
16. $53 + (-29)$ 24
17. $28 + (-42)$ −14
18. $-61 + 39$ −22
19. $-5.8 + (-7.7)$ −13.5
20. $-0.29 + (-0.58)$ −0.87
21. $-5\frac{3}{4} + 12\frac{1}{4}$ $6\frac{1}{2}$
22. $5\frac{3}{8} + (-13\frac{1}{8})$ $-7\frac{3}{4}$
23. $-10\frac{5}{8} + (-3\frac{1}{4})$ $-13\frac{7}{8}$

SECTION 1.3
Write each difference as a sum. Then compute.

24. $17 - 29$ 17 + (−29), −12
25. $42 - 68$ 42 + (−68), −26
26. $-27 - (-18)$ −27 + 18, −9
27. $-53 - (-26)$ −53 + 26, −27
28. $19.2 - (-4.7)$ 19.2 + 4.7, 23.9
29. $42.9 - (-18.5)$ 42.9 + 18.5, 61.4
30. $-3\frac{1}{2} - 2\frac{1}{4}$ $-3\frac{1}{2} + (-2\frac{1}{4}), -5\frac{3}{4}$
31. $75 - (-13)$ 75 + 13, 88
32. $0 - (-0.09)$ 0 + 0.09, 0.09

SECTION 1.4
Multiply.

33. $(12)(-17)$ −204
34. $(-15)(21)$ −315
35. $(-18)(-25)$ 450
36. $(-52)(-14)$ 728
37. $(-\frac{1}{5})(45)$ −9
38. $(\frac{1}{4})(-28)$ −7
39. $(-24)(0.35)$ −8.4
40. $(18)(-0.45)$ −8.1
41. $(-4.2)(-2.4)$ 10.08

SECTION 1.5
Divide.

42. $\frac{-63}{9}$ −7
43. $\frac{84}{-7}$ −12
44. $\frac{-144}{-12}$ 12
45. $\frac{-128}{-8}$ 16
46. $13 \div (-\frac{1}{4})$ −52
47. $\frac{2}{3} \div (-12)$ $-\frac{1}{18}$
48. $(-1\frac{1}{4}) \div (-1\frac{7}{8})$ $\frac{2}{3}$
49. $(-3\frac{1}{2}) \div (-2\frac{5}{8})$ $1\frac{1}{3}$

SECTION 1.6
Evaluate.

50. $12 - 27 + 8$ −7
51. $23 - 38 + 6$ −9
52. $16 + 4(-8)$ −16
53. $(-13) + 12 \cdot 3$ 23
54. $15 - 42 \div (-6)$ 22
55. $24 - (-16) \div 4$ 28

SECTION 1.7
Evaluate.

56. 4^3 64
57. $(-2)^3$ −8
58. $(6)^2 - 3(-5)$ 51
59. $(-12)(8) \div 24 + 3^2$ 5
60. $4(-3)^2 \div (-12) - 25$ −28
61. $-4(3)^2 \div 12 - (-15)$ 12

Evaluate each expression when n = 3.

62. $n^2 - 13$ −4
63. $4n^2 - 45$ −9
64. $-2n^2 - n$ −21
65. $-n - 5n^2$ −48
66. $n^3 - n^2 + n$ 21
67. $n^3 - 3n^2 + 1$ 1
68. $-n^3 + 3n^2 - 1$ −1
69. $-n^3 + n^2 - n$ −21
70. $-3n^3 + 2n^2 - 2n$ −69

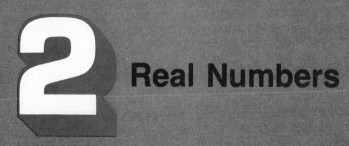

CHAPTER **2** **Real Numbers**

Sections 2.1 **Real Numbers**

2.2 **Addition Properties**

2.3 **Multiplication Properties**

2.4 **Special Properties**

2.5 **Multiplying and Factoring**

2.6 **Combining Like Terms**

Features *Career:* Statistician

Calculator Exercises: Finding the Average

Review and Testing *Review Capsules*

Mid-Chapter Review

Chapter Summary

Chapter Review

OBJECTIVES: To write a rational number as a quotient of two integers
To express a fraction as a repeating decimal
To identify a number as Rational or Irrational

2.1 Real Numbers

The **set of whole numbers** consists of zero and the <u>counting numbers</u>.

Counting Numbers
$\{1, 2, 3, 4, 5, \cdots\}$

Whole Numbers
$\{0, 1, 2, 3, 4, 5, \cdots\}$

The three dots mean "and so on."

The **set of integers** consists of the set of whole numbers and their opposites. For example, 2 and −2 are opposites.

$$\{\cdots, -3, -2, -1, 0, 1, 2, 3, \cdots\}$$

P-1 **What is the opposite of each of the following?**
a. −2 2   **b.** 6 −6   **c.** 0 0   **d.** 213 −213

The number $-2\frac{1}{2}$ is a <u>rational number</u>. Here are other names for $-2\frac{1}{2}$.

$$-\frac{5}{2} \qquad \frac{-5}{2} \qquad \frac{5}{-2} \qquad \frac{-10}{4} \qquad \frac{20}{-8} \qquad -2.5 \qquad -2\frac{5}{10}$$

> A **rational number** is a number that can be expressed as a quotient of two integers, in which the denominator is not zero.
>
> $-\frac{3}{5} = \frac{-3}{5}$
>
> $3\frac{1}{3} = \frac{10}{3}$

example 1

Write each number as a quotient of two integers in two ways.
a. 4   **b.** 0   **c.** $3\frac{3}{4}$ **d.** $-\frac{5}{8}$ **e.** 0.3

Solutions: **a.** $\frac{4}{1}; \frac{8}{2}$ **b.** $\frac{0}{1}; \frac{0}{5}$ **c.** $\frac{15}{4}; \frac{45}{12}$ **d.** $\frac{-5}{8}$ or $\frac{5}{-8}; \frac{-10}{16}$ **e.** $\frac{3}{10}; \frac{30}{100}$

(Other solutions are possible.)

Rational numbers can also be expressed as <u>repeating decimals</u>. Also, <u>all</u> repeating decimals are names for rational numbers.

example 2

Express $\frac{3}{11}$ as a repeating decimal.

Solution: $\frac{3}{11}$ means $3 \div 11$.

$$\begin{array}{r} 0.2727 \cdots \\ 11\overline{)3.0000} \cdots \end{array}$$

A repeating decimal has a digit or sequence of digits that is infinitely repeated.

The repeating decimal 0.2727 · · · can be abbreviated as 0.$\overline{27}$. The bar indicates the digits that repeat.

The decimal form of many rational numbers is a <u>terminating decimal</u>. For example, $\frac{1}{4} = 0.25$, $-3\frac{1}{2} = -3.5$, and $1\frac{7}{8} = 1.875$. However, you can consider 0 as the repeating digit for these numbers.

$$\frac{1}{4} = 0.25000 \cdots \qquad -3\frac{1}{2} = -3.5000 \cdots \qquad 1\frac{7}{8} = 1.875000 \cdots$$

Positive numbers such as 1, 4, 9, 16, 25, and 36 are **perfect squares,** because each is the square of a counting number.

$$1 = 1^2, 4 = 2^2, 9 = 3^2, 16 = 4^2, 25 = 5^2, 36 = 6^2$$

Thus, square roots of perfect squares are rational.

Emphasize that these are not the only rational numbers.

Rational Numbers: $\sqrt{1} = 1, \sqrt{4} = 2, \sqrt{9} = 3, \sqrt{16} = 4, \sqrt{25} = 5, \cdots$

Square roots of counting numbers that are not perfect squares are <u>irrational</u>.

An **irrational number** <u>cannot</u> be expressed as a quotient of integers. Thus, the decimal form of an irrational number is <u>nonrepeating</u>. For example,

$$\sqrt{2} = 1.41421356 \cdots .$$

example 3

Write <u>Rational</u> or <u>Irrational</u> to describe each number.
a. 12.326326 · · ·   b. 0.050050005 · · ·
c. $\sqrt{14}$ d. $-\sqrt{9}$

Solutions: a. <u>Rational</u>, because 326 repeats.
b. <u>Irrational</u>, because the decimal is nonrepeating.
c. <u>Irrational</u>, because 14 is not a perfect square.
d. <u>Rational</u>, because 9 is a perfect square: $-\sqrt{9} = -3$.

The **set of real numbers** contains all the rational numbers and all the irrational numbers.

example 4

Refer to the set below to list the numbers named.
$$\{-\tfrac{13}{4}, -\tfrac{12}{4}, -2.7, -\sqrt{2}, 0, \sqrt{3}, \pi, 4.9, \sqrt{49}\}$$

a. Integers   **b.** Rational numbers

c. Irrational numbers   **d.** Real numbers

Solutions: **a.** $-\tfrac{12}{4}, 0, \sqrt{49}$ **b.** $-\tfrac{13}{4}, -\tfrac{12}{4}, -2.7, 0, 4.9, \sqrt{49}$

           c. $-\sqrt{2}, \sqrt{3}, \pi$ **d.** All are real numbers.

CLASSROOM EXERCISES

Name each number as a quotient of two integers in two ways. (Example 1)

1. $3\tfrac{1}{2}$ $\tfrac{7}{2}, \tfrac{14}{4}$ **2.** -15 $\tfrac{-15}{1}, \tfrac{-30}{2}$ **3.** 0 $\tfrac{0}{1}, \tfrac{0}{3}$ **4.** -0.9 $\tfrac{-9}{10}, \tfrac{-18}{20}$ **5.** $-\tfrac{1}{4}$ $\tfrac{-2}{8}, \tfrac{-4}{16}$ **6.** $\sqrt{9}$ $\tfrac{3}{1}, \tfrac{6}{2}$ **7.** $-\sqrt{25}$ $\tfrac{-5}{1}, \tfrac{-10}{2}$

Name each rational number as a repeating decimal. (Example 2)

8. 5 5.000 $\cdots$ **9.** $\tfrac{1}{2}$ 0.5000 $\cdots$ **10.** $\tfrac{1}{3}$ 0.3333 $\cdots$ **11.** $\tfrac{4}{7}$ 0.571428571428 $\cdots$ **12.** $\tfrac{1}{9}$ 0.1111 $\cdots$ **13.** $-\tfrac{3}{8}$ $-.375000 \cdots$ **14.** $-1\tfrac{2}{5}$ $-1.4000 \cdots$

Describe each number as <u>Rational</u> *or* <u>Irrational</u>. (Example 3)

15. 1.123123 $\cdots$ Rational   **16.** 6.121231234 $\cdots$ Irrational   **17.** 19   Rational   **18.** -16 Rational

Refer to the set of numbers below. Then list the numbers named in each exercise. (Example 4)

$$\{28, -1.8, 3\tfrac{1}{4}, 0.1010010001\cdots, -124, 17, -\tfrac{22}{7}, 5.436436436\cdots\}$$

19. Whole numbers $\{28, 17\}$ **20.** Integers $\{28, -124, 17\}$ **21.** Negative numbers $\{-1.8, -124, -\tfrac{22}{7}\}$

22. Real numbers   See below.   **23.** Rational numbers $\{28, -1.8, 3\tfrac{1}{4}, -124, 17, -\tfrac{22}{7}, 5.436436436\cdots\}$ **24.** Irrational numbers $\{0.1010010001\cdots\}$

WRITTEN EXERCISES

See the Teacher's Manual for the suggested assignments.

Goal: To identify rational and irrational numbers

Sample Problem: List the rational and irrational numbers in
$$\{\tfrac{4}{2}, \sqrt{16}, -3.5, -\sqrt{27}, 5.222\cdots, \sqrt{33}\}.$$

Answer: Rationals: $\tfrac{4}{2}, \sqrt{16}, -3.5, 5.222\cdots$; Irrationals: $-\sqrt{27}, \sqrt{33}$

Write each number as a quotient of two integers in two ways. (Example 1)

1. $-\tfrac{7}{8}$ $\tfrac{-14}{16}, \tfrac{-28}{32}$ **2.** $-\tfrac{13}{16}$ $\tfrac{-26}{32}, \tfrac{-39}{48}$ **3.** $4\tfrac{3}{8}$ $\tfrac{35}{8}, \tfrac{70}{16}$ **4.** $-5\tfrac{3}{4}$ $\tfrac{-23}{4}, \tfrac{-46}{8}$ **5.** -1.83 See below.

6. 3.47 $\tfrac{347}{100}, \tfrac{694}{200}$ **7.** 20 $\tfrac{20}{1}, \tfrac{40}{2}$ **8.** -46 $\tfrac{-46}{1}, \tfrac{-92}{2}$ **9.** $-\sqrt{9}$ $\tfrac{-3}{1}, \tfrac{-6}{2}$ **10.** $-\sqrt{64}$ $\tfrac{-8}{1}, \tfrac{-16}{2}$

22. $\{28, -1.8, 3\tfrac{1}{4}, 0.1010010001\cdots, -124, 17, -\tfrac{22}{7}, 5.436436436\cdots\}$ **5.** $\tfrac{-183}{100}, \tfrac{-366}{200}$

Write each rational number as a repeating decimal. (Example 2)

11. -24 **12.** $\frac{5}{9}$ **13.** $\frac{7}{11}$ **14.** $-3\frac{5}{8}$ **15.** $\frac{3}{7}$ **16.** $\frac{11}{12}$

$-24.000\cdots$ $0.555\cdots$ $0.6363\cdots$ $-3.625000\cdots$ $0.4285714285714\cdots$ $0.91666\cdots$

Write Rational or Irrational to describe each number. (Example 3)

17. -3.7 Rational **18.** 7.9 Rational   **19.** $\sqrt{29}$ Irrational   **20.** $-\sqrt{13}$ Irrational

21. $-1\frac{5}{8}$ Rational **22.** $3\frac{3}{4}$ Rational   **23.** $\sqrt{49}$ Rational   **24.** $-\sqrt{36}$ Rational

25. $-\pi$ Irrational **26.** $-7.1000\cdots$ Rational **27.** $0.24681012\cdots$ Irrational **28.** $-0.3691215\cdots$

Irrational

Refer to the set of numbers below. Then list the number in each exercise.
(Example 4)

$\{\frac{10}{2}, -2, 4.7, 0, \pi, -1\frac{3}{4}, \frac{7}{8}, 19, -\frac{17}{4}, -6, -0.9\}$

$\{\frac{10}{2}, -2, 4.7, 0, -1\frac{3}{4}, \frac{7}{8}, 19, -\frac{17}{4}, -6, -0.9\}$ $\{-2, -1\frac{3}{4}, -\frac{17}{4}, -6, -0.9\}$
29. Rational numbers   **30.** Irrational numbers $\{\pi\}$ **31.** Negative numbers

32. Positive integers   **33.** Positive irrational numbers $\{\pi\}$ **34.** Real numbers
$\{\frac{10}{2}, 19\}$ $\{\frac{10}{2}, -2, 4.7, 0, \pi, -1\frac{3}{4}, \frac{7}{8}, 19, -\frac{17}{4},$
Select one or more letters below to describe each of the following numbers. $-6, -0.9\}$
(Examples 3–4)

a. Whole numbers   **b.** Integers   **c.** Rational numbers

d. Irrational numbers   **e.** Real numbers   **f.** Counting numbers

35. 7 a, b, c, e, f **36.** -4 b, c, e **37.** $\frac{5}{8}$ c, e   **38.** -20 b, c, e **39.** -1.7 c, e **40.** $7\frac{1}{5}$ c, e

41. $-6\frac{1}{9}$ c, e **42.** $\frac{22}{7}$ c, e **43.** $1.4238\cdots$ d, e **44.** $-\frac{28}{7}$ b, c, e **45.** 101 **46.** -8.0 b, c, e

a, b, c, e, f

REVIEW CAPSULE FOR SECTION 2.2

Rewrite the following as sums. (Section 1.3)

1. $6-4$ 6 + (−4)   **2.** $7-6$ 7 + (−6)   **3.** $15-8$ 15 + (−8)   **4.** $4-9$ 4 + (−9)

5. $5-12$ 5 + (−12)   **6.** $23-19$ 23 + (−19)   **7.** $14-18$ 14 + (−18)   **8.** $2-25$ 2 + (−25)

Add. (Section 1.2)

9. $4+13$ 17   **10.** $8+9$ 17   **11.** $\frac{5}{16}+(-\frac{1}{4})$ $\frac{1}{16}$ **12.** $\frac{1}{12}+(-\frac{2}{5})$ $-\frac{19}{60}$

13. $1.3+(-0.2)$ 1.1   **14.** $2.3+(-1.1)$ 1.2   **15.** $-4+(-5)$ −9   **16.** $-8+(-1)$ −9

17. $-\frac{1}{3}+\frac{2}{9}$ $-\frac{1}{9}$ **18.** $\frac{1}{2}+3\frac{2}{3}$ $4\frac{1}{6}$ **19.** $-1.5+(-5.6)$ −7.1   **20.** $0.8+(-5.9)$ −5.1

Subtract. (Section 1.3)

21. $5-3$ 2   **22.** $12-9$ 3   **23.** $\frac{1}{3}-\frac{1}{4}$ $\frac{1}{12}$ **24.** $\frac{3}{4}-\frac{2}{15}$ $\frac{37}{60}$

25. $-0.6-1.2$ −1.8   **26.** $-0.2-0.7$ −0.9   **27.** $-4-(-5)$ 1   **28.** $-6-(-1)$ −5

29. $1\frac{2}{3}-\frac{3}{4}$ $\frac{11}{12}$ **30.** $-\frac{5}{6}-(-\frac{11}{12})$ $\frac{1}{12}$ **31.** $0.5-3.1$ −2.6   **32.** $2.4-(-8.3)$ 10.7

2.2 Addition Properties

To simplify an arithmetic expression involving addition and subtraction
To simplify an algebraic expression involving addition and subtraction

The following properties apply to addition of real numbers.

Addition Property of Zero

For any real number a,
$$a + 0 = a \text{ and } 0 + a = a.$$

$-3.4 + 0 = -3.4$
$0 + 6\frac{1}{2} = 6\frac{1}{2}$

Addition Property of Opposites

For any real number a,
$$a + (-a) = 0.$$

$9.1 + (-9.1) = 0$
$8\frac{1}{3} + (-8\frac{1}{3}) = 0$

Commutative Property of Addition

Any two real numbers can be added in either order.
For any real numbers a and b,
$$a + b = b + a.$$

$\left(-\frac{3}{4}\right) + 7 = 7 + \left(-\frac{3}{4}\right)$
$y + 5 = 5 + y$

Associative Property of Addition

The way real numbers are grouped for addition does not affect their sum.
For any real numbers a, b, and c,
$$(a + b) + c = a + (b + c).$$

$(9 + \frac{2}{5}) + \frac{3}{10} = 9 + (\frac{2}{5} + \frac{3}{10})$
$(6 + x) + x = 6 + (x + x)$

---

example 1

An __equation__ is a sentence that contains the equality symbol "=."

Find a value of the variable that will make each __equation__ true. Name the property that gives the reason for your choice.

a. $2.9 + x = 0$ **b.** $3 + n = 8\frac{1}{2} + 3$
c. $y + 0 = 4$ **d.** $(35 + 67) + 72 = 35 + (67 + a)$

Solutions:

	Equation	Value	Property
a.	$2.9 + x = 0$	$x = -2.9$	Addition Property of Opposites
b.	$3 + n = 8\frac{1}{2} + 3$	$n = 8\frac{1}{2}$	Commutative Property
c.	$y + 0 = 4$	$y = 4$	Addition Property of Zero
d.	$(35 + 67) + 72 = 35 + (67 + a)$	$a = 72$	Associative Property

P-1 **What value of *y* makes each equation true? by which property?**

  a. $8.2 + 7.1 = 7.1 + y$ **b.** $\left(7 + 3\frac{1}{2}\right) + y = 7 + \left(3\frac{1}{2} + 6\right)$

  8.2; Commutative Property for Addition   6; Associative Property for Addition

The addition properties can be used to simplify expressions. The first step is to write the expression as a sum.

example 2   Simplify: $-12 + 19 - 13 + 15$

Solution: Use the Commutative and Associative Properties.

① Write as a sum. ⟶ $-12 + 19 - 13 + 15 = -12 + 19 + (-13) + 15$

② Add. ⟶ $= \left(-12 + (-13)\right) + (19 + 15)$

  $= \quad\quad -25 \quad + \quad 34$

  $= 9$

example 3   Simplify: $12 + t - 17$

Solution:

① Write as a sum. ⟶ $12 + t - 17 = 12 + t + (-17)$

② Add. ⟶ $= t + \left(12 + (-17)\right)$

③ Simplify. ⟶ $= t + (-5)$

  $= t - 5$

▶ *By the Commutative and Associative Properties*

example 4   Simplify: $5.2 + x - 8.3 + y$

Solution: $5.2 + x - 8.3 + y = \left(5.2 + (-8.3)\right) + x + y$

  $= -3.1 + x + y$

The result can also be written as $x + y - 3.1$

P-2 **Simplify each of the following.**

  a. $3 + 4 - 7 + 9$ 9 **b.** $9 - 2\frac{1}{2} - 7\frac{3}{8}$ $-\frac{7}{8}$ **c.** $1\frac{1}{2} + y - \frac{2}{3}$ **d.** $3.2 + b - 4.0$

  $\frac{5}{6} + y$ $b - 0.8$

CLASSROOM EXERCISES

  Add.

1. $6 + (-6)$ 0

2. $-12 + 0$ −12

3. $4\frac{1}{3} + 0$ $4\frac{1}{3}$

4. $\left(-\frac{1}{3}\right) + \frac{1}{3}$ 0

5. $0 + (-0.7)$ −0.7

6. $(-0.4) + 0.4$ 0

7. $1\frac{1}{2} + \left(-1\frac{1}{2}\right)$ 0

8. $0 + \frac{3}{8}$ $\frac{3}{8}$

Write the value of the variable that makes each equation true. (Example 1)

9. $1.4 + x = 0.6 + 1.4$ 0.6

10. $4.3 + d = 4.3$ 0

11. $3\frac{1}{2} + (4 + \frac{1}{3}) = (a + 4) + \frac{1}{3}$ $3\frac{1}{2}$

12. $6\frac{1}{2} + 0 = n$ $6\frac{1}{2}$

13. $k = 4 + (-4)$ 0

14. $3 + (4 + b) = (3 + 4) + 5$ 5

Simplify. (Example 2)

15. $-3\frac{1}{2} + 1\frac{2}{3} - \frac{1}{6} + 2$ 0

16. $4\frac{1}{5} - 5\frac{8}{10} + 2\frac{3}{10} - \frac{1}{2}$ 0.2

17. $4 - 5 - 2 + 6$ 3

18. $-11 + 2 - 7 + 3$ −13

(Example 3)

19. $2.6 + x - 0.5$ $2.1 + x$

20. $y - 3.2 + 1.7$ $y - 1.5$

21. $3\frac{1}{2} - a + \frac{2}{3}$ $4\frac{1}{6} - a$

22. $-d + 2\frac{1}{3} - 3\frac{1}{2}$ $-d - 1\frac{1}{6}$

(Example 4)

23. $x - 4 + y - 2$ $x + y - 6$

24. $-z + 6 - 9 - p$ $-z - p - 3$

25. $12.0 - a - b - 6.9$ $5.1 - a - b$

26. $-3.9 - 9.3 - m - k$ $-13.2 - m - k$

WRITTEN EXERCISES

See the Teacher's Manual for the suggested assignments.

Goal: To simplify expressions using the addition properties
Sample Problem: $-3\frac{1}{3} - a + \frac{2}{3} + c$ **Answer:** $-a + c - 2\frac{2}{3}$

Write the value of the variable that makes each equation true. Name the property that gives the reason for your choice. (Example 1)

1. $4\frac{1}{2} + (-4\frac{1}{2}) = b$ 0; Add. Property of Opposites

2. $(a + \frac{3}{8}) + 1\frac{1}{2} = \frac{2}{3} + (\frac{3}{8} + 1\frac{1}{2})$ $\frac{2}{3}$; Assoc. Prop. of Add.

3. $15 + 7 = x + 15$ 7; Comm. Property of Addition

4. $y + 0 = -12$ −12; Add. Property of zero

5. $8 + r = 0$ −8; Add. Property of Opposites

6. $0 + 6 = t$ 6; Add. Property of zero

Simplify. (Example 2)

7. $2.5 - 1.2 - 0.8 + 2.0$ 2.5

8. $-0.3 - 5.9 + 2.8 + 12.9$ 9.5

9. $\frac{1}{2} - \frac{1}{4} + 2 - \frac{3}{4}$ $1\frac{1}{2}$

10. $-3\frac{1}{8} + \frac{3}{4} - \frac{1}{8} - \frac{7}{8}$ $-3\frac{3}{8}$

11. $7 + 5 - 13 + 6$ 5

12. $12 - 10 + 23 - 15$ 10

13. $2.7 + 3.6 - 4.8 + 0.2$ 1.7

14. $-8.9 - 2.6 + 11.2 - 1.2$ −1.5

(Example 3)

15. $-a - 0.5 + 0.2$ $-a - 0.3$

16. $3.8 + b - 6.4$ $b - 2.6$

17. $1\frac{7}{8} + p - \frac{1}{2} - \frac{3}{8}$ $p + 1$

18. $4\frac{1}{4} - y - 7\frac{1}{3} - 5\frac{3}{4}$ $-y - 8\frac{5}{6}$

19. $5 - 1 - 2 - u$ $2 - u$

20. $s - 16 - 0 + 9$ $s - 7$

21. $-3.9 + f - 0.5$ $f - 4.4$

22. $-r + 6.8 - 8.1$ $-r - 1.3$

(Example 4)

23. $6 + k - 23 - b$ $-17 + k - b$

24. $-d + 56 - 39 + w$ $-d + w + 17$

25. $d - 2\frac{1}{2} + \frac{3}{8} - f$ $d - 2\frac{1}{8} - f$

26. $h - 0.7 + 2.4 - m$ $h + 1.7 - m$

27. $a - 5 + 4.95 - b$ $a - 0.05 - b$

28. $s - 4\frac{3}{4} + \frac{2}{3} + t$ $s - 4\frac{1}{12} + t$

29. $r - 14 - g - 16$ $r - g - 30$

30. $-19.1 + k + 19.1 - x$ $k - x$

(Examples 2–4)

31. $4\frac{1}{4} - 6\frac{1}{2} - 2\frac{3}{4} + 1\frac{1}{4}$ $-3\frac{3}{4}$

32. $16 - 35 + 17 + 35$ 33

33. $7\frac{5}{8} + a - b - 13\frac{1}{4}$ $a - b - 5\frac{5}{8}$

34. $-18 - y + 18$ $-y$

35. $-63 + 15 + q - 34$ $-82 + q$

36. $0.9 - 1.3 - 4.8 + 3.7$ -1.5

37. $c - 7\frac{5}{6} - d - 3\frac{2}{3}$ $c - d - 11\frac{1}{2}$

38. $31 + x - 17$ $x + 14$

39. $16 + 34 - 21 + 10$ 39

40. $44 + j - 17 + w$ $27 + j + w$

41. $3 + 6.1 - 0.8 + 2.3$ 10.6

42. $p + 3\frac{1}{5} - \frac{9}{10}$ $p + 2\frac{3}{10}$

MORE CHALLENGING EXERCISES

Simplify.

43. $-123 + 86 + 114 - 230 - 75 - 28$ -256

44. $-0.56 + j - 0.98 - 0.09 + k$ $j + k - 1.63$

45. $3\frac{1}{2} + 4\frac{1}{4} - \frac{7}{8} + \frac{1}{8} - 5\frac{3}{8}$ $1\frac{5}{8}$

46. $14.9 + r - 23.4 - s + t - 15.8$ $-24.3 + r - s + t$

47. $217 - 83 + 142 + 96 - 38 - 62 - 129$ 143

48. $0.87 - 0.49 - 0.08 + 0.33 - 0.91 - 0.39$ -0.67

49. $5\frac{5}{6} + \frac{11}{12} - m - 1\frac{1}{3} - n - p - \frac{1}{6}$ $-m - n - p + 5\frac{1}{4}$

50. $2 + 12 - 33 - 52 + 14 - 76 + 38 + 18$ -77

51. $6.5 + a - c + 7.02 + 3.59 - 8.2$ $8.91 + a - c$

52. $2\frac{1}{10} - \frac{1}{2} - d - f + \frac{4}{5} - \frac{9}{10} - 7\frac{1}{5} - \frac{3}{5} - q$

$-6.3 - d - f - q$

REVIEW CAPSULE FOR SECTION 2.3

Multiply. (Section 1.4)

1. $(5)(-6)$ -30

2. $3 \cdot 15$ 45

3. $\left(\frac{1}{3}\right)\left(-\frac{3}{4}\right)$ $-\frac{1}{4}$

4. $\frac{1}{5} \cdot \frac{6}{5}$ $\frac{6}{25}$

5. $-0.4 \cdot 6.2$ -2.48

6. $(-1.8)(-3.9)$ 7.02

7. $(-14)(5)$ -70

8. $(-8)(-11)$ 88

9. $\left(-\frac{3}{8}\right)\left(-1\frac{2}{3}\right)$ $\frac{5}{8}$

10. $-1\frac{1}{2} \cdot 3\frac{1}{5}$ -4.8

11. $1.9 \cdot 2.6$ 4.94

12. $6.8(-5.3)$ 36.04

Write the reciprocal of the following. (Section 1.5)

13. 5 $\frac{1}{5}$

14. $\frac{2}{5}$ $\frac{5}{2}$

15. -4 $-\frac{1}{4}$

16. $\frac{1}{3}$ 3

17. $-\frac{3}{8}$ $-\frac{8}{3}$

18. 10 $\frac{1}{10}$

19. 1 1

20. $-\frac{1}{12}$ $-\frac{12}{1}$

21. -13 $-\frac{1}{13}$

22. 11 $\frac{1}{11}$

23. -1 -1

24. $\frac{8}{5}$ $\frac{5}{8}$

OBJECTIVES: To find the value of the variable that will make an equation true based on one
of the Multiplication Properties
To simplify an arithmetic expression involving multiplication

2.3 Multiplication Properties

To simplify an algebraic expression involving multiplication

The following properties apply to multiplication of real numbers.

Multiplication Property of One

For any real number a,

$$a \cdot 1 = a \text{ and } 1 \cdot a = a.$$

$(-4)(1) = -4$

$1(0.3x) = 0.3x$

Multiplication Property of Reciprocals

The product of any nonzero real
number and its reciprocal is 1.

$$a \cdot \frac{1}{a} = 1, a \neq 0$$

$\frac{3}{5} \cdot \frac{5}{3} = 1$

$(-7)\left(-\frac{1}{7}\right) = 1$

Commutative Property of Multiplication

Any two real numbers can be
multiplied in either order.
For any real numbers a and b,

$$a \cdot b = b \cdot a.$$

$(-3)(2.5) = (2.5)(-3)$

$\left(4\frac{1}{5}\right)(-8) = (-8)\left(4\frac{1}{5}\right)$

Associative Property of Multiplication

The way real numbers are grouped
for multiplication does not affect
their product.
For any real numbers a, b, and c,

$$(ab)c = a(bc).$$

$\left(9 \cdot \frac{2}{3}\right)5 = 9\left(\frac{2}{3} \cdot 5\right)$

$5.2(3x) = (5.2 \cdot 3)x$

---

example 1

Find the value of the variable that makes each
equation true. Name the property that gives the
reason for your choice.

a. $\frac{1}{3} \cdot y = 1$ **b.** $(4.1) \cdot m = (-3.5)(4.1)$

c. $n \cdot 1 = 6$ **d.** $\left(\frac{2}{3}d\right)4\frac{1}{2} = \frac{2}{3}\left(5 \cdot 4\frac{1}{2}\right)$

Solution:

	Equation	Value	Property
a.	$\frac{1}{3} \cdot y = 1$	$y = \frac{3}{1}$, or 3	Multiplication Property of Reciprocals
b.	$(4.1) \cdot m = (-3.5)(4.1)$	$m = -3.5$	Commutative Property
c.	$n \cdot 1 = 6$	$n = 6$	Multiplication Property of One
d.	$\left(\frac{2}{3}d\right)4\frac{1}{2} = \frac{2}{3}\left(5 \cdot 4\frac{1}{2}\right)$	$d = 5$	Associative Property

What value of x makes each equation true?   by which property?

   a. $(8.1)(6.3) = (6.3)x$ **b.** $(7 \cdot 9)\frac{1}{2} = x(9 \cdot \frac{1}{2})$ **c.** $(-9)x = 1$

   8.1; Comm. Property of Mult.   7; Assoc. Property of Mult. $-\frac{1}{9}$; Mult. Property of Reciprocals

   The multiplication properties can be used to simplify expressions.

example 2   Multiply: $(-\frac{1}{2})(\frac{1}{4})(-4)(-12)$

Solution: Use the Associative and Commutative Properties.

1️⃣ Rewrite the expression ⟶ $(-\frac{1}{2})(\frac{1}{4})(-4)(-12) = (-\frac{1}{2})(-12)(\frac{1}{4})(-4)$

2️⃣ Multiply from left to right. ⟶ $(-\frac{1}{2})(-12)(\frac{1}{4})(-4) = (6)(-1)$

$$= -6$$

example 3   Multiply: $(9)(x)(-\frac{1}{3})(y)$.

Solution:

1️⃣ $(9)(x)(-\frac{1}{3})(y) = (9)(-\frac{1}{3})(x)(y)$ ◀ **By the Commutative and Associative Properties**

2️⃣ $(9)(-\frac{1}{3})(x)(y) = (-3)(x \cdot y)$

$$= -3xy$$

Multiply in each expression.

   a. $(0.6)(3.2)(-5)$ −9.6   **b.** $(\frac{1}{8})(n)(24)(16)$ 48n   **c.** $(-25)(p)(q)(-4)$ 100pq

CLASSROOM EXERCISES

Multiply. (Table)

1. $(\frac{1}{4})(4)$ 1   **2.** $-16(-\frac{1}{16})$ 1   **3.** $62 \cdot 1$ 62   **4.** $(1)(-23)$ −23

5. $(\frac{10}{9})(\frac{9}{10})$ 1   **6.** $(-\frac{2}{3})(-\frac{3}{2})$ 1   **7.** $1(17.8)$ 17.8   **8.** $(0.03)(1)$ 0.03

Write the value of the variable that makes each equation true. (Example 1)

9. $(12.8)(3.04) = n(12.8)$ 3.04   **10.** $(1)(-0.24) = d$ −0.24   **11.** $7(16) = y(7)$ 16

12. $(17 \cdot 3)b = 17(3 \cdot 5)$ 5   **13.** $54 \cdot 5 = 5q$ 54   **14.** $(4.1 \cdot 0.2)a = 4.1(0.2 \cdot 5)$ 5

15. $\frac{3}{8}(\frac{1}{3} \cdot k) = (\frac{3}{8} \cdot \frac{1}{3})\frac{4}{5}$ $\frac{4}{5}$ **16.** $1 = \frac{5}{12} \cdot z$ $\frac{12}{5}$ **17.** $\frac{2}{5}(\frac{5}{7} \cdot m) = (\frac{2}{5} \cdot \frac{5}{7})\frac{1}{2}$ $\frac{1}{2}$

Multiply. (Examples 2 and 3)

18. $(4)(17)(5)(-3)$ -1020

19. $(-3)(19)(5)(-2)$ 570

20. $(\frac{1}{3})(\frac{4}{5})(-6)(-\frac{5}{4})$ 2

21. $(-\frac{3}{2})(-\frac{1}{8})(48)(-\frac{4}{3})$ -12

22. $(14)(-4)(9)(-11)$ 5544

23. $(35)(\frac{1}{7})(10)(\frac{2}{5})$ 20

24. $(a)(0.25)(b)(0.4)$ $0.1ab$

25. $(1.6)(y)(-0.5)(z)$ $-0.8yz$

26. $(-j)(-3)(6)(k)$ $18jk$

27. $(-12)(m)(-n)(-10)$ $-120mn$

28. $(x)(-6.1)(1.3)(y)$ $-7.93xy$

29. $(-b)(1.8)(h)(0.6)$ $-1.08bh$

WRITTEN EXERCISES

See the Teacher's Manual for the suggested assignments.
Goal: To multiply in expressions using the multiplication properties

Sample Problem: $(-\frac{5}{8})(y)(\frac{8}{5})(-z)$ **Answer:** yz

Write the value of the variable that makes each equation true. Name the property that gives the reason for your choice. (Example 1)

1. $-\frac{5}{7} = f \cdot 1$ $-\frac{5}{7}$; Mult. Prop. of 1

2. $\frac{6}{11} \cdot \frac{11}{6} = h$ 1; Mult. Prop. of Reciprocals

3. $(-2.3 \cdot 6.4)8 = -2.3(6.4 \cdot s)$ 8; Assoc. Prop. of Mult.

4. $1 \cdot (-9) = x$ -9; Mult. Prop. of 1

5. $a \cdot 3 = 3 \cdot (-\frac{1}{2})$ $-\frac{1}{2}$; Commut. Prop. of Mult.

6. $(-6.8)(3.5) = m(-6.8)$
3.5; Commut. Prop. of Mult.

Multiply. (Examples 2 and 3)

7. $(-2)(-5)4$ 40

8. $(-1)(-8)(-3)$ -24

9. $(-\frac{1}{3})(12)(-9)$ 36

10. $(-4)(-\frac{3}{2})(-\frac{2}{3})(-\frac{1}{4})$ 1

11. $(0.6)(-p)(0.7)(-q)$ $0.42pq$

12. $(-3.5)(c)(-d)(-40)$ $-140cd$

13. $(-8)(18)(m)(-2)$ $288m$

14. $(d)(4)(39)(f)(2)$ $312df$

15. $(-3)(-3)(t)(-3)$ $-27t$

16. $(4)(-3)(-\frac{1}{2})(-\frac{1}{5})$ $-1\frac{1}{5}$

17. $(1.8)(m)(p)(-3)$ $-5.4mp$

18. $(-40)(3)(-10)(-4)$ -4800

19. $(-5)(x)(9)(y)(-5)$ $225xy$

20. $(-0.3)(a)(-0.7)(5)(b)$ $1.05ab$

21. $(1\frac{3}{10})(\frac{5}{6})(\frac{6}{5})$ $1\frac{3}{10}$

22. $(-\frac{1}{8})(-y)(\frac{3}{5})(-8)(m)$ $-\frac{3}{5}ym$

23. $(2.8)(5.7)(-0.5)$ -7.98

24. $(-k)(14)(12)(-\frac{1}{7})(t)$ $24kt$

MORE CHALLENGING EXERCISES

Multiply.

25. $(-1)(-1)(-1)(-1)(-1)(-1)$ 1

26. $(a)(-0.4)(13)(-b)(5)(-c)(-1)$ $26abc$

27. $(-\frac{1}{12})(\frac{1}{5})(x)(z)(5)(-12)(-y)$ $-xyz$

28. $(-40)(15)(0.2)(0.1)(-0.5)$ 6

29. $(-t)(-2)(r)(-2)(s)(-2)(-2)$ $-16trs$

30. $(-4)(d)(-\frac{1}{2})(-12)(e)(f)(\frac{1}{3})$ $-8def$

MID-CHAPTER REVIEW

NOTE: After completing the Mid-Chapter Review, you may want to administer a quiz covering the same sections. See pages M-12 and M-13 of the Teacher's Manual for the suggested quiz.

Write each number as a quotient of two integers in two ways. (Section 2.1)

1. $-\frac{5}{6}$ $\frac{-10}{12}; \frac{-15}{18}$ **2.** $-\frac{14}{17}$ $\frac{-28}{34}; \frac{-42}{51}$ **3.** $2\frac{4}{5}$ $\frac{14}{5}; \frac{28}{10}$ **4.** $-3\frac{1}{7}$ $\frac{-22}{7}; \frac{-44}{14}$ **5.** 3.5 $\frac{35}{10}; \frac{70}{20}$ **6.** -4.8 $\frac{-48}{10}; \frac{-96}{20}$

Write each rational number as a repeating decimal. (Section 2.1)

7. $\frac{4}{9}$ $0.444\cdots$ **8.** $\frac{2}{3}$ $0.666\cdots$ **9.** $\frac{8}{11}$ $0.7272\cdots$ **10.** $-\frac{4}{7}$ $0.571428571428\cdots$ **11.** $5\frac{1}{4}$ $5.2500\cdots$ **12.** $-6\frac{1}{7}$ $-6.142857142857\cdots$

Write <u>Rational</u> or <u>Irrational</u> to describe each number. (Section 2.1)

13. -2.8 Rational **14.** 8.1 Rational **15.** 31 Rational **16.** $\sqrt{81}$ Rational

17. $-4\frac{2}{3}$ Rational **18.** $\frac{\pi}{4}$ Irrational **19.** $6.13000\cdots$ Rational **20.** $2.323323332\cdots$ Irrational

Refer to the set of numbers below. Then list the numbers named in each exercise. (Section 2.1)

$$\{\tfrac{2}{3}, -\sqrt{5}, -1\tfrac{2}{7}, \sqrt{36}, -9.3\}$$

21. Integers $\sqrt{36}$ **22.** Irrational numbers $-\sqrt{5}$ **23.** Real numbers $\frac{2}{3}, -\sqrt{5}, -1\frac{2}{7}, \sqrt{36}, -9.3$

Simplify. (Section 2.2)

24. $18 + x - 18$ x **25.** $-6.3 - a + b - 9.2$ $-15.5 - a + b$ **26.** $75 + 50 - 85 + 90$ 130

27. $-12\frac{3}{4} + 5\frac{1}{2} - 7\frac{1}{2} + 8\frac{1}{4}$ $-6\frac{1}{2}$ **28.** $-43 + w - 82 + 37$ $w - 88$ **29.** $5\frac{3}{8} + r - 9\frac{3}{4} - s$ $r - s - 4\frac{3}{8}$

30. $t - 0.25 - w - 0.75$ $t - w - 1$ **31.** $y - 12 + 8 + z$ $y + z - 4$ **32.** $-8.4 - 2.5 - 0.6 - 1.3$ -12.8

Multiply. (Section 2.3)

33. $(6)(-2)(-3)$ 36 **34.** $\left(-\frac{1}{4}\right)(-24)(8)$ 48 **35.** $(4)(-3)(-2)(-5)$ -120

36. $(5)(-3)(x)\left(\frac{1}{5}\right)$ $-3x$ **37.** $(-40)(-k)(-10)(4)$ $-1600k$ **38.** $(n)(-2)(-2)(-2)(-2)$ $16n$

39. $(6.3)(a)(-1.4)(y)$ $-8.82ay$ **40.** $(2.2)(-0.4)(d)(-s)$ $0.88ds$ **41.** $(p)(8)(-3)(f)$ $-24pf$

REVIEW CAPSULE FOR SECTION 2.4

Simplify.

1. $(-3 \cdot 4)(x \cdot y \cdot y)$ $-12xy^2$ **2.** $(5 \cdot 7)(a \cdot a \cdot b \cdot b)$ $35a^2b^2$ **3.** $\left(9 \cdot \frac{1}{3}\right)(p^2 \cdot q \cdot r)$ $3p^2qr$

4. $\left(-\frac{1}{5} \cdot 10\right)(m \cdot n^2 \cdot s)$ $-2mn^2s$ **5.** $x + (-8)$ $x - 8$ **6.** $-t + (-1)$ $-t - 1$

7. $(1.3 \cdot 5)(f^2 \cdot g \cdot t^2)$ $6.5f^2gt^2$ **8.** $w + (-16)$ $w - 16$ **9.** $-22 + (p)$ $-22 + p$

OBJECTIVES: To simplify expressions of the form $-(a + b)$
To simplify expressions of the form $-1(a)$ or $-1(a + b)$
To simplify expressions of the form $-a(b)$ or $(-a)(-b)$

2.4 Special Properties

To simplify expressions of the form $a - (b + c)$

The following special properties are helpful when simplifying an expression that contains parentheses.

Opposite of a Sum

$$-(a + b) = (-a) + (-b) \qquad -(4 + x) = (-4) + (-x)$$
$$= -a - b \qquad\qquad = -4 - x$$

Multiplication Property of −1

$$-1(a) = -a \qquad -1(7.2) = -7.2; \ -1(-y) = y$$
$$-1(a + b) = -a - b \qquad -1(4 + x) = -4 - x; \ -1(-t - s) = t + s$$

Opposites and Products

$$(-a)b = -ab \qquad (-6)(m) = -6m; \ (8)(-z) = -8z$$
$$(-a)(-b) = ab \qquad (-4)(-y) = 4y; \ -(5x)(-y) = 5xy$$

Subtraction of a Sum

$$a - (b + c) = a - b - c \qquad 5 - (m - q) = 5 - m + q$$
$$6 - (c - 2) = 6 - c + 2$$

Emphasize that a, b, and c, can represent 0 or a negative number as well as a positive number.

Note that the first two special properties above are equivalent. That is,

$$-(a + b) = -1(a + b)$$

Thus, finding the opposite of a sum is the same as multiplying the sum by -1.

P-1 **Simplify.**

a. $-1(x + 2)$ **b.** $-(4 - t)$ **c.** $-1(\sqrt{2})$ $-\sqrt{2}$ **d.** $(-m)(-k)$ mk

     $-x - 2$ $-4 + t$

example 1   Simplify: $(-rs)(5rt)$

Solution:

1. Use the Multiplication Property of −1. $\longrightarrow$ $(-rs)(5rt) = (-1rs)(5rt)$
2. Use the Commutative and Associative Properties. $\longrightarrow$ $= (-1 \cdot 5)(r \cdot r \cdot s \cdot t)$
3. Multiply. $\longrightarrow$ $= (-5)(r^2st)$
$$= -5r^2st$$

example 2

Simplify: $(-2a)(-a)(-x)(-\frac{1}{2}x)$

Solution:

[1] Multiply from the left to right. ⟶ $(-2a)(-a)(-x)(-\frac{1}{2})x = (2a^2)(\frac{1}{2}x^2)$

[2] Use the Commutative and Associative Properties. ⟶ $= (2 \cdot \frac{1}{2})(a^2 \cdot x^2)$

[3] Use the Multiplication Property of 1. ⟶ $= 1 \cdot a^2x^2$

$$= a^2x^2$$

In the following special properties, note that no divisor is 0.

Special Properties of Division

$$\frac{a}{1} = a \qquad\qquad \frac{7qr}{1} = 7qr$$

$$\frac{a}{a} = 1, a \neq 0 \qquad\qquad \frac{-3s + 4t}{-3s + 4t} = 1$$

Opposites and Quotients

$$\frac{-a}{b} = -\frac{a}{b}; \frac{a}{-b} = -\frac{a}{b}; b \neq 0 \qquad\qquad \frac{-2k}{m} = -\frac{2k}{m}; \frac{7y}{-9x} = -\frac{7y}{9x}$$

$$\frac{-a}{-b} = \frac{a}{b}, b \neq 0 \qquad\qquad \frac{-3c}{-5d^2} = \frac{3c}{5d^2}$$

P-2　**Simplify.**

a. $\dfrac{-5k}{7}$ $-\frac{5k}{7}$　b. $\dfrac{-3cd}{-3cd}$ 1　c. $\dfrac{6t + 4m}{6t + 4m}$ 1　d. $\dfrac{2xy}{-2xy}$ −1

example 3

Simplify: $\dfrac{-(4 - t)}{t - 4}, t \neq 4$

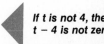
If t is not 4, then
t – 4 is not zero.

Solution:

[1] Simplify the numerator. ⟶ $\dfrac{-(4 - t)}{t - 4} = \dfrac{-4 + t}{t - 4}$

[2] Use the Commutative Property. ⟶ $= \dfrac{t + (-4)}{t - 4}$

[3] Simplify. ⟶ $= \dfrac{t - 4}{t - 4} = 1$

CLASSROOM EXERCISES

Simplify. (Examples 1–3)

1. $-(-a + b)$ $a - b$

2. $-1(-x)$ x

3. $-(-x - y)$ $x + y$

4. $(-5p)(-3)$ $15p$

5. $-(x + y)$ $-x - y$

6. $3(-k)$ $-3k$

7. $(x - 2) - (y - a)$ $x - 2 - y + a$

8. $-(x^2 + 2x - 3)$ $-x^2 - 2x + 3$

9. $a - (6 - b)$ $a - 6 + b$

10. $(-\frac{1}{2})(-a)$ $\frac{1}{2}a$

11. $(-20h)(\frac{1}{5})$ $-4h$

12. $(xy)(-7)$ $-7xy$

13. $(-x)(2y)$ $-2xy$

14. $(-a)(-a)$ a^2

15. $(-xy)(3x)$ $-3x^2y$

16. $(-a)(-b)(-c)$ $-abc$

17. $(-\frac{2}{3}c)(-3ac)(-a)$ $-2a^2c^2$

18. $(\frac{1}{5})(-\frac{7}{8}g)(10h)(-4g)$ $7g^2h$

19. $(-y)(-\frac{1}{2}y)(\frac{1}{2}z)(-2z)$ $-\frac{1}{2}y^2z^2$

20. $(2r)(-3s)(-r)(-6)$ $-36r^2s$

21. $(-m)(-4n)(-4n)(m)$ $-16m^2n^2$

22. $\dfrac{a}{-b}$ $-\dfrac{a}{b}$

23. $\dfrac{-cd}{-cd}$ 1

24. $\dfrac{-9 - m}{1}$ $-9 - m$

25. $\dfrac{-9}{f}$ $-\dfrac{9}{f}$

26. $\dfrac{d^2}{1}$ d^2

27. $\dfrac{9a}{-9a}$ -1

28. $\dfrac{x - 7}{x - 7}, x \neq 7$ 1

29. $\dfrac{-(a - b)}{b - a}, b \neq a$ 1

30. $\dfrac{16 - c}{-(c - 16)}, c \neq 16$ 1

WRITTEN EXERCISES

See the Teacher's Manual for the suggested assignments.

Goal: To simplify expressions using special properties

Sample Problems. **a.** $-6r - (r + 3)$ **b.** $(-3.2)(-x)(y)$

c. $\dfrac{2a - 5}{-(5 - 2a)}, a \neq 2\frac{1}{2}$

Answers: a. $-7r - 3$ **b.** $3.2xy$ **c.** 1

Simplify. (Examples 1–3)

1. $(-a)(-c)$ ac

2. $x - (y + 10)$ $x - y - 10$

3. $(-1)(f)$ $-f$

4. $2t - (r - 1)$ $2t - r + 1$

5. $(-d)(4)$ $-4d$

6. $-(z + 11)$ $-z - 11$

7. $(m + n)(-1)$ $-m - n$

8. $-(14 + p)$ $-14 - p$

9. $2a - (11 + b)$ $2a - 11 - b$

10. $(8a)(-ab)$ $-8a^2b$

11. $(-4c)(-4d)$ $16cd$

12. $(-\frac{1}{3}t)(-15)$ $5t$

13. $(-16)(\frac{1}{4}q)$ $-4q$

14. $(-2.3x)(-2y)$ $4.6xy$

15. $(-5a)(1.8a)$ $-9a^2$

16. $(-3s)(-t)(s)(2t)$ $6s^2t^2$

17. $(2x)(-y)(-x)(3y)$ $6x^2y^2$

18. $(-\frac{1}{2}xy)(-\frac{1}{3}xy)(3)$ $\frac{1}{2}x^2y^2$

19. $(4b)(-\frac{2}{3}ab)(-\frac{1}{2}a)$ $\frac{4}{3}a^2b^2$

20. $(-5ab)(1.8ac)(-\frac{1}{5}b)$ $1.8a^2b^2c$

21. $(1.3r)(-0.6s)(2rs)$ $-1.56r^2s^2$

22. $\dfrac{-7}{a}$ $-\dfrac{7}{a}$

23. $\dfrac{-(2 + y)}{x}$ $\dfrac{-2 - y}{x}$

24. $\dfrac{mn}{1}$ mn

25. $\dfrac{bc}{bc}$ 1

26. $\dfrac{-h}{-k}$ $\dfrac{h}{k}$

27. $\dfrac{3}{-p}$ $-\dfrac{3}{p}$

28. $\dfrac{-(2-x)}{x-2}, x \neq 2$ 1

29. $\dfrac{f-g}{f-g}, f \neq g$ 1

30. $\dfrac{a-7}{-(a-7)}, a \neq 7$ -1

31. $\dfrac{-(k-g)}{-(k-g)}, k \neq g$ 1

32. $(\frac{1}{2}xy)(-4x)(-y)$ $2x^2y^2$

33. $(-7)(-fg)$ $7fg$

34. $\dfrac{abc}{abc}$ 1

35. $\dfrac{-2b+3}{-(-3+2b)}, b \neq \dfrac{3}{2}$ 1

36. $(p+q)-(r-s)$ $p+q-r+s$

37. $(1.3r)(-0.6r)$ $-0.78r^2$

38. $(-3a)(5b)(\frac{1}{10}a)(-4b)$ $6a^2b^2$

39. $(\frac{1}{5}x)(\frac{2}{3}xy)$ $\frac{2}{15}x^2y$

40. $\dfrac{mp}{-(mp)}$ -1

41. $12-(r-3s+15)$ $-3-r+3s$

42. $-(18+t)$ $-18-t$

43. $\dfrac{-3b}{t}$ $-\dfrac{3b}{t}$

44. $(-1)(0.3c+4d)$ $-0.3c-4d$

45. $\dfrac{-(y-2)}{y-2}, y \neq 2$ -1

MORE CHALLENGING EXERCISES

Simplify.

46. $(-2)3+4(-5)-(-7)(-6)$ -68

47. $(-15)9-(-3a)(-a)-(-6)(-10)+(-b)(5b)$ $-195-3a^2-5b^2$

48. $(-1)(-1)-(-1)(-1)(-1)+(-1)(-2)-(-2)(-1)(-3)$ 10

49. $\dfrac{-(y-z)}{-(z-y)}, y \neq z$ -1

50. $(-\frac{1}{2}a)(4d)(15ab)(\frac{1}{8}c)(-\frac{1}{2}d)(-2bc)$ $-3\frac{3}{4}a^2b^2c^2d^2$

51. $(0.5x)(-3y)+(-12r)(-9x)(0.5st)-(-8w)(2wx)(2.5x)$ $-1.5xy+54rstx+40w^2x^2$

REVIEW CAPSULE FOR SECTION 2.5

Simplify.

1. $(2 \cdot 7)a+(2)(8)$ $14a+16$

2. $3 \cdot 7+(3 \cdot 8)x$ $21+24x$

3. $(-5 \cdot 2)+(-5 \cdot 6)b$ $-10-30b$

4. $(-8)y+(-8 \cdot 4)$ $-8y-32$

5. $(4p)(3q)+(4p)(-2)$ $12pq-8p$

6. $(\frac{1}{2}x)(-y)+(8x^2)(-y)$ $-\frac{1}{2}xy-8x^2y$

Write Yes or No to indicate whether 3xy is a factor of both given expressions.

7. $-6xy, 3x^2y$ Yes

8. $2xy, 6xy^2$ No

9. $-18x^3y, 3xy$ Yes

10. $4x^2y^2, 6xy$ No

11. $9x^2y^2, -13xy$ No

12. $21yx, -15x^2y^2$ Yes

OBJECTIVES: To apply the Distributive Property in writing an expression of the form
$a(b + c)$ or $a(b - c)$ as a sum or difference in simplest form
To apply the Distributive Property in factoring expressions of the form $ab + ac$ or $ab - ac$

2.5 Multiplying and Factoring

The Distributive Property can be used to express a product as a sum.

Distributive Property

For any real numbers a, b, and c:

1. $a(b + c) = ab + ac$ $3(2c + 5b) = 3(2c) + 3(5b)$
2. $(b + c)a = ba + ca$ $(-5a - 7b)2c = (-5a)2c + (-7b)2c$

---

example 1

Multiply and simplify: $-3(4x + 7)$

Solution:

☐1 Use the Distributive Property. ⟶ $-3(4x + 7) = -3(4x) + (-3)(7)$

☐2 Use the Associative Property. ⟶ $= (-3 \cdot 4)x + (-3)(7)$

$= -12x + (-21)$

☐3 Simplify. ⟶ $= -12x - 21$

P-1   **Multiply and simplify.**

    a. $5(-3a + 2)$ **b.** $(6m + 4)\left(-\frac{1}{2}\right)$ **c.** $-3r(-2s + 5)$ $6rs - 15r$

      $-15a + 10$ $-3m - 2$

Note in Example 2 that $(3x - 2y)$ is written as the sum $[3x + (-2y)]$
<u>before</u> multiplying.

example 2

Multiply and simplify: $(3x - 2y)5x$

Solution: $(3x - 2y)5x = [3x + (-2y)]5x$

$= (3x)(5x) + (-2y)(5x)$

$= 15x^2 + (-10xy)$

$= 15x^2 - 10xy$

The Distributive Property can be used to express a sum as a product.

$$7x + 14 = 7(x + 2)$$

This process is called **factoring.** The number 7 is the <u>common</u>
<u>factor</u> of $7x$ and 14 because each is divisible by 7.

P-2 **Find the common factors of each pair.**

a. $3x^2$ and $3xy$ $3x$ b. $12ac$ and $4bc$ $4c$ c. $-21rt$ and $-7t$ $-7t$

example 3   Factor: $3x^2 + 3xy$

Solution: ① Find the common factor. ⟶ $3x^2 + 3xy = (3x)\,(x) + (3x)\,(y)$

② Rewrite using the common factor
as one factor of the product. ⟶ $= (3x)\,(x + y)$

Note in Example 4 that $12ac - 4bc$ and $-21rt - 7t$ are written as sums
<u>before</u> factoring.

example 4   Factor: a. $12ac - 4bc$ b. $-21rt - 7t$

Solutions:

a. $12ac - 4bc = 12ac + (-4bc)$ b. $-21rt - 7t = -21rt + (-7t)$

$\qquad = 3a(4c) + (-b)\,(4c)$ $= (-7t)\,(3r) + (-7t)\,(1)$

$\qquad = [3a + (-b)]4c$ $= (-7t)\,(3r + 1)$

$\qquad = (3a - b)4c$ $= -7t(3r + 1)$

P-3 **What is the factored form of each of the following?**

a. $6y + 24$ b. $10mn - 4n$ 3. $15x^2 - 3x$ d. $-9v - 3vw$

$6(y + 4)$ $2n(5m - 2)$ $3x(5x - 1)$ $-3v(3 + w)$

CLASSROOM EXERCISES

Multiply and simplify. (Examples 1 and 2)

$20x^2 + 28x$

1. $10(p + q)$ $10p + 10q$ 2. $12(k - 1)$ $12k - 12$ 3. $\frac{1}{2}(4k - 12)$ $2k - 6$ 4. $-4x(-5x - 7)$

5. $(r + s)8$ $8r + 8s$ 6. $(a - b)14a$ 7. $(9m - 3)\,(-\frac{1}{3}m)$ $-3m^2 + m$ 8. $(3m - 5n)\,(-m)$

$14a^2 - 14ab$ $-3m^2 + 5mn$

Factor. (Examples 3 and 4)

$a(3x + 5y)$

9. $8m + 8n$ $8(m + n)$ 10. $3xa + 5ya$ 11. $6x + 10y$ $2(3x + 5y)$ 12. $2a + 10a^2$ $2a(1 + 5a)$

13. $5x - 5y$ $5(x - y)$ 14. $4 - 6b$ $2(2 - 3b)$ 15. $4mt - 9nt$ $t(4m - 9n)$ 16. $x^2 - 3x$ $x(x - 3)$

17. $-3a - 3b$ 18. $-5x - 10y$ 19. $-6r^2 - r$ $-r(6r + 1)$ 20. $-4st + 8s^2t$

$-3(a + b)$ $-5(x + 2y)$ $4st(-1 + 2s)$

WRITTEN EXERCISES

See the Teacher's Manual for the suggested assignments.

Goal: To use the Distributive Property to multiply and factor expressions

Sample Problem: a. $-5t(3r - 4s)$ **b.** $21mt - 9nt$

Answers: a. $-15tr + 20ts$ **b.** $3t(7m - 3n)$

Multiply and simplify. (Examples 1 and 2)

1. $10(a + b)$ $10a + 10b$ **2.** $5(x + y)$ $5x + 5y$ **3.** $-3(x + 2)$ $-3x - 6$ **4.** $-5(t + 4)$ $-5t - 20$

5. $7(r - 8)$ $7r - 56$ **6.** $12(s - 5)$ $12s - 60$ **7.** $8(3p + 2)$ $24p + 16$ **8.** $6(4r + 5)$ $24r + 30$

9. $(r + 3)4r$ $4r^2 + 12r$ **10.** $(m + 6)3m$ $3m^2 + 18m$ **11.** $(y - 6)(-2y)$ $-2y^2 + 12y$ **12.** $(n - 10)(-4n)$ $-4n^2 + 40n$

13. $(6t - 5u)4t$ $24t^2 - 20ut$ **14.** $(8k - 7j)5k$ $40k^2 - 35kj$ **15.** $(-8t + 12)(\frac{1}{4}t)$ $-2t^2 + 3t$ **16.** $(2.8b - 1.4c)(-0.2ab)$ $-0.56ab^2 + 0.28abc$

Factor. (Examples 3 and 4)

17. $5a + 5b$ $5(a + b)$ **18.** $14m + 7n$ $7(2m + n)$ **19.** $4r + 20s$ $4(r + 5s)$ **20.** $3ax + 6ay$ $3a(x + 2y)$

21. $2km + 4kn$ See below. **22.** $y + 13y^2$ $y(1 + 13y)$ **23.** $p^2q + pq^2$ $pq(p + q)$ **24.** $6m + 18n$ $6(m + 3n)$

25. $3r - 3s$ $3(r - s)$ **26.** $4a - 4$ $4(a - 1)$ **27.** $8x - 8$ $8(x - 1)$ **28.** $12rk - 18sk$ $6k(2r - 3s)$

29. $8kx - 16yx$ See below. **30.** $\frac{3}{4}rx - \frac{3}{4}ry$ See below. **31.** $13x^2 - 26xy^2$ See below. **32.** $\frac{1}{3}am - \frac{1}{3}an$ $\frac{1}{3}a(m - n)$

33. $-14ab - 7b$ $-7b(2a + 1)$ **34.** $-24rs - 8s$ $-8s(3r + 1)$ **35.** $-3x^2 + 6x$ $3x(-x + 2)$ **36.** $-5n^2 + 15n$ $5n(-n + 3)$

37. $-2xy + 5xy$ $xy(-2 + 5)$ or $3xy$ **38.** $-4x^2 - x$ $-x(4x + 1)$ **39.** $-10a - 2b$ $-2(5a + b)$ **40.** $-11rs^2 + 33r^2s$ $11rs(-s + 3r)$

MORE CHALLENGING EXERCISES

Multiply and simplify.

41. $7(a + b - c)$ $7a + 7b - 7c$ **42.** $(2a^2 + 3a - 1)3a$ $6a^3 + 9a^2 - 3a$ **43.** $-8k(4p + 3q - 2r)$ $-32kp - 24kq + 16kr$

44. $(7 + xy + y^2)(-y^2)$ $-7y^2 - xy^3 - y^4$ **45.** $-rs(r^2 - 2rs + 3s^2)$ $-r^3s + 2r^2s^2 - 3rs^3$ **46.** $(-4x - 3x^2 - 30)2x$ $-8x^2 - 6x^3 - 60x$

Factor.

EXAMPLE: $6a^3 + 9a^2 - 3a$

SOLUTION: $6a^3 + 9a^2 - 3a = (3a)(2a^2) + (3a)(3a) + (3a)(-1)$
$$= 3a(2a^2 + 3a - 1)$$

47. $5a - 15b + 10c$ $5(a - 3b + 2c)$ **48.** $4r + 8s - 24t$ $4(r + 2s - 6t)$ **49.** $6x^3 + 3x^2 - 18x$ $3x(2x^2 + x - 6)$

50. $7y^3 - 14y^2 + 21y$ $7y(y^2 - 2y + 3)$ **51.** $30r - 36x - 138$ $6(5r - 6x - 23)$ **52.** $-2x^2 - 4x^2y - 8x^2y^2$ $-2x^2(1 + 2y + 4y^2)$

REVIEW CAPSULE FOR SECTION 2.6

Add or subtract, as indicated. (Sections 1.2 and 1.3)

1. $12 + (-5)$ 7 **2.** $-8 + (-2)$ -10 **3.** $7 + (-13)$ -6 **4.** $-4 + (-9)$ -13

5. $8 - 14$ -6 **6.** $3 - (-2)$ 5 **7.** $-5 - 15$ -20 **8.** $-1 - (-6)$ 5

44 / Chapter 2

21. $2k(m + 2n)$ **29.** $8x(k - 2y)$

30. $\frac{3}{4}r(x - y)$ **31.** $13x(x - 2y^2)$

2.6   Combining Like Terms

To combine like terms in an expression of three or more terms and then simplify

The first and third terms in $3x + 4x^2 - 2x$ are <u>like terms</u>.

> **Like terms** have exactly the same variables
> and the same powers of these variables.

P-1   **Which of the following are like terms?**

a. $3x$ and $-5x$ Like   **b.** $5y$ and $2y^2$ Unlike   **c.** a^2b and $-2ab^2$ Unlike

You can add and subtract only <u>like terms</u>. When you add or subtract like terms, you are **combining** like terms.

example 1   Simplify: $x^2 - 8x^2$

Solution: ☐1 Factor. ⟶ $x^2 - 8x^2 = (1 - 8)x^2$

☐2 Add. ⟶ $= (-7)x^2$ $1 - 8 = 1 + (-8)$

$= -7x^2$

It may be helpful to write the expression as a sum.

example 2   Simplify: $x - 5 - 11x + 7$

Solution:

☐1 Write as a sum. ⟶ $x - 5 - 11x + 7 = 1x + (-5) + (-11x) + 7$

☐2 Group like terms. ⟶ $= [1x + (-11x)] + (-5 + 7)$

☐3 Factor. ⟶ $= [1 + (-11)]x + (-5 + 7)$

$= -10x + 2$

It is not necessary to show detailed steps as in Examples 1 and 2.

example 3   Simplify: $-2x^2 - 3x + 5 - 5x + 11x^2$

The detailed steps are helpful when a student has trouble with the short-cut method shown in Example 3.

Solution: $-2x^2 - 3x + 5 - 5x + 11x^2 = 9x^2 - 8x + 5$

CLASSROOM EXERCISES

Simplify. (Examples 1–3)

1. $3y + 8y$ $11y$

2. $2ax + 7ax$ $9ax$

3. $7x - 5x$ $2x$

4. $6y^2 - 9y^2$ $-3y^2$

5. $ab + ab$ $2ab$

6. $-t - t^2$ $-t - t^2$

7. $2r - 2r$ 0

8. $-3b^2 + b^2$ $-2b^2$

9. $2z + 10z$ $12z$

10. $2a^2b + 3ba^2$ $5a^2b$

11. $3x - 1 + 5x$ $8x - 1$

12. $5a - a + 2$ $4a + 2$

13. $-7 + 2x - 2x$ -7

14. $-x^2 - 5x^2 - 3$ $-6x^2 - 3$

15. $-3t + t + 5$ $-2t + 5$

16. $2a^2 - 3a - 7a^2$ $-5a^2 - 3a$

17. $a^2 - 3a + 2a + 5$ $a^2 - a + 5$

18. $d^2 + 9 + d + 3d^2$ $4d^2 + d + 9$

19. $x^2 + x + 1 - x + x^2$ $2x^2 + 1$

20. $\frac{1}{4}x + 2 - 4 - \frac{1}{2}x + 2x^2$ $2x^2 - \frac{1}{4}x - 2$

21. $\frac{1}{9}a^2 + \frac{1}{3} + \frac{1}{2}a + \frac{1}{6} + 2a$ $\frac{1}{9}a^2 + 2\frac{1}{2}a + \frac{1}{2}$

22. $0.6y^2 - 0.5y - 0.3y + y^2 + 1$ $1.6y^2 - 0.8y + 1$

23. $1.5m + 0.9n + 2.1m^2 + 4.2m + 0.1n$ $5.7m + 2.1m^2 + n$

24. $5d - 16f + 23d - 41 - 12f$ $28d - 28f - 41$

25. $15p^2 - 31 - 81p^2 - 42 - p$ $-66p^2 - p - 73$

26. $14n + 5n^2 + 5n^2 + 16m^2 - 16n^2$ $-6n^2 + 14n + 16m^2$

WRITTEN EXERCISES

See the Teacher's Manual for the suggested assignments.

Goal: To combine like terms

Sample Problems: a. $-3y + 5y$ **b.** $-3x^2 + 6 - x^2 - 4$

Answers: a. $2y$ **b.** $2 - 4x^2$

Simplify. (Examples 1–3)

1. $13y + 7y$ $20y$

2. $5q^2 - q^2$ $4q^2$

3. $17t + 2t$ $19t$

4. $5a - 11a$ $-6a$

5. $-2x - 15x$ $-17x$

6. $-m + 5m$ $4m$

7. $3t^2 - 5t^2$ $-2t^2$

8. $2r^2 - 11r^2$ $-9r^2$

9. $-4z^2 + 11z^2$ $7z^2$

10. $2x - x - 6x$ $-5x$

11. $-3a - 6 + 9a$ $6a - 6$

12. $9m + 2n - 3m - 5n$ $6m - 3n$

13. $0.3t^2 + 2t - 0.5t^2$ $-0.2t^2 + 2t$

14. $3c^2 - 3x - 3c + 5$ See below.

15. $-2.1g + 5.3 - 8.7 - 0.9g$ See below.

16. $5.4d - 0.6 - 8.9d - 8.5$ $-3.5d - 9.1$

17. $\frac{1}{4}a - b + \frac{3}{5}a - \frac{1}{2}b$ $\frac{17a}{20} - 1\frac{1}{2}b$

18. $\frac{2}{3}r + \frac{5}{3}s - \frac{1}{3}s + \frac{2}{3}r$ $1\frac{1}{3}r + 1\frac{1}{3}s$

19. $a^2 - 6 - 3a^2 - 12 - 5a$ $-2a^2 - 5a - 18$

20. $15m - 17 - 17m - 4n - 11n$ See below.

21. $0.9t + 1.6t^2 + 0.3 + 1.7t^2 + 1.9t$ $3.3t^2 + 2.8t + 0.3$

22. $0.05 + 13n^2 + 3.15 - 2.1n^2 - 3.4n$ See below.

23. $\frac{1}{3}r^2 - \frac{1}{5}s^2 - \frac{1}{3}s^2 + \frac{1}{8}r^2 + \frac{1}{3}$ $\frac{11}{24}r^2 - \frac{8}{15}s^2 + \frac{1}{3}$

24. $\frac{2}{3} - \frac{4}{5}b - \frac{3}{4}b^2 - \frac{7}{8}b^2 - \frac{3}{10}$ $-1\frac{5}{8}b^2 - \frac{4}{5}b + \frac{11}{30}$ See below.

25. $12f^2 - 15f - 62f^2 - 45 - 2f$ $-50f^2 - 17f - 45$

26. $50b + 200z + 5bz - 300bz - 112b$ See below.

27. $-0.3t + 0.7t + 0.1t$ $0.5t$

28. $-5y^2 - 3y + y^2 - y$ $-4y^2 - 4y$

29. $ab^2 - a^2b + ab - a^2b^2 - ba^2$ $ab^2 - 2a^2b + ab - a^2b^2$

30. $1.8ab - 0.7ab + 2.1ab$ $3.2ab$

31. $8v^2 + 8w^2 + 2w + 2w^2 - 6w$ $8v^2 + 10w^2 - 4w$

32. $17a^2 + 19a^2$ $36a^2$

33. $77a^2 + 35 - 2a^2 - 10$ $75a^2 + 25$

34. $12k^2 + 9k - 12k + 6k^2 + 6$ $18k^2 - 3k + 6$

35. $\frac{1}{2}x - x^2 - \frac{3}{4}x - 3x^2 - \frac{1}{3}x^2 + \frac{1}{5}$ $-4\frac{1}{3}x^2 - \frac{1}{4}x + \frac{1}{5}$

36. $\frac{1}{3}d + \frac{1}{8}d^2 - \frac{1}{2}d$ $\frac{1}{8}d^2 - \frac{1}{6}d$

14. $3c^2 - 3x - 3c + 5$ **15.** $-3g - 3.4$

46 / Chapter 2 **20.** $-2m - 15n - 17$ **22.** $10.9n^2 - 3.4n + 3.2$

26. $-62b - 295bz + 200z$

Statistician

Statisticians plan and carry out studies that help to make sound decisions. Some statisticians work in city planning where they predict population growth and future needed services. Others are involved in quality control work.

The **arithmetic mean** or **average** is one of the most important measures that statisticians compute. To compute the mean or average, M, of two or more numbers, add the measures and divide by the number of measures.

EXAMPLE: The low temperatures in degrees Celsius in a city for five straight days are listed below. Find the mean low temperature for the five–day period to the nearest tenth.

$$-12.2°, \quad -14.4°, \quad -10.0°, \quad -12.8°, \quad -15.0°$$

SOLUTION: $M = \dfrac{(-12.2) + (-14.4) + (-10.0) + (-12.8) + (-15.0)}{5}$

By calculator:

[1] [2] [.] [2] [+] [1] [4] [.] [4] [+] [1] [0]

[+] [1] [2] [.] [8] [+] [1] [5] [÷] [5] [=]   `12.88`

$M = -12.9°$

EXERCISES

1. Compute the average score of a student who had these scores on 6 exams. Round to the nearest tenth.
86, 93, 96, 88, 74, 83   86.7

2. Compute the average number of years of formal education reported by seven persons. Round to the nearest tenth.
14, 12, 10, 11, 16, 13, 9   12.1 years

3. Compute the average number of wins by a pitcher who won the following number of games in an 8–year career. Round to the nearest whole number.
17, 12, 22, 25, 19, 22, 20, 16

4. Compute the average starting salary for a certain position as reported by 8 companies. Round to the nearest dollar.
$19,500 $21,250 $22,000 $18,000
$19,800 $20,500 $17,700 $22,600

CHAPTER SUMMARY

IMPORTANT TERMS

Counting numbers *(p. 26)*
Whole numbers *(p. 26)*
Integers *(p. 26)*
Rational numbers *(p. 26)*
Repeating decimal *(p. 26)*
Terminating decimal *(p. 27)*
Perfect squares *(p. 27)*

Irrational numbers *(p. 27)*
Nonrepeating decimal *(p. 27)*
Real numbers *(p. 27)*
Equation *(p. 30)*
Factoring *(p. 42)*
Like terms *(p. 45)*
Combining like terms *(p. 45)*

IMPORTANT IDEAS

1. Rational numbers can be expressed as repeating decimals.

2. The decimal forms of irrational numbers are nonrepeating.

3. The following addition properties are true for any real numbers.
   a. Addition Property of Zero: $a + 0 = a$
   b. Addition Property of Opposites: $a + (-a) = 0$
   c. Commutative Property of Addition: $a + b = b + a$
   d. Associative Property of Addition: $(a + b) + c = a + (b + c)$

4. The following multiplication properties are true for any real numbers.
   a. Multiplication Property of One: $a \cdot 1 = a$
   b. Multiplication Property of Reciprocals: $a \cdot \dfrac{1}{a} = 1, a \neq 0$
   c. Commutative Property of Multiplication: $a \cdot b = b \cdot a$
   d. Associative Property of Multiplication: $(ab)c = a(bc)$

5. The following special properties are true for any real numbers.
   a. Property of the Opposite of a Sum: $-(a + b) = (-a) + (-b)$
   b. Multiplication Property of -1: $-1(a) = -a; -1(a + b) = -a - b$
   c. Opposites and Products: $(-a)(b) = -ab; (-a)(-b) = ab$
   d. Subtraction of a Sum: $a - (b + c) = a - b - c$
   e. Special Division Properties: $\dfrac{a}{1} = a; \dfrac{a}{a} = 1, a \neq 0$
   f. Opposites and Division: $\dfrac{-a}{b} = -\dfrac{a}{b}; \dfrac{a}{-b} = -\dfrac{a}{b}; \dfrac{-a}{-b} = \dfrac{a}{b}; b \neq 0$

6. *Distributive Property:* For any real numbers a, b, and c,
   a. $a(b + c) = ab + ac$, and
   b. $(b + c)a = ba + ca$.

7. Steps for Combining Like Terms
   a. Add or subtract the numerical factors.
   b. Use the same variable(s) and exponent(s) to write one term.

CHAPTER REVIEW

SECTION 2.1

Write each number as a quotient of two integers in two ways.

1. $-\frac{13}{16}$ $\frac{-26}{32}; \frac{-39}{48}$ **2.** $-\frac{4}{5}$ $\frac{-8}{10}; \frac{-12}{15}$ **3.** $3\frac{7}{8}$ $\frac{31}{8}, \frac{62}{16}$ **4.** $-2\frac{3}{4}$ $\frac{-11}{4}; \frac{-22}{8}$ **5.** -37 $\frac{-37}{1}, \frac{-74}{2}$ **6.** 16 $\frac{16}{1}, \frac{32}{2}$

Write each rational number as a repeating decimal.

7. -21 $-21.000\cdots$ **8.** $\frac{4}{5}$ $0.8000\cdots$ **9.** $-\frac{1}{3}$ $-0.333\cdots$ **10.** $\frac{7}{12}$ $0.58333\cdots$ **11.** $4\frac{1}{2}$ $4.5000\cdots$ **12.** $8\frac{1}{7}$

12. $8.142857142857\cdots$

Refer to the set of numbers below. Then list the numbers named in Exercises 13–18.

$$\{13\tfrac{1}{2}, -5, 0, -\sqrt{5}, 4.1, 13, -\sqrt{9}, \tfrac{5}{8}, \pi, -0.5\}$$

13. Rational numbers $13\frac{1}{2}, -5, 0, 4.1, 13, -\sqrt{9}, \frac{5}{8}, -0.5$

14. Irrational numbers $-\sqrt{5}, \pi$

15. Positive real numbers $13\frac{1}{2}, 4.1, 13, \frac{5}{8}, \pi$

16. Negative real numbers $-5, -\sqrt{5}, -\sqrt{9}, -0.5$

17. Integers $-5, 0, 13, -\sqrt{9}$

18. Whole numbers $0, 13$

SECTION 2.2

Simplify.

19. $23 - 15 - 18 + 5$ -5

20. $-37 + 14 - 9 + 21$ -11

21. $-12.9 + 8.6 + 13.7 - 18.3$ -8.9

22. $16.8 - 13.4 - 25.7 + 17.8$ -4.5

23. $f - 3\frac{1}{4} + 2\frac{1}{2} - d$ $f - d - \frac{3}{4}$

24. $9\frac{5}{8} - 6\frac{1}{2} - a + 2\frac{7}{8}$ $6 - a$

25. $56 + r - 92 + 26 - s - 18$ $-28 + r - s$

26. $-73 - r + 39 + w - 14 + 58$ $10 - r + w$

SECTION 2.3

Multiply.

27. $(-4)(7)(-3)$ 84

28. $(-5)(20)(-4)$ 400

29. $(-30)(-2)(-4)$ -240

30. $(-10)(-40)(-5)$ -2000

31. $(12)(-3)\left(\frac{1}{4}\right)\left(-\frac{1}{9}\right)(-17)$ -17

32. $\left(\frac{1}{6}\right)(-8)(3)\left(-\frac{1}{4}\right)(-63)$ -63

33. $(-2)(-2)(-3)(-1)$ 12

34. $(-1)(-2)(-2)(-3)(-3)$ -36

35. $(-6)(12)(x)(-4)$ $288x$

36. $\left(\frac{1}{4}\right)(y)(8)(-5)$ $-10y$

37. $(7)(-c)\left(-\frac{1}{3}\right)(21)$ $49c$

38. $(-18)(5)(-d)\left(-\frac{1}{9}\right)$ $-10d$

SECTION 2.4

Simplify.

39. $-(s - 5)$ $_{-s + 5}$

40. $w - (k + 12)$ $_{w - k - 12}$

41. $-5a + 3b - c$ **44.** $r + s - p + q$

41. $-5a - (-3b + c)$ $_{\text{See above.}}$

42. $-(12m - 2n - p)$ $_{\text{See below.}}$

43. $(m - n) - (a + b)$ $_{m - n - a - b}$

44. $(r + s) - (p - q)$ $_{\text{See above.}}$

45. $(-4s)(-t)$ $_{4st}$

46. $(-k)(-12n)$ $_{12kn}$

47. $(\frac{1}{4}x)(-12x)$ $_{-3x^2}$

48. $(-\frac{1}{3}t)(-21t)$ $_{7t^2}$

49. $(-10ab)(5b)(-2ac)$ $_{100a^2b^2c}$

50. $(-4qr)(6q)(-3qr)$

51. $\dfrac{-xy}{-xy}$ $_1$

52. $\dfrac{-8t}{8t}$ $_{-1}$

53. $\dfrac{5}{-s}$ $_{-\frac{5}{s}}$ $_{72q^3r^2}$

54. $\dfrac{a - 4}{a - 4}, a \neq 4$ $_1$

55. $\dfrac{t - 1}{1 - t}, t \neq 1$ $_{-1}$

56. $\dfrac{-(7 - x)}{x - 7}, x \neq 7$ $_1$

42. $-12m + 2n + p$

SECTION 2.5

Multiply and simplify.

57. $-8(b + 9)$ $^{-8b - 72}$

58. $(r + 10)(-7)$ $^{-7r - 70}$

59. $(-5 + 6t)(-3)$ $^{15 - 18t}$

60. $-9(2a + 1)$ $_{-18a - 9}$

61. $3r(-2r + 5)$ $_{-6r^2 + 15r}$

62. $6m(-3m + 5)$ $_{-18m^2 + 30m}$

63. $(-9t - 12)(\frac{1}{4}t)$ $_{-2\frac{1}{4}t^2 - 3t}$

64. $(3.4a + 2.6)(-0.3b)$ $_{-1.02ab - 0.78b}$

Factor.

65. $10t - 10w$ $^{10(t - w)}$

66. $\frac{1}{2}a - \frac{1}{2}b$ $\frac{1}{2}(a - b)$

67. $2x + 6y$ $_{2(x + 3y)}$

68. $15r + 10s$ $_{5(3r + 2s)}$

69. $6x^2 + 3x$ $_{3x(2x + 1)}$

70. $-4y^2 + 2y$ $_{2y(-2y + 1)}$

71. $-12x - 3y$ $_{-3(4x + y)}$

72. $-22xy^2 + 44xy$ $_{22xy(-y + 2)}$

SECTION 2.6

Simplify.

73. $5k - 8k$ $_{-3k}$

74. $-12t^2 - 15t^2 - 5$ $_{-27t^2 - 5}$

75. $6.3n - 4.7n - 3.2 - 3.9n$ $_{-2.3n - 3.2}$

76. $7.2q - 5.9q - 12.1 - 2.7q$ $_{-1.4q - 12.1}$

77. $r^2s - 4s^2 + r^2s + s^2$ $_{2r^2s - 3s^2}$

78. $-p^2q + 2pq^2 - qp^2 - pq^2$ $_{-2p^2q + pq^2}$

CHAPTER 3 Equations

Sections   3.1   Addition and Subtraction

3.2   Multiplication and Division

3.3   Two or More Operations

3.4   Like Terms in Equations

3.5   A Variable on Both Sides

3.6   Problem Solving with Formulas

Features   *Calculator Exercises:* Checking Equations

Special Topic Application: Unit Price

Review
and
Testing
Review Capsules

Mid-Chapter Review

Chapter Summary

Chapter Review

3.1 Addition and Subtraction

NOTE: Computer programming sections A-1 and A-2 on pages 479-483 can be studied any time after Chapter 3 has been studied. All computer programming sections are optional.

Recall from Section 2.2 that an **equation** is a sentence that contains the equality symbol "=". The **solution** or **root** of an equation is a number that makes the equation true.

P-1

Which equations are true when x is replaced by 19?

a. $x - 9 = 10$ **b.** $x - 9 + 9 = 10 + 9$ **c.** $x = 19$

   True   True   True

Equations **a, b,** and **c** are <u>equivalent</u>. **Equivalent equations** have the same solution. Note that 9 was added to each side of Equation **a** to get Equation **b** and Equation **c**.

"$x - 6 + 6 = 10 + 6$" and "$x = 16$" are both equivalent to "$x - 6 = 10$."

> **Addition Property for Equations**
>
> Adding the same real number to each side of an equation forms an equivalent equation.
>
> $x - 6 = 10$
> $x - 6 + 6 = 10 + 6$
> $x = 16$

The goal in finding the solution of an equation is to get the variable alone on one side of the equation. To **solve** an equation means to find its solution.

example 1

Solve: **a.** $n - 8 = -15$ **b.** $73 = t - 9$

Solution: a. $n - 8 = -15$ **Check:** $n - 8 = -15$

$\boxed{1}$ Add 8 to each side. ⟶ $n - 8 + 8 = -15 + 8$ $-7 - 8$

                               $n = -7$ -15

Solution: b. $73 = t - 9$ **Check:** $73 = t - 9$

$\boxed{1}$ Add 9 to each side. ⟶ $73 + 9 = t - 9 + 9$ $82 - 9$

                               $82 = t$ 73

As Example 1 shows, you check the answer by replacing the variable with your answer to see if it is the solution.

P-2   **Solve.**

a. $y - 12 = -13$ **b.** $14 = x - 15$ **c.** $t - 18 = -18$ **d.** $11 = k - 11$

    $y = -1$ $x = 29$ $t = 0$ $k = 22$

As you would expect, there is a subtraction property for equations.

> **Subtraction Property for Equations**
>
> Subtracting the same real number from each side of an equation forms an equivalent equation.
>
> $x + 7 = -2$
> $x + 7 - 7 = -2 - 7$
> $x = -9$

The checks are left for you to do in Example 2.

example 2

Solve: **a.** $3.4 + x = -7.9$.   **b.** $\frac{2}{5} = y + \frac{3}{5}$

Solution: a.
$$3.4 + x = -7.9$$

$\boxed{1}$ Subtract 3.4 from each side. $\longrightarrow$ $3.4 + x - 3.4 = -7.9 - 3.4$

$$x = -11.3$$

◄ $-7.9 - 3.4 =$
$-7.9 + (-3.4)$

Solution: b.
$$\frac{2}{5} = y + \frac{3}{5}$$

$\boxed{1}$ Subtract $\frac{3}{5}$ from each side. $\longrightarrow$ $\frac{2}{5} - \frac{3}{5} = y + \frac{3}{5} - \frac{3}{5}$

$$-\frac{1}{5} = y$$

◄ $\frac{2}{5} - \frac{3}{5} =$
$\frac{2}{5} + (-\frac{3}{5})$

P-3   **Solve.**

a. $n + 13 = 12$ **b.** $17 + k = 18$ **c.** $24 = x + 24$
    $n = -1$ $k = 1$ $x = 0$

CLASSROOM EXERCISES

What number must be added to or subtracted from each side of each equation? (Step 1, Examples 1 and 2)

1. $k + 12 = -9$ Subtract 12.   **2.** $x - 8 = 14$ Add 8.   **3.** $8 + t = 29$ Subt. 8.

4. $m - 12.9 = -4.7$ Add 12.9.   **5.** $9.2 = w - 13.7$ Add 13.7.   **6.** $8\frac{3}{4} + r = 1\frac{1}{8}$ Subt. $8\frac{3}{4}$.

7. $\frac{13}{8} = p - \frac{5}{2}$ Add $\frac{5}{2}$.   **8.** $8 + m = 3$ Subtract 8.   **9.** $14 = 23 + s$ Subt. 23.

Solve. Check each answer. (Examples 1 and 2)

10. $x - 7 = 14$ $x = 21$ **11.** $y - 12 = -7$ $y = 5$ **12.** $p - 23 = -18$ $p = 5$

13. $17 = q - 9$ $q = 26$ **14.** $-0.8 = r - 0.8$ $r = 0$ **15.** $2.5 = b - 1.5$ $b = 4$

16. $f + \frac{3}{8} = 2\frac{1}{4}$ $f = 1\frac{7}{8}$ **17.** $h + 6\frac{1}{2} = 3\frac{2}{3}$ $h = -2\frac{5}{6}$ **18.** $12 + v = -9$ $v = -21$

19. $32 = y + 15$ $y = 17$ **20.** $-12 = 20 + x$ $x = -32$ **21.** $-6 = 11 + c$ $c = -17$

Goal: To solve equations by using the Addition and Subtraction Properties

Sample Problems: **a.** $x - 19 = 12$ **b.** $-30 = 27 + n$

Answers: **a.** $x = 31$ **b.** $-57 = n$

Solve. Check each answer. (Example 1)

1. $x - 9 = 24$ $x = 33$
2. $y - 15 = 27$ $y = 42$
3. $z - 21 = -9$ $z = 12$
4. $a - 32 = -15$ $a = 17$
5. $b - 1\frac{3}{8} = -5\frac{5}{8}$ $b = -4\frac{1}{4}$
6. $c - 27\frac{1}{10} = 19\frac{3}{10}$ $c = 46\frac{2}{5}$
7. $23 = d - 15$ $d = 38$
8. $-46 = r - 31$ $r = -15$
9. $23 = f - 1$ $f = 24$
10. $-236 = p - 407$ $p = 171$
11. $\frac{1}{2} = g - \frac{1}{2}$ $g = 1$
12. $-5\frac{1}{6} = h - 2\frac{5}{6}$ $h = -2\frac{1}{3}$

(Example 2)

13. $j + 11 = 28$ $j = 17$
14. $14 + k = 33$ $k = 19$
15. $n + 15 = -9$ $n = -24$
16. $38 + q = 26$ $q = -12$
17. $\frac{3}{5} + x = -\frac{2}{5}$ $x = -1$
18. $t + \frac{1}{4} = \frac{3}{4}$ $t = \frac{1}{2}$
19. $10.0 = b + 5.2$ $b = 4.8$
20. $30.7 = x + 27.6$ $x = 3.1$
21. $9 = 7 + k$ $k = 2$
22. $413 = w + 198$ $w = 215$
23. $-\frac{4}{5} = \frac{2}{5} + y$ $y = -1\frac{1}{5}$
24. $9\frac{3}{4} = z + 2\frac{1}{2}$ $z = 7\frac{1}{4}$

(Examples 1 and 2)

25. $x + 20 = -13$ $x = -33$
26. $a + 2\frac{3}{4} = -7\frac{1}{4}$ $a = -10$
27. $7.5 = b - 2.6$ $b = 10.1$
28. $c - 59.2 = -34.5$ $c = 24.7$
29. $3\frac{1}{4} = d + 6\frac{1}{2}$ $d = -3\frac{1}{4}$
30. $\frac{5}{6} = t - \frac{1}{6}$ $t = 1$
31. $10.5 + f = 19.3$ $f = 8.8$
32. $-59.6 = 80.7 + g$ $g = -140.3$
33. $1\frac{3}{4} + x = -\frac{7}{4}$ $x = -3\frac{1}{2}$
34. $h + 26 = 405$ $h = 379$
35. $k - 60.2 = -47.4$ $k = 12.8$
36. $-7.3 = 4.1 + m$ $m = -11.4$
37. $16.2 = p + 14.9$ $p = 1.3$
38. $s - 59 = -102$ $s = -43$
39. $74 + z = 12$ $z = -62$
40. $3\frac{3}{4} = v - \frac{7}{8}$ $v = 4\frac{5}{8}$
41. $9.3 = -24.1 + b$ $b = 33.4$
42. $k - 12\frac{1}{5} = 17\frac{1}{2}$ $k = 29\frac{7}{10}$

REVIEW CAPSULE FOR SECTION 3.2

Perform the indicated operations. (Section 1.4)

1. $3\left(\frac{1}{3}\right)$ 1
2. $\frac{1}{8} \cdot 8$ 1
3. $\left(-\frac{1}{7}\right)\left(-7\right)$ 1
4. $(-16)\left(-\frac{1}{16}\right)$ 1
5. $\left(\frac{3}{4}\right)\left(\frac{4}{3}\right)$ 1
6. $\left(-\frac{7}{2}\right)\left(-\frac{2}{7}\right)$ 1
7. $\left(-\frac{5}{16}\right)\left(-\frac{16}{5}\right)$ 1
8. $\left(\frac{8}{3}\right)\left(\frac{3}{8}\right)$ 1
9. $33 \div 33$ 1
10. $(-4.5) \div (-4.5)$ 1
11. $\frac{5}{8} \div \frac{5}{8}$ 1
12. $312 \div 312$ 1
13. $15 \cdot \frac{3}{5}$ 9
14. $(-1.8)(3.9)$ -7.02
15. $\left(\frac{5}{8}\right)(-12)$ $-7\frac{1}{2}$
16. $(-9)(-13)$ 117
17. $\left(-\frac{3}{4}\right)\left(-\frac{7}{2}\right)$ $2\frac{5}{8}$
18. $(13)(-76)$ -988
19. $(58)(8)$ 464
20. $-12.5 \cdot 8.2$ -102.5
21. $-7.2 \div -0.9$ 8
22. $\frac{1}{6} \div \frac{2}{3}$ $\frac{1}{4}$
23. $135 \div 9$ 15
24. $-13 \div \frac{1}{4}$ -52
25. $-15.5 \div 0.6$ $-25\frac{5}{6}$
26. $0.1 \div 0.25$ 0.4
27. $\left(-\frac{2}{3}\right) \div \left(\frac{4}{15}\right)$ -2.5
28. $-\frac{4}{5} \div 16$ -0.05

3.2 Multiplication and Division

OBJECTIVES: To solve and check an equation of the form $\frac{x}{a} = b$, showing all steps

To solve and check an equation of the form $ax = b$, showing all steps

Equations involving multiplication or division are solved somewhat like equations that involve addition or subtraction.

P-1 **Which equations are true when n is replaced by 27?**

a. $\frac{n}{9} = 3$ True **b.** $\frac{n}{9} \cdot 9 = 3 \cdot 9$ True **c.** $n = 27$ True

Equations **a, b,** and **c** are equivalent. Note that each side of Equation **a** was multiplied by 9 to get Equation **b** and Equation **c.**

All three of these equations are equivalent.

> **Multiplication Property for Equations**
>
> Multiplying each side of an equation by the same nonzero real number forms an equivalent equation.
>
> $\frac{x}{5} = 1.6$
>
> $\frac{x}{5}(5) = 1.6(5)$
>
> $x = 8$

Recall that $\frac{x}{4}$ means $\frac{1}{4}x$. Thus, in the example below,

$$\frac{x}{4}(4) \text{ means } \left(\frac{1}{4}x\right)(4) \text{ or, } 1 \cdot x.$$

example 1

Solve: **a.** $\frac{x}{4} = -12$ **b.** $40 = \frac{y}{-8}$

Solution: a.

$$\frac{x}{4} = -12$$

1 Multiply each side by 4. ⟶ $\frac{x}{4}(4) = -12(4)$

$$x = -48$$

Check: $\frac{x}{4} = -12$

$$\frac{-48}{4}$$

$$-12$$

Solution: b.

$$40 = \frac{y}{-8}$$

1 Multiply each side by -8. ⟶ $40(-8) = \frac{y}{-8}(-8)$

$$-320 = y$$

Check: $40 = \frac{y}{-8}$

$$\frac{-320}{-8}$$

$$40$$

P-2 **Solve.**

a. $\frac{b}{6} = -6$ **b.** $20 = \frac{x}{-5}$ **c.** $\frac{n}{3} = \frac{1}{3}$ **d.** $-32 = \frac{b}{-8}$

$b = -36$ $x = -100$ $n = 1$ $b = 256$

As you would expect, there is a division property for equations.

All three of
these are
equivalent.

> **Division Property for Equations**
>
> Dividing each side of an equation
> by the same nonzero real number
> forms an equivalent equation.
>
> $7x = -3$
>
> $\dfrac{7x}{7} = \dfrac{-3}{7}$
>
> $x = -\dfrac{3}{7}$

example 2 Solve: $-6x = -8.4$

Solution: $-6x = -8.4$ **Check:** $-6x = -8.4$

☐1 Divide each side by -6. ⟶ $\dfrac{-6x}{-6} = \dfrac{-8.4}{-6}$ $-6(1.4)$

$x = 1.4$ $-8.4 \leftarrow$

P-3   **Solve.**

a. $3y = 0.3$ **b.** $21 = -7x$ **c.** $-5n = -5$ **d.** $-12 = 4t$
$\ y = 0.1$ $\ x = -3$ $\ n = 1$ $\ t = -3$

Recall that <u>dividing by a number is the same as multiplying by its
reciprocal</u>. This idea is used in the next example.

example 3 Solve: $12 = -\frac{3}{5}y$

Solution: $12 = -\dfrac{3}{5}y$

☐1 Multiply each side by $-\frac{5}{3}$. ⟶ $12\left(-\frac{5}{3}\right) = \left(-\frac{3}{5}y\right)\left(-\frac{5}{3}\right)$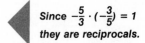
Since $-\frac{5}{3} \cdot \left(-\frac{3}{5}\right) = 1$
they are reciprocals.

☐2 Rewrite the equation. ⟶ $12\left(-\frac{5}{3}\right) = \left(-\frac{3}{5} \cdot -\frac{5}{3}\right)y$

☐3 Multiply. ⟶ $\left(\overset{4}{\cancel{\frac{12}{1}}}\right)\left(-\frac{5}{\cancel{3}}\right) = 1 \cdot y$

$-20 = y$
The check is
left for you.

P-4   **What number should you multiply each side of the equation by to get
the variable alone?**

a. $\frac{1}{2}a = 19$ $_2$ **b.** $12 = -\frac{3}{4}m$ $-\frac{4}{3}$ **c.** $-1\frac{2}{3}x = 16$ $-\frac{3}{5}$ **d.** $-9 = \frac{4}{5}y$ $\frac{5}{4}$

CLASSROOM EXERCISES

What number should you multiply by or divide by to get the variable alone?
(Step 1, Examples 1, 2, and 3)

1. $\frac{n}{12} = -89$ Mult. by 12. **2.** $\frac{r}{-1.9} = 3.4$ Multi. by −1.9. **3.** $14a = -72$ Divide by 14. **4.** $-23m = -59$ Divide by −23.

5. $5.6 = -8.9k$ Divide by −8.9. **6.** $-8.65 = 0.29q$ Divide by 0.29. **7.** $127 = -\frac{2}{3}w$ Mult. by $-\frac{3}{2}$. **8.** $-28 = \frac{15}{4}x$ Multi. by $\frac{4}{15}$.

Solve. Check each answer (Examples 1, 2, and 3)

9. $\frac{j}{7} = 4$ $j = 28$ **10.** $\frac{y}{-6} = -11$ $y = 66$ **11.** $\frac{z}{7} = 20$ $z = 140$ **12** $\frac{a}{12} = -5$ $a = -60$

13. $-4 = \frac{r}{1.2}$ $r = -4.8$ **14.** $8 = \frac{s}{-7}$ $s = -56$ **15.** $-9 = \frac{t}{-9}$ $t = 81$ **16.** $0 = \frac{w}{32}$ $w = 0$

17. $5t = -30$ $t = -6$ **18.** $-8y = 56$ $y = -7$ **19.** $8a = -2.4$ $a = -0.3$ **20.** $-0.6x = -5.4$ $x = 9$

21. $-24 = \frac{3}{2}k$ $k = -16$ **22.** $-15 = -\frac{1}{2}x$ $x = 30$ **23.** $-24 = -\frac{2}{3}k$ $k = 36$ **24.** $-27 = \frac{3}{4}p$ $p = -36$

WRITTEN EXERCISES

See the Teacher's Manual for the suggested assignments.

Goal: To solve equations using the Multiplication and Division Properties

Sample Problems: a. $\frac{w}{5} = -7.2$ **b.** $4\frac{2}{3} = -3x$

Answers: a. $w = -36$ **b.** $-\frac{14}{9} = x$

Solve. Check each answer. (Examples 1, 2, and 3)

1. $\frac{x}{-5} = 13$ $x = -65$ **2.** $\frac{g}{-3} = 30$ $g = -90$ **3.** $\frac{y}{8} = -12\frac{1}{2}$ $y = -100$ **4.** $\frac{k}{12} = -9\frac{1}{2}$ $k = -114$

5. $\frac{x}{8.3} = -14$ $x = -116.2$ **6.** $\frac{s}{0.2} = 1000$ $s = 200$ **7.** $\frac{t}{-4} = -15$ $t = 60$ **8.** $\frac{m}{-5} = 75$ $m = -375$

9. $23 = \frac{v}{8}$ $v = 184$ **10.** $-14 = \frac{w}{-7}$ $w = 98$ **11.** $-16 = \frac{x}{5.2}$ $x = -83.2$ **12.** $-2.08 = \frac{m}{-12}$ See below.

13. $8\frac{1}{4} = \frac{s}{-4}$ $s = -33$ **14.** $5\frac{1}{8} = \frac{z}{16}$ $z = 82$ **15.** $0.34 = \frac{r}{-1.6}$ See below. **16.** $-70 = \frac{b}{0.5}$ $b = -35$

17. $4a = -28$ $a = -7$ **18.** $6c = -54$ $c = -9$ **19.** $-9d = 72$ $d = -8$ **20.** $-11e = 77$ $e = -7$

21. $-1.8x = 18.36$ $x = -10.2$ **22.** $-5b = 3.5$ $-0.7 = b$ **23.** $-108 = 12x$ $x = -9$ **24.** $-72 = -0.9y$ $y = 80$

25. $-140 = -16x$ $x = 8\frac{3}{4}$ **26.** $-y = 99$ $y = -99$ **27.** $-62r = 0$ $r = 0$ **28.** $-90 = -6y$ $y = 15$

29. $\frac{1}{2}z = -44$ $z = -88$ **30.** $\frac{2}{3}r = -54$ $r = -81$ **31.** $30 = \frac{2}{5}k$ $k = 75$ **32.** $15 = \frac{3}{4}c$ $c = 20$

33. $-\frac{2}{3}w = 20$ $w = -30$ **34.** $-\frac{1}{4}a = 8$ $a = -32$ **35.** $36 = \frac{3}{4}m$ $m = 48$ **36.** $24 = \frac{5}{6}e$ $e = 28\frac{4}{5}$

37. $\frac{2}{5}x = -14$ $x = -35$ **38.** $-100 = \frac{1}{5}y$ $y = -500$ **39.** $-\frac{7}{8}p = -49$ $p = 56$ **40.** $56 = -\frac{1}{4}s$ $s = -224$

15. $r = -0.544$ 12. $m = 24.96$

MORE CHALLENGING EXERCISES

41. $-\frac{5}{6}x = 1\frac{2}{3}$ $x = -2$ **42.** $1\frac{3}{4}x = -2\frac{5}{8}$ $x = -1\frac{1}{2}$ **43.** $1.8x = -432.9$ $x = -240.5$ **44.** $-0.07x = -36.988$ $x = 528.4$

Simplify. (Section 3.1)

1. $5n + 10 - 10$ $5n$ **2.** $3r - 7 + 7$ $3r$ **3.** $6b \div 6$ b

4. $(12t + 1.8 - 1.8) \div 12$ t **5.** $(18x - 3\frac{1}{3} + 3\frac{1}{3}) \div 18$ x **6.** $(\frac{y}{4} + 4 - 4)4$ y

OBJECTIVES: To solve and check an equation with the variable on one side and involving multiplication and either addition or subtraction, showing all steps

3.3   Two or More Operations

To solve and check equation with the variable on one side and involving division and either addition or subtraction, showing all steps

To solve an equation that involves more than one operation, use the Addition or Subtraction Property for Equations before using the Multiplication or Division Property.

example 1

Solve: $5n - 7 = 14$

Solution:

$5n - 7 = 14$

1. Add 7 to each side. ⟶ $5n - 7 + \mathbf{7} = 14 + \mathbf{7}$

$5n = 21$

2. Divide each side by 5. ⟶ $\dfrac{5n}{\mathbf{5}} = \dfrac{21}{\mathbf{5}}$

$n = 4\frac{1}{5}$

Check: $5n - 7 = 14$

$5(4\frac{1}{5}) - 7$

$21 - 7$

14

Sometimes the variable is on the right side of an equation. The steps for solving are still the same.

example 2

Solve: $-40 = 8 - 4y$

Solution:

$-40 = 8 - 4y$

1. Subtract 8 from each side. ⟶ $-40 - \mathbf{8} = 8 - 4y - \mathbf{8}$

$-48 = -4y$

2. Divide each side by -4. ⟶ $\dfrac{-48}{\mathbf{-4}} = \dfrac{-4y}{\mathbf{-4}}$

$12 = y$

Check: $-40 = 8 - 4y$

$8 - 4(12)$

$8 - 48$

-40

P-1   **Solve.**

a. $3t - 7 = 14$ $t = 7$ **b.** $-k + 16 = 8$ $k = 8$ **c.** $29 = -3 - 8r$ $r = -4$

Recall that $\frac{x}{12}$ means $\frac{1}{12}x$. Thus, in the example below,

$$\frac{x}{12}\,(12) \text{ means } (\tfrac{1}{12}x)\,(12) \text{ or, } 1 \cdot x.$$

example 3   Solve: $\frac{x}{12} - 14 = -8$

Solution: $\frac{x}{12} - 14 = -8$

$\boxed{1}$ Add 14 to each side. $\longrightarrow$ $\frac{x}{12} - 14 + \mathbf{14} = -8 + \mathbf{14}$

$$\frac{x}{12} = 6$$

$\boxed{2}$ Multiply each side by 12. $\longrightarrow$ $\frac{x}{12}(12) = 6(12)$ ◀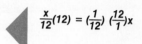

$$x = 72$$

The check is left for you.

P-2   **Solve.**

a. $\frac{b}{7} + 6 = 5$ $\;b = -7$ b. $11 + \frac{s}{5} = 16$ $\;s = 25$ c. $-33 = -3 - \frac{d}{2}$ $\;d = 60$

CLASSROOM EXERCISES

What number must be added to or subtracted from each side of each equation? (Step 1, Examples 1–3)

1. $2n + 5 = 8$ Subt. 5. **2.** $7w - 12 = -3$ Add 12. **3.** $6p - 5.6 = 7.3$ Add 5.6. **4.** $1.4 + 0.9k = 0.5$ Subt. 1.4.

5. $3 - 2t = -9$ Subt. 3. **6.** $12 = 8w + 7$ Subt. 7. **7.** $-25 = 5 + 7q$ Subt. 5. **8.** $16 = 2 - 12x$ Subt. 2.

9. $\frac{a}{4} - 6 = 23$ Add 6. **10.** $\frac{m}{-5} + 3 = -7$ Subt. 3. **11.** $6.5 - 1.3r = -3.7$ Subt. 6.5. **12.** $0.5 + 0.8w = -2.7$ Subt. 0.5.

Write <u>Yes</u> *or* <u>No</u> *after checking whether the solution of each equation below is correct. (Checks in Examples 1–3)*

13. $4x - 9 = -21$ Yes
     $x = -3$

14. $-3y + 7 = -6$ No
     $y = 4$

15. $12 - 3c = -15$ No
     $c = 1$

16. $16 = -8 + 3f$ Yes
     $f = 8$

17. $25 - b = 17$ No
     $b = -8$

18. $12 + \frac{1}{2}n = 18$ No
     $n = 3$

19. $-\frac{1}{3}r + 5 = -2$ Yes
     $r = 21$

20. $-19 + \frac{a}{5} = -23$ Yes
     $a = -20$

21. $-5.9 = 1.3p - 2$
     No
     $p = 3$

WRITTEN EXERCISES

See the Teacher's Manual for the suggested assignments.

Goal: To solve equations using the Addition, Subtraction, Multiplication, and Division Properties for Equations

Sample Problems: a. $-8 + 4r = -20$ **b.** $8.5 = 5x + 6$

Answers: a. $r = -3$ **b.** $0.5 = x$

Solve. Show all steps. Check each answer. (Example 1)

1. $3x - 8 = 13$ $x = 7$ **2.** $4a - 12 = 16$ $a = 7$ **3.** $2b + 9 = -17$ $b = -13$

4. $6x + 5 = 25$ $x = 3\frac{1}{3}$ **5.** $16 + 3c = -50$ $c = -22$ **6.** $-56 + 24d = -254$ $d = -8\frac{1}{4}$

(Example 2)

7. $-31 = 2e + 7$ $e = -19$ **8.** $17 = -4x + 3$ $x = -3\frac{1}{2}$ **9.** $-52 = 12 + 8y$ $y = -8$

10. $-16\frac{1}{2} = -5\frac{1}{2} + 3x$ $x = -3\frac{2}{3}$ **11.** $-17\frac{1}{4} = 4y - 2\frac{1}{4}$ $y = -3\frac{3}{4}$ **12.** $250 = 5f - 100$ $f = 70$

(Example 3)

13. $\frac{x}{7} - 4 = -12$ $x = -56$ **14.** $\frac{h}{10} - 6 = -15$ $h = -90$ **15.** $-26 + \frac{x}{1.2} = -34$ $x = -9.6$

16. $-19 + \frac{k}{2.7} = -33$ **17.** $20 = \frac{a}{5} - 10$ $a = 150$ **18.** $70 = 8 + \frac{b}{2}$ $b = 124$
$k = -37.8$

(Examples 1–3)

19. $3x - 4.8 = -21.3$ $x = -5.5$ **20.** $-32 + 30t = -287$ $t = -8.5$ **21.** $\frac{h}{4} + 15 = -60$ $h = -300$

22. $-2.4 = 10.6 - 2k$ $k = 6.5$ **23.** $\frac{2}{3}g - \frac{1}{3} = \frac{2}{3}$ $g = 1\frac{1}{2}$ **24.** $50 = \frac{1}{2}d + 30$ $d = 40$

25. $12 - 5z = 48$ $z = -7.2$ **26.** $1.5f + 8.5 = 11.5$ $f = 2$ **27.** $125 = 10c - 25$ $c = 15$

28. $\frac{n}{6} - 13 = 20$ $n = 198$ **29.** $4x - 12.3 = -18.5$ $x = -1.55$ **30.** $12 - \frac{3}{4}m = 15$ $m = -4$

31. $\frac{j}{3} - 4 = 7$ $j = 33$ **32.** $2a - 9.3 = -6.7$ $a = 1.3$ **33.** $\frac{1}{5}b + 15 = 25$ $b = 50$

34. $-10.4 - p = 12.1$ **35.** $\frac{r}{8} + 15 = 12$ $r = -24$ **36.** $\frac{2}{7}w + \frac{1}{7} = -\frac{5}{7}$ $w = -3$
$p = -22.5$

37. $86 = 9 + 3x$ $x = 25\frac{2}{3}$ **38.** $12 - \frac{t}{5} = 7$ $t = 25$ **39.** $-36 = -4x + 6$ $x = 10\frac{1}{2}$

40. $-\frac{p}{6} + 7 = -2.5$ $p = 57$ **41.** $5\frac{1}{3} = 12 - 8k$ $k = \frac{5}{6}$ **42.** $6.2 = -2x - 5.4$ $x = 5.8$

MORE CHALLENGING EXERCISES

Solve. Check each answer.

43. $4\frac{1}{2} - \frac{1}{4}d = -3\frac{1}{8}$ $d = 30\frac{1}{2}$ **44.** $-3\frac{1}{4} + \frac{1}{2}t = -10\frac{3}{8}$ $t = -14\frac{1}{4}$ **45.** $\frac{11}{4} = \frac{15}{8} + \frac{3}{2}h$ $h = \frac{7}{12}$

46. $\frac{13}{4} = -\frac{9}{2} - \frac{3}{8}u$ $u = -20\frac{2}{3}$ **47.** $74 + 16z - 102 = -92$ $z = -4$ **48.** $324 = -56 - 18a + 92$
$a = -16$

49. $\frac{7}{6} + \frac{4}{5}v = 2\frac{1}{2}$ $v = \frac{5}{3}$ **50.** $-19 + 4x - 23 = -2$ $x = 10$ **51.** $48 - 3c - 6 = 84$
$c = -14$

MID-CHAPTER REVIEW NOTE: After completing the Mid-Chapter Review, you may want to administer a quiz covering the same sections. See pages M-14 and M-15 of the Teacher's Manual for the suggested quiz.

Solve. Check each answer. (Section 3.1)

1. $b + 9 = -3$ $b = -12$

2. $10 + w = 40$ $w = 30$

3. $y - 1.5 = 3$ $y = 4.5$

4. $-3\frac{1}{8} = k - 2\frac{1}{4}$ $k = -\frac{7}{8}$

5. $t - 67 = 83$ $t = 150$

6. $0.75 = a + 0.25$ $a = 0.5$

Solve. Check each answer. (Section 3.2)

7. $-39 = 13a$ $a = -3$

8. $\frac{m}{-2} = -3$ $m = 6$

9. $-9z = 30$ $z = -3\frac{1}{3}$

10. $\frac{r}{0.5} = 16.5$ $r = 8.25$

11. $6\frac{1}{2} = \frac{x}{2}$ $x = 13$

12. $-42 = -13h$ $h = 3\frac{3}{13}$

Solve. Check each answer. (Section 3.3)

13. $3y + 7 = 28$ $y = 7$

14. $40 = \frac{h}{3} - 10$ $h = 150$

15. $15 = 7\frac{1}{2} - \frac{1}{2}t$ $t = -15$

16. $-20 = 15 + 15n$ $n = -2\frac{1}{3}$

17. $1.7 + \frac{j}{6} = 3.7$ $j = 12$

18. $8v - 17 = -33$ $v = -2$

─────── *CHECKING EQUATIONS* ───────

You can use a calculator to check an equation. However, a calculator does not automatically follow the rules for the order of operations. You may have to rewrite the equation for the calculator.

EXAMPLE Check the answer to Sample Problem **a** on page 60.

SOLUTION Equation: $-8 + 4r = -20$ Answer to be checked: -3
First rewrite the left side for the calculator: $4r - 8$

Multiplication is performed before addition.

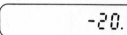 −20.

Note: For "−3" press "⌊3⌋ ⌊⁺∕₋⌋."

Since both sides have the same value, -20, the answer, -3, is correct.

Check the given "answer" to each equation below.

1. $5n - 7 = 14$; 4.2 Correct

2. $24 = 6 + 2x$; 3 Incorrect

3. $4 + 3x = -11$; -5
Correct

REVIEW CAPSULE FOR SECTION 3.4

Simplify. (Sections 2.6 and 2.5)

1. $5n + 3 - 2n$ $3n + 3$

2. $2.4t - t + 1.3t$ $2.7t$

3. $k + 1\frac{1}{4} - 3\frac{1}{2}k - 1\frac{3}{4}$ $-2\frac{1}{2}k - \frac{1}{2}$

4. $16m - 14 - 6 - 3m + m$ $14m - 20$

5. $5(6 - x)$ $30 - 5x$

6. $15(3 + 2n)$ $45 + 30n$

7. $-8(k - 6)$ $-8k + 48$

8. $-12(-5 - 3x)$ $60 + 36x$

9. $\frac{1}{4}(2y + 3)$ $\frac{1}{2}y + \frac{3}{4}$

3.4 Like Terms in Equations

OBJECTIVES: To solve and check an equation with the variable in two or more like terms on the same side
To solve and check an equation with the variable on one side that requires use of the Distributive Property and combining like terms

In solving some equations, you should combine like terms first.

example 1

Solve and check: $5x - 7 - 3x = -19$

Solution:

|1| Combine like terms.

$$5x - 7 - 3x = -19$$
$$5x - 7 - 3x = -19$$
$$2x - 7 = -19$$

|2| Add 7 to each side.

$$2x - 7 + 7 = -19 + 7$$
$$2x = -12$$

|3| Divide each side by 2. $\longrightarrow$

$$\frac{2x}{2} = \frac{-12}{2}$$
$$x = -6$$

Check: $5x - 7 - 3x = -19$
$$5(-6) - 7 - 3(-6)$$
$$-30 - 7 + 18$$
$$-37 + 18$$
$$-19 \leftarrow$$

P-1 Solve.

a. $7m - 3 + 4m = 30$ $m = 3$ **b.** $9k + 6 - 3k = -36$ $k = -7$

In solving some equations, you have to use the Distributive Property first to remove parentheses. The check in the following examples is left for you to do.

example 2

Solve and check: $26 = 5 - 3(2t + 3)$

Solution: |1| Use the Distributive Property. $\longrightarrow$ $26 = 5 - 3(2t + 3)$

|2| Simplify. $\longrightarrow$ $26 = 5 - 6t - 9$

$$26 = -4 - 6t$$

|3| Add 4 to each side. $\longrightarrow$ $26 + 4 = -4 - 6t + 4$

$$30 = -6t$$

|4| Divide each side by -6. $\longrightarrow$ $\dfrac{30}{-6} = \dfrac{-6t}{-6}$

$$-5 = t$$

P-2 Solve.

a. $24 = 8 - 4(3y - 1)$ $y = -1$ **b.** $17 = 12 + 5(r - 4)$ $r = 5$

example 3

Solve: $2(3x - 4) - 4(x + 1) = -15$

Solution:

1. Use the Distributive Property twice. $\longrightarrow$ $2(3x - 4) - 4(x + 1) = -15$

2. Combine like terms. $\longrightarrow$ $6x - 8 - 4x - 4 = -15$

   $2x - 12 = -15$

3. Add 12 to each side. $\longrightarrow$ $2x - 12 + \mathbf{12} = -15 + \mathbf{12}$

   $2x = -3$

4. Divide each side by 2. $\longrightarrow$ $\dfrac{2x}{2} = \dfrac{-3}{2}$

   $x = -1\frac{1}{2}$

CLASSROOM EXERCISES

Write the equation that results after combining like terms. (Step 1, Example 1)

1. $5y + 6 - y = 13$ $4y + 6 = 13$

2. $-10 = 8t - 3t - 7$ $-10 = 5t - 7$

3. $-4r + 8 - r = 17$ $-5r + 8 = 17$

4. $10q - 6 - 2q - 3q = 7$ $5q - 6 = 7$

5. $-9.7 = 5.8m - 2.7m - 4.8$ $-9.7 = 3.1m - 48$

6. $-3.2a - 1.6 + 4.1a = 9.3$ $0.9a - 1.6 = 9.3$

7. $10x - 5 - 12x + 8 = 19$ $-2x + 3 = 19$

8. $-27 = 5k + 2 - 8k - 10$ $-27 = -3k - 8$

9. $\frac{1}{4}n - 5 - 2\frac{1}{2}n = 3\frac{1}{2} - 2\frac{1}{4}$ $-2\frac{1}{4}n - 5 = 1\frac{1}{4}$

10. $\frac{1}{4}(3x - 1) = 2\frac{1}{8}$ $\frac{3}{4}x - \frac{1}{4} = 2\frac{1}{8}$

    a. *Write the equation that results after removing parentheses.*
    b. *Then write the equation that results after combining like terms.*
    (Steps, 1 and 2 in Examples 2 and 3)

11. $3(4x - 1) + 6 = 10$ $12x - 3 + 6 = 10;\ 12x + 3 = 10$

12. $-5(2x + 3) - 7 = 12$ $-10x - 15 - 7 = 12;$ $-10x - 22 = 12$

13. $-5 = 5t - 3(1 - t)$ $-5 = 5t - 3 + 3t;\ -5 = 8t - 3$

14. $17 - 4(n - 5) = 10$ See below.

15. $\frac{1}{3} - 2(q - 5) + \frac{1}{4}q = 6$ See below.

16. $-7 = -\frac{1}{2}(4r - 6) + 13$ $-7 = -2r + 3 + 13;$ $-7 = -2r + 16$

17. $\frac{3}{4}(x - 2) + 2(3x + \frac{1}{4}) = -11$ See below.

18. $5(k - \frac{1}{3}) - 3(2k + \frac{1}{3}) = 19$ See below.

19. $-6 = 4(3 - 2t) + 5(t - 4)$ $-6 = 12 - 8t + 5t - 20;$ $-6 = -8 - 3t$

20. $-6 + 5w - 3(4 - w) = 25$ $-6 + 5w - 12 + 3w = 25;$ $-18 + 8w = 25$

Evaluate each expression for the given value of the variable.
(Check, Example 1)

21. $3y - 8$ when $y = 5$ 7

22. $12 - 2p$ when $p = -3$ 18

23. $z - 5z - 3$ when $z = 2$ -11

24. $3r - 5 - 5r$ when $r = -1$ -3

25. $2(d - 3) - 5$ when $d = 4$ -3

26. $-3(c - 2) - 4$ when $c = -2$ 8

14. $17 - 4n + 20 = 10;\ 37 - 4n = 10$

15. $\frac{1}{3} - 2q + 10 + \frac{1}{4}q = 6;\ -1\frac{3}{4}q + 10\frac{1}{3} = 6$

17. $\frac{3}{4}x - \frac{3}{2} + 6x + \frac{1}{2} = -11;\ 6\frac{3}{4}x - 1 = -11$

Equations / **63**

18. $5k - \frac{5}{3} - 6k - 1 = 19;\ -k - 2\frac{2}{3} = 19$

WRITTEN EXERCISES

See the Teacher's Manual for the suggested assignments.

Goal: To solve equations having like terms

Sample Problem: $-5(2x + 1) - 7x = 29$

Answer: $x = -2$

Solve. Check each answer. (Examples 1, 2, and 3)

1. $3x + 5 + x = 33$ $x = 7$

2. $2y - 8 - 5y = -47$ $y = 13$

3. $-z + 1.2 - 3z = 2.8$ $z = -0.4$

4. $4.6a - 5.8a - 30 = -12$ $a = -15$

5. $37 = 8x - 19 - 15x$ $x = -8$

6. $-26 = 22 - c - 5c$ $c = 8$

7. $\frac{1}{4}(b + 3) = 2\frac{1}{2}$ $b = 7$

8. $15 = 3(\frac{2}{3}d - \frac{1}{3})$ $d = 8$

9. $-2(x + 1) - 7 = 15$ $x = -12$

10. $-3(4n + 1) + 8n = -35$ $n = 8$

11. $-32 = -5(f - 2) + 2f$ $f = 14$

12. $15 - 4(2g - 3) + 4g = 39$ $g = -3$

13. $(4k - 3) - (7k + 8) = 6\frac{1}{2}$ $k = -5\frac{5}{6}$

14. $17\frac{1}{2} = \frac{1}{3}(y + 1) - (2y - \frac{1}{2})$ $y = -10$

15. $92 = (m + 4) - (3m - 12)$ $m = -38$

16. $2(3 - 2x) - 4(x + 4) = -118$ $x = 13\frac{1}{2}$

17. $-0.5(3n + 3) - 2(n + 0.6) = 0.8$ $n = -1$

18. $-7 = 6(4 + 0.3) + 0.5(2r - 5)$ $r = -30.3$

Solve each equation. (Examples 1–3)

19. $\frac{1}{2}x + 6 + 4x = 5\frac{1}{2}$ $x = -\frac{1}{9}$

20. $7(n + 1) = 21$ $n = 2$

21. $-12 + 2(5 - h) - 3h = -57$ $h = 11$

22. $-3.6b + 26 - 0.8b = -84$ $b = 25$

23. $19.2 - 23.8 = 5d - 14.8 - 7d$ $d = -5.1$

24. $-2(5 - x) - 6(x + 3) = -102$ $x = 18.5$

25. $0.9 - 5.7 = 10.4 - e - 3e$ $e = 3.8$

26. $16 = 2r - 4(r - 6) + 6r$ $r = -2$

27. $-85 = 5t - 9t - (14 - 2t)$ $t = 35\frac{1}{2}$

28. $4z + 6z - (20 - 8z) = 25$ $z = 2\frac{1}{2}$

29. $2\frac{1}{2}y - 3(y + \frac{1}{4}) + 6y = 13$ $y = 2\frac{1}{2}$

30. $70 = 6(2t - 1) - 3(2t + 1)$ $t = 13\frac{1}{6}$

MORE CHALLENGING EXERCISES

Solve each equation.

31. $z + 5 = 2z - 4$ $z = 9$

32. $3y - 12 = 4y + 7$ $y = -19$

33. $4 - 6y = 12 - 4y$ $y = -4$

REVIEW CAPSULE FOR SECTION 3.5

For Exercises 1–6, evaluate both expressions for the given value of the variable. (Section 1.7)

1. $\left.\begin{array}{l} 5x + 3 \\ 4x - 9 \end{array}\right\}$ $x = 6$ 33; 15

2. $\left.\begin{array}{l} 20 - 2y \\ 56 - 5y \end{array}\right\}$ $y = 12$ -4; -4

3. $\left.\begin{array}{l} 4 - 3z \\ z + 22 \end{array}\right\}$ $z = -4\frac{1}{2}$ 17.5; 17.5

4. $\left.\begin{array}{l} 21 + m \\ -19 - 7m \end{array}\right\}$ $m = -5$ 16; 16

5. $\left.\begin{array}{l} 5r + 2(r - 1) \\ 3(r + 1) \end{array}\right\}$ $r = 1\frac{1}{4}$ $6\frac{3}{4}$; $6\frac{3}{4}$

6. $\left.\begin{array}{l} 8p - 2(2p - 1) \\ 6(p + 2) \end{array}\right\}$ $p = -5$ -18; -18

3.5 A Variable on Both Sides

To solve and check an equation with the variable on both sides but requiring use of the Distributive Property at the first step

When a variable appears on both sides of an equation, the first step is to eliminate the variable from one side.

example 1

Solve: $5x + 12 = 3x - 6$

Solution: $5x + 12 = 3x - 6$

1. Subtract $3x$ from each side. ⟶ $5x + 12 - \mathbf{3x} = 3x - 6 - \mathbf{3x}$

                                                                $2x + 12 = -6$

2. Subtract 12 from each side. ⟶ $2x + 12 - \mathbf{12} = -6 - \mathbf{12}$ ◀ $-6 - 12 = -6 + (-12)$

                                                                $2x = -18$

3. Divide each side by 2. ⟶ $\dfrac{2x}{2} = \dfrac{-18}{2}$

                                                                $x = -9$

Check: $5x + 12 = 3x - 6$

$5(-9) + 12 \mid 3(-9) - 6$

$-45 + 12 \mid -27 - 6$ ◀ $-27 - 6 = -27 + (-6)$

$-33 \mid -33$

You will want to demonstrate optional ways to solve the equations of the Examples.

P-1   Solve.

a. $11t + 16 = 4t + 2$ $t = -2$ **b.** $9j + 6 = 4j - 14$ $j = -4$

example 2

Solve: $12 - 7r = 42 - 3r$

Solution: $12 - 7r = 42 - 3r$

1. Add $7r$ to each side. ⟶ $12 - 7r + \mathbf{7r} = 42 - 3r + \mathbf{7r}$

                                                                $12 = 42 + 4r$

2. Subtract 42 from each side. ⟶ $12 - \mathbf{42} = 42 + 4r - \mathbf{42}$

                                                                $-30 = 4r$

3. Divide each side by 4. ⟶ $\dfrac{-30}{4} = \dfrac{4r}{4}$

                                                                $-7\frac{1}{2} = r$ ◀ **The check is left for you.**

P-2   Solve.

a. $3 - 2p = 17 - p$ **b.** $15 - 3f = 3 + 6f$ $f = 1\frac{1}{3}$

   $p = -14$

In equations that contain parentheses, use the Distributive Property first. Then eliminate the variable from one side of the equation.

example 3

Solve: $5 + 2x = 2(x - 3) + x$

Solution:

1. Use the Distributive Property. $\longrightarrow$ $5 + 2x = 2(x - 3) + x$

2. Combine like terms. $\longrightarrow$ $5 + 2x = 2x - 6 + x$

$$5 + 2x = 3x - 6$$

3. Subtract 2x from each side. $\longrightarrow$ $5 + 2x - \mathbf{2x} = 3x - 6 - \mathbf{2x}$

$$5 = x - 6$$

4. Add 6 to each side. $\longrightarrow$ $5 + \mathbf{6} = x - 6 + \mathbf{6}$

$$11 = x$$

Check:

$5 + 2x = 2(x - 3) + x$	
$5 + 2(11)$	$2(11 - 3) + 11$
$5 + 22$	$2(8) + 11$
27	27

P-3 **Solve.**

a. $9 + 4y = 3(y + 4) - y$
$y = 1\frac{1}{2}$

b. $2 + 10g = 6(2g + 3) + 2g$ $g = -4$

CLASSROOM EXERCISES

Write the two equations that are formed in eliminating the variable from each side of the following equations. (Step 1, Examples 1–2)

1. $3x - 2 = 2x + 5$ $x - 2 = 5;\ -2 = -x + 5$

2. $3 - 4y = 7 - 5y$ $3 + y = 7;\ 3 = 7 - y$

3. $8 + a = -3a + 6$ $8 + 4a = 6;\ 8 = -4a + 6$

4. $10 + 5g = -8 + 3g$ $10 + 2g = -8;\ 10 = -8 - 2g$

5. $-4d - 6 = 12 - d$ $-3d - 6 = 12;\ -6 = 12 + 3d$

6. $10b - 7 = 9 - 4b$ $14b - 7 = 9;\ -7 = 9 - 14b$

For each equation, write an equivalent equation that has the variable on one side. (Steps 1 and 2, Examples 1–2)

EXAMPLE: $3x - 7 = 2x + 8$ **ANSWER:** $x - 7 = 8$ or $-7 = -x + 8$

7. $4p + 2 = 6 - p$ $5p + 2 = 6$

8. $5 - 2r = 3r - 2$ $5 = 5r - 2$

9. $-3z - 8 = z + 5$ $-8 = 4z + 5$

10. $3\frac{1}{4}m + 2\frac{1}{4} = 1\frac{1}{2}m - 4\frac{1}{2}$
$1\frac{3}{4}m + 2\frac{1}{4} = -4\frac{1}{2}$

11. $10.8 - 3.4j = 9.2 + 7.1j$
$10.8 = 9.2 + 10.5j$

12. $8 - h = 2h - 3 - 6h$
$8 = -3 - 3h$

WRITTEN EXERCISES

Goal: To solve equations that have a variable on both sides

Sample Problem: Solve: $5 + 4x = 3x - 10 - x$

Answer: $x = -7\frac{1}{2}$

Solve. Check each answer. (Example 1)

1. $3x - 5 = 2x + 12$ $x = 17$

2. $5x - 3 = 4x + 9$ $x = 12$

3. $12a - 9 = 10a + 17$ $a = 13$

4. $8b - 14 = 6b + 28$ $b = 21$

5. $1.6c - 7.5 = 14.1 + 3.4c$ $c = -12$

6. $0.5d - 3 - d = -1.8 + d$ $d = -0.8$

7. $3\frac{1}{2}k + 17 = 2\frac{3}{4}k + 12$ $k = -6\frac{2}{3}$

8. $\frac{1}{20} + \frac{1}{5}s - 11 = \frac{3}{5}s - 11$ $s = \frac{1}{8}$

(Example 2)

9. $12 - x = 26 - 3x$ $x = 7$

10. $20 - 2y = 56 - 5y$ $y = 12$

11. $4 - 3z = z + 22$ $z = -4\frac{1}{2}$

12. $5 - 2m = -22 - 4m$ $m = -13\frac{1}{2}$

13. $2\frac{1}{4} - 1\frac{4}{5}p - 19 = \frac{2}{3}p + 38 - 2\frac{1}{3}$ $p = -21\frac{1}{4}$

14. $9 - 5\frac{1}{4}x = 27 - 2\frac{1}{4}x - 2\frac{3}{4}x$ $x = -72$

15. $2t + 1.2 - 5t = 2.8 - t$ $t = -0.8$

16. $3.2 + z = -6.5 - 1.2z$
$z = -4.4090909\cdots$

(Example 3)

17. $3(4 - x) - 22 = x + 48$ $x = -14\frac{1}{2}$

18. $-4(d - 2) - 15 = 36 + 2d$ $d = -7\frac{1}{6}$

19. $14 - 3y = -3(4 + 2y) - 9$ $y = -11\frac{2}{3}$

20. $-6g - 8 = 12 - 4(3g + 9)$ $g = -2\frac{2}{3}$

21. $0.2(n + 1) = 0.6(n - 1) - 0.7$ $n = 3\frac{3}{4}$

22. $3(y + 0.5) = 0.5y + 1.5$ $y = 0$

23. $\frac{4}{5}y - \frac{1}{2}(y - 1) = \frac{3}{4}(y + 1)$ $y = -\frac{5}{9}$

24. $\frac{1}{2}(z + 1) - 2z = 6z + \frac{1}{2}$ $z = 0$

Solve. Check each answer. (Examples 1–3)

25. $10 - 5y = y + 61$ $y = -8\frac{1}{2}$

26. $14 - 3b = -16 - 7b$ $b = -7\frac{1}{2}$

27. $6 - 15q = 11q - 44$ $q = 1\frac{12}{13}$

28. $2.3x - 31.5 = 14.9 + 5.2x$ $x = -16$

29. $\frac{3}{4}(\frac{1}{2} - k) - 1\frac{7}{8} = k + 3\frac{1}{6}$ $k = -2\frac{2}{3}$

30. $5z + 2(z - 1) = 3(z + 1)$ $z = \frac{5}{4}$

31. $-10 - 18d = 26 - 12d$ $d = -6$

32. $-4f - 19 = 17 + f$ $f = -7\frac{1}{5}$

33. $6(2r + 3) - 10r = 20r + 1$ $r = \frac{17}{18}$

34. $21 + m = -19 - 7m$ $m = -5$

35. $8p - 2(2p - 1) = 6(p + 2)$ $p = -5$

36. $7p - 6 = 10p - 0.5(2p + 5)$ $p = -17.5$

MORE CHALLENGING EXERCISES

Solve each equation.

$f = -\frac{1}{3}$

37. $(d - 3) - (-2d + 5) = 2d - 7 - 3d$ $d = \frac{1}{4}$

38. $(5f - 2) - (6 - 2f) = -f - 9 + 5f$

39. $5g^2 - 2g - 3g^2 = 3g + 2g^2 + 10$ $g = -2$

40. $x(2x - 3) + 4x = 2x^2 - 9$ $x = -9$

OBJECTIVES: Given a word problem describing values of two of the variables in the formula
$d = rt$ to solve for the third variable
Given a word problem describing values of p and either l or w in the formula $p = 2(l + w)$, to solve
for the third variable

3.6 Problem Solving with Formulas

The following word rule and formula relate distance, rate, and time.

Word Rule: Distance equals rate multiplied by time.

Formula: $d = rt$

In a formula, variables and symbols are used to represent words. If you know the values of two of the variables in $d = rt$, you use the techniques for solving equations to find the third value.

example 1

In 1903, Orville Wright flew his airplane a distance of 37 meters at an average speed (rate) of 3.08 meters per second. To the nearest tenth, how long did the flight last?

Solution:

$d = distance$
$r = rate$
$t = time$

1	Write the formula. $\longrightarrow$	$d = rt$
2	Identify the known variables. $\longrightarrow$	$d = 37$ meters; $r = 3.08$ meters per second
3	Replace the variables. $\longrightarrow$	$37 = 3.08t$
4	Solve the equation. $\longrightarrow$	$\dfrac{37}{3.08} = t$ or, $12.01 = t$

To the nearest tenth, the flight lasted 12.0 seconds.

Word Rule: The perimeter of a rectangle equals the sum of the measures of the sides.

Formula: $p = l + l + w + w$
$p = 2l + 2w$ or, $\mathbf{p = 2(l + w)}$

Combine like terms. Then factor.

example 2

The perimeter of this postage stamp is 9.4 centimeters (cm). The width is 2.2 centimeters. Find the length.

Solution:

It is a common error for students to write a product such as $2(l + 2.2)$ as $2l + 2.2$.

1	Write the formula. $\longrightarrow$	$p = 2(l + w)$
2	Identify the known variables. $\longrightarrow$	$p = 9.4$ cm; $w = 2.2$ cm
3	Replace the variables. $\longrightarrow$	$9.4 = 2(l + 2.2)$
4	Solve the equation. $\longrightarrow$	$9.4 = 2l + 4.4$
		$2.5 = l$ The length is 2.5 cm.

CLASSROOM EXERCISES

Find the value of the unknown variable. (Example 1)

1. $d = 1200$ kilometers; $r = 400$ kilometers per hour; $t = $ __?__ 3 hours
2. $d = $ __?__ ; $r = 25$ meters per minute; $t = 30$ minutes 750 meters
3. $d = 280$ feet; $r = $ __?__ ; $t = 4$ seconds 70 feet per second

(Example 2)

4. $p = $ __?__ ; $l = 18$ meters; $w = 12$ meters 60 meters
5. $p = 150$ kilometers; $l = $ __?__ ; $w = 30$ kilometers 45 kilometers
6. $p = 29.2$ millimeters; $l = 6.4$ millimeters; $w = $ __?__ 8.2 millimeters

WRITTEN EXERCISES

See the Teacher's Manual for the suggested assignments.

Sample Problems: **a.** Given: $d = 60.2$ m and $r = 7$ meters per second. Find t.
   b. Given $p = 37.0$ mm and $l = 12.7$ mm. Find w.
Answers: **a.** 8.6 seconds   **b.** $w = 5.8$ mm

For each problem, find the rate, r, or the time, t. Round your answer to the nearest tenth. (Example 1)

1. On a certain day, it took 1.2 seconds for light to travel from the moon to the earth 360,000 kilometers away. Find the speed of light in kilometers per second.
   300,000 kilometers per second

2. During a thunderstorm, lightning was observed 5100 feet away. The thunderclap followed 4.5 seconds later. Find the speed of sound in feet per second. 1133.3 ft per second

3. A cheetah ran a distance of 80 yards traveling at an average speed of 35 yards per second. How long did it take the cheetah to run that distance? 2.3 seconds

4. In 1932, Amelia Earhart flew a plane from Newfoundland to Ireland, a distance of 3260 kilometers, at an average speed of 217 kilometers per hour. How long did her trip take? 15.0 hours

For each problem, find the width, w, or length, l. Round your answer to the nearest tenth. (Example 2)

5. The perimeter of a picture frame is 3.8 meters. The length of the frame is 1.2 meters. Find the width. 0.7 meters

6. The perimeter of a hand calculator is 12.6 inches. The width is 2.5 inches. Find the length. 3.8 inches

Unit Price

When you shop you want to obtain the best value for your shopping dollar. One factor in finding the best value is the <u>unit price</u>. **Unit price** is the price of an item per unit, such as price per gram, price per kilogram, price per pound, price per ounce and so on.

You can use the following formula to find the unit price.

$$U = \frac{p}{n}$$

U = unit price
p = price of an item
n = number of units

FRUIT SALAD		26Z
UNIT PRICE	B4702	YOU PAY
$1.01	Z5	$1.65
PER POUND	050281	

EXAMPLE: A package of 100 trash bags sells for $12.95. A smaller package of 20 bags costs $2.95. Which is the better buy?

SOLUTION: **Larger Package**   **Smaller Package**

$$U = \frac{p}{n} \qquad\qquad U = \frac{p}{n}$$

$$= \frac{12.95}{100} \qquad\qquad = \frac{2.95}{20}$$

$$= 0.1295 \qquad\qquad = 0.1475$$

$0.1295 = 12.95 cents
$0.1475 = 14.75 cents

The price per bag in the larger package is about 13 cents. The price per bag in the smaller package is almost 15 cents. The larger package is the better buy.

In Ex. 1-6, the "better buy" is indicated by an asterisk (*).

Find the unit price. Then tell which size is the "better buy."

1. 0.22¢ per gram; 0.18¢ per gram
1. 397 grams of catsup for $0.87
  * 907 grams of catsup for $1.63

2. 10.2¢ per ounce; 9.8¢ per ounce
2. 6 ounces of rice for $0.61
  * 10 ounces of rice for $0.98

3. 12 ounces of cheese for $1.10
  * 16 ounces of cheese for $1.42

3. 9.2¢ per ounce; 8.9¢ per ounce

4. * 450 grams of cereal for $1.22
  570 grams of cereal for $1.60

4. 0.27¢ per gram; 0.28¢ per gram

Find the cost per serving. Then tell which is the "better buy."

5. 49¢ per serving; 43¢ per serving
5. Flank steak gives 6 servings per pound and costs $2.95 per pound.
  * Ground meat gives 3 servings per pound and costs $1.29 per pound.

6. * Poultry costs $2.00 per kilogram and gives 4 servings per kilogram.
  Fresh fish costs $3.50 per kilogram and gives 6 servings per kilogram.

6. 50¢ per serving; 58¢ per serving

Special Topic Application

CHAPTER SUMMARY

IMPORTANT TERMS	Equation *(p. 52)* Solution *(p. 52)*	Root *(p. 52)* Equivalent equations *(p. 52)*

IMPORTANT IDEAS

1. *Addition Property for Equations:* Adding the same real number to each side of an equation forms an equivalent equation.

2. *Subtraction Property for Equations:* Subtracting the same real number from each side of an equation forms an equivalent equation.

3. *Multiplication Property for Equations:* Multiplying each side of an equation by the same nonzero real number forms an equivalent equation.

4. *Division Property for Equations:* Dividing each side of an equation by the same nonzero real number forms an equivalent equation.

5. To solve an equation that involves more than one operation, the Addition or Subtraction Property for Equations is generally used before the Multiplication or Division Property.

6. In equations that contain parentheses, use the Distributive Property first.

CHAPTER REVIEW NOTE: The Teacher's Resource Book contains two forms of each Chapter Test.

In Exercises 1–40, solve each equation. Check each answer.

SECTION 3.1

1. $x + 23 = 16$ $x = -7$ **2.** $y + 29 = -18$ $y = -47$ **3.** $b - 47 = -28$ $b = 19$ **4.** $d - 37 = 49$ $d = 86$

5. $-28 = 14 + f$ $f = -42$ **6.** $76 = -32 + g$ $g = 108$ **7.** $5.6 = t - 24.7$ $t = 30.3$ **8.** $-12.3 = x + 19.8$ $x = 32.1$

SECTION 3.2

9. $-7k = 63$ $k = -9$ **10.** $-96 = 12n$ $n = -8$ **11.** $-8 = \dfrac{m}{14}$ $m = -112$ **12.** $\dfrac{x}{-8} = 19$ $x = -152$

13. $-\dfrac{3}{4}t = -27$ $t = 36$ **14.** $60 = -\dfrac{12}{4}z$ $z = -20$ **15.** $12y = -99.6$ $y = -8.3$ **16.** $131.4 = -9r$ $r = -14.6$

SECTION 3.3

17. $4z - 3 = 42$ $z = 11\frac{1}{4}$ **18.** $6t - 14 = 38$ $t = 8\frac{2}{3}$ **19.** $-68 = 8m + 12$ $m = -10$ **20.** $-54 = 18 + 12p$ $p = -6$

21. $78 - 6x = 34$ $x = 7\frac{1}{3}$ **22.** $69 = 102 - 8n$ $n = 4\frac{1}{8}$ **23.** $-22 + \dfrac{v}{2.4} = -46$ $v = -57.6$ **24.** $-9 = \dfrac{w}{1.9} + 48$ $w = -108.3$

25. $8x + 6 - 5x = 39$ $\quad x = 11$

26. $56 = 12k - 8 - 8k$ $\quad k = 16$

27. $-19.3y - 16 + 5.9y = -83$ $\quad y = 5$

28. $-55 = 2.4n + 74 - 15.3n$ $\quad n = 10$

29. $35 = 4(t - 2) - 6t$ $\quad t = -21.5$

30. $7z - 3(z + 7) = -67$ $\quad z = -11.5$

31. $-28 = (3p - 2) - 2(5p + 12)$ $\quad p = \frac{2}{7}$

32. $(18 - x) - (3x + 4) = -48$ $\quad x = 15\frac{1}{2}$

33. $8h + 3 = 5h - 18$ $\quad h = -7$

34. $2x + 5 = 6x + 29$ $\quad x = -6$

35. $28 - 7y = y - 48$ $\quad y = 9.5$

36. $44 - a = -18 + 2a$ $\quad a = 20\frac{2}{3}$

37. $\frac{1}{2}(4t - 6) - 3t = 2t - 7$ $\quad t = \frac{4}{3}$

38. $-2v + 6 = 8 - \frac{1}{3}(9 - 3v)$ $\quad v = \frac{1}{3}$

39. $4.3g - 28 = -1.9g + 65$ $\quad g = 15$

40. $62 - 3.7x = 1.9x + 34$ $\quad x = 5$

For each problem, find the rate, r, or the time, t. Round your answer to the nearest tenth.

41. A wildebeest was observed racing a distance of 86.4 meters in 4.5 seconds. Find the speed of the wildebeest in meters per second.
19.2 meters per second

42. The speed of a radio signal is 186,000 miles per second. How long does it take for a radio signal to travel from the earth to Mars, which is about 35,000,000 miles away?
188.2 seconds or about 3.1 minutes

For each problem, find the width, w, or length, l. Round your answer to the nearest tenth.

43. The perimeter of a wall mirror is 204 inches. The width is 18.1 inches. Find the length of the mirror. **83.9 inches**

44. A steel ribbon 3.8 meters long is exactly long enough to wrap around a packing carton once. The base of the carton is 1.2 meters long. How wide is the base of the carton? **0.7 meters**

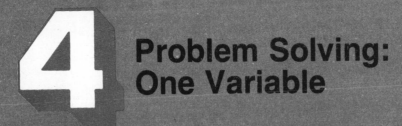

CHAPTER 4

Problem Solving: One Variable

Sections   4.1   **Problem Solving: Words to Equations**

   4.2   **Problem Solving: Conditions to Equations**

   4.3   **Problem Solving: Perimeter**

   4.4   **Problem Solving: Using Per Cent**

   4.5   **Problem Solving with Formulas**

Features   *Calculator Exercises:* **Using Formulas**

   Career: **Engineering Technician**

**Review
and
Testing**   *Review Capsules*

   Mid-Chapter Review

   Chapter Summary

   Chapter Review

4.1 Problem Solving: Words to Equations

NOTE: Computer programming section A-3 on pages 484 and 485 can be studied anytime after Chapter 4 has been studied. All computer programming sections are optional.

In order to solve word problems by algebra it is necessary to translate key words of the problem to algebraic symbols. Table 1 shows some word expressions and the corresponding algebraic expressions.

Table 1	Operation	Word Expression	Algebraic Expression
	Addition	The <u>sum</u> of a number and 12	$n + 12$
		Thirteen <u>plus</u> some number	$13 + r$
		Six <u>more than</u> some number	$t + 6$
		Some number <u>increased by</u> $3\frac{2}{3}$	$y + 3\frac{2}{3}$
	Subtraction	Some number <u>decreased by</u> $5\frac{1}{2}$	$x - 5\frac{1}{2}$
		The <u>difference</u> between some number and 9.4	$p - 9.4$
		Fifty-four <u>minus</u> some number	$54 - k$
		Some number <u>less</u> 5	$w - 5$
		Five <u>less than</u> some number	$w - 5$
	Multiplication	The <u>product</u> of 4.9 and some number	$4.9n$
		Some number <u>multiplied by</u> $\frac{2}{3}$	$\frac{2}{3}t$
		Twenty-four <u>times</u> an unknown number	$24a$
		An unknown number <u>doubled</u>	$2y$
	Division	The <u>quotient</u> of some number and 15	$\frac{q}{15}$
		An unknown number <u>divided by</u> 2.9	$\frac{m}{2.9}$
		Twenty-one <u>divided by</u> some number	$\frac{21}{n}$

The usual agreement is to write "difference between" in the order in which the numbers appear.

Also consider:
Some number less than 5
$5 - w$

example 1

Write an algebraic expression for this word expression.

Fourteen points <u>less than</u> the record number scored

Solution: [1] Choose a variable. ⟶ Let $n =$ the record number scored

        [2] Identify the operation. ⟶ subtraction ("less than")

        [3] Write an algebraic expression. ⟶ $n - 14$

Table 2 shows some sentences and their corresponding equations.

Table 2

Word Sentence	Equation
19.8 **is** the <u>sum</u> of some number and 4.3.	$19.8 = t + 4.3$
An unknown number of cars <u>decreased by</u> 37 **equals** 196.	$n - 37 = 196$
The <u>product</u> of the number of hours worked and the rate per hour, $5.25, **is** $183.75	$5.25w = 183.75$
The <u>quotient</u> of the total cost and the number of payments, 36, **equals** $173.50.	$\dfrac{c}{36} = 173.50$

example 2

Write an equation for this sentence. Then solve the equation.

The list price of a lamp less a discount of $3.00 equals the sale price of $26.95.

Solution:

1. Choose a variable. ——————→ Let p = the list price.
2. Identify the operation. ——————→ subtraction ("less")
3. Write an equation. ——————→ $p - 3.00 = 26.95$
4. Solve the equation. ——————→ $p - 3.00 + 3.00 = 26.95 + 3.00$
   $$p = 29.95$$

The list price of the lamp is $29.95.

CLASSROOM EXERCISES

Write an algebraic expression for each word expression. Use the variable n.
(Table 1 and Example 1)

1. Twelve <u>more than</u> a number of stamps $n + 12$

2. Four dollars <u>less than</u> the cost of two tickets $n - 4$

3. The total number of points <u>divided by</u> 8 $\dfrac{n}{8}$

4. A savings account balance <u>increased by</u> $1200 $n + 1200$

5. Eighteen hundred entries in the race <u>times</u> the entry fee $1800n$

6. The number of swimmers <u>decreased by</u> eighteen $n - 18$

7. The <u>quotient</u> of 1200 miles and the number of gallons of fuel $\dfrac{1200}{n}$

8. The number of shoppers over the last year <u>tripled</u> $3n$

9. The <u>difference</u> between twenty-six and the number of fish caught today $26 - n$

10. Six thousand <u>plus</u> the number of records sold this year $6000 + n$

Choose a variable and write an equation for each word sentence. Then solve the equation. (Table 2 and Example 2) In Exercise 11-20, the choice of variable may vary.

11. The low temperature for the month increased by 27° is 50°. Let n = low temperature; $n + 27 = 50$; $n = 23°$

12. The high temperature for the day decreased by 18° is 78°. Let t = high temperature; $t - 18 = 78$; $t = 96°$

13. The total number of points divided by 20 games equals 18 points per game. Let p = total points; $\frac{p}{20} = 18$; $p = 360$

14. The cost of an unknown number of tickets multiplied by 4 dollars equals 940 dollars. Let c = cost of tickets; $4c = 940$, $c = 235$

15. The total number of persons on the flight, 104, is the number of passengers plus a flight crew of eleven. Let n = number of passengers; $104 = n + 11$; $n = 93$

16. The number of kilometers driven divided by 75 liters equals 10.2 kilometers per liter. See below.

17. The average number of centimeters of rainfall less 9.4 centimeters is 69.3 centimeters, the amount of rainfall for the past year. Let r = average amount of rainfall; $r - 9.4 = 69.3$; $r = 78.7$cm

18. The total number of runners starting the race less the 36 runners who dropped out leaves 218 runners to finish. Let n = number of runners starting the race; $r - 36 = 218$; $r = 254$km

19. The total amount of this year's sales tripled would represent $372,000 in sales next year. Let s = this year's sales; $3s = 372,000$; $s = \$124,000$

20. The cost of a new car decreased by a rebate of $325 equals a net cost of $7520. Let c = cost of car before rebate; $c - 325 = 7520$; $c = \$7845$.

16. Let k = number of kilometers driven; $\frac{k}{75} = 10.2$; $k = 765$ km

WRITTEN EXERCISES

See the Teacher's Manual for the suggested assignments.

Goal: To write and solve an algebraic equation for a word sentence involving one operation

Sample Problem: The low temperature for one day of −35° equals the high temperature decreased by 12°.

Answer: $-35 = h - 12$; $h = -23°$

Choose a variable and write an expression for each word expression. (Example 1) In Exercises 1-18, the choice of variable may vary.

1. Twice the number of taxicabs $2t$

2. Three times the number of musicians $3m$

3. The number of TV viewers increased by 25,000 $v + 25,000$

4. Twenty-nine less than the number of pro golfers $g - 29$

5. The number of meters decreased by 15.8 $m - 15.8$

6. Five hundred sixty dollars more than the amount of a loan $l + 560$

7. A bowler's total score divided by 28 games $\frac{b}{28}$

8. The quotient of the number of kilometers sailed and 3.2 hours $\frac{k}{3.2}$

9. The difference between the number of accidents reported and 512 $a - 512$

10. The product of the number of cartons shipped and 14.3 kilograms $14.3c$

Let c = total cost; $\frac{c}{24} = 86$; c = \$2064

Choose a variable and write an equation for each word sentence. Then solve the equation. (Example 2)

11. The quotient of the total cost and 24 payments is 86 dollars. **See above.**

12. The product of the number of tickets sold and \$6.50 equals \$6916. **Let t = tickets sold; $6.50t = 6916$; $t = 1064$**

13. The width of a rectangle, 14.2 meters, is 5.8 meters less than the length. **Let l = length of rectangle; $14.2 = l - 5.8$, $l = 20$ m**

14. The quotient of the total cost and 288 cans of tennis balls equals the cost per can of \$1.75. **Let c = total cost; $\frac{c}{288} = 1.75$; $c = \$504$**

15. The low temperature of $-5.3°$C is 7.9 degrees less than the high temperature for the day. **Let h = high temperature for day; $-5.3 = h - 7.9$; $h = 2.6°$**

16. The high temperature of $-12.6°$F is 8.7 degrees more than the low temperature for the day. **Let l = low temperature for day; $-12.6 = l + 8.7$; $l = -21.30$**

17. The amount of the sale multiplied by 0.06 equals the sales tax of \$33.60. **Let a = amount of sale; $0.06a = 33.60$; $a = \$560$**

18. Fifty-four dollars is \$7.75 more than the cost of the items one year ago. **Let c = cost of items a year ago; $54 = c + 7.75$; $c = \$46.25$**

Match each word expression or word sentence in Exercises 19–26 with the corresponding expression or equation from a–t. (Examples 1–2)

19. Thirty-five more than the number of horses. **l**

20. The number of shoppers increased by 4500 equals 12,700. **p**

21. The number of books in a collection less 485 books is 714. **n**

22. The paper carrier's daily supply of papers less 17, the number not sold. **r**

23. Three times the number of state senators is 72. **o**

24. The number of players on the squad who played plus 24, the number who did not play. **j**

25. Twice the number of planes landing each day. **k**

26. A golfer's score of 86 is 3 strokes less than his handicap score. **m**

a. $17 - w$

b. $2p = 58$

c. $28.6 + 2.3 = m$

d. $4500n = 12,700$

e. $n + 24 = 56$

f. $86 - 3$

g. $485 - r = 714$

h. $3 + n = 72$

i. $r + 2.3 = 28.6$

j. $24 + q$

k. $2(y)$

l. $t + 35$

m. $s - 3 = 86$

n. $714 = k - 485$

o. $72 = 3s$

p. $12,700 = 4500 + x$

q. $r + 2\frac{2}{3} = 84\frac{1}{8}$

r. $p - 17$

s. $2\frac{3}{4} + b$

t. $76\frac{5}{8} + 2\frac{3}{4}$

REVIEW CAPSULE FOR SECTION 4.2

Solve each equation. (Section 3.4)

1. $x + x + 19 = 73$ $x = 27$

2. $y + 7y - 4 = 28$ $y = 4$

3. $6.6 = w - 4.2 + w$ $w = 5.4$

4. $r + 13.6 + r = 25.2$ $r = 5.8$

5. $5k + 3k - 18 = 86$ $k = 13$

6. $430 = 6t + 14 - t$ $t = 83.2$

4.2 Problem Solving: Conditions to Equations

To help students achieve success, Condition 1 appears before Condition 2 in each stated problem of this lesson.

To solve word problems it is helpful to identify the conditions in the problem. One condition is used to represent the unknowns of the problem. Call this Condition 1. Another condition is used to write the equation. Call this Condition 2. Then solve the equation.

example 1

One model of subcompact car has 71 cubic feet more passenger space than luggage space. (Condition 1) The total amount of passenger and luggage space is 87 cubic feet. (Condition 2) Find the amount of both types of space.

Solution:

1. Use Condition 1 to represent the unknowns. $\longrightarrow$ Let s = the luggage space.
Then $s + 71$ = the passenger space.

2. Use Condition 2 to write an equation. $\longrightarrow$ $s + s + 71 = 87$

3. Solve the equation. $\longrightarrow$

$$2s + 71 = 87$$
$$2s = 16$$
$$s = 8$$
$$s + 71 = 79$$

4. **Check:** Condition 1   Are there 71 more cubic feet of passenger space than luggage space?

Does $79 = 8 + 71$?   Yes ✔

Condition 2   Does the total amount of space equal 87 cubic feet?

Does $8 + 79 = 87$?   Yes ✔

The passenger space is 79 cubic feet, and the luggage space is 8 cubic feet.

The following summary of steps can help you solve word problems.

Steps for Solving Word Problems

1. Identify Condition 1. Use Condition 1 to represent the unknowns.
2. Identify Condition 2. Use Condition 2 to write an equation.
3. Solve the equation.
4. Check the results with the conditions. Answer the question.

---

example 2

The number of eleventh grade members of the Ski Club this year is 5 fewer than twice the number of twelfth grade members (Condition 1). The total membership is 82 (Condition 2). How many eleventh grade members are there?

Solution:

$\boxed{1}$ Use Condition 1 to represent the unknowns. $\longrightarrow$ Let n = the number of twelfth graders.
Then $2n - 5$ = the number of eleventh graders.

$\boxed{2}$ Use Condition 2 to write an equation. $\longrightarrow n + 2n - 5 = 82$

$\boxed{3}$ Solve the equation. $\longrightarrow$

$$3n - 5 = 82$$
$$3n = 87$$
$$n = 29$$
$$2n - 5 = 53$$

$\boxed{4}$ **Check:** Condition 1   Is the number of eleventh grade members 5 less than twice the number of twelfth grade members?

Does $53 = 2(29) - 5$?   Yes ✔

Condition 2   Is the total membership 82?

Does $29 + 53 = 82$?   Yes ✔

There are 29 twelfth grade members and 53 eleventh grade members.

CLASSROOM EXERCISES

In Exercises 1–12:
a. Use Condition 1 to represent the unknowns. Use p as the variable.
b. Use Condition 2 to write an equation for the problem. (Example 1)

1. There were 186 more seats for tourist class than for first class on one flight. The total number of seats was 234. Let p = number of first class seats; $p + 186 + p = 234$

2. The number of parking spaces for small cars in a lot is 75 less than the number for standard cars. The total number of spaces is 425. Let p = number of spaces for small cars; $p + p - 75 = 425$

3. In June a sales representative drove 775 kilometers less than in May. The total distance driven in May and June was 3521 kilometers. See below.

4. The number of points scored by the winning bowl team was 13 more than by the losing team. The sum of the scores was 457 See below.

5. The parts for a repair job on a car cost $3.58 more than the labor. The total bill was $75.62. Let p = cost of labor; then $p + 3.58$ = cost of parts; $p + p + 3.58 = 75.62$

6. One model of compact car has 69 cubic feet more passenger space than cargo space. The total amount of space is 101 cubic feet. Let p = amount of cargo space; then $p + 69$ = amount of passenger space; $p + p + 69 = 101$

3. Let p = number of miles driven in May; then $p - 775$ = number of miles driven in June; $p + p - 775 = 3521$

Problem Solving: One Variable / **79**

4. Let p = number of points scored by losing team; then $p + 13$ = number of points scored by winning team; $p + p + 13 = 457$

7. Let p = rainfall in May; then $2p - 4\frac{3}{5}$ = rainfall in June;
$p + 2p - 4\frac{3}{5} = 14\frac{9}{10}$
(Example 2)

7. A city's rainfall in June was $4\frac{3}{5}$ inches less than twice the amount in May. The total rainfall for the two months was $14\frac{9}{10}$ inches. See above.

8. Let p = amount of gas bill; then $2p - 0.35$ = electric bill; $p + 2p - 0.35 = 76.30$

8. A family's electric bill one month was $0.35 less than twice the gas bill. The total amount of the two bills was $76.30. See above.

9. A professional golfer earned $5,000 less than twice the amount earned the previous year. The total amount earned in the two years was $93,000.   Let p = amount earned first year; then $2p - 5000$ = amount earned second year; $p + 2p - 5000 = 93{,}000$

10. The number of students in a certain college is 153 more than ten times the number of teachers. The total number of students and teachers is 3244.   Let p = number of teachers; then $10p + 153$ = number of students; $p + 10p + 153 = 3244$

11. The number of multiple-choice questions on a test was seven less than three times the number of true-false questions. The total number of questions on the test was 105.   Let p = the number of true-false questions; $3p - 7$ = the number of multiple choice questions; $p + 3p - 7 = 105$.

12. The mass of a machine is 7.6 kilograms less than 20 times the mass of its shipping crate. The total mass of the shipment is 239.4 kilograms.   Let p = mass of shipping crate; then $20p - 7.6$ = mass of machine; $p + 20p - 7.6 = 239.4$

WRITTEN EXERCISES

See the Teacher's Manual for the suggested assignments.

Goal: To represent the conditions of a word problem and to solve the problem

Sample Problem: The attendance at the first performance of an orchestra was 560 more than at the second performance. The total attendance for the two performances was 5320. Find the number attending each performance.

For Exercises 1–18, all answers are given. For the solutions to the odd numbered exercises, see the *Answers to Selected Exercises* on page 504 of the student's book.

Answers: 1st performance: 2940; 2nd performance: 2380

In Exercises 1–18:
a. Use Condition 1 to represent the unknowns.
b. Use Condition 2 to write an equation for the problem.
c. Solve the problem. (Example 1)   In Exercises 1–18, the choice of variable may vary.

1. A marathon race had 448 more local participants than visiting runners. The total number in the race was 3640. Find the number of local runners and the number of visiting runners. **1596 visiting runners 2044 local runners**

2. A coach's teams during his career won 121 more games than they lost. The total number of games was 531. Find the number of wins and the number of losses.   Let l = number of games lost; then $l + 121$ = no. of games won; $l + l + 121 = 531$; $l = 205$ games lost; $l + 121 = 326$ games won

3. In an aerobic dance class there are five fewer men than women. The total number in the class is 35. Find the number of men and the number of women in the class.   20 women; 15 men

12. Let l = amt. of carpeting for living room; then $l + 120$ = amt. needed for bedroom; $l + l + 120 = 968$; $l = 424$ m² (living room); $l + 120 = 544$ m² (bedroom)

4. Let f = no. of games (1st set); then $f + 4$ = no. of games (2nd set); $f + f + 4 = 20$; $f = 8$ games (1st set); $f + 4 = 12$ games (2nd set)

4. A tennis match ending in two sets had 4 more games in the second set than in the first. The total number of games was 20. Find the number played in each set. See above.

6. Let f = amt. spent on feed; then $2f - 150$ = amt. spent on housing and transportation; $f + 2f - 150 = 8500$; $f = \$2883.33$ on feed; $2f - 150 = \$5616.67$ on housing and transportation

(Example 2)

6. In one year, a retired couple spent $150 less on housing and transportation than twice the amount spent on food. The total amount spent on housing, transportation, and food was $8500. Find the amount spent for food. See above.

8. At one point of a season the leading scorer in pro basketball had scored four fewer points on field goals than four times the number of points on free throws. Her total number of points was 1776. Find the number of points scored on field goals and the number scored on free throws. See above.

9. The number of general admission seats at a concert was 1000 less than twice the number of reserved seats. The total number of seats available was 12,500. Find the number of general admission seats and the number of reserved seats. 9. 4500 reserved seats; 8000 general admission seats

11. The passenger space in one car contains 5 cubic feet more than five times the cargo space. The total passenger and cargo space is 131 cubic feet. Find the size of each space. 11. Cargo: 21 ft³; passengers: 110 ft³

13. Simon has a part-time job. In one two-week period he worked $2\frac{3}{4}$ hours more the second week than the first. His total time for the two weeks was $45\frac{3}{4}$ hours. Find the number of hours worked each week. 13. 1st. week: $21\frac{1}{2}$ hours; 2nd week: $24\frac{1}{4}$ hours

8. Let f = no. of pts. scored on free throws; then $4f - 4$ = no. of pts. scored on field goals; $f + 4f - 4 = 1776$; $f = 356$ pts. on free throws; $4f - 4 = 1420$ pts. on field goals

5. A collector has paintings and sculptures. The paintings are valued at $350,000 more than the sculptures. The total collection is valued at $1,260,000. Find the value of the paintings and the value of the sculptures. Sculptures: $455,000; Paintings: $805,000

7. A family's large car holds 2.3 liters more fuel than twice the capacity of its compact car. The total fuel capacity of the two cars is 140.9 liters. Find the fuel capacity of each car. Smaller car: 46.2 liters; Larger car: 94.7 liters

10. An art book contains 16 fewer pages of illustrations than three times the number of printed pages. The total number of pages is 512. Find the number of pages of illustrations. See below.

12. A bedroom requires 120 square meters more carpeting than a living room. The total amount of carpeting needed is 968 square meters. Find the amount needed for the bedroom and the living room. 12. See bottom of p. 80.

14. A trip from a family's home to the coast required 4.5 liters more fuel returning than going. The total amount needed for the round-trip was 180.3 liters. Find the amount of fuel needed for each leg of the trip. See below.

10. Let p = no. of printed pages; then $3p - 16$ = no. of illustrated pages; $p + 3p - 16 = 512$; $p = 132$ printed pages; $3p - 16 = 380$ illustrated pages

14. Let a = amt. needed going; then $a + 4.5$ = amt. needed returning; $a + a + 4.5 = 180.3$; $a = 87.9$ liters going; $a + 4.5 = 92.4$ liters returning

15. Alfredo has a coin collection. He has 26 fewer U.S. coins than three times the number of foreign coins. The collection consists of 998 coins. Find the number of each type of coin. **256 foreign coins**
742 U.S. coins

16. The average snowfall for a city is 5.4 inches less than twice the amount of rainfall. The total amount of precipitation is 100.9 inches. Find the average amount of snowfall. **See below.**

17. Mary Ann enters customer records on a computer. In a two-day period she entered 12 more records the second day than the first day. In the two days she entered 256 records. Find the number of records entered each day. **First day: 122 records**
Second day: 134 records

18. An insurance analyst set a goal of doubling her annual sales from the previous year. Her sales actually were $50,000 less than twice the previous year's sales. The total for the two years was $980,000. Find her sales for the second year. **Let f = first year sales; then 2f − 50,000 = second year sales; f + 2f − 50,000 = 980,000, f = $343,333.33; 2f − 50,000 = $636,666.67**

USING FORMULAS

You can use a calculator to solve problems using formulas such as $d = rt$ and $p = 2l + 2w$.

EXAMPLE Find the distance, d, when $r = 102$ km/hr and $t = 16\frac{1}{2}$ hours.

SOLUTION Substitute the known values in the formula $d = rt$.

[1] [0] [2] [×] [1] [6] [·] [5] [=]   │ 1683. │

Find the perimeter of a rectangle, p, or the distance, d.   27,167.75m

1. $l = 16.96$ cm; $w = 9.23$ cm; $p = $? **52.38 cm**   **2.** $r = 13.55$ m/sec; $t = 2005$ sec; $d = $?

3. $l = 195.5$ km; $w = 112.3$ km; $p = $? **615.6 km**   **4.** $r = 750$ km/hr; $t = 313.472$ hr; $d = $?
235,104 km

REVIEW CAPSULE FOR SECTION 4.3

Solve and check each equation. (Section 3.4)   n = 4.2

1. $2t + 2(t - 10) = 84$ t = 26   **2.** $256 = 2w + 2(w + 5)$ w = 61.5   **3.** $2(5n) + 2(13n) = 151.2$

4. $143 = 2(7p) + 2(15p)$ p = 3¼ **5.** $3x + 8x + 13x = 163.2$ x = 6.8   **6.** $185.4 = 4r + 5r + 9r$ r = 10.3

Represent the unknowns in each problem. Use the variable d.

EXAMPLE: The ratio of rainy days to sunny days is 1:6.   **ANSWER:** 1d; 6d

7. The ratio of tin to copper in an alloy is 1:4. d; 4d

8. The ratio of gaining stocks to losing stocks is 7:2. 7d; 2d

9. The ratio of orange, grapefruit, and pineapple sections in a fruit cup is 5:4:2. 5d; 4d; 2d

10. Stainless steel contains steel, chromium, and nickel in the ratio 37:9:4. 37d; 9d; 4d

16. Let r = amt. of rainfall; then $2r - 5.4$ = amt. of snowfall; $r + 2r - 5.4 = 100.9$; $r = 35.43$ in of rainfall; $2r - 5.4 = 65.46$ in of snowfall

4.3 Problem Solving: Perimeter

To solve word problems involving perimeters of triangles and rectangles with the lengths of sides described by ratios

The **perimeter** of a geometric figure such as a triangle, square, or rectangle is the sum of the lengths of its sides.

P-1 **What is the perimeter of each figure below?**

a.

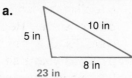

5 in   10 in   8 in

23 in

b.

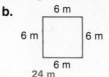

6 m   6 m   6 m

6 m

24 m

c.

8 cm

4 cm   4 cm

8 cm

24 cm

example 1

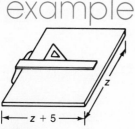

The length of a drawing board is 5 inches more than the width. (Condition 1) The perimeter is 94 inches. (Condition 2) Find the length and width.

z

$z + 5$

Solution:

1. Use Condition 1 to represent the unknowns. ⟶   Let z = the width. Then $z + 5$ = the length.

$$p = 2l + 2w$$

◄ **Formula for the perimeter of a rectangle**

2. Use Condition 2 to write an equation. ⟶ $94 = 2(z + 5) + 2z$

3. Solve the equation. ⟶

$$94 = 2z + 10 + 2z$$
$$94 = 4z + 10$$
$$84 = 4z$$
$$21 = z$$
$$z + 5 = 26$$

4. **Check:**   Condition 1   Is the length 5 inches more than the width?

Does $26 = 21 + 5$?   Yes ✔

Condition 2   Is the perimeter 94 inches?

Does $2(26) + 2(21) = 94$?   Yes ✔

The length is 26 inches and the width is 21 inches.

The ratio of the lengths of the sides of a figure are sometimes given. If the lengths of the sides of a triangle are in the ratio 5:8:11, the lengths can be represented as $5x$, $8x$, and $11x$.

example 2

A cross country ski course is along a triangular route. The three legs of the course in order from the starting point have lengths in the ratio 2:3:4. (Condition 1) The length of the entire course is 45 kilometers. (Condition 2) Find the length of each leg.

Solution:

1. Use Condition 1 to represent the unknowns. —————————→ Let $2x$ = the length of the first leg.
Then $3x$ = the length of the second leg.
And $4x$ = the length of the third leg.

2. Use Condition 2 to write an equation. ——→ $2x + 3x + 4x = 45$

3. Solve the equation. ————————————————→ $9x = 45$

$$x = 5$$
$$2x = 10$$
$$3x = 15$$
$$4x = 20$$

4. **Check:** Condition 1   Are the lengths of the legs in the ratio 2:3:4?

Does $\frac{10}{15} = \frac{2}{3}$? (Does $10 \cdot 3 = 15 \cdot 2$?)

Does $\frac{15}{20} = \frac{3}{4}$?   Does $\frac{10}{20} = \frac{2}{4}$?   Yes ✓

Condition 2   Does the sum of the lengths of the legs equal 45 km?

Does $10 + 15 + 20 = 45$?   Yes ✓

The lengths of the legs of the course are 10 kilometers, 15 kilometers, and 20 kilometers.

CLASSROOM EXERCISES

In Exercises 1–12:
a. Use Condition 1 to represent the unknowns. Use the variable m.
b. Use Condition 2 to write an equation for the problem. (Example 1)

1. The width of a screen for viewing photo slides is 10 inches less than the length. The perimeter is 140 inches.   Let m = length; then $m - 10$ = width; $2m + 2(m - 10) = 140$

2. One size of American flag has a length that is 27 inches more than its width. The perimeter is 174 inches.   Let m = width; then $m + 27$ = length; $2m + 2(m + 27) = 174$

3. The top of a stereo cabinet is a rectangle with its length 16 inches more than its width. The perimeter is 102 inches. Let m = width; then $m + 16$ = length; $2m + 2(m + 16) = 102$

4. The length of one size of photo slide is 1.1 centimeters more than the width. The perimeter is 11.4 centimeters. Let m = width; then $m + 1.1$ = length; $2m + 2(m + 1.1) = 11.4$

5. A scout troop hikes along a triangular route. The first leg is twice as long as the second leg. The third leg is 17 miles long. The entire hike is for 50 miles. Let m = length of second leg; then $2m$ = length of first leg; $m + 2m + 17 = 50$
(Example 2)

6. A sailboat race is along a triangular route. The first leg is 25.3 kilometers. The third leg is three times as long as the second leg. The race has a length of 67.3 kilometers. Let m = length of second leg; then $3m$ = length of third leg; $25.3 + m + 3m = 67.3$

7. One special triangle has the lengths of its sides in the ratio 3:4:5. The perimeter is 38.4 centimeters. Let lengths of sides be $3m$, $4m$, and $5m$; $3m + 4m + 5m = 38.4$

8. Three cities form a triangle and the distances between the cities are in the ratio 4:5:6. The perimeter of the triangle is 184.5 kilometers. Let distances be $4m$, $5m$, and $6m$; $4m + 5m + 6m = 184.5$

9. The ratio of the width to the length of a tennis court is 6:13. The perimeter is 228 feet. Let $6m$ = width; then $13m$ = length; $2(6m) + 2(13m) = 228$

10. The ratio of the length to the width of a door is 20:9. The perimeter is 232 inches. Let length = $20m$; then width = $9m$; $2(20m) + 2(9m) = 232$

11. A surveyor working on a highway locates three stakes to form a triangle. One side of the triangle measures 34.3 meters. The ratio of the lengths of the other sides is 5:9. The perimeter is 70.7 meters. Let lengths of the two sides be $5m$ and $9m$; $34.3 + 5m + 9m = 70.7$

12. A guy wire supports a pole and is anchored 9.8 meters from the base of the pole. The ratio of the length of the guy wire to the height of the pole is 7:5. The perimeter of the triangle formed is 33.8 meters. Let $7m$ = length of the guy wire; then $5m$ = length of pole; $9.8 + 5m + 7m = 33.8$

WRITTEN EXERCISES
See the Teacher's Manual for the suggested assignments.

Goal: To solve word problems involving perimeters of triangles and rectangles

Sample Problem: The ratio of the length to the width of a flag is 19:10. Find the length and width of a flag having a perimeter of 174 feet.

Answer: 57 feet by 30 feet

In Exercises 1–14:
a. Use Condition 1 to represent the unknowns.
b. Use Condition 2 to write an equation for the problem.
c. Solve the problem. (Example 1)

1. A sign is rectangular in shape. Its length is 6 feet greater than its height. Its perimeter is 84 feet. Find its length and height. Let h = height; then $h + 6$ = length; $2h + 2(h + 6) = 84$; $h = 18$ ft; $h + 6 = 24$ ft

2. A mailing carton has a rectangular base. The length is 3 inches greater than the width. The perimeter is 36 inches. Find the length and width. Let w = width; then $w + 3$ = length; $2w + 2(w + 3) = 36$; $w = 7.5$ in; $w + 3 = 10.5$ in

See page 504 for the answers to
Exercises 3, 5, 7, 9, 11, and 13.

6. Let width = $15x$; then length = $22x$; $2(15x) + 2(22x) = 370$
$x = 5$; width: 75 m; length: 110 m

3. A sculptor designs a monument that includes a triangle with a base of 8.5 meters. The longer of the other two sides has a length 1.7 meters greater than the other. The perimeter of the triangle is 51.2 meters. Find the two unknown lengths. *20.5 ; 22.2*

(Example 2)

4. A company's trademark is triangular. One side of the original design is 12.5 centimeters long. The shorter of the other two sides has a length 6.6 centimeters less than the length of the other. The perimeter of the triangle is 36.1 centimeters. Find the two unknown lengths.

Let x = length of longer side; then $x - 6.6$ = length of shorter side
$12.5 + x + x - 6.6 = 36.1$; $x = 15.1$ cm; $x - 6.6 = 8.5$ cm

5. One special triangle has sides in the ratio 5:12:13. Find the lengths of the sides if the perimeter is 204.0 meters. *34 ; 81.6 ; 88.4*

6. The ratio of the width to the length of a soccer field is 15:22. The perimeter is 370 meters. Find the length and width. See above.

7. A pilot flies a plane on a triangular route. The ratio of the lengths of the three legs of the flight is 4:7:9. The entire route is 684 kilometers long. Find the lengths of the legs of the route. *136.8 ; 239.4 ; 307.8*

8. A picture is to be framed with its length and width in the ratio 50:31. The length of the frame needed (perimeter) is 243 centimeters. Find the length and width of the picture.

Let $50x$ = length; then $31x$ = width: $2(50x) + 2(31x) =$
243, $x = 1.5$; length: 75 cm; width: 46.5 cm

(Examples 1–2)

10. Let $19x$ and $10x$ be the dimensions: $2(19x) + 2(10x) = 87$;
$x = 1.5$; length: 28.5 in, width: 15

9. A house has a rectangular floor plan. The length is 4 feet less than twice the width. The perimeter is 148 feet. Find the length and width. *26 48*

10. An official U.S. flag must have a ratio of length to width of 19:10. Find the length and width of a flag with a perimeter of 87 inches.

11. The width of a computer terminal screen is $2\frac{1}{2}$ inches more than the height. The perimeter of the screen is 44 inches. Find the height and width. *9 ¾   12 ¼*

12. A computer printout sheet is 9.9 centimeters longer than it is wide. The perimeter is 131.4 centimeters. Find the length and width. See below.

13. A cable attached to the top of a tower is anchored 35.6 meters from the base of the tower. The perimeter of the triangle formed is 108.1 meters. The ratio of the cable's length to the tower's height is 18:11. Find the tower's height. *27.5*

14. A punch press stamps a rectangular opening in a metal part. The length of the opening is 4.5 centimeters more than the width. The perimeter is 37.8 centimeters. Find the length and width of the opening.

12. Let w = width; then $w + 9.9$ = length; $2w + 2(w + 9.9) = 131.4$;
$w = 27.9$; width: 27.9 cm, length: 37.8 cm

Let w = width; $w + 4.5$ = length, $2w + 2(w + 4.5) = 37.8$;
$w = 7.2$ cm; width: 7.2 cm; length: 11.7 cm

MID-CHAPTER REVIEW   NOTE: After completing the Mid-Chapter Review, you may want to administer a quiz covering the same sections. See pages M-16 and M-17 of the Teacher's Manual for the suggested quiz.

Choose a variable and write an equation for each word sentence. Then solve the equation. (Section 4.1)

1. The number of visitors to the park this past year, 356,000, was 45,000 more than the number of visitors the previous year.

2. The difference between the number of persons playing tennis at a club last month and 512, the number playing raquetball, was 74.   Let p = number playing tennis; $p - 512 = 74$; $p = 586$

3. One month's phone bill of $38.50 for long distance calls was exactly twice the charge for local calls.

4. A company sells one product for $11.25 which is 1.8 times the cost of the product.   Let p = cost of product: $1.8p = 11.25$; $p = 6.25$

In Exercises 5–10, use Condition 1 to represent unknowns. Use Condition 2 to write an equation for the problem. Solve the problem. (Section 4.2)

5. A tumbling class for 5-6 year olds at the Y had seven more girls than boys. The total number enrolled for the class was 45. Find the number of girls and the number of boys.   19; 26

6. Joel bought a sports coat for $15 less than five times the cost of a pair of slacks. The total cost of the coat and slacks was $273. Find the cost of each item.

7. A traffic count between 6:00 a.m. and 8:00 a.m. on a highway showed 2900 fewer cars the first hour than the second hour. The total number of cars for the two-hour period was 24,500. Find the number for each hour.   13700; 10800

8. A school club's receipts from special projects was $5.00 more than three times the receipts from dues. The amount of total receipts was $485. Find the amounts received from dues and from special projects.   Let d = receipts from dues; then $3d + 5$ = receipts from special projects; $d + 3d + 5 = 485$; $d = 120$; dues: $120, special projects: $365

(Section 4.3)

9. A rectangular parking lot has a length that is 6.2 meters greater than twice its width. The perimeter is 106.6 meters. Find the length and width.   15.7 ; 37.6

10. An Olympic-size swimming pool has a length and width in the ratio 25:12. The pool's perimeter is 148 meters. Find the length and width.   Let $25x$ = length, $12x$ = width; $2(25x) + 2(12x) = 148$, $x = 2$; length: 50 m; width: 24 m

6. Let c = cost of slacks; then $5c - 15$ = cost of sports coat. $c + 5c - 15 = 273$; $c = 48$; slacks: $48, sports coat: $225

REVIEW CAPSULE FOR SECTION 4.4

Compute.

EXAMPLE: 8.5% of 350   **ANSWER:** 8.5% $= 0.085$; $0.085 \cdot 350 = 29.75$

1. 12% of $960   115.2
2. 8% of $87.50   7
3. 5% of 2780   139
4. 40% of $29.95   11.98
5. 75% of 56   42
6. 17% of 250   42.5
7. 4.5% of $750   33.75
8. $33\frac{1}{3}$% of 915   305

4.4 Problem Solving: Using Per Cent

To solve sports problems involving averages expressed as per cents
To solve miscellaneous word problems involving per cents

Merchandise is often offered on sale to consumers at a reduction in price. The price before the reduction is called the **list price** or **regular price.** The amount that the item is reduced is called the **discount.** The reduced price is called the **sale price.**

The following word rule and formula relate sale price, list price, and discount.

Word Rule: The <u>sale price</u> equals the <u>list price</u> less the <u>discount</u>.

Formula: $s = p - d$ ◀ s = sale price
p = list price
d = discount

Discount expressed as a per cent of the list price is called the **rate of discount.**

The following word rule and formula relate discount, rate of discount, and list price.

Word Rule: <u>Discount</u> equals the <u>rate of discount</u> times the <u>list price</u>.

Formula: $d = r \cdot p$ ◀ r = rate of discount

List Price	Rate of Discount	Discount
$60	20%	(0.20) (60) = $12.00
$150	10%	(0.10) (150) = 15.00
$225	8%	(0.08) (225) = 18.00

example 1

A lamp was on sale at a rate of discount of 20%. The sale price was $25.00. Find the list price of the lamp and the discount.

Solution:

1. Use Condition 1 to represent ⟶ Let p = the list price.
the unknowns. Then $0.20p$ = the discount.

2. Use Condition 2 to write an equation. ⟶ $p - 0.20p = 25.00$

3. Solve the equation. ⟶ $0.80p = 25.00$

$p = 31.25$

$0.20p = 6.25$

4 **Check:** Condition 1   Was the discount 20% of the list price?

Does $6.25 \div 31.25 = 0.2$ or 20%?   Yes ✔

Condition 2   Did the list price less the discount equal the sale price?

Does $31.25 - 6.25 = 25.00$?   Yes ✔

The list price was $31.25 and the discount was $6.25.

In Example 2, you are asked to organize the information given so that you can answer the question that is asked. Making a table will help you to do this and to write an equation for the problem.

example 2   Team A had a shooting average of 48% in a game. Team B attempted 5 more shots than Team A and had a shooting average of 55%. (Condition 1) Team B had 8 more shots than Team A. (Condition 2) Find the number attempted by each team.

Solution:

	Shooting Per Cent	Shots Attempted (Condition 1)	Shots Made
1 Team A	48%	x	$0.48x$
Team B	55%	$x + 5$	$0.55(x + 5)$

2 Use Condition 2 to write an equation. ⟶ $0.55(x + 5) = 0.48x + 8$

3 Solve the equation. ⟶ $0.55x + 2.75 = 0.48x + 8$

$$0.55x = 0.48x + 5.25$$
$$0.07x = 5.25$$
$$x = 75$$
$$x + 5 = 80$$

4 **Check:** Condition 1   Did Team B attempt 5 more shots than Team A?

Does $80 = 75 + 5$?   Yes ✔

Condition 2   Did Team B make 8 more shots than Team A?

Does $0.55(80) = 0.48(75) + 8$?   Yes ✔

Team A attempted 75 shots and Team B attempted 80 shots.

CLASSROOM EXERCISES

Find the discount on each item. (Table 1)

1. A dining table listed at $640 with a discount rate of 20% $128

2. A shirt listed at $36 with a discount rate of 25% $9

3. A record album listed at $9.50 with a discount rate of 40% $3.80

4. A pick-up truck listed at $8500 with a discount rate of 6% $510

In Exercises 5–8:
   a. *Use Condition 1 to represent the unknowns. Use the variable p.*
   b. *Use Condition 2 to write an equation for the problem.* (Example 1)

5. The rate of discount of a radio on sale was 35%. The discount was $31.50. Find the list price. Let p = list price; $0.35p = 31.50$

6. The rate of discount of a pair of skis on sale was 20%. The discount was $75. Find the list price. Let p = list price; $0.20p = 75$

7. A typewriter was on sale with a discount rate of 12%. The sale price was $396. Find the list price and the discount. Let p = list price; then $0.12p$ = discount; $p - 0.12p = 396$

8. A sweater was on sale with a discount rate of 35%. The sale price was $39. Find the list price and the discount. Let p = list price; then $0.35p$ = discount; $p - 0.35p = 39$

In Exercises 9–10:
   a. *Use the given information (Condition 1 and Condition 2) to complete the table.*
   b. *Use Condition 2 to write an equation for the problem.* (Example 2)

9. Last season in the City Softball League, Emily had a batting average of .300 (30%), but got 3 fewer hits than this season. Her batting average this season was .280 (28%). She was at bat 15 more times this season than last season. Find the number of times she was at bat each season.

Equation: $0.30t = 0.28 (t + 15) - 3$

	Batting Average	Times at Bat	Number of Hits
Last Season	30%	t	? $0.30t$
This Season	28%	? $t + 15$	? $0.28(t + 15)$

10. In a basketball game the high scorer on the winning team had a shooting average of 60%. He made 3 fewer shots than the high scorer on the losing team. The shooting average of the high scorer on the losing team was 75%, and he attempted one less shot. Find the number of shots attempted by the high scorer of each team.

High Scorer	Shooting Average	Shots Attempted	Number of Goals
Winning Team	60%	s	? $0.60s$
Losing Team	75%	? $s - 1$	? $0.75(s - 1)$

Equation: $0.60s = 0.75 (s - 1) - 3$

WRITTEN EXERCISES

See the Teacher's Manual for the suggested assignments.

Goal: To solve problems involving per cent

Sample Problem: A stereo was on sale for $328 at a discount of 18%. Find the list price and the discount.

Answers: List Price: $400; Discount: $72

2. Let p = list price; then $0.15p$ = discount; $p - 0.15p = 331.50$; $p = 390$; list price: $390, discount: $58.50

In Exercises 1–7:

a. Use Condition 1 to represent the unknowns.

b. Use Condition 2 to write an equation for the problem.

c. Solve the problem. (Examples 1 and 2)

1. The rate of discount of a refrigerator on sale was 20%. The discount was $115. Find the list price. Let p = list price; then $0.20p$ = discount; $0.20p = 115$; p = $575 (list price)

2. A color TV was on sale for $331.50. The discount rate was 15%. Find the list price and the discount. See above.

3. A woman's warmup suit was on sale at a rate of discount of 20%. The sale price was $48. Find the list price and the discount. Let p = list price; then $0.20p$ = discount; $p - 0.20p = 48$; $p = 60$; list price: $60, discount: $12

4. A store offers customers a 2% discount if bills are paid within 15 days. This discount would save one customer $5.12. Find the original amount of the customer's bill. See below.

5. The number of players selected for the girls' tennis team was 75% of the number who tried out. There were 4 more who tried out for the boys' team than for the girls' team, but only 60% of the boys were selected. The two teams had the same number of members. Find how many tried out for each team. See below.

6. Jon spends 25% of his monthly income for rent and 20% for food. The amount spent for rent is $70 more than the amount spent for food. Find his monthly income. See below.

7. A symphony concert was a sell-out with 65% of the seats at a price of $8 each and 35% at a price of $10. There were 960 more of the $8 seats than the $10 seats. Find the total number of tickets sold. Let t = number of tickets sold; then $0.65t$ = number at $8, $0.35t$ = number at $10; $0.65t = 0.35t + 960$, $t = 3200$ tickets sold

4. Let a = amt. of original bill; then $0.02a$ = discount; $0.02a = 512$; a = $256 (original bill)

REVIEW CAPSULE FOR SECTION 4.5

5. Let g = no. trying out for girls' team; then $g + 4$ = no. trying out for boys' team; $0.75g = 0.60(g + 4)$; $g = 16$; girls: 16, boys: 20

Use $d = rt$ to compute the distance traveled. (Section 3.6)

1. 4.5 hours at a rate of 460 mi/hr 2070 mi

2. 8 hours at a rate of 52.4 mi/hr 419.2 mi

3. 18.5 seconds at a rate of 3.4 m/sec 62.9 mi

4. 1.4 hours at a rate of 205 km/hr 287 km

6. Let i = monthly income; then $0.25i$ = rent and $0.20i$ = food costs; $0.25i = 0.20i + 70$; i = $1400 (monthly income)

4.5 Problem Solving With Formulas

DISTANCE/RATE/TIME

The following word rule and formula are used to solve time/rate/distance problems.

Word Rule: Distance equals <u>rate</u> multiplied by <u>time</u>.

Formula: $d = r \cdot t$ or $d = rt$

◄ d = *distance*
r = *rate*
t = *time*

In solving these problems, make a table showing the rate, time and distance for each trip. For <u>round trips</u>,

distance going equals distance returning.

This is Condition 2 in the problems for this section. Note that Condition 2 is sometimes stated before Condition 1 in time/rate/distance problems.

example 1

A salesperson took a round-trip flight to another city. (Condition 2) The first half of the trip took 5 hours and the return trip took 4.5 hours. The average rate returning was 54 miles per hour (abbreviated mi/hr) more than the average rate going. (Condition 1) Find the average speed returning.

Solution:	Rate (Condition 1)	Time	Distance (Condition 2) $d = rt$
1 Going	x mi/hr	5 hr	$x(5)$, or $5x$ mi
Returning	$(x + 54)$ mi/hr	4.5 hr	$(x + 54)4.5$, or $4.5(x + 54)$ mi

2 Use Condition 2 to write an equation. ────► Distance going = Distance returning

$$5x = 4.5(x + 54)$$

3 $$5x = 4.5x + 243$$

$$0.5x = 243$$

$$\frac{0.5x}{0.5} = \frac{243}{0.5}$$

$$x = 486$$

◄ *Don't forget to find x + 54.*

$$x + 54 = 540$$

4 **Check:** Condition 1 Was the average rate returning 54 miles per hour more than the average rate going?

Does $540 = 486 + 54$? Yes ✔

Condition 2 Does the distance going equal the distance returning?

Does $486(5) = 540(4.5)$? Yes ✔

The average rate returning was 540 miles per hour.

The following word rule and formula are similar to the distance formula. The **cruising range** of a car is the distance it can travel on a full tank of fuel. **Mileage** means miles per gallon (mi/gal) or kilometers per liter (km/L).

Word Rule: The <u>cruising range</u> (distance) of a car equals the <u>fuel tank capacity</u> multiplied by the <u>mileage</u>.

Suggest to students that *mileage* is a rate of use of fuel.

Formula: $r = m \cdot c$ or $r = mc$ ◀

r = cruising range
m = mileage
c = fuel tank capacity

example 2

The fuel tank capacity of Car B is 36 liters less than that of Car A. Car A averages 7 kilometers per liter of fuel. Car B averages 9 kilometers per liter. (Condition 1) The range of Car B is 132 kilometers less than that of Car A. (Condition 2) Find the fuel tank capacity of each car.

Solution:

		Mileage	Fuel Tank Capacity (Condition 1)	Range (Condition 2) $r = mc$
1	Car A	7 km/L	x L	$7x$ km
	Car B	9 km/L	$(x - 36)$ L	$9(x - 36)$ km

2 Range of Car B = Range of Car A − 132 ◀ *Condition 2*

$$9(x - 36) = 7x - 132$$

3
$$9x - 324 = 7x - 132$$

$$9x - 7x - 324 = 7x - 132 - 7x$$

$$2x - 324 + 324 = -132 + 324$$

$$2x = 192$$

$$x = 96$$

$$x - 36 = 60$$

◀ **Tank capacity of Car A: 96 L**
Tank capacity of Car B: 60 L

$\boxed{4}$ **Check:** Condition 1   Is the fuel tank capacity of Car B 36 liters less than that of Car A?

Does $60 = 96 - 36$?   Yes $\checkmark$

Condition 2   Is the range of Car B 132 kilometers less than that of Car A?

Does $9(60) = 7(96) - 132$ Yes $\checkmark$

The fuel tank capacity of Car A is 96 liters.
The fuel tank capacity of Car B is 60 liters.

CLASSROOM EXERCISES

In Exercises 1–3:
a. Use the given information to complete the table.
b. Use Condition 2 to write an equation for the problem.
(Examples 1 and 2)

1. Sarah traveled to New Orleans and back by train. The trip to New Orleans took 6 hours and the trip returning took 6.4 hours. The average rate returning was 6 kilometers per hour less than the average rate going.   Equation: $6x = 6.4(x - 6)$

	Rate (Condition 1)	Time	Distance (Condition 2) $d = rt$
Going	x km/hr	6 hr	? $6x$
Returning	? $x - 6$	6.4 hr	? $6.4(x - 6)$

2. On a round trip to another city, José spent 3 hours going and $2\frac{3}{4}$ hours returning. The average rate returning was 4 miles per hour faster than the average rate going.   Equation: $3r = 2\frac{3}{4}(r + 4)$

	Rate (Condition 1)	Time	Distance (Condition 2) $d = rt$
Going	r mi/hr	? 3	? $3r$
Returning	? $r + 4$	? $2\frac{3}{4}$	? $2\frac{3}{4}(r + 4)$

3. The fuel tank capacity of Car B is 2 liters less than that of Car A. Car A averages 10 km/L of fuel and Car B averages 12 km/L. The range of Car B is 112 kilometers more than that of Car A.   Equation: $10x = 12(x - 2) - 112$

	Mileage	Fuel Tank Capacity (Condition 1)	Range (Condition 2) $r = mc$
Car A	10 km/L	x L	? $10x$
Car B	12 km/L	? $x - 2$	? $12(x - 2) - 112$

4. Rate going: x; rate returning: $x + 80$; $5x = 4(x + 80)$; Going: 320 km/hr; returning: 400 km/hr

WRITTEN EXERCISES

See the Teacher's Manual for the suggested assignments.

Goal: To solve distance/rate/time problems

Sample Problem: A round-trip jet flight takes 2.25 hours to reach Miami and 2 hours to return. The rate returning is 80 kilometers per hour greater than the rate going. Find the average rate going and the average rate returning.

Answers: Average rate going: 640 km/hr; Average rate returning: 720 km/hr

For Exercises 1–7:
a. Use Condition 1 and Condition 2 to complete a table.
b. Use Condition 2 to write an equation for the problem.
c. Solve the problem. (Examples 1 and 2)

2. Rate returning: x; rate going: $x + 6$; $4(x + 6) = 5x$; Avg. speed returning: 24 km/hr

1. A bus makes a round-trip run. The average rate going is 15 miles per hour more than the average rate returning. The first half of the trip takes $2\frac{4}{5}$ hours and the return trip takes 4 hours. Find the average speed on the first half of the trip.

1. Rate returning: x; rate going: $x + 15$; $(x + 15) 2\frac{4}{5} = 4x$; rate (1st half of trip): 50 mi/hr

2. An excursion boat makes a round-trip to a park. The return trip is 6 kilometers per hour slower than the rate going to the park. The trip to the park takes 4 hours and the return trip takes 5 hours. Find the average speed returning.

3. In going back and forth to work every day, Marge finds that the average rate returning is 7 miles per hour less than the rate going. It takes Marge 1 hour to go to work and $1\frac{1}{4}$ hours to return home. Find the average rate going and the average rate returning.

3. Rate going: x; rate returning: $x - 7$; $x = 1\frac{1}{4}(x - 7)$; Rate going: 35 mi/hr; Rate returning: 28mi/hr

4. A jet makes a round-trip to San Francisco. The first half of the trip takes 5 hours and the return trip takes 4 hours. The average rate returning is 80 kilometers per hour more than the average rate going. Find the average rate going and returning. See above.

5. Two cars have the same cruising range. Car B's fuel tank holds 35 fewer liters than Car A. Car B averages 8.5 kilometers per liter of fuel. Car A averages 5 kilometers per liter. Find the fuel tank capacity of each car. 5. Car A: x liters; car B: $x - 35$ liters; $5x = 8.5(x - 35)$; Car A: 85 L; car B: 50 L

6. A car averages 18 miles per gallon of fuel for city driving and 27 miles per gallon on the highway. The car's cruising range on the highway is 225 miles greater than its cruising range in the city. Find the car's fuel tank capacity.
Fuel capacity (gallons): x; $18x + 225 = 27x$; 25 gallons

7. The Lee family decided to drive to the beach and back. The trip going took 4 hours. The trip returning took 5 hours. The average rate returning was 10 miles per hour slower than the rate going. Find the average rate returning. Rate going: r; rate returning: $r - 10$; $4r = 5(r - 10)$; 50 mi/hr going; 40 mi/hr returning

Problem Solving: One Variable / 95

Career Engineering Technician

Engineering technicians work with engineers and perform some of the same tasks that engineers do. They are often involved with the construction of devices that engineers have designed.

In construction work, it is important to know the greatest safe load that a beam can bear. The following formula applies to a steel beam with a rectangular cross section. Its load is in pounds, distributed along the beam.

Greatest Safe Load

$$S = \frac{1780Ad}{l}$$

A = cross-sectional area (in²)
d = depth of beam (in)
l = distance between supports (ft)

EXAMPLE: Compute the greatest safe load in pounds for a solid steel beam 20 feet long with a cross section 8 inches wide and 6 inches deep.

SOLUTION: $S = \dfrac{1780Ad}{l}$

$A = 48$ in²(6″ × 8″), $l = 20$ ft, $d = 6$ in

$S = \dfrac{(1780)(48)(6)}{20}$

By calculator:

| 1 | 7 | 8 | 0 | × | 4 | 8 |

| × | 6 | ÷ | 2 | 0 | = |

25632.

The greatest safe load is **25,632 pounds.**

EXERCISES

Compute the greatest safe load in pounds of a solid rectangular steel beam that has the given dimensions.

1. Length: 16 ft
Width: 2 in
Depth: 4 in 3560 pounds

2. Length: 12 ft
Width: 3 in
Depth: 5 in 11,125 pounds

3. Length: 18 ft
Width: 6 in
Depth: 6 in 21,360 pounds

4. Length: 9 ft
Width: 3 in
Depth: 4 in 9493.33 pounds

5. The formula $S = \dfrac{1795Ad}{l}$ is used to calculate the greatest safe load in pounds of a steel I-beam with the load in the middle of the beam. One such beam has a length of 24 feet, a depth of 4 inches, and a cross-sectional area of 16 square inches. Find its greatest safe load.

4786.67 pounds

Career

CHAPTER SUMMARY

IMPORTANT TERMS	Perimeter *(p. 83)* Rate of discount *(p. 88)*
	List price *(p. 88)* Mileage *(p. 93)*
	Discount *(p. 88)* Cruising range *(p. 93)*
	Sale price *(p. 88)*

IMPORTANT IDEAS

1. The words <u>sum</u>, <u>plus</u>, <u>more than</u>, and <u>increased by</u> suggest the operation of addition.

2. The words <u>decreased by</u>, <u>difference</u>, <u>minus</u>, <u>less</u>, and <u>less than</u> suggest the operation of subtraction.

3. The words <u>product</u>, <u>multiplied by</u>, <u>times</u>, and <u>doubled</u> suggest the operation of multiplication.

4. The words <u>quotient</u> and <u>divided by</u> suggest the operation of division.

5. Steps for Solving Word Problems.
   a. Identify Condition 1. Use Condition 1 to represent the unknowns.
   b. Identify Condition 2. Use Condition 2 to write an equation.
   c. Solve the equation.
   d. Check the results with the two conditions. Answer the question.

CHAPTER REVIEW NOTE: The Teacher's Resource Book contains two forms of each Chapter Test.

SECTION 4.1

Choose a variable and write an equation for the word sentence. Then solve the equation.

Let c = cost of each box; then $24c = 30.72$; $c = 1.28$

1. The total distance traveled less 25.6 kilometers equals 278.3 kilometers. Let d = total distance traveled; then $d - 25.6 = 278.3$; $d = 303.9$

2. Twenty-four times the cost of each box equals $30.72.

3. A bowler's total score divided by 5 games equals her average game score of 168. Let b = total score; then $\frac{b}{5} = 168$; $b = 840$

4. The low temperature for one day increased by 24° equals the high temperature of 30.5°. Let t = low temperature; then $t + 24 = 30.5$; $t = 6.5$

SECTION 4.2

In Exercises 5–18, use Condition 1 to represent the unknowns. Use Condition 2 to write an equation for the problem. Solve the problem.

5. A librarian issued 82 more fiction books in one day than nonfiction books. The total number of books issued was 372. Find the number of each kind that were issued. Let n = number of nonfiction books; then $n + 82$ = number of fiction books; $n + n + 82 = 372$; $n = 145$; nonfiction books: 145; fiction books: 227

6. In a 2-day period the amount of rainfall the first day was 3.7 centimeters less than the amount the second day. In two days it rained 15.3 centimeters. Find the amount it rained each day. Let r = amount of rainfall second day; then $r - 3.7$ = amount of rainfall first day; $r + r - 3.7 = 15.3$; $r = 9.5$; first day: 5.8 cm; second day: 9.5 cm

7. On a family trip Alice drove 100 miles more than twice the number of miles her father drove. The total number of miles was 1150. Find how many miles Alice and her father each drove. See above.

8. The labor cost of producing a machine part is $0.05 less than twice the cost of materials. The total unit production cost of the part is $1.72. Find the cost of materials and the cost of labor.

SECTION 4.3

9. A helicopter pad on top of a building is rectangular in shape. The length is 11.8 meters more than the width. The perimeter is 80.0 meters. Find the length and width. See above.

10. A ceiling of a room is covered with rectangular panels. The length of each panel is twice the width. The perimeter is 365.76 centimeters. Find the length and width. See above.

11. The ratio of the length to the width of a rectangle is 7:3. The perimeter is 166.0 millimeters. Find the length and width.

12. A triangular plane route has legs in the ratio 5:9:13. The total route has a length of 3681 kilometers. Find the length of each leg.

SECTION 4.4

13. A tape deck is on sale at a discount rate of 40%. The sale price is $274.50. Find the list price. See below.

14. An airline offered a special fare at a discount of 18%. The special fare was $479.70. Find the regular fare for this flight. See below.

15. The first and second place teams in a division had winning records of .900 (90%) and .850 (85%). The first place team won one more game than the second place team. They played the same number of games. Find the number of games played by each team.

16. A store offered a special tire sale with one radial tire at the regular price and a second tire at a discount of 50%. Lucy purchased two tires at a total cost of $140.70. Find the regular price of a tire.

SECTION 4.5

17. Juan and Maria computed the average speed of the family car on a vacation trip. The trip to their vacation spot took 4.25 hours and the return trip took 4 hours. The average speed going was 5 kilometers per hour less than the speed returning. Find the average speed each direction.

18. The fuel tank capacity of Car B is 5 liters less than that of Car A. Car A averages 11.9 kilometers per liter and Car B averages 9.8 kilometers per liter. The range of Car A is 154 kilometers more than that of Car B. Find the fuel tank capacity of each car.

CHAPTER

5 Properties of Order

Sections 5.1 Graphs of Inequalities

5.2 Properties of Order

5.3 Addition and Subtraction

5.4 Solving Inequalities

5.5 Multiplication and Division

5.6 Problem Solving with Inequalities

Features *Calculator Exercises:* Checking Inequalities

Special Topic Application: Compound Interest

Review
and
Testing *Review Capsules*

Mid-Chapter Review

Chapter Summary

Chapter Review

5.1 Graphs of Inequalities

To draw a graph of an inequality based on its given or implied domain

NOTE: Computer programming section A-4 on pages 486-488 can be studied any time after Chapter 5 has been studied. All computer programming sections are optional.

The sentence "$x = 2$" means "x is equal to two". The sentence "$x < 2$" means "x is less than two". The solutions of these sentences are illustrated in the <u>graphs</u> below. The set of replacements for x is {integers}.

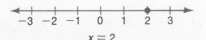

$x = 2$

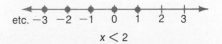

$x < 2$

P-1 **Why is "etc." necessary in the second graph?** To show that all integers less than 2 are solutions

The set of replacements for a variable is the **domain.** In the second graph above the domain of x is {integers}. If the domain is {real numbers}, then the graph of $x < 2$ is as shown below.

The point corresponding to 2 is circled in order to show that 2 is not a solution.

Sentences such as $x < 2$ are called **inequalities.** Other kinds of inequalities are shown below.

Inequality	Meaning
$x > 2$	"x is greater than two."
$x \neq 2$	"x is not equal to two."
$x \leq 2$	"x is less than or equal to two."

Examples 1 & 2 show the importance of defining the domain of the variable.

P-2 **Why is 2 a solution of $x \leq 2$?** 2 is equal to 2.

P-3 **Why is 3 a solution of $x \neq 2$?** 3 is not equal to 2.

example 1

Draw a graph of the solutions of $x < 3$ on a number line. Domain = {counting numbers}.

Solution:

The solutions are 1 and 2. The <u>solution set</u> is {1, 2}.

example 2

Draw a graph of the solution set of $x < 3$.
Domain = {integers}.

Solution:

etc. −5 −4 −3 −2 −1 0 1 2 3 4 5

If no domain is stated, it is assumed to be {real numbers}.   *Underscore the importance of this statement.*

example 3

Draw a graph of $x \leq 3$.   ◄ *"Graph of $x \leq 3$" means "graph of the solution set of $x \leq 3$."*

Solution:

−5 −4 −3 −2 −1 0 1 2 3 4 5

P-4   **Why is the point corresponding to 3 darkened?**   *To show that 3 is a solution of $x \leq 3$*

The solution set of an inequality in the domain {real numbers} can be shown by a set description.

Inequality	Solution Set
$x \leq 8$	$\{x : x \leq 8\}$

You may read $\{x : x \leq 8\}$ as follows: "The set of numbers, x, such that x is less than or equal to 8."

example 4

Graph $x \geq -\frac{1}{2}$.   ◄ *"Graph" means "draw a graph."*

Solution:

$-\frac{1}{2}$

−5 −4 −3 −2 −1 0 1 2 3 4 5

P-5   **What solution sets are graphed below?   What domain is assumed?**   {real numbers}

a.

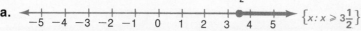

$3\frac{1}{2}$

−5 −4 −3 −2 −1 0 1 2 3 4 5 $\left\{x : x \geq 3\frac{1}{2}\right\}$

b.

$-2\frac{1}{2}$

−5 −4 −3 −2 −1 0 1 2 3 4 5 $\left\{x : x < -2\frac{1}{2}\right\}$

CLASSROOM EXERCISES

Find the solution set that is graphed. If necessary, name the domain that you are assuming. (P-5)

1. $\{x : x \geq -1\}; \{\text{integers}\}$
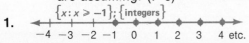
-4 -3 -2 -1 0 1 2 3 4 etc.

2. $\{x : x < 1\}; \{\text{real numbers}\}$
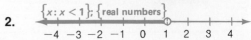
-4 -3 -2 -1 0 1 2 3 4

3.
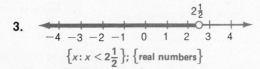
$2\frac{1}{2}$
-4 -3 -2 -1 0 1 2 3 4
$\{x : x < 2\frac{1}{2}\}; \{\text{real numbers}\}$

4.
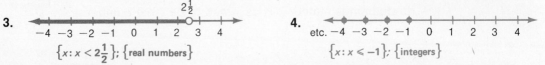
etc. -4 -3 -2 -1 0 1 2 3 4
$\{x : x \leq -1\}; \{\text{integers}\}$

Name three solutions of each inequality. (Examples 1–4) In Exercises 5-10 answers will vary.

5. $x \leq 10$; Domain = {whole numbers} 0; 4; 9

6. $x < -9$; Domain = {integers}   -83; -20; -10

7. $x \leq 3.9$ $-\pi$; 0; 3.9

8. $x > -\pi$ $-3; \sqrt{17}$; 43

9. $x \geq -5$; Domain = {rational numbers} $-5; 3\frac{1}{4}; 8\frac{1}{3}$

10. $x \geq -2$; Domain = {integers}   -2; 0; 19

WRITTEN EXERCISES

See the Teacher's Manual for the suggested assignments.

Goals: To write the solution set of an inequality from a graph and to graph an inequality

Sample Problem: Graph $x < 6$. Domain = {integers}.

Answer:

etc. -3 -2 -1 0 1 2 3 4 5 6 7

Write a set description of each solution set that is graphed. If necessary, show the domain you are assuming. (P-5)

1. $\{-2, -1, 0, 1\}$
-4 -3 -2 -1 0 1 2 3 4

2. $\{-1, 0, 1, 2, 3\}$
-4 -3 -2 -1 0 1 2 3 4

3. $\{x : x \leq 0\}; \{\text{integers}\}$
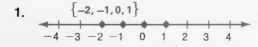
etc. -5 -4 -3 -2 -1 0 1 2 3

4. $\{x : x \geq -1\}; \{\text{integers}\}$
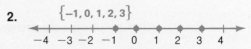
-3 -2 -1 0 1 2 3 4 5 etc.

5. $\{x : x > -2\}; \{\text{real numbers}\}$
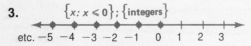
-4 -3 -2 -1 0 1 2 3 4

6. $\{x : x < -1\}; \{\text{real numbers}\}$
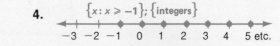
-4 -3 -2 -1 0 1 2 3 4

7. $\{x : x \le -1\}$; $\{$real numbers$\}$

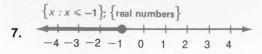

8. $\{x : x \ge -2\}$; $\{$real numbers$\}$

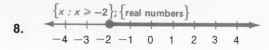

9. $-1\frac{1}{2}$

$\{x : x \ge -1\frac{1}{2}\}$; $\{$real numbers$\}$

10. π

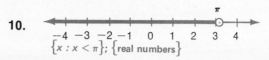

$\{x : x < \pi\}$; $\{$real numbers$\}$

Draw a graph of each inequality. (Examples 1–4)

On a number line, the points 2, 3, 4, 5, etc.

11. $x \ge 2$; Domain = $\{$whole numbers$\}$

On a number line, the points 5, 4, 3, 2, 1, 0

12. $x < 6$; Domain = $\{$whole numbers$\}$

13. $x < -2$; Domain = $\{$integers$\}$ See below.

14. $x \ge 5$; Domain = $\{$integers$\}$ See below.

15. $x < -\frac{3}{4}$ On a number line, all points to the left of, and not including $-\frac{3}{4}$

16. $x \ge -3\frac{1}{2}$ On a number line all points to the right of, and including, $-3\frac{1}{2}$

17. $x \ge 2.7$

On a number line, all points to the right of, and including, 2.7

18. $x < -1.9$

On a number line, all points to the left of, and not including, -1.9

MORE CHALLENGING EXERCISES

Write the solution set of each inequality. Domain = $\{0, 1, 2, 3, 4, 5, 6, 7, 8, 9\}$.

19. $2x + 5 < 10$ $\{0, 1, 2\}$

20. $3x - 1 < 13$ $\{0, 1, 2, 3, 4\}$

21. $5x - 3 \le 25$ See below.

22. $7 + 5x \le 42$ $\{0, 1, 2, 3, 4, 5, 6, 7\}$

23. $x + 3 > 11$ $\{9\}$

24. $x - 5 \le 2$ See below.

25. $x - 7 \le 2$ $\{0, 1, 2, 3, 4, 5, 6, 7, 8, 9\}$

26. $x - 3 \ge 1$ $\{4, 5, 6, 7, 8, 9\}$

27. $x + 5 \ge 2$ See below.

21. $\{0, 1, 2, 3, 4, 5\}$ 24. $\{0, 1, 2, 3, 4, 5, 6, 7\}$ 27. $\{0, 1, 2, \cdots, 9\}$

Write <u>Yes</u> *or* <u>No</u> *to show whether each graph below describes the solution set of the sentence. Domain = $\{$real numbers$\}$.*

28. $-x = 2$ No

29. $-x = -3$ No

30. $-x > -3$ Yes

31. $-x \ge -2\frac{1}{2}$ $-2\frac{1}{2}$ No

13. On a number line, the points $-3, -4, -5$, etc.
14. On a number line, the points 5, 6, 7, 8, etc.

REVIEW CAPSULE FOR SECTION 5.2

Change each fraction to decimal form. Then identify the greater number of each pair.

EXAMPLES: a. $\frac{2}{5}$ and $\frac{3}{5}$ **b.** $-\frac{7}{10}$ and $-\frac{8}{10}$

SOLUTIONS: a. $\frac{2}{5} = 0.4$; $\frac{3}{5} = 0.6$; $0.6 > 0.4$ Thus, $\frac{3}{5} > \frac{2}{5}$.   4. 0.75, 0.875; $\frac{7}{8} > \frac{6}{8}$

b. $-\frac{7}{10} = -0.7$; $-\frac{8}{10} = -0.8$; $-0.7 > -0.8$ Thus, $-\frac{7}{10} > -\frac{8}{10}$.
0.4, -0.6;

1. $\frac{3}{10}$ and $\frac{5}{10}$ 0.3, 0.5; $\frac{5}{10} > \frac{3}{10}$ **2.** $\frac{3}{4}$ and $\frac{1}{4}$ 0.75, 0.25; $\frac{3}{4} > \frac{1}{4}$ **3.** $\frac{2}{5}$ and $-\frac{3}{5}$ $\frac{2}{5} > -\frac{3}{5}$ **4.** $\frac{6}{8}$ and $\frac{7}{8}$ See above.

5. $-\frac{4}{10}$ and $-\frac{5}{10}$

$-0.4, -0.5; -\frac{4}{10} > -\frac{5}{10}$

6. $-\frac{3}{8}$ and $-\frac{5}{8}$

$-0.375, -0.625; -\frac{3}{8} > -\frac{5}{8}$

7. $\frac{4}{6}$ and $\frac{5}{6}$

$0.6\cdots, 0.833\cdots; \frac{5}{6} > \frac{4}{6}$

8. $-\frac{1}{3}$ and $-\frac{2}{3}$

$-0.33\cdots, -0.66\cdots,$

$-\frac{1}{3} > -\frac{2}{3}$

5.2   Properties of Order

To write an equivalent inequality of the opposites of two real numbers from a given inequality
To write an inequality for *x* and *y* from two inequalities such as $x < a$ and $a < y$

Comparison Property

If *a* and *b* are real numbers, then exactly one
of the following is true.

1. $a > b$ 2. $a = b$ 3. $a < b$

P-1   **If $a = -1.7$ and $b = -1.8$, what inequality can you form by use of the Comparison Property?** $a > b$

P-2   **If $a = -1.3$ and $b = \frac{-13}{-10}$, what inequality can you form by use of the Comparison Property?** $a < b$

example 1

Write an inequality by taking the opposite of each side of $-3 < 5$.

Solution:
$$-3 < 5$$
$$-(-3) \;\underline{?}\; -(5)$$
$$3 > -5$$

Taking the opposite of each side reverses the order.

Order Property of Opposites

If *a* and *b* are real numbers and
$a < b$, then $-a > -b$.

$$-5.2 < -4.7$$
$$5.2 > 4.7$$

You will need to emphasize again and again that taking the opposite of the numbers reverses the inequality.

You can write $-3 < 5$ as $5 > -3$ and $3 > -5$ as $-5 < 3$. Similarly, you can write $a < b$ as $b > a$ and $-a > -b$ as $-b < -a$.

P-3   **What two inequalities can you form by applying the Order Property of Opposites to each of the following inequalities?**

a. $y > -6$ **b.** $-1\frac{3}{4} < t$ **c.** $-r < s$
$6 > -y; -y < 6$ $-t < 1\frac{3}{4}; 1\frac{3}{4} > -t$ $-s < r; r > -s$

P-4   **What inequality relates *r* and 1.8 in the graph below?** $r < 1.8$

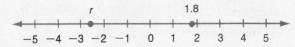

P-5 What inequality relates 1.8 and *t* in the graph below? $1.8 < t$

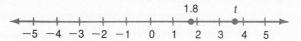

P-6 What inequality relates *r* and *t*? $r < t$

Transitive Property of Order

If $a < b$ and $b < c$, then $a < c$.

$-3.4 < 0$ and $0 < 1.9$.
Then $-3.4 < 1.9$.

P-7 If $x < -2$ and $-2 < y$, what inequality relates *x* and *y*? $x < y$

example 2 Suppose that "$-1.5 > q$" and "$-1.5 < p$" are both true. Write an inequality for *p* and *q*. Use "$<$".

Solution: $q < -1.5$ and $-1.5 < p$ ◄ **Transitive Property of Order**

$q < p$

You know that you can write $a < b$ as $b > a$, $b < c$ as $c > b$, and $a < c$ as $c > a$.

P-8 How would you state a Transitive Property of Order using "$>$"?
If $a > b$ and $b > c$, then $a > c$.

CLASSROOM EXERCISES

Write an inequality for each pair of numbers. (P-1, P-2)

For Ex. 1-8, only one of two possible inequalities is given for each pair.

1. -5; 2 $-5 < 2$ **2.** 15; -13 $15 > -13$ **3.** -12; -9 $-12 < -9$ **4.** $\frac{3}{4}$; $-\frac{3}{4}$ $\frac{3}{4} > -\frac{3}{4}$

5. 1.3; 1.03 $1.3 > 1.03$ **6.** -1.6; -1.7 $-1.6 > -1.7$ **7.** $\frac{3}{4}$; $\frac{3}{8}$ $\frac{3}{4} > \frac{3}{8}$ **8.** $-\frac{3}{5}$; $-\frac{2}{5}$ $-\frac{3}{5} < -\frac{2}{5}$

Answer each question. a, b, and c are real numbers. (Example 1, P-7)

9. If $-c > -a$, what is the order of *a* and *c*? $a > c$

10. If $c < b$ and $b < a$, what is the order of *c* and *a*? $c < a$

11. If $a > c$ and $b > c$, can you say anything about the order of *a* and *b*? No

12. If $c < -5$ and $a > -5$, what is the order of *a* and *c*? $a > c$

Goal: To write inequalities using the Comparison Property, the Order Property of Opposites, and the Transitive Property of Order

Sample Problem: Suppose that "$x < -31$" and "$y > -31$" are both true. Write an inequality for x and y. Use "$<$".

Answer: $x < y$

Write an inequality for the two numbers. Use "$<$". (P-1, P-2)

$-2\frac{1}{8} < -2\frac{1}{9}$

1. -1.7; 1.6 $-1.7 < 1.6$ 2. 0.7; -0.9 $-0.9 < 0.7$ 3. $-1\frac{3}{4}$; $-1\frac{7}{8}$ $-1\frac{7}{8} < -1\frac{3}{4}$ 4. $-2\frac{1}{8}$; $-2\frac{1}{9}$

5. $\frac{5}{13}$; $\frac{5}{12}$ $\frac{5}{13} < \frac{5}{12}$ 6. $\frac{11}{16}$; $\frac{11}{19}$ $\frac{11}{19} < \frac{11}{16}$ 7. $-\frac{13}{16}$; $-\frac{12}{17}$ $-\frac{13}{16} < -\frac{12}{17}$ 8. $-\frac{6}{19}$; $-\frac{7}{18}$

$-\frac{7}{18} < -\frac{6}{19}$

Write a new inequality by applying the Order Property of Opposites. (Example 1)

$\frac{7}{8} < b$

9. $3 < -b$ $-3 > b$ 10. $-a < 5$ $a > -5$ 11. $-a < -\frac{1}{2}$ $a > \frac{1}{2}$ 12. $-\frac{7}{8} > -b$

13. $-(a + b) < 2$ $a + b > -2$ 14. $-10 < -(b + a)$ $10 > a + b$ 15. $-b > a$ $b < -a$ 16. $-a < b$

$a > -b$

Write True or False for each sentence. a, b, and c are real numbers. (Example 2)

17. If $c < -2$ and $-2 < a$, then $c < a$. True   18. If $b > 5$ and $5 > c$, then $b > c$. True

19. If $a < -2$, then $a < -5$ is true.   False   20. If $c > -3$, then $-1 < c$ is true.   False

21. If $a < c$ and $b < c$, then $a < b$.   False   22. If $c < a$ and $b > c$, then $b < a$. False

23. If $-a > 4$ and $-4 < b$, then $a < b$. True   24. If $a < -7$ and $a > -c$, then $c > 7$. True

Write an inequality for x and y. Use "$<$". (Example 2)

25. $y < -2$ and $-2 < x$ $y < x$ 26. $y < 5$ and $5 < x$ $y < x$

27. $x < -3.8$ and $y > -3.8$ $x < y$ 28. $y < 0.9$ and $x > 0.9$ $y < x$

29. $213 > -x$ and $y < -213$ $y < x$ 30. $-56 > y$ and $-x < 56$ $y < x$

31. $-x > 19.3$ and $19.3 > -y$ $x < y$ 32. $-y < -10.3$ and $-x > -10.3$ $x < y$

REVIEW CAPSULE FOR SECTION 5.3

Solve each equation. (Section 3.1)

1. $64 = t - 71$ $t = 135$ 2. $x + 7 = -8$ $x = -15$ 3. $y - 5 = 8$ $y = 13$

4. $3.7 = w - 4.2$ $w = 7.9$ 5. $t + 0.9 = -5.2$ $t = -6.1$ 6. $-\frac{3}{4} = \frac{7}{8} - r$ $r = 1\frac{5}{8}$

7. $-d - 1\frac{2}{3} = -\frac{5}{6}$ $d = -\frac{5}{6}$ 8. $-2.07 = p - 5.93$ $p = 3.86$ 9. $s + 0.87 = 0.34$

$s = -0.53$

5.3 Addition and Subtraction

To solve inequalities of the forms $x + a > b$ or $x + a < b$

P-1 **What addition problem is shown below?** $5 + (-2) = 3$

The number -2 is added to 5 by moving two units to the left of the point with coordinate 5.

P-2 **From the graph below, what inequality can you write using "<"?**
$-1 < x - 2$

P-3 **What number can be added to $x - 2$ to get x?** 2

The number 2 is added to both $x - 2$ and -1 on the number line.

P-4 **What inequality can be formed with x and 1 using ">"?** $x > 1$

---

example 1

Solve: $x - 2 > -1$ ◀ **Solve** *means to find the solution set.*

Solution: $\qquad x - 2 > -1$

1. Add 2 to each side. ⟶ $x - 2 + 2 > -1 + 2$
2. Simplify. ⟶ $x > 1$

The solution set of $x > 1$ is $\{x : x > 1\}$. It is the same as the solution set of $x - 2 > -1$.

◀ $x > 1$ *and* $x - 2 > -1$ *are equivalent.*

Point out the analogy between this property and the Addition Property for Equations.

> **Addition Property for Inequalities**
>
> Adding the same real number to each side of an inequality does not change the order of the inequality. The new inequality is equivalent to the first.
>
> $x - 12 > 3$
> $x - 12 + 12 > 3 + 12$
> $x > 15$

example 2 Solve: $x - 5 > -1$

Solution:

$x - 5 > -1$

1	Add 5 to each side. ──────────►	$x - 5 + 5 > -1 + 5$
2	Simplify. ──────────►	$x > 4$
3	Write the solution set. ──────────►	$\{x : x > 4\}$

The inequality $x + 7 + (-7) < 12 + (-7)$ is equivalent
to $x + 7 - 7 < 12 - 7$. This suggests a subtraction property.

Subtraction Property for Inequalities

Subtracting the same real number from each
side of an inequality does not change the
order of the inequality. The new inequality
is equivalent to the first.

$$x + \tfrac{1}{2} < \tfrac{3}{4}$$
$$x + \tfrac{1}{2} - \tfrac{1}{2} < \tfrac{3}{4} - \tfrac{1}{2}$$
$$x < \tfrac{1}{4}$$

---

example 3 Solve: $x + 5.3 < 2.9$

Example 3 may also be solved
by adding −5.3 to each side.

Solution:

$x + 5.3 < 2.9$

1	Subtract 5.3 from each side. ──────────►	$x + 5.3 - 5.3 < 2.9 - 5.3$
2	Simplify. ──────────►	$x < -2.4$
3	Write the solution set. ──────────►	$\{x : x < -2.4\}$

CLASSROOM EXERCISES

*Tell what number to add to, or subtract from, each side of the inequality to
get the variable by itself. (Step 1 in Examples 1–3)*

Subtract 7.

1. $r + 5 < 3$ Subtract 5. **2.** $w - \frac{1}{2} > 2$ Add $\frac{1}{2}$. **3.** $-13 > a + 7$

4. $-5.6 < 1.8 + c$ Subtract 1.8. **5.** $-0.8 + x < 5.9$ Add 0.8. **6.** $-3\frac{1}{4} > t - 5\frac{1}{8}$

Add $5\frac{1}{8}$.

Solve. (Examples 1–3)

7. $x - 1 < 10$ $\{x : x < 11\}$ **8.** $y + 2 > 8$ $\{y : y > 6\}$ **9.** $a - \frac{1}{2} < 1\frac{1}{2}$

$\{a : a < 2\}$

10. $t + 7 > -2$ $\{t : t > -9\}$

11. $w - 5 < -1$ $\{w : w < 4\}$

12. $10 > -3 + s$ $\{s : s < 13\}$

13. $-5 + r < -1$ $\{r : r < 4\}$

14. $p - 2\frac{1}{2} > -3\frac{1}{2}$ $\{p : p > -1\}$

15. $-0.5 + x > -8.5$ See above.

16. $3.6 < -1.4 + y$ $\{y : y > 5\}$

17. $2x - 3 - x < 5$ $\{x : x < 8\}$

18. $-7 > 3a + 5 - 2a$

$\{a : a < -12\}$

WRITTEN EXERCISES

See the Teacher's Manual for the suggested assignment.

Goal: To solve an inequality using the Addition or Subtraction Property for Inequalities

Sample Problems: Solve: **a.** $x - 5.3 < 2.9$ **b.** $x + 5.3 < 2.9$

Answers: a. $\{x : x < 8.2\}$ **b.** $\{x : x < -2.4\}$

Write <u>Yes</u> *or* <u>No</u> *to show whether the two inequalities are equivalent.* (Examples 1–3)

1. $x + 2 < 3$; $x < 5$ No

2. $-5 < y - 2$; $-7 < y$ No

3. $2a - 7 < -2$; $2a < 5$ Yes

4. $5r + 6 > -1$; $5r > -7$ Yes

5. $x + 2 < 5$; $x + 1 < 6$ No

6. $y - 3 < 4$; $y - 2 < 5$ Yes

7. $2x + 2 < 5x$; $2x < 5x - 2$ Yes

8. $3t < 4t - 1$; $3t - 1 < 4t$ No

9. $3w - 1 > w + 7$; $3w - 2 > w + 8$ No

10. $9g - 5 > g + 3$; $9g - 3 > g + 5$ Yes

Solve. (Examples 1–3)

11. $y + 2 > -3$ $\{y : y > -5\}$

12. $x + 5 < 8$ $\{x : x < 3\}$

13. $-3 + t < -10$ $\{t : t < -7\}$

14. $-7 + r > -13$ $\{r : r > -6\}$

15. $x - \frac{1}{2} < -2$ $\{x : x < -1\frac{1}{2}\}$

16. $p - \frac{3}{4} > -3$ See below.

17. $-3.4 > -0.3 + q$ $\{q : q < -3.1\}$

18. $-4.5 < b - 1.2$ $\{b : b > -3.3\}$

19. $-\frac{3}{4} + w > 1\frac{5}{8}$ See below.

20. $-\frac{2}{3} + y > -3\frac{1}{6}$ $\{y : y > -2\frac{1}{2}\}$

21. $4.2 < y - 3.7$ $\{y : y > 7.9\}$

22. $3.9 < y + 1.6$

$\{y : y > 2.3\}$

MORE CHALLENGING EXERCISES

Solve. Domain = {integers}.

23. $2 - x < 3$ $\{x : x > -1\}$

24. $-y - 7 > -2$ $\{y : y < -5\}$

25. $-12 > -5 - a$ $\{a : a > 7\}$

26. $15 < -b + 12$ $\{b : b < -3\}$

27. $-p + \frac{1}{2} \le 5\frac{1}{2}$ $\{p : p \ge -5\}$

28. $\frac{2}{3} - q \ge -4\frac{1}{3}$ $\{q : q \le 5\}$

Solve. Graph each solution set. Graphs are not shown.

29. $x + 1 \le 5$ $\{x : x \le 4\}$

30. $y - 2 \le 3$ $\{y : y \le 5\}$

31. $a - 3 \ge -7$ $\{a : a \ge -4\}$

32. $b + 7 \ge 10$ $\{b : b \ge 3\}$

33. $-7 \le -12 + r$ $\{r : r \ge 5\}$

34. $-13 \le t - 19$ $\{t : t \ge 6\}$

16. $\{p : p > -2\frac{1}{4}\}$

19. $\{w : w > 2\frac{3}{8}\}$

1. the points to the right of, and not including, −4
2. the points to the left of, and including, 3
3. the points 4, 3, 2, 1, 0, −1, etc.
4. the points −2, −1, 0, 1, 2, 3, etc.

MID-CHAPTER REVIEW

NOTE: After completing the Mid-Chapter Review, you may want to administer a quiz covering the same sections. See pages M-18 and M-19 of the Teacher's Manual for the suggested quiz.

Draw a graph of each inequality. (Section 5.1) For Ex. 1-6, the graphs are described as points on a number line.

1. $x > -4$; Domain = {real numbers} See above.   **2.** $x \le 3$; Domain = {real numbers} See above.

3. $x < 5$; Domain = {integers} See above.   **4.** $x \ge -2$; Domain = {integers} See above.

5. $x \le 6$; Domain = {whole numbers}   **6.** $x > 4$; Domain = {real numbers}
   the points 0, 1, 2, 3, 4, 5, 6   the points to the right of, and not including, 4

Write an inequality for a and b. Use "<." (Section 5.2)

7. $a < 3$ and $b > 5$ $a < b$ **8.** $a > 2$ and $b < -3$ $b < a$ **9.** $-3.8 < a$ and $-4.3 > b$
                                                                                 $b < a$

10. $4 < -a$ and $b > -4$ $a < b$ **11.** $a > -3\frac{1}{2}$ and $b < -4$ $b < a$ **12.** $-a < 0$ and $-5 > b$
                                                                                                   $b < a$

Solve. (Section 5.3)

13. $t - 8 < -3$ $t < 5$ **14.** $-\frac{1}{2} + w > 5\frac{1}{4}$ $w > 5\frac{3}{4}$ **15.** $8.2 < x + 9.4$ $x > -1.2$

16. $-4.7 > -2.3 + q$ $q < -2.4$ **17.** $r + \frac{3}{4} < \frac{1}{2}$ $r < -\frac{1}{4}$ **18.** $-1.7 < y - 8.3$ $y > 6.6$

─────────── *CHECKING INEQUALITIES* ───────────

You can use a calculator to check a given number in an inequality. First, substitute the number in the inequality. Then compare the two sides of the inequality.

Note that it is unnecessary to press 0 when entering 0.43. On most calculators 0 shows automatically.

EXAMPLE   In $2.1 + t < 2.9 - t$, is 0.43 a solution?

SOLUTION

Left side: [2] [·] [1] [+] [·] [4] [3] [=] | 2.53

Right side: [2] [·] [9] [−] [·] [4] [3] [=] | 2.47

Since 2.53 > 2.47, 0.43 is not a solution.

Check whether the given number is a solution for the inequality.

1. $8.01 + t < 2t - 4.8$; 13 Yes   **2.** $7.64 - t > t + 3.18$; 2.25 No   **3.** $2t - 19.6 < t - 7.1$; 11.9 Yes

REVIEW CAPSULE FOR SECTION 5.4

Solve each equation. (Sections 3.4 and 3.5)

1. $6n + 5 - n = 14$ $n = 1\frac{4}{5}$ **2.** $-12t + 16 = -8 - 3t$ $t = 2\frac{2}{3}$ **3.** $4(w - 8) = 9w + 3$ $w = -7$

4. $1 - 5y = -3(y - 7)$ $y = -10$ **5.** $-6(2 - p) = 2(-3p + 4)$ $p = 1\frac{2}{3}$ **6.** $-\frac{1}{4}(8m - 4) = -\frac{1}{3}(12 + 3m)$ $m = 5$

5.4 Solving Inequalities

To solve an inequality in which the variable appears on both sides
To solve an inequality in which the variable appears on both sides and requires use of the Distributive Property

example 1

Solve: $4x + 2 - 5x < -12$

Solution:

$$4x + 2 - 5x < -12$$

1. Combine like terms. ⟶ $-x + 2 < -12$
2. Subtract 2 from each side. ⟶ $-x + 2 - 2 < -12 - 2$
3. Simplify. ⟶ $-x < -14$
4. Order Property of Opposites ⟶ $x > 14$

◀ The solution set is $\{x : x > 14\}$.

The variable often appears on both sides of an inequality.

example 2

Solve: $2x - 5 > 3x + 2$

Solution:

1. Subtract 2x from each side. ⟶ $2x - 5 - 2x > 3x + 2 - 2x$
2. Simplify. ⟶ $-5 > x + 2$
3. Subtract 2 from each side. ⟶ $-5 - 2 > x + 2 - 2$
4. Simplify. ⟶ $-7 > x$

◀ The solution set is $\{x : x < -7\}$.

example 3

Solve: $3(x - 3) < 2x + 1$

Solution:

1. Distributive Property ⟶ $3x - 9 < 2x + 1$
2. Subtract 2x from each side. ⟶ $3x - 9 - 2x < 2x + 1 - 2x$
3. Simplify. ⟶ $x - 9 < 1$
4. Add 9 to each side. ⟶ $x - 9 + 9 < 1 + 9$
5. Simplify. $x < 10$

◀ The solution set is $\{x : x < 10\}$.

example 4

Solve: $2x - 5 > 2(x + 3)$

Solution:

1. Distributive Property ⟶ $2x - 5 > 2x + 6$
2. Subtract 2x from each side. ⟶ $2x - 5 - 2x > 2x + 6 - 2x$
3. Simplify. ⟶ $-5 > 6$

◀ "$-5 > 6$" is false. The solution set is empty.

The inequality $-5 > 6$ is false. There is <u>no</u> replacement for x that will make $2x - 5 > 2(x + 3)$ true. The solution set is empty. (The symbol for the <u>empty</u> <u>set</u> is "ϕ".)

example 5 Solve: $3x + 7 - 2x > x - 3$

Solution:

1. Combine like terms. ⟶ $x + 7 > x - 3$
2. Subtract x from each side. ⟶ $x + 7 - x > x - 3 - x$
3. Simplify. ⟶ $7 > -3$

The inequality $7 > -3$ is true. Thus, $3x + 7 - 2x > x - 3$ is true for any number that replaces x. The solution set is {real numbers}.

CLASSROOM EXERCISES

See page 507 for the answers to the odd-numbered Classroom Exercises.

Write the inequality you get as the first step in solving each inequality in the Written Exercises. (Step 1 of Examples 1–5) 2. $8 > x - 3$ 4. $t + 7 < -9$ 6. $3\frac{1}{8} > -r - \frac{1}{4}$

8. $s - 2 - s < 2s - 8 - s$ 10. $\frac{2}{3}x - 5 + \frac{1}{3}x > -\frac{1}{3}x - 2 + \frac{1}{3}x$ 12. $1.2n - 3.6 - 0.2n < 0.2n + 5.1 - 0.2n$ 14. $x - 6 > 2x$

WRITTEN EXERCISES 16. $2x - \frac{3}{2} + \frac{1}{2} < x - 6$ 18. $10 - 5a > -3a - 7 - a$ 20. $3n - 12 >$
$^-n - 2 + 2n$

See the Teacher's Manual for the suggested assignments.

Goal: To solve an inequality in which the variable appears more than once

Sample Problem: $4x - 5 < 3(x + 2)$ **Answer:** $\{x : x < 11\}$

See page 507 for the answers to the odd-numbered Written Exercises.

Solve each inequality. (Examples 1–5)

1. $\{t : t < -16\}$ $-3 < -7x + 2 + 8x$
2. $8 > 4x - 3 - 3x$ $\{x : x < 11\}$
3. $3\frac{1}{2}a - 2 - 2\frac{1}{2}a < -7$

4. $-5\frac{1}{4}t + 7 + 6\frac{1}{4}t < -9$
5. $12y + \frac{1}{2} - 13y > -12\frac{1}{4}$
6. $3\frac{1}{8} > -7r - \frac{1}{4} + 6r$ See below.

7. $3w - 5 < 2w + 12$
8. $s - 2 < 2s - 8$ $\{s : s > 6\}$
9. $3\frac{1}{2}x - 2 > 2\frac{1}{2}x + 10$

10. $\frac{2}{3}x - 5 > -\frac{1}{3}x - 2$ $\{x : x > 3\}$
11. $0.6m - 0.7 < -0.4m + 0.2$
12. $1.2n - 3.6 < 0.2n + 5.1$
See below.

13. $3(-x + 2) < -5 - 2x$
14. $x - 6 > 2(x - 5)$ See below.
15. $5 - x < -2(x - 3) - 2$

16. $\frac{1}{2}(4x - 3) + \frac{1}{2} < x - 6$ See below.
17. $5y - 2 - 3y < \frac{1}{2}(6y - 8)$
18. $5(2 - a) > -3a - 7 - a$
See below.

19. $3a - 5 - 2a < a + 2$
20. $3(n - 4) > n - 2 + 2n$ ϕ
21. $5(x - 1) < 2x - 6 + 3x$

6. $\{r : r > -3\frac{3}{8}\}$ 12. $\{n : n < 8.7\}$ 14. $\{x : x < 4\}$ 16. $\{x : x < -5\}$ 18. $\{a : a < 17\}$

REVIEW CAPSULE FOR SECTION 5.5

Solve each equation. (Section 3.2)

1. $\frac{3}{4}x = 27$ $x = 36$
2. $\frac{8}{7}n = -96$ $n = -84$
3. $-12 = -\frac{1}{5}t$ $t = 60$
4. $\frac{r}{-6} = 2\frac{2}{3}$ $r = -16$

5. $-0.8 = \frac{w}{7}$ $w = -5.6$
6. $4p = -22$ $p = -5\frac{1}{2}$
7. $-3q = -12\frac{3}{5}$ $q = 4\frac{1}{5}$
8. $0.3s = -7.8$
$s = -26$

5.5 Multiplication and Division

To solve inequalities of the forms $ax > b$ or $ax < b$ by the Division Property of Inequalities

P-1 **For each inequality below, what inequality do you get if each side is multiplied by $\frac{1}{2}$?**

    a. $-4 < 6$ **b.** $-2 > -10$ **c.** $3 > -8$ **d.** $-12 < 0$

      $-2 < 3$ $-1 > -5$ $\frac{3}{2} > -4$ $-6 < 0$

P-2 **What happens if each side of an inequality is multiplied by 0?**

Each side becomes zero.

Consider a case in which each side of an inequality is multiplied by a negative number. Start with $-3 < 7$.

$$-3 \ < \ 7$$

1⃞ Multiply each side by -2.   ⟶ $-2(-3) \ \underline{\ ? \ } \ -2(7)$

2⃞ Simplify.   ————————⟶ $6 \ \underline{\ ? \ } \ -14$

P-3 **Should __?__ be replaced by $<$ or $>$?**   by $>$

Multiplication Property for Inequalities

If each side of an inequality is multiplied by the same nonzero real number, an equivalent inequality is obtained as follows.

1. The direction of the inequality is unchanged when each side is multiplied by the same positive number.
2. The direction of the inequality is reversed when each side is multiplied by the same negative number.

$\frac{1}{2}x > 12$
$2(\frac{1}{2}x) > 2(12)$
$x > 24$

$-\frac{2}{3}x < 6$
$-\frac{3}{2}(-\frac{2}{3}x) > -\frac{3}{2}(6)$
$x > -9$

Students tend to forget to reverse the inequality when multiplying each side by a negative number.

P-4 **What do you multiply each side of these inequalities by to get the variable alone?**

    a. $\frac{1}{2}x > 3$ 2   **b.** $-\frac{1}{3}x < 8$ -3 **c.** $\frac{4}{5}x > 9$ $\frac{5}{4}$ **d.** $-\frac{2}{3}x > 10$ $-\frac{3}{2}$

example 1

Solve: $-\frac{2}{3}x > 10$ The reciprocal of $-\frac{2}{3}$ is $-\frac{3}{2}$.

Solution:

1⃞ Multiply each side by $-\frac{3}{2}$. ⟶ $-\frac{3}{2}(-\frac{2}{3}x) < -\frac{3}{2}(10)$

2⃞ Simplify. ————————⟶ $x < -15$ Solution set: $\{x : x < -15\}$

P-5 For each inequality below, what inequality do you get if each side is divided by 3?   by -3?

a. $3x < 9$
$x < 3; -x > -3$

b. $-6x > 6$
$-2x > 2; 2x < -2$

c. $12x < -3$
$4x < -1; -4x > 1$

d. $-15x < 1$
$-5x < \frac{1}{3}; 5x > -\frac{1}{3}$

Division Property for Inequalities

If each side of an inequality is divided by the same nonzero real number, an equivalent inequality is obtained as follows.

1. The direction of the inequality is unchanged when each side is divided by the same positive number.
2. The direction of the inequality is reversed when each side is divided by the same negative number.

$5x < 15$

$\dfrac{5x}{5} < \dfrac{15}{5}$

$x < 3$

$-3x > 9$

$\dfrac{-3x}{-3} < \dfrac{9}{-3}$

$x < -3$

---

example 2

Solve: $3x < 15$

This can also be solved by multiplying each side by $\frac{1}{3}$.

Solution:

1. Divide each side by 3. ⟶ $\dfrac{3x}{3} < \dfrac{15}{3}$

2. Simplify. ⟶ $x < 5$ Solution set: $\{x : x < 5\}$

---

example 3

Solve: $-5x < 20$

This can also be solved by multiplying each side by -5.

Solution:

1. Divide each side by -5. ⟶ $\dfrac{-5x}{-5} > \dfrac{20}{-5}$

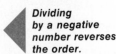

Dividing by a negative number reverses the order.

2. Simplify. ⟶ $x > -4$ Solution set: $\{x : x > -4\}$

CLASSROOM EXERCISES

Multiply each side by 5. Then write an equivalent inequality.
(P-1, Multiplication Property for Inequalities)

1. $x > 2$ $5x > 10$ **2.** $y < -3$ $5y < -15$ **3.** $2a > 10$ $10a > 50$ **4.** $\frac{1}{5}t < \frac{3}{5}$
$t < 3$

Multiply each side by −3. Then write an equivalent inequality.
(Step 1 of Example 1, Multiplication Property for Inequalities)

5. $y > 2$ $-3y < -6$　　**6.** $s < -5$　$-3s > 15$　　**7.** $-\frac{1}{3}r < 2$ $r > -6$　　**8.** $-\frac{1}{3}y > -10$ $y < 30$

Write the number you would multiply or divide each side by to get the variable by itself. (Step 1 of Examples 1–3)

9. $2x < 1$ Divide by 2.　**10.** $-\frac{1}{2}x > \frac{2}{3}$ Multiply by −2.　**11.** $-\frac{3}{2}x < 0.6$ Multiply by $-\frac{2}{3}$.　**12.** $-0.6x > 15$ Divide by −0.6; or Multiply by $-\frac{5}{3}$.

To form pairs of equivalent inequalities, indicate if < or > should be used as the missing symbol. (P-1, P-3, P-5, Multiplication or Division Property for Inequalities)

13. $5y > 35$; y __?__ 7 $>$　　　　　　**14.** $\frac{1}{2}t < -1$; -2 __?__ t $>$

15. $-3 > -\frac{1}{3}x$; 9 __?__ x $<$　　　　**16.** $2 < -0.1y$; y __?__ -20 $<$

WRITTEN EXERCISES

See the Teacher's Manual for the suggested assignments.

Goal: To solve an inequality using the Multiplication or Division Property for Inequalities

Sample Problems: a. $-\frac{3}{4}x > 12$　　**b.** $4x < -8$

Answers: a. $\{x : x < -16\}$　　**b.** $\{x : x < -2\}$　　12. $\{y : y > 6\}$　　16. $\{t : t > \frac{12}{5}\}$

Solve. (Examples 1–3)

$\{t : t < 2\}$

1. $3y < 15$ $\{y : y < 5\}$　　**2.** $5y > 30$ $\{y : y > 6\}$　　**3.** $\frac{1}{4}t > -5$ $\{t : t > -20\}$　　**4.** $-10t > -20$

5. $-7r < 21$ $\{r : r > -3\}$　**6.** $\frac{1}{3} < -\frac{1}{6}y$ $\{y : y < -2\}$　**7.** $\frac{1}{2} > -\frac{1}{4}x$ $\{x : x > -2\}$　**8.** $\frac{1}{2}x < -8$ $\{x : x < -16\}$

9. $\frac{2}{3}w < -4$ $\{w : w < -6\}$　**10.** $\frac{3}{5}p > -9$ $\{p : p > -15\}$　**11.** $|-\frac{1}{2}|x < |-3|$ $\{x : x < 6\}$　**12.** $|-\frac{1}{3}|y > |-2|$ See above.

13. $-\frac{4}{3}q > 12$ $\{q : q < -9\}$　**14.** $-\frac{8}{7}b < 16$ $\{b : b > -14\}$　**15.** $-3x > 11$ $\{x : x < -\frac{11}{3}\}$　**16.** $-5t < -12$ See above.

17. $0.6n < -6$　　　**18.** $-0.9m > 18$　　　**19.** $-4.5 < 1.5x$　　　**20.** $3.4 > -17y$
$\{n : n < -10\}$　　　$\{m : m < -20\}$　　　$\{x : x > -3\}$　　　$\{y : y > -0.2\}$

REVIEW CAPSULE FOR SECTION 5.6

Solve each equation. (Section 3.3)

1. $10x - 3 = 17$ $x = 2$　　**2.** $-14 = 6n + 10$ $n = -4$　　**3.** $8t = 6t - 15$ $t = -7\frac{1}{2}$

4. $18 - t = -5t$ $t = -4\frac{1}{2}$　　**5.** $\frac{3}{8}p - \frac{1}{8} = \frac{3}{4} - \frac{1}{2}p$ $p = 1$　　**6.** $-\frac{2}{3}r - \frac{1}{6} = \frac{5}{6}r + \frac{1}{3}$ $r = -\frac{1}{3}$

7. $-3(\frac{5}{12}y - \frac{5}{6}) = \frac{3}{8}y - \frac{1}{4}$ $y = 1\frac{9}{13}$　　　**8.** $-\frac{3}{4}m + \frac{5}{2} = -5(\frac{4}{5} - \frac{3}{10}m)$ $m = 2\frac{8}{9}$

5.6　Problem Solving with Inequalities

To solve inequalities of the forms $ax + b < c$ and $ax + b > c$
To solve inequalities of the forms $ax - b < c$ and $ax - b > c$
To solve a word problem by writing and solving a related inequality

Point out to students that solving inequalities is analogous to solving equations.

When you multiply each side of an inequality by a positive number to get the variable alone, you are using the same steps as you used to solve an equation.

example 1　Solve: $3x - 2 < 10$

Solution:

1　Add 2 to each side. ⟶ $3x - 2 + 2 < 10 + 2$

2　Simplify. ⟶ $3x < 12$

3　Multiply by the reciprocal of 3. ⟶ $\frac{1}{3}(3x) < \frac{1}{3}(12)$

4　Simplify. ⟶ $x < 4$

The solution set is $\{x : x < 4\}$.

P-1　**Why is the order symbol "<" not reversed in any of the steps in Example 1?** The order of an inequality is unchanged if each side is multiplied by a positive number.

In solving inequalities, use the Addition and Subtraction Properties for Inequalities before the Multiplication and Division Properties.

example 2　Solve: $-11 > -\frac{1}{3}x + 5$

Solution:

1　Subtract 5 from each side. ⟶ $-11 - 5 > -\frac{1}{3}x + 5 - 5$

2　Simplify. ⟶ $-16 > -\frac{1}{3}x$

3　Multiply each side by -3. ⟶ $-3(-16) < -3(-\frac{1}{3}x)$

◄ *−3 is the reciprocal of $-\frac{1}{3}$.*

4　Simplify. ⟶ $48 < x$

The solution set is $\{x : x > 48\}$.

P-2　**Why must the order be reversed in Step　3 ?**
Each side is multiplied by a negative number.

P-3　**Why was −3 chosen in Step　3 ?**
−3 is the reciprocal of $-\frac{1}{3}$, the coefficient of x.

example 3

One less than five times a number is less than the same number increased by 3. For what set of numbers is this statement true?

Solution:

Let $x =$ any number in the set.
Then $5x - 1 =$ one less than five times the number.
$x + 3 =$ the number increased by 3.

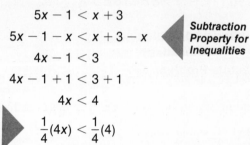

$$5x - 1 < x + 3$$
$$5x - 1 - x < x + 3 - x$$

Subtraction Property for Inequalities

$$4x - 1 < 3$$
$$4x - 1 + 1 < 3 + 1$$
$$4x < 4$$

Multiplication Property for Inequalities

$$\frac{1}{4}(4x) < \frac{1}{4}(4)$$

$$x < 1 \qquad \text{The solution set is } \{x : x < 1\}.$$

P-4 **What is the solution set of the inequality in a below? in b?**

$\{$real numbers$\}$; the empty set, ϕ

a

$2(3 - 2x) > x - 1 - 5x$
$6 - 4x > -1 - 4x$
$6 - 4x + 4x > -1 - 4x + 4x$
$6 > -1$

b

$-\frac{1}{2}x - \frac{1}{3} + \frac{3}{4}x > \frac{3}{8}x + 1 - \frac{1}{8}x$
$-\frac{1}{3} + \frac{1}{4}x > \frac{2}{8}x + 1$
$-\frac{1}{3} + \frac{1}{4}x - \frac{1}{4}x > \frac{1}{4}x + 1 - \frac{1}{4}x$
$-\frac{1}{3} > 1$

The steps in **a** lead to a true sentence. The solution set is {real numbers}. The steps in **b** lead to a false sentence. Its solution set is the empty set, ϕ.

CLASSROOM EXERCISES

Write the equivalent sentence you get as the first step in solving each inequality. (Step 1 of Examples 1 and 2)

1. $2x + 1 > 3$ $2x > 2$

2. $-3x + 4 < -2$ $-3x < -6$

3. $\frac{1}{2}x - 3 < -7$ $\frac{1}{2}x < -4$

4. $-\frac{2}{3}x + 1 > \frac{3}{4}$ $-\frac{2}{3}x > -\frac{1}{4}$

5. $-12 < 3 - 5x$ $-15 < -5x$

6. $9.3 < -4.8 + 3x$ $14.1 < 3x$

7. $3x + 2 < x - 3$ $2x + 2 < -3$

8. $5 - 2x > 4x - 3$ $5 > 6x - 3$

9. $\frac{1}{2}x - 6 > \frac{3}{2}x + 4$ $-6 > x + 4$

Solve. (Examples 1 and 2)

10. $-2x + 2 < 4 \{x : x > -1\}$ **11.** $3x - 6 > -12 \{x : x > -2\}$ **12.** $\frac{1}{3}x + 1 > -2 \{x : x > -9\}$

15. $\{x : x > -2\}$

13. $-\frac{1}{2}x < 5 \{x : x > -10\}$ **14.** $3x - 1 > 5 \{x : x > 2\}$ **15.** $1 - 2x < -x + 3$ See above.

16. $2x + 3 < 5 \{x : x < 1\}$ **17.** $3x + 4 < 3x - 2 \ \phi$ **18.** $2.3x - 3 < 5 + 2.3x$ $\{\text{real numbers}\}$

WRITTEN EXERCISES

See the Teacher's Manual for the suggested assignments.

Goal: To solve an inequality using at least two of the Properties of Inequalities

Sample Problem: $2x - 1 < 5$ **Answer:** $\{x : x < 3\}$

Solve. Show the steps. (Examples 1 and 2)

1. $3x - 1 < 7 \ \{x : x < \frac{8}{3}\}$

2. $5x + 3 < 28 \ \{x : x < 5\}$

3. $-10 > 2x + 3 \ \{x : x < -\frac{13}{2}\}$

4. $-12 > 2x - 5 \ \{x : x < -\frac{7}{2}\}$

5. $-\frac{1}{2}y - 3 < -7 \ \{y : y > 8\}$

6. $-\frac{1}{3}a + 1 > -10 \ \{a : a < 33\}$

7. $3b + 7 < 5b \ \{b : b > \frac{7}{2}\}$

8. $2 - 2n < -n \ \{n : n > 2\}$

9. $2m - 5 > 5m + 1 \ \{m : m < -2\}$

10. $5t + 3 < 3t - 4 \ \{t : t < -\frac{7}{2}\}$

11. $3x + 2 - 8x < 3 \ \{x : x > -\frac{1}{5}\}$

12. $-p - 2 - 3p > -1 \ \{p : p < -\frac{1}{4}\}$

13. $\frac{4}{3}q - \frac{1}{2} > \frac{7}{2} + \frac{2}{3}q \ \{q : q > 6\}$

14. $\frac{3}{5}r + \frac{5}{3} < -\frac{1}{3} + \frac{1}{5}r \ \{r : r < -5\}$

15. $-2(3x - 3) < 6 \ \{x : x > 0\}$

16. $-3 > \frac{1}{2}(-4x - 6) \ \{x : x > 0\}$

17. $-3x + \frac{1}{2} + x < -\frac{1}{2}(4x + 1) \ \phi$

18. $-5(2x - 3) > 3 - 9x - x \{\text{real numbers}\}$

19. $-2(\frac{1}{2}x - \frac{1}{4}) < -\frac{1}{4}x + 1 - \frac{3}{4}x \{\text{real numbers}\}$

20. $6(3 - \frac{1}{3}x) < -\frac{1}{4}(8x + 1) \ \phi$

Solve each problem. (Example 3)

21. If 1 is added to three times a number, the sum is less than twice that number. For what set of numbers is this statement true? $\{x : x < -1\}$

22. If 1 is subtracted from five times a number, the result is greater than 15. For what set of number is this statement true? $\{x : x > 3\frac{1}{5}\}$

23. The sum of two consecutive whole numbers is less than 5. What values may the lesser of the two numbers have? 0 or 1

24. The sum of two consecutive even negative integers is greater than -7. What value may the lesser of the two numbers have? -4

Compound Interest

It is popular today for lending institutions to pay interest that is **compounded daily**. This means that interest earned each day is added to the principal to compute the succeeding day's interest.

The following formula can be used to calculate the amount of principal and accrued interest on one dollar invested for n days at an annual rate of 12% compounded daily.

$$A = (1.0003333)^n$$

The above formula is used to construct a table for computing the interest on one dollar earned after a certain number of days. Here are selected lines from the table.

DAILY COMPOUNDING		ANNUAL RATE 12%	
Days	Factor	Days	Factor
10	0.0033383	50	0.0168035
20	0.0066878	60	0.0201979
30	0.0100485	70	0.0236037
40	0.0134204	80	0.0270208

EXAMPLE: Find the interest earned in 30 days on an investment of $4800 at an annual rate of 12% with daily compounding.

SOLUTION: Multiply $4800 by the appropriate factor from the table.

$$(0.0100485)(4800) = \$48.23$$

In the formula, $(1.0003333)^n$ is an approximation of $(1 + \frac{0.12}{360})^n$. (Many banks use a 360-day year to calculate interest.) The factors in the table can be approximately verified using a calculator. See page 21.

EXERCISES

Find the interest earned for each investment after the given number of days at an annual rate of 12% with daily compounding.

1. $650 after 20 days $4.35
2. $1750 after 80 days $47.29
3. $12,700 after 50 days $213.40
4. $8650 after 60 days $174.71
5. $22,350 after 30 days $224.59
6. $158,000 after 10 days $527.45
7. $643,000 after 70 days $15,177.18
8. $6,000,000 after 20 days $40,126.80

Special Topic Application

CHAPTER SUMMARY

IMPORTANT TERMS	Graph *(p. 100)* Inequality *(p. 100)* Solution set *(p. 100)* Empty set *(p. 112)* Domain of a variable *(p. 100)*

IMPORTANT IDEAS

1. *Comparison Property:* If a and b are real numbers, then exactly one of the following is true: $a > b$, $a = b$, or $a < b$.

2. *Order Property of Opposites:* If a and b are real numbers and $a < b$, then $-a > -b$.

3. *Transitive Property of Order:* If $a < b$ and $b < c$, then $a < c$.

4. *Addition Property for Inequalities:* Adding the same real number to each side of an inequality does not change the direction of the inequality. The new inequality is equivalent to the first.

5. *Subtraction Property for Inequalities:* Subtracting the same real number from each side of an inequality does not change the direction of the inequality. The new inequality is equivalent to the first.

6. *Multiplication Property for Inequalities:* If each side of an inequality is multiplied by the same nonzero real number, an equivalent inequality is obtained as follows.
   a. The direction of the inequality is unchanged if each side is multiplied by the same positive number.
   b. The direction of the inequality is reversed if each side is multiplied by the same negative number.

7. *Division Property for Inequalities:* If each side of an inequality is divided by the same nonzero real number, an equivalent inequality is obtained as follows.
   a. The direction of the inequality is unchanged if each side is divided by the same positive number.
   b. The direction of the inequality is reversed if each side is divided by the same negative number.

CHAPTER REVIEW

NOTE: The Teacher's Resource Book contains two forms of each Chapter Test.

SECTION 5.1

Write a set description of each solution set that is graphed. Show the domain that you are assuming, if necessary.

1. 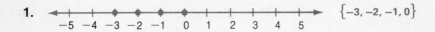 $\left\{-3, -2, -1, 0\right\}$

2.  $\left\{x : x \geqslant -1\right\}$; $\left\{\text{integers}\right\}$

3.

$\{x : x < 1\frac{1}{2}\}$; $\{$real numbers$\}$

4.

$\{x : x \geqslant -\frac{1}{2}\}$; $\{$real numbers$\}$

Draw a graph of each set. For Ex. 5-10, the graphs are described as points on a number line.

5. $\{x : x < 5\}$; Domain = $\{$whole numbers$\}$ **6.** $\{x : x < -2\}$; Domain = $\{$integers$\}$
   the points 4, 3, 2, 1, 0   the points −3, −4, −5, −6, etc.

7. $\{x : x > -3\}$ **8.** $\{x : x > 1\}$ **9.** $\{x : x < 4\}$ **10.** $\{x : x < -1\}$

All points to the right of, and not including, −3   All points to the right of, and not including, 1   All points to the left of, and not including, 4   All points to the left of, and not including, −1

SECTION 5.2

Write a new inequality by applying the Order Property of Opposites.

11. $r < -12$ $-r > 12$ **12.** $x > -8$ $-x < 8$ **13.** $a > -3$ $-a < 3$ **14.** $-4.5 < t$ $4.5 > -t$

15. $-x > -4.2$ $x < 4.2$ **16.** $3\frac{1}{4} > -t$ $-3\frac{1}{4} < t$ **17.** $-1 > -x$ $1 < x$ **18.** $k < -n$ $-k > n$

19. If $a \geq b$ is false, what is the order of a and b? $a < b$

20. If $-b < c$ and $-c > a$, what is the order of b and a? $a < b$

Write True or False for each sentence.

21. If $a < -5$ and $-5 < b$, then $a < b$.   True

22. If $a > 6$ and $6 > b$, then $a < b$.   False

SECTION 5.3

Write Yes or No to show whether the two inequalities are equivalent.

23. $x + 3 < 5$; $x + 1 < 7$ No   **24.** $x - 4 < 10$; $x - 5 < 9$ Yes

25. $-5 > 2x - 2$; $-7 > 2x$ No   **26.** $5x - 8 > 2$; $5x > 10$ Yes

27. $2a - 7 > -2$; $2a > 5$ Yes   **28.** $3b - 1 < b + 7$; $3b - 2 < b + 8$ No

Write the solution set of each inequality by applying the Addition or Subtraction Property for Inequalities.

29. $x - 3 < -2$ $\{x : x < 1\}$ **30.** $x + 9 > -3$ $\{x : x > -12\}$ **31.** $-4 + x < -6$ $\{x : x < -2\}$

32. $-8 + x > -10$ $\{x : x > -2\}$ **33.** $-8.3 > 1.4 + x$ $\{x : x < -9.7\}$ **34.** $5.6 < x - 3.9$ $\{x : x > 9.5\}$

SECTION 5.4

Solve.

35. $4x + 3 - 3x < -5$ $x < -8$

36. $3 > 5x + 7 - 4x$ $x < -4$

37. $3x - 5 > 2(x + 3)$ $x > 11$

38. $3(2x - 1) < x - 2 + 4x$ $x < 1$

SECTION 5.5

Solve.

39. $4x < 30$ $x < 7\frac{1}{2}$

40. $8x > -20$ $x > -2\frac{1}{2}$

41. $-9x > 45$ $x < -5$

42. $-5x < -60$ $x > 12$

43. $-6 < -\frac{3}{2}x$ $x < 4$

44. $\frac{1}{2} > -\frac{1}{4}x$ $x > -2$

SECTION 5.6

Solve.

45. $0.3 - 0.6x < 1.4x - 2.9$ $x > 1.6$

46. $3.2x - 1.1 > 0.2x + 1.3$ $x > 0.8$

47. $x - 19 > 12 - 2x$ $x > 10\frac{1}{3}$

48. $2x - 5 + 3x < -x + 7$ $x < 2$

49. $-2 + 3x > 3(1 + x)$ ϕ

50. $2x - 4 + x < -1 + 3x$ $\{\text{real numbers}\}$

CHAPTER

6 Relations and Functions

Sections   6.1   **Graphs of Ordered Pairs**

6.2   **Points and Ordered Pairs**

6.3   **Relations**

6.4   **Functions**

6.5   **Graphs of Functions**

6.6   **Problem Solving: Using Functions**

Features   *Calculator Exercises:* **Magic Squares**

Career: **Air Conditioning Technician**

Review and Testing   *Review Capsules*

Mid-Chapter Review

Chapter Review

Cumulative Review: **Chapters 1-6**

6.1 Graphs of Ordered Pairs

To write the integral coordinates of a point from a graph of the point

NOTE: Computer programming section A-5 on pages 488-489 can be studied any time after Chapter 6 has been studied. All computer programming sections are optional.

Figure 1 shows two intersecting real-number lines and two points, P and Q. The horizontal line is the **X axis**, and the vertical line is the **Y axis**. The point O where the two lines meet is called the **origin**.

P-1   **On the X axis, what direction is positive?   negative?**   Right   Left

P-2   **On the Y axis, what direction is positive?   negative?**   Up   Down

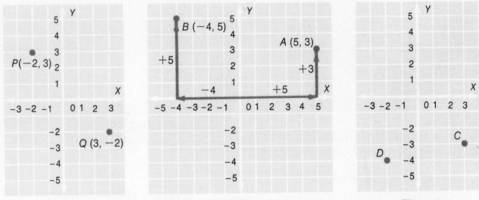

Figure 1   Figure 2   Figure 3

The pair of real numbers (−2, 3) are the **coordinates** of point P in Figure 1. Their order is important. For that reason they are called an **ordered pair.**

P-3   **What is the first coordinate of point Q in Figure 1? 3 the second coordinate of point Q?   −2**

P-4   **How does Figure 1 show that (−2, 3) and (3, −2) are not the same?**
They do not have the same location.

example 1

In Figure 2, locate A(5, 3).   ◀ A(5, 3) is the Point A which corresponds to the ordered pair (5, 3).

Solution:

1. Start at 0, and move five units to the <u>right</u> along the X axis.

2. Next, move <u>up</u> three units in a direction parallel to the Y axis.

P-5   **Why is the move of five units made along the X axis?**
The first number is x.

P-6 **Why do you move five units to the <u>right</u>?** The first coordinate, 5, is positive.

P-7 **Why is the second move of three units <u>up</u> and not <u>down</u>?** The second coordinate, 3, is positive.

example 2   Locate B(−4, 5) in Figure 2.

Solution:
⬜1 Start at 0, and move four units to the <u>left</u> along the X axis.

◄ **Left because the first coordinate is negative.**

⬜2 Next, move five units <u>up</u> in a direction parallel to the Y axis.

example 3   Write the ordered pair that corresponds to point C in Figure 3.

Solution:

⬜1 Start at the origin.

⬜2 Move to the right, directly over point C.

◄ **Right means a positive coordinate.**

⬜3 Write the first coordinate, 3.

⬜4 Move down, counting the units.

◄ **Down means a negative coordinate.**

⬜5 Write the second coordinate, −3.

P-8 **To name the ordered pair that corresponds to point D, what move do you make first? What is the first coordinate?** Start at 0, and move left 2 units along the x axis; −2

P-9 **What is the second move?   the second coordinate?** Down 4 units, parallel to the y axis; −4

P-10 **What is the ordered pair for point D?** (−2, −4)

CLASSROOM EXERCISES   For Exercises 1-10, the moves described locate the desired points. Always start at the origin.

Write the two moves needed to locate the point corresponding to each ordered pair. (Examples 1 and 2)

Right 3, Down 2	Left 10, Down 3	Left 3, Up 7	Right 5, Up 5	Right 7, Down 1
1. (3, −2)	**2.** (−10, −3)	**3.** (−3, 7)	**4.** (5, 5)	**5.** (7, −1)

Right 10, Down 10	Right 8, Up 3	Right 1, Down 1	Left 3, Down 3	Left 5, Up 5
6. (10, −10)	**7.** (8, 3)	**8.** (1, −1)	**9.** (−3, −3)	**10.** (−5, 5)

Tell the ordered pair that corresponds to each point. (Example 3, P-8, P-9)

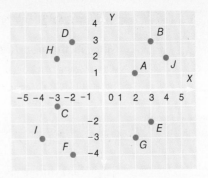

11. A (2, 1)   **12.** B (3, 3)

13. C (−3, −1)   **14.** D (−2, 3)

15. E (3, −2)   **16.** F (−2, −4)

17. G (2, −3)   **18.** H (−3, 2)

19. I (−4, −3)   **20.** J (4, 2)

WRITTEN EXERCISES

See the Teacher's Manual for the suggested assignments.

Goals: To locate the point that corresponds to a given ordered pair of integers, and to name the ordered pair that corresponds to a given point

Sample Problems: a. Locate $G(4, -1)$ **b.** Name the ordered pair for Z in Figure 4 below.

Answers: a. Move four units right, one unit down, and draw the point. Label it $G(4, -1)$.   **b.** (−5, 4)

For Ex. 1-12, the moves described locate the desired points. Always start at the origin.

Draw an X axis and Y axis on graph paper. Locate the point corresponding to each of the following. Name it with the capital letter. (Examples 1 and 2)

1. $A(1, 4)$ Right 1, Up 4   **2.** $B(5, 2)$ Right 5, Up 2   **3.** $C(-5, 3)$ Left 5, Up 3   **4.** $D(-2, 4)$ Left 2, Up 4

5. $E(6, -1)$ Right 6, Down 1   **6.** $F(3, -5)$ Right 3, Down 5   **7.** $G(-4, -1)$ Left 4, Down 1   **8.** $H(-2, -5)$ See below.

9. $I(-4, -4)$ Left 4, Down 4   **10.** $J(-5, 5)$ Left 5, Up 5   **11.** $K(3, 3)$ Right 3, Up 3   **12.** $L(2, -2)$ Right 2, Down 2

8. Left 2, Down 5

Write the ordered pair that corresponds to each point. (Example 3)

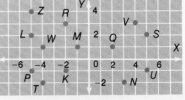

	(−5, −1)	(2, 1)	(−2, 3)	(5, 2)	(−4, −2)	(5, −1)
	13. P	**14.** Q	**15.** R	**16.** S	**17.** T	**18.** U
	19. V	**20.** W	**21.** M	**22.** N	**23.** K	**24.** L
	(4, 3)	(−4, 1)	(−1, 1)	(3, −2)	(−2, −1)	(−5, 2)

Figure 4

REVIEW CAPSULE FOR SECTION 6.2

Name the two consecutive integers that each number is between.

EXAMPLE: −1.6   **SOLUTION:** $-2 < -1.6$; $-1.6 < -1$;   The integers are −2 and −1.

1. $-3\frac{1}{4}$ **2.** $5\frac{7}{8}$ **3.** −0.9   **4.** −3.08   **5.** $-\pi$ **6.** $-\sqrt{3}$

−3 and −4   5 and 6   −1 and 0   −3 and −4   −3 and −4   −2 and −1

6.2 Points and Ordered Pairs

OBJECTIVE: To graph a point having real-number coordinates

The plane of Figure 1 is called a **coordinate plane**. Any point of the coordinate plane may be represented as an ordered pair of real numbers (x, y).

The four regions in Figure 1 are called **quadrants**. Both x and y are positive real numbers for each point in quadrant I. In quadrant II, x is negative, and y is positive.

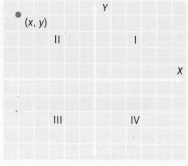

Figure 1

P-1   **How can you describe the ordered pair of coordinates corresponding to each point in quadrant III? in quadrant IV?** *x negative, y negative; x positive, y negative*

example 1 Graph $A(3\frac{1}{2}, 5)$.

Solution: [1] Start at the origin, and move three and one-half units to the <u>right</u> on the X axis.

[2] Move <u>up</u> five units parallel to the Y axis. ◀ **See Figure 2.**

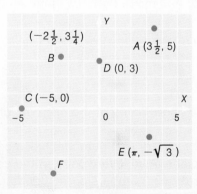

Figure 2

P-2   **To locate $B(-2\frac{1}{2}, 3\frac{1}{4})$ in Figure 2 what move is made first?**
Start at 0 and move $2\frac{1}{2}$ units left.

P-3   **What move is made to represent the y value?**
Move $3\frac{1}{4}$ units up, parallel to the y axis.

Relations and Functions / **127**

example 2

Graph $C(-5, 0)$.

A coordinate of 0 indicates no motion.

Give special attention to Examples 2 and 3. Students are prone to make mistakes when 0 is one of the coordinates.

Solution:
1. Start at 0 and move five units to the left.

2. Do not move up or down.

Point C is on the X axis.

C is between quadrants II and III.
(Figure 2, p. 127)

example 3

Graph $D(0, 3)$.

Solution:
1. Start at 0 and do not move to the left or right.

2. Move up three units.

Point D is on the Y axis.

D is between quadrants I and II.
(Figure 2, p. 127)

example 4

Graph $E(\pi, -\sqrt{3})$.
Use approximate values of π and $-\sqrt{3}$.

$$\pi \approx 3.1 \qquad -\sqrt{3} \approx -1.7$$

The symbol "$\approx$" means "is approximately equal to."

Solution:
1. Start at 0 and move right 3.1 units.

2. Move down 1.7 units.

See Figure 2.

P-4 **What are the coordinates of the origin? of point F on page 127?**

$(0, 0)$ $(-3, -4)$

Every ordered pair of real numbers has a corresponding point in the coordinate plane. Also, every point in the coordinate plane has an ordered pair of real numbers corresponding to it.

> There is a one-to-one correspondence between points of a coordinate plane and ordered pairs of real numbers.

CLASSROOM EXERCISES

Write the quadrant in which each point lies. (Figure 1)

1. $A(-2, 7)$ II

2. $B(-5, -6)$ III

3. $C(1.7, 2.9)$ I

4. $D(3\frac{1}{2}, -5)$ IV

Locate each point. (Examples 2 and 3)

5. $E(0, -5)$ On the y axis, 5 units down from the origin

6. $F(10, 0)$ On the x axis, 10 units to the right of the origin

7. $G(-5\frac{1}{2}, 0)$ On the x axis, $5\frac{1}{2}$ units to the left of the origin

8. $H(0, 2.7)$ On the y axis, 2.7 units above the origin

WRITTEN EXERCISES

See the Teacher's Manual for the suggested assignments.

Goal: To graph points with real-number coordinates

Sample Problem: Graph $P(2\frac{1}{4}, -1\frac{1}{2})$. **Answer:**

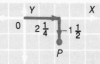

For Ex. 1-20, each point may be located by the directions following each coordinate pair. Always start at the origin. Note that in Ex. 9-12 and 15, there is only one move to locate each point.

Represent a coordinate plane on graph paper. Graph the point that corresponds to each ordered pair. Label each point. (Examples 1-4)

1. $(4\frac{1}{2}, 3)$ Right $4\frac{1}{2}$, Up 3

2. $(2\frac{1}{2}, 5)$ Right $2\frac{1}{2}$, Up 5

3. $(-2, -4\frac{1}{2})$ Left 2, Down $4\frac{1}{2}$

4. $(4, -3\frac{1}{2})$ Right 4, Down $3\frac{1}{2}$

5. $(-2\frac{3}{4}, 4\frac{1}{4})$ Left $2\frac{3}{4}$, Up $4\frac{1}{4}$

6. $(-3\frac{2}{3}, -4\frac{1}{2})$ Left $3\frac{2}{3}$, Down $4\frac{1}{2}$

7. $(-3.5, 2.2)$ Left 3.5, Up 2.2

8. $(1.7, -2.5)$ Right 1.7, Down 2.5

9. $Q(0, 4)$ Up 4

10. $R(5, 0)$ Right 5

11. $R(-3\frac{1}{2}, 0)$ Left $3\frac{1}{2}$

12. $U(0, -5\frac{1}{2})$ Down $5\frac{1}{2}$

Graph these points in the same coordinate plane. (Examples 1-4)

13. $A(-6, -2)$ Left 6, Down 2

14. $E(9, 3)$ Right 9, Up 3

15. $B(0, -2)$ Down 2

16. $F(3, 3)$ Right 3, Up 3

17. $C(-1, 2)$ Left 1, Down 2

18. $G(3, -3)$ Right 3, Down 3

19. $D(-7, 2)$ Left 7, Up 2

20. $H(9, -3)$ Right 9, Down 3

21. Connect points A and B, B and C, C and D, and D and A with line segments. What name is given to this geometric figure? parallelogram

22. Connect points E and F, F and G, G and H, and H and E with line segments. What kind of figure do you get? square

REVIEW CAPSULE FOR SECTION 6.3

In each formula, find the value for y corresponding to the value of x. (Section 6.1)

1. $y = -x + \frac{3}{4}$ when $x = -\frac{1}{2}$ $\frac{5}{4}$

2. $y = x^2 - x + 3$ when $x = \frac{1}{2}$ $2\frac{3}{4}$

3. $y = -x^2 - 5$ when $x = -5$ -30

4. $y = |x - 1.2|$ when $x = -0.9$ 2.1

6.3 Relations

To graph a relation when its roster form is given
To graph a relation when its rule and a set of x values is given

P-1 **What are the coordinates of the six points graphed at the right?** (2, 1), (0, 1), (−2, 1), (2, −1), (0, −1), (2, −1)

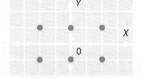

Y

X

0

Coordinates of these points are elements of set A below.

A = {(2, 1), (2, −1), (0, 1), (0, −1), (−2, 1), (−2, −1)}

Elements of set A are ordered pairs.

Set A is a <u>relation</u>.

You may want to give other examples of relations besides "number" relations, e.g. (city, state).

> A **relation** is a set of ordered pairs.

P-2 **What are the unknown y values in the table at the right using the formula y = 2x − 1?**

The <u>formula</u> y = 2x − 1 describes a relation. This relation can also be described by a <u>table</u>, in <u>roster form</u>, and by a <u>graph</u>.

x	y
−2	? −5
−1	? −3
0	? −1
1	? 1
2	? 3

Table

Note the various ways in which relations can be described.

x	−2	−1	0	1	2
y	−5	−3	−1	1	3

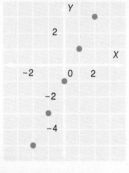

Roster

S = {(−2, −5), (−1, −3), (0, −1), (1, 1), (2, 3)}

Relation S can be shown by a <u>set description</u>.

S = {(x, y) : y = 2x − 1}

Read, "The set of ordered pairs (x, y) such that y = 2x − 1."

example 1

Write relation T in roster form if the x values are −2, −1, 0, 1, and 2.

$$T = \{(x, y) : y = x^2 + 1\}$$

Read, "The set of ordered pairs (x, y) such that y = x² + 1."

Solution:

x	y
−2	?
−1	?
0	?
1	?
2	?

$y = x^2 + 1$

$y = (-2)^2 + 1 = 5$
$y = (-1)^2 + 1 = 2$
$y = (0)^2 + 1 = 1$
$y = (1)^2 + 1 = 2$
$y = (2)^2 + 1 = 5$

x	y
−2	5
−1	2
0	1
1	2
2	5

$T = \{(-2, 5), (-1, 2), (0, 1), (1, 2), (2, 5)\}$

example 2

Draw a graph of relation K if the x values are −2, −1, 0, 1, and 2.

$$K = \{(x, y) : y = |x| + 1\}$$

Solution:

x	y
−2	?
−1	?
0	?
1	?
2	?

$y = |x| + 1$

$y = |-2| + 1 = 3$
$y = |-1| + 1 = 2$
$y = |0| + 1 = 1$
$y = |1| + 1 = 2$
$y = |2| + 1 = 3$

x	y
−2	3
−1	2
0	1
1	2
2	3

CLASSROOM EXERCISES

Write a word description for each of the following relations. (Example 1)

For Ex. 1-6, the answers are read thus, "the set of ordered pairs (x, y) such that

1. $\{(x, y) : y = x\}$ y equals x.

2. $\{(x, y) : y < x\}$ y is less than x.

3. $\{(x, y) : y = x^2\}$ y equals x squared.

4. $\{(x, y) : y = x - 1\}$ y equals x less one.

5. $\{(x, y) : y = x^2 + 2x + 1\}$ y equals x squared plus two x plus 1.

6. $\{(x, y) : y = |x|\}$ y equals the absolute value of x.

Name two ordered pairs of each relation if the x values are 1 and −1. (Examples 1 and 2) For Ex. 8, answers will vary.

7. $\{(x, y) : y = x\}$ (1, 1), (−1, −1)

8. $\{(x, y) : y < x\}$ (1, 0), (−1, −2)

9. $\{(x, y) : y = x^2\}$ (1, 1), (−1, 1)

10. $\{(x, y) : y = x - 1\}$ (1, 0), (−1, −2)

11. $\{(x, y) : y = x^2 + 2x + 1\}$ (1, 4), (−1, 0)

12. $\{(x, y) : y = |x|\}$ (1, 1), (−1, 1)

Name three ordered pairs of each relation below. (P-1)

13. $(-3, 3), (0, 0), (2, 2)$ **14.** $(-3, 2), (-2, 1), (-1, 3)$ **15.** $(-1, 2), (0, 1), (1, 0)$ **16.** $(1, 0), (1, \frac{1}{2}), (1, -\frac{1}{4})$

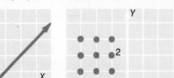
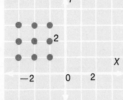
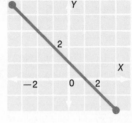
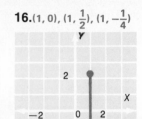

WRITTEN EXERCISES

See the Teacher's Manual for the suggested assignments.

Goals: To write a relation in roster form and to graph a relation

Sample Problem: Draw a graph of $\{(x, y) : y = x\}$ **Roster:** $\{(0, 0), (1, 1), (2, 2)\}$
if the x values are 0, 1, and 2.   **Graph:**

Write each relation in roster form if the x values are 1, 2, 3, and 4.
(Example 1)

1. $\{(x, y) : y = x - 1\}$ $\{(1, 0), (2, 1), (3, 2), (4, 3)\}$ **2.** $\{(x, y) : y = x - 3\}$ $\{(1, -2), (2, -1), (3, 0) (4, 1)\}$

3. $\{(x, y) : y = x^2\}$ $\{(1, 1), (2, 4), (3, 9), (4, 16)\}$ **4.** $\{(x, y) : y = x^2 - 1\}$ $\{(1, 0), (2, 3), (3, 8), (4, 15)\}$

5. $\{(x, y) : y = |x|\}$ $\{(1, 1), (2, 2), (3, 3), (4, 4)\}$ **6.** $\{(x, y) : y = \sqrt{x^2}\}$ $\{(1, 1), (2, 2), (3, 3), (4, 4)\}$

7. $\{(x, y) : y = \sqrt{x}\}$ $\{(1, 1), (2, \sqrt{2}), (3, \sqrt{3}), (4, 2)\}$ **8.** $\{(x, y) : y = -\sqrt{x}\}$ $\{(1, -1), (2, -\sqrt{2}), (3, -\sqrt{3}), (4, -2)\}$

9. $\{(x, y) : y = 0 \cdot x + 1\}$ $\{(1, 1), (2, 1), (3, 1), (4, 1)\}$ **10.** $\{(x, y) : y = 0 \cdot x - 2\}$ $\{(1, -2), (2, -2), (3, -2), (4, -2)\}$

11. $\{(x, y) : y = x^2 - x + 1\}$ **12.** $\{(x, y) : y = x^2 + x - 1\}$
$\{(1, 1), (2, 3), (3, 7), (4, 13)\}$ $\{(1, 1), (2, 5), (3, 11), (4, 19)\}$

Draw a graph of each relation in a separate coordinate plane. (Example 2)

(Right 1, Up 2), (Right 1, Up 3), (Left 3, Up 5), (Left 3, Down 4$\frac{1}{2}$)   (Left 3, Up 4), (Left 3, Down 2), (Right 4, Up 1),

13. $\{(1, 2), (1, 3), (-3, 5), (-3, -4\frac{1}{2})\}$ **14.** $\{(-3, 4), (-3, -2), (4, 1), (4, 6\frac{1}{2})\}$ (Right 4, Up 6$\frac{1}{2}$)

15. $\{(0, 0), (0, \pi), (0, -\pi), (\pi, 0)\}$ **16.** $\{(\pi, 3), (\pi, -3), (\pi, 5\frac{1}{2}), (\pi, 0)\}$
(Origin), (Up π), (Down π), (Right π); Note: $\pi \approx 3.14$ (Right π, Up 3), (Right π, Down 3), (Right π, Up 5$\frac{1}{2}$), (Right π)

Draw a graph of each relation in a separate coordinate plane. The x values
are $-1, 0, 1$ and 2. (Example 2) Each group consists of 4 pairs. Ordered pairs are given.

(-1, 0), (0, 1), (1, 2), (2, 3)   (-1, -4), (0, -3), (1, -2), (2, -1)   (-1, -6), (0, -7), (1, -6), (2, -3)

17. $\{(x, y) : y = x + 1\}$ **18.** $\{(x, y) : y = x - 3\}$ **19.** $\{(x, y) : y = x^2 - 7\}$

20. $\{(x, y) : y = x^2 - 10\}$ See below. **21.** $\{(x, y) : y = |x|\}$ (-1, 1), (0, 0), (1, 1), (2, 2) **22.** $\{(x, y) : y = \sqrt{x^2}\}$

23. $\{(x, y) : y = 0 \cdot x + 1\}$ **24.** $\{(x, y) : y = 0 \cdot x - 2\}$ See below.
(-1, 1), (0, 1), (1, 1), (2, 1)   (-1, -2), (0, -2), (1, -2), (2, -2)

25. $\{(x, y) : y = x^2 - x + 1\}$ **26.** $\{(x, y) : y = x^2 + x - 1\}$
(-1, 3), (0, 1), (1, 1), (2, 3)   (-1, -1), (0, -1), (1, 1), (2, 5)

20. $(-1, -9), (0, -10), (1, -9), (2, -6)$

22. $(-1, 1), (0, 0), (1, 1), (2, 2)$

MID-CHAPTER REVIEW

NOTE: After completing the Mid-Chapter Review, you may want to administer a quiz covering the same sections. See pages M-20 and M-21 of the Teacher's Manual for the suggested quiz.

Write the ordered pair that corresponds to each point of the graph. (Section 6.1)

1. A $(-4, -2)$ **2.** B $(0, -2)$ **3.** C $(-2, 0)$ **4.** D $(5, 3)$

5. E $(0, 3)$ **6.** F $(3, 0)$ **7.** G $(-5, 3)$ **8.** H $(4, -2)$

In Ex. 9-13, each point will be located by moving the direction of the stated number of units.

Graph these points in the same coordinate plane. (Section 6.2)

9. $A(2, -1)$ **10.** $B(-4, -3)$ **11.** $C(-3, 5)$ **12.** $D(4, 3.5)$ **13.** $E(-2.5, -3.5)$

Right 2, Down 1   Left 4, Down 3   Left 3, Up 5   Right 4, Up 3.5   Left 2.5, Down 3.5

Write each relation in roster form and then draw its graph. The x values are –2, –1, 0, 1, and 2. (Section 6.3) Each graph consists of the given points.

14. $\{(x, y): y = -2x + 3\}$
Line: $(-2,7)$, $(-1,5)$, $(0, 3)$, $(1, 1)$, $(2, -1)$

15. $\{(x, y): y = |-x| + 2\}$
Two lines (v-shaped): $(-2, 4)$, $(-1, 3)$, $(0, 2)$, $(1, 3)$, $(2, 4)$

16. $\{(x, y): y = -x^2 - 1\}$
Curve: $(-2, -5)$, $(-1, -2)$, $(0, -1)$, $(1, -2)$, $(2, -5)$

MAGIC SQUARES

Complete the Magic Square shown by filling it in with your calculator solutions to the exercises below. Then add <u>across</u> (three rows), <u>down</u> (three columns) and <u>diagonally</u> (two ways).

EXAMPLE   Find y when $x = 1.2$: $y = \sqrt{x^3 + 1.162}$

SOLUTION

1. 1.2	2. 1.9	3. 1.4
Ex. 1.7	4. 1.5	5. 1.3
6. 1.6	7. 1.1	8. 1.8

In Exercises 1–8, $x = 1.2$ Write each value of y in the Magic Square.

1. $y = \sqrt{x^2}$ 1.2   **2.** $y = x^2 + 0.46$ 1.9   **3.** $y = \sqrt{x + 0.76}$ 1.4   **4.** $y = \sqrt{x^2 + 0.81}$ 1.5

5. $y = 3x - 2.3$ 1.3   **6.** $y = \sqrt{x^2 + 1.12}$ 1.6   **7.** $y = |x^3 - 2.828|$ 1.1   **8.** $y = \sqrt{(3 - x)^2}$ 1.8

REVIEW CAPSULE FOR SECTION 6.4

Write the ordered pairs for the points A, B, C, and D. (Section 6.1)

1.

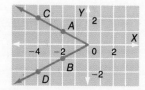

$A(-2, 1)$; $B(-2, -1)$;
$C(-4, 2)$; $D(-4, -2)$

2.

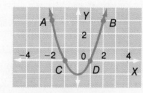

$A(-2, 3)$; $B(2, 3)$;
$C(-1, 0)$; $D(1, 0)$

3.

$A(-3, -2)$; $B(-1, -3)$;
$C(2, 1)$; $D(2, -1)$

Relations and Functions   /   **133**

6.4   Functions

P-1   **What are the x values of relation T below?   the y values?**

−1, 0, 4, −3   3, −2, 0

$$T = \{(-1, 3), (0, -2), (4, 0), (-3, -2)\}$$

Remember, no element of **Set D below is the <u>domain</u> of relation T. Set R is the <u>range</u>.**
a set is written more than
once. Thus, D and R do $$D = \{-1, 0, 4, -3\} \qquad R = \{3, -2, 0\}$$
not have the same number
of elements.

> The **domain** of a relation is the set of x values
> of its ordered pairs. The **range** of a relation
> is the set of y values of its ordered pairs.

example 1   Write the domain D and range R of relation W.

$$W = \{(-\tfrac{1}{2}, 0), (-2, 3), (-\tfrac{1}{4}, 2), (-\tfrac{1}{2}, -1), (2, -1)\}$$

Solution: $$D = \{-\tfrac{1}{2}, -2, -\tfrac{1}{4}, 2\} \qquad R = \{0, 3, 2, -1\}$$

Two x values are equal in A; no two x values are equal in B.

P-2   **What is different about the domains of relations A and B?**

$$A = \{(-2, 5), (4, 8), (-2, 3)\}$$
$$B = \{(-2, 5), (4, 8), (9, 3)\}$$

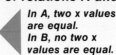 *In A, two x values
are equal.
In B, no two x
values are equal.*

Relation B is an example of a special relation called a <u>function</u>.

> A **function** is a relation in which no two ordered pairs
> have the same x value. In a function, each different
> x value has only one y value.

P-3   **How can you show that relation T following P-1 is a function?**
Show that no two x values of relation T are equal.

P-4   **Which of the following relations are also functions?**   P and S

$$P = \{(-1, 3), (2, 7), (0, 0)\}$$
$$Q = \{(1.3, 2), (-0.5, 1), (1.3, 0)\}$$
$$R = \{(\tfrac{1}{2}, \tfrac{1}{4}), (-\tfrac{1}{4}, 0), (\tfrac{2}{3}, 5), (0.5, 0.7)\}$$
$$S = \{(\pi, -2), (3, \sqrt{5}), (-1, -\sqrt{5})\}$$

The graph of a certain function is shown in Figure 1. The "hollow dot" means that $(-1, -2)$ is not in the function. The "heavy dot" emphasizes that $(3, 1)$ is in the function.

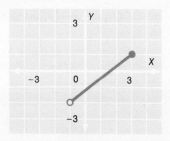

Figure 1

The graph of this function consists of all points on the portion of the line as shown.

There is a simple test to tell whether or not a graph represents a function.

> If any vertical line has more than one point in common with a graph, then the graph does not represent a function. Otherwise, it is the graph of a function.

P-5 **Does the graph in Figure 1 represent a function? Why?** Yes.
A vertical line will have only one point in common with the graph.

example 2

Write <u>Yes</u> or <u>No</u> to show whether the graph in Figure 2 represents a function.

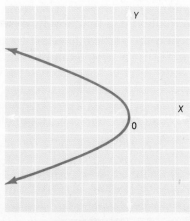

Figure 2

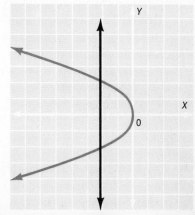

Figure 3

Solution: A vertical line is shown in Figure 3. It has two points in common with the graph. <u>No</u>, the graph of Figure 2 does not represent a function.

CLASSROOM EXERCISES

Write the domain and range of each relation. (Example 1)

Domain: $\{3, -5, 4, 0\}$; Range: $\{7, 2, -1, 0\}$
1. $\{(3, 7), (-5, 2), (4, -1), (0, 0)\}$

Domain: $\{\frac{1}{2}, \frac{1}{4}, \frac{1}{5}, 0\}$ Range: $\{3, 5, 7, 0\}$
2. $\{(\frac{1}{2}, 3), (\frac{1}{4}, 5), (\frac{1}{5}, 7), (0, 0)\}$

3. $\{(3, 8), (\sqrt{2}, -1), (\pi, -2), (\frac{1}{3}, -1)\}$

Domain: $\{3, \sqrt{2}, \pi, \frac{1}{3}\}$; Range: $\{8, -1, -2\}$

4. $\{(10, 1), (11, 2), (12, 3), (10, \frac{1}{2})\}$

Domain: $\{10, 11, 12\}$; Range: $\{1, 2, 3, \frac{1}{2}\}$

5.

x	2	3	4	5
y	3	4	5	6

Domain: $\{2, 3, 4, 5\}$
Range: $\{3, 4, 5, 6\}$

6.

x	$\frac{1}{2}$	$\frac{1}{3}$	$\frac{1}{4}$
y	$-\frac{1}{2}$	$-\frac{1}{3}$	$-\frac{1}{4}$

Domain: $\{\frac{1}{2}, \frac{1}{3}, \frac{1}{4},\}$
Range: $\{-\frac{1}{2}, -\frac{1}{3}, -\frac{1}{4}\}$

7.

x	1	−1	0	$\frac{1}{2}$	$-\frac{1}{2}$
y	1	1	0	$\frac{1}{2}$	$\frac{1}{2}$

Domain: $\{1, -1, -\frac{1}{2}, 0, \frac{1}{2}\}$; Range: $\{1, 0, \frac{1}{2}\}$

8.

x	1	1	4	4	9
y	1	−1	2	−2	3

Domain: $\{1, 4, 9\}$; Range: $\{1, -1, 2, -2, 3\}$

Write Yes or No to indicate if each set is a function. (P-2, P-3, P-4)

9. $\{(-1, 2), (2, -1)\}$ Yes

10. $\{(3, -1), (3, -2), (3, -3)\}$ No

11. $\{(\frac{1}{2}, 1), (\frac{1}{3}, 1), (\frac{1}{4}, 1)\}$ Yes

12. $\{(1.6, 2), (0.5, -3), (\frac{1}{2}, 0.7)\}$ No

13. $\{(1, 2), (3, 4), (5, 6)\}$ Yes

14. $\{(1, 1), (1, 2), (1, 3), (1, 4)\}$ No

15.

x	0	−3	2	−1
y	2	5	7	2

Yes

16.

x	$\frac{1}{2}$	$-\frac{1}{2}$	$\frac{3}{4}$	$-\frac{3}{4}$
y	5	6	7	8

Yes

WRITTEN EXERCISES

See the Teacher's Manual for the suggested assignments.

Goals: To determine whether a relation is a function by examining its set of ordered pairs or by applying the vertical line test to its graph

Sample Problems: a. $\{(0, 1), (1, 1)\}$ **b.** See Example 2.

Answers: a. Yes.   **b.** No.

1. D: $\{5, -3, -1, 1\}$; R: $\{10, 2, 0, -3\}$

2. D: $\{6, 2, 0, -3\}$; R: $\{5, 3, 0, -1\}$

3. D: $\{\frac{1}{2}, -1, -\frac{1}{2}, 2\}$; R: $\{2, \frac{1}{2}, -1\}$

4. D: $\{\frac{2}{3}, 0, -\frac{1}{2}, \frac{1}{4}\}$; R: $\{-1, \frac{1}{2}, 0, \frac{1}{4}\}$

Write the domain, D, and range, R, of each relation. (Example 1)

1. $\{(5, 10), (-3, 2), (-1, 0), (1, -3)\}$ See above.

2. $\{(6, 5), (2, 3), (0, 0), (-3, -1)\}$ See above.

3. $\{(\frac{1}{2}, 2), (-1, \frac{1}{2}), (-\frac{1}{2}, -1), (2, -1)\}$ See above.

4. $\{(\frac{2}{3}, -1), (0, \frac{1}{2}), (-\frac{1}{2}, 0), (\frac{1}{4}, \frac{1}{4})\}$ See above.

5. $\{(-1, \sqrt{2}), (-2, \sqrt{3}), (\pi, -1), (0, -\pi)\}$

D: $\{-1, -2, \pi, 0\}$; R: $\{\sqrt{2}, \sqrt{3}, -1, -\pi\}$

6. $\{(\sqrt{3}, -1), (0, \sqrt{2}), (0, \pi), (-1, \sqrt{2})\}$

D: $\{\sqrt{3}, 0, -1\}$; R: $\{-1, \sqrt{2}, \pi\}$

7.

x	0	1	1.5	−1	$-\pi$
y	0	1	1	−1	−1

See below.

8.

x	0	1	2	1.5	−1	−1.5
y	0	1	2	2	0	−1

See below.

9.

x	0	$\frac{1}{2}$	1	$1\frac{1}{2}$	$-\frac{1}{2}$	−1
y	0	0	1	1	−1	−1

D: $\{0, \frac{1}{2}, 1, 1\frac{1}{2}, -\frac{1}{2}, -1\}$; R: $\{0, 1, -1\}$

10.

x	0	1	2	$\frac{1}{2}$	−1	$-\frac{1}{2}$
y	0	1	4	$\frac{1}{4}$	1	$\frac{1}{4}$

D: $\{0, 1, 2, \frac{1}{2}, -1, -\frac{1}{2}\}$; R: $\{0, 1, 4, \frac{1}{4}\}$

7. D: $\{0, 1, 1.5, -1, \pi\}$; R: $\{0, 1, -1\}$

8. D: $\{0, 1, 2, 1.5, -1, -1.5\}$; R: $\{0, 1, 2, -1\}$

Write __Yes__ or __No__ to show whether each relation is a function. (P-2, P-3, P-4)

11. {(5, 7), (9, 11)} Yes

12. {(2, 4), (6, 8)} Yes

13. {(−2, 3), (−3, 4), (−5, 3)} Yes

14. {(−$\frac{1}{2}$, 1), (−$\frac{3}{2}$, 2), ($\frac{5}{2}$, 1)} Yes

15. {(0, 0), (2, 10), (−1, 3), (0, 5)} No

16. {(−2, −1), (0, −3), (−2, 0), (−3, 0)} No

17. {(π, 3), ($\frac{1}{2}$, $\frac{1}{3}$), (0.5, 5)} No

18. {($\sqrt{2}$, 3), (−π, 2), (−$\sqrt{2}$, 1)} Yes

Write __Yes__ or __No__ to show whether each graph represents a function. Explain your answer. (Example 2) Apply the vertical line test to each graph. If the line has more than one point in common with a graph, the graph is not a function.

19. Yes

20. Yes

21. No

22. No

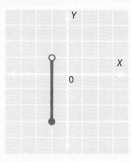
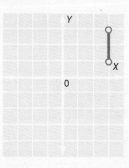

23. Yes

24. No

25. No

26. No

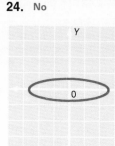
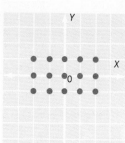
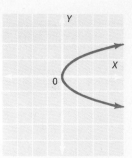

REVIEW CAPSULE FOR SECTION 6.5

Find which of these ordered pairs are in each relation. (Section 6.3)

(−3, 3) (−2, 2) (1, 4) (−2, −2) (1, 1) (0, 0) (0, 2) (7, −1) (−4, −2)

1. {(x, y) : y = −$\frac{1}{3}$x + $\frac{4}{3}$}
(1, 1), (7, −1), (−2, 2)

2. {(x, y) : y = −x² + 2}
(0, 2), (1, 1), (−2, −2)

3. {(x, y) : y = |x|}
(0, 0), (1, 1), (−2, 2), (−3, 3)

4. {(x, y) : y = −$\sqrt{x^2}$}
(0, 0), (−2, −2)

5. {(x, y) : y = −|x|}
(0, 0), (−2, −2)

6. {(x, y) : y = x² − x}
(0, 0)

6.5 Graphs of Functions

OBJECTIVE: To graph a function when its rule is given as a set description when (a) its domain is not more than five real numbers and (b) its domain is {real numbers}

example 1
Using real numbers as the domain, draw a graph of $\{(x, y) : y = 2x + 1\}$.

Solution: Choose a few x values that are small in absolute value. The corresponding y values are obtained from the formula to complete the table.

Values Chosen for x

x	y
−1	?
0	?
1	?
2	?

Values for y Obtained from the Formula
$$y = 2x + 1$$

For $x = -1$, $y = 2(-1) + 1 = -1$.
For $x = 0$, $y = 2(0) + 1 = 1$.
For $x = 1$, $y = 2(1) + 1 = 3$.
For $x = 2$, $y = 2(2) + 1 = 5$.

x	y
−1	−1
0	1
1	3
2	5

These ordered pairs are graphed in Figure 1. You can see that the points appear to lie on a line, which is shown as a dashed line. The complete graph is shown in Figure 2.

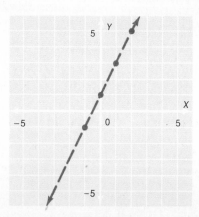

Figure 1

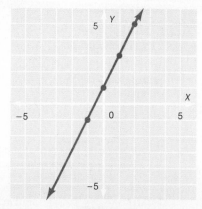

Figure 2

P-1   If $x = -2$, what is the corresponding value for y from the formula $y = 2x + 1$? −3

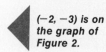

$(-2, -3)$ is on the graph of Figure 2.

example 2

Using {real numbers} as the domain, draw a graph of $\{(x, y) : y = x^2 - 1\}$.

Solution: Choose values for x and compute the corresponding values for y.

x	y
−2	?
−1	?
0	?
1	?
2	?

For $x = -2$, $y = (-2)^2 - 1 = 3$.
For $x = -1$, $y = (-1)^2 - 1 = 0$.
For $x = 0$, $y = (0)^2 - 1 = -1$.
For $x = 1$, $y = (1)^2 - 1 = 0$.
For $x = 2$, $y = (2)^2 - 1 = 3$.

x	y
−2	3
−1	0
0	−1
1	0
2	3

These ordered pairs are graphed in Figure 3, and a curved dashed line is drawn through the points. The complete graph is shown in Figure 4.

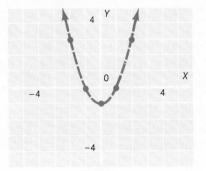

Figure 3

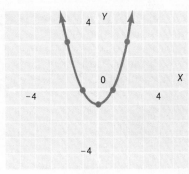

Figure 4

P-2 What is the range of the function shown in Figure 4? $\{y : y \geqslant -1\}$

P-3 If $x = \frac{3}{2}$, what is the corresponding y value from the formula $y = x^2 - 1$? $\frac{5}{4}$

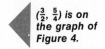

$(\frac{3}{2}, \frac{5}{4})$ is on the graph of Figure 4.

CLASSROOM EXERCISES

Write the y values that correspond to the given x values. (Examples 1 and 2)

1. $\{(x, y) : y = 2x\}$

x	0	−1	1	−2	2
y	?	?	?	?	?
	0	−2	2	−4	4

2. $\{(x, y) : y = 3x + 1\}$

x	−2	−1	0	1	2
y	?	?	?	?	?
	−5	−2	1	4	7

Relations and Functions / **139**

Refer to Figure 5 for Exercises 3–7. (P-1, P-2, P-3)

3. Why does the graph represent a function?   No vertical line
can cut the graph in more than one point.

4. What is the domain?   4. {real numbers}

5. What is the range?   5. {real numbers}

6. What y value corresponds to $x = -1$?   −1

7. What x value corresponds to $y = 1$?   0

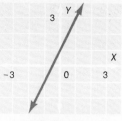

Figure 5

Refer to Figure 6 for Exercises 8–12. (P-1, P-2, P-3)

8. Why does the graph represent a function?   No vertical line
can cut the graph in more than one point.

9. What is the domain?   9. {$x: -1 \leqslant x < 3$}

10. What is the range?   10. {$y: 1 < y \leqslant 2$}

11. What y value corresponds to $x = 1$? $1\frac{1}{2}$

12. What x value corresponds to $y = 1\frac{3}{4}$?   0

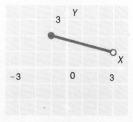

Figure 6

WRITTEN EXERCISES

See the Teacher's Manual for the suggested assignments.

Goal: To draw the graph of a function given the set description and domain

Sample Problem: Using {real numbers} as the domain,
draw a graph of {$(x, y) : y = |x|$}

Answer:

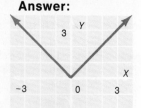

In Exercises 1-15, the graph is one of the following: a straight line, a "v", an
inverted "v", *Draw a graph of each function in a separate*
or a curve *coordinate plane. First graph five ordered pairs with x*
(parabola). *values −2, −1, 0, 1, and 2. The domain is {real*
Points on
the graph *numbers}. (Examples 1 and 2)*
are given.

Line: (0, 0), (2, −4)   Line: (0, 0), (2, −6)   Line: (0, 1), (2, −1)
1. {$(x, y) : y = -2x$}   **2.** {$(x, y) : y = -3x$}   **3.** {$(x, y) : y = -x + 1$}
        Line: (0, 1),   Inverted "v": (0, 0),
4. {$(x, y) : y = -2x + 1$}$(2, -3)$ **5.** {$(x, y) : y = -|x|$}$(-2, -2), (2, -2)$ **6.** {$(x, y) : y = -\sqrt{x^2}$}
                                                        See below.
7. {$(x, y) : y = |x + 1|$}   **8.** {$(x, y) : y = |x - 1|$}   **9.** $(x, y) : y = 0 \cdot x - 3$
V: (−2, 1), (−1, 0), (0, 1), (2, 3)   V: (−2, 3), (−1, 2), (0, 1), (1, 0), (2, 1)   See below.
10. {$(x, y) : y = 0 \cdot x + 4$}   **11.** {$(x, y) : y = -x^2 + 2$}   **12.** {$(x, y) : y = x^2 - 3$}
Line parallel to x axis: (0, 4), (2, 4)   Curve: (−2, −2), (−1, 1), (0, 2)   Curve: (−2, 1), (−1, −2),
                                                        (0, −3), (1, −2), (2, 1)
MORE CHALLENGING EXERCISES (1, 1), (2, −2)

13. {$(x, y) : y = \frac{1}{2}x^2 - x$}   **14.** {$(x, y) : y = x^2 - x + 1$}   **15.** {$(x, y) : y = -x^2 + x$}
Curve: (−2, 4), (−1, 1$\frac{1}{2}$),   Curve: (−2, 7), (−1, 3), (0, 1),   Curve: (−2, −6), (−1, −2),
(0, 0), (1, −$\frac{1}{2}$), (2, 0)   (2, 3)   (0, 0), (1, 0), (2, −2)

REVIEW CAPSULE FOR SECTION 6.6

Use the formula M = 0.4E to estimate the weight of a person on Mars.

EXAMPLE: Earth weight (E) = 160 pounds   **SOLUTION:** $M = 0.4(160) = 64$ pounds

1. 115 pounds   **2.** 178 pounds   **3.** 92 pounds   **4.** 210 pounds   **5.** 133 pounds
46 pounds   71.2 pounds   36.8 pounds   84 pounds   53.2 pounds

6. Inverted "v"; same as Ex. 5.   9. Line parallel to x axis; (0, −3), (2, −3)

6.6 Problem Solving: Using Functions

Suppose an object is dropped from a height above ground. The object will hit the ground after a certain number of seconds. This number can be used together with the function below to find the number of meters that the object falls.

$$\{(x, y) : y = 4.9x^2\}$$

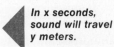

x : number of seconds
y : number of meters

P-1 **What is the value of y if x equals 1 second?   if x equals 2 seconds?**
4.9   19.6

Notice that for each value of x in seconds, there is exactly one corresponding value of y in meters. Thus, this relation *is* a function.

example 1

A rock that is dropped from the Golden Gate Bridge will hit the water about 3.7 seconds later. Solve for the distance from the bridge to the water.

Solution:

$y = 4.9x^2$

$y \approx 4.9(3.7)^2$

$y \approx 4.9(13.7)$

$y \approx 67$ meters

Sound travels in water at an approximate speed of 1450 meters per second. Here is a function relating distance and time for underwater sound.

$$\{(x, y) : y = 1450x\}$$

In x seconds, sound will travel y meters.

The distance to the object is computed by measuring the time taken for a sound wave to be reflected from the object.

example 2

A sound wave takes 1.6 seconds from the instant it leaves a ship until it is reflected back from an object. Compute the distance in meters to the object.

Solution:

$$y = 1450x$$

$$y \approx 1450(1.6) \quad \text{or} \quad 2320$$

The sound wave travels about 2320 meters (twice the distance to the object). The distance from the ship to the object is about 1160 meters.

The graph at the right represents the distance in meters a car will travel each second for speeds given in kilometers per hour.

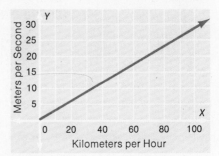

P-2 **What distance will a car travel in one second at a speed of 50 kilometers per hour?** 15 meters

P-3 **Which function below best describes this graph?** c

a. $\{(x, y) : y = 3.56x\}$ b. $\{(x, y) : y = 2.8x\}$ c. $\{(x, y) : y = 0.28x\}$

CLASSROOM EXERCISES

Refer to the table below which shows some ordered pairs of the function $\{(x, y) : y = 4.9x^2\}$. (Example 1)

x	1	2	3	4	5	6	10
y	4.9	19.6	44.1	78.4	122.5	176.4	490

1. How long would an object take to fall 78.4 meters?   4 seconds

2. How far would an object fall in 5 seconds?   122.5 meters

3. How far would an object fall between the first and second seconds?   14.7 meters

4. Does an object fall twice as far in the first 4 seconds as it does in the first 2 seconds?   No

5. How long would it take an object to fall 490 meters?   10 seconds

6. How long would it take an object to fall 441 decimeters?   3 seconds

7. How does the distance between the second and third seconds compare with the distance between the fourth and fifth seconds?

Distance fallen between second and third seconds (24.5 m) is less than distance fallen between fourth and fifth seconds (44.1 m).

WRITTEN EXERCISES
See the Teacher's Manual for the suggested assignments.

Goal: To use a formula or graph of a function to solve word problems

Sample Problem: Use $y = 4.9x^2$ to determine how far an object has fallen 10 seconds after it has been dropped.

Answer: 490 meters

Use the formula $y = 1450x$ for Exercises 1–4. (Example 2)

1. Compute the underwater distance from a ship to an object if a sound wave takes 2.5 seconds to be reflected from the object.   1812.5 meters

2. Compute the depth of water beneath a ship if a sound wave takes 3.2 seconds to be reflected from the bottom.   2320 meters

3. Compute the number of seconds for a sound wave to be reflected from an object 2175 meters from a ship.   3 seconds

4. Compute the number of seconds for a sound wave to be reflected from an object 580 meters from a ship. $\frac{4}{5}$ seconds

Assume that the graph in Figure 1 represents the cost of sending first-class mail. Each x value represents the amount in grams. Each y value represents the corresponding costs in cents. Find the cost of sending the amounts of mail given in Exercises 5–8.

5. 30 grams   10 cents   **6.** 60 grams   20 cents   **7.** 15 grams   10 cents   **8.** 45 grams   20 cents

9. How much mail can you send for 30 cents?   for 40 cents?   From 90 grams up to and including 120 grams
From 60 grams up to and including 90 grams

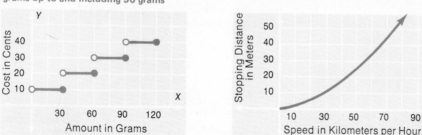

Figure 1   Figure 2

Figure 2 shows the average stopping distance for a car traveling at various speeds. Write the stopping distance for each speed given in Exercises 10–13.

10. 30 km/hr   12 meters   **11.** 50 km/hr   27 meters   **12.** 60 km/hr   34 meters   **13.** 80 km/hr
58 meters

14. What speed requires a stopping distance of 30 meters?   54 km/hr

15. What speed requires a stopping distance of 50 meters?   75 km/hr

Career   **Air Conditioning Technician**

Air conditioning technicians design, manufacture, sell, and service air conditioning equipment. One of their skills is the ability to determine whether an air conditioner is of the right <u>cooling capacity</u> for a particular room. The **cooling capacity** of an air conditioner is measured in **British Thermal units (BTU'S).**

Monitoring a large air conditioning unit

The graph shown at the right can be used to estimate how much cooling capacity is needed for a given room of a house or apartment. (The graph can be used for any room that is about eight feet high, provided that it is not a kitchen and not directly below an attic floor.) The exposure of the room's exterior wall determines which part of the shaded band you should use.

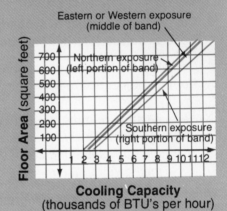

Cooling Capacity
(thousands of BTU's per hour)

EXAMPLE: A room of a house has a northern exposure. Its floor area is 300 square feet. What must be the size (cooling capacity) of the air conditioner for this room?

SOLUTION:
1. On the vertical scale, find the room's floor area, 300 square feet.

2. Since the room has a northern exposure, find the point on the <u>left</u> portion of the band directly to the right of the 300 reading.

3. From this point on the band read directly <u>down</u> on the horizontal scale to find the correct cooling capacity, **5500 BTU's per hour.**

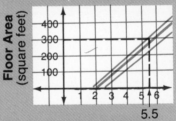

Cooling Capacity
(thousands of BTU's per hour)

EXERCISES

Estimate the size of an air conditioner needed to cool each room described. Round your answer to the nearest 500 BTU's.

1. Southern exposure;
   400 square feet   8000 BTU's

2. Northern exposure;
   500 square feet   8000 BTU's

3. Eastern exposure;
   300 square feet   6000 BTU's

4. Southern exposure;
   250 square feet   6000 BTU's

5. Western exposure;
   100 square feet   3500 BTU's

6. Northern exposure;
   700 square feet   10,500 BTU's

CHAPTER SUMMARY

IMPORTANT TERMS	
X axis *(p. 124)*	Quadrants *(p. 127)*
Y axis *(p. 124)*	Relation *(p. 130)*
Origin *(p. 124)*	Domain *(p. 134)*
Coordinates *(p. 124)*	Range *(p. 134)*
Ordered pair *(p. 124)*	Function *(p. 134)*
Coordinate plane *(p. 127)*	

IMPORTANT IDEAS

1. There is a one-to-one correspondence between points of a coordinate plane and ordered pairs of real numbers.

2. A relation can be described in roster form, by a graph in a co-ordinate plane, by a formula, or by a general set description.

3. If any vertical line has more than one point in common with a graph, then the graph does not represent a function.

CHAPTER REVIEW

NOTE: The Teacher's Resource Book contains two forms of each Chapter Test.

SECTION 6.1   In Ex. 1-8, each point is located by moving in the stated direction, the stated number of units.

Draw an X axis and Y axis. Then locate these points.

1. $A(-3, 2)$ Left 3, Up 2   **2.** $B(4, -3)$ Right 4, Down 3   **3.** $C(-3, -4)$ Left 3, Down 4   **4.** $D(2, 5)$ Right 2, Up 5

5. $E(3, -3)$ Right 3, Down 3   **6.** $F(-4, 0)$ Left 4   **7.** $G(0, -4)$ Down 4   **8.** $H(0, 0)$ Origin

SECTION 6.2   In Ex. 9-16, each point is located by moving in the stated direction the stated number of units.

Graph these points in the same coordinate plane.

9. $P(2, -3\frac{1}{2})$ Right 2, Down 3$\frac{1}{2}$ **10.** $Q(-3, 2\frac{1}{2})$ Left 3, Up 2$\frac{1}{2}$ **11.** $R(2.25, 1.75)$ Right 2.25, Up 1.75   **12.** $S(-4.5, -2.5)$ Left 4.5, Down 2.5

13. $T(0, 3)$ Up 3   **14.** $W(-3, 0)$ Left 3   **15.** $U(-2\frac{1}{2}, -3\frac{1}{2})$ Left 2$\frac{1}{2}$, Down 3$\frac{1}{2}$ **16.** $Z(-3\frac{1}{2}, -2\frac{1}{2})$ Left 3$\frac{1}{2}$, Down 2$\frac{1}{2}$

SECTION 6.3

Write each relation in roster form if the x values are −1, 0, 2, and 3. Then draw its graph.

17. $\{(x, y) : y = 3x - 5\}$ $\{(-1, -8), (0, -5), (2, 1), (3, 4)\}$ **18.** $\{(x, y) : y = 4 - x\}$ $\{(-1, 5), (0, 4), (2, 2), (3, 1)\}$

19. $\{(x, y) : y = x^2 - 1\}$ $\{(-1, 0), (0, -1), (2, 3), (3, 8)\}$ **20.** $\{(x, y) : y = 3 - x^2\}$ $\{(-1, 2), (0, 3), (2, -1), (3, -6)\}$

21. $\{(x, y) : y = |x - 1|\}$ $\{(-1, 2), (0, 1), (2, 1), (3, 2)\}$ **22.** $\{(x, y) : y = 2 - |x|\}$ $\{(-1, 1), (0, 2), (2, 0), (3, -1)\}$

Relations and Functions / **145**

SECTION 6.4

Write the domain D and the range R of each relation.

24. D: $\{1.7, -2.3, 0\}$; R: $\{-2, -0.9, -6\}$

23. $\{(-\frac{1}{2}, 0), (2, 6), (4, -3)\}$ D: $\{-\frac{1}{2}, 2, 4\}$; R: $\{0, 6, -3\}$ **24.** $\{(1.7, -2), (-2.3, -0.9), (0, -6)\}$

25. $\{(-3, \frac{1}{2}), (0, -5), (-3, 0), (-2, -4)\}$ **26.** $\{(3, 2), (-1.6, 3), (3.5, -2.7), (-1, 2)\}$
D: $\{-3, 0, -2\}$; R: $\{\frac{1}{2}, -5, 0, -4\}$ D: $\{3, -1.6, 3.5, -1\}$; R: $\{2, 3, -2.7\}$

Write Yes or No to show whether each relation is a function.

27. $\{(12, -10), (-25, 5), (-4, -10), (17, 5)\}$ Yes **28.** $\{(1, 6), (0, 5), (-4, -2.7), (1.8, -5.3)\}$
Yes

29. No

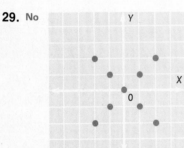

30. Yes

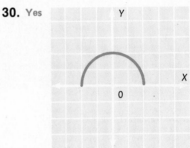

SECTION 6.5

Draw a graph of each function in a separate coordinate plane.
The domain is {real numbers}. For Ex. 31-32, each graph is a line through the points located by the stated ordered pairs.

31. $\{(x, y) : y = x - 3\}$ (0, −3), (1, −2), (2, −1), (3, 0) **32.** $\{(x, y) : y = -2x + 1\}$ (−1, 3), (0, 1), (1, −1)

33. $\{(x, y) : y = |x| - 2\}$ Two lines; (−2, 0), (0, −2), (2, 0) **34.** $\{(x, y) : y = 3 - \sqrt{x^2}\}$ Two lines; (−2, 1),
(−1, 2), (0, 3), (1, 2), (3, 0)

SECTION 6.6

Use the formula d = 0.21r to compute the distance d, in meters, traveled by car at a speed of r kilometers per hour in $\frac{3}{4}$ second (average time it takes a driver to apply the brakes).

35. $r = 40$ km/hr
8.4 meters

36. $r = 60$ km/hr
12.6 meters

37. $r = 100$ km/hr
21 meters

38. $r = 80$ km/hr
16.8 meters

The graph at the right represents
$\{(r, d) : d = 0.21r\}$.

39. At approximately what speed in kilometers per hour would a car travel 8 meters in $\frac{3}{4}$ second?
40 km/hr

40. At approximately what speed in kilometers per hour would a car travel 12 meters in $\frac{3}{4}$ second?
58 km/hr

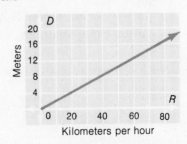

CUMULATIVE REVIEW: CHAPTERS 1–6

Simplify. (Section 1.1)

1. $|29|$ 29

2. $|-39|$ 39

3. $|3 - 17|$ 14

4. $|-(-4.9)|$ 4.9

Add. (Section 1.2)

5. $(-13) + 9$ −4

6. $24 + (-17)$ 7

7. $(-16) + (-27)$ −43

8. $(-48) + (-23)$ −71

Subtract. (Section 1.3)

9. $(-13) - 22$ −35

10. $(-28) - (-9)$ −19

11. $5.6 - 8.7$ −3.1

12. $12.3 - (-14.9)$ 27.2

Multiply. (Section 1.4)

13. $(-5)(-13)$ 65

14. $(7)(-8)$ −56

15. $(-2.4)(1.6)$ −3.84

16. $(-3.2)(-7)$ 22.4

Divide. (Section 1.5)

17. $\dfrac{28}{-7}$ −4

18. $\dfrac{-54}{-9}$ 6

19. $(-120) \div (-8)$ 15

20. $(-72) \div 9$ −8

Simplify. (Section 1.6)

21. $12 + 3 \cdot 5$ 27

22. $36 - 20 \div 4$ 31

23. $48 - 2^3 \div 2 + 6$ 50

24. $(-72) \div 4(-3) - 15$ −9

Evaluate. (Section 1.7)

25. $3 \cdot 2^4$ 48

26. $5 - (-2)^3$ 13

27. $(-54) \div 3^3$ −2

28. $(-5)^3 - 12^2$ −269

Write <u>Rational</u> *or* <u>Irrational</u> *to describe each number.* (Section 2.1)

29. $-\sqrt{81}$
Rational

30. $2\frac{3}{4}$
Rational

31. $0.51015202530\cdots$
Irrational

32. $\sqrt{45}$
Irrational

Simplify. (Section 2.2)

33. $15 - 24 + 6 - 19$ −22

34. $-2.7 + 3.1 - 5.3 + 0.8$ −4.1

35. $9.4 + x - 12.8 - y$ −3.4 + x − y

36. $15.6 - t - 13.9 + s$ 1.7 − t + s

Multiply. (Section 2.3)

37. $(-4)(6)(-3)$ 72

38. $(-2)(-12)(-5)$ −120

39. $(-3)(x)(-6)(-2)(y)$ −36xy

40. $(-1)(-2)(a)(-1)(b)(-3)(-1)$ −6ab

Simplify. (Section 2.4)

41. $4x - (y - 3)$
4x − y + 3

42. $13 - (2x - 3y + 19)$
−6 − 2x + 3y

43. $(3r)(-2)(-5rs)$
30r²s

44. $(-4p)(-q)(-3qr)$
−12q²pr

Multiply and simplify. (Section 2.5)

45. $-3r(2r - 5)$ $-6r^2 + 15r$

46. $(5s + 3t)(-2t)$ $-10st - 6t^2$

Factor each expression. (Section 2.5)

47. $6x^2 - 24x$ $6x(x - 4)$

48. $-15rs - 3s$ $-3s(5r + 1)$

Simplify. (Section 2.6)

49. $13s - t - 9s - 5t$ $4s - 6t$

50. $-3p^2q - pq^2 + 2p^2q - 2pq^2$
  $-p^2q - 3pq^2$

Solve. Show all steps. Check each answer. (Section 3.1)

51. $x + 19 = 5$ -14 **52.** $x - 37 = -44$ -7 **53.** $-27 = x + 15$ -42 **54.** $23 = x + 51$ -28

Solve. Show all steps. Check each answer (Section 3.2)

55. $-8x = -104$ 13 **56.** $2.6x = -18.2$ -7 **57.** $\dfrac{x}{3.7} = -12$ -44.4 **58.** $-\dfrac{1}{4}x = -17$ 68

Solve. Show all steps. Check each answer. (Section 3.3)

59. $4x - 9 = 43$ 13 **60.** $3x + 7 = -32$ -13 **61.** $-13 + \dfrac{x}{6} = -17$ -24 **62.** $18 = \dfrac{x}{1.4} + 29$
  -15.4

Solve. Show all steps. Check each answer. (Section 3.4)

63. $x + 17 + 3x = -9$ $-\dfrac{13}{2}$ or $-6\dfrac{1}{2}$

64. $24 = x + 35 - 3x$ $\dfrac{11}{2}$ or $5\dfrac{1}{2}$

65. $2(x + 2) - 3(2x - 1) = -32$ $\dfrac{39}{4}$ or $9\dfrac{3}{4}$

66. $3x - 5x - (7 + x) = -35$ $\dfrac{28}{3}$ or $9\dfrac{1}{3}$

Solve. Show all steps. Check each answer. (Section 3.5)

67. $4x - 5 = 2x + 9$ 7

68. $3x + 7 = 25 - x$ $\dfrac{9}{2}$ or $4\dfrac{1}{2}$

69. $5 - 2x - 13 = 4x + 8 - x$ $-\dfrac{16}{5}$ or $-3\dfrac{1}{5}$

70. $x + 14 - 3x = 12 - 4x - 21$
  $-\dfrac{23}{2}$ or $-11\dfrac{1}{2}$

Solve each problem. (Section 3.6)

71. The perimeter of a rectangular construction site is 880 meters. Find the width of the site if the length is 280 meters.   160 meters

72. The winner of the Indianapolis 500 mile race one year finished in $3\dfrac{2}{5}$ hours. Find the speed to the nearest mile per hour.   147 mi/hr

Choose a variable and write an equation for the word sentence. Solve the equation. (Section 4.1)

73. A selling price of $15.95 less the cost equals a profit of $6.23.
cost: c; $15.95 - c = 6.23$
       $c = \$9.72$

74. The product of the number of licenses and a $15 fee equals $3825.
No. of licenses: n; $15n = 3825$
       $n = 255$ licenses

77. Adv. classes: x persons; begin. classes: $2x - 18$ persons;
$x + 2x - 18 = 477$; Adv. classes: 165; Beginning classes: 312

75. The scenic route for the trip to the county fair is 214.7 kilometers. This is 23.4 kilometers longer than the same trip using the expressway.
Expressway distance: x; $214.7 = x + 23.4$;
$x = 191.3$ kilometers

76. The quotient of the total cost and 15 cans of tomato soup equals the cost per can of $0.79.
Total cost: c; $\frac{c}{15} = 0.79$; $c = \$11.85$

In Exercises 75–78, use Condition 1 to represent the unknowns. Use Condition 2 to write an equation for the problem. Solve the problem. (Sections 4.2, 4.3, 4.4, 4.5)

77. See above.

77. The number of persons enrolled in beginning tennis classes in a city program was 18 less than twice the number enrolled in advanced classes. The total number in beginning and advanced classes was 477. Find the number in each.

78. Length: l; width: $l - 2.5$; $2l + 2(l - 2.5) = 43.0$;
Length: 12 cm; width: 9.5 cm
78. A color transparency of a product photo is rectangular in shape with its width 2.5 centimeters less than its length. The perimeter is 43.0 centimeters. Find the length and width. See above.

79. A distributor of a product is allowed a discount of 4% by the manufacturer on any quantity purchase exceeding $1000. On one order the distributor's net cost was $1204.32. Find what the cost would have been without the discount.
Amt. of purchase without discount: x; $1204.32 = 0.96x$;
$x = \$1254.50$

80. The fuel tank capacity of one midsize car is 2.5 gallons more than a subcompact car. The mid-size car averages 14 miles per gallon and the subcompact averages 18 miles per gallon. The range of the subcompact car is 29 miles more than the range of the mid-size car. Find the fuel tank capacity of each car. Subcompact's capacity: x; mid-size's capacity: $x + 2.5$; $18x = 14(x + 2.5) + 29$; Sub-compact: 16 gallons; Mid-size: 18.5 gallons

Draw a graph of each inequality. (Section 5.1)

81. $x \leq 5$; Domain = {whole numbers}
On a number line, the points 0, 1, 2, 3, 4, 5

82. $x > -2$; Domain = {real numbers}
On a number line, the points to the right of, and not including, -2

Write a new inequality by applying the Order Property of Opposites. (Section 5.2)

83. $-t > 9$ $t < -9$

84. $-13 < -k$ $13 > k$

Solve. (Section 5.3)

85. $x - 12 < -19$ $x < -7$

86. $23 + x > 5$ $x > -18$

Solve. (Section 5.4)

87. $3 > 2x + 7 - 3x$ $x > 4$

88. $3(a - 1) < 5a + 3 - 3a$ $a < 6$

Solve. (Section 5.5)

89. $\frac{3}{4}x < -15$ $x < -20$

90. $-0.9r > -27$ $r < 30$

Solve. (Section 5.6)

91. $3x - 2 > 5x + 12$ $\quad x < -7$

92. $-2(x - 2) < 19 - 5x$ $\quad x < 5$

Write the ordered pair for each point. (Section 6.1)

93. R $\quad$ (−1, 2)

94. S $\quad$ (−2, −1)

95. T $\quad$ (2, 2)

96. W $\quad$ (1, 0)

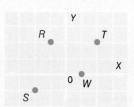

Graph the following points in one coordinate plane.
(Section 6.2) $\quad$ Each point is located by moving in the stated direction. Start at the origin.

97. $A(-4, -3)$
Left 4, Down 3

98. $B(5, -2)$
Right 5, Down 2

99. $C(0, -3\frac{1}{2})$
Down $3\frac{1}{2}$

100. $D(-2\frac{1}{2}, 0)$
Left $2\frac{1}{2}$

Draw a graph of each relation. The x values are −2, −1, 0, 1, and 2.
(Section 6.3) $\quad$ Each graph contains points for which the ordered pairs are given.

101. $\{(x, y) : y = -x^2 + 1\}$ (−2, −3), (−1, 0), (0, 1), (1, 0)

102. $\{(x, y) : y = |x| - 2\}$ (−2, 0), (−1, −1), (0, −2), (1, −1), (2, 0)

Write <u>Yes</u> *or* <u>No</u> *to show whether each relation is a function.* (Section 6.4)

103. $\{(-\frac{1}{2}, 0), (3, -5), (-1, 0)\}$ $\quad$ Yes

104. $\{(2, -1), (-3, 7), (0, 1), (-3, -4)\}$ $\quad$ No

105. No

106. Yes
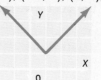

In Ex. 107 and 108, each graph is a straight line containing the given points.

Draw a graph of each function. The domain is {*real numbers*}. (Section 6.5)

107. $\{(x, y) : y = \frac{1}{2}x - 3\}$
(0, −3), (2, −2), (−2, −4)

108. $\{(x, y) : y = -\frac{3}{2}x + 1\}$
(0, 1), (2, −2), (−2, 4)

Use the formula $y = 490x^2$ *to compute the distance in centimeters an object will fall in x seconds.* (Section 6.6)

109. $x = 10$ seconds $\quad$ 49,000 centimeters

110. $x = 12$ seconds $\quad$ 70,560 centimeters

CHAPTER **7** Powers

Sections 7.1 **Products of Powers**

7.2 **Quotients of Powers and Zero Exponents**

7.3 **Negative Exponents**

7.4 **Powers of Products and Quotients**

7.5 **Powers of Powers**

7.6 **Scientific Notation**

Features *Calculator Exercises:* **Evaluating Fractions**

Special Topic Application: **Space Technology**

Review and Testing *Review Capsules*

Mid-Chapter Review

Chapter Summary

Chapter Review

7.1 Products of Powers

OBJECTIVES: To write a product of powers of the same base as one power
To write a product of one power and the sum or difference of two powers all with the same base as a sum or difference using the Distributive Property and the Product Property of Powers
To solve a special equation by applying the Product Property of Powers

P-1 **Write each power below as a product.**

a. 2^4 **b.** x^3 **c.** y^5 **d.** 4^3 **e.** z^2 $z \cdot z$

$2 \cdot 2 \cdot 2 \cdot 2$ $x \cdot x \cdot x$ $y \cdot y \cdot y \cdot y \cdot y$ $4 \cdot 4 \cdot 4$

2 is a factor of 2^4 four times. x is a factor of x^3 three times.

P-2 **How many times is y a factor of y^5?**   5

> If a is a positive integer, then x^a means that x is a factor a times.
>
> $$x^a = \underbrace{x \cdot x \cdot x \cdots x}_{a \text{ factors}}$$

example 1

Write $2^3 \cdot 2^5$ as one power.

Solution:
$$2^3 \cdot 2^5 = (2 \cdot 2 \cdot 2)(2 \cdot 2 \cdot 2 \cdot 2 \cdot 2)$$
$$= (2 \cdot 2 \cdot 2 \cdot 2 \cdot 2 \cdot 2 \cdot 2 \cdot 2)$$
$$= 2^8$$

P-3 **How can you express $(-3)^2$ as a product?**   **$(-3)^4$ as a product?**

$(-3) \cdot (-3)$ $(-3) \cdot (-3) \cdot (-3) \cdot (-3)$

example 2

Write $(-3)^2(-3)^4$ as one power.

Solution:
$$(-3)^2(-3)^4 = (-3 \cdot -3)(-3 \cdot -3 \cdot -3 \cdot -3)$$
$$= (-3 \cdot -3 \cdot -3 \cdot -3 \cdot -3 \cdot -3)$$
$$= (-3)^6$$

P-4 **How many times is x used as a factor in $x^a \cdot x^b$ if a and b are positive integers?** $a + b$ times

$$x^a \cdot x^b = \underbrace{(x \cdot x \cdot x \cdots x)}_{a \text{ factors}}\underbrace{(x \cdot x \cdot x \cdots x)}_{b \text{ factors}}$$

Product Property of Powers

If a and b are integers and x is any nonzero real number, then $x^a \cdot x^b = x^{a+b}$.

$$13^4 \cdot 13^5 = 13^9$$

$$(-5.6)^2(-5.6) = (-5.6)^3$$

P-5 **Write each product below as one power.**

a. $(-1.9)^2(-1.9)^3$ $(-1.9)^5$ b. $(\frac{1}{2})^4(\frac{1}{2})^3$ $(\frac{1}{2})^7$ c. $t^2 \cdot t^7$ t^9

◀ **Keep the same base. Add the exponents.**

example 3 Write the product as a sum: $r^3(r^2 + r)$

1 Distributive Property ⟶ $r^3(r^2 + r) = r^3 \cdot r^2 + r^3 \cdot r$

2 Product Property of Powers ⟶ $= r^5 + r^4$

P-6 **Write each product below expressed as a sum or difference.**

a. $t^2(t^4 + t^3)$ $t^6 + t^5$ b. $k^3(3k^2 - 2k + 3)$ $3k^5 - 2k^4 + 3k^3$

example 4 Solve: $12^4 \cdot 12^x = 12^9$

Solution: $12^4 \cdot 12^x = 12^9$

$12^{4+x} = 12^9$

$4 + x = 9$

$x = 5$

◀ **Since the bases are equal, the exponents are also equal.**

P-7 **Solve:** $(-4.8)^3 \cdot (-4.8)^4 = x^7$ -4.8

CLASSROOM EXERCISES

Write each product as one power. (Examples 1-2)

1. $2^3 \cdot 2^2$ 2^5
2. $a^5 \cdot a^2$ a^7
3. $(-5)^2(-5)^4$ $(-5)^6$
4. $(-1.8)^5(-1.8)^2$ $(1.8)^7$

5. $(\frac{1}{2})^2(\frac{1}{2})^3$ $(\frac{1}{2})^5$
6. $n \cdot n^4$ n^5
7. $k^{10} \cdot k^{12}$ k^{22}
8. $a^3 \cdot a \cdot a^2$ a^6

9. $7 \cdot 7^2 \cdot 7^3$ 7^6
10. $(-1)^3(-1)^5$ $(-1)^8$
11. $2^x \cdot 2^3$ 2^{x+3}
12. $m^x \cdot m^y$ m^{x+y}

Solve each equation. (Example 4)

13. $10^5 = x^5$ $x = 10$ **14.** $10^x \cdot 10^2 = 10^9$ $x = 7$ **15.** $x^6 \cdot 3^5 = 3^{11}$ $x = 3$

16. $(\frac{1}{2})^3(\frac{1}{2})^5 = (\frac{1}{2})^x$ $x = 8$ **17.** $3 \cdot 3^2 = x$ $x = 27$ **18.** $5^3 \cdot 5^x = 5^4$ $x = 1$

WRITTEN EXERCISES

See the Teacher's Manual for the suggested assignments.

Goal: To write a product of powers as one power
Sample Problem: $r^4 \cdot r \cdot r^3$ **Answer:** r^8

Write each product as one power. (Examples 1–2)

1. $12^3 \cdot 12^7$ 12^{10} **2.** $10^5 \cdot 10^4$ 10^9 **3.** $5 \cdot 5^3$ 5^4 **4.** $6 \cdot 6^4$ 6^5

5. $(3.2)^5(3.2)^7$ $(3.2)^{12}$ **6.** $(3.14)^3(3.14)^2(3.14)^5$ **7.** $(-15)^4(-15)^5$ $(-15)^9$ **8.** $(-10)^4(-10)^2$ $(-10)^6$

9. $(-6)^2(-6)^9$ $(-6)^{11}$ **10.** $(-\frac{1}{4})^3(-\frac{1}{4})^2(-\frac{1}{4})^5$ **11.** $(-\frac{2}{3})(-\frac{2}{3})^2(-\frac{2}{3})^5(-\frac{2}{3})^8$ **12.** $x^2 \cdot x^5$ x^7

13. $a^4 \cdot a^3$ a^7 **14.** $y^m \cdot y^n$ y^{m+n} **15.** $r^8 \cdot r^t$ r^{8+t} **16.** $r^4 \cdot r \cdot r^3$ r^8

17. $a^3 \cdot a^2 \cdot a^6$ a^{11} **18.** $b^4 \cdot b \cdot b^3$ b^8 **19.** $5^2 \cdot 5^m$ 5^{2+m} **20.** $12^x \cdot 12^3$ 12^{x+3}

Write each product as a sum or difference. (Example 3)

21. $y^2(y + y^2)$ $y^3 + y^4$ **22.** $a^3(a^2 + a)$ $a^5 + a^4$ **23.** $x^4(x^5 + x^3)$ $x^9 + x^7$ **24.** $m^5(m^2 + m^3)$ $m^7 + m^8$

25. $(2^3 - 2^5)2^2$ $2^5 - 2^7$ **26.** $(10^4 - 10^2)10^3$ $10^7 - 10^5$ **27.** $n(n^3 - n^2 + n)$ $n^4 - n^3 + n^2$ **28.** $s^3(s^5 - s^3 - s)$ $s^8 - s^6 - s^4$

Solve each equation. (Example 4)

29. $10^5 \cdot 10^6 = 10^x$ $x = 11$ **30.** $8^3 \cdot 8^9 = 8^x$ $x = 12$

31. $(0.5)^x(0.5)^2 = (0.5)^7$ $x = 5$ **32.** $(1.2)^5(1.2)^x = (1.2)^9$ $x = 4$

33. $x^5 \cdot 3^5 = 3^{10}$ $x = 3$ **34.** $5^5 \cdot x^5 = 5^{10}$ $x = 5$

35. $(\pi)^6(\pi)^3 = x^9$ $x = \pi$ **36.** $(-\frac{2}{3})^2(-\frac{2}{3})^9 = x^{11}$ $x = -\frac{2}{3}$

REVIEW CAPSULE FOR SECTION 7.2

Evaluate both sides of each equation. Then write <u>True</u> or <u>False</u> for the equation. (Section 1.7)

1. $\dfrac{2^5}{2^2} = 2^3$ True   **2.** $\dfrac{3^5}{3^3} = 3^2$ True   **3.** $\dfrac{2^6}{2^2} = 2^3$ False   **4.** $\dfrac{x^5}{y^3} = \left(\dfrac{x}{y}\right)^2$ when $x = -2$, $y = 1$ False

7.2 Quotients of Powers and Zero Exponents

OBJECTIVES: To write a quotient of two powers of the same base as one power
To identify whether or not an equation involving a quotient of powers is true
To solve a special equation by applying the Quotient Property of Powers
To simplify an expression involving one or more powers with 0 as an exponent

P-1   How can you express x^5 as a product? x^3 as a product?

$x \cdot x \cdot x \cdot x \cdot x$ $x \cdot x \cdot x$

example 1   Write $\dfrac{x^5}{x^3}$ as one power.

Solution:

1️⃣ Meaning of a power ⟶ $\dfrac{x^5}{x^3} = \dfrac{x \cdot x \cdot x \cdot x \cdot x}{x \cdot x \cdot x}$

2️⃣ Product Rule for Fractions ⟶ $= \dfrac{x \cdot x \cdot x}{x \cdot x \cdot x} \cdot \dfrac{x \cdot x}{1}$ ◀ **Remember that** $\dfrac{x \cdot x \cdot x}{x \cdot x \cdot x} = 1.$

3️⃣ Multiplication Property of 1 ⟶ $= \dfrac{x \cdot x}{1}$

4️⃣ Simplify. ⟶ $= x^2$

> **Quotient Property of Powers**
>
> If a and b are integers and x is a nonzero real number, then $\dfrac{x^a}{x^b} = x^{a-b}.$ $\dfrac{5^{12}}{5^3} = 5^{12-3}$
>
> $= 5^9$

P-2   **Write each quotient below as one power.**

a. $\dfrac{17^7}{17^4}$ 17^3 **b.** $(1.8)^8 \div (1.8)^3$ $(1.8)^5$ **c.** $\dfrac{m^{12}}{m^5}$ m^7 ◀ **Keep the same base. Subtract the exponents.**

example 2   Solve: $\dfrac{12^t}{12^3} = 12^4$

Solution: $\dfrac{12^t}{12^3} = 12^4$

$12^{t-3} = 12^4$

$t - 3 = 4$ ◀ **Since the bases are equal, the exponents are also equal.**

$t = 7$

P-3 How can you express $\dfrac{113^5}{113^5}$ as one power by using the Quotient Property of Powers? 113^0

P-4 Simplify $\dfrac{a}{a}$ if a is any nonzero real number. 1

This discussion inductively establishes the Property of a Zero Exponent stated below.

$$\dfrac{113^5}{113^5} = 113^{5-5}$$ ◄ **By the Quotient Property of Powers**

$$= 113^0$$

$$\dfrac{113^5}{113^5} = 1$$ ◄ **By the special property:** $\dfrac{a}{a} = 1$

Thus, it is clear that 113^0 equals 1.

P-5 **What is the value of any nonzero real number raised to the 0 power?** 1

Consider $\dfrac{x^m}{x^m}$, in which m is any integer and x is any nonzero real number.

$$\dfrac{x^m}{x^m} = x^{m-m}$$ ◄ **By the Quotient Property of Powers**

$$= x^0$$

$$\dfrac{x^m}{x^m} = 1$$ ◄ **By the special property:** $\dfrac{a}{a} = 1$

This shows that x^0 equals 1. Thus, the following property has been proved.

Property of a Zero Exponent

If x is any nonzero real number, then $x^0 = 1$.

$(-27)^0 = 1$

$(\sqrt{5})^0 = 1$

P-6 **Simplify each expression below.**

a. $\left(\dfrac{3}{4}\right)^0 + 12^0$ 2   **b.** $(-5.2)^0 - (\sqrt{3})^0$ 0   **c.** $\left(\dfrac{t}{25}\right)^0$ 1

CLASSROOM EXERCISES

Write each quotient as one power. No divisor equals 0. (Example 1)

1. $\dfrac{3^5}{3^2}$ 3^3

2. $\dfrac{10^8}{10^3}$ 10^5

3. $\dfrac{(-3)^6}{(-3)^2}$ $(-3)^4$

4. $\dfrac{x^{10}}{x^7}$ x^3

5. $\dfrac{a^7}{a^5}$ a^2

6. $\dfrac{b^4}{b}$ b^3

7. $2^7 \div 2^4$ 2^3

8. $y^{12} \div y^7$ y^5

9. $\left(\dfrac{1}{2}\right)^{10} \div \left(\dfrac{1}{2}\right)^3$ $(\frac{1}{2})^7$

10. $12^3 \div 12^k$ 12^{3-k}

11. $\dfrac{(-5)^t}{(-5)^4}$ $(-5)^{t-4}$

12. $\dfrac{(0.5)^p}{(0.5)^q}$ $(0.5)^{p-q}$

Write <u>True</u> *or* <u>False</u> *for each sentence.* (Example 1)

13. $\dfrac{6^4}{3^2} = 2^2$ False

14. $\dfrac{10^{10}}{10^5} = 1^5$ False

15. $\dfrac{2^7}{3^2} = \left(\dfrac{2}{3}\right)^5$ False

16. $\dfrac{5^4}{5^3} = \dfrac{1}{5}$ False

17. $\dfrac{2^4}{4^1} = 2^2$ True

18. $\dfrac{13}{7^2} = (13-7)^3$ False

Simplify. (P-5, P-6)

19. 2^0 1

20. 100^0 1

21. $(-5)^0$ 1

22. $\left(-\dfrac{2}{3}\right)^0$ 1

23. $(0.5)^0$ 1

24. $(-\pi)^0$ 1

25. $w^0; w \neq 0$ 1

26. $\left(\dfrac{1}{t}\right)^0; t \neq 0$ 1

WRITTEN EXERCISES

See the Teacher's Manual for the suggested assignments.

Goal: To write a quotient of powers as one power
Sample Problem: $y^{12} \div y^4$
Answer: y^8

Write each quotient as one power. (Example 1)

1. $\dfrac{10^5}{10^3}$ 10^2

2. $\dfrac{8^6}{8^3}$ 8^3

3. $\left(\dfrac{1}{2}\right)^3 \div \left(\dfrac{1}{2}\right)^2$ $(\frac{1}{2})^1$ or $\frac{1}{2}$

4. $\left(\dfrac{1}{4}\right)^5 \div \left(\dfrac{1}{4}\right)^3$ $(\frac{1}{4})^2$

5. $\dfrac{x^{12}}{x^8}$ x^4

6. $\dfrac{a^{15}}{a^{12}}$ a^3

7. $\dfrac{2^{12}}{2^9}$ 2^3

8. $\dfrac{10^7}{10^3}$ 10^4

9. $\dfrac{(0.6)^3}{(0.6)^2}$ $(0.6)^1$ or 0.6

10. $\dfrac{(1.3)^6}{(1.3)^5}$ $(1.3)^1$ or 1.3

11. $\dfrac{\pi^5}{\pi^2}$ π^3

12. $\dfrac{(-\pi)^5}{(-\pi)^3}$ $(-\pi)^2$

Write True or False for each equation. (Example 1)

13. $\dfrac{10^{11}}{10^{10}} = 10$ True

14. $\dfrac{100^{98}}{100^{96}} = 10,000$ True

15. $\dfrac{10^5}{5^2} = 2^3$ False

16. $\dfrac{12^7}{3^4} = 4^3$ False

17. $\dfrac{3^8}{3^4} = 3^2$ False

18. $\dfrac{5^6}{5^2} = 5^3$ False

19. $\dfrac{(\sqrt{2})^7}{(\sqrt{2})^2} = (\sqrt{2})^5$ True

20. $\dfrac{(-\sqrt{3})^{10}}{(-\sqrt{3})^6} = 3^2$ True

21. $\dfrac{10^3 \cdot 10^5}{10^4} = 10^4$ True

22. $\dfrac{10^9}{10^2 \cdot 10^3} = 10,000$ True

Solve each equation. (Example 2)

23. $\dfrac{2^x}{2^2} = 2^3$ $x = 5$

24. $\dfrac{3^y}{3^5} = 3^2$ $y = 7$

25. $\dfrac{x^5}{10^3} = 10^2$ $x = 10$

26. $\dfrac{5^9}{a^3} = 5^6$ $a = 5$

27. $\dfrac{10^7}{10^2} = 10^x$ $x = 5$

28. $\dfrac{10^{10}}{10^3} = 10^y$ $y = 7$

29. $\dfrac{11^{2x}}{11^x} = 11^4$ $x = 4$

30. $\dfrac{5^{3x}}{5^x} = 5^{12}$ $x = 6$

31. $10^0 = x$ $x = 1$

32. $7^0 = n$ $n = 1$

33. $\left(\dfrac{1}{2}\right)^0 = y$ $y = 1$

34. $\left(-\dfrac{1}{4}\right)^0 = a$ $a = 1$

35. $(0.7)^a = 1$ $a = 0$

36. $(-1.3)^x = 1$ $x = 0$

37. $7^x - 5^x = 0$ $x = 0$

38. $\left(\dfrac{\sqrt{2}}{\sqrt{7}}\right)^x = 1$ $x = 0$

39. $1 = p^0$ p = any nonzero real number

40. $y^0 = 1$ y = any nonzero real number

Simplify. (P-6)

41. $93^0 - 2$ -1

42. $(-114)^0 + 5$ 6

43. $3x^0 + 2y^0$ 5

44. $5m^0 + 3n^0$ 8

45. $-2r^0 + t^0$ -1

46. $p^0 - 4q^0$ -3

REVIEW CAPSULE FOR SECTION 7.3

Subtract. (Section 1.3)

1. $4 - 6$ -2 **2.** $2 - (-3)$ 5   **3.** $(-5) - (-1)$ -4 **4.** $(-3) - 7$ -10 **5.** $0 - (-5)$ 5

7.3 Negative Exponents

OBJECTIVES: To simplify powers involving negative exponents
To simplify products or quotients of powers involving negative exponents

The Product and Quotient Properties of Powers apply to negative exponents as well as to positive and zero exponents.

example 1

Simplify $\dfrac{x^3}{x^6}$.

Solution:

1. Meaning of a power $\longrightarrow$ $\dfrac{x^3}{x^6} = \dfrac{x \cdot x \cdot x}{x \cdot x \cdot x \cdot x \cdot x \cdot x}$

2. Product Rule for Fractions $\longrightarrow$ $= \dfrac{x \cdot x \cdot x}{x \cdot x \cdot x} \cdot \dfrac{1}{x \cdot x \cdot x}$

3. Multiplication Property of 1 $\longrightarrow$ $= \dfrac{1}{x \cdot x \cdot x}$

4. Simplify. $\longrightarrow$ $= \dfrac{1}{x^3}$

The Quotient Property of Powers is used for the same expression.

$$\frac{x^3}{x^6} = x^{3-6}$$

Exponent of numerator less the exponent of denominator

$$= x^{-3}$$

Thus, the following sentence is true for all nonzero real numbers.

$$\frac{1}{x^3} = x^{-3}$$

$\dfrac{1}{x^3}$ **is considered to be the simplest form.**

Since x cannot equal 0 in $\dfrac{1}{x^3}$, it cannot equal 0 in x^{-3}.

You may want to discuss why $x^{-a} = \dfrac{1}{x^a}$ is also true when a is *any* integer.

> ### Property of Negative Exponents
>
> If $-a$ represents a negative integer and x is a nonzero real number, then $x^{-a} = \dfrac{1}{x^a}$.
>
> $$3^{-2} = \frac{1}{3^2}$$
>
> $$(-1.3)^{-5} = \frac{1}{(-1.3)^5}$$

P-1 **Simplify.**

a. r^{-3} $\quad \dfrac{1}{r^3}$ b. m^{-6} $\quad \dfrac{1}{m^6}$ c. 3^{-2} d. 2^{-4} e. 10^{-3} $\quad \dfrac{1}{10^3}$ or $\dfrac{1}{1000}$

$\dfrac{1}{3^2}$ or $\dfrac{1}{9}$ $\qquad$ $\dfrac{1}{2^4}$ or $\dfrac{1}{16}$

Powers / **159**

P-2 **What is the rule for multiplying powers of the same base?**
Add the exponents. Keep the same base.

example 2   Write $y^{-5} \cdot y^3$ as one power. Then simplify.

Solution:

$\boxed{1}$ Product Property of Powers $\longrightarrow$ $y^{-5} \cdot y^3 = y^{-5+3}$

$\boxed{2}$ Add the exponents. $\longrightarrow$ $= y^{-2}$

$\boxed{3}$ Simplify. $\longrightarrow$ $= \dfrac{1}{y^2}$

P-3 **Write each product below as one power.**

a. $17^{-2} \cdot 17$ 17^{-1} **b.** $(1.2)^{-2}(1.2)^6$ $(1.2)^4$ **c.** $r^{-1} \cdot r^3 \cdot r^{-5}$ r^{-3}

P-4 **What is the rule for dividing powers of the same base?**
Subtract the exponents. Keep the same base.

example 3   Write $\dfrac{x^{-5}}{x^{-2}}$ as one power.

Solution:

$\boxed{1}$ Quotient Property of Powers $\longrightarrow$ $\dfrac{x^{-5}}{x^{-2}} = x^{-5-(-2)}$

$\boxed{2}$ Subtract the exponents. $\longrightarrow$ $= x^{-3}$ ◀ **The simplest name is $\dfrac{1}{x^3}$.**

P-5 **Write each quotient below as one power.**

a. $\dfrac{5^{-1}}{5^{-3}}$ 5^2 **b.** $\dfrac{(3.7)^2}{(3.7)^5}$ 3.7^{-3} **c.** $\dfrac{y^0}{y^{-2}}$ y^2 **d.** $\dfrac{x^0}{x^{-5}}$ x^5 **e.** $\dfrac{r^{-4}}{r^0}$ r^{-4}

example 4   Write as one power and simplify: $\dfrac{m^6 \cdot m^{-3}}{m^4}$

Solution:

$\boxed{1}$ Product Property of Powers $\longrightarrow$ $\dfrac{m^6 \cdot m^{-3}}{m^4} = \dfrac{m^3}{m^4}$

$\boxed{2}$ Quotient Property of Powers $\longrightarrow$ $= m^{-1}$

$\boxed{3}$ Simplify. $\longrightarrow$ $= \dfrac{1}{m}$

CLASSROOM EXERCISES

Write each expression as a power with a negative exponent. (Property of Negative Exponents)

1. $\dfrac{1}{5^{10}}$ $\quad 5^{-10}$

2. $\dfrac{1}{(-3)^4}$ $\quad (-3)^{-4}$

3. $\dfrac{1}{(5.2)^2}$ $\quad (5.2)^{-2}$

4. $\dfrac{1}{(325)^5}$ $\quad 325^{-5}$

5. $\dfrac{1}{r^8}$ $\quad r^{-8}$

6. $\dfrac{1}{t}$ $\quad t^{-1}$

Write each product or quotient as one power. (Examples 2–3)

7. $x^2 \cdot x^5$ $\quad x^7$

8. $(2^{-3})(2^5)$ $\quad 2^2$

9. $\dfrac{2^5}{2^3}$ $\quad 2^2$

10. $\dfrac{10^{-2}}{10^{-1}}$ $\quad 10^{-1}$

WRITTEN EXERCISES

See the Teacher's Manual for the suggested assignments.

Goal: To simplify powers and products and quotients of powers involving positive and negative exponents

Sample Problem: $\dfrac{a^2 \cdot a^{-7}}{a^{-10}}$ **Answer:** a^5

Simplify each expression. (Examples 2–3)

1. r^{-4} $\quad \dfrac{1}{r^4}$

2. t^{-8} $\quad \dfrac{1}{t^8}$

3. $2y^{-5}$ $\quad \dfrac{2}{y^5}$

4. $6m^{-2}$ $\quad \dfrac{6}{m^2}$

5. 4^{-2} $\quad \dfrac{1}{4^2}$ or $\dfrac{1}{16}$

6. 3^{-3} $\quad \dfrac{1}{3^3}$ or $\dfrac{1}{27}$

7. $(-3)^{-3}$ $\quad \dfrac{1}{(-3)^3}$ or $-\dfrac{1}{27}$

8. $(-2)^{-3}$ $\quad \dfrac{1}{(-2)^3}$ or $-\dfrac{1}{8}$

9. ab^{-3} $\quad \dfrac{a}{b^3}$

10. rs^{-2} $\quad \dfrac{r}{s^2}$

11. $\dfrac{2^3}{2^{-2}}$ $\quad 2^5$ or 32

12. $\dfrac{10^{-1}}{10^{-3}}$ $\quad 10^2$ or 100

13. $\dfrac{a^2}{a^5}$ $\quad a^{-3}$

14. $\dfrac{y}{y^3}$ $\quad y^{-2}$

15. $(2^{50})(2^{-49})$ $\quad 2$

16. $(10^{100})(10^{-99})$ $\quad 10$

Write each product or quotient as one power. Then simplify where necessary. (Examples 2–4)

17. $a^5 \cdot a^{-3}$ $\quad a^2$

18. $b^{-2} \cdot b^7$ $\quad b^5$

19. $x^{-3} \cdot x^{-2}$ $\quad x^{-5}; \dfrac{1}{x^5}$

20. $y^{-1} \cdot y^{-2}$ $\quad y^{-3}; \dfrac{1}{y^3}$

21. $\dfrac{n^2}{n^3}$ $\quad n^{-1}; \dfrac{1}{n}$

22. $\dfrac{m^5}{m^7}$ $\quad m^{-2}; \dfrac{1}{m^2}$

23. $\dfrac{r^{-2}}{r^{-5}}$ $\quad r^3$

24. $\dfrac{s^{-6}}{s^{-3}}$ $\quad s^{-3}; \dfrac{1}{s^3}$

25. $\dfrac{t^0}{t^{-3}}$ $\quad t^3$

26. $\dfrac{w^0}{w^{-5}}$ $\quad w^5$

27. $\dfrac{p^{-2}}{p^0}$ $\quad p^{-2}; \dfrac{1}{p^2}$

28. $\dfrac{g^5}{g^0}$ $\quad g^5$

29. $(10^2)(10^7)(10^{-5})$ $\quad 10^4$

30. $(5^{-2})(5^4)(5^{-3})$ $\quad 5^{-1}; \dfrac{1}{5}$

31. $(y^{-5})(y^6)(y^{-3})$ $\quad y^{-2}; \dfrac{1}{y^2}$

32. $(b^7)(b^{-3})(b^{-2})$ $\quad b^2$

33. $\dfrac{r^3 \cdot r^{-5}}{r^{-2}}$ $\quad r^0; 1$

34. $\dfrac{s^{-2} \cdot s^{-3}}{s^{-7}}$ $\quad s^2$

MID-CHAPTER REVIEW

NOTE: After completing the Mid-Chapter Review, you may want to administer a quiz covering the same sections. See pages M-22 and M-23 of the Teacher's Manual for the suggested quiz.

Write each product as one power. (Section 7.1)

1. $12^x \cdot 12^y$ 12^{x+y}

2. $(1.4)^2(1.4)^5$ $(1.4)^7$

3. $(-6)^4(-6)^{10}$ $(-6)^{14}$

4. $(\frac{3}{4})^m \cdot (\frac{3}{4})^5$ $(\frac{3}{4})^{m+5}$

5. $(-0.9)^3(-0.9)$ $(-0.9)^4$

6. $(-\frac{5}{4})^x \cdot (-\frac{5}{4})^y$ $(-\frac{5}{4})^{x+y}$

7. $r^2 \cdot r^3 \cdot r^5$ r^{10}

8. $(3.7)^4(3.7)^{24}$ $(3.7)^{28}$

Write each quotient as one power (Section 7.2)

9. $\dfrac{(21)^5}{(21)^3}$ 21^2

10. $\dfrac{(-7)^8}{(-7)^3}$ $(-7)^5$

11. $\left(\dfrac{3}{4}\right)^6 \div \left(\dfrac{3}{4}\right)^3$ $(\frac{3}{4})^3$

12. $\dfrac{(5.3)^{10}}{(5.3)^5}$ $(5.3)^5$

Simplify.

13. $(0.9)^0$ 1

14. $(-\frac{5}{8})^0$ 1

15. $5^0 - 144^0$ 0

16. $-7t^0, t \neq 0$ -7

Write each product or quotient as one power. Then simplify. (Section 7.3)

17. $(0.6)^{-7}(0.6)^4$ $(0.6)^{-3}; \dfrac{1}{(0.6)^3}$

18. $(8.1)^{-2}(8.1)^{-3}$ $(8.1)^{-5}; \dfrac{1}{8.1^5}$

19. $w^{-1} \cdot w^{-5}$ $w^{-6}; \dfrac{1}{w^6}$

20. $p^8 \cdot p^{-3}$ p^5

21. $(12)^3 \div (12)^5$ $12^{-2}; \dfrac{1}{12^2}$

22. $(5.9)^{-2} \div (5.9)^4$ $(5.9)^{-6}; \dfrac{1}{(5.9)^6}$

23. $\dfrac{m^2}{m^5}, m \neq 0$ $m^{-3}; \dfrac{1}{m^3}$

24. $\dfrac{t^{-1}}{t^4}, t \neq 0$ $t^{-5}; \dfrac{1}{t^5}$

EVALUATING FRACTIONS

You can use a calculator to evaluate a fraction with a power in the denominator.

EXAMPLE   Evaluate $\dfrac{1}{(2.9)^3}$

SOLUTION

   $\boxed{2} \; \boxed{\cdot} \; \boxed{9} \; \boxed{\times} \; \boxed{=} \; \boxed{=} \; \boxed{\div} \; \boxed{=} \; \boxed{=}$ 0.041002

Note how much more efficient this method is than to divide 1 by the cube of 2.9.

▲ **On some calculators press "=" twice here.**

Evaluate.

1. $\dfrac{1}{2^{10}}$ 0.0009765

2. $\dfrac{1}{3^{12}}$ 0.0000018

3. $\dfrac{1}{(4.8)^5}$ 0.0003924

4. $\dfrac{1}{(0.9)^4}$ 1.5241579

5. $\dfrac{1}{(0.86)^{12}}$ 6.1096827

6. $\dfrac{1}{(0.92)^{15}}$ 3.492875

7. $\dfrac{1}{(3^8)(3.14)}$ 0.0000485

8. $\dfrac{1}{(0.6)^7(3140)}$ 0.0113765

REVIEW CAPSULE FOR SECTION 7.4

Multiply. (Section 2.3)

1. $(2w)(2w)(2w)$ $8w^3$

2. $(-3t)(-3t)(-3t)$ $-27t^3$

3. $(-0.1r)(-0.1r)(-0.1r)$ $-0.001r^3$

4. $(\frac{p}{5})(\frac{p}{5})(\frac{p}{5})(\frac{p}{5})$ $\dfrac{p^4}{625}$

7.4 Powers of Products and Quotients

OBJECTIVES: To simplify a power of a product by use of the Property of the Power of a Product
To simplify a power of a quotient by use of the Property of the Powers of a Quotient

P-1 **What is the value of $2x^3$ if x equals 1?** 2 ◀ Raise 1 to the third power. Then multiply by 2.

P-2 **What is the value of $(2x)^3$ if x equals 1?** 8 ◀ Multiply $2 \cdot 1$. Then raise to the third power.

You can see that $2x^3$ does not equal $(2x)^3$.

example 1   Simplify $(2x)^3$.

Solution:

$\boxed{1}$ Meaning of a power ⟶ $(2x)^3 = (2x)(2x)(2x)$

$\boxed{2}$ Commutative and Associative
Properties of Multiplication ⟶ $= (2 \cdot 2 \cdot 2)(x \cdot x \cdot x)$ ◀ **Thus, $(2x)^3 = 2^3x^3$.**

$\boxed{3}$ Simplify. ⟶ $= 8x^3$

Property of the Power of a Product	$(-3t)^3 = (-3)^3t^3$
If x and y are nonzero real numbers and a is any integer, then $(xy)^a = x^ay^a$.	$= -27t^3$ $(pq)^{-2} = p^{-2}q^{-2}$

P-3 **Simplify.**

a. $(xy)^2$ x^2y^2 **b.** $(3a)^2$ $9a^2$ **c.** $(2r)^3$ $8r^3$ **d.** $(-3r)^2$ $9r^2$

P-4 **What is the name for $(rs)^{-3}$ based on the Property of the Power of a Product?** $r^{-3}s^{-3}$

example 2   Simplify $(rs)^{-3}$.

Solution:

$\boxed{1}$ Property of the Power of a Product ⟶ $(rs)^{-3} = r^{-3}s^{-3}$

$\boxed{2}$ Property of Negative Exponents ⟶ $= \dfrac{1}{r^3} \cdot \dfrac{1}{s^3}$

$\boxed{3}$ Product Rule for Fractions ⟶ $= \dfrac{1}{r^3s^3}$

example 3　Simplify $\left(\dfrac{x}{3}\right)^3$.

Solution:

1. Meaning of a power ⟶ $\left(\dfrac{x}{3}\right)^3 = \left(\dfrac{x}{3}\right)\left(\dfrac{x}{3}\right)\left(\dfrac{x}{3}\right)$

2. Product Rule of Fractions ⟶ $= \dfrac{x \cdot x \cdot x}{3 \cdot 3 \cdot 3}$

3. Meaning of a power ⟶ $= \dfrac{x^3}{3^3}$, or $\dfrac{x^3}{27}$　◀ **Simplest form**

Property of the Power of a Quotient

If x and y are nonzero real numbers and a is any integer, then $\left(\dfrac{x}{y}\right)^a = \dfrac{x^a}{y^a}$.

$\left(\dfrac{2}{3}\right)^2 = \dfrac{2^2}{3^2}$

$\left(\dfrac{r}{s}\right)^{-3} = \dfrac{r^{-3}}{s^{-3}}$

P-5　**Simplify.**

a. $\left(\dfrac{3}{t}\right)^2$　$\dfrac{9}{t^2}$　**b.** $\left(\dfrac{p}{q}\right)^4$　$\dfrac{p^4}{q^4}$　**c.** $\left(\dfrac{2r}{s}\right)^3$　$\dfrac{8r^3}{s^3}$　**d.** $\left(\dfrac{1}{r}\right)^4$　$\dfrac{1}{r^4}$

Expression **c** above involves both properties.

$$\left(\dfrac{2r}{s}\right)^3 = \dfrac{(2r)^3}{s^3} = \dfrac{2^3 r^3}{s^3} = \dfrac{8r^3}{s^3}$$

example 4　Simplify $\left(\dfrac{2}{x}\right)^{-3}$.

Solution:

1. Property of the Power of a Quotient ⟶ $\left(\dfrac{2}{x}\right)^{-3} = \dfrac{2^{-3}}{x^{-3}}$

2. Property of a Negative Exponent ⟶ $= \dfrac{1}{2^3} \div \dfrac{1}{x^3}$

3. Meaning of division ⟶ $= \dfrac{1}{2^3} \cdot \dfrac{x^3}{1}$

4. Simplify. ⟶ $= \dfrac{x^3}{8}$

CLASSROOM EXERCISES

Simplify. (Examples 1–3)

1. $(2a)^2$ $4a^2$
2. $(3x)^2$ $9x^2$
3. $(\frac{1}{2}y)^2$ $\frac{1}{4}y^2$
4. $(2y)^3$ $8y^3$

5. $(5n)^2$ $25n^2$
6. $(4t)^2$ $16t^2$
7. $(-2b)^2$ $4b^2$
8. $(-x)^2$ x^2

9. $(0.5a)^2$ $0.25a^2$
10. $(-3m)^2$ $9m^2$
11. $(-2r)^3$ $-8r^3$
12. $(-2a)^4$ $16a^4$

13. $(xy)^2$ x^2y^2
14. $(mn)^3$ m^3n^3
15. $(ab)^4$ a^4b^4
16. $(st)^5$ s^5t^5

17. $\left(\frac{3}{x}\right)^2$ $\frac{9}{x^2}$
18. $\left(\frac{y}{2}\right)^3$ $\frac{y^3}{8}$
19. $\left(\frac{m}{n}\right)^5$ $\frac{m^5}{n^5}$
20. $\left(\frac{2a}{b}\right)^2$ $\frac{4a^2}{b^2}$

21. $\left(\frac{-x}{y}\right)^2$ $\frac{x^2}{y^2}$
22. $\left(\frac{r}{-3s}\right)^2$ $\frac{r^2}{9s^2}$
23. $\left(\frac{-2}{x}\right)^3$ $-\frac{8}{x^3}$
24. $\left(\frac{-1}{y}\right)^4$ $\frac{1}{y^4}$

WRITTEN EXERCISES

See the Teachers Manual for the suggested assignments.

Goal: To simplify a power of a product or a power of a quotient

Sample Problems: a. $(4xy)^3$ **b.** $\left(\frac{4x}{y}\right)^3$ **Answers: a.** $64x^3y^3$ **b.** $\frac{64x^3}{y^3}$

Simplify. (Examples 1–4)

1. $(3r)^3$ $27r^3$
2. $(4t)^3$ $64t^3$
3. $(-2a)^2$ $4a^2$
4. $(-3y)^2$ $9y^2$
5. $(-3p)^3$ $-27p^3$

6. $(-2q)^3$ $-8q^3$
7. $(-ab)^2$ a^2b^2
8. $(-xy)^2$ x^2y^2
9. $(-rs)^3$ $-r^3s^3$
10. $(-mn)^3$ See below.

11. $(2xy)^2$ $4x^2y^2$
12. $(3ab)^2$ $9a^2b^2$
13. $(-3pq)^2$ $9p^2q^2$
14. $(-2mn)^2$ $4m^2n^2$
15. $(-2ab)^3$ See below.

16. $(-4cd)^3$ $-64c^3d^3$
17. $\left(\frac{2}{x}\right)^3$ $\frac{8}{x^3}$
18. $\left(\frac{3}{y}\right)^2$ $\frac{9}{y^2}$
19. $\left(\frac{a}{-2}\right)^3$ $-\frac{a^3}{8}$
20. $\left(\frac{b}{-3}\right)^2$ $\frac{b^2}{9}$

21. $\left(\frac{-x}{-y}\right)^2$ $\frac{x^2}{y^2}$
22. $\left(\frac{-2a}{-2b}\right)^3$ $\frac{a^3}{b^3}$
23. $(2y)^{-2}$ $\frac{1}{4y^2}$
24. $(3r)^{-1}$ $\frac{1}{3r}$
25. $(pq)^{-3}$ $\frac{1}{p^3q^3}$

26. $(cd)^{-5}$ $\frac{1}{c^5d^5}$
27. $(-3t)^{-1}$ $-\frac{1}{3t}$
28. $(-4k)^{-2}$ $\frac{1}{16k^2}$
29. $\left(\frac{3a}{b}\right)^3$ $\frac{27a^3}{b^3}$
30. $\left(\frac{2r}{3s}\right)^3$ $\frac{8r^3}{27s^3}$

REVIEW CAPSULE FOR SECTION 7.5

10. $-m^3n^3$

15. $-8a^3b^3$

Write each product as one power. (Section 7.1)

1. $m^4 \cdot m^4 \cdot m^4$ m^{12}
2. $(-3)^2 \cdot (-3)^2 \cdot (-3)^2$ $(-3)^6$
3. $t^{-3} \cdot t^{-3} \cdot t^{-3}$ t^{-9}

4. $(2a)^{-2} \cdot (2a)^{-2} \cdot (2a)^{-2}$ $(2a)^{-6}$
5. $g^{-5} \cdot g^{-5} \cdot g^{-5} \cdot g^{-5}$ g^{-20}
6. $(-0.5)^3 \cdot (-0.5)^3$
   $(-0.5)^6$

7.5   Powers of Powers

OBJECTIVES: To simplify a power of a power
To simplify a power of an expression involving a product having one or more powers
To simplify a power of an expression involving a quotient where each term
has one or more powers

P-1   **Write $(x^2)^3$ as a product of three factors.** $(x^2)(x^2)(x^2)$

example 1   Simplify $(x^2)^3$.

Solution:

1️⃣ Meaning of a positive integral power ⟶ $(x^2)^3 = x^2 \cdot x^2 \cdot x^2$

2️⃣ Product Property of Powers ⟶ $= x^6$

P-2   **How is the exponent 6 related to the exponents 2 and 3?** $2 \cdot 3 = 6$

example 2   Simplify $(y^{-4})^{-3}$.

Solution:

1️⃣ Property of a Negative Exponent ⟶ $(y^{-4})^{-3} = \dfrac{1}{(y^{-4})^3}$

2️⃣ Meaning of a positive integral power ⟶ $= \dfrac{1}{(y^{-4})(y^{-4})(y^{-4})}$

3️⃣ Product Property of Powers ⟶ $= \dfrac{1}{y^{-12}}$

4️⃣ Property of a Negative Exponent ⟶ $= y^{12}$

P-3   **How is the exponent 12 related to the exponents -4 and -3?**

$(-4)(-3) = 12$

Property of the Power of a Power

To raise a power
to a power, multiply
exponents.

If x is a nonzero real number and a
and b are integers, then $(x^a)^b = x^{ab}$

$(r^{-2})^4 = r^{(-2)(4)}$

$= r^{-8}$

P-4   **Simplify.**

a. $(m^3)^5$ m^{15} **b.** $(k^{-4})^{-2}$ k^8 **c.** $(t^4)^{-1}$

t^{-4}

◀ **Keep the same base.
Multiply the exponents.**

example 3
Simplify $(2x^2y^3)^{-2}$

Solution:

1. Property of the Power of a Product ⟶ $(2x^2y^3)^{-2} = 2^{-2}(x^2)^{-2}(y^3)^{-2}$
2. Property of the Power of a Power ⟶ $= 2^{-2}x^{-4}y^{-6}$
3. Property of a Negative Exponent ⟶ $= \dfrac{1}{2^2} \cdot \dfrac{1}{x^4} \cdot \dfrac{1}{y^6}$
4. Product Rule for Fractions ⟶ $= \dfrac{1}{4x^4y^6}$

The table below shows powers of 2.

Base	Exponent	Power
2	12	4096
2	11	2048
2	10	1024
2	9	512
2	8	256
2	7	128
2	6	64
2	5	32
2	4	16
2	3	8
2	2	4
2	1	2
2	0	1
2	−1	$\frac{1}{2}$
2	−2	$\frac{1}{4}$
2	−3	$\frac{1}{8}$
2	−4	$\frac{1}{16}$
2	−5	$\frac{1}{32}$
2	−6	$\frac{1}{64}$
2	−7	$\frac{1}{128}$
2	−8	$\frac{1}{256}$
2	−9	$\frac{1}{512}$

P-5   **Simplify.**

a. 2^9 512 **b.** 2^{-11} $\frac{1}{2048}$ **c.** $(2^{-5})^2$ $\frac{1}{1024}$ **d.** $(m^{-1})^{-5}$ m^5

example 4   Simplify $\left(\frac{2^4 s^3 t^2}{r^4}\right)^3$.

Solution:

☐1 Property of the Power of a Quotient $\longrightarrow$ $\left(\frac{2^4 s^3 t^2}{r^4}\right)^3 = \frac{(2^4 s^3 t^2)^3}{(r^4)^3}$

☐2 Property of the Power of a Product $\longrightarrow$ $= \frac{(2^4)^3 (s^3)^3 (t^2)^3}{(r^4)^3}$

☐3 Property of the Power of a Power $\longrightarrow$ $= \frac{2^{12} s^9 t^6}{r^{12}}$

☐4 Simplify. $\longrightarrow$ $= \frac{4096 s^9 t^6}{r^{12}}$ ◀ *Use the table of powers of 2.*

CLASSROOM EXERCISES

Simplify. (Examples 1–2)

1. $(3^2)^3$ 3^6

2. $(10^4)^3$ 10^{12}

3. $(a^{-1})^3$ $\frac{1}{a^3}$

4. $(b^2)^{-3}$ $\frac{1}{b^6}$

5. $(y^{-2})^{-3}$ y^6

6. $(t^{-5})^0$ 1

7. $(0.5^2)^4$ $(0.5)^8$

8. $(100^{-2})^{10}$ $\frac{1}{100^{20}}$

9. $(-3^4)^6$ $(-3)^{24}$

Simplify. (Examples 2–4)

10. $(r^2)^{-1}$ $\frac{1}{r^2}$

11. $(t^{-3})^2$ $\frac{1}{t^6}$

12. $(m^2 n^{-1})^3$ $\frac{m^6}{n^3}$

13. $(3q^{-2})^{-2}$ $\frac{q^4}{9}$

14. $(r^{-10})^{-2}$ r^{20}

15. $\left(\frac{x^2}{x^3}\right)^2$ $\frac{1}{x^2}$

16. $\left(\frac{a^3}{b^4}\right)^3$ $\frac{a^9}{b^{12}}$

17. $\left(\frac{r^{-2}}{s^3}\right)^3$ $\frac{1}{r^6 s^9}$

18. $\left(\frac{m^{-1}}{m^{-2}}\right)^{-5}$ $\frac{1}{m^5}$

19. $\left(\frac{x^2}{y^{-3}}\right)^{-3}$ $\frac{1}{x^6 y^9}$

20. $\left(\frac{10^{-2}}{y^{-3}}\right)^{-1}$ $\frac{100}{y^3}$

21. $\left(\frac{-2^3}{-5^2}\right)^0$ 1

22. $\left(\frac{6^{-2}}{8^{-3}}\right)^0$ 1

23. $\left(\frac{s^{-4}}{m^{-2}}\right)^{-2}$ $\frac{s^8}{m^4}$

24. $\left(\frac{-x^2}{y^{-2}}\right)^{-3}$

$\frac{1}{-x^6 y^6}$

WRITTEN EXERCISES

See the Teacher's Manual for the suggested assignments.

Goal: To simplify powers of powers

Sample Problem: $(t^{-2})^{-5}$ **Answer:** t^{10}

Simplify. (Examples 1–4)

1. $(a^2)^4$ a^8

2. $(p^3)^2$ p^6

3. $(y^{-2})^5$ $\dfrac{1}{y^{10}}$

4. $(r^2)^{-4}$ $\dfrac{1}{r^8}$

5. $(m^{-1})^5$ $\dfrac{1}{m^5}$

6. $(n^{-2})^{-5}$ n^{10}

7. $(t^2)^{-2}$ $\dfrac{1}{t^4}$

8. $(w^{-3})^4$ $\dfrac{1}{w^{12}}$

9. $(3r^3)^2$ $9r^6$

10. $(4s^5)^2$ $16s^{10}$

11. $(2a^2b)^3$ $8a^6b^3$

12. $(2ab^3)^2$ $4a^2b^6$

13. $(2xy^2)^5$ $32x^5y^{10}$

14. $(2x^3y^2)^4$ $16x^{12}y^8$

15. $\left(\dfrac{x^3}{2}\right)^5$ $\dfrac{x^{15}}{32}$

16. $\left(\dfrac{y^2}{2}\right)^6$ $\dfrac{y^{12}}{64}$

17. $\left(\dfrac{2a^2b^3}{c^{21}}\right)^5$ $\dfrac{32a^{10}b^{15}}{c^{105}}$

18. $\left(\dfrac{2xy^3}{r^4}\right)^6$ $\dfrac{64x^6y^{18}}{r^{24}}$

19. $(-2t^3)^3$ $-8t^9$

20. $(-2m^{-2}n^3)^{-1}$ $-\dfrac{m^2}{2n^3}$

21. $(2xy^2)^{-3}$ $\dfrac{1}{8x^3y^6}$

22. $(3r^2s^3)^{-2}$ $\dfrac{1}{9r^4s^6}$

23. $(4m^{-2}n^3)^{-1}$ $\dfrac{m^2}{4n^3}$

24. $(10a^{-4}b^2)^{-1}$ $\dfrac{a^4}{10b^2}$

25. $(2^{-3}r^{-1}s^3)^{-2}$ $\dfrac{64r^2}{s^6}$

26. $(2^{-4}p^4q^{-2})^{-3}$ $\dfrac{4096q^6}{p^{12}}$

27. $(-2x^2y^{-1}z^3)^{-5}$ See below.

28. $(-2r^{-2}s^4t^3)^{-6}$ $\dfrac{r^{12}}{64s^{24}t^{18}}$

29. $(0.2m^4n^5)^7$ $0.0000128m^{28}n^{35}$

30. $(-0.2x^5y^2)^5$

$-0.00032x^{25}y^{10}$

MORE CHALLENGING EXERCISES

31. $\left(\dfrac{1}{t^3}\right)^{-4}$ t^{12}

32. $\left(\dfrac{1}{m^{-2}}\right)^5$ m^{10}

33. $\left(\dfrac{2r^2}{s^3}\right)^{-3}$ $\dfrac{s^9}{8r^6}$

34. $\left(\dfrac{3x^4}{y^3}\right)^{-2}$ $\dfrac{y^6}{9x^8}$

35. $\left(\dfrac{4a^{-2}}{b^3}\right)^{-3}$ $\dfrac{a^6b^9}{64}$

36. $\left(\dfrac{-2p^3}{q^{-1}r^{-2}}\right)^{-4}$ See below.

37. $\left(\dfrac{-3n^{-3}}{x^{-3}}\right)^{-3}$ $-\dfrac{n^9}{27x^9}$

38. $\left(\dfrac{4s^{-4}}{m^{-4}}\right)^{-4}$ $\dfrac{s^{16}}{256m^{16}}$

39. $\left(\dfrac{-5r^3}{m^{-2}n^{-3}}\right)^{-2}$ See below.

27. $-\dfrac{y^5}{32x^{10}z^{15}}$ 36. $\dfrac{1}{16p^{12}q^4r^8}$

39. $\dfrac{1}{25m^4n^6r^6}$

REVIEW CAPSULE FOR SECTION 7.6

Multiply each number (a) by 1000 and (b) by 100,000.

1. 0.0015678 $\begin{array}{l}1.5678\\156.78\end{array}$

2. 0.826605027 $\begin{array}{l}826.605027\\82660.5027\end{array}$

3. 48.2783 $\begin{array}{l}48278.3\\4827830\end{array}$

4. $5280.$ $\begin{array}{l}5{,}280{,}000\\528{,}000{,}000\end{array}$

Divide each number (a) by 10,000 and (b) by 1,000,000.

5. $675{,}928$ $\begin{array}{l}67.5928\\0.675928\end{array}$

6. $5{,}026{,}500$ $\begin{array}{l}502.6500\\5.026500\end{array}$

7. 0.18 $\begin{array}{l}0.000018\\0.00000018\end{array}$

8. $160{,}000{,}000$ $\begin{array}{l}16{,}000\\160\end{array}$

7.6 Scientific Notation

OBJECTIVES: To write a number in regular decimal form when it is given in scientific notation
To write a given number in scientific notation

Scientists use very large and very small numbers. Such numbers are often expressed in <u>scientific notation</u>. Here are some examples.

a. 3×10^5 **b.** 1.6×10^2 **c.** 2.3×10^{-7}

Scientific notation is a numeral of the form $N \times 10^a$, in which a is an integer and N is a rational number such that $1 \le N < 10$.

$53{,}000. = 5.3 \times 10^4$

$0.0048 = 4.8 \times 10^{-3}$

The sentence $1 \le N < 10$ means that "$N \ge 1$ <u>and</u> $N < 10$."

P-1 **What is the value of N in each number below? the value of a?**

a. 5.8×10^3 **b.** 3.76×10^{-1} **c.** 1.0059×10^{-6}

$N = 5.8; a = 3$ $N = 3.76; a = -1$ $N = 1.0059; a = -6$

The table below shows some powers of 10.

Powers of Ten
$10^4 = 10{,}000$
$10^3 = 1{,}000$
$10^2 = 100$
$10^1 = 10$
$10^0 = 1$
$10^{-1} = 0.1$ or $\frac{1}{10}$
$10^{-2} = 0.01$ or $\frac{1}{100}$
$10^{-3} = 0.001$ or $\frac{1}{1000}$
$10^{-4} = 0.0001$ or $\frac{1}{10{,}000}$

example 1

Write 1.2×10^4 in decimal form.

Solution:

1 Find the value of 10^4 from the table. ⟶ $10^4 = 10{,}000$

2 Substitute. ⟶ $1.2 \times 10^4 = (1.2)(10{,}000)$

3 Multiply. ⟶ $= 12{,}000.$

The result is the same as moving the decimal point four places to the right in 1.2.

example 2

Write 5.3×10^{-3} in decimal form.

Solution:

1. Find the value of 10^{-3} from the table. ⟶ $10^{-3} = 0.001$

2. Substitute. ⟶ $5.3 \times 10^{-3} = (5.3)(0.001)$

3. Multiply. ⟶ $= 0.0053$

◄ *The result is the same as moving the decimal point three places to the left in 5.3.*

P-2 **How is the exponent of 10 in scientific notation related to the location of the decimal point in decimal form?**

The exponent shows how many places to "move" the decimal point.

> To change scientific notation $N \times 10^a$ to decimal form:
> 1. move the decimal point of N to the right a places if a is positive, or
> 2. move the decimal point of N to the left a places if a is negative.

example 3

Write 186,000 in scientific notation.

Solution:

1. Place a caret to locate the decimal point in N. ⟶ 186000.

2. Count the number of places from the caret to the decimal point. ⟶ 186000. ⟶ 5 places

3. Write in scientific notation. ⟶ 1.86×10^5

Remind students to check by converting the result to ordinary decimal form. The result should equal the original number.

example 4

Write 0.0000053 in scientific notation.

Solution:

1. Place a caret to locate the decimal point in N. ⟶ 0.0000053

2. Count the number of places from the caret to the decimal point. ⟶ 0.0000053 ⟶ 6 places

3. Write in scientific notation. ⟶ 5.3×10^{-6}

CLASSROOM EXERCISES

Tell the decimal form for each number. (Examples 1-2)

1. 3×10^2 300

2. 2.0×10^{-2} 0.02

3. 7.03×10^3 7030

4. 3.9×10^{-3} 0.0039

5. 4.62×10^1 46.2

6. 8.1627×10^{-1} 0.81627

7. 5.0001×10^4 50,001

8. 9.99×10^{-4} 0.000999

Tell the scientific notation for each number. (Examples 3-4)

9. 530 5.3×10^2

10. 0.0926 9.26×10^{-2}

11. 48.6 4.86×10^1

12. 0.2738 2.738×10^{-1}

13. 76,000. 7.6×10^4

14. 6.318 6.318×10^0

15. 0.000483 4.83×10^{-4}

16. 0.008092 8.092×10^{-3}

WRITTEN EXERCISES

See the Teacher's Manual for the suggested assignments.
Goal: To write numbers in scientific notation
Sample Problems: a. 418,200 **b.** 0.00531
Answers: a. 4.182×10^5 **b.** 5.31×10^{-3}

Write the decimal form of each number. (Examples 1-2)

1. 4.2×10^3 4200

2. 3.7×10^2 370

3. 2.9×10^{-4} 0.00029

4. 9.1×10^{-3} 0.0091

5. 8.62×10^4 86,200

6. 6.01×10^5 601,000

7. 1.00726×10^{-1} 0.100726

8. 2.053×10^{-2} 0.02053

9. 7.280×10^6 7,280,000

10. 3.1709×10^7 31,709,000

11. 5.607×10^{-5} 0.00005607

12. 9.090×10^{-6} 0.000009090

Write the scientific notation for each number. (Examples 3-4)

13. 0.0092 9.2×10^{-3}

14. 0.000184 1.84×10^{-4}

15. 2705. 2.705×10^3

16. 937. 9.37×10^2

17. 0.01734 1.734×10^{-2}

18. 0.80672 8.0672×10^{-1}

19. 27,000,000. 2.7×10^7

20. 186,000. 1.86×10^5

21. 0.0000275 2.75×10^{-5}

22. 0.00000031801 3.1801×10^{-7}

23. 2 million 2×10^6

24. 3.5 billion 3.5×10^9

25. The diameter of the earth is about 1.28×10^7 meters. Write the distance in decimal form. 12,800,000 meters

26. The diameter of the sun is about 1.39×10^9 meters. Write this distance in decimal form.
1,390,000,000 meters

MORE CHALLENGING EXERCISES

27. A light year is the distance light travels in one year. The number of kilometers in a light year is 9.45×10^{12}. Write this in decimal form. 9,450,000,000,000

28. The distance from earth to the sun is about 150,000,000 kilometers. In light years, this is $\frac{1.5}{9.4} \times \frac{10^8}{10^{12}}$.
Write this in scientific notation.
about 1.6×10^{-5}

Space Technology

Speeds and distances in space are so great that scientific notation is useful in representing them and in performing computations.

Here are some approximate distances and speeds.

Minimum Distance from Earth to:
Mars: 56,000,000 (5.6×10^7) kilometers
Sun: 147,000,000 (1.47×10^8) kilometers
Saturn: 1,200,000,000 (1.2×10^9) kilometers
Pluto: 4,270,000,000 (4.27×10^9) kilometers
Proxima Centauri (nearest star):
    40,000,000,000,000 (4.0×10^{13}) kilometers

Speed of Light or of a Radio Signal:
    300,000 (3.0×10^5) kilometers per second

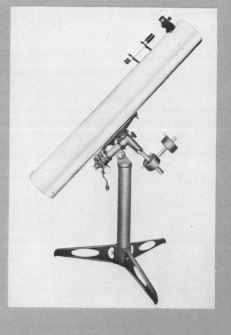

EXAMPLE: Find the approximate time in seconds needed for a radio signal to reach the earth from Saturn.

SOLUTION: Use $d = rt$

$$d \quad = \quad r \quad \times t$$
$$1.2 \times 10^9 = (3.0 \times 10^5) \times t \text{ or,}$$
$$(3.0 \times 10^5)t = 1.2 \times 10^9$$
$$t = \frac{1.2 \times 10^9}{3.0 \times 10^5}$$
$$= 0.4 \times 10^4 \text{ or, } \mathbf{4000 \text{ seconds}}$$

◄ $d = 1.2 \times 10^9$ *kilometers*
$r = 3.0 \times 10^5$ *km per second*

EXERCISES

Refer to the distance and speeds given above to find each of the following. Round your answer to the nearest whole number.

1. The approximate time in seconds for light from the sun to reach the earth   490 seconds

2. The approximate time in minutes (60 seconds) for a radio signal from Mars to reach the earth   3 minutes

3. The approximate time in hours for a radio signal from Pluto to reach the earth   4 hours

4. The approximate time in years (365 days) for light to reach the earth from the nearest star   4 years

Special Topic Application

CHAPTER SUMMARY

IMPORTANT TERMS	Power of a power *(p. 166)* Scientific notation *(p. 170)*

IMPORTANT IDEAS

1. If a is a positive integer, then x^a means that x is a factor a times.

2. *Product Property of Powers:* If a and b are integers and x is any nonzero real number, then $x^a \cdot x^b = x^{a+b}$.

3. *Quotient Property of Powers:* If a and b are integers and x is a nonzero real number, then $\dfrac{x^a}{x^b} = x^{a-b}$.

4. *Property of a Zero Exponent:* If x is any nonzero real number, then $x^0 = 1$.

5. *Property of Negative Exponents:* If $-a$ represents a negative integer and x is a nonzero real number, then $x^{-a} = \dfrac{1}{x^a}$.

6. *Property of the Power of a Product:* If x and y are nonzero real numbers and a is any integer, then $(xy)^a = x^a y^a$.

7. *Property of the Power of a Quotient:* If x and y are nonzero real numbers and a is any integer, then $\left(\dfrac{x}{y}\right)^a = \dfrac{x^a}{y^a}$.

8. *Property of the Power of a Power:* If x is a nonzero real number and a and b are integers, then $(x^a)^b = x^{ab}$.

9. To change scientific notation $N \times 10^a$ to decimal form:
   a. move the decimal point of N to the right a places if a is positive, or
   b. move the decimal point of N to the left a places if a is negative.

CHAPTER REVIEW

NOTE: The Teacher's Resource Book contains two forms of each Chapter Test.

SECTION 7.1

Write each product as one power.

1. $(27)^6(27)^3$ 27^9

2. $(-8.5)^4(-8.5)^4$ $(-8.5)^8$

3. $r^2 \cdot r^5$ r^7

4. $m^3 \cdot m^{12}$ m^{15}

5. $t^3 \cdot t \cdot t^5$ t^9

6. $p^4 \cdot p^5 \cdot p$ p^{10}

SECTION 7.2

Write each quotient as one power.

7. $\dfrac{19^8}{19^3}$ 19^5

8. $\dfrac{24^{12}}{24^7}$ 24^5

9. $\dfrac{(2.7)^{15}}{(2.7)^{13}}$ $(2.7)^2$

10. $\dfrac{(-3.9)^6}{(-3.9)^3}$ $(-3.9)^3$

11. $\dfrac{(\sqrt{7})^8}{(\sqrt{7})^5}$ $(\sqrt{7})^3$

12. $\dfrac{\pi^{19}}{\pi^{10}}$ π^9

Simplify.

13. $(35)^0$ 1

14. $(242)^0$ 1

15. $(-23.9)^0$ 1

16. $\left(\dfrac{5}{4}\right)^0$ 1

17. $(13.4)^0 - 2x^0$ -1

18. $5n^0 + (-95)^0$ 6

SECTION 7.3

Simplify.

19. $(t)^{-10}$ $\dfrac{1}{t^{10}}$

20. $(2)^{-6}$ $\dfrac{1}{64}$

21. $5x^{-2}$ $\dfrac{5}{x^2}$

22. $100y^{-1}$ $\dfrac{100}{y}$

23. $p^{-2}q$ $\dfrac{q}{p^2}$

24. $m^{-3}n$ $\dfrac{n}{m^3}$

Write each product or quotient as one power. Then simplify where necessary.

25. $k^{-4} \cdot k^2$ $k^{-2}; \dfrac{1}{k^2}$

26. $r^{-5} \cdot r^{-3}$ $r^{-8}; \dfrac{1}{r^8}$

27. $\dfrac{m^{-2}}{m^3}$ $m^{-5}; \dfrac{1}{m^5}$

28. $\dfrac{t^4}{t^{-3}}$ t^7

29. $\dfrac{p^2 \cdot p^{-3}}{p^4}$ $p^{-5}; \dfrac{1}{p^5}$

30. $\dfrac{x^{-1} \cdot x^{-3}}{x^4}$ $x^{-8}; \dfrac{1}{x^8}$

SECTION 7.4

Simplify.

31. $(4t)^2$ $16t^2$

32. $(2q)^4$ $16q^4$

33. $(-2r)^5$ $-32r^5$

34. $(-3y)^3$ $-27y^3$

35. $\left(\dfrac{5}{p}\right)^2$ $\dfrac{25}{p^2}$

36. $\left(\dfrac{-3}{s}\right)^3$ $-\dfrac{27}{s^3}$

37. $(-4m)^{-2}$ $\dfrac{1}{16m^2}$

38. $(-3n)^{-3}$ $-\dfrac{1}{27n^3}$

39. $\left(\dfrac{-1}{-y}\right)^3$ $\dfrac{1}{y^3}$

SECTION 7.5

Simplify.

40. $(d^3)^5$ d^{15}

41. $(g^5)^{-2}$ $\dfrac{1}{g^{10}}$

42. $\left(\dfrac{y^4}{2}\right)^5$ $\dfrac{y^{20}}{32}$

43. $\left(\dfrac{3m^2n^3}{p}\right)^3$ $\dfrac{27m^6n^9}{p^3}$

44. $(-2p^{-2}q^3r^{-4})^2$ $\dfrac{4q^6}{p^4r^8}$

45. $(2^{-2}x^2y^{-1}z^{-4})^3$

$\dfrac{x^6}{64y^3z^{12}}$

SECTION 7.6

Write the decimal form of each number.

46. 1.83×10^{-2} 0.0183

47. 3.187×10^{4} 31,870

48. 2.1692×10^{5} 216,920

49. 5.279×10^{-3} 0.005279

50. 7.10036×10^{-4} 0.000710036

51. 8.00002×10^{3} 8000.02

Write the scientific notation for each number.

52. 47,280. 4.728×10^{4}

53. 0.005219 5.219×10^{-3}

54. 0.00002009 2.009×10^{-5}

55. 512,000,000. 5.12×10^{8}

56. The speed of light is approximately 300,000 kilometers per second. Write 300,000 in scientific notation. 3×10^{5}

57. There are about 31,536,000 seconds in one year. Write 31,536,000 in scientific notation. 3.1536×10^{7}

CHAPTER **8** Roots

Sections   **8.1**   **Numbers in Radical Form**

8.2   **Products**

8.3   **Simplifying Radicals**

8.4   **Simplifying Radical Expressions**

8.5   **Sums and Differences**

8.6   **Quotients**

8.7   **Approximations**

Features   *Calculator Exercises:* **Evaluating Radicals**

Career: **Meteorologist**

**Review
and
Testing**   *Review Capsules*

Mid-Chapter Review

Chapter Summary

Chapter Review

To write the positive square root of a perfect square real number by using the
meaning of a square root
To write the prime factorization of a composite number

8.1 Numbers in Radical Form

To write the positive square root of a perfect square counting number by using
prime factorization

P-1 **What is the simplest form of $\sqrt{36}$?** 6
of $-\sqrt{36}$? −6

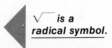 $\sqrt{}$ *is a*
radical symbol.

Emphasize that $\sqrt{}$
is used to represent
a nonnegative square
root.
$-\sqrt{}$ is used for a
negative square root.

A *square root* is one of two equal factors of a number. Both 6 and −6
are square roots of 36. Also, 36 is the *square* of both 6 and −6.

$$(6)(6) = 36 \qquad (-6)(-6) = 36$$

P-2 **What is the value of $\sqrt{0}$?** 0

P-3 **Why doesn't $\sqrt{-16}$ have a real-number value?** There are no two
equal factors of −16.

The square of a positive number is positive.
The square of a negative number is positive.
The square of 0 is 0.

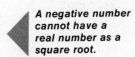 *A negative number*
cannot have a
real number as a
square root.

P-4 **What is the square of each number below?**

a. −7 49 **b.** $\frac{1}{2}$ $\frac{1}{4}$ **c.** −0.3 0.09 **d.** 20 400 **e.** $-\frac{3}{4}$ $\frac{9}{16}$

P-5 **Simplify each expression below.**

a. $-\sqrt{49}$ −7 **b.** $\sqrt{\frac{1}{4}}$ $\frac{1}{2}$ **c.** $-\sqrt{0.09}$ −0.3 **d.** $\sqrt{10,000}$ 100

It may be helpful to review prime factorization at this time.
The set of prime numbers less than 25 is shown below.

This is a good set of
prime numbers for
students to remember.
Not often will a prime
factor greater than 23
be needed.

$$\{2, 3, 5, 7, 11, 13, 17, 19, 23\}$$

A *prime number* is a counting number greater than 1 that has
exactly two counting-number factors, 1 and the number itself.

P-6 **Why is 15 not a prime number?** 1, 3, 5 and 15 are factors of 15.

The set of counting-number factors of 15
is {1, 3, 5, 15}.

The prime
factorization
of 15 is 3 · 5.

You will recall that *prime factorization* is writing a number as a product of its prime-number factors. The table below shows the prime factorization of some numbers. The numbers 4, 9, 25, and 36 in the table are *perfect squares*. Note that each prime factor of a perfect square occurs an even number of times.

Number	Prime Factorization	Number	Prime Factorization
4	$2 \cdot 2$	20	$2 \cdot 2 \cdot 5$
6	$2 \cdot 3$	25	$5 \cdot 5$
9	$3 \cdot 3$	27	$3 \cdot 3 \cdot 3$
12	$2 \cdot 2 \cdot 3$	36	$2 \cdot 2 \cdot 3 \cdot 3$

example 1   Write the prime factorization of 150.

Solution:

1. Divide by 2 (the smallest prime number). Write the quotient 75.

$$\begin{array}{r|r} 2 & 150 \\ \hline & 75 \end{array}$$

2. Check to see whether 2 is a factor of 75. It is not.

3. Select the next greater prime number 3. It is a factor of 75. Divide and write the quotient 25.

$$\begin{array}{r|r} 2 & 150 \\ \hline 3 & 75 \\ \hline & 25 \end{array}$$

4. Check again to see whether 3 is a factor of 25. It is not.

5. Select the next greater prime number 5. Divide by 5 and write the quotient 5. The quotient is prime.

$$\begin{array}{r|r} 2 & 150 \\ \hline 3 & 75 \\ \hline 5 & 25 \\ \hline & 5 \end{array}$$

6. Write the prime factorization of 150.

$$150 = 2 \cdot 3 \cdot 5 \cdot 5$$

example 2   Simplify $\sqrt{441}$.

◄ *Prime factorization can help in simplifying radicals.*

Solution:

1. Write the prime factorization of 441. ⟶ $\sqrt{441} = \sqrt{3 \cdot 3 \cdot 7 \cdot 7}$

2. Write two equal factors of 441. ⟶ $= \sqrt{(3 \cdot 7)(3 \cdot 7)}$

$$= \sqrt{21 \cdot 21}$$

3. Simplify. ⟶ $= 21$

$$\begin{array}{r|r} 3 & 441 \\ \hline 3 & 147 \\ \hline 7 & 49 \\ \hline & 7 \end{array}$$

CLASSROOM EXERCISES

Write the square of each number. (P-4)

1. −10 100   **2.** 11 121   **3.** −12 144   **4.** $\frac{1}{2}$ $\frac{1}{4}$ **5.** $-\frac{1}{3}$ $\frac{1}{9}$

6. −0.2 0.04   **7.** 0.4 0.16   **8.** −13 169   **9.** $\frac{5}{2}$ $\frac{25}{4}$ **10.** −1.2 1.44

Simplify. (P-1, P-5)

11. $\sqrt{9}$ 3   **12.** $-\sqrt{1}$ −1   **13.** $\sqrt{0}$ 0   **14.** $-\sqrt{36}$ −6   **15.** $\sqrt{100}$ 10

16. $\sqrt{\frac{9}{4}}$ $\frac{3}{2}$ **17.** $-\sqrt{\frac{1}{16}}$ $-\frac{1}{4}$ **18.** $\sqrt{\frac{9}{25}}$ $\frac{3}{5}$ **19.** $-\sqrt{0.01}$ −0.1   **20.** $\sqrt{0.0004}$ 0.02

Write the prime factorization. (Example 1)

21. 21 3·7   **22.** 12 2·2·3   **23.** 8 2·2·2   **24.** 25 5·5

25. 26 2·13   **26.** 35 5·7   **27.** 49 7·7   **28.** 77 7·11

29. 39 3·13   **30.** 18 2·3·3   **31.** 45 3·3·5   **32.** 81 3·3·3·3

WRITTEN EXERCISES

See the Teacher's Manual for the suggested assignments.

Goal: To write square roots of numbers
Sample Problems: a. $\sqrt{225}$ **b.** $-\sqrt{2^2 \cdot 3^4}$
Answers: a. 15   **b.** −18

Simplify. (Steps 2 and 3 of Example 2)

1. $\sqrt{121}$ 11   **2.** $\sqrt{196}$ 14   **3.** $-\sqrt{100}$ −10   **4.** $-\sqrt{81}$ −9   **5.** $\sqrt{\frac{4}{25}}$ $\frac{2}{5}$

6. $\sqrt{\frac{9}{49}}$ $\frac{3}{7}$ **7.** $-\sqrt{\frac{1}{9}}$ $-\frac{1}{3}$ **8.** $-\sqrt{\frac{25}{36}}$ $-\frac{5}{6}$ **9.** $\sqrt{0.81}$ 0.9   **10.** $\sqrt{0.25}$ 0.5

11. $\sqrt{(2 \cdot 5)(2 \cdot 5)}$ 10   **12.** $\sqrt{(5 \cdot 11)(5 \cdot 11)}$ 55   **13.** $\sqrt{2 \cdot 3 \cdot 3 \cdot 2 \cdot 2 \cdot 2}$ 12

14. $\sqrt{3 \cdot 2 \cdot 5 \cdot 3 \cdot 2 \cdot 5}$ 30   **15.** $\sqrt{2^2 \cdot 5^4}$ 50   **16.** $\sqrt{3^4 \cdot 5^2 \cdot 11^2}$ 495

Write the prime factorization. (Example 1)

17. 65 5·13   **18.** 99 3·3·11   **19.** 18 2·3·3   **20.** 400 2·2·2·2·5·5   **21.** 54 2·3·3·3

22. 60 2·2·3·5   **23.** 120 2·2·2·3·5   **24.** 108 2·2·3·3·3   **25.** 198 2·3·3·11   **26.** 264 2·2·2·3·11

Simplify. (Example 2)

27. $\sqrt{484}$ 22   **28.** $\sqrt{676}$ 26   **29.** $\sqrt{784}$ 28   **30.** $\sqrt{1225}$ 35   **31.** $\sqrt{1936}$ 44

32. $\sqrt{4096}$ 64   **33.** $\sqrt{3136}$ 56   **34.** $\sqrt{4624}$ 68   **35.** $\sqrt{5776}$ 76   **36.** $\sqrt{6561}$ 81

37. $\sqrt{5184}$ 72   **38.** $\sqrt{7225}$ 85   **39.** $\sqrt{9025}$ 95   **40.** $\sqrt{4356}$ 66   **41.** $\sqrt{3844}$ 62

8.2 Products

OBJECTIVE: To simplify the product of two or more square root radicals

Radicals such as $\sqrt{9}$, $-\sqrt{49}$, and $\sqrt{64}$ represent rational numbers. **A square root of a perfect square is rational.**

Radicals such as $\sqrt{7}$, $\sqrt{15}$, $-\sqrt{34}$, and $\sqrt{50}$ represent irrational numbers.

> Any whole number that is not a perfect square has an irrational square root.

P-1 **Which numbers below are rational?   Which are irrational?**

a. $\sqrt{19}$ **b.** $-\sqrt{144}$ **c.** $-\sqrt{80}$ **d.** $\sqrt{0}$

Irrational   Rational   Irrational   Rational

example 1   Multiply and simplify: $\sqrt{13} \cdot \sqrt{13}$

Solution: $\sqrt{13} \cdot \sqrt{13} = (\sqrt{13})^2$ ◀ **A square root is one of two equal factors of a number.**

$= 13$

Even though simple, the logic of this solution may elude some students. Review the meaning of a square root.

> If a is any nonnegative real number, then $\sqrt{a} \cdot \sqrt{a} = a$.
>
> $\sqrt{20} \cdot \sqrt{20} = 20$
> $\sqrt{3.2} \cdot \sqrt{3.2} = 3.2$

P-2 **Multiply and simplify.**

a. $\sqrt{29} \cdot \sqrt{29}$ 29   **b.** $\sqrt{\dfrac{1}{4}} \cdot \sqrt{\dfrac{1}{4}}$ $\dfrac{1}{4}$ **c.** $\sqrt{1029} \cdot \sqrt{1029}$ 1029

example 2   Multiply and simplify: $(\sqrt{3} \cdot \sqrt{10})^2$

Solution:

1 Property of the Power of a Product ────▶ $(\sqrt{3} \cdot \sqrt{10})^2 = (\sqrt{3})^2(\sqrt{10})^2$

2 Simplify. ────────────────────────▶ $= (3)(10)$ or 30

The product $\sqrt{3} \cdot \sqrt{10}$ is positive. Example 2 shows that $\sqrt{3} \cdot \sqrt{10}$ represents the positive square root of 30.

$$\sqrt{3} \cdot \sqrt{10} = \sqrt{30}$$

Product Property of Radicals

If a and b are nonnegative real numbers, then $\sqrt{a} \cdot \sqrt{b} = \sqrt{ab}$.

$$\sqrt{5} \cdot \sqrt{11} = \sqrt{55}$$
$$\sqrt{2} \cdot \sqrt{8} = \sqrt{16}$$
$$= 4$$

P-3   **Multiply and simplify.**

a. $\sqrt{7} \cdot \sqrt{5}$ $\sqrt{35}$ b. $\sqrt{6} \cdot \sqrt{11}$ $\sqrt{66}$ c. $\sqrt{3} \cdot \sqrt{12}$ 6

example 3   Multiply and simplify: $-\sqrt{10} \cdot \sqrt{13}$

Solution:

1. Product of a positive and negative number $\longrightarrow$ $-\sqrt{10} \cdot \sqrt{13} = -(\sqrt{10} \cdot \sqrt{13})$

2. Product Property of Radicals $\longrightarrow$ $= -(\sqrt{130})$

3. Simplify. $\longrightarrow$ $= -\sqrt{130}$

example 4   Multiply and simplify: $(-\sqrt{8})(-\sqrt{18})$

Solution:

$$(-\sqrt{8})(-\sqrt{18}) = (\sqrt{8})(\sqrt{18})$$
$$= \sqrt{8 \cdot 18}$$
$$= \sqrt{144}$$
$$= 12$$

example 5   Multiply and simplify: $\sqrt{3} \cdot \sqrt{10} \cdot \sqrt{7}$

Solution:

$$\sqrt{3} \cdot \sqrt{10} \cdot \sqrt{7} = (\sqrt{3} \cdot \sqrt{10}) \cdot \sqrt{7}$$
$$= (\sqrt{30})(\sqrt{7})$$
$$= \sqrt{210}$$

◀ *You may group the factors as you please.*

CLASSROOM EXERCISES

Multiply and simplify. (Examples 1-4)

1. $\sqrt{2} \cdot \sqrt{5}$ $\sqrt{10}$ **2.** $\sqrt{3} \cdot \sqrt{7}$ $\sqrt{21}$ **3.** $\sqrt{8} \cdot \sqrt{8}$ 8   **4.** $\sqrt{8} \cdot \sqrt{2}$ 4

5. $\sqrt{2} \cdot \sqrt{50}$ 10   **6.** $\sqrt{4} \cdot \sqrt{25}$ 10   **7.** $\sqrt{\frac{1}{5}} \cdot \sqrt{10}$ $\sqrt{2}$ **8.** $\sqrt{\frac{1}{2}} \cdot \sqrt{10}$ $\sqrt{5}$

9. $\sqrt{\frac{1}{3}} \cdot \sqrt{\frac{1}{3}}$ $\frac{1}{3}$ **10.** $\sqrt{0.5} \cdot \sqrt{0.5}$ 0.5   **11.** $\sqrt{0} \cdot \sqrt{5}$ 0   **12.** $(-\sqrt{4})(\sqrt{9})$ -6

13. $(-\sqrt{16})(-\sqrt{25})$ 20   **14.** $(-\sqrt{2})(-\sqrt{3})$ $\sqrt{6}$ **15.** $(-\sqrt{2})(\sqrt{2})$ -2 **16.** $(-\sqrt{3})^2$ 3

WRITTEN EXERCISES

See the Teacher's Manual for the suggested assignments.

Goal: To simplify the products of radicals

Sample Problem: $(\sqrt{2})(\sqrt{5})(-\sqrt{7})$ **Answer:** $-\sqrt{70}$

Multiply and simplify. (Examples 1-5)

1. $\sqrt{13} \cdot \sqrt{13}$ 13   **2.** $\sqrt{17} \cdot \sqrt{17}$ 17   **3.** $\sqrt{13\frac{3}{8}} \cdot \sqrt{13\frac{3}{8}}$ $13\frac{3}{8}$ **4.** $\sqrt{19\frac{1}{3}} \cdot \sqrt{19\frac{1}{3}}$ $19\frac{1}{3}$

5. $\sqrt{81} \cdot \sqrt{36}$ 54   **6.** $\sqrt{144} \cdot \sqrt{16}$ 48   **7.** $\sqrt{2} \cdot \sqrt{18}$ 6   **8.** $\sqrt{3} \cdot \sqrt{27}$ 9

9. $\sqrt{3} \cdot \sqrt{17}$ $\sqrt{51}$ **10.** $\sqrt{2} \cdot \sqrt{19}$ $\sqrt{38}$ **11.** $(-\sqrt{5})(\sqrt{2})$ $-\sqrt{10}$ **12.** $(\sqrt{7})(-\sqrt{2})$ $-\sqrt{14}$

13. $(-\sqrt{3})(-\sqrt{10})$ $\sqrt{30}$ **14.** $(-\sqrt{5})(-\sqrt{6})$ $\sqrt{30}$ **15.** $\sqrt{\frac{1}{3}} \cdot \sqrt{15}$ $\sqrt{5}$ **16.** $\sqrt{\frac{1}{2}} \cdot \sqrt{34}$ $\sqrt{17}$

17. $\sqrt{\frac{1}{2}} \cdot \sqrt{\frac{1}{2}}$ $\frac{1}{2}$ **18.** $\sqrt{\frac{2}{3}} \cdot \sqrt{\frac{2}{3}}$ $\frac{2}{3}$ **19.** $\sqrt{\frac{1}{3}} \cdot \sqrt{48}$ 4   **20.** $\sqrt{\frac{1}{5}} \cdot \sqrt{20}$ 2

21. $\sqrt{2} \cdot \sqrt{3} \cdot \sqrt{6}$ 6   **22.** $\sqrt{3} \cdot \sqrt{5} \cdot \sqrt{15}$ 15

23. $\sqrt{2} \cdot \sqrt{3} \cdot \sqrt{5}$ $\sqrt{30}$ **24.** $\sqrt{3} \cdot \sqrt{5} \cdot \sqrt{7}$ $\sqrt{105}$

25. $\sqrt{2} \cdot \sqrt{5} \cdot \sqrt{10}$ 10   **26.** $\sqrt{3} \cdot \sqrt{7} \cdot \sqrt{21}$ 21

MORE CHALLENGING EXERCISES

Solve each equation.

27. $\frac{1}{\sqrt{3}}x = \sqrt{12}$ $x = 6$ **28.** $\frac{1}{\sqrt{5}}x = \sqrt{20}$ $x = 10$ **29.** $\frac{1}{\sqrt{7}}x \stackrel{!}{=} \sqrt{2}$ $x = \sqrt{14}$ **30.** $\frac{1}{\sqrt{11}}x = \sqrt{3}$ $x = \sqrt{33}$

31. $x^2 = 36$ $x = 6$ or $x = -6$ **32.** $x^2 = 100$ $x = 10$ or $x = -10$ **33.** $x^2 = 14$ $x = \sqrt{14}$ or $x = -\sqrt{14}$ **34.** $x^2 = 33$ $x = \sqrt{33}$ or $x = -\sqrt{33}$

REVIEW CAPSULE FOR SECTION 8.3

Find each power. (Section 1.7)

1. 5^3 125   **2.** 6^3 216   **3.** 7^3 343   **4.** 8^3 512   **5.** 9^3 729   **6.** 5^4 625   **7.** 6^4 1296   **8.** 7^4

2401

8.3 Simplifying Radicals

To simplify a cube root or a fourth root radical in which the radicand has a perfect cube factor or perfect fourth power factor, respectively

P-1   **Simplify each radical below.**

a. $\sqrt{49}$ 7   b. $-\sqrt{81}$ −9   c. $\sqrt{5^2}$ 5   d. $-\sqrt{13^2}$ −13

▶ $\sqrt{49}$ is a **radical** and 49 is the **radicand**.

example 1   Simplify $\sqrt{12}$.

Solution:

1 Write the prime factorization of 12. ⟶ $\sqrt{12} = \sqrt{2 \cdot 2 \cdot 3}$

2 Product Property of Radicals ⟶ $= \sqrt{2 \cdot 2} \cdot \sqrt{3}$

3 Meaning of square root ⟶ $= 2\sqrt{3}$

The simplest form of $\sqrt{12}$ is $2\sqrt{3}$.

▶ $\sqrt{12}$ is **irrational because 12 is not a perfect square.**

A square root radical is in <u>simplest form</u> if its radicand has no perfect square factor.

example 2   Simplify $\sqrt{200}$.

Solution:

1 Write the prime factorization. ⟶ $\sqrt{200} = \sqrt{2^3 \cdot 5^2}$

2 Product Property of Radicals ⟶ $= \sqrt{2^2 \cdot 5^2} \cdot \sqrt{2}$

3 Meaning of square root ⟶ $= 2 \cdot 5\sqrt{2}$

4 Simplify. ⟶ $= 10\sqrt{2}$

The simplest form of $\sqrt{200}$ is $10\sqrt{2}$.

▶ *Even powers of factors are grouped under one radical symbol.*

Other roots besides square roots are possible. A **cube root** of a number is one of its three equal factors. A **fourth root** of a number is one of its four equal factors.

$2 \cdot 2 \cdot 2 = 8$ ◀ *2 is a cube root of 8.*

$3 \cdot 3 \cdot 3 \cdot 3 = 81$ ◀ *3 is a fourth root of 81.*

The Product Property of Radicals can be extended to other roots.

$$\sqrt[3]{x} \cdot \sqrt[3]{y} = \sqrt[3]{xy}$$

$$\sqrt[4]{x} \cdot \sqrt[4]{y} = \sqrt[4]{xy}$$

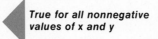 **True for all nonnegative values of x and y**

You may want to show that

$$\sqrt[3]{-8} \cdot \sqrt[3]{-27} = \sqrt[3]{(-8)(-27)}.$$

example 3   Simplify $\sqrt[3]{54}$.

Solution:

1. Write the prime factorization. ⟶ $\sqrt[3]{54} = \sqrt[3]{2 \cdot 3 \cdot 3 \cdot 3}$

2. Product Property of Radicals ⟶ $= \sqrt[3]{3 \cdot 3 \cdot 3} \cdot \sqrt[3]{2}$

3. Simplify. ⟶ $= 3\sqrt[3]{2}$

The simplest form of $\sqrt[3]{54}$ is $3\sqrt[3]{2}$. **Read "3 times the cube root of 2."**

The table below shows the third and fourth powers of some counting numbers.

n	n^3	n^4		n	n^3	n^4
1	1	1		6	216	1296
2	8	16		7	343	2401
3	27	81		8	512	4096
4	64	256		9	729	6561
5	125	625		10	1000	10,000

P-2   **Simplify each radical below.**

a. $\sqrt[4]{2^4}$ 2   **b.** $\sqrt[3]{2^3 \cdot 3^3}$ 6   **c.** $\sqrt[3]{125}$ 5   **d.** $\sqrt[4]{256}$ 4

CLASSROOM EXERCISES

Simplify. (Examples 1–2)

1. $\sqrt{2^2}$ 2   **2.** $\sqrt{3^2}$ 3   **3.** $-\sqrt{5^2}$ −5   **4.** $\sqrt{7^2}$ 7   **5.** $\sqrt{2^4}$ 4

6. $\sqrt{3^4}$ 9   **7.** $\sqrt{5^4}$ 25   **8.** $\sqrt{7^4}$ 49   **9.** $\sqrt{11^2}$ 11   **10.** $\sqrt{3^6}$ 27

11. $\sqrt{6^4}$ 36   **12.** $-\sqrt{10^2}$ −10   **13.** $\sqrt{2^2 \cdot 5^2}$ 10   **14.** $\sqrt{3^2 \cdot 5^2}$ 15   **15.** $\sqrt{2^2 \cdot 7^2}$ 14

16. $\sqrt{2^4 \cdot 5^2}$ 20   **17.** $\sqrt{2^2 \cdot 3^2 \cdot 5^2}$ 30   **18.** $\sqrt{2 \cdot 5 \cdot 2}$ $2\sqrt{5}$ **19.** $\sqrt{3 \cdot 3 \cdot 5}$ $3\sqrt{5}$ **20.** $\sqrt{2 \cdot 3 \cdot 2}$ $2\sqrt{3}$

Simplify. (Examples 1–3)

21. $\sqrt{2 \cdot 3 \cdot 2 \cdot 3 \cdot 2}$ $6\sqrt{2}$ **22.** $\sqrt{3 \cdot 5 \cdot 3 \cdot 3 \cdot 5}$ $15\sqrt{3}$ **23.** $\sqrt[3]{3^3}$ 3

24. $\sqrt[4]{5^4}$ 5   **25.** $\sqrt[3]{8}$ 2   **26.** $\sqrt[4]{1296}$ 6

27. $\sqrt[3]{729}$ 9   **28.** $\sqrt[4]{2401}$ 7   **29.** $\sqrt[3]{2^3 \cdot 7}$ $2\sqrt[3]{7}$

30. $\sqrt[3]{3 \cdot 5 \cdot 3 \cdot 5 \cdot 5}$ $5\sqrt[3]{9}$ **31.** $\sqrt[4]{5^4 \cdot 11^4}$ 55   **32.** $\sqrt[4]{2 \cdot 3 \cdot 2 \cdot 3 \cdot 5 \cdot 3 \cdot 3}$

$3\sqrt[4]{20}$

WRITTEN EXERCISES

See the Teacher's Manual for the suggested assignments.

Goal: To simplify radicals

Sample Problem: $\sqrt{288}$ **Answer:** $12\sqrt{2}$

Simplify. (Examples 1–3)

1. $\sqrt{6^2}$ 6   **2.** $\sqrt{4^2}$ 4   **3.** $\sqrt{38^2}$ 38   **4.** $\sqrt{19^2}$ 19

5. $\sqrt{2^2 \cdot 3^2} \cdot \sqrt{3}$ $6\sqrt{3}$ **6.** $\sqrt{3^2 \cdot 5^2} \cdot \sqrt{5}$ $15\sqrt{5}$ **7.** $\sqrt{5^2 \cdot 7^2} \cdot \sqrt{5 \cdot 7}$ $35\sqrt{35}$

8. $\sqrt{2^2 \cdot 11^2} \cdot \sqrt{2 \cdot 11}$ $22\sqrt{22}$ **9.** $\sqrt{2^4} \cdot \sqrt{2 \cdot 3}$ $4\sqrt{6}$ **10.** $\sqrt{3^4} \cdot \sqrt{3 \cdot 5}$ $9\sqrt{15}$

11. $\sqrt{2^4 \cdot 3^2} \cdot \sqrt{5 \cdot 2}$ $12\sqrt{10}$ **12.** $\sqrt{3^4 \cdot 5^2} \cdot \sqrt{2 \cdot 11}$ $45\sqrt{22}$ **13.** $\sqrt{2 \cdot 3 \cdot 3 \cdot 5 \cdot 2}$ $6\sqrt{5}$

14. $\sqrt{3 \cdot 5 \cdot 2 \cdot 3 \cdot 5}$ $15\sqrt{2}$ **15.** $\sqrt{5 \cdot 7 \cdot 5 \cdot 3 \cdot 2 \cdot 2}$ $10\sqrt{21}$ **16.** $\sqrt{3 \cdot 11 \cdot 7 \cdot 3 \cdot 7 \cdot 3}$ See below.

17. $\sqrt{8}$ $2\sqrt{2}$ **18.** $\sqrt{18}$ $3\sqrt{2}$ **19.** $\sqrt{27}$ $3\sqrt{3}$ **20.** $\sqrt{20}$ $2\sqrt{5}$ **21.** $\sqrt{24}$ $2\sqrt{6}$

22. $\sqrt{28}$ $2\sqrt{7}$ **23.** $\sqrt{40}$ $2\sqrt{10}$ **24.** $\sqrt{44}$ $2\sqrt{11}$ **25.** $-\sqrt{48}$ $-4\sqrt{3}$ **26.** $-\sqrt{60}$ $-2\sqrt{15}$

27. $\sqrt{120}$ $2\sqrt{30}$ **28.** $\sqrt{108}$ $6\sqrt{3}$ **29.** $\sqrt{96}$ $4\sqrt{6}$ **30.** $\sqrt{180}$ $6\sqrt{5}$ **31.** $\sqrt[3]{27}$ 3

32. $\sqrt[3]{64}$ 4   **33.** $\sqrt[4]{16}$ 2   **34.** $\sqrt[4]{625}$ 5   **35.** $\sqrt[3]{81}$ $3\sqrt[3]{3}$ **36.** $\sqrt[3]{72}$ $2\sqrt[3]{9}$

37. $\sqrt[4]{144}$ $2\sqrt[4]{9}$ **38.** $\sqrt[4]{243}$ $3\sqrt[4]{3}$ **39.** $\sqrt[3]{1250}$ $5\sqrt[3]{10}$ **40.** $\sqrt[3]{2160}$ $6\sqrt[3]{10}$ **41.** $\sqrt[4]{1250}$ $5\sqrt[4]{2}$

42. $\sqrt[3]{-512}$ -8 **43.** $\sqrt[3]{-1000}$ -10 **44.** $\sqrt[3]{-24}$ $-2\sqrt[3]{3}$ **45.** $\sqrt[3]{-56}$ $-2\sqrt[3]{7}$ **46.** $\sqrt[3]{-375}$ $-5\sqrt[3]{3}$

16. $21\sqrt{33}$

REVIEW CAPSULE FOR SECTION 8.4

Replace the variables with the given values. Then simplify. (Section 1.7)

1. $\sqrt{2s^2}$ if $s = 3$ $3\sqrt{2}$ **2.** $\sqrt{3r^3}$ if $r = 5$ $5\sqrt{15}$ **3.** $\sqrt{5t^3}$ if $t = 2$ $2\sqrt{10}$

4. $\sqrt{m^2n^3}$ if $m = 7, n = 3$ $21\sqrt{3}$ **5.** $\sqrt{x^3y^3}$ if $x = 5, y = 2$ $10\sqrt{10}$ **6.** $\sqrt{2ab^3}$ if $a = 7, b = 3$

$3\sqrt{42}$

8.4 Simplifying Radical Expressions

OBJECTIVE: To simplify a square root or a cube root radical in which the radicand is a product involving powers of one or more variables

P-1 **What is $\sqrt{x}$ for each value of x below?**

a. $x = 100$ 10   b. $x = \frac{1}{4}$ $\frac{1}{2}$ c. $x = 17$ $\sqrt{17}$ d. $x = \frac{4}{9}$ $\frac{2}{3}$

P-2 **Why cannot x have a negative value in $\sqrt{x}$?**   A negative number cannot have a real number as a square root.

The domain of each variable will be {nonnegative real numbers} unless stated otherwise.

example 1   Simplify $\sqrt{x^2 y^4}$.

Solution:

1. Product Property of Radicals ⟶ $\sqrt{x^2 y^4} = \sqrt{x^2} \cdot \sqrt{y^4}$

2. Meaning of square root ⟶ $= xy^2$

An even power of a variable is called a perfect square because each of its square roots can be expressed without the radical symbol.

P-3 **Simplify each radical.**

a. $\sqrt{a^6}$ a^3 b. $\sqrt{x^8}$ x^4 c. $\sqrt{b^{12}}$ b^6 d. $\sqrt{y^{28}}$ y^{14}

Warn students not to "take the square root of" the exponent.

$$\sqrt{x^9} \neq x^3$$

example 2   Simplify $\sqrt{x^3 y^5}$.

Solution:

1. Product Property of Powers ⟶ $\sqrt{x^3 y^5} = \sqrt{(x^2 \cdot x)(y^4 \cdot y)}$

  ◀ x^2 and y^4 are perfect squares.

2. Commutative and Associative Properties of Multiplication ⟶ $= \sqrt{(x^2 y^4)(xy)}$

  ◀ Group the perfect square factors.

3. Product Property of Radicals ⟶ $= \sqrt{x^2 y^4} \cdot \sqrt{xy}$

4. Meaning of square root ⟶ $= xy^2 \sqrt{xy}$

The simplest form is $xy^2 \sqrt{xy}$.

example 3   Simplify $\sqrt{12c^3d^7}$.

Solution:
$$\sqrt{12c^3d^7} = \sqrt{(2 \cdot 2 \cdot 3)(c \cdot c^2)(d \cdot d^6)}$$
$$= \sqrt{(2^2 \cdot c^2 \cdot d^6)(3cd)}$$
$$= \sqrt{2^2 \cdot c^2 \cdot d^6} \cdot \sqrt{3cd}$$
$$= 2cd^3\sqrt{3cd}$$

example 4   Simplify $\sqrt[3]{r^4s^5}$.

Solution:

1. Find the greatest third power factors of r^4 and s^5. ⟶ $r^4 = r^3 \cdot r; \ s^5 = s^3 \cdot s^2$

2. Product Property of Powers ⟶ $\sqrt[3]{r^4s^5} = \sqrt[3]{(r^3 \cdot r)(s^3 \cdot s^2)}$

3. Associative and Commutative Properties of Multiplication ⟶ $= \sqrt[3]{(r^3s^3)(rs^2)}$ **Group the perfect cube factors.**

4. Product Property of Radicals ⟶ $= \sqrt[3]{r^3s^3} \cdot \sqrt[3]{rs^2}$

5. Meaning of cube root ⟶ $= rs\sqrt[3]{rs^2}$

P-4   **What is $\sqrt[3]{a^3}$? $\sqrt[3]{x^6}$? $\sqrt[3]{y^9}$?**

$\qquad\qquad a \qquad\quad x^2 \qquad\quad y^3$

You know that a square root radical is in simplest form if its radicand has no perfect square factor. A cube root radical is in simplest form if its radicand has no perfect cube factor.

The following radicals are in simplest form.

a. $\sqrt{x}$ **b.** $\sqrt{10}$ **c.** $\sqrt[3]{p^2q}$ **d.** $\sqrt{2t}$

P-5   **Which of the following radicals are in simplest form?**

a. $\sqrt{28x^3}$ No   **b.** $\sqrt{21st}$ Yes   **c.** $\sqrt[3]{9m^2n^2}$ Yes   **d.** $\sqrt[3]{24c^5d^7}$ No

CLASSROOM EXERCISES

Simplify. (Examples 1–3)

1. $\sqrt{a^2}$ a **2.** $\sqrt{x^4}$ x^2 **3.** $\sqrt{a^2b^2}$ ab **4.** $\sqrt{x^6}$ x^3 **5.** $\sqrt{x^2y^4}$

$\qquad\qquad\qquad\qquad\qquad\qquad\qquad\qquad\qquad\qquad\qquad\qquad\qquad\qquad\qquad\qquad\qquad\qquad xy^2$

6. $\sqrt{4x^2}$ $2x$ **7.** $\sqrt{9y^2}$ $3y$ **8.** $\sqrt{16a^2}$ $4a$ **9.** $\sqrt{25n^2}$ $5n$ **10.** $\sqrt{4x^4}$ $2x^2$

11. $\sqrt{9x^6}$ $3x^3$ **12.** $\sqrt{16x^2y^4}$ $4xy^2$ **13.** $\sqrt{x^4} \cdot \sqrt{x}$ $x^2\sqrt{x}$ **14.** $\sqrt{a^6} \cdot \sqrt{a}$ $a^3\sqrt{a}$

15. $\sqrt{2^2 \cdot a^2} \cdot \sqrt{2a}$ **16.** $\sqrt{3^2 \cdot x^4} \cdot \sqrt{2x}$ **17.** $\sqrt{x^2y^2} \cdot \sqrt{2x}$ **18.** $\sqrt{3^4 \cdot x^4} \cdot \sqrt{2x}$

19. $\sqrt{6x^2}$ $x\sqrt{6}$ $2a\sqrt{2a}$ **20.** $\sqrt{10y^4}$ $3x^2\sqrt{2x}$ **21.** $\sqrt[3]{r^3t^3}$ $xy\sqrt{2x}$ **22.** $\sqrt[3]{m^6n^3}$ $9x^2\sqrt{2x}$

23. $\sqrt[3]{x^{12}}$ x^4 **24.** $\sqrt[3]{p^3q^9}$ $y^2\sqrt{10}$ **25.** $\sqrt[3]{8k^6}$ rt **26.** $\sqrt[3]{27r^3}$ m^2n

pq^3 $2k^2$ $3r$

WRITTEN EXERCISES

See the Teacher's Manual for the suggested assignments.

Goal: To simplify radicals containing variables

Sample Problem: $\sqrt[3]{16a^4b^6}$

Answer: $2ab^2\sqrt[3]{2a}$

Simplify. The domain is {nonnegative real numbers}. (Examples 1–4)

1. $\sqrt{36y^2}$ $6y$ **2.** $\sqrt{9a^4}$ $3a^2$ **3.** $\sqrt{y^2z^6}$ yz^3 **4.** $\sqrt{a^6b^8}$ a^3b^4

5. $\sqrt{x^5}$ $x^2\sqrt{x}$ **6.** $\sqrt{a^3}$ $a\sqrt{a}$ **7.** $\sqrt{4x}$ $2\sqrt{x}$ **8.** $\sqrt{9y}$ $3\sqrt{y}$

9. $\sqrt{16y^3}$ $4y\sqrt{y}$ **10.** $\sqrt{25y^5}$ $5y^2\sqrt{y}$ **11.** $\sqrt{8x^2}$ $2x\sqrt{2}$ **12.** $\sqrt{8y^4}$ $2y^2\sqrt{2}$

13. $\sqrt{8a^5}$ $2a^2\sqrt{2a}$ **14.** $\sqrt{8x^3}$ $2x\sqrt{2x}$ **15.** $\sqrt{12ab}$ $2\sqrt{3ab}$ **16.** $\sqrt{18xy}$ $3\sqrt{2xy}$

17. $\sqrt{49a^3b^3}$ $7ab\sqrt{ab}$ **18.** $\sqrt{36x^3y^3}$ $6xy\sqrt{xy}$ **19.** $\sqrt{24a^2b^3}$ $2ab\sqrt{6b}$ **20.** $\sqrt{40x^3y^2}$ $2xy\sqrt{10x}$

21. $\sqrt{75r^5s^6}$ $5r^2s^3\sqrt{3r}$ **22.** $\sqrt{45c^4d^7}$ $3c^2d^3\sqrt{5d}$ **23.** $\sqrt{20r^2s^3t^5}$ See below.   **24.** $\sqrt{27a^5b^4c^3}$ See below.

25. $\sqrt[3]{x^{12}}$ x^4 **26.** $\sqrt[3]{r^6}$ r^2 **27.** $\sqrt[3]{x^{13}}$ $x^4\sqrt[3]{x}$ **28.** $\sqrt[3]{8y^7}$ $2y^2\sqrt[3]{y}$

29. $\sqrt[3]{27x^3y^6}$ $3xy^2$ **30.** $\sqrt[3]{64r^6s^9}$ $4r^2s^3$ **31.** $\sqrt[3]{16a^2b^3}$ $2b\sqrt[3]{2a^2}$ **32.** $\sqrt[3]{24m^4n^6}$ $2mn^2\sqrt[3]{3m}$

33. $\sqrt[3]{54m^5n^8}$ **34.** $\sqrt[3]{32a^{11}b^5}$ **35.** $\sqrt[3]{32r^7s^{10}}$ **36.** $\sqrt[3]{128a^4b^9}$

$3mn^2\sqrt[3]{2m^2n^2}$ $2a^3b\sqrt[3]{4a^2b^2}$ $2r^2s^3\sqrt[3]{4rs}$ $4ab^3\sqrt[3]{2a}$

MORE CHALLENGING EXERCISES

23. $2rst^2\sqrt{5st}$

24. $3a^2b^2c\sqrt{3ac}$

Write each product as one radical. Then simplify.

EXAMPLE: $\sqrt{2x} \cdot \sqrt{2x^3}$ **SOLUTION:** $\sqrt{2x} \cdot \sqrt{2x^3} = \sqrt{4x^4}$
$$= 2x^2$$

37. $\sqrt{x} \cdot \sqrt{x^3}$ x^2 **38.** $\sqrt{x} \cdot \sqrt{x^5}$ x^3 **39.** $\sqrt{2} \cdot \sqrt{2x}$ $2\sqrt{x}$

40. $\sqrt{3} \cdot \sqrt{3y}$ $3\sqrt{y}$ **41.** $\sqrt{2x} \cdot \sqrt{2x^3}$ $2x^2$ **42.** $\sqrt{3y^3} \cdot \sqrt{3y}$ $3y^2$

43. $\sqrt[3]{4x} \cdot \sqrt[3]{3x^2}$ $x\sqrt[3]{12}$ **44.** $\sqrt[3]{2r^4} \cdot \sqrt[3]{4r^2}$ $2r^2$ **45.** $\sqrt[3]{9a} \cdot \sqrt[3]{3a^5}$ $3a^2$

46. $\sqrt[3]{16r^2s^2} \cdot \sqrt[3]{4rs^4}$ $4rs^2$ **47.** $\sqrt[3]{8b^2} \cdot \sqrt[3]{8b^7}$ $4b^3$ **48.** $\sqrt[3]{27rs^{11}} \cdot \sqrt[3]{r^8s}$

$3r^3s^4$

MID-CHAPTER REVIEW

NOTE: After completing the Mid-Chapter Review, you may want to administer a quiz covering the same sections. See pages M-24 and M-25 of the Teacher's Manual for the suggested quiz.

Simplify. (Section 8.1)

1. $\sqrt{(13 \cdot 17)(13 \cdot 17)}$ _221_ 2. $\sqrt{2 \cdot 5 \cdot 7 \cdot 2 \cdot 7 \cdot 5}$ _70_ 3. $\sqrt{5^4 \cdot 7^2 \cdot 11^2}$ _1925_ 4. $\sqrt{3^2 \cdot 5^4 \cdot 13^2}$ _975_

5. $\sqrt{729}$ _27_ 6. $\sqrt{1024}$ _32_ 7. $\sqrt{1296}$ _36_ 8. $\sqrt{2025}$ _45_ 9. $\sqrt{2304}$ _48_

Multiply and simplify. (Section 8.2)

10. $\sqrt{23} \cdot \sqrt{23}$ _23_ 11. $\sqrt{9} \cdot \sqrt{49}$ _21_ 12. $\sqrt{12} \cdot \sqrt{3}$ _6_ 13. $(-\sqrt{7})(\sqrt{2})$ _$-\sqrt{14}$_

14. $(-\sqrt{\frac{1}{2}})(-\sqrt{162})$ _9_ 15. $\sqrt{\frac{1}{5}} \cdot \sqrt{125}$ _5_ 16. $\sqrt{\frac{5}{6}} \cdot \sqrt{\frac{5}{6}}$ _$\frac{5}{6}$_ 17. $\sqrt{5} \cdot \sqrt{7} \cdot \sqrt{6}$ _$\sqrt{210}$_

Simplify. (Section 8.3)

18. $\sqrt{360}$ _$6\sqrt{10}$_ 19. $\sqrt{490}$ _$7\sqrt{10}$_ 20. $\sqrt{320}$ _$8\sqrt{5}$_ 21. $\sqrt{700}$ _$10\sqrt{7}$_ 22. $\sqrt{98}$ _$7\sqrt{2}$_

23. $\sqrt{405}$ _$9\sqrt{5}$_ 24. $\sqrt[3]{40}$ _$2\sqrt[3]{5}$_ 25. $\sqrt[3]{108}$ _$3\sqrt[3]{4}$_ 26. $\sqrt[4]{48}$ _$2\sqrt[4]{3}$_ 27. $\sqrt[4]{162}$ _$3\sqrt[4]{2}$_

Simplify. The domain is {nonnegative real numbers}. (Section 8.4)

28. $\sqrt{81a^4b^2}$ _$9a^2b$_ 29. $\sqrt{49m^6n^2}$ _$7m^3n$_ 30. $\sqrt{24p^3}$ _$2p\sqrt{6p}$_ 31. $\sqrt{27r^4s^5}$ _$3r^2s^2\sqrt{3s}$_

32. $\sqrt{75p^2q^3r^6}$ _$5pqr^3\sqrt{3q}$_ 33. $\sqrt{108a^3b^5c^7}$ _$6ab^2c^3\sqrt{3abc}$_ 34. $\sqrt[3]{216m^3n^4}$ _$6mn\sqrt[3]{n}$_ 35. $\sqrt[3]{54p^7q^6}$ _$3p^2q^2\sqrt[3]{2p}$_

EVALUATING RADICALS

A calculator with a square root key, $\boxed{\sqrt{}}$, can be used to find not only square roots but other roots also. For, example, you can think of a fourth root as a "square root of a square root."

EXAMPLE 1 $\sqrt{39}$ SOLUTION $\boxed{3}$ $\boxed{9}$ $\boxed{\sqrt{}}$ $\boxed{6.2449979}$

EXAMPLE 2 $\sqrt[4]{36}$ SOLUTION Think of $\sqrt[4]{36}$ as $\sqrt{\sqrt{36}}$.

$\boxed{3}$ $\boxed{6}$ $\boxed{\sqrt{}}$ $\boxed{\sqrt{}}$ $\boxed{2.4494897}$

Evaluate each square root or fourth root.

1. $\sqrt{64}$ _8_ 2. $\sqrt{121}$ _11_ 3. $\sqrt{43}$ _6.5574385_ 4. $\sqrt{99}$ _9.9498743_ 5. $\sqrt[4]{16}$ _2_ 6. $\sqrt[4]{1296}$ _6_

REVIEW CAPSULE FOR SECTION 8.5

Combine like terms. (Section 2.6)

1. $9m + 8m$ _17m_ 2. $5.6t - 2.9t$ _2.7t_ 3. $76k + k$ _77k_ 4. $4.8w - 5.9w + 0.8w$ _−0.3w_

8.5 Sums and Differences

To add or subtract radicals having equal radicands
To simplify radicals in a sum or difference and then write the sum or difference in simplest form by adding or subtracting like radicals

P-1 **How is each sum or difference below expressed as a product by the Distributive Property?**

a. $7x + ax$ **b.** $ty - ry$ **c.** $11m + 3m$ *Find a common factor.*

$(7 + a)x$ $(t - r)y$ $(11 + 3)m$ or $14m$

The Distributive Property can also be applied to sums or differences of radicals.

example 1
Add: $3\sqrt{5} + 4\sqrt{5}$

Solution:

1. Distributive Property ⟶ $3\sqrt{5} + 4\sqrt{5} = (3 + 4)\sqrt{5}$ *Adding $3\sqrt{5}$ and $4\sqrt{5}$ is much like adding 3x and 4x.*

2. Simplify. ⟶ $= 7\sqrt{5}$

P-2 **Add and simplify: $6\sqrt{2} + 5\sqrt{2}$** $11\sqrt{2}$

Radicals such as $6\sqrt{2}$ and $5\sqrt{2}$ are called *like radicals.* They have equal radicands.

The Distributive Property is used in these Examples to show how like radicals are combined. Students will soon learn to combine like radicals just as they combine like terms.

P-3 **Add and simplify.**

a. $4\sqrt{5} + \sqrt{5}$ $5\sqrt{5}$ **b.** $9\sqrt{3} - 2\sqrt{3}$ $7\sqrt{3}$ **c.** $\sqrt{10} - 4\sqrt{10}$ $-3\sqrt{10}$

P-4 **What are the prime factors of 12?**   2, 2, and 3

example 2
Add and simplify: $\sqrt{12} + 7\sqrt{3}$

Solution:

1. Write the prime factorization of 12. ⟶ $\sqrt{12} + 7\sqrt{3} = \sqrt{2 \cdot 2 \cdot 3} + 7\sqrt{3}$

2. Product Property of Radicals ⟶ $= \sqrt{2^2} \cdot \sqrt{3} + 7\sqrt{3}$

3. Meaning of square root ⟶ $= 2\sqrt{3} + 7\sqrt{3}$

4. Distributive Property ⟶ $= (2 + 7)\sqrt{3}$

5. Simplify. ⟶ $= 9\sqrt{3}$ *Simplest form*

P-5   Simplify: **a.** $\sqrt{3}$ $\sqrt{3}$ **b.** $\sqrt{15}$ $\sqrt{15}$

example 3   Add and simplify: $\sqrt{3} + \sqrt{15}$

Solution: Each radical is in simplest form. Therefore, $\sqrt{3} + \sqrt{15}$ is in simplest form.

P-6   **What is the prime factorization of 8?   of 50?** $2 \cdot 5 \cdot 5$
$2 \cdot 2 \cdot 2$

example 4   Add and simplify: $\sqrt{8} + 3\sqrt{2} + \sqrt{50}$

Solution:
$$\sqrt{8} + 3\sqrt{2} + \sqrt{50} = \sqrt{2 \cdot 2 \cdot 2} + 3\sqrt{2} + \sqrt{2 \cdot 5 \cdot 5}$$
$$= \sqrt{2^2} \cdot \sqrt{2} + 3\sqrt{2} + \sqrt{5^2} \cdot \sqrt{2}$$
$$= 2\sqrt{2} + 3\sqrt{2} + 5\sqrt{2}$$
$$= (2 + 3 + 5)\sqrt{2}$$
$$= 10\sqrt{2} \qquad \textbf{Simplest form}$$

example 5   Subtract and simplify: $\sqrt{12n} - \sqrt{27n}$

Solution:

1. Write the prime factorization. → $\sqrt{12n} - \sqrt{27n} = \sqrt{2 \cdot 2 \cdot 3 \cdot n} - \sqrt{3 \cdot 3 \cdot 3 \cdot n}$

2. Product Property of Radicals → $= \sqrt{2^2} \cdot \sqrt{3n} - \sqrt{3^2} \cdot \sqrt{3n}$

3. Meaning of square root → $= 2\sqrt{3n} - 3\sqrt{3n}$

4. Distributive Property → $= (2 - 3)\sqrt{3n}$

5. Simplify. → $= -1\sqrt{3n}$ or $-\sqrt{3n}$

CLASSROOM EXERCISES

Add or subtract as indicated. (Example 1)

1. $2\sqrt{3} + 5\sqrt{3}$ $7\sqrt{3}$

2. $3\sqrt{5} + 2\sqrt{5}$ $5\sqrt{5}$

3. $3\sqrt{2} + \sqrt{2}$ $4\sqrt{2}$

4. $\sqrt{7} + \sqrt{7}$ $2\sqrt{7}$

5. $7\sqrt{10} + 5\sqrt{10}$ $12\sqrt{10}$

6. $8\sqrt{3} - 5\sqrt{3}$ $3\sqrt{3}$

Add or subtract as indicated. Simplify where necessary. (Examples 1 and 3)

7. $4\sqrt{2} - \sqrt{2}$ $3\sqrt{2}$ **8.** $5\sqrt{5} - 4\sqrt{5}$ $\sqrt{5}$ **9.** $3\sqrt{11} - 5\sqrt{11}$ $-2\sqrt{11}$ **10.** $3\sqrt{13} - 4\sqrt{13}$ $-\sqrt{13}$

11. $2\sqrt{x} + 3\sqrt{x}$ $5\sqrt{x}$ **12.** $\frac{1}{2}\sqrt{y} + 2\sqrt{y}$ $\frac{5}{2}\sqrt{y}$ **13.** $\frac{3}{4}\sqrt{a} - \frac{1}{4}\sqrt{a}$ $\frac{1}{2}\sqrt{a}$ **14.** $\sqrt{n} + \sqrt{n}$ $2\sqrt{n}$

15. $9\sqrt{m} + \sqrt{m}$ $10\sqrt{m}$ **16.** $\sqrt{16} - \sqrt{1}$ 3 **17.** $\sqrt{4} + \sqrt{9}$ 5 **18.** $\sqrt{2} + \sqrt{5}$ $\sqrt{2} + \sqrt{5}$

WRITTEN EXERCISES

See the Teacher's Manual for the suggested assignments.
Goal: To add and subtract radicals
Sample Problem: $3\sqrt{5} - 7\sqrt{5} + \sqrt{5}$ **Answer:** $-3\sqrt{5}$

Add or subtract as indicated. Simplify where necessary. (Examples 1–3, 5)

1. $10\sqrt{3} + 5\sqrt{3}$ $15\sqrt{3}$ **2.** $8\sqrt{5} + 3\sqrt{5}$ $11\sqrt{5}$ **3.** $7\sqrt{2} - 3\sqrt{2}$ $4\sqrt{2}$

4. $8\sqrt{7} - 3\sqrt{7}$ $5\sqrt{7}$ **5.** $2\sqrt{3} - 5\sqrt{3}$ $-3\sqrt{3}$ **6.** $3\sqrt{14} - 7\sqrt{14}$ $-4\sqrt{14}$

7. $5\sqrt{2} - \sqrt{2}$ $4\sqrt{2}$ **8.** $6\sqrt{6} - \sqrt{6}$ $5\sqrt{6}$ **9.** $\sqrt{11} + \sqrt{11}$ $2\sqrt{11}$

10. $\sqrt{15} + \sqrt{15}$ $2\sqrt{15}$ **11.** $\sqrt{5} + \sqrt{15}$ $\sqrt{5} + \sqrt{15}$ **12.** $2\sqrt{3} + \sqrt{7}$ $2\sqrt{3} + \sqrt{7}$

13. $\sqrt{19} - \sqrt{3}$ $\sqrt{19} - \sqrt{3}$ **14.** $3\sqrt{5} - 2\sqrt{3}$ $3\sqrt{5} - 2\sqrt{3}$ **15.** $3\sqrt{x} + 9\sqrt{x}$ $12\sqrt{x}$

16. $5\sqrt{a} + 10\sqrt{a}$ $15\sqrt{a}$ **17.** $-2\sqrt{t} - 3\sqrt{t}$ $-5\sqrt{t}$ **18.** $-\sqrt{r} - 5\sqrt{r}$ $-6\sqrt{r}$

19. $\sqrt{s} + \sqrt{s}$ $2\sqrt{s}$ **20.** $\sqrt{12} + 3\sqrt{3}$ $5\sqrt{3}$ **21.** $3\sqrt{8} + 5\sqrt{2}$ $11\sqrt{2}$

22. $3\sqrt{12} + 5\sqrt{3}$ $11\sqrt{3}$ **23.** $\sqrt{20} - 2\sqrt{5}$ 0 **24.** $\sqrt{18} - 6\sqrt{2}$ $-3\sqrt{2}$

25. $\sqrt{27} + \sqrt{12}$ $5\sqrt{3}$ **26.** $\sqrt{32} + \sqrt{8}$ $6\sqrt{2}$ **27.** $2\sqrt{45} + \sqrt{5}$ $7\sqrt{5}$

28. $\sqrt{24} + \sqrt{96}$ $6\sqrt{6}$ **29.** $2\sqrt{72} - \sqrt{2}$ $11\sqrt{2}$ **30.** $4\sqrt{27} - \sqrt{12}$ $10\sqrt{3}$

31. $\sqrt{28a} + 3\sqrt{7a}$ $5\sqrt{7a}$ **32.** $\sqrt{44n} + 5\sqrt{11n}$ $7\sqrt{11n}$ **33.** $\sqrt{2r} + \sqrt{18r}$ $4\sqrt{2r}$

34. $\sqrt{16x} - \sqrt{4x}$ $2\sqrt{x}$ **35.** $\sqrt{25y} + \sqrt{49y}$ $12\sqrt{y}$ **36.** $\sqrt{2x} - 3\sqrt{32x}$ $-11\sqrt{2x}$

(Example 4)

37. $2\sqrt{3} + \sqrt{3} + 4\sqrt{3}$ $7\sqrt{3}$ **38.** $7\sqrt{2} + \sqrt{2} + 2\sqrt{2}$ $10\sqrt{2}$

39. $3\sqrt{7} - 4\sqrt{7} + 2\sqrt{7}$ $\sqrt{7}$ **40.** $4\sqrt{5} - 6\sqrt{5} + \sqrt{5}$ $-\sqrt{5}$

41. $7\sqrt{y} - 2\sqrt{y} - 5\sqrt{y}$ 0 **42.** $-3\sqrt{b} + 10\sqrt{b} - 7\sqrt{b}$ 0

REVIEW CAPSULE FOR SECTION 8.6

Multiply and simplify. (Section 8.2)

1. $\sqrt{3} \cdot \sqrt{12}$ 6 **2.** $\sqrt{5x^3} \cdot \sqrt{5x}$ $5x^2$ **3.** $\sqrt{13x} \cdot \sqrt{13x}$ $13x$ **4.** $\sqrt{\frac{1}{9}x} \cdot \sqrt{x^3}$ $\frac{1}{3}x^2$

8.6 Quotients

To simplify a quotient of two square root radicals
To rationalize the denominator in the quotient of two square root radicals and then simplify

P-1 **Simplify:** a. $\sqrt{\dfrac{4}{9}}$ $\frac{2}{3}$ b. $\dfrac{\sqrt{4}}{\sqrt{9}}$ $\frac{2}{3}$

Quotient Property of Radicals

If a is any nonnegative real number and b is any positive real number, then $\sqrt{\dfrac{a}{b}} = \dfrac{\sqrt{a}}{\sqrt{b}}$.

$$\sqrt{\frac{4}{9}} = \frac{\sqrt{4}}{\sqrt{9}}$$

$$\sqrt{\frac{3}{7}} = \frac{\sqrt{3}}{\sqrt{7}}$$

Explain that the numerator can equal 0 but the denominator cannot equal 0.

---

example 1

Simplify $\sqrt{\dfrac{8}{r^2}}$.

Solution:

1. Quotient Property of Radicals ⟶ $\sqrt{\dfrac{8}{r^2}} = \dfrac{\sqrt{8}}{\sqrt{r^2}}$

2. Product Property of Radicals ⟶ $= \dfrac{\sqrt{4} \cdot \sqrt{2}}{\sqrt{r^2}}$

3. Meaning of square root ⟶ $= \dfrac{2\sqrt{2}}{r}$ ◄ **Simplest form**

P-2 **Simplify each radical.**

a. $\sqrt{\dfrac{n^2}{9}}$ $\frac{n}{3}$ b. $\sqrt{\dfrac{2}{x^2}}$ $\frac{\sqrt{2}}{x}$ c. $\sqrt{\dfrac{r^3}{16}}$ $\frac{r\sqrt{r}}{4}$ d. $\sqrt{\dfrac{64}{a^2}}$ $\frac{8}{a}$

---

example 2

Simplify $\dfrac{\sqrt{18x^3}}{\sqrt{2x}}$.

Solution:

1. Quotient Property of Radicals ⟶ $\dfrac{\sqrt{18x^3}}{\sqrt{2x}} = \sqrt{\dfrac{18x^3}{2x}}$

2. Divide. ⟶ $= \sqrt{9x^2}$

3. Meaning of square root ⟶ $= 3x$ ◄ **Simplest form**

Sometimes it is inconvenient to have a radical in a denominator. The procedure used in Example 3 below is called **rationalizing the denominator.**

example 3 Rationalize the denominator of $\dfrac{\sqrt{a}}{\sqrt{b}}$.

Solution:

1. Multiplication Property of One ⟶ $\dfrac{\sqrt{a}}{\sqrt{b}} = \dfrac{\sqrt{a}}{\sqrt{b}} \cdot \dfrac{\sqrt{b}}{\sqrt{b}}$ ◀ $\dfrac{\sqrt{b}}{\sqrt{b}}$ is another name for 1.

2. Product Property of Radicals ⟶ $= \dfrac{\sqrt{ab}}{\sqrt{b^2}}$

3. Meaning of square root ⟶ $= \dfrac{\sqrt{ab}}{b}$ ◀ $\dfrac{\sqrt{ab}}{b}$ has no radical in the denominator.

P-3 **What name for 1 would be used to rationalize the denominator of each fraction below?**

a. $\dfrac{\sqrt{2}}{\sqrt{5}}$ $\dfrac{\sqrt{5}}{\sqrt{5}}$ b. $\dfrac{\sqrt{m}}{\sqrt{2n}}$ $\dfrac{\sqrt{2n}}{\sqrt{2n}}$ c. $\dfrac{\sqrt{5r}}{\sqrt{12s}}$ d. $\dfrac{\sqrt{3y}}{\sqrt{x^3}}$ ◀ **Remember that** $\sqrt{x^3}\sqrt{x} = x^2$.

$\dfrac{\sqrt{12s}}{\sqrt{12s}}$ or $\dfrac{\sqrt{3s}}{\sqrt{3s}}$ $\dfrac{\sqrt{x}}{\sqrt{x}}$

example 4 Rationalize the denominator of $\dfrac{\sqrt{5r}}{\sqrt{12s}}$.
Then simplify.

Solution:

1. Multiplication Property of One ⟶ $\dfrac{\sqrt{5r}}{\sqrt{12s}} = \dfrac{\sqrt{5r}}{\sqrt{12s}} \cdot \dfrac{\sqrt{12s}}{\sqrt{12s}}$ You may want to show also the method in this Example of multiplying by

2. Product Property of Radicals ⟶ $= \dfrac{\sqrt{60rs}}{12s}$ $\dfrac{\sqrt{3s}}{\sqrt{3s}}$ in Step 1 .

3. Product Property of Radicals ⟶ $= \dfrac{\sqrt{4} \cdot \sqrt{15rs}}{12s}$

4. Meaning of square root ⟶ $= \dfrac{2\sqrt{15rs}}{12s}$

5. Simplify. ⟶ $= \dfrac{\overset{1}{2}\sqrt{15rs}}{\underset{6}{12}s}$ or $\dfrac{\sqrt{15rs}}{6s}$

CLASSROOM EXERCISES

Simplify. (Example 1)

1. $\sqrt{\frac{1}{4}}$ $\frac{1}{2}$
2. $\sqrt{\frac{1}{9}}$ $\frac{1}{3}$
3. $\sqrt{\frac{9}{25}}$ $\frac{3}{5}$
4. $\sqrt{\frac{36}{49}}$ $\frac{6}{7}$
5. $\sqrt{\frac{64}{100}}$ $\frac{4}{5}$
6. $\sqrt{\frac{100}{144}}$ $\frac{5}{6}$

Simplify. (Example 2)

7. $\frac{\sqrt{12}}{\sqrt{3}}$ 2
8. $\frac{\sqrt{8}}{\sqrt{2}}$ 2
9. $\frac{\sqrt{20}}{\sqrt{5}}$ 2
10. $\frac{\sqrt{24}}{\sqrt{6}}$ 2
11. $\frac{\sqrt{28}}{\sqrt{7}}$ 2

WRITTEN EXERCISES

See the Teacher's Manual for the suggested assignments.

Goal: To simplify quotients of radicals

Sample Problem: $\dfrac{\sqrt{132r^3}}{\sqrt{6r}}$ **Answer:** $r\sqrt{22}$

Simplify. (Example 1)

1. $\sqrt{\frac{x^2}{16}}$ $\frac{x}{4}$
2. $\sqrt{\frac{y^2}{25}}$ $\frac{y}{5}$
3. $\sqrt{\frac{49}{a^2}}$ $\frac{7}{a}$
4. $\sqrt{\frac{64}{y^2}}$ $\frac{8}{y}$
5. $\sqrt{\frac{y^4}{100}}$ $\frac{y^2}{10}$

6. $\sqrt{\frac{x^4}{121}}$ $\frac{x^2}{11}$
7. $\sqrt{\frac{2}{x^2}}$ $\frac{\sqrt{2}}{x}$
8. $\sqrt{\frac{3}{r^2}}$ $\frac{\sqrt{3}}{r}$
9. $\sqrt{\frac{12}{a^2}}$ $\frac{2\sqrt{3}}{a}$
10. $\sqrt{\frac{18}{t^2}}$ $\frac{3\sqrt{2}}{t}$

Simplify. (Example 2)

11. $\frac{\sqrt{50}}{\sqrt{2}}$ 5
12. $\frac{\sqrt{75}}{\sqrt{3}}$ 5
13. $\frac{\sqrt{108}}{\sqrt{3}}$ 6
14. $\frac{\sqrt{72}}{\sqrt{2}}$ 6
15. $\frac{\sqrt{98}}{\sqrt{2}}$ 7

16. $\frac{\sqrt{180}}{\sqrt{5}}$ 6
17. $\frac{\sqrt{125}}{\sqrt{5}}$ 5
18. $\frac{\sqrt{147}}{\sqrt{3}}$ 7
19. $\frac{\sqrt{x^3}}{\sqrt{x}}$ x
20. $\frac{\sqrt{a}}{\sqrt{a^3}}$ $\frac{1}{a}$

21. $\frac{\sqrt{4y}}{\sqrt{y^3}}$ $\frac{2}{y}$
22. $\frac{\sqrt{r^3}}{\sqrt{9r}}$ $\frac{r}{3}$
23. $\frac{\sqrt{ab^2}}{\sqrt{a^3}}$ $\frac{b}{a}$
24. $\frac{\sqrt{x^3y^3}}{\sqrt{xy}}$ xy
25. $\frac{\sqrt{10}}{\sqrt{2}}$ $\sqrt{5}$

26. $\frac{\sqrt{14}}{\sqrt{7}}$ $\sqrt{2}$
27. $\frac{\sqrt{18}}{\sqrt{3}}$ $\sqrt{6}$
28. $\frac{\sqrt{22}}{\sqrt{11}}$ $\sqrt{2}$
29. $\frac{\sqrt{33}}{\sqrt{3}}$ $\sqrt{11}$
30. $\frac{\sqrt{38}}{\sqrt{2}}$ $\sqrt{19}$

Rationalize each denominator. Then simplify. (Examples 3–4)

31. $\frac{\sqrt{3}}{\sqrt{5}}$ $\frac{\sqrt{15}}{5}$
32. $\frac{\sqrt{2}}{\sqrt{7}}$ $\frac{\sqrt{14}}{7}$
33. $\frac{\sqrt{a^2}}{\sqrt{b}}$ $\frac{a\sqrt{b}}{b}$
34. $\frac{\sqrt{r^3}}{\sqrt{p}}$ $\frac{r\sqrt{rp}}{p}$
35. $\frac{\sqrt{3s}}{\sqrt{5t}}$ $\frac{\sqrt{15st}}{5t}$
36. $\frac{\sqrt{2x}}{\sqrt{3y}}$ $\frac{\sqrt{6xy}}{3y}$

REVIEW CAPSULE FOR SECTION 8.7

Write the prime factorization. (Section 8.1)

1. 168 $2 \cdot 2 \cdot 2 \cdot 3 \cdot 7$
2. 180 $2 \cdot 2 \cdot 3 \cdot 3 \cdot 5$
3. 244 $2 \cdot 2 \cdot 61$
4. 288 $2 \cdot 2 \cdot 2 \cdot 2 \cdot 2 \cdot 3 \cdot 3$
5. 207 $3 \cdot 3 \cdot 23$
6. 234 $2 \cdot 3 \cdot 3 \cdot 13$

8.7 Approximations

OBJECTIVES: To approximate positive square roots of certain counting numbers, not in a given Table of Squares and Square Roots by forming a product involving one or more radicals that are within the range of the table. To rationalize the denominator of a fraction and approximate the given radical by use of a Table

A Table of Squares and Square Roots is provided on page 198 for the positive integers from 1 to 150. Square roots in this table are approximated to three decimal places.

P-1 **What is each power below based on the table?**

a. 28^2 784 **b.** 76^2 5776 **c.** 26^2 676

Each number in the **Number** column is the positive square root of a number in the **Square** column.

P-2 **What is the value of each square root below?**

a. $\sqrt{784}$ 28 **b.** $-\sqrt{6084}$ −78 **c.** $\sqrt{729}$ 27

P-3 **What is the approximate value of each square root below?**

a. $\sqrt{26}$ 5.099 **b.** $\sqrt{78}$ 8.832 **c.** $-\sqrt{28}$ −5.292

P-4 **What is the prime factorization of 160?** $2 \cdot 2 \cdot 2 \cdot 2 \cdot 2 \cdot 5$

example 1

Approximate $\sqrt{160}$ to three decimal places.

Write the radical in simplest form. → Use the table of square roots.

Solution:

1. Write the prime factorization. ⟶ $\sqrt{160} = \sqrt{2 \cdot 2 \cdot 2 \cdot 2 \cdot 2 \cdot 5}$

2. Product Property of Radicals ⟶ $= \sqrt{2^4} \cdot \sqrt{2 \cdot 5}$

3. Simplify. ⟶ $= 4\sqrt{10}$

4. Use the table on page 198. ⟶ $\approx 4(3.162)$

≈ 12.648

The approximate value of $\sqrt{160}$ is 12.648.

Table of Squares and Square Roots

No.	Square	Square Root	No.	Square	Square Root	No.	Square	Square Root
1	1	1.000	51	2601	7.141	101	10,201	10.050
2	4	1.414	52	2704	7.211	102	10,404	10.100
3	9	1.732	53	2809	7.280	103	10,609	10.149
4	16	2.000	54	2916	7.348	104	10,816	10.198
5	25	2.236	55	3025	7.416	105	11,025	10.247
6	36	2.449	56	3136	7.483	106	11,236	10.296
7	49	2.646	57	3249	7.550	107	11,449	10.344
8	64	2.828	58	3364	7.616	108	11,664	10.392
9	81	3.000	59	3481	7.681	109	11,881	10.440
10	100	3.162	60	3600	7.746	110	12,100	10.488
11	121	3.317	61	3721	7.810	111	12,321	10.536
12	144	3.464	62	3844	7.874	112	12,544	10.583
13	169	3.606	63	3969	7.937	113	12,769	10.630
14	196	3.742	64	4096	8.000	114	12,996	10.677
15	225	3.873	65	4225	8.062	115	13,225	10.724
16	256	4.000	66	4356	8.124	116	13,456	10.770
17	289	4.123	67	4489	8.185	117	13,689	10.817
18	324	4.243	68	4624	8.246	118	13,924	10.863
19	361	4.359	69	4761	8.307	119	14,161	10.909
20	400	4.472	70	4900	8.367	120	14,400	10.954
21	441	4.583	71	5041	8.426	121	14,641	11.000
22	484	4.690	72	5184	8.485	122	14,884	11.045
23	529	4.796	73	5329	8.544	123	15,129	11.091
24	576	4.899	74	5476	8.602	124	15,376	11.136
25	625	5.000	75	5625	8.660	125	15,625	11.180
26	676	5.099	76	5776	8.718	126	15,876	11.225
27	729	5.196	77	5929	8.775	127	16,129	11.269
28	784	5.292	78	6084	8.832	128	16,384	11.314
29	841	5.385	79	6241	8.888	129	16,641	11.358
30	900	5.477	80	6400	8.944	130	16,900	11.402
31	961	5.568	81	6561	9.000	131	17,161	11.446
32	1024	5.657	82	6724	9.055	132	17,424	11.489
33	1089	5.745	83	6889	9.110	133	17,689	11.533
34	1156	5.831	84	7056	9.165	134	17,956	11.576
35	1225	5.916	85	7225	9.220	135	18,225	11.619
36	1296	6.000	86	7396	9.274	136	18,496	11.662
37	1369	6.083	87	7569	9.327	137	18,769	11.705
38	1444	6.164	88	7744	9.381	138	19,044	11.747
39	1521	6.245	89	7921	9.434	139	19,321	11.790
40	1600	6.325	90	8100	9.487	140	19,600	11.832
41	1681	6.403	91	8281	9.539	141	19,881	11.874
42	1764	6.481	92	8464	9.592	142	20,164	11.916
43	1849	6.557	93	8649	9.644	143	20,449	11.958
44	1936	6.633	94	8836	9.695	144	20,736	12.000
45	2025	6.708	95	9025	9.747	145	21,025	12.042
46	2116	6.782	96	9216	9.798	146	21,316	12.083
47	2209	6.856	97	9409	9.849	147	21,609	12.124
48	2304	6.928	98	9604	9.899	148	21,904	12.166
49	2401	7.000	99	9801	9.950	149	22,201	12.207
50	2500	7.071	100	10,000	10.000	150	22,500	12.247

example 2

Approximate $\sqrt{\dfrac{3}{8}}$ to three decimal places.

Rationalize the denominator. → Use the table of square roots. → Divide.

Solution:

1 Quotient Property of Radicals ⟶ $\sqrt{\dfrac{3}{8}} = \dfrac{\sqrt{3}}{\sqrt{8}}$

2 Multiplication Property of One ⟶ $= \dfrac{\sqrt{3}}{\sqrt{8}} \cdot \dfrac{\sqrt{8}}{\sqrt{8}}$

Discuss the use of $\dfrac{\sqrt{2}}{\sqrt{2}}$ as a name for 1 in Step 2 . Also, note the importance of rationalizing the denominator. $\dfrac{\sqrt{6}}{4}$ is easier to approximate than $\dfrac{\sqrt{3}}{\sqrt{8}}$.

3 Product Property of Radicals ⟶ $= \dfrac{\sqrt{24}}{8}$

4 Write the simplest name of the numerator. ⟶ $= \dfrac{2\sqrt{6}}{8}$

5 Simplify. ⟶ $= \dfrac{\sqrt{6}}{4}$

6 Use the table on page 198. ⟶ $\approx \dfrac{2.449}{4}$

≈ 0.612 ◄ **Approximate value of** $\sqrt{\dfrac{3}{8}}$

P-5   **What is the prime factorization of 210?** $2 \cdot 3 \cdot 5 \cdot 7$

example 3

Approximate $\sqrt{210}$ to two decimal places.

Solution:

Method 1

$\sqrt{210} = \sqrt{2 \cdot 3 \cdot 5 \cdot 7}$

$= \sqrt{2} \cdot \sqrt{3} \cdot \sqrt{5} \cdot \sqrt{7}$

$\approx (1.414)(1.732)(2.236)(2.646)$

≈ 14.49

Method 2

$\sqrt{210} = \sqrt{10} \cdot \sqrt{21}$

$\approx (3.162)(4.583)$

≈ 14.49

You can see that there is less computation in Method 2.

CLASSROOM EXERCISES

Tell each value by referring to the Table of Squares and Square Roots.
(P-1, P-2, P-3)

1. 29^2 841
2. 56^2 3136
3. 93^2 8649
4. 117^2 13,689

5. $\sqrt{5184}$ 72
6. $\sqrt{961}$ 31
7. $-\sqrt{7744}$ −88
8. $\sqrt{13,225}$ 115

9. $\sqrt{38}$ 6.164
10. $\sqrt{131}$ 11.446
11. $\sqrt{78}$ 8.832
12. $-\sqrt{43}$ −6.557

13. $\sqrt{90}$ 9.487
14. $\sqrt{139}$ 11.790
15. $-\sqrt{150}$ −12.247
16. $\sqrt{109}$ 10.440

17. $\sqrt{8649}$ 93
18. $\sqrt{18,496}$ 136
19. $\sqrt{3481}$ 59
20. $\sqrt{13,456}$ 116

WRITTEN EXERCISES

See the Teacher's Manual for the suggested assignments.

Goal: To approximate the values of square roots to two or three decimal places

Sample Problem: Approximate $\sqrt{304}$ to three decimal places.

Answer: 17.436

Approximate each square root to three decimal places. Use the table on page 198. (Examples 1–2)

1. $\sqrt{168}$ 12.962
2. $\sqrt{180}$ 13.416
3. $\sqrt{244}$ 15.620
4. $\sqrt{288}$ 16.968

5. $\sqrt{207}$ 14.388
6. $\sqrt{234}$ 15.297
7. $\sqrt{275}$ 16.585
8. $\sqrt{425}$ 20.615

9. $\sqrt{468}$ 21.633
10. $\sqrt{684}$ 26.154
11. $\sqrt{\frac{3}{4}}$ 0.866
12. $\sqrt{\frac{5}{16}}$ 0.559

13. $\sqrt{\frac{2}{3}}$ 0.816
14. $\sqrt{\frac{5}{6}}$ 0.913
15. $\sqrt{\frac{7}{8}}$ 0.935
16. $\sqrt{\frac{5}{8}}$ 0.791

17. $\sqrt{\frac{11}{12}}$ 0.958
18. $\sqrt{\frac{7}{12}}$ 0.764
19. $\sqrt{\frac{3}{32}}$ 0.306
20. $\sqrt{\frac{7}{18}}$ 0.624

Approximate each square root to two decimal places. (Example 3)

21. $\sqrt{161}$ 12.69
22. $\sqrt{209}$ 14.46
23. $\sqrt{155}$ 12.45
24. $\sqrt{259}$ 16.10

25. $\sqrt{187}$ 13.67
26. $\sqrt{205}$ 14.32
27. $\sqrt{75}$ 8.66
28. $\sqrt{192}$ 13.86

MORE CHALLENGING EXERCISES

29. $\sqrt{3\frac{1}{2}}$ 1.87
30. $\sqrt{5\frac{2}{3}}$ 2.38
31. $\sqrt{12\frac{3}{4}}$ 3.57
32. $\sqrt{10\frac{4}{5}}$ 3.29

Meteorologist

Meteorology is the study of the atmosphere. The best known activity of meteorologists is weather forecasting. Meteorologists are employed by commercial airlines, by radio and television stations, by utility companies, by insurance companies, and many others. The largest employer is the National Oceanic and Atmospheric Administration.

A bachelor's degree with a major in meteorology is the usual minimum requirement for beginning jobs in weather forecasting. Beginning meteorologists often start in jobs involving routine collection of data. Meteorological technicians assist meteorologists. They calibrate instruments, record atmospheric data, and assist in research.

One statistic that is often given in daily weather reports in winter in cold climates is **wind chill temperature.** This was developed in order to describe the relative discomfort humans experience due to both temperature and wind speed. Data for wind chill temperatures were derived from experiments conducted in Antarctica by U.S. scientists. Weather forecasters obtain the wind chill temperatures from tables such as the one shown below.

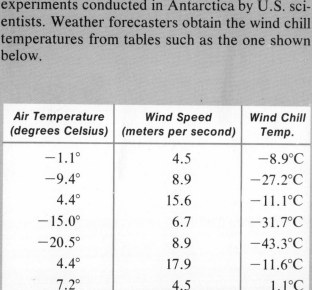

Air Temperature (degrees Celsius)	Wind Speed (meters per second)	Wind Chill Temp.
−1.1°	4.5	−8.9°C
−9.4°	8.9	−27.2°C
4.4°	15.6	−11.1°C
−15.0°	6.7	−31.7°C
−20.5°	8.9	−43.3°C
4.4°	17.9	−11.6°C
7.2°	4.5	1.1°C

The following formula can also be used to approximate the data available in tables.

$$C = 33 - \frac{(10\sqrt{r} + 10.45 - r)(33 - t)}{22.1}$$

C = the wind chill temperature in degree Celsius.
t = the air temperature in degrees Celsius.
r = the wind speed in meters per second.

The numbers 33, 10.45, 10, and 22.1 are constants.

EXAMPLE: On a Fall day the air temperature is 5°C. The wind speed is 8 meters per second. Find the wind chill temperature.

SOLUTION: $C = 33 - \dfrac{(10\sqrt{r} + 10.45 - r)(33 - t)}{22.1}$

$r = 8; t = 5$

$C = 33 - \dfrac{(10\sqrt{8} + 10.45 - 8)(33 - 5)}{22.1}$

$= 33 - \dfrac{(10\sqrt{8} + 10.45 - 8)(28)}{22.1}$

By calculator:

$\boxed{8}\ \boxed{\sqrt{}}\ \boxed{\times}\ \boxed{1}\ \boxed{0}\ \boxed{+}\ \boxed{1}\ \boxed{0}\ \boxed{.}\ \boxed{4}\ \boxed{5}$

$\boxed{-}\ \boxed{8}\ \boxed{\times}\ \boxed{2}\ \boxed{8}\ \boxed{\div}\ \boxed{2}\ \boxed{2}\ \boxed{.}\ \boxed{1}\ \boxed{=}$

$\boxed{+/_-}\ \boxed{+}\ \boxed{3}\ \boxed{3}\ \boxed{=}$ 　　　　　$\boxed{-5.939347}$

The wind chill temperature is about **−5.9°C**.

EXERCISES

In Exercises 1–4, the air temperature is given in degrees Celsius (°C) and the wind speed is given in meters per second (m/s). Find the wind chill temperature in each case. Compare your answer with the value found in the table on page 201.

1. Air temperature: 7.2°C   1.3° C
Wind speed: 4.5 m/s   (Table: 1.1° C)

2. Air temperature: −9.4°C   −27.2° C
Wind speed: 8.9 m/s   (Table: −27.2° C)

3. Air temperature: −15.0°C
Wind speed: 6.7 m/s
−31.4° C   (Table: −31.7° C)

4. Air temperature: 4.4°C
Wind speed: 15.6 m/s
−11.4° C   (Table: −11.1° C)

Career

CHAPTER SUMMARY

IMPORTANT TERMS	Radical symbol *(p. 178)* Square root *(p. 178)* Square *(p. 178)* Prime number *(p. 178)* Prime-factorization *(p. 179)* Perfect square *(p. 179)* Radical *(p. 184)*	Radicand *(p. 184)* Cube root *(p. 184)* Fourth root *(p. 184)* Perfect cube *(p. 188)* Like radicals *(p. 191)* Rationalizing the denominator *(p. 195)*

IMPORTANT IDEAS

1. A negative number cannot have a real number as a square root.

2. Each prime factor of a perfect square occurs an even number of times.

3. A square root of a perfect square counting number is rational.

4. Any whole number that is not a perfect square has an irrational square root.

5. If a is any nonnegative real number, then $\sqrt{a} \cdot \sqrt{a} = a$.

6. *Product Property of Radicals:* If a and b are nonnegative real numbers, then $\sqrt{a} \cdot \sqrt{b} = \sqrt{ab}$.

7. A square root radical is in simplest form if its radicand has no perfect square factor.

8. A cube root radical is in simplest form if its radicand has no perfect cube factor.

9. *Quotient Property of Radicals:* If a is any nonnegative real number and b is any positive real number, then $\sqrt{\dfrac{a}{b}} = \dfrac{\sqrt{a}}{\sqrt{b}}$.

CHAPTER REVIEW

NOTE: The Teacher's Resource Book contains two forms of each Chapter Test.

SECTION 8.1

Simplify.

1. $-\sqrt{49}$ –7

2. $\sqrt{\dfrac{1}{16}}$ $\frac{1}{4}$

3. $\sqrt{0.36}$ 0.6

4. $\sqrt{3^4 \cdot 7^2}$ 63

SECTION 8.2

Multiply and simplify.

5. $\sqrt{23} \cdot \sqrt{23}$ 23

6. $\sqrt{81} \cdot \sqrt{36}$ 54

7. $(\sqrt{3})(-\sqrt{11})$ $-\sqrt{33}$

8. $(\sqrt{2})(\sqrt{7})$ $\sqrt{14}$

9. $\left(\sqrt{\dfrac{1}{2}}\right)(\sqrt{72})$ 6

10. $\left(\sqrt{\dfrac{1}{3}}\right)(\sqrt{27})$ 3

SECTION 8.3

Simplify.

11. $\sqrt{2 \cdot 3 \cdot 2 \cdot 3 \cdot 3}$ $6\sqrt{3}$ **12.** $\sqrt{3 \cdot 5 \cdot 5 \cdot 2 \cdot 2 \cdot 2}$ $10\sqrt{6}$

13. $\sqrt{52}$ $2\sqrt{13}$ **14.** $\sqrt{60}$ $2\sqrt{15}$ **15.** $\sqrt{99}$ $3\sqrt{11}$ **16.** $\sqrt{63}$ $3\sqrt{7}$ **17.** $\sqrt[3]{24}$ $2\sqrt[3]{3}$ **18.** $\sqrt[3]{56}$

$2\sqrt[3]{7}$

SECTION 8.4

Simplify.

19. $\sqrt{r^6}$ r^3 **20.** $\sqrt{t^{10}}$ t^5 **21.** $\sqrt{9x^5}$ $3x^2\sqrt{x}$ **22.** $\sqrt{16y^3}$ $4y\sqrt{y}$

23. $\sqrt{28a^3b^5}$ $2ab^2\sqrt{7ab}$ **24.** $\sqrt{45r^4s^7}$ $3r^2s^3\sqrt{5s}$ **25.** $\sqrt[3]{16m^3n^4}$ $2mn\sqrt[3]{2n}$ **26.** $\sqrt[3]{27p^5q^6}$

$3pq^2\sqrt[3]{p^2}$

SECTION 8.5

Add or subtract as indicated. Simplify where necessary.

$9\sqrt{3}$

27. $8\sqrt{13} + 2\sqrt{13}$ $10\sqrt{13}$ **28.** $12\sqrt{3} - \sqrt{3}$ $11\sqrt{3}$ **29.** $2\sqrt{12} + 5\sqrt{3}$

30. $3\sqrt{8} + 5\sqrt{2}$ $11\sqrt{2}$ **31.** $\sqrt{24} - 9\sqrt{6}$ $-7\sqrt{6}$ **32.** $12\sqrt{5} - \sqrt{45}$

$9\sqrt{5}$

SECTION 8.6

Simplify.

33. $\sqrt{\dfrac{3}{24}}$ $\dfrac{\sqrt{2}}{4}$ **34.** $\sqrt{\dfrac{x}{81}}$ $\dfrac{\sqrt{x}}{9}$ **35.** $\sqrt{\dfrac{20}{t^2}}$ $\dfrac{2\sqrt{5}}{t}$ **36.** $\sqrt{\dfrac{54}{y^4}}$ $\dfrac{3\sqrt{6}}{y^2}$

Rationalize each denominator. Then simplify.

37. $\dfrac{\sqrt{7}}{\sqrt{10}}$ $\dfrac{\sqrt{70}}{10}$ **38.** $\dfrac{\sqrt{3}}{\sqrt{14}}$ $\dfrac{\sqrt{42}}{14}$ **39.** $\dfrac{\sqrt{3x^3}}{\sqrt{2y}}$ $\dfrac{x\sqrt{6xy}}{2y}$ **40.** $\dfrac{\sqrt{2a^5}}{\sqrt{5m}}$

$\dfrac{a^2\sqrt{10am}}{5m}$

SECTION 8.7

Approximate each square root to three decimal places. Use the table on page 198.

41. $\sqrt{153}$ **42.** $\sqrt{200}$ 14.14 **43.** $\sqrt{\dfrac{11}{16}}$ 0.829 **44.** $\sqrt{\dfrac{7}{25}}$ 0.529 **45.** $\sqrt{\dfrac{17}{24}}$ 0.842 **46.** $\sqrt{\dfrac{11}{20}}$

12.368 0.742

CHAPTER **9** Polynomials

Sections
9.1 **Monomials**

9.2 **Operations with Monomials**

9.3 **Polynomials**

9.4 **Addition and Subtraction**

9.5 **Multiplication**

9.6 **Division**

9.7 **Division with Remainders**

Features
Calculator Exercises: **Evaluating Polynomials**

Special Topic Application: **Distance to the Horizon**

Review and Testing
Review Capsules

Mid-Chapter Review

Chapter Summary

Chapter Review

9.1 Monomials

The numerals and expressions below are monomials.

a. $\frac{1}{3}x$ **b.** 5   **c.** $3x^2$ **d.** $-x$

Explain that the
domains of *a*, *x*, and
n are all different.

A ***monomial*** of one variable over
{rational numbers} is an expression
of the form ax^n in which *a* is any rational
number and *n* is any nonnegative integer.

$-5x^3$

$\frac{1}{4}x^5$

$-3x^0$ or -3

P-1   **What are the values of *a* and *n* in each monomial below?**

                                         Since $-15 = -15x^0$,

a. $3.7x^2$ **b.** $-x$ **c.** -15 *-15 is a*
$a = 3.7; n = 2$ $a = -1, n = 1$ *monomial.*
                           $a = -15; n = 0$

If ax^n is a monomial, *n* cannot be negative. The following expressions
are <u>not</u> monomials.

a. $3x^{-2}$ **b.** $-\frac{1}{5}x^{-1}$ **c.** $0.7x^{-3}$

P-2   **Why is $\dfrac{3}{x^2}$ not a monomial?**

                             $\frac{3}{x^2}$ *is equivalent*
                             to $3x^{-2}$.

$n = -2$, which is a negative number.

In a monomial of the form ax^n, the number represented by *a* is the
coefficient or ***numerical coefficient.***

P-3   **What is the coefficient of each monomial below?**

a. $\frac{1}{3}x^2$ $\frac{1}{3}$ **b.** x^3 1   **c.** $-x$ -1 **d.** $-\dfrac{x}{5}$ $-\frac{1}{5}$

Monomials are classified by their numerical coefficients. The
monomials below are monomials ***over the set of integers.***

a. $2x^3$ **b.** -10 **c.** $5x$ **d.** $-x^5$

---

example 1

Evaluate $-8x^3$ if *x* equals -2.

Solution: $-8x^3 = -8(-2)^3$ 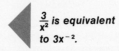   **Raise to a
power first.**

                 $= (-8)(-8)$

                 $= 64$

CLASSROOM EXERCISES

Write Yes or No to tell whether each numeral or expression is a monomial over {rational numbers}. (P-2)

1. $5x^3$ Yes   **2.** $5x^{-1}$ No   **3.** $\dfrac{3}{x}$ No   **4.** $\dfrac{x}{3}$ Yes   **5.** $\sqrt{4} \cdot x^3$ Yes   **6.** $-7x^0$
Yes

Write the coefficient of each monomial. (P-3)

7. $2x^2$ 2   **8.** $-x^3$ −1   **9.** $-7\frac{1}{2}$ $-7\frac{1}{2}$ **10.** $-2.8x^3$ −2.8   **11.** $3\frac{2}{3}x^0$
$3\frac{2}{3}$

WRITTEN EXERCISES

See the Teacher's Manual for the suggested assignments.

Goal: To evaluate monomials
Sample Problem: Evaluate $0.6x^3$ if $x = 20$.   **Answer:** 4800

Write Yes or No to show whether each numeral or expression is a monomial over {rational numbers}. (P-2)

1. $13x$ Yes   **2.** $27x^2$ Yes   **3.** $-5x^3$ Yes   **4.** $-3x^5$ Yes   **5.** $2x^{-2}$ No

6. $-3x^{-5}$ No   **7.** $\dfrac{x^2}{10}$ Yes   **8.** $\dfrac{-x^3}{7}$ Yes   **9.** $\dfrac{3}{x^2}$ No   **10.** $\dfrac{-2}{x^2}$ No

11. $0.6x^0$ Yes   **12.** $5.7x^0$ Yes   **13.** $\sqrt{7} \cdot x^2$ No   **14.** $-\sqrt{3} \cdot x^3$ No   **15.** $x + 3$ No

Write the coefficient of each monomial. (P-3)

16. $2x^2$ 2   **17.** $5x^4$ 5   **18.** $\frac{1}{3}x^2$ $\frac{1}{3}$ **19.** $\frac{3}{5}x^3$ $\frac{3}{5}$ **20.** $-0.3x$ −0.3   **21.** $1.8x^3$ 1.8

22. x 1   **23.** $-x^3$ −1   **24.** $\dfrac{x}{10}$ $\frac{1}{10}$ **25.** $\frac{3}{5}$ $\frac{3}{5}$ **26.** $2x^0$ 2   **27.** $\dfrac{3x}{5}$ $\frac{3}{5}$

Evaluate each monomial. (Example 1)

28. $-5x^2$ if $x = 3$ −45   **29.** $3x^3$ if $x = -1$ −3   **30.** $\frac{1}{4}x^4$ if $x = -2$ 4

31. $\frac{3}{4}x^5$ if $x = 2$ 24   **32.** $-0.5x^3$ if $x = 10$ −500   **33.** $-8.3x^0$ if $x = -19$
−8.3

REVIEW CAPSULE FOR SECTION 9.2

Write each product or quotient as one power. (Sections 7.1 and 7.2)

1. $m^2 \cdot m^4$ m^6 **2.** $t \cdot t^7$ t^8 **3.** $r^5 \cdot r^3 \cdot r^2$ r^{10} **4.** $y^4 \cdot y^4 \cdot y^4$ y^{12}

5. $\dfrac{w^6}{w^2}$ w^4 **6.** $\dfrac{q^4}{q}$ q^3 **7.** $\dfrac{n^8}{n^4}$ n^4 **8.** $\dfrac{a^{10}}{a^5}$ a^5

9.2 Operations with Monomials

OBJECTIVES: To multiply two or more monomials
To divide two monomials

P-1   **Multiply.**

Some students will
forget and try to
multiply exponents.

a. $x^3 \cdot x^4$ **b.** $y^2 \cdot y^9$ **c.** $r \cdot r^5$ ◄ **Remember to add exponents.**

x^7 y^{11} r^6

example 1   Multiply: $(3x^2)(-2x^3)$

Solution:

☐1 Commutative and Associative Properties
of Multiplication ──────────► $(3 \cdot -2)(x^2 \cdot x^3)$

☐2 Simplify. ──────────────► $-6x^5$ ◄ **Product Property of Powers**

Monomials of more than one variable are shown below.

a. $2x^3y$ **b.** $-3r^2st$ **c.** $\frac{1}{2}p^3q^2$

example 2   Multiply: $(8st^2)(-7r^2st)$

Solution:

☐1 Commutative and Associative Properties
of Multiplication ──────────► $(8 \cdot -7)(r^2)(s \cdot s)(t^2 \cdot t)$

☐2 Simplify. ──────────────► $-56r^2s^2t^3$

P-2   **What is the simplest form of $4 \cdot -5 \cdot -\frac{1}{2}$?**   10

P-3   **What is the simplest form of $(rs)(s^2)(r)$?** r^2s^3

example 3   Multiply: $(4rs)(-5s^2)(-\frac{1}{2}r)$

Solution:

☐1 Commutative and Associative Properties
of Multiplication ──────────► $(4 \cdot -5 \cdot -\frac{1}{2})(r \cdot r)(s \cdot s^2)$

☐2 Simplify. ──────────────► $10r^2s^3$

> **Steps for multiplying two or more monomials**
>
> 1. Multiply the numerical factors.
> 2. Add exponents of powers of the same base.

$$(6x^2y)(-7xy^3) =$$
$$-42x^3y^4$$

P-4   **Simplify each quotient.**

   a. $\dfrac{x^5}{x^2}$ $_{x^3}$ b. $\dfrac{y^4}{y}$ $_{y^3}$ c. $\dfrac{r^6}{r^5}$ $_r$

◄ **Remember to subtract exponents.**

example 4   Divide: $\dfrac{-36n^8}{9n^5}$

Solution:

1. Product Rule of Fractions ⟶ $\dfrac{-36}{9} \cdot \dfrac{n^8}{n^5}$

2. Simplify. ⟶ $-4n^3$ ◄ **Quotient Property of Powers**

example 5   Divide: $\dfrac{-7r^3s^2}{-4rs}$

Solution:

1. Product Rule of Fractions ⟶ $\dfrac{-7}{-4} \cdot \dfrac{r^3}{r} \cdot \dfrac{s^2}{s}$

2. Simplify. ⟶ $\dfrac{7}{4}r^2s$ or $1\tfrac{3}{4}r^2s$

> **Steps for dividing monomials**
>
> 1. Divide the numerical factors.
> 2. Subtract exponents of powers of the same base.

$$\dfrac{56a^4bc^3}{-7a^2b} =$$
$$-8a^2c^3$$

CLASSROOM EXERCISES

Multiply. (Examples 1–3)

1. $(4y^2)(5y)$ $_{20y^3}$

2. $(-r^3)(2r^2)$ $_{-2r^5}$

3. $(-6x^2)(7x^3)$ $_{-42x^5}$

4. $(-8t^5)(-4t)$ $_{32t^6}$

5. $(16xy)(-\tfrac{1}{2}x^2y)$ $_{-8x^3y^2}$

6. $(2x)(3x)(5x)$ $_{30x^3}$

7. $(-x)(2x^2)(3y)$ $_{-6x^3y}$

8. $(r^2)(-4rs)(-s^3)$ $_{4r^3s^4}$

9. $(2xy)(3x^2)(4xy^2)$
   $_{24x^4y^3}$

Divide. (Examples 4 and 5)

10. $\dfrac{12t^5}{-3t^2}$ $\;-4t^3$

11. $\dfrac{-9x^4}{-x^2}$ $\;9x^2$

12. $\dfrac{-15x^3}{5x}$ $\;-3x^2$

13. $\dfrac{14b^6}{-7b^2}$ $\;-2b^4$

14. $\dfrac{-63r^5s^4}{-9rs^3}$ $\;7r^4s$

15. $\dfrac{-54s^5t^3}{6st^2}$ $\;-9s^4t$

16. $\dfrac{18r^2s^3t}{6rs}$ $\;3rs^2t$

17. $\dfrac{-48p^3qr^5}{6pr^4}$
$\;-8p^2qr$

WRITTEN EXERCISES

See the Teacher's Manual for the suggested assignments.

Goals: To multiply and to divide monomials

Examples: a. $(-12r^3s^2)(5r^2s)$ **b.** $\dfrac{-24x^3y}{-8xy}$ **Answers: a.** $-60r^5s^3$ **b.** $3x^2$

Multiply. (Examples 1–3)

1. $(8m^3)(9m^2)$ $\;72m^5$

2. $(7a^4)(3a^3)$ $\;21a^7$

3. $(-12r^3t^2)(8t^3)$ $\;-96r^3t^5$

4. $(15xy^4)(-4x^2)$ $\;-60x^3y^4$

5. $(-\frac{1}{3}pq^3)(-15p^3q^2)$ $\;5p^4q^5$

6. $(-20s^4t^2)(-\frac{1}{4}st^4)$ $\;5s^5t^6$

7. $(4t^2)(-3t)(2t)$ $\;-24t^4$

8. $(5n)(3n^2)(-3n^3)$ $\;-45n^6$

9. $(3mn)(-7n^2)(-m^2n)$ $\;\substack{\text{See} \\ \text{below.}}$

10. $(-4rt^2)(2rt)(-t^2)$ $\;8r^2t^5$

11. $(-3ab)(-3ab^2)(-3a^2b^3)$ $\;-27a^4b^6$

12. $(-2q^2r)(-2qr^2)(-2qr^3)$ $\;\substack{\text{See} \\ \text{below.}}$

13. $(0.4rs^2t)(-3.8rst^3)$
$\;-1.52r^2s^3t^4$

14. $(-2.8a^2bc^3)(7ab^2c)$ $\;-19.6a^3b^3c^4$

15. $(-6xy^2z^3)(-1.4u^3x^2y)$
$\;8.4u^3x^3y^3z^3$

Divide. (Examples 4 and 5)

16. $\dfrac{-20y^5}{4y^2}$ $\;-5y^3$

17. $\dfrac{12k^4}{-3k}$ $\;-4k^3$

18. $\dfrac{-32r^2}{-8r}$ $\;4r$

19. $\dfrac{-36y^3}{-9y}$ $\;4y^2$

20. $\dfrac{9.6p^6q^3}{-6p^2q}$ $\;-1.6p^4q^2$

21. $\dfrac{-4.8m^8n^5}{8m^2n^3}$ $\;-0.6m^6n^2$

22. $\dfrac{-13pq^3r}{-qr}$ $\;13pq^2$

23. $\dfrac{-29a^4bc^3}{-a^3c}$ $\;29abc^2$

24. $\dfrac{-17r^5s^6t^9}{-5r^2s^2t^3}$ $\;3\frac{2}{5}r^3s^4t^6$

25. $\dfrac{22x^{12}y^8z^6}{-7x^4y^2z^2}$ $\;-3\frac{1}{7}x^8y^6z^4$

26. $\dfrac{-5k^7p^{10}y^5}{12k^3py^4}$ $\;-\frac{5}{12}k^4p^9y$

27. $\dfrac{-4m^{12}n^7q^3}{-15m^3n^5q}$ $\;\frac{4}{15}m^9n^2q^2$

9. $21m^3n^4$

12. $-8q^4r^6$

REVIEW CAPSULE FOR SECTION 9.3

Write each expression as a sum. (Section 1.3)

1. $x^2 - 2x$
$\;x^2 + (-2x)$

2. $2n^3 - 5$ $\;2n^3 + (-5)$ **3.** $4y^2 - y$ $\;4y^2 + (-y)$ **4.** $3a^4 - 5a$
$\;3a^4 + (-5a)$

5. $-5t^3 - 4t$
$\;-5t^3 + (-4t)$

9.3 Polynomials

To simplify a polynomial by combining like terms and arranging terms in descending order of powers
To evaluate a polynomial for values of its variable or variables

P-1 **What monomials are in the following expression?** $2x^2$, $(-9x)$, and $\frac{1}{4}$

$$2x^2 + (-9x) + \frac{1}{4}$$ ◄ *A polynomial*

> A *polynomial* is a monomial or the sum of two or more monomials.
>
> $-1.8x^6$
> $-5x^4 + 2x^2 - 3x + 1$

The monomials that form a polynomial are called **terms**.

A **binomial** is a polynomial of two terms.

A **trinomial** is a polynomial of three terms.

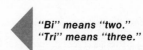 *"Bi" means "two."*
"Tri" means "three."

P-2 **Which polynomials below are binomials? trinomials?**

a and d   b and c

a. $2x^2 + 6$ **b.** $x^2 - x + 1$

c. $\frac{1}{2} - \frac{1}{4}x^2 + \frac{3}{4}x$ **d.** $3.8x^2 - 1.3x$

The table below shows three polynomials expressed in simplest form.

Polynomials	Simplest Form	
$3x^2 - 2x - x + 7$	$3x^2 - 3x + 7$	This order of terms is called "descending order of powers."
$5x - x^3 - 10 + 2x^2$	$-x^3 + 2x^2 + 5x - 10$	
$1.3x^2 + 0.6 - x^4 + 5.6x^4 - x$	$4.6x^4 + 1.3x^2 - x + 0.6$	

 example 1   Simplify $2x^2 - 2x^3 + 3x - 5x - x^2 - 12 + x^4$.

Solution:

⊡ Combine like terms. $2x^2 - 2x^3 + 3x - 5x - x^2 - 12 + x^4 = x^2 - 2x^3 - 2x - 12 + x^4$

⊡ Arrange terms in order by exponents. ⎯⎯⎯⎯⎯⎯→ $= x^4 - 2x^3 + x^2 - 2x - 12$

Polynomials of more than one variable are shown below.

a. x^2y **b.** $3r^2st + 5rst^2$ **c.** $4x^3y^2 - 2x^2y + 5xy^3$

example 2 Simplify $1.3rs - 2.4r^2 + 3.8rs + 6.7s^2$.

Solution:

① Combine like terms. ⟶ $1.3rs - 2.4r^2 + 3.8rs + 6.7s^2 = 5.1rs - 2.4r^2 + 6.7s^2$

② Arrange in descending order of powers of r. ⟶ $= -2.4r^2 + 5.1rs + 6.7s^2$

OR

② Arrange in descending order of powers of s. ⟶ $= 6.7s^2 + 5.1rs - 2.4r^2$

Since monomials represent real numbers in this course, polynomials also represent real numbers.

example 3 Evaluate $2x^2 - 5x + 7$ if $x = -2$.

Solution:
$$2x^2 - 5x + 7 = 2(-2)^2 - 5(-2) + 7$$
$$= 2(4) + 10 + 7$$
$$= 8 + 10 + 7$$
$$= 25$$

CLASSROOM EXERCISES

Write Yes or No to tell whether each numeral or expression is a polynomial over {rational numbers}. (Definition)

1. $3x + 5$ Yes

2. $-5x^2$ Yes

3. x^3 Yes

4. $\frac{1}{2}$ Yes

5. $-\frac{2}{3}x^3 + 3x^2$ Yes

6. $\frac{x}{2}$ Yes

7. $\frac{2}{x}$ No

8. $5x^0$ Yes

9. $3x^{-1}$ No

10. $100x^{100}$ Yes

11. $\sqrt{16} \cdot x - 1$ Yes

12. $0.3x^2$ Yes

13. $3x^3 + \frac{1}{2}x^2$ Yes

14. $\sqrt{2} \cdot x^2 + x$ No

15. 0 Yes

Simplify. (Examples 1 and 2)

16. $x^2 - 3x - 7x + 1$ $x^2 - 10x + 1$

17. $3 + 5x^2 - 2x$ $5x^2 - 2x + 3$

18. $x^2 - 3 + x - x^3 + 2x^4$ $2x^4 - x^3 + x^2 + x - 3$

19. $12 - 2x^3 + 5x^3$ $3x^3 + 12$

20. $8 - 3x + 7 - 2x^2$ $-2x^2 - 3x + 15$

21. $2x^2y + 3x^2y - 5$ $5x^2y - 5$

22. $4x^2y^2 - 1 - 3x^2y^2 - 8$ $x^2y^2 - 9$

23. $-3x^5 + 5x^8 - 3x^2 + x^{12}$ $x^{12} + 5x^8 - 3x^5 - 3x^2$

WRITTEN EXERCISES
See the Teacher's Manual for the suggested assignments.

Goals: To simplify and to evaluate polynomials

Sample Problems: a. $x^2 + y^2 + 5x^2$ **b.** Evaluate $-2x^3 + x$ if $x = -3$.

Answers: a. $6x^2 + y^2$ **b.** 51

Write <u>Yes</u> or <u>No</u> to show whether each numeral or expression is a polynomial over {rational numbers}. (Definition)

1. $2x - 5$ Yes

2. $4x + 3$ Yes

3. $x^2 + 3\pi$ No

4. $5x^2 - \sqrt{3}$ No

5. $\dfrac{x^2}{2} - \dfrac{3}{x} + 5$ No

6. $\dfrac{-x^2}{5} + \dfrac{x}{2} + 5$ Yes

7. $-3x^0$ Yes

8. $\frac{1}{3}x^5$ Yes

9. $1.3x^2 + 8.5x - 7.2$ Yes

10. $3x^{-2} + 4x^{-1} - 5^0$ No

19. $m^3 - 2m^2n + 5mn - 10$

14. $-2x^4 + x^3 + 12x^2 - 5x + 3$

Simplify. (Examples 1 and 2)

11. $3x^2 - x - 3x + 7$ $3x^2 - 4x + 7$

12. $-2x^3 + x^2 - 4x^2 + 5$ $-2x^3 - 3x^2 + 5$

13. $5x - 3x^2 + x^5 - 1 + 4x^3$ $x^5 + 4x^3 - 3x^2 + 5x - 1$

14. $12x^2 - 5x + x^3 - 2x^4 + 3$ See above.

15. $7x^2 - 9x + 8 - 3x^2 - x^2$ $3x^2 - 9x + 8$

16. $15x^2 - x + 12 - 3x^2 - 6x$ $12x^2 - 7x + 12$

17. $3x^3y - 5 + xy^3 + 5x^2y^2$ $3x^3y + 5x^2y^2 + xy^3 - 5$

18. $6rs^3 - r^2s^2 + 3r^4s - 5s^4$ $-5s^4 + 6rs^3 - r^2s^2 + 3r^4s$

19. $m^2n + 5mn - 3m^2n + m^3 - 10$ See above.

20. $p^3q + 5q^3 + 3p^3q - pq^2$ $5q^3 - pq^2 + 4p^3q$

21. $1.5x - 2.3x^4 + 0.9x - 1.9x^2 + 1.8x^4$
$$-0.5x^4 - 1.9x^2 + 2.4x$$

22. $0.3x^3 + 2.9x^5 - 5.2x + 6.3x - 1.8x^3$
$$2.9x^5 - 1.5x^3 + 1.1x$$

Evaluate each polynomial. (Example 3)

23. $-x^2 + 3x - 5$ if $x = -3$ -23

24. $3x^2 - 4x + 5$ if $x = -4$ 69

25. $x^3 - x^2 + x - 1$ if $x = -2$ -15

26. $-x^3 + x^2 - x + 1$ if $x = -2$ 15

27. $2x^4 - x^3 + 3x + 2$ if $x = 2$ 32

28. $x^5 - 2x^4 - x^2 + 5$ if $x = 1$ 3

29. $x^2y^2 - 2xy + 1$ if $x = -2$ and $y = 3$ 49

30. $r^3s - r^2s^2 + 2$ if $r = -1$ and $s = 2$ -4

MORE CHALLENGING EXERCISES
Simplify.

31. $x^2 - (3x + 5)$ $x^2 - 3x - 5$

32. $2x^3 - (-x^2 + x)$ $2x^3 + x^2 - x$

33. $(x^2 + 4x) + (12 - 3x)$ $x^2 + x + 12$

34. $(x^3 - 2x^2) + (5x - 4x^2)$ $x^3 - 6x^2 + 5x$

Evaluate each monomial. (Section 9.1)

1. $-4x^3$ if $x = -2$ 32   **2.** $\frac{1}{2}x^2$ if $x = \frac{1}{2}$ $\frac{1}{8}$ **3.** $0.5x^4$ if $x = -2$ 8   **4.** $-(x^5)$ if $x = -1$
1

Multiply or divide. (Section 9.2)

5. $(-3rt)(2r^2)$ $-6r^3t$ **6.** $(-10m^2n)(mn)$ **7.** $\dfrac{-30s^2t}{6st}$ $-5s$ **8.** $\dfrac{-48m^3n^2}{-8mn}$ $6m^2n$

$-10m^3n^2$

Simplify. (Section 9.3)

10. $-6x^3 + 2x^2 - 5x - 12$

9. $-x + 3 - 2x^2 + 7x - x^2 + 9$ $-3x^2 + 6x + 12$ **10.** $-5x^3 - 12 + 3x - x^3 + 2x^2 - 8x$

11. $-1.9x^2 + 0.2x^3 - 1.3x^2 + 2.8x - 1.4$ **12.** $0.9x - 1.8x^4 - 1.3x + 4.3x^3 - 2.7x^4$

$0.2x^3 - 3.2x^2 + 2.8x - 1.4$ $-4.5x^4 + 4.3x^3 - 0.4x$

Evaluate for the given value of the variable. (Section 9.3)

13. $r^2 - 2r + 5$; $r = -3$ 20   **14.** $-5x^3 - x^2 + 2x - 3$; $x = 2$ -43 **15.** $-p^2 + 7p - 10$; $p = -10$
-180

EVALUATING POLYNOMIALS

Polynomials can easily be evaluated with a calculator by grouping terms with
parentheses in a special way.

Have some students
compare the efficiency
of this method with
evaluating the poly-
nomial directly.

$$5n^3 - 4n^2 + 12n - 17 = ((5n - 4)n + 12)n - 17$$

EXAMPLE Evaluate $5x^2 - 16x + 3$ if $x = 42$.

SOLUTION $\boxed{1}$ Group terms in a special way. $\longrightarrow$ $5x^2 - 16x + 3 = (5x - 16)x + 3$

$\boxed{2}$ Substitute and evaluate. $\longrightarrow$ $= (5 \cdot 42 - 16)42 + 3$

8151.

Note that you can:
1. **work from left to right;**
2. **"ignore" the exponent.**

Evaluate each polynomial for the given value of x.

1. $120x^2 - 75x + 29$; $x = 24$ **2.** $76x^2 + 128x - 97$; $x = 29$ **3.** $x^3 - 2x^2 + 3x - 4$; $x = 12$
67,349   67,531   1472

REVIEW CAPSULE FOR SECTION 9.4

Arrange the terms of each polynomial in descending order of powers.
(Section 9.3)

1. $2x - 3x^2$ **2.** $-4x - 3x^3$ **3.** $12 - 6x^2 + 4x$ **4.** $7 - 5x$ **5.** $3x - 5 + x^2$
$-3x^2 + 2x$ $-3x^3 - 4x$ $-6x^2 + 4x + 12$ $-5x + 7$ $x^2 + 3x - 5$

9.4   Addition and Subtraction

OBJECTIVES: To add two or more polynomials arranged either vertically or horizontally
To subtract two polynomials arranged either vertically or horizontally

example 1   Add: $(x^2 - 3x + 4) + (3x^2 + 5x - 7)$

Solution:

1. Write the sum
   of all terms. ——————→ $(x^2 - 3x + 4) + (3x^2 + 5x - 7) = x^2 - 3x + 4 + 3x^2 + 5x - 7$

2. Combine like terms. ——————————————————→ $= 4x^2 + 2x - 3$ ◀ **Simplest form**

P-1   **Add.**

  a. $(x^2 - 8x) + (7x + 3)$ **b.** $(3x^2 - 5) + (4x - x^2)$ $2x^2 + 4x - 5$
  $x^2 - x + 3$

Polynomials can be added by arranging them vertically in columns.

example 2 $(3x^3 - x^2 + 4) + (3x^2 - 7x - 9) + (-x^3 + 3x - 6)$

Solution:

$$
\begin{array}{r}
3x^3 - x^2 \quad\;\; + 4 \\
+ 3x^2 - 7x - 9 \\
(+)\; -x^3 \qquad\; + 3x - 6 \\
\hline
2x^3 + 2x^2 - 4x - 11
\end{array}
$$

◀ **Leave space for the missing term, and write in the + or − between terms.**

> The sum of any two polynomials is a polynomial.

example 3   Subtract: $(x^2 - 12x) - (3x^2 + 7x - 5)$

Solution:

1. Meaning of
   subtraction ——————→ $(x^2 - 12x) - (3x^2 + 7x - 5) = (x^2 - 12x) + -(3x^2 + 7x - 5)$

2. Property of the Opposite of a Sum ——————————→ $= x^2 - 12x - 3x^2 - 7x + 5$

3. Simplify. ——————————————————————→ $= -2x^2 - 19x + 5$

P-2   **Simplify each difference below.**

  a. $(2x^2 + 6x) - (2x - 3)$ $2x^2 + 4x + 3$ **b.** $(x^3 - 2x^2) - (-5x + 1)$ $x^3 - 2x^2 + 5x - 1$

Polynomials / 215

P-3 **Subtract.**

a. $x^3 - (-3x^3)$ $_{4x^3}$ **b.** $0 - 2x^2$ $_{-2x^2}$ **c.** $(-4x) - (-3x)$ $_{-x}$ **d.** $7 - (-1)$ $_8$

example 4 Subtract: $x^3 - 4x + 7 - (-3x^3 + 2x^2 - 3x - 1)$

Solution:

$$
\begin{array}{r}
x^3 \qquad\ \ - 4x + 7 \\
(-)\ \underline{-3x^3 + 2x^2 - 3x - 1} \\
4x^3 - 2x^2 -\ \ x + 8
\end{array}
$$

**Compare this with
your answers to P-3.**

In adding or subtracting polynomials vertically, you arrange the terms in descending order of powers.

example 5 Subtract: $(3x - 2 - 5x^2) - (7 - x^2 + x)$

Solution:

$$
\begin{array}{r}
-5x^2 + 3x - 2 \\
(-)\ \underline{-x^2 +\ \ x + 7} \\
-4x^2 + 2x - 9
\end{array}
$$

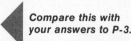

**Descending
powers
of x**

The difference of any two polynomials is a polynomial.

CLASSROOM EXERCISES

Add. (Example 2)

1. $4x - 9$
$\underline{3x + 2}$
$7x - 7$

2. $-x + 15$
$\underline{5x -\ \ 7}$
$4x + 8$

3. $2x^2 -\ \ x + 3$
$-x^2 \qquad\ - 4$
$\underline{-3x^2 - 4x}$
$-2x^2 - 5x - 1$

Subtract. (Example 4)

4. $6x + 12$
$(-)\ \underline{5x +\ \ 3}$
$x + 9$

5. $3x^2 + 6x + 4$
$(-)\ \underline{x^2 + 2x + 3}$
$2x^2 + 4x + 1$

6. $4x^2 \qquad\ - 1$
$(-)\ \underline{6x^2 - x + 5}$
$-2x^2 + x - 6$

Add or subtract as indicated. (Examples 1 and 3)

7. $(3x^2 - 2x) + (5x - 3)$
$3x^2 + 3x - 3$

8. $(-7x^2 + 8x) - (x + 5)$
$-7x^2 + 7x - 5$

9. $(2x^2 - 3x) - (3x^2 + x)$
$-x^2 - 4x$

WRITTEN EXERCISES

See the Teacher's Manual for the suggested assignments.

Goals: To add and subtract polynomials

Sample Problem: $(-4x^2 + 7) + (9x - 12) - (x - x^2)$ **Answer:** $-3x^2 + 8x - 5$

Add. (Example 2)

1. $\begin{array}{r} 14x^2 - 9x + 4 \\ -3x^2 + 7x - 12 \end{array}$ $11x^2 - 2x - 8$

2. $\begin{array}{r} -10x^2 + 11x - 6 \\ 7x^2 - 9x + 13 \end{array}$ $-3x^2 + 2x + 7$

3. $\begin{array}{r} 3.2x^2 + 0.5x - 1.8 \\ -1.7x^2 + 2.4x + 2.6 \end{array}$ $1.5x^2 + 2.9x + 0.8$

4. $\begin{array}{r} -4.1x^2 + 0.9x - 3.3 \\ 2.7x^2 - 2.4x - 1.6 \end{array}$ $-1.4x^2 - 1.5x - 4.9$

5. $\begin{array}{r} x^3 - 6x + 10 \\ -2x^3 + x^2 + 3x - 7 \\ -x^3 - 5x^2 + 6 \end{array}$ $-2x^3 - 4x^2 - 3x + 9$

6. $\begin{array}{r} -23x^3 + 14x^2 - 11 \\ x^3 - 9x^2 + 17 \\ -8x^3 + 15x - 2 \end{array}$

    $-30x^3 + 5x^2 + 15x + 4$

Subtract. (Examples 4–5)

7. $\begin{array}{r} x^2 + 5x - 10 \\ (-) 3x^2 - x + 8 \end{array}$ $-2x^2 + 6x - 18$

8. $\begin{array}{r} -4x^2 + x - 9 \\ (-) x^2 - 3x + 8 \end{array}$ $-5x^2 + 4x - 17$

9. $\begin{array}{r} 2x^3 + 6x - 3 \\ (-) -x^3 + 5x^2 + 9x - 5 \end{array}$ $3x^3 - 5x^2 - 3x + 2$

10. $\begin{array}{r} 3x^3 + 8x^2 - 5 \\ (-) 4x^3 + 12x - 13 \end{array}$ $-x^3 + 8x^2 - 12x + 8$

Add or subtract as indicated. (Examples 1–5)

11. $(5x^2 - 3x + 12) + (3 - x^2 - 4x)$ $4x^2 - 7x + 15$

12. $(8 - 6x - 4x^2) + (5x^2 - x - 13)$ $x^2 - 7x - 5$

13. $(x^3 - 2x + 5) - (4x^3 - 5x^2 + x - 2)$ $-3x^3 + 5x^2 - 3x + 7$

14. $(8x^3 - 2x^2 + 3x - 4) - (x^3 + 5x^2 - x + 7)$ $7x^3 - 7x^2 + 4x - 11$

15. $(1.3x^2 - 2.7x - 0.5) + (2.5x^2 + 4.3x + 2.3) - (1.7x^2 - 2.8x - 4.9)$ $2.1x^2 + 4.4x + 6.7$

16. $(0.9x^2 + 4.1x - 2.8) - (1.4x^2 - 2.7x + 5.1) + (-3.2x^2 + 4.5x - 1.8)$ $-3.7x^2 + 11.3x - 9.7$

17. $(4x^3 - 5x^2 - 6) - (2x^2 + 3x + 10) - (-3x^3 + x - 7)$ $7x^3 - 7x^2 - 4x - 9$

18. $(12x^2 - x - 10) - (x^3 + 4x^2 + 8) - (-3x^3 + 5x + 7)$ $2x^3 + 8x^2 - 6x - 25$

REVIEW CAPSULE FOR SECTION 9.5

Multiply. (Section 2.5)

1. $-2x(3x - 5)$ $-6x^2 + 10x$

2. $5x(-4x + 2)$ $-20x^2 + 10x$

3. $(10x - 3)(-4x)$ $-40x^2 + 12x$

4. $(-12x - 8)\frac{1}{2}$ $-6x - 4$

9.5 Multiplication

OBJECTIVES: To multiply two binomials
To multiply a binomial and a quadratic trinomial
To multiply any two polynomials

P-1 **Find each of the following products.**

a. $(-2x)(x)$ $-2x^2$ **b.** $(3x)(-5)$ $-15x$ **c.** $(-3)(-4)$ 12 *Products of monomials*

example 1 Multiply: $(x + 3)(3x - 4)$ ◀ *Two binomials*

Solution:

1 Distributive Property ──────▶ $(x + 3)(3x - 4) = (x + 3)3x + (x + 3)(-4)$

2 Distributive Property ──────────────▶ $= x(3x) + 3(3x) + x(-4) + 3(-4)$

3 Simplest forms of products ──────▶ $= 3x^2 + 9x - 4x - 12$

4 Combine like terms. ──────────────▶ $= 3x^2 + 5x - 12$ ◀ *Simplest form*

In a polynomial, a term with no variables is called the **constant term.**

P-2 **What is the constant term in each polynomial below?**

a. $x^2 + 5$ 5 **b.** $3x^2 + 5x - 12$ –12 **c.** $x^3 - 7x + 9$ 9

Binomials can be multiplied by a short method.

The mnemonic device FOIL may help some students remember the method shown here.
F: First terms
O: Outside terms
I: Inside terms
L: Last terms

example 2 Multiply: $(5x - 2)(x - 3)$

Multiply the first terms.	Multiply the outside terms.	Multiply the inside terms.	Multiply the last terms.

Solution: $(5x - 2)(x - 3)$ $(5x - 2)(x - 3)$ $(5x - 2)(x - 3)$ $(5x - 2)(x - 3)$

$5x^2$ $-15x$ $-2x$ 6

$(5x - 2)(x - 3) = 5x^2 - 15x - 2x + 6$

$= 5x^2 - 17x + 6$

P-3 **Find each of the following products.**

a. $(2x + 1)(x + 4)$
$2x^2 + 9x + 4$

b. $(3x - 2)(2x + 3)$
$6x^2 + 5x - 6$

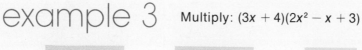
Try to combine like terms mentally.

Any two polynomials are multiplied by multiplying each term of one polynomial by each term of the other.

example 3   Multiply: $(3x + 4)(2x^2 - x + 3)$

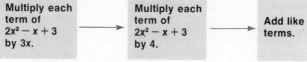

Multiply each term of $2x^2 - x + 3$ by $3x$. → Multiply each term of $2x^2 - x + 3$ by 4. → Add like terms.

Solution: **Method 1**

$(3x + 4)(2x^2 - x + 3) = 3x(2x^2) + 3x(-x) + 3x(3) + 4(2x^2) + 4(-x) + 4(3)$

$= 6x^3 - 3x^2 + 9x + 8x^2 - 4x + 12$

$= 6x^3 + 5x^2 + 5x + 12$

Method 2

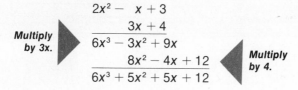

Multiply by 3x.
$$2x^2 - x + 3$$
$$\underline{ 3x + 4}$$
$$6x^3 - 3x^2 + 9x$$
$$\underline{ 8x^2 - 4x + 12}$$
$$6x^3 + 5x^2 + 5x + 12$$
Multiply by 4.

example 4   Multiply: $(x - 3)(5 + 3x^3 - x^2)$

Solution:

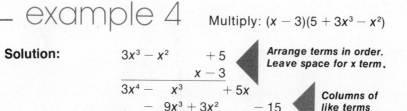

$$3x^3 - x^2 + 5$$
$$\underline{ x - 3}$$
Arrange terms in order. Leave space for x term.
$$3x^4 - x^3 + 5x$$
$$\underline{ - 9x^3 + 3x^2 - 15}$$
$$3x^4 - 10x^3 + 3x^2 + 5x - 15$$
Columns of like terms

The product of any two polynomials is a polynomial.

CLASSROOM EXERCISES

Multiply. (Example 2)

1. $(x + 1)(x + 2)$ $x^2 + 3x + 2$

2. $(x + 3)(x + 4)$ $x^2 + 7x + 12$

3. $(x - 1)(x + 3)$ $x^2 + 2x - 3$

4. $(x + 2)(x - 3)$ $x^2 - x - 6$

5. $(x - 2)(x - 4)$ $x^2 - 6x + 8$

6. $(x - 3)(x - 7)$ $x^2 - 10x + 21$

7. $(x + 8)(x - 5)$ $x^2 + 3x - 40$

8. $(x - 2)(x + 7)$ $x^2 + 5x - 14$

9. $(2x + 1)(x + 2)$ $2x^2 + 5x + 2$

10. $(3x - 1)(x + 2)$ $3x^2 + 5x - 2$

11. $(4x + 1)(x - 3)$ $4x^2 - 11x - 3$

12. $(2x - 1)(2x - 1)$ $4x^2 - 4x + 1$

Write the missing row in each multiplication problem. (Examples 3–4)

13. $2x + 5$
 $\underline{x - 6}$
 $\boxed{}$ $2x^2 + 5x$
 $\underline{-\ 12x - 30}$
 $2x^2 -\ 7x - 30$

14. $-3x - 4$
 $\underline{2x + 1}$
 $-6x^2 -\ 8x$
 $\underline{\boxed{}}$ $-3x - 4$
 $-6x^2 - 11x - 4$

15. $x^2 - 2x + 3$
 $\underline{x - 2}$
 $x^3 - 2x^2 + 3x$
 $\underline{-\ 2x^2 + 4x - 6}$
 $\boxed{}$ $x^3 - 4x^2 + 7x - 6$

16. $2x^2 + 3x - 1$
 $\underline{3x + 4}$
 $\boxed{}$ $6x^3 + 9x^2 - 3x$
 $\underline{8x^2 + 12x - 4}$
 $6x^3 + 17x^2 +\ 9x - 4$

17. $3x^2 -\ 5$
 $\underline{2x + 3}$
 $6x^3 -\ 10x$
 $9x^2 -\ 15$
 $\boxed{}$ $6x^3 + 9x^2 - 10x - 15$

18. $x^3 - 2x^2 +\ 5$
 $\underline{2x - 1}$
 $2x^4 - 4x^3 +\ 10x$
 $-\ x^3 + 2x^2 -\ 5$
 $\boxed{}$
 $2x^4 - 5x^3 + 2x^2 + 10x - 5$

WRITTEN EXERCISES

See the Teacher's Manual for the suggested assignments.

Goal: To multiply a polynomial by a polynomial

Sample Problem: $(5x^2 - 2x + 3)(x + 2)$ **Answer:** $5x^3 + 8x^2 - x + 6$

Multiply. (Examples 1 and 2)

1. $(x + 3)(x + 5)$ $x^2 + 8x + 15$

2. $(x + 2)(x + 7)$ $x^2 + 9x + 14$

3. $(x - 4)(x + 2)$ $x^2 - 2x - 8$

4. $(x - 3)(x + 1)$ $x^2 - 2x - 3$

Multiply. (Examples 1 and 2)

5. $(x - 5)(x - 3)$ $x^2 - 8x + 15$

6. $(x - 2)(x - 4)$ $x^2 - 6x + 8$

7. $(x + 7)(x - 5)$ $x^2 + 2x - 35$

8. $(x + 10)(x - 6)$ $x^2 + 4x - 60$

9. $(2x + 3)(x + 5)$ $2x^2 + 13x + 15$

10. $(3x + 2)(x + 4)$ $3x^2 + 14x + 8$

11. $(3x - 1)(x + 4)$ $3x^2 + 11x - 4$

12. $(4x - 3)(x + 5)$ $4x^2 + 17x - 15$

13. $(5x - 2)(x - 3)$ $5x^2 - 17x + 6$

14. $(3x - 4)(x - 4)$ $3x^2 - 16x + 16$

15. $(4x + 5)(2x - 3)$ $8x^2 - 2x - 15$

16. $(2x + 5)(3x - 7)$ $6x^2 + x - 35$

Multiply. (Examples 3 and 4)

17. $x^2 - 2x + 3$
   $\underline{\quad\quad x - 4}$
   $x^3 - 6x^2 + 11x - 12$

18. $x^2 + 3x - 2$
   $\underline{\quad\quad x - 3}$
   $x^3 - 11x + 6$

19. $2x^2 + 3x - 4$
   $\underline{\quad\quad x + 5}$
   $2x^3 + 13x^2 + 11x - 20$

20. $3x^2 - x + 4$
   $\underline{\quad\quad x + 4}$
   $3x^3 + 11x^2 + 16$

21. $x^2 \quad\quad - 5$
   $\underline{\quad\quad x + 6}$
   $x^3 + 6x^2 - 5x - 30$

22. $x^2 - 4x$
   $\underline{\quad\quad x - 5}$
   $x^3 - 9x^2 + 20x$

23. $2x^2 - 3x + 7$
   $\underline{\quad\quad 3x - 2}$
   $6x^3 - 13x^2 + 27x - 14$

24. $3x^2 - 2x - 4$
   $\underline{\quad\quad 2x + 3}$
   $6x^3 + 5x^2 - 14x - 12$

25. $-5x^2 + 2x - 4$
   $\underline{\quad\quad 4x + 5}$
   $-20x^3 - 17x^2 - 6x - 20$

26. $-2x^2 + 3x - 6$
   $\underline{\quad\quad 5x - 2}$
   $-10x^3 + 19x^2 - 36x + 12$

27. $3x^3 - 2x + 4$
   $\underline{\quad\quad 4x - 2}$
   $12x^4 - 6x^3 - 8x^2 + 20x - 8$

28. $6x^3 + 7x - 8$
   $\underline{\quad\quad 2x - 5}$
   $12x^4 - 30x^3 + 14x^2 - 51x + 40$

29. $5x^3 + 4x^2 \quad\quad - 6$
   $\underline{\quad\quad\quad - 2x + 5}$
   $-10x^4 + 17x^3 + 20x^2 + 12x - 30$

30. $7x^3 + 6x^2 \quad\quad + 5$
   $\underline{\quad\quad\quad 6x + 3}$
   $42x^4 + 57x^3 + 18x^2 + 30x + 15$

31. $2x^3 \quad\quad - x + 2$
   $\underline{\quad\quad\quad 4x - 5}$
   $8x^4 - 10x^3 - 4x^2 + 13x - 10$

MORE CHALLENGING EXERCISES

32. $x^3 - 3x^2 + 2x - 3$
   $\underline{\quad\quad\quad 2x + 3}$
   $2x^4 - 3x^3 - 5x^2 \quad - 9$

33. $2x^3 + 5x^2 - 3x + 2$
   $\underline{\quad\quad\quad 3x - 4}$
   $6x^4 + 7x^3 - 29x^2 + 18x - 8$

34. $-3x^3 \quad\quad - 4x + 10$
   $\underline{\quad\quad\quad 5x - 4}$
   $-15x^4 + 12x^3 - 20x^2 + 66x - 40$

35. $-5x^3 + 2x^2 \quad\quad - 6$
   $\underline{\quad\quad\quad 4x + 5}$
   $-20x^4 - 17x^3 + 10x^2 - 24x - 30$

36. $x^3 - 2x^2 + 3x - 1$
   $\underline{\quad\quad x^2 - 3x + 2}$
   $x^5 - 5x^4 + 11x^3 - 14x^2 + 9x - 2$

37. $-2x^3 + x^2 - 5x + 3$
   $\underline{\quad\quad x^2 + 2x - 3}$
   $-2x^5 - 3x^4 + 3x^3 - 10x^2 + 21x - 9$

REVIEW CAPSULE FOR SECTION 9.6

Subtract. (Section 9.4)

1. $4x^2 - 3x + 2$
   $\underline{4x^2 + \ x}$
   $\quad\quad -4x + 2$

2. $5x^2 \quad\quad - 4$
   $\underline{5x^2 + 2x}$
   $\quad\quad -2x - 4$

3. $-2x^2 + 4x - 3$
   $\underline{-2x^2 - 4x}$
   $\quad\quad 8x - 3$

4. $x^4 - 3x^2 + 6$
   $\underline{x^4 - 5x^2 - 2}$
   $\quad\quad 2x^2 + 8$

9.6 Division

OBJECTIVES: To divide a polynomial of two or more terms by a monomial and write the quotient and a zero remainder
To divide a polynomial of two or more terms by a binomial and write the quotient and a zero remainder

To divide a polynomial by a monomial, divide each term of the polynomial by the monomial.

P-1   **Simplify: a.** $\dfrac{12x^3}{2x}$ $6x^2$ **b.** $\dfrac{8x^2}{2x}$ $4x$ **c.** $\dfrac{4x}{2x}$ 2

example 1

Divide: $(12x^3 + 8x^2 - 4x) \div 2x$

> $2x$ is the *divisor*.
> $12x^3 + 8x^2 - 4x$ is the *dividend*.

Solution:

$$(12x^3 + 8x^2 - 4x) \div 2x = \frac{12x^3}{2x} + \frac{8x^2}{2x} - \frac{4x}{2x}$$

$$= 6x^2 + 4x - 2$$

Examples 2 and 3 show division of a trinomial by a binomial.

example 2

Divide: $(2x^2 + x - 15) \div (x + 3)$

Explain that division can be checked by multiplying the quotient and the divisor.

Solution:

1. Divide $2x^2$, the first term of $2x^2 + x - 15$, by x, the first term of $x + 3$. ⟶

$$\begin{array}{r} 2x \\ x + 3 \overline{)2x^2 + x - 15} \end{array}$$

2. Multiply $(x + 3)$ by $2x$. Subtract the product from $2x^2 + x - 15$. ⟶

$$\begin{array}{r} 2x \\ x + 3 \overline{)2x^2 + x - 15} \\ 2x(x+3) \longrightarrow \underline{2x^2 + 6x } \\ -5x - 15 \end{array}$$

3. Divide $-5x$ by x. This is the second term of the quotient. ⟶

$$\begin{array}{r} 2x - 5 \\ x + 3 \overline{)2x^2 + x - 15} \\ \underline{2x^2 + 6x } \\ -5x - 15 \end{array}$$

4. Multiply $(x + 3)$ by -5. Subtract the product from $-5x - 15$. ⟶

$$\begin{array}{r} 2x - 5 \\ x + 3 \overline{)2x^2 + x - 15} \\ \underline{2x^2 + 6x } \\ -5x - 15 \\ -5(x+3) \longrightarrow \underline{-5x - 15} \\ 0 \end{array}$$

The quotient is $2x - 5$.

P-2   **Simplify: a.** $\dfrac{4x^3}{2x}$ $_{2x^2}$ **b.** $\dfrac{-2x^2}{2x}$ $_{-x}$

example 3   Divide: $(4x^3 - 3x - 1) \div (2x + 1)$

Solution:

1. Divide $4x^3$ by $2x$ to get the
   first term of the quotient. ⟶

$$2x + 1 \overline{)4x^3 \qquad - 3x - 1}$$
$$2x^2$$

◀ *Leave space for an x^2 term.*

2. Multiply $(2x + 1)$ by $2x^2$. Subtract
   the product from $4x^3 - 3x - 1$. ⟶

$$
\begin{array}{r}
2x^2 \qquad\qquad\quad \\
2x + 1 \overline{)4x^3 \qquad - 3x - 1} \\
2x^2(2x+1) \longrightarrow \quad 4x^3 + 2x^2 \qquad\qquad \\
\hline
-2x^2 - 3x - 1
\end{array}
$$

3. Divide $-2x^2$ by $2x$ for the second
   term of the quotient. ⟶

$$
\begin{array}{r}
2x^2 - x \qquad\qquad \\
2x + 1 \overline{)4x^3 \qquad - 3x - 1} \\
4x^3 + 2x^2 \qquad\qquad \\
\hline
-2x^2 - 3x - 1
\end{array}
$$

4. Multiply $(2x + 1)$ by $-x$. Subtract
   the product from $-2x^2 - 3x - 1$. ⟶

$$
\begin{array}{r}
2x^2 - x \qquad\qquad \\
2x + 1 \overline{)4x^3 \qquad - 3x - 1} \\
4x^3 + 2x^2 \qquad\qquad \\
\hline
-2x^2 - 3x - 1 \\
-x(2x+1) \longrightarrow \quad -2x^2 - x \qquad\quad \\
\hline
-2x - 1
\end{array}
$$

5. Divide $-2x$ by $2x$ for the last term
   of the quotient. Multiply
   $(2x + 1)$ by -1 and subtract. ⟶

$$
\begin{array}{r}
2x^2 - x - 1 \qquad\quad \\
2x + 1 \overline{)4x^3 \qquad - 3x - 1} \\
4x^3 + 2x^2 \qquad\qquad \\
\hline
-2x^2 - 3x - 1 \\
-2x^2 - x \qquad\quad \\
\hline
-2x - 1 \\
-1(2x+1) \longrightarrow \quad -2x - 1 \\
\hline
0
\end{array}
$$

The quotient is $2x^2 - x - 1$.

CLASSROOM EXERCISES

Divide. (Example 1)

1. $\dfrac{25x^4}{-5x^2}$ $_{-5x^2}$ **2.** $\dfrac{-20x^5}{4x}$ $_{-5x^4}$ **3.** $(15x^4 - 25x^2) \div 5x^2$ $_{3x^2 \,-\, 5}$ **4.** $(9x^3 + 6x^2) \div 3x^2$
$_{3x + 2}$

Complete each division problem. (Examples 2–3)

5.
$$\begin{array}{r} x+5 \\ x-2\overline{)x^2+3x-10} \\ \underline{x^2-2x} \end{array}$$

6.
$$\begin{array}{r} x-12 \\ x+5\overline{)x^2-7x-60} \\ \underline{x^2+5x} \end{array}$$

7.
$$\begin{array}{r} 3x+2 \\ 2x-3\overline{)6x^2-5x-6} \\ \underline{6x^2-9x} \end{array}$$

8.
$$\begin{array}{r} 2x-5 \\ 5x-3\overline{)10x^2-31x+15} \\ \underline{10x^2-\;6x} \end{array}$$

WRITTEN EXERCISES

See the Teacher's Manual for the suggested assignment.

Goal: To divide a polynomial by a binomial

Sample Problem: $(2x^3+3x^2-1) \div (2x-1)$ **Answer:** x^2+2x+1

Divide. (Example 1)

1. $(4x^2+6x) \div 2x$ $2x+3$

2. $(9y^3-12y) \div 3y$ $3y^2-4$

3. $(18xy-12x^2y^2) \div 6xy$ $3-2xy$

4. $(36x^3+12x) \div 12x$ $3x^2+1$

Divide. (Examples 2 and 3)

5. $x-3\overline{)3x^2-5x-12}$ $3x+4$

6. $x+2\overline{)4x^2+5x-6}$ $4x-3$

7. $2x-1\overline{)10x^2-17x+6}$ $5x-6$

8. $3x-1\overline{)12x^2+2x-2}$ $4x+2$

9. $4x+1\overline{)12x^2-13x-4}$ $3x-4$

10. $2x+3\overline{)8x^2+10x-3}$ $4x-1$

11. $x-5\overline{)x^3-8x^2+17x-10}$ x^2-3x+2

12. $x+4\overline{)x^3+8x^2+14x-8}$ x^2+4x-2

13. $2x+3\overline{)4x^3\qquad-7x+3}$ $2x^2-3x+1$

14. $3x+1\overline{)9x^3+6x^2+4x+1}$ $3x^2+x+1$

15. $x^2-2\overline{)x^3-5x^2-2x+10}$ $x-5$

16. $x^2+3\overline{)2x^3-5x^2+6x-15}$ $2x-5$

17. $x^2-2x\overline{)x^4-2x^3+3x^2-6x}$ x^2+3

18. $x^2-5\overline{)x^4\qquad-3x^2\qquad-10}$ x^2+2

19. $(10x^3-29x^2+60x-20) \div (5x-2)$
$2x^2-5x+10$

20. $(18x^3+9x^2-62x+35) \div (6x-5)$
$3x^2+4x-7$

21. $(x^3-8) \div (x-2)$ x^2+2x+4

22. $(x^3+27) \div (x+3)$ x^2-3x+9

23. $(x^4-81) \div (x-3)$ $x^3+3x^2+9x+27$

24. $(x^4-16) \div (x-2)$ x^3+2x^2+4x+8

REVIEW CAPSULE FOR SECTION 9.7

Multiply. (Section 7.1)

1. $(2x+5)5x$ $10x^2+25x$

2. $(2x^2-1)6x$ $12x^3-6x$

3. $-4x(3x^2+5)$
$-12x^3-20x$

4. $-3x(4x+1)$
$-12x^2-3x$

5. $x^2(x^2+x-1)$ $x^4+x^3-x^2$

6. $x^2(2x^2-x+1)$ $2x^4-x^3+x^2$

7. $(x^2-x-1)2x^2$
$2x^4-2x^3-2x^2$

9.7   Division with Remainders

OBJECTIVE: To divide a polynomial of three or more terms by a binomial or a trinomial and write the quotient as a polynomial plus a fraction formed by the remainder and the divisor

P-1   **Simplify** $\dfrac{3x^2}{x}$. $3x$

example 1

Divide: $x - 4\overline{)3x^2 - 10x - 6}$

Solution:

1. Divide $3x^2$ by x. Multiply $(x - 4)$ by $3x$ and subtract. ⟶

$$
\begin{array}{r}
3x \\
x - 4\overline{)3x^2 - 10x - 6} \\
\end{array}
$$

$3x(x - 4)$ ⟶ $\underline{3x^2 - 12x}$

$2x - 6$

2. Divide $2x$ by x. Multiply $(x - 4)$ by 2 and subtract. ⟶

$$
\begin{array}{r}
3x + 2 \\
x - 4\overline{)3x^2 - 10x - 6} \\
3x^2 - 12x \\
\end{array}
$$

$2x - 6$

$2(x - 4)$ ⟶ $\underline{2x - 8}$

2

To check this kind of division problem, multiply the quotient, $3x + 2$, and the divisor, $x - 4$, and add the remainder. The result should equal the dividend, $3x^2 - 10x - 6$.

The remainder is 2. The quotient can be written as $3x + 2 + \dfrac{2}{x - 4}$.

P-2   **Why is** $\dfrac{2}{x - 4}$ **not a polynomial?**

◀ The quotient of polynomials is not necessarily a polynomial.

It is not in the form ax^n, with a real and n a nonnegative integer.

P-3   **What is** $10x^2 - 12x - 8x^3 - 19$ **arranged in descending powers of** x**?**

$-8x^3 + 10x^2 - 12x - 19$

example 2

Divide: $(10x^2 - 12x - 8x^3 - 19) \div (2x^2 + 3)$

Solution:

1. Arrange terms in order. ⟶ $2x^2 + 3\overline{)-8x^3 + 10x^2 - 12x - 19}$

2. Divide $-8x^3$ by $2x^2$. Multiply $(2x^2 + 3)$ by $-4x$ and subtract. ⟶

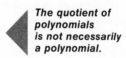

$$
\begin{array}{r}
-4x \\
2x^2 + 3\overline{)-8x^3 + 10x^2 - 12x - 19} \\
\end{array}
$$

$-4x(2x^2 + 3)$ ⟶ $\underline{-8x^3 \qquad - 12x}$

$10x^2 \qquad - 19$

3 Divide $10x^2$ by $2x^2$. Multiply $(2x^2 + 3)$ by 5 and subtract. $\longrightarrow$

$$
\begin{array}{r}
-4x + 5 \\
2x^2 + 3\overline{)-8x^3 + 10x^2 - 12x - 19} \\
-8x^3 \qquad\quad - 12x \\
\hline
10x^2 \qquad\quad - 19
\end{array}
$$

$5(2x^2 + 3) \longrightarrow$

$$
\begin{array}{r}
10x^2 \qquad + 15 \\
\hline
-34
\end{array}
$$

The quotient is written as $-4x + 5 - \dfrac{34}{2x^2 + 3}$. ◀ **Not a polynomial**

P-4   **What is the first term of $4x - 3y\overline{)8x^3 - 10x^2y - xy^2 + 2y^3}$?**

example 3   Divide: $4x - 3y\overline{)8x^3 - 10x^2y - xy^2 + 2y^3}$

Solution:

1 Divide $8x^3$ by $4x$. Multiply $(4x - 3y)$ by $2x^2$ and subtract. $\longrightarrow$

$$
\begin{array}{r}
2x^2 \\
4x - 3y\overline{)8x^3 - 10x^2y - xy^2 + 2y^3}
\end{array}
$$

$2x^2(4x - 3y) \longrightarrow$

$$
\begin{array}{r}
8x^3 - 6x^2y \\
\hline
-4x^2y - xy^2 + 2y^3
\end{array}
$$

2 Divide $-4x^2y$ by $4x$. Multiply $(4x - 3y)$ by $-xy$ and subtract. $\longrightarrow$

$$
\begin{array}{r}
2x^2 - xy \\
4x - 3y\overline{)8x^3 - 10x^2y - xy^2 + 2y^3} \\
8x^3 - 6x^2y \\
\hline
-4x^2y - xy^2 + 2y^3
\end{array}
$$

$-xy(4x - 3y) \longrightarrow$

$$
\begin{array}{r}
-4x^2y + 3xy^2 \\
\hline
-4xy^2 + 2y^3
\end{array}
$$

3 Divide $-4xy^2$ by $4x$. Multiply $(4x - 3y)$ by $-y^2$ and subtract. $\longrightarrow$

$$
\begin{array}{r}
2x^2 - xy - y^2 \\
4x - 3y\overline{)8x^3 - 10x^2y - xy^2 + 2y^3} \\
8x^3 - 6x^2y \\
\hline
-4x^2y - xy^2 + 2y^3 \\
-4x^2y + 3xy^2 \\
\hline
-4xy^2 + 2y^3
\end{array}
$$

$-y^2(4x - 3y) \longrightarrow$

$$
\begin{array}{r}
-4xy^2 + 3y^3 \\
\hline
-y^3
\end{array}
$$

The quotient is $2x^2 - xy - y^2 - \dfrac{y^3}{4x - 3y}$.

CLASSROOM EXERCISES

Note: Q stands for quotient; R stands for remainder.

Write the quotient and remainder in each problem. (Examples 1 and 2)

1. $x + 2 \overline{) x^2 - 3x - 7}$ Q: $x - 5$
             R: 3

$\underline{x^2 + 2x}$

$-5x - 7$

$\underline{-5x - 10}$

2. $x - 3 \overline{) x^2 + x + 5}$ Q: $x + 4$
             R: 17

$\underline{x^2 - 3x}$

$4x + 5$

$\underline{4x - 12}$

3. $3x - 1 \overline{) 6x^2 + 4x - 3}$ Q: $2x + 2$
             R: -1

$\underline{6x^2 - 2x}$

$6x - 3$

$\underline{6x - 2}$

4. $2x + 1 \overline{) 4x^2 - 6x + 1}$ Q: $2x - 4$
             R: 5

$\underline{4x^2 + 2x}$

$-8x + 1$

$\underline{-8x - 4}$

5. $x^2 - 1 \overline{) x^3 + x^2 - 3x + 1}$ Q: $x + 1$
             R: $-2x + 2$

$\underline{x^3 \quad - x}$

$x^2 - 2x + 1$

$\underline{x^2 \quad - 1}$

6. $x - 1 \overline{) x^3 \qquad - 6}$ Q: $x^2 + x + 1$
             R: -5

$\underline{x^3 - x^2}$

$x^2 \qquad - 6$

$\underline{x^2 - x}$

$x - 6$

$\underline{x - 1}$

Write the polynomial missing from each row. (Example 2)

7. $2x - 3 \overline{) \overset{\textstyle 5x + 3}{10x^2 - 9x - 11}}$

$\boxed{}$ $10x^2 - 15x$

$\underline{6x - 11}$

$\boxed{}$ $6x - 9$

-2

8. $4x + 1 \overline{) \overset{\textstyle 3x - 5}{12x^2 - 17x - 1}}$

$\boxed{}$ $12x^2 + 3x$

$\underline{-20x - 1}$

$\boxed{}$ $-20x - 5$

4

9. $x^2 - 3 \overline{) \overset{\textstyle x + 2}{x^3 + 2x^2 - x + 5}}$

$\boxed{}$ $x^3 - 3x$

$\underline{2x^2 + 2x + 5}$

$\boxed{}$ $2x^2 - 6$

$\boxed{}$ $2x + 11$

10. $x^2 + 2 \overline{) \overset{\textstyle x^2 + x - 3}{x^4 + x^3 - x^2 + 2x - 6}}$

$\underline{x^4 \qquad + 2x^2}$

$\boxed{}$ $x^3 - 3x^2 + 2x - 6$

$\underline{x^3 \qquad + 2x}$

$\boxed{}$ $-3x^2 \qquad - 6$

$\boxed{}$ $-3x^2 - 6$

0

WRITTEN EXERCISES

See the Teacher's Manual for the suggested assignments.

Goal: To divide a polynomial by a polynomial

Sample Problem: $x + 2 \overline{) x^3 + 6x^2 + 11x + 10}$ **Answer:** $x^2 + 4x + 3 + \dfrac{4}{x + 2}$

Divide. (Examples 1–3)

1. $x + 4 \overline{)2x^2 + 3x - 17}$ $2x - 5 + \dfrac{3}{x + 4}$

2. $x - 3 \overline{)4x^2 - 11x - 1}$ $4x + 1 + \dfrac{2}{x - 3}$

3. $2x - 3 \overline{)4x^2 + 8x - 25}$ $2x + 7 - \dfrac{4}{2x - 3}$

4. $3x + 2 \overline{)12x^2 - x - 10}$ $4x - 3 - \dfrac{4}{3x + 2}$

5. $5x - 6 \overline{)15x^2 + 2x - 29}$ $3x + 4 - \dfrac{5}{5x - 6}$

6. $6x - 1 \overline{)18x^2 + 27x - 11}$ $3x + 5 - \dfrac{6}{6x - 1}$

7. $2x + 5 \overline{)10x^2 + 13x - 40}$ $5x - 6 - \dfrac{10}{2x + 5}$

8. $4x + 1 \overline{)12x^2 - 33x - 15}$ $3x - 9 - \dfrac{6}{4x + 1}$

9. $2x^2 - 1 \overline{)12x^3 - 10x^2 - 5x + 5}$ $6x - 5 + \dfrac{x}{2x^2 - 1}$

10. $3x^2 + 5 \overline{)-12x^3 + 9x^2 - 21x + 15}$ $-4x + 3 - \dfrac{x}{3x^2 + 5}$

11. $x^2 + x - 1 \overline{)x^4 - 2x^3 + 2x^2 + x + 2}$ $x^2 - 3x + 6 - \dfrac{8x - 8}{x^2 + x - 1}$

12. $2x^2 - x + 1 \overline{)2x^4 - x^3 - 3x^2 + x - 1}$ $x^2 - 2 - \dfrac{x - 1}{2x^2 - x + 1}$

13. $x^2 + 8x + 2 \overline{)x^3 + 3x^2 - 38x - 16}$ $x - 5 - \dfrac{6}{x^2 + 8x + 2}$

14. $x^2 - x - 1 \overline{)2x^4 - 2x^3 - 5x^2 + 3x + 7}$ $2x^2 - 3 + \dfrac{4}{x^2 - x - 1}$

15. $2x^2 + 9x + 4 \overline{)2x^4 + 13x^3 + 16x^2 - 19x + 12}$ $x^2 + 2x - 3 + \dfrac{24}{2x^2 + 9x + 4}$

16. $a^2 - 4a + 4 \overline{)a^3 - 6a^2 + 13a - 9}$ $a - 2 + \dfrac{a - 1}{a^2 - 4a + 4}$

17. $x + y \overline{)x^3 + x^2y - xy^2 - 2y^3}$ $x^2 - y^2 - \dfrac{y^3}{x + y}$

18. $x - y \overline{)x^3 + x^2y - xy^2 - 2y^3}$ $x^2 + 2xy + y^2 - \dfrac{y^3}{x - y}$

MORE CHALLENGING EXERCISES

19. $x + 2 \overline{)x^3 - 8}$ $x^2 - 2x + 4 - \dfrac{16}{x + 2}$

20. $x - 3 \overline{)x^3 + 27}$ $x^2 + 3x + 9 + \dfrac{54}{x - 3}$

21. $2x - 3y \overline{)2x^3 - 7x^2y + 8xy^2 - 2y^3}$ See below.

22. $3y - x \overline{)-9y^3 + 9y^2x - 5yx^2 - x^3}$ See below.

23. $2x - 1 \overline{)8x^3 - 1}$ $4x^2 + 2x + 1$

24. $5y + 4 \overline{)125y^3 + 64}$ $25y^2 - 20y + 16$

25. $a^2 - 2 \overline{)a^3 + 6a^2 - 2a - 12}$ $a + 6$

26. $3x + 2y \overline{)3x^3 + 8x^2y + 7xy^2 + 5y^3}$ See below.

27. $x + 5 \overline{)x^3 + 4x - 3}$ $x^2 - 5x + 29 - \dfrac{148}{x + 5}$

28. $x + 2 \overline{)x^3 - 6x^2 + 1}$ $x^2 - 8x + 16 - \dfrac{31}{x + 2}$

29. $2a - 1 \overline{)5a + 6a^2 - 4}$ $3a + 4$

30. $x + 5 \overline{)4 - 6x^2 + 3x}$ $-6x + 33 - \dfrac{161}{x + 5}$

31. $a - 3 \overline{)4a^3 - 24a - 3a^2 - 9}$ $4a^2 + 9a + 3$

32. $2a + 3 \overline{)2a^3 + 18 - 3a - 7a^2}$ $a^2 - 5a + 6$

33. $x + y \overline{)x^3 + y^3}$ $x^2 - xy + y^2$

34. $x - y \overline{)x^3 - y^3}$ $x^2 + xy + y^2$

35. $x^2 + xy + y^2 \overline{)x^3 - y^3}$ $x - y$

36. $a^2 - ab + b^2 \overline{)a^3 + b^3}$ $a + b$

37. $x - 1 \overline{)x^4 - 1}$ $x^3 + x^2 + x + 1$

38. $x^2 + x + 1 \overline{)x^4 + x^2 + 2}$ $x^2 - x + 1 + \dfrac{1}{x^2 + x + 1}$

21. $x^2 - 2xy + y^2 + \dfrac{y^3}{2x - 3y}$

22. $-3y^2 + 2xy - x^2 - \dfrac{2x^3}{3y - x}$

26. $x^2 + 2xy + y^2 + \dfrac{3y^3}{3x + 2y}$

Distance to the Horizon

If you are sitting in a plane that is high in the air, you can see the earth's horizon several kilometers away. The distance to the horizon depends upon the plane's <u>altitude</u>. The **altitude** is the plane's distance above the ground.

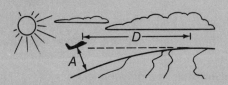

The approximate distance to the horizon is given by the following formula.

$$D = 3.57\sqrt{A}$$

D is the distance to the horizon in kilometers.
A is the altitude of the plane in meters.

EXAMPLE: Find the distance to the horizon from a plane that is at an altitude of 3000 meters. Write the answer to the nearest whole kilometer.

SOLUTION: $D = 3.57\sqrt{A}$

$D = 3.57\sqrt{3000}$ *A = 3000 meters*

$ = 3.57\sqrt{100 \cdot 30}$

$ = 3.57\sqrt{100} \cdot \sqrt{30}$

$ = 3.57 \cdot 10 \cdot \sqrt{30}$

$ = 3.57 \cdot 10 \cdot 5.477$ *From the table on page 198*

$ =$ **196 kilometers**

EXERCISES

In Exercises 1–6 find the distance to the horizon from a plane at each altitude. Write the answer to the nearest whole kilometer.

1. 1500 meters   138 kilometers   2. 2000 meters   160 kilometers   3. 4000 meters   226 kilometers

4. 10,000 meters   357 kilometers   5. 12,000 meters   391 kilometers   6. 15,000 meters   437 kilometers

7. A television transmitter is on top of a mountain 1200 meters above a desert below. Find, to the nearest kilometer, how far away a television set on the ground can receive the transmitter's signal.   124 kilometers

CHAPTER SUMMARY

IMPORTANT TERMS	Monomial *(p. 206)* Trinomial *(p. 211)*
	Coefficient *(p. 206)* Constant term *(p. 218)*
	Polynomial *(p. 211)* Divisor *(p. 222)*
	Term *(p. 211)* Dividend *(p. 222)*
	Binomial *(p. 211)*

IMPORTANT IDEAS

1. Monomials or polynomials are said to be over {integers} if all the coefficients are integers.

2. The sum of any two polynomials is a polynomial.

3. In adding or subtracting polynomials vertically, you arrange the terms in descending order of powers.

4. The difference of any two polynomials is a polynomial.

5. Any two polynomials are multiplied by multiplying each term of one polynomial by each term of the other.

6. The product of any two polynomials is a polynomial.

7. To divide a polynomial by a monomial, divide each term of the polynomial by the monomial.

8. The quotient of two polynomials is not necessarily a polynomial.

CHAPTER REVIEW

Note: The Teacher's Resource Book contains two forms of each Chapter test.

SECTION 9.1

Write Yes or No to show whether each numeral or expression is a polynomial over {rational numbers}.

1. $\frac{1}{3}x^2$ Yes

2. $\frac{3}{x^2}$ No

3. $-5x^{-3}$ No

4. $\sqrt{3} \cdot x$ No

Evaluate each monomial.

5. $4x^3$ if $x = -2$ −32

6. $-5x^2$ if $x = -3$ −45

7. $-0.8x^4$ if $x = 2$ −12.8

8. $1.2x^3$ if $x = -4$ −76.8

SECTION 9.2

Multiply.

9. $(3t^2)(7t^4)$ $21t^6$

10. $(-5xy^3)(13x^2y)$ $-65x^3y^4$

11. $(\frac{1}{3}ab)(-6ab^2)(-a^2b^2)$ $2a^4b^5$

12. $(1.4mn^2)(7m^2n)(-2n^2)$ $-19.6m^3n^5$

Divide.

13. $\dfrac{-108t^5}{9t^3}$ $-12t^2$

14. $\dfrac{1.44r^3s^6t^2}{-12rs^5t}$ $-0.12r^2st$

15. $\dfrac{-3x^{12}y^7z^9}{-18x^3y^5z^7}$ $\frac{1}{6}x^9y^2z^2$

16. $\dfrac{23a^4bc^2}{a^3c}$ $23abc$

17. $\dfrac{-13x^4y^5}{-4x^2y}$ $\frac{13}{4}x^2y^4$

18. $\dfrac{16a^5c^6}{2a^4c^5}$ $8ac$

SECTION 9.3

Write Yes or No to show whether each numeral or expression is a polynomial over {rational numbers}.

19. $\dfrac{2}{x^2} - \dfrac{1}{x} + \dfrac{1}{2}$ No

20. $x^3 - 10$ Yes

21. $3\sqrt{x} - \sqrt{3}$ No

22. $x^{-3} + 2x^{-2} - 5x^{-1} - 7$ No

Simplify.

23. $7x^2 - 2x + 5x - 16$ $7x^2 + 3x - 16$

24. $4x^3 - 2x^2 - x^2 + 5x$ $4x^3 - 3x^2 + 5x$

25. $12x - x^2 + 5 - 3x^3$ $-3x^3 - x^2 + 12x + 5$

26. $3x^2 - 5 + 4x - 2x^3 + x^4$ $x^4 - 2x^3 + 3x^2 + 4x - 5$

SECTION 9.4

Add.

27. $\begin{aligned} -3x^2 + 2x - 5 \\ \underline{7x^2 - 9x - 12} \end{aligned}$ $4x^2 - 7x - 17$

28. $\begin{aligned} 4.3x^2 - 1.7x + 2.5 \\ \underline{-3.9x^2 + 4.8x - 8.3} \end{aligned}$ $0.4x^2 + 3.1x - 5.8$

29. $(5x^3 - 3x + 7) + (2x^2 - 8x - 12)$ $5x^3 + 2x^2 - 11x - 5$

30. $(-2x^3 + x^2 - 5) + (5x^3 - x^2 + 7x - 12)$ $3x^3 + 7x - 17$

Subtract.

31. $\begin{aligned} x^2 - 3x + 4 \\ \underline{-5x^2 + 4x + 9} \end{aligned}$ $6x^2 - 7x - 5$

32. $\begin{aligned} 2x^3 \qquad - 3x - 5 \\ \underline{6x^3 - x^2 + 5x - 6} \end{aligned}$ $-4x^3 + x^2 - 8x + 1$

33. $(x^4 - 3x^2 + 7) - (5x^3 - x^2 + 2x - 5)$ $x^4 - 5x^3 - 2x^2 - 2x + 12$

34. $(3x^3 - x^2 - 4x) - (-x^3 + 4x^2 - x - 10)$ $4x^3 - 5x^2 - 3x + 10$

SECTION 9.5

Multiply.

35. $(2x + 7)(x - 3)$ $2x^2 + x - 21$

36. $(3x - 8)(x + 4)$ $3x^2 + 4x - 32$

37. $(5x - 2)(4x + 5)$ $20x^2 + 17x - 10$

38. $(6x - 5)(2x - 9)$ $12x^2 - 64x + 45$

39.
$$3x^3 - x^2 \qquad + 5$$
$$\underline{\qquad\qquad 2x - 7}$$
$6x^4 - 23x^3 + 7x^2 + 10x - 35$

40.
$$-4x^3 \qquad - 5x + 3$$
$$\underline{\qquad\qquad 4x - 3}$$
$-16x^4 + 12x^3 - 20x^2 + 27x - 9$

SECTION 9.6

Divide.

41. $2x - 5 \overline{)2x^2 + 9x - 35}$ $x + 7$

42. $3x - 4 \overline{)15x^2 + 4x - 32}$ $5x + 8$

43. $x^2 - 3 \overline{)x^4 - 3x^3 + x^2 + 9x - 12}$ $x^2 - 3x + 4$

44. $x^2 + 2 \overline{)-x^4 + x^3 - 7x^2 + 2x - 10}$
$-x^2 + x - 5$

SECTION 9.7

Divide.

45. $4x + 11 \overline{)-8x^2 - 2x + 60}$ $-2x + 5 + \dfrac{5}{4x + 11}$

46. $6x - 4 \overline{)-18x^2 + 36x - 35}$
$-3x + 4 - \dfrac{19}{6x - 4}$

47. $x^2 + 3 \overline{)x^4 - x^3 - 3x - 11}$
$x^2 - x - 3 - \dfrac{2}{x^2 + 3}$

48. $2x^2 - 5 \overline{)2x^4 + 3x^2 - 26}$
$x^2 + 4 - \dfrac{6}{2x^2 - 5}$

CHAPTER

10 Factoring Polynomials

Sections 10.1 Common Monomial Factors

10.2 Quadratic Polynomials

10.3 Factoring $x^2 + bx + c$

10.4 Factoring $ax^2 + bx + c$

10.5 Difference of Two Squares

10.6 Trinomial Squares

10.7 Combined Types of Factoring

Features *Calculator Exercises:* Formula for Finding a Sum

Career: Life Scientist

Review
and
Testing

Review Capsules

Mid-Chapter Review

Chapter Summary

Chapter Review

10.1 Common Monomial Factors

OBJECTIVES: To factor a polynomial over {integers} by common monomial factoring

P-1   **Express $4x^2 - 6x$ as a product.** $2x(2x - 3)$

Here are some ways to factor $4x^2 - 6x$.

> "Factor" means "write as a product of factors."

$$4x^2 - 6x = 2(2x^2 - 3x) \qquad 4x^2 - 6x = \tfrac{1}{2}x(8x - 12)$$

$$4x^2 - 6x = 4x(x - 1.5) \qquad 4x^2 - 6x = x^{-1}(4x^3 - 6x^2)$$

$$4x^2 - 6x = 2x(2x - 3)$$

The factors $2x$ and $(2x - 3)$ in the last factorization are special.

1. They are both polynomials.
2. Their coefficients are integers.
3. They are prime.

> The coefficients are 2, 2, and −3.

There are only two ways to write $7x^2 - 2$ as a product of two or more polynomials that have integers as their coefficients.

$$7x^2 - 2 = 1(7x^2 - 2)$$
$$7x^2 - 2 = -1(-7x^2 + 2)$$

> Either 1 times the polynomial or −1 times the opposite of the polynomial.

For this reason polynomials such as $7x^2 - 2$ are called **prime polynomials.**

example 1

Factor $6x^2 - 9x$.

> Always find the prime polynomial factors.

Solution:

1. Find the greatest number that is a common factor of 6 and 9. ——————→ 3

> $6 = 3 \cdot 2$
> $9 = 3 \cdot 3$

2. Find the greatest power of x that is common to x^2 and x. ——————→ x

> $x^2 = x \cdot x$
> $x = x$

3. Write the common monomial factor. ——→ $3x(\quad)$

4. Divide each term of $6x^2 - 9x$ by $3x$. ——————————→ $3x(2x - 3)$

Check your answer by multiplying the factors.

$$\begin{array}{r} 2x - 3 \\ 3x \\ \hline 6x^2 - 9x \end{array}$$

> Explain that this is only a partial check. Refer to P-1 to show why.

The **greatest common factor** of two or more counting numbers is the greatest number that is a factor of all the numbers.

The greatest common factor of 6 and 9 is 3.

example 2   Factor $8x^3 + 12x^2$.

Solution:

1. Write the greatest common factor of 8 and 12. $\longrightarrow$ 4

2. Write the greatest power of x common to x^3 and x^2. $\longrightarrow$ x^2

3. Write the common monomial factor. $\longrightarrow$ $4x^2(\qquad)$

4. Divide each term of $8x^3 + 12x^2$ by $4x^2$. $\longrightarrow$ $4x^2(2x + 3)$

P-2   **What is the common monomial factor of $8x^3 + 12x^2$?** $4x^2$

The prime factors of $8x^3 + 12x^2$ are $2 \cdot 2 \cdot x \cdot x(2x + 3)$. The simplest factored form is $4x^2(2x + 3)$. Expressing $8x^3 + 12x^2$ as $4x^2(2x + 3)$ is an example of **common monomial factoring.**

example 3   Factor $10x^4 - 15x^3 + 25x^2$.

Solution:

1. Find the greatest common factor of 10, 15, and 25. $\longrightarrow$ 5

2. Find the greatest power of x common to x^4, x^3, and x^2. $\longrightarrow$ x^2

3. Write the common monomial factor. $\longrightarrow$ $5x^2(\qquad)$

4. Divide each term of $10x^4 - 15x^3 + 25x^2$ by $5x^2$. $\longrightarrow$ $5x^2(2x^2 - 3x + 5)$

Check: $\dfrac{\begin{array}{r} 2x^2 - 3x + 5 \\ 5x^2 \end{array}}{10x^4 - 15x^3 + 25x^2}$ ◄ *Multiply the factors.*

In factoring, you should always check two conditions.

1. Any polynomial factors other than monomial factors should be prime.
2. The product of the factors must equal the given polynomial.

CLASSROOM EXERCISES

Say <u>Yes</u> or <u>No</u> to tell whether each polynomial is prime.

1. $x + 2$ Yes
2. $x - 5$ Yes
3. $2x + 4$ No
4. $5x + 10$ No

5. $x^2 + x$ No
6. $x^2 + 2$ Yes
7. $3x - 2$ Yes
8. $x^2 + 3x$ No

Factor. (Examples 1 and 2)

9. $4x + 2$ $2(2x + 1)$
10. $3x - 3$ $3(x - 1)$
11. $5x + 15$ $5(x + 3)$
12. $x^2 - 3x$ $x(x - 3)$

13. $2x^2 + 10$ $2(x^2 + 5)$
14. $3x^2 + 9x$ $3x(x + 3)$
15. $-3x + 6$ $-3(x - 2)$
16. $-x^2 + 3x$
$-x(x - 3)$

17. $5x^3 - 10x$ $5x(x^2 - 2)$
18. $12x^2 + 18x$ $6x(2x + 3)$
19. $24 - 8x^2$ $8(3 - x^2)$
20. $14x^5 - 21x^2$
$7x^2(2x^3 - 3)$

WRITTEN EXERCISES

See the Teacher's Manual for the suggested assignments.

Goal: To factor a polynomial by common monomial factoring
Sample Problem: Factor $9x^4 - 54x^3 + 18x^2$.   **Answer:** $9x^2(x^2 - 6x + 2)$

Factor. (Examples 1–3)

8. $-4x(x - 5)$

1. $4x - 4$ $4(x - 1)$
2. $3x + 3$ $3(x + 1)$
3. $5x + 10$ $5(x + 2)$
4. $6x - 18$
$6(x - 3)$

5. $2x^2 + 3x$ $x(2x + 3)$
6. $4x^2 - 5x$ $x(4x - 5)$
7. $-3x^2 + 9x$ $-3x(x - 3)$
8. $-4x^2 + 20x$
8. See above.

9. $8x^3 - 12x^2$ $4x^2(2x - 3)$
10. $10x^3 + 25x^2$ $5x^2(2x + 5)$
11. $12x^3 - 18x$ $6x(2x^2 - 3)$
12. $18x^3 - 27x$
$9x(2x^2 - 3)$

13. $x^3 - 2x^2 + 3x$ $x(x^2 - 2x + 3)$
14. $3x^3 + x^2 - 5x$ $x(3x^2 + x - 5)$

15. $2x^4 - 4x^2 - 10x$ $2x(x^3 - 2x - 5)$
16. $6x^4 + 8x^3 - 26x$ $2x(3x^3 + 4x^2 - 13)$

17. $-5x^2 - 10x$ $-5x(x + 2)$
18. $-4x^2 - 16x$ $-4x(x + 4)$

19. $8x^5 - 12x^3 + 20x^2$ $4x^2(2x^3 - 3x + 5)$
20. $18x^4 + 12x^3 - 30x^2$ $6x^2(3x^2 + 2x - 5)$

21. $5x^4 - 35x^2 - 10$ $5(x^4 - 7x^2 - 2)$
22. $3x^5 + 12x^3 - 9$ $3(x^5 + 4x^3 - 3)$

23. $21x^6 + 14x^5 - 10$ Prime polynomial
24. $18x^7 - 27x^4 + 9x^3$ $9x^3(2x^4 - 3x + 1)$

REVIEW CAPSULE FOR SECTION 10.2

Write each trinomial in the form $x^2 + rx + sx + rs$.

EXAMPLE: $x^2 + 7x + 10$ **SOLUTION:** $x^2 + 5x + 2x + 5 \cdot 2$

3. $x^2 + 7x + 3x + 7 \cdot 3$

1. $x^2 + 4x + 4$ $x^2 + 2x + 2x + 2 \cdot 2$
2. $x^2 + 6x + 8$ $x^2 + 4x + 2x + 4 \cdot 2$
3. $x^2 + 10x + 21$

4. $x^2 + 5x + 6$ $x^2 + 2x + 3x + 2 \cdot 3$
5. $x^2 + 12x + 11$ $x^2 + x + 11x + 1 \cdot 11$
6. $x^2 + 9x + 20$
$x^2 + 4x + 5x + 4 \cdot 5$

10.2 Quadratic Polynomials

OBJECTIVES: To factor a polynomial of the form $x^2 + rx + sx + rs$ in which r and s are integers
To factor a quadratic trinomial of the form $x^2 + bx + c$ in which b and c are positive integers

A monomial such as $2x^5$ is said to be of the <u>fifth degree</u>.

> The **degree of a monomial** in one variable is determined by the exponent of the variable.　　　$-8x^3$ is of the <u>third degree</u>.

P-1　**What is the degree of each of these monomials?**

a. $-3x^2$　　**b.** $5x$　　**c.** -16　　**d.** $16x^8$
　Second　　　　First　　　　Zero　　　　Eighth

> The **degree of a polynomial** is the highest degree of the monomials of the polynomial.　　　$5x^2 - 2x + 6$ is of <u>second degree</u>.

Second degree polynomials are called **quadratic polynomials.**　◀ $5x^2 - 2x + 6$ is a **quadratic trinomial.**

P-2　**What is the degree of each of these polynomials?**

a. $x - 5$　　**b.** $x^3 - 2x^2 + 3x - 7$　　**c.** $3x^2 - 2x + 2x^4 - 7$
　First　　　　　　　Third　　　　　　　　　　　Fourth

example 1

Factor $x^2 + 2x + 3x + 6$.　◀ Remember always to write the **prime** factors.

Solution:

1. Write as the sum of two binomials. ⟶ $x^2 + 2x + 3x + 6 = (x^2 + 2x) + (3x + 6)$

2. Factor each binomial. ⟶ $= x(x + 2) + 3(x + 2)$

3. Distributive Property ⟶ $= (x + 3)(x + 2)$

example 2

Factor $x^2 + rx + sx + rs$. (r and s represent integers.)

Solution:

1. Write as the sum of two binomials. ⟶ $x^2 + rx + sx + rs = (x^2 + rx) + (sx + rs)$

2. Factor each binomial. ⟶ $= x(x + r) + s(x + r)$

3. Distributive Property ⟶ $= (x + s)(x + r)$

P-3 What are the two binomial factors in each of the following?

a. $x(x + 3) + 7(x + 3)$ **b.** $x(x + 10) + 2(x + 10)$

    $(x + 3)$ and $(x + 7)$ $(x + 10)$ and $(x + 2)$

P-4 What number in $x^2 + 5x + 2x + 10$ corresponds to r in
$x^2 + rx + sx + rs$? to s? to rs?
   5   2   10

example 3   Factor $x^2 + 5x + 2x + 10$. ◀ $x^2 + rx + sx + rs$

Solution: $x^2 + 5x + 2x + 10 = (x^2 + 5x) + (2x + 10)$

$$= x(x + 5) + 2(x + 5)$$

$$= (x + 2)(x + 5)$$

P-5 What two integers have a sum of 13 and a product of 36? 9 and 4

example 4   Write $x^2 + 13x + 36$ in the form $x^2 + rx + sx + rs$.
Then factor.

Solution: $x^2 + 13x + 36 = x^2 + 4x + 9x + 36$ ◀ $r = 4$
                                                                $s = 9$

Values of r and s are to be formed intuitively. An explicit rule will be discussed in Section 10-3

$$= (x^2 + 4x) + (9x + 36)$$

$$= x(x + 4) + 9(x + 4)$$

$$= (x + 9)(x + 4)$$

CLASSROOM EXERCISES

Write the degree of each polynomial. (P-2)

1. $x^2 - 5$ Second   **2.** $3x^3 - 5x + 6$ Third   **3.** $x - 3x^0$ First

4. $5 + 2x - x^2$ Second   **5.** $x - x^5 + x^3 - x^2$ Fifth   **6.** $-3x + 7x^5 - 5x^{10}$
                                                                                   Tenth

Write the two binomial factors. (P-3)

7. $x(x + 3) + 4(x + 3)$ $(x + 4), (x + 3)$ **8.** $x(x + 2) + 7(x + 2)$ $(x + 7), (x + 2)$

9. $x(x + 5) + 3(x + 5)$ $(x + 3), (x + 5)$ **10.** $x(x + 2) + 8(x + 2)$ $(x + 8), (x + 2)$

11. $x(x + 4) + 5(x + 4)$ $(x + 5), (x + 4)$ **12.** $x(x + 7) + 3(x + 7)$ $(x + 3), (x + 7)$

13. $x(x + 8) + 4(x + 8)$ $(x + 4), (x + 8)$ **14.** $x(x + 9) + 5(x + 9)$ $(x + 5), (x + 9)$

WRITTEN EXERCISES

See the Teacher's Manual for the suggested assignments.

Goal: To write two binomial factors of a quadratic trinomial
Sample Problem: Factor $x^2 + 16x + 63$.
Answer: $(x + 9)(x + 7)$

Factor. (Examples 1–3)

1. $x^2 + 3x + 4x + 12$ $(x + 3)(x + 4)$

2. $x^2 + 2x + 7x + 14$ $(x + 2)(x + 7)$

3. $x^2 + 5x + 3x + 15$ $(x + 5)(x + 3)$

4. $x^2 + 2x + 8x + 16$ $(x + 2)(x + 8)$

5. $x^2 + 4x + 5x + 20$ $(x + 4)(x + 5)$

6. $x^2 + 7x + 3x + 21$ $(x + 7)(x + 3)$

7. $x^2 + 8x + 4x + 32$ $(x + 8)(x + 4)$

8. $x^2 + 9x + 5x + 45$ $(x + 9)(x + 5)$

9. $x^2 + 3x + 11x + 33$ $(x + 3)(x + 11)$

10. $x^2 + 6x + 8x + 48$ $(x + 6)(x + 8)$

Write each trinomial in the form $x^2 + rx + sx + rs$. Then factor. (Example 4)

EXAMPLE: $x^2 + 18x + 77$

SOLUTION: $x^2 + 18x + 77 = x^2 + (7x + 11x) + 77$
$$= (x^2 + 7x) + (11x + 77)$$
$$= x(x + 7) + 11(x + 7)$$
$$= (x + 11)(x + 7)$$

11. $x^2 + 7x + 10$ $(x + 5)(x + 2)$

12. $x^2 + 9x + 14$ $(x + 7)(x + 2)$

13. $(x + 3)(x + 2)$
13. $x^2 + 5x + 6$

14. $x^2 + 8x + 15$ $(x + 5)(x + 3)$

15. $x^2 + 10x + 21$ $(x + 7)(x + 3)$

16. $x^2 + 13x + 22$
$(x + 11)(x + 2)$

17. $x^2 + 15x + 26$ $(x + 13)(x + 2)$

18. $x^2 + 14x + 33$ $(x + 11)(x + 3)$

19. $x^2 + 13x + 30$
$(x + 10)(x + 3)$

20. $x^2 + 11x + 18$ $(x + 9)(x + 2)$

21. $x^2 + 11x + 28$ $(x + 7)(x + 4)$

22. $x^2 + 11x + 10$
$(x + 10)(x + 1)$

MORE CHALLENGING EXERCISES

23. $x^2 + 23x + 132$ $(x + 11)(x + 12)$

24. $x^2 + 19x + 90$ $(x + 9)(x + 10)$

$(x + 15)(x + 10)$
25. $x^2 + 25x + 150$

26. $x^2 + 32x + 247$ $(x + 13)(x + 19)$

27. $x^2 + 29x + 208$
$(x + 13)(x + 16)$

28. $x^2 + 49x + 558$
$(x + 18)(x + 31)$

REVIEW CAPSULE FOR SECTION 10.3

Factor. (Section 2.5)

1. $x(x + 5) - 2(x + 5)$ $(x - 2)(x + 5)$

$(x + 2)(x - 3)$
2. $x(x - 3) + 2(x - 3)$

$(x - 4)(x - 6)$
3. $x(x - 6) - 4(x - 6)$

4. $x(x - 10) - 2(x - 10)$
$(x - 10)(x - 2)$

5. $x(x - 5) - 5(x - 5)$
$(x - 5)(x - 5)$

6. $x(x - 9) - 9(x - 9)$
$(x - 9)(x - 9)$

10.3 Factoring $x^2 + bx + c$

To write a quadratic trinomial in the form $x^2 + rx + sx + s$
To write the binomial factors of a quadratic trinomial in the form $x^2 + bx + c$

The simplest polynomial form of $x^2 + rx + sx + rs$ is shown below.

$$x^2 + (r + s)x + rs$$

P-1 In the polynomial $x^2 + 10x + 16$, what integer corresponds to $r + s$? 10
What integer corresponds to rs? 16

P-2 What represents the value of b when $x^2 + (r + s)x + rs$ is compared
with $x^2 + bx + c$? $r + s$

P-3 What represents the constant term c? rs

> To factor a trinomial of the form $x^2 + bx + c$, find
> two integers r and s such that
>
> $$r + s = b \quad \text{and} \quad r \cdot s = c.$$

Explain that if integers exist that make $r + s = b$ and $r \cdot s = c$ both true, there is just one such pair of integers.

example 1   Factor $x^2 + 10x + 16$.

◀ **Find two numbers whose
sum is 10 and whose
product is 16.**

Solution: $\qquad r + s = 10 \qquad rs = 16$

1. Write all pairs of integers with product 16.

(1)(16)	(−1)(−16)
(2)(8)	(−2)(−8)
(4)(4)	(−4)(−4)

2. Select the pair with a sum of 10. $\longrightarrow$ $\begin{cases} r = 8 \\ s = 2 \end{cases}$

3. Write in the form
$x^2 + rx + sx + rs$. $\longrightarrow$ $x^2 + 10x + 16 = x^2 + 8x + 2x + 16$

4. Write as the sum of two binomials. $\longrightarrow = (x^2 + 8x) + (2x + 16)$

5. Factor each binomial. $\longrightarrow = x(x + 8) + 2(x + 8)$

6. Distributive Property $\longrightarrow = (x + 2)(x + 8)$

P-4   **What integer in $x^2 - 7x + 12$ corresponds to $r + s$?   to rs?**

                                                                        −7   12

example 2   Factor $x^2 - 7x + 12$.

Solution:

1. Write all pairs of integers with product 12.

$$(1)(12) \qquad (-1)(-12)$$
$$(2)(6) \qquad (-2)(-6)$$
$$(3)(4) \qquad (-3)(-4)$$

2. Select the pair with a sum of −7. ⟶ $\begin{cases} r = -3 \\ s = -4 \end{cases}$

3. Write in the form
$x^2 + rx + sx + rs$. ⟶ $x^2 - 7x + 12 = x^2 - 3x - 4x + 12$

4. Write as a sum of two binomials. ⟶ $= (x^2 - 3x) + (-4x + 12)$

5. Factor each binomial. ⟶ $= x(x - 3) - 4(x - 3)$ ◀   *Use* $-4(x - 3)$, *not* $\frac{4(-x + 3)}{}$.

6. Distributive Property ⟶ $= (x - 4)(x - 3)$

P-5   **What integer in $x^2 - x - 20$ corresponds to $r + s$?   to rs?**

                                                                      −1   −20

example 3   Factor $x^2 - x - 20$.

Solution:

1. Write all pairs of integers with product −20.

$$(1)(-20) \qquad (-1)(20)$$
$$(2)(-10) \qquad (-2)(10)$$
$$(4)(-5) \qquad (-4)(5)$$

2. Select the pair with a sum of −1. ⟶ $\begin{cases} r = 4 \\ s = -5 \end{cases}$

3. $x^2 - x - 20 = x^2 + 4x - 5x - 20$

4. $= (x^2 + 4x) + (-5x - 20)$

5. $= x(x + 4) - 5(x + 4)$

6. $= (x - 5)(x + 4)$

example 4   Factor $x^2 + 5x + 10$.

Solution:

1. Write all pairs of integers with product 10.

$$(1)(10) \qquad (-1)(-10)$$
$$(2)(5) \qquad (-2)(-5)$$

◀ **Pairs of integers with product 10**

2. Select the pair with a sum of 5.

◀ **None of the pairs of integers meet this condition.**

Since no two integers meet both conditions, $x^2 + 5x + 10$ is a prime polynomial.

CLASSROOM EXERCISES

Name two integers, if they exist, that have a product and a sum as given.
(Examples 1 and 2)

1. The product is 6 and the sum is 5.   3, 2   **2.** The product is 12 and the sum is 8. 6, 2

3. The product is 18 and the sum is 9.   6, 3   **4.** The product is 2 and the sum is 3. 2, 1

5. The product is 3 and the sum is 2.   None   **6.** The product is 8 and the sum is −2. None

7. The product is −8 and the sum is 2. 4, −2   **8.** The product is −8 and the sum is −2.
                                                   −4, 2

9. The product is 8 and the sum is 6. 2, 4   **10.** The product is 8 and the sum is −6.
                                                   −2, −4

11. The product is 10 and the sum is 3. None   **12.** The product is 12 and the sum is 6.
                                                   None

Express each trinomial in the form $x^2 + rx + sx + rs$. (Examples 1–3)

13. $x^2 + 7x + 12$ $x^2 + 4x + 3x + 12$ **14.** $x^2 + 6x + 9$ $x^2 + 3x + 3x + 9$ **15.** $x^2 + 8x + 15$ $x^2 + 5x + 3x + 15$

16. $x^2 + 11x + 10$ $x^2 + 10x + x + 10$ **17.** $x^2 - 5x + 6$ $x^2 - 3x - 2x + 6$ **18.** $x^2 - 10x + 16$ $x^2 - 8x - 2x + 16$

19. $x^2 + 4x - 5$ $x^2 + 5x - x - 5$ **20.** $x^2 - 7x - 8$ $x^2 - 8x + x - 8$ **21.** $x^2 + 5x - 6$ $x^2 + 6x - x - 6$

22. $x^2 - 5x - 6$ $x^2 - 6x + x - 6$ **23.** $x^2 + 6x - 7$ $x^2 + 7x - x - 7$ **24.** $x^2 - 6x - 7$ $x^2 - 7x + x - 7$

WRITTEN EXERCISES

See the Teacher's Manual for the suggested assignments.

Goal: To factor quadratic trinomials of the form $x^2 + bx + c$

Sample Problems: a. $x^2 + 11x + 30$ **b.** $x^2 - 8x - 20$

Answers: a. $(x + 6)(x + 5)$ **b.** $(x - 10)(x + 2)$

For each trinomial, write the values of $r + s$ and $r \cdot s$. (P-1, P-4, P-5, P-6)

1. $x^2 + 7x + 12$ 7; 12

2. $x^2 + 14x + 15$ 14; 15

3. $x^2 + 14x + 33$ 14; 33

4. $x^2 + 9x + 20$ 9; 20

5. $x^2 + 4x - 32$ 4; −32

6. $x^2 + x - 30$ 1; −30

7. $x^2 - 8x - 48$ −8; −48

8. $x^2 - 10x - 64$ −10; −64

9. $x^2 - 17x + 72$ −17; 72

10. $x^2 + 5x - 36$ 5; −36

11. $x^2 - 3x + 2$ −3; 2

12. $x^2 + 7x - 30$ 7; −30

Write each trinomial in the form $x^2 + rx + sx + rs$. (Examples 1–3)

13. $x^2 + 13x + 12$ $x^2 + 12x + x + 12$

14. $x^2 + 16x + 15$ $x^2 + 15x + x + 15$

15. $x^2 + 11x + 30$ $x^2 + 5x + 6x + 30$

16. $x^2 + 13x + 42$ $x^2 + 6x + 7x + 42$

17. $x^2 - 8x + 15$ $x^2 - 5x - 3x + 15$

18. $x^2 - 9x + 14$

19. $x^2 - 11x + 24$ $x^2 - 8x - 3x + 24$

20. $x^2 - 14x + 45$ $x^2 - 9x - 5x + 45$

21. $x^2 - 3x - 40$

22. $x^2 - 2x - 35$ $x^2 - 7x + 5x - 35$

23. $x^2 + 4x - 21$ $x^2 + 7x - 3x - 21$

24. $x^2 + 4x - 32$

25. $x^2 - 9x - 36$ $x^2 - 12x + 3x - 36$

26. $x^2 - 13x + 36$ $x^2 - 9x - 4x + 36$

27. $x^2 - 7x + 6$

28. $x^2 - 7x - 8$ $x^2 - 8x + x - 8$

29. $x^2 - 11x - 42$ $x^2 - 14x + 3x - 42$

30. $x^2 - 3x + 2$ $x^2 - 2x - x + 2$

See below. (for 18, 21, 24, 27)

18. $x^2 - 7x - 2x + 14$ 21. $x^2 - 8x + 5x - 40$
24. $x^2 + 8x - 4x - 32$ 27. $x^2 - 6x - x + 6$

Factor. (Examples 1–4)

31. $x^2 + 2x + 1$ $(x + 1)(x + 1)$

32. $x^2 + 4x + 4$ $(x + 2)(x + 2)$

33. $x^2 + 12x + 35$ $(x + 5)(x + 7)$

34. $x^2 + 10x + 21$ $(x + 7)(x + 3)$

35. $x^2 - 7x + 12$ $(x - 4)(x - 3)$

36. $x^2 - 9x + 20$

37. $x^2 - 11x + 30$ $(x - 6)(x - 5)$

38. $x^2 - 10x + 24$ $(x - 6)(x - 4)$

39. $x^2 - x - 12$

40. $x^2 - x - 20$ $(x - 5)(x + 4)$

41. $x^2 - x - 30$ $(x - 6)(x + 5)$

42. $x^2 - 2x - 24$

43. $x^2 + x - 30$ $(x + 6)(x - 5)$

44. $x^2 + 2x - 24$ $(x + 6)(x - 4)$

45. $x^2 - 9x + 14$

46. $x^2 - 11x + 24$ $(x - 8)(x - 3)$

47. $x^2 + 5x - 14$ $(x + 7)(x - 2)$

48. $x^2 + 5x - 24$

49. $x^2 - 13x + 36$ $(x - 9)(x - 4)$

50. $x^2 - 20x + 64$ $(x - 16)(x - 4)$

51. $x^2 - 2x - 15$

52. $x^2 - 10x - 24$ $(x - 12)(x + 2)$

53. $x^2 + 19x + 34$ $(x + 17)(x + 2)$

54. $x^2 - 11x + 28$

55. $x^2 - 22x - 48$ $(x - 24)(x + 2)$

56. $x^2 - 26x + 48$ $(x - 24)(x - 2)$

57. $x^2 + 3x + 2$

58. $x^2 + 10x + 16$ $(x + 8)(x + 2)$

59. $x^2 - x - 56$ $(x - 8)(x + 7)$

60. $x^2 - 10x - 56$ $(x - 14)(x + 4)$

See below. (for 36, 39, 42, 45, 48, 51, 54, 57)

36. $(x - 5)(x - 4)$ 39. $(x - 4)(x + 3)$ 42. $(x - 6)(x + 4)$ 45. $(x - 7)(x - 2)$
48. $(x + 8)(x - 3)$ 51. $(x - 5)(x + 3)$ 54. $(x - 7)(x - 4)$ 57. $(x + 2)(x + 1)$

10.4 Factoring $ax^2 + bx + c$

OBJECTIVES: To multiply two binomials
To write the binomial factors of a quadratic trinomial of the form $ax^2 + bx + c$

In the last section you factored quadratic trinomials. Each of these trinomials had a <u>leading coefficient</u> of 1.

> The coefficient of the term of highest degree in a polynomial is called the **leading coefficient.**
>
> The leading coefficient of $x - 2x^2 - 5$ is -2.

P-1 **What is the leading coefficient in each polynomial below?**

a. $5x^3 - 2x^2 + 3x - 7$ 5 **b.** $x - 5$ 1 **c.** $2x^3 - x^4 + 3$ −1

Example 1 reviews multiplying two binomials.

example 1   Multiply: $(2x + 1)(x + 3)$

Solution:

1. Distributive Property ⟶ $(2x + 1)(x + 3) = (2x + 1)x + (2x + 1)3$

2. Distributive Property ⟶ $= 2x^2 + x + 6x + 3$

3. Add like terms. ⟶ $= 2x^2 + 7x + 3$

Quadratic trinomials are factored by reversing steps 1, 2, and 3 above. The key step is in writing $2x^2 + 7x + 3$ as $2x^2 + x + 6x + 3$. You must find values for r and s in the polynomial form

$$2x^2 + rx + sx + 3$$
$$\text{or}$$
$$2x^2 + (r + s)x + 3.$$

 $2x^2 + x + 6x + 3$

> To factor a quadratic trinomial of the form $ax^2 + bx + c$, you must find two integers, r and s, that meet these conditions.
> 1. The sum of r and s equals the coefficient of the first-degree term. $(r + s = b)$
> 2. The product of r and s equals the product of the leading coefficient and the constant term. $(r \cdot s = a \cdot c)$

example 2   Factor $6x^2 + 11x - 10$.

Solution: $r + s = 11$ $rs = -60$ ◀   *Find two numbers whose sum is 11 and whose product is −60.*

1. Write all pairs of integers with product −60.   It may not be necessary for students to write all pairs. Have them check each pair of numbers as they write them.

(−1)(60)	(1)(−60)	(−2)(30)	(2)(−30)	(−3)(20)	(3)(−20)
(−4)(15)	(4)(−15)	(−5)(12)	(5)(−12)	(−6)(10)	(6)(−10)

2. Select the pair with a sum of 11. ⟶ $r = -4$ and $s = 15$
3. Write in the form $6x^2 + rx + sx - 10$. ⟶ $6x^2 + 11x - 10 = (6x^2 - 4x) + (15x - 10)$
4. Factor each binomial. ⟶ $= 2x(3x - 2) + 5(3x - 2)$
5. Distributive Property ⟶ $= (2x + 5)(3x - 2)$

example 3   Factor $2x^2 + 7x + 3$.

Solution: $r + s = 7$ $rs = 6$ ◀ $2x^2 + 7x + 3 =$ $2x^2 + (r + s)x + 3$

1. Write all pairs of integers with product 6.

     (1)(6)   (2)(3)   (−1)(−6)   (−2)(−3)

2. Select the pair with a sum of 7. ⟶ $r = 1$ and $s = 6$
3. $2x^2 + 7x + 3 = (2x^2 + x) + (6x + 3)$
4. $= x(2x + 1) + 3(2x + 1)$
5. $= (x + 3)(2x + 1)$

example 4   Factor $12x^2 - 11x + 2$.

Solution: $r + s = -11$ $rs = 24$

1.

(1)(24)	(2)(12)	(3)(8)	(4)(6)	*Pairs of integers with product 24*
(−1)(−24)	(−2)(−12)	(−3)(−8)	(−4)(−6)	

2. $r = -3$ and $s = -8$
3. $12x^2 - 11x + 2 = (12x^2 - 3x) + (-8x + 2)$
4. $= 3x(4x - 1) - 2(4x - 1)$
5. $= (3x - 2)(4x - 1)$

CLASSROOM EXERCISES

Tell the value of r + s. Then tell the value of rs. (Examples 2–4)

1. $2x^2 + 3x + 1$ 3; 2

2. $2x^2 + 5x + 2$ 5; 4

3. $3x^2 + 10x + 3$ 10; 9

4. $3x^2 + 7x + 2$ 7; 6

5. $3x^2 + 11x + 6$ 11; 18

6. $3x^2 + 14x + 15$ ⎞

7. $6x^2 + 11x + 3$ 11; 18

8. $6x^2 + 7x + 2$ 7; 12

9. $6x^2 + 17x + 5$ ⎟

10. $6x^2 + 13x + 6$ 13; 36

11. $3x^2 - x - 2$ −1; −6

12. $3x^2 - 5x - 2$ ⎟ See below.

13. $2x^2 - 5x - 25$ −5; −50

14. $2x^2 - 3x - 9$ −3; −18

15. $15x^2 - 7x - 2$ ⎠

16. $15x^2 + 4x - 4$ 4; −60

17. $6x^2 - 17x + 12$ −17; 72

18. $10x^2 - 29x + 10$
    −29; 100

6. 14; 45   9. 17; 30   12. −5; −6   15. −7; −30

WRITTEN EXERCISES

See the Teacher's Manual for the suggested assignments.

Goal: To factor trinomials of the form $ax^2 + bx + c$

Sample Problem: $10x^2 - 11x - 6$

Answer: $(5x + 2)(2x - 3)$

Multiply. (Example 1)

1. $(2x - 1)(x - 1)$
   $2x^2 - 3x + 1$

2. $(2x - 1)(x - 2)$
   $2x^2 - 5x + 2$

3. $(3x - 2)(x + 1)$
   $3x^2 + x - 2$

4. $(3x - 1)(x + 2)$
   $3x^2 + 5x - 2$

Factor. (Examples 2–4)

5. $2x^2 + 3x + 1$ $(2x + 1)(x + 1)$

6. $2x^2 + 5x + 2$ $(2x + 1)(x + 2)$

7. $3x^2 + 10x + 3$
   $(3x + 1)(x + 3)$

8. $3x^2 + 7x + 2$ $(3x + 1)(x + 2)$

9. $3x^2 + 11x + 6$ $(3x + 2)(x + 3)$

10. $3x^2 + 14x + 15$ ⎞

11. $6x^2 + 11x + 3$ $(3x + 1)(2x + 3)$

12. $6x^2 + 7x + 2$ $(3x + 2)(2x + 1)$

13. $6x^2 + 17x + 5$ ⎟

14. $6x^2 + 13x + 6$ $(3x + 2)(2x + 3)$

15. $3x^2 - x - 2$ $(3x + 2)(x - 1)$

16. $3x^2 - 5x - 2$ ⎟

17. $2x^2 - 5x - 25$ $(2x + 5)(x - 5)$

18. $2x^2 - 3x - 9$ $(2x + 3)(x - 3)$

19. $15x^2 - 7x - 2$ ⎟ See below.

20. $15x^2 + 4x - 4$ $(5x - 2)(3x + 2)$

21. $2x^2 - 7x + 6$ $(2x - 3)(x - 2)$

22. $3x^2 - 10x + 3$ ⎟

23. $8x^2 - 14x + 3$ $(4x - 1)(2x - 3)$

24. $15x^2 - 13x + 2$ $(5x - 1)(3x - 2)$

25. $2x^2 + 5x - 3$ ⎟

26. $3x^2 - 7x - 6$ $(3x + 2)(x - 3)$

27. $15x^2 + 14x - 8$ $(5x - 2)(3x + 4)$

28. $12x^2 - 7x - 5$ ⎟

29. $18x^2 + 23x + 7$ $(9x + 7)(2x + 1)$

30. $15x^2 + 11x - 12$ $(5x - 3)(3x + 4)$

31. $12x^2 - 33x - 9$ ⎠

32. $4x^2 - 29x + 7$ $(4x - 1)(x - 7)$

33. $8x^2 + 35x + 12$ $(8x + 3)(x + 4)$

34. $12x^2 + 25x + 12$
    $(4x + 3)(3x + 4)$

10. $(3x + 5)(x + 3)$ 13. $(3x + 1)(2x + 5)$ 16. $(3x + 1)(x - 2)$ 19. $(5x + 1)(3x - 2)$

22. $(3x - 1)(x - 3)$ 25. $(2x - 1)(x + 3)$ 28. $(12x + 5)(x - 1)$ 31. $(12x + 3)(x - 3)$ or $3(4x + 1)(x - 3)$

MID-CHAPTER REVIEW

NOTE: After completing the Mid-Chapter Review, you may want to administer a quiz covering the same sections. See pages M-28 and M-29 of the Teacher's Manual for the suggested quiz.

Factor. (Section 10.1)

1. $12x^2 - 4x$
$4x(3x - 1)$

2. $-5x^3 - 10x^2$
$-5x^2(x + 2)$

3. $3x^3 + 9x^2 - 15x$
$3x(x^2 + 3x - 5)$

4. $4x^4 - 12x^2 - 2x$
$2x(2x^3 - 6x - 1)$

5. $2x^2y + 6xy$
$2xy(x + 3)$

6. $3xy^2 - 9x^2y$
$3xy(y - 3x)$

7. $5x^3y - 10x^2y + 25x^2y^2$
$5x^2y(x - 2 + 5y)$

8. $12rs^2t - 6r^2st^2$
$(6rst(2s - rt)$

Factor. (Section 10.2)

9. $x^2 + 12x + 35$
$(x + 5)(x + 7)$

10. $x^2 + 15x + 54$
$(x + 9)(x + 6)$

11. $x^2 + 15x + 50$
$(x + 5)(x + 10)$

12. $x^2 + 16x + 48$
$(x + 4)(x + 12)$

Factor. (Section 10.3)

13. $x^2 + 3x - 40$
$(x + 8)(x - 5)$

14. $x^2 - 16x + 60$
$(x - 6)(x - 10)$

15. $x^2 - 3x - 88$
$(x - 11)(x + 8)$

16. $x^2 - 2x - 63$
$(x - 9)(x + 7)$

17. $x^2 + 6x - 72$
$(x + 12)(x - 6)$

18. $x^2 + x - 72$
$(x + 9)(x - 8)$

19. $x^2 - 20x + 99$
$(x - 11)(x - 9)$

20. $x^2 - x - 99$
Prime

Factor. (Section 10.4)

21. $2x^2 + x - 6$
$(2x - 3)(x + 2)$

22. $8x^2 - 6x - 5$
$(2x + 1)(4x - 5)$

23. $20x^2 - 3x - 2$
$(4x + 1)(5x - 2)$

24. $6x^2 - 19x - 20$
$(6x + 5)(x - 4)$

 —————— *FORMULA FOR FINDING A SUM* ——————

The formula for the sum of the first n counting numbers is $S = \dfrac{n(n + 1)}{2}$.
Thus, if $n = 4$ then,

$$S = \frac{4(4 + 1)}{2} \quad \text{or} \quad 10.$$
 $1 + 2 + 3 + 4 = 10$

EXAMPLE Find the sum of the first 853 counting numbers.

SOLUTION $n = 853$ $\qquad S = \dfrac{853(853 + 1)}{2} \quad \text{or} \quad \dfrac{853(854)}{2}$

$\boxed{8}\ \boxed{5}\ \boxed{3}\ \boxed{\times}\ \boxed{8}\ \boxed{5}\ \boxed{4}\ \boxed{\div}\ \boxed{2}\ \boxed{=}$ $\qquad$ **$364231.$**

Find the sum of the first n counting numbers for the given value of n.

1. 6   21
2. 12   78
3. 20   210
4. 30   465
5. 90   4,095
6. 500   125,250
7. 1000   500,500

REVIEW CAPSULE FOR SECTION 10.5

Factor. (Section 10.2)

1. $(x^2 + 12x) - (12x + 144)$
$(x + 12)(x - 12)$

2. $(x^2 + 2xy) - (2xy + 4y^2)$
$(x + 2y)(x - 2y)$

3. $4x^2 - 6x + 6x - 9$
$(2x + 3)(2x - 3)$

Factoring Polynomials / **247**

10.5 Difference of Two Squares

OBJECTIVES: To write the product of two binomials of the form $(a + b)$ and $(a - b)$
To factor a binomial that is the difference of two squares

A binomial such as $x^2 - 16$ is called a **difference of two squares.**

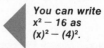
You can write $x^2 - 16$ as $(x)^2 - (4)^2$.

The first term and the absolute value of the constant term are perfect squares.

P-1 **Which polynomials below represent the difference of two squares?**

a. $x^2 - 4$ **b.** $x^3 - 9$ **c.** $x^4 - 1$ **d.** $x^2 + 25$ *a and c*

The product of two special binomials suggests how to factor a difference of two squares.

example 1   Multiply: $(x + a)(x - a)$

Solution: $(x + a)(x - a) = x^2 + ax - ax - a^2$

$= x^2 - a^2$ **◄** *Difference of two squares*

P-2 **What are the binomial factors of $x^2 - a^2$?** $(x + a)(x - a)$

You may want to mention that the sum of two squares is not factorable.

The prime factorization of a binomial such as $x^2 - a^2$ is $(x + a)(x - a)$. $x^2 - 49 = (x + 7)(x - 7)$

P-3 **What is the positive square root of 121?**   11

example 2   Factor $x^2 - 121$.

Solution: $x^2 - 121 = (x + 11)(x - 11)$ **◄** *(Sum of square roots) times (Difference of square roots)*

example 3 · Factor $x^4 - 9$.

Solution: Both x^4 and 9 are perfect squares. You can write x^4 as $(x^2)^2$ and 9 as 3^2.

$$x^4 - 9 = (x^2 + 3)(x^2 - 3)$$

example 4 · Factor $4x^2 - 9y^2$.

Solution: You can write $4x^2$ as $(2x)^2$ and $9y^2$ as $(3y)^2$.

$$4x^2 - 9y^2 = (2x + 3y)(2x - 3y)$$

P-4 **Simplify.**

a. $\sqrt{x^6}$ **b.** $\sqrt{r^8}$ **c.** $\sqrt{t^{12}}$

x^3 r^4 t^6

> **Any power with an even exponent is a perfect square.**

example 5 · Factor $x^{10} - y^8$.

Write one factor as a sum of square roots. ⟶ **Write one factor as a difference of square roots.**

Solution: $$x^{10} - y^8 = (x^5 + y^4)(x^5 - y^4)$$

> To factor the difference of squares, write one factor as the sum of square roots and the other factor as the difference of square roots.

6. $(a + 6)(a - 6)$
7. $(t + 7)(t - 7)$
8. $(x + 8)(x - 8)$
9. $(b + 9)(b - 9)$
10. $(x + 10)(x - 10)$

CLASSROOM EXERCISES

Factor. (Examples 2–4)

$(a + 1)(a - 1)$ $(a + 2)(a - 2)$ $(p + 3)(p - 3)$ $(r + 4)(r - 4)$ $(x + 5)(x - 5)$
1. $a^2 - 1$ **2.** $y^2 - 4$ **3.** $p^2 - 9$ **4.** $r^2 - 16$ **5.** $x^2 - 25$

6. $a^2 - 36$ See above.   **7.** $t^2 - 49$ See above.   **8.** $x^2 - 64$ See above.   **9.** $b^2 - 81$ See above.   **10.** $x^2 - 100$ See above.

11. $p^2 - q^2$ **12.** $c^2 - d^2$ **13.** $4x^2 - y^2$ **14.** $x^2 - 9y^2$ **15.** $x^4 - 25$
$(p + q)(p - q)$ $(c + d)(c - d)$ $(2x + y)(2x - y)$ $(x + 3y)(x - 3y)$ $(x^2 + 5)(x^2 - 5)$

WRITTEN EXERCISES

Goal: To factor the difference of two squares
Sample Problem: $25a^2 - 9b^2$ 3. $x^2 - 121$ 6. $9a^2 - b^2$ 9. $25x^2 - 9$
Answer: $(5a + 3b)(5a - 3b)$ 12. $y^4 - 9$ 16. $(3y + 1)(3y - 1)$ 20. $(y^2 + 3)(y^2 - 3)$

Multiply. (Example 1)

1. $(x - 8)(x + 8)$ $x^2 - 64$
2. $(x - 9)(x + 9)$ $x^2 - 81$
3. $(x + 11)(x - 11)$ See above.

4. $(x + 12)(x - 12)$ $x^2 - 144$
5. $(2x - y)(2x + y)$ $4x^2 - y^2$
6. $(3a - b)(3a + b)$ See above.

7. $(xy - 3)(xy + 3)$ $x^2y^2 - 9$
8. $(rs - 5)(rs + 5)$ $r^2s^2 - 25$
9. $(5x + 3)(5x - 3)$ See above.

10. $(4x + 3)(4x - 3)$ $16x^2 - 9$
11. $(x^2 + 2)(x^2 - 2)$ $x^4 - 4$
12. $(y^2 + 3)(y^2 - 3)$ See above.

Factor. (Examples 2-5) 24. $(4a + 3b)(4a - 3b)$ 28. $(5r + 4)(5r - 4)$ 32. $(3ab^2 + 5)(3ab^2 - 5)$

13. $a^2 - 25$ $(a + 5)(a - 5)$
14. $y^2 - 36$ $(y + 6)(y - 6)$
15. $4x^2 - 1$ $(2x + 1)(2x - 1)$
16. $9y^2 - 1$ See above.

17. $9a^2 - 16$
$(3a + 4)(3a - 4)$
18. $4b^2 - 25$
$(2b + 5)(2b - 5)$
19. $x^4 - 4$ $(x^2 + 2)(x^2 - 2)$
20. $y^4 - 9$ See above.

21. $4x^4 - 9$
$(2x^2 + 3)(2x^2 - 3)$
22. $9a^4 - 1$
$(3a^2 + 1)(3a^2 - 1)$
23. $4x^2 - y^2$
$(2x + y)(2x - y)$
24. $16a^2 - 9b^2$ See above.

25. $a^2b^2 - 1$
$(ab + 1)(ab - 1)$
26. $x^2y^2 - 4$
$(xy + 2)(xy - 2)$
27. $16t^2 - 81$
$(4t + 9)(4t - 9)$
28. $25r^2 - 16$ See above.

29. $x^2y^2 - r^2$
$(xy + r)(xy - r)$
30. $a^2b^2 - c^2$
$(ab + c)(ab - c)$
31. $16x^2y^4 - 9$
$(4xy^2 + 3)(4xy^2 - 3)$
32. $9a^2b^4 - 25$ See above.

33. $x^6 - 4$
$(x^3 + 2)(x^3 - 2)$
34. $a^6 - 9$
$(a^3 + 3)(a^3 - 3)$
35. $x^{10} - y^8$
$(x^5 + y^4)(x^5 - y^4)$
36. $r^8 - s^{14}$
$(r^4 + s^7)(r^4 - s^7)$

MORE CHALLENGING EXERCISES

Multiply by the method shown in the example below.

EXAMPLE: $(19)(21) = (20 - 1)(20 + 1)$
$= 400 - 1 = 399$

37. $(14)(16)$ 224
38. $(15)(17)$ 255
39. $(11)(15)$ 165
40. $(14)(18)$
252

41. $(22)(18)$ 396
42. $(23)(17)$ 391
43. $(26)(34)$ 884
44. $(36)(44)$
1584

45. $(43)(37)$ 1591
46. $(54)(46)$ 2484
47. $(59)(61)$ 3599
48. $(89)(91)$
8099

REVIEW CAPSULE FOR SECTION 10.6

Multiply. (Section 9.5)

1. $(x + 6)(x + 6)$
$x^2 + 12x + 36$
2. $(x - 3)(x - 3)$
$x^2 - 6x + 9$
3. $(2x - 5)(2x - 5)$
$4x^2 - 20x + 25$
4. $(5x + 1)(5x + 1)$
$20x^2 + 9x + 1$

5. $(2x + 7)(2x + 7)$
$4x^2 + 28x + 49$
6. $(x - y)(x - y)$
$x^2 - 2xy + y^2$
7. $(3x + 2)(3x + 2)$
$9x^2 + 12x + 4$
8. $(5x - 1)^2$
$25x^2 + 10x + 1$

10.6 Trinomial Squares

OBJECTIVES: To identify whether or not a trinomial is a perfect square
To square a binomial
To factor a perfect square trinomial

A trinomial such as $x^2 + 6x + 9$ is called a **trinomial square** because it has two equal binomial factors.

$$x^2 + 6x + 9 = (x + 3)(x + 3)$$

A trinomial of the form $ax^2 + bx + c$ is a trinomial square if <u>both</u> of the following conditions are true.

1. ax^2 and c are perfect squares.
2. $(\frac{1}{2}b)^2 = ac$

In $x^2 + 6x + 9$, both x^2 and 9 are perfect squares.

P-1   **What is the value of $\frac{1}{2}b$?** ³ **of $(\frac{1}{2}b)^2$?** ⁹ **of ac?** ⁹

You can see that $x^2 + 6x + 9$ meets both conditions.

example 1

Write <u>Yes</u> or <u>No</u> to show whether $4x^2 - 20x + 25$ is a trinomial square.

Solution: ☐1 $4x^2$ and 25 are both perfect squares.

$$4x^2 = (2x)(2x) \qquad 25 = (5)(5)$$

☐2 "$(\frac{1}{2}b)^2 = ac$" is true.

$(\frac{1}{2}b)^2 = (\frac{1}{2} \cdot -20)^2 \qquad ac = 4 \cdot 25$

Explain that $4x^2 - 20x - 25$ is not a trinomial square. Students often have trouble with this concept.

$= (-10)^2 \qquad\qquad = 100$

$= 100$

<u>Yes</u>, $4x^2 - 20x + 25$ is a trinomial square.

◀ *A trinomial square is also called a "perfect square trinomial."*

example 2

Factor $4x^2 - 20x + 25$.   *This is a trinomial square.*

Solution:

☐1 Write the first term of each binomial as a square root of $4x^2$. ⟶ $4x^2 - 20x + 25 = (2x\quad)(2x\quad)$

☐2 Write the second term as a square root of 25. ⟶ $= (2x\quad 5)(2x\quad 5)$

☐3 Write each binomial as a difference. ⟶ $= (2x - 5)(2x - 5)$

P-2 **Why is each factor of Example 2 a difference?** The value of b is negative.

P-3 **Multiply.**

a. $(2x + 5)(2x + 5)$ **b.** $(x - 7)(x - 7)$ **c.** $(3x - 1)(3x - 1)$
$4x^2 + 20x + 25$ $x^2 - 14x + 49$ $9x^2 - 6x + 1$

Trinomials in more than one variable can be trinomial squares.

example 3   Factor $x^2y^2 + 8xy + 16$.

Solution: 1 x^2y^2 and 16 are perfect squares. $x^2y^2 + 8xy + 16$ **is a trinomial square.**

          2   "$(\frac{1}{2} \cdot 8)^2 = 1 \cdot 16$" is true.

              $x^2y^2 + 8xy + 16 = (xy + 4)(xy + 4)$ **To check, multiply the factors.**

P-4 **Factor.**

a. $x^2 + 2x + 1$ **b.** $x^2 - 12x + 36$ **c.** $9x^2 - 24x + 16$
$(x + 1),(x + 1)$ $(x - 6),(x - 6)$ $(3x - 4),(3x - 4)$

CLASSROOM EXERCISES

Write Yes or No to tell whether each trinomial is a trinomial square.
(Example 1)

1. $16x^2 + 8x + 1$ Yes   2. $x^2 + 9x - 16$ No   3. $x^2 + 10x + 25$ Yes

4. $x^2 + 4x + 3$ No   5. $x^2 - 2x + 1$ Yes   6. $100 - 20x + x^2$ Yes

7. $x^2 - 49x + 14$ No   8. $x^2 + 20x + 100$ Yes   9. $2x^2 + 8x - 8$ No

10. $2x^2 - 8x + 8$ No   11. $81x^2 + 50x + 3$ No   12. $64x^2 + 48x + 9$ Yes

Factor each trinomial square. (Example 2)

13. $x^2 + 4x + 4$ $(x + 2)(x + 2)$ 14. $x^2 - 2x + 1$ $(x - 1)(x - 1)$

15. $x^2 - 6x + 9$ $(x - 3)(x - 3)$ 16. $x^2 - 10x + 25$ $(x - 5)(x - 5)$

17. $x^2 + 16x + 64$ $(x + 8)(x + 8)$ 18. $x^2 + 18x + 81$ $(x + 9)(x + 9)$

19. $x^2 - 24x + 144$ $(x - 12)(x - 12)$ 20. $x^2 - 14x + 49$ $(x - 7)(x - 7)$

21. $4x^2 + 4x + 1$ $(2x + 1)(2x + 1)$ 22. $25x^2 - 20x + 4$ $(5x - 2)(5x - 2)$

WRITTEN EXERCISES

Goal: To factor trinomial squares
Sample Problem: $4x^2 - 20x + 25$ **Answer:** $(2x - 5)(2x - 5)$

Write Yes or No to show whether each trinomial is a trinomial square.
(Example 1)

1. $x^2 - 8x + 25$ No
2. $x^2 + 10x + 36$ No
3. $x^2 - 22x + 121$ Yes

4. $x^2 - 14x + 49$ Yes
5. $x^2 + 14x - 49$ No
6. $x^2 + 16x - 64$ No

7. $2x^2 - 12x + 25$ No
8. $3x^2 - 22x + 36$ No
9. $9x^2 + 18x + 1$ No

10. $16x^2 + 32x + 1$ No
11. $4x^2 - 4x + 1$ Yes
12. $5x^2 - 10x + 25$ No

Multiply. (P-3)

13. $(x - 5)(x - 5)$ $x^2 - 10x + 25$
14. $(x - 3)(x - 3)$ $x^2 - 6x + 9$
15. $(x + 7)(x + 7)$ $x^2 + 14x + 49$

16. $(x + 9)(x + 9)$ $x^2 + 18x + 81$
17. $(2x + 3)(2x + 3)$ $4x^2 + 12x + 9$
18. $(3x + 2)(3x + 2)$ $9x^2 + 12x + 4$

19. $(5x - 1)(5x - 1)$ $25x^2 - 10x + 1$
20. $(4x - 3)(4x - 3)$ $16x^2 - 24x + 9$
21. $(4x + 5)^2$ $16x^2 + 40x + 25$

22. $(6x + 5)^2$ $36x^2 + 60x + 25$
23. $(2x - 1)^2$ $4x^2 - 4x + 1$
24. $(3x - 7)^2$ $9x^2 - 42x + 49$

Factor. (Examples 2–3)

25. $36x^2 - 12x + 1$ $(6x - 1)(6x - 1)$
26. $25x^2 - 10x + 1$ $(5x - 1)(5x - 1)$
27. $25x^2 + 20x + 4$ $(5x + 2)(5x + 2)$

28. $16x^2 + 24x + 9$ $(4x + 3)(4x + 3)$
29. $9x^2 - 24x + 16$ $(3x - 4)(3x - 4)$
30. $4x^2 - 20x + 25$ $(2x - 5)(2x - 5)$

31. $49x^2 + 140x + 100$ $(7x + 10)(7x + 10)$
32. $36x^2 + 84x + 49$ $(6x + 7)(6x + 7)$
33. $49x^2 - 14x + 1$ $(7x - 1)(7x - 1)$

34. $81x^2 + 18x + 1$ $(9x + 1)(9x + 1)$
35. $x^2 + 4xy + 4y^2$ $(x + 2y)(x + 2y)$
36. $x^2 + 6xy + 9y^2$ $(x + 3y)(x + 3y)$

37. $4x^2 + 12xy + 9y^2$ $(2x + 3y)(2x + 3y)$
38. $16x^2 + 40xy + 25y^2$ $(4x + 5y)(4x + 5y)$
39. $x^2y^2 - 16xy + 64$ $(xy - 8)(xy - 8)$

40. $4x^2y^2 - 20xy + 25$ $(2xy - 5)(2xy - 5)$
41. $9x^2y^2 + 42xy + 49$ $(3xy + 7)(3xy + 7)$
42. $x^2y^2 - 2xy + 1$ $(xy - 1)(xy - 1)$

REVIEW CAPSULE FOR SECTION 10.7

Match each polynomial with its prime factors. (Sections 10.1–10.6)

1. $4x^2 - 8x + 3$ B
2. $4x^2 - 10x - 6$ D
3. $4x^2 + 4x - 3$ A
4. $4x^2 - 9$ C

A. $(2x + 3)(2x - 1)$
B. $(2x - 3)(2x - 1)$
C. $(2x - 3)(2x + 3)$
D. $2(x - 3)(2x + 1)$

10.7 Combined Types of Factoring

OBJECTIVE: To write the prime factors of a polynomial by using one or more factoring methods

You have learned the following ways of factoring polynomials.

1. Common monomial factoring
2. Factoring the difference of two squares
3. Factoring quadratic trinomials
4. Factoring trinomial squares

When you factor a polynomial always write it as a product of prime polynomial factors.

In factoring a polynomial, always look for a common monomial factor as the <u>first</u> step.

P-1 **What is a common monomial factor of $2x^2 - 32$?** 2

example 1   Factor $2x^2 - 32$.

Solution:

1. Write the common monomial factor. ⟶ $2x^2 - 32 = 2($ $)$

2. Divide each term of $2x^2 - 32$ by 2. ⟶ $= 2(x^2 - 16)$

3. Factor $x^2 - 16$ as a difference of two squares. ⟶ $= 2(x + 4)(x - 4)$

▲ *Prime polynomial factors*

When you write a polynomial as the product of prime polynomial factors, you are factoring completely. To "factor" always means to "factor completely."

P-2 **What is a common monomial factor of $3x^2 - 6x + 3$?** 3

example 2   Factor $3x^2 - 6x + 3$.

Solution:

1. Write the common factor. ⟶ $3x^2 - 6x + 3 = 3($ $)$

2. Divide each term of $3x^2 - 6x + 3$ by 3. ⟶ $= 3(x^2 - 2x + 1)$

3. Factor $x^2 - 2x + 1$ as a trinomial square. ⟶ $= 3(x - 1)(x - 1)$

example 3   Factor $30x^2 - 5x - 10$.

Solution:

1. Use common monomial factoring. ⟶ $30x^2 - 5x - 10 = 5(6x^2 - x - 2)$

2. Determine whether $6x^2 - x - 2$ is a trinomial square. ⟶ ◄ **$6x^2 - x - 2$ is not a trinomial square.**

3. Write $-x$ as a sum. ⟶ $6x^2 - x - 2 = 6x^2 + rx + sx - 2$

4. Write all pairs of integers with product -12.

$$(-1)(12) \qquad (-2)(6) \qquad (-3)(4)$$
$$(1)(-12) \qquad (2)(-6) \qquad (3)(-4)$$

5. Select the pair with a sum of -1. ⟶ $\begin{cases} r = 3 \\ s = -4 \end{cases}$

6. $\qquad\qquad 6x^2 - x - 2 = 6x^2 + 3x - 4x - 2$

7. $\qquad\qquad\qquad\qquad = 3x(2x + 1) - 2(2x + 1)$ ◄ **Remember: 5 is also a factor of $30x^2 - 5x - 10$.**

8. $\qquad\qquad\qquad\qquad = (3x - 2)(2x + 1)$

Thus, $\quad 30x^2 - 5x - 10 = 5(6x^2 - x - 2)$
$$= 5(3x - 2)(2x + 1)$$

example 4   Factor $4x^2 - 16y^2$.

Solution: You can see that $4x^2 - 16y^2$ is a difference of two squares.

$$4x^2 - 16y^2 = 4(x^2 - 4y^2)$$ ◄ **Common monomial factor**

$$= 4(x + 2y)(x - 2y)$$

CLASSROOM EXERCISES

Tell the common factor. Then divide each term by it. (P-1, P-2)

1. $4x^2 - 12$ $4; (x^2 - 3)$

2. $3x^2 + 6x + 6$ $3; (x^2 + 2x + 2)$

3. $4x^2 - 20x + 28$ $4; (x^2 - 5x + 7)$

4. $2x^2 - 8x + 12$ $2; (x^2 - 4x + 6)$

5. $15x^2 - 5x - 25$ $5; (3x^2 - x - 5)$

6. $16x^2 - 64$ $16; (x^2 - 4)$

Write the common factor. Then divide each term by it. (P-1, P-2)

7. $x^2y^2 - 3xy + 5y$ $\quad y; (x^2y - 3x + 5)$

8. $ax^2 - 3ax + 12a$ $\quad a; (x^2 - 3x + 12)$

9. $-4x^2 - 20$ $\quad -4; (x^2 + 5)$

10. $12ax^2 + 3a$ $\quad 3a; (4x^2 + 1)$

11. $3a^2b^2 - 9ab + 6b$ $\quad 3b; (a^2b - 3a + 2)$

12. $24 - 36x^2$ $\quad 12; (2 - 3x^2)$

13. $3x^2y - 30xy + 75y$ $\quad 3y; (x^2 - 10x + 25)$

14. $-12x^2y - 14xy + 6y$ $\quad -2y; (6x^2 + 7x - 3)$

WRITTEN EXERCISES

See the Teacher's Manual for the suggested assignments.

Goal: To factor polynomials using more than one type of factoring

Sample Problem: $2a^2b^2 + 14a^2b + 24a^2$

Answer: $2a^2(b + 4)(b + 3)$

3. $2(x+2)(x+2)$ 6. $3(x + 7)(x + 5)$
9. $5(x - 5)(x + 4)$ 12. $(xy + 4)(xy - 4)$

Factor. Remember factors should be prime polynomials. (Examples 1–4)

1. $2y^2 - 18$ $\quad 2(y + 3)(y - 3)$

2. $2a^2 - 50$ $\quad 2(a + 5)(a - 5)$

3. $2x^2 + 8x + 8$

4. $2x^2 + 4x + 2$ $\quad 2(x + 1)(x + 1)$

5. $3x^2 + 30x + 63$ $\quad 3(x + 7)(x + 3)$

6. $3x^2 + 36x + 105$

7. $4x^2 - 40x + 96$ $\quad 4(x - 6)(x - 4)$

8. $5x^2 - 55x + 150$ $\quad 5(x - 6)(x - 5)$

9. $5x^2 - 5x - 100$

10. $3x^2 - 3x - 36$ $\quad 3(x - 4)(x + 3)$

11. $4y^2 - 9$ $\quad (2y + 3)(2y - 3)$

12. $x^2y^2 - 16$

} See above

13. $ax^2 + 4ax + 4a$ $\quad a(x + 2)(x + 2)$

14. $x^2y + 6xy + 9y$ $\quad y(x + 3)(x + 3)$

15. $6x^2 - 10x - 4$

16. $6x^2 - 2x - 4$ $\quad 2(3x + 2)(x - 1)$

17. $12x^2 - 40x + 12$ $\quad 4(3x - 1)(x - 3)$

18. $20x^2 - 70x + 60$

19. $-3x^2 - 12$ $\quad -3(x^2 + 4)$

20. $-5a^2 - 125$ $\quad -5(a^2 + 25)$

21. $4ax^2 - 9a$

22. $8ab^2 - 18a$ $\quad 2a(2b + 3)(2b - 3)$

23. $x^2y - 10xy + 25y$ $\quad y(x - 5)(x - 5)$

24. $a^2b^2 - 6a^2b + 9a^2$

} See below

25. $3x^2 - 75$ $\quad 3(x + 5)(x - 5)$

26. $27y^2 - 3$ $\quad 3(3y + 1)(3y - 1)$

27. $32 - 16d + 2d^2$

28. $-36 + 15a^2 - 12a$ $\quad 3(5a + 6)(a - 2)$

29. $3x^2 - 6x - 24$ $\quad 3(x - 4)(x + 2)$

30. $10y^2 - 26y + 12$

31. $2 - 128x^2$ $\quad 2(1 + 8x)(1 - 8x)$

32. $x^3 - x$ $\quad x(x + 1)(x - 1)$

33. $ab^2 - ab - 20a$

34. $pq^2 + p^2q^2 - p$ $\quad p(q^2 + pq^2 - 1)$

35. $24a^2 - 30a + 9$ $\quad 3(2a - 1)(4a - 3)$

36. $30a^2 - 5a - 10$

MORE CHALLENGING EXERCISES

15. $2(3x + 1)(x - 2)$ 18. $10(x - 2)(2x - 3)$
21. $a(2x + 3)(2x - 3)$ 24. $a^2(b - 3)(b - 3)$

37. $4a^2b^2 + 4abc + c^2$ $\quad (2ab + c)(2ab + c)$

38. $9x^2y^2 - 30xy + 25$ $\quad (3xy - 5)(3xy - 5)$

39. $32x^2y^4 - 18t^2$ $\quad 2(4xy^2 + 3t)(4xy^2 - 3t)$

40. $50a^2b^2 - 2c^4$ $\quad 2(5ab + c^2)(5ab - c^2)$

41. $30x^2 - 22x + 4$ $\quad 2(5x - 2)(3x - 1)$

42. $20x^2 - 54x + 10$ $\quad 2(5x - 1)(2x - 5)$

43. $10x^2y^3 - 12x^3y^4 + 18x^2y^2$ $\quad 2x^2y^2(5y - 6xy^2 + 9)$

44. $9a^3b^3 + 15ab^2 - 21a^2b^2$ $\quad 3ab^2(3a^2b - 7a + 5)$

27. $2(4 - d)(4 - d)$ 30. $2(5y - 3)(y - 2)$
33. $a(b - 5)(b + 4)$ 36. $5(2a + 1)(3a - 2)$

Life Scientist

Life scientists are specialists in living things. Since biology is the science of life, many life scientists call themselves biologists. However, most are named by the type of living thing that they study or by the nature of the work that they perform. Some life scientist careers are agronomist, biochemist, botanist, horticulturist, microbiologist, nutritionist, and zoologist.

In the study of genetics, life scientists learn that the traits of parents are transmitted to their offspring by tiny particles called genes. Each living thing has two genes for each trait — one gene from each parent.

The genes for tall and short pea plants are represented below.

TT Pure tall T = gene for tallness
tt Pure short t = gene for shortness
Tt Hybrid tall

When a pure tall pea plant and a pure short pea plant are crossed, all offspring are hybrid tall.

Suppose that two hybrid tall pea plants are mated. This problem is related to the algebra problem of squaring a binomial.

Let $(\frac{1}{2}T + \frac{1}{2}t)$ represent the two genes for tallness and shortness in each hybrid tall pea plant. Then

$$(\tfrac{1}{2}T + \tfrac{1}{2}t)(\tfrac{1}{2}T + \tfrac{1}{2}t) = \tfrac{1}{4}TT + \tfrac{1}{2}Tt + \tfrac{1}{4}tt.$$

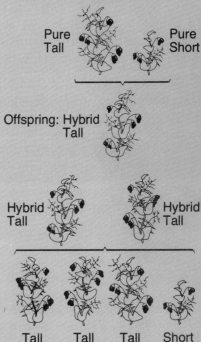

This result indicates the following probabilities.

The probability is $\frac{1}{4}$ that an offspring will be pure tall (TT).
This means that, over a long enough period of time, you can expect about one fourth of all such offspring to be pure tall.

The probability is $\frac{1}{2}$ that an offspring will be hybrid tall (Tt).
That is, over a long period of time about one half of all such offspring can be expected to be hybrid tall.

The probability is $\frac{1}{4}$ that an offspring will be pure short (tt).

EXAMPLE 1: There are 24 offspring of two hybrid tall parent pea plants. Find the probable number of each type.

SOLUTION: Refer to the trinomial on page 257.

$$\frac{1}{4}TT + \frac{1}{2}Tt + \frac{1}{4}tt \begin{cases} \frac{1}{4} \times 24 = 6 \text{ pure tall} \\ \frac{1}{2} \times 24 = 12 \text{ hybrid tall} \\ \frac{1}{4} \times 24 = 6 \text{ pure short} \end{cases}$$

Since this is merely the *probable* distribution, you would not expect always to obtain exactly these numbers of the various types.

In guinea pigs a rough coat R is **dominant** to a smooth coat r. This means that guinea pigs will have coats as shown below according to their genes.

RR: Rough coat Rr: Rough coat rr: Smooth coat

EXAMPLE 2: A guinea pig with a pure coat (RR) is mated with a guinea pig that is hybrid for its coat (Rr). There are 36 offspring of these parents. Find the probable number of each type.

SOLUTION: $(\frac{1}{2}R + \frac{1}{2}R)(\frac{1}{2}R + \frac{1}{2}r) = \frac{1}{4}RR + \frac{1}{4}Rr + \frac{1}{4}RR + \frac{1}{4}Rr$

$$= \frac{1}{2}RR + \frac{1}{2}Rr$$

$\frac{1}{2} \times 36 = 18$ rough coat (RR) $\frac{1}{2} \times 36 = 18$ rough coat (Rr)

All of the offspring will have rough coats.

E X E R C I S E S

There are 128 offspring of two pea plants. Find the probable number of pure tall (TT), pure short (tt), and hybrid tall (Tt) for each combination of parent plants. 1. 64 hybrid tall; 64 pure short

2. 128 pure short

1. Hybrid tall and pure short
2. Pure short and pure short
3. Pure tall and hybrid short
4. Hybrid tall and pure short

64 pure tall; 64 hybrid tall   64 hybrid tall; 64 pure short

There are 56 offspring of two guinea pigs. Find the probable number of offspring with pure rough coats (RR), hybrid rough coats (Rr), and pure smooth coats (rr) for each combination of parents.

5. Hybrid rough coat; hybrid rough coat
6. Pure rough coat; pure smooth coat
7. Pure rough coat; hybrid rough coat

14 pure rough coats;
28 hybrid rough coats; **258**   56 hybrid rough coats   28 pure rough coats;
14 pure smooth coats   28 hybrid rough coats   **Career**

CHAPTER SUMMARY

IMPORTANT TERMS	Prime polynomial *(p. 234)* Quadratic polynomial *(p. 237)*

IMPORTANT TERMS

Prime polynomial *(p. 234)*
Common monomial factor *(p. 234)*
Greatest common factor *(p. 235)*
Degree of a monomial *(p. 237)*
Degree of a polynomial *(p. 237)*

Quadratic polynomial *(p. 237)*
Leading coefficient *(p. 244)*
Difference of two squares *(p. 248)*
Trinomial square *(p. 251)*

IMPORTANT IDEAS

1. In a prime polynomial the only polynomial factors with coefficients that are integers are
   a. 1 and the polynomial, and
   b. −1 and the opposite of the polynomial.

2. To factor a quadratic trinomial you must find two integers *r* and *s* meeting the following conditions.
   a. The sum of *r* and *s* equals the coefficient of the first-degree term.
   b. The product of *r* and *s* equals the product of the leading coefficient and the constant term.

3. The prime factorization of $x^2 - a^2$ is $(x + a)(x - a)$.

4. For a quadratic trinomial such as $ax^2 + bx + c$ to be a trinomial square,
   a. ax^2 and *c* must be perfect squares, and
   b. "$(\frac{1}{2}b)^2 = ac$" must be true.

5. In factoring a polynomial, always look for a common monomial factor as the first step.

CHAPTER REVIEW   NOTE: The Teacher's Resource Book contains two forms of each Chapter Test.

SECTION 10.1

Factor.

1. $4x^2 - 10x$ $2x(2x - 5)$

2. $3a^3 + 15a^2$ $3a^2(a + 5)$

3. $18a^2b + 30a^2b^2 - 42ab$ $6ab(3a + 5ab - 7)$

4. $24ax + 48ay - 96at$ $24a(x + 2y - 4t)$

5. $a^2bc^3 - ab^2c + a^2b^2c^2$ $abc(ac^2 - b + abc)$

6. $2x^5 - 4x^4 + 6x^3 - 8x^2 + 10x$

$2x(x^4 - 2x^3 + 3x^2 - 4x + 5)$

SECTION 10.2

Factor.

7. $x^2 + 7x + 3x + 21$ $(x + 7)(x + 3)$

8. $x^2 + 8x + 5x + 40$ $(x + 8)(x + 5)$

9. $x^2 + 5x + 10x + 50$ $(x + 5)(x + 10)$

10. $x^2 + 9x + 6x + 54$ $(x + 9)(x + 6)$

11. $x^2 + 10x + 21$ $(x + 7)(x + 3)$

12. $x^2 + 13x + 22$ $(x + 11)(x + 2)$

SECTION 10.3

Factor.

13. $x^2 + 3x - 18$ $(x + 6)(x - 3)$ **14.** $x^2 - x - 20$ $(x - 5)(x + 4)$ **15.** $x^2 - 9x + 18$
$(x - 6)(x - 3)$

16. $x^2 - 14x + 33$ $(x - 11)(x - 3)$ **17.** $x^2 - 5x - 81$ Prime   **18.** $x^2 - 5x - 36$
$(x - 9)(x + 4)$

SECTION 10.4

Factor.

$(4x - 1)(x + 2)$

19. $2x^2 - x - 3$ $(2x - 3)(x + 1)$ **20.** $3x^2 - 5x - 2$ $(3x + 1)(x - 2)$ **21.** $4x^2 + 7x - 2$

22. $5x^2 + 4x - 1$ $(5x - 1)(x + 1)$ **23.** $3x^2 - 2x - 5$ $(3x - 5)(x + 1)$ **24.** $4x^2 - 4x - 3$
$(2x + 1)(2x - 3)$

SECTION 10.5

Factor.

$(rs + xy)(rs - xy)$

25. $9a^2 - 16b^2$ $(3a + 4b)(3a - 4b)$ **26.** $4m^2 - 81n^2$ $(2m + 9n)(2m - 9n)$ **27.** $r^2s^2 - x^2y^2$

28. $4t^2 - 121x^2$ $(2t + 11x)(2t - 11x)$ **29.** $x^4 - 169$ $(x^2 + 13)(x^2 - 13)$ **30.** $25a^2b^4 - 144c^2$
$(5ab^2 + 12c)(5ab^2 - 12c)$

SECTION 10.6

Write Yes or No to show whether each trinomial is a trinomial square.

31. $x^2 - 12x + 36$ Yes   **32.** $x^2 + 3x + 9$ No

33. $4x^2 + 10x + 13$ No   **34.** $9x^2y^2 - 16xy + 25$ No

35. $8x^2 - 12x + 9$ No   **36.** $4x^2 - 20x + 25$ Yes

Factor.

$(2x - 3)(2x - 3)$

37. $x^2 - 8x + 16$ $(x - 4)(x - 4)$ **38.** $x^2 + 12x + 36$ $(x + 6)(x + 6)$ **39.** $4x^2 - 12x + 9$

40. $9x^2 - 6x + 1$ $(3x - 1)(3x - 1)$ **41.** $x^2 - 4xy + 4y^2$ $(x - 2y)(x - 2y)$ **42.** $16x^2 - 24x + 9$
$(4x - 3)(4x - 3)$

SECTION 10.7

Factor.

43. $5x^2 - 20$ $5(x + 2)(x - 2)$ **44.** $28x^2 - 7$ $7(2x + 1)(2x - 1)$

45. $3x^2 - 12x + 12$ $3(x - 2)(x - 2)$ **46.** $2x^2 + 4x - 70$ $2(x + 7)(x - 5)$

47. $3x^2 - 12x + 96$ $3(x^2 - 4x + 32)$ **48.** $x^2y - 2xy - 24y$ $y(x - 6)(x + 4)$

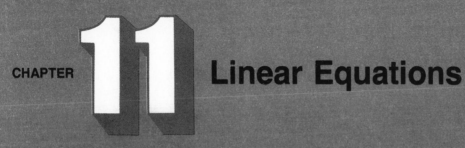

CHAPTER **11** **Linear Equations**

Sections   11.1   **Graphs of Linear Equations**

11.2   **Y Intercept**

11.3   **Slope of a Line**

11.4   **Slope Formula**

11.5   **Parallel Lines**

11.6   **X Intercept**

11.7   **Problem Solving: Linear Functions**

Features   *Calculator Exercises:* **A Paper Caper**

Special Topic Application: **Latitude and Longitude**

Review
and
Testing

Review Capsules

Mid-Chapter Review

Chapter Summary

Chapter Review

11.1 Graphs of Linear Functions

To identify from the rule of a function whether or not the function is linear

The steps for graphing a function are reviewed.

| Select values for x. | → | Compute the y values. | → | Graph the ordered pairs. | → | Draw a line containing the points. |

example 1

Draw a graph of $\{(x, y) : y = 2x - 1\}$. The domain is {real numbers}.

Solution: $y = 2x - 1$ ◀ **Rule** for the **function**

x	−2	−1	0	1	2
y	−5	−3	−1	1	3

If $x = -2$, $y = 2(-2) - 1$
$= -5.$

If $x = -1$, $y = 2(-1) - 1$
$= -3.$

If $x = 0$, $y = 2(0) - 1$
$= -1.$

If $x = 1$, $y = 2(1) - 1$
$= 1.$

If $x = 2$, $y = 2(2) - 1$
$= 3.$

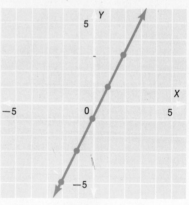

Figure 1

These ordered pairs are graphed in Figure 1. The points lie on a line.

P-1   **What are the coordinates of some other points on the line?**
(3, 5), (−4, −9), etc.

P-2   **How do you know whether (3, 5) belongs to this function?**
Substitute 3 for x and 5 for y in y = 2x − 1.

1 Replace x with 3. ────────────→ $y = 2(3) - 1$

2 Solve for y. ────────────→ $y = 5$

Thus, (3, 5) belongs to the function. The point (3, 5) lies on the graph of Figure 1.

example 2

Draw a graph of $\{(x, y) : y = -\frac{1}{2}x + 2\}$.

Solution: When the domain is not given, assume that it is {real numbers}.

$$y = -\frac{1}{2}x + 2$$

$$y = -\frac{1}{2}(-4) + 2 = 4$$

$$y = -\frac{1}{2}(-2) + 2 = 3$$

$$y = -\frac{1}{2}(0) + 2 = \underline{\quad?\quad}$$

$$y = -\frac{1}{2}(2) + 2 = \underline{\quad?\quad}$$

$$y = -\frac{1}{2}(4) + 2 = \underline{\quad?\quad}$$

x	−4	−2	0	2	4
y	4	3	?	?	?

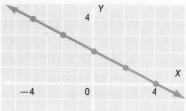

The graph of the function is shown in Figure 2.

Figure 2

A function that has the points of its graph lying in a nonvertical straight line is a ***linear function.***

You will want to explain that a vertical line can be the graph of a relation but not a function.

The rule for a linear function is **y = ax + b** (*a* and *b* are real numbers.)

$\{(x, y) : y = 3x + 5\}$

$\{(x, y) : y = -\frac{5}{2}x + \sqrt{3}\}$

P-3 **What are the values of *a* and *b* in the rule $y = -x + \frac{1}{2}$? in the rule $y = \frac{2}{3}x - \frac{1}{4}$? in the rule $y = 10 - 3x$?** $a: -3; b: 10$ $a: -1; b: \frac{1}{2}$

$a: \frac{2}{3}; b: -\frac{1}{4}$

P-4 **Which functions below are linear?**   *Functions a and b*

a. $y = 2x + 5$ **b.** $y = x - 3$ **c.** $y = x^2 + 1$ **d.** $y = \sqrt{x}$

CLASSROOM EXERCISES

Write the y values that are missing from each table. (Examples 1 and 2)

1. $\{(x, y) : y = 3x\}$

x	−2	−1	0	2
y	?	?	?	?
	−6	−3	0	6

2. $\{(x, y) : y = x + 3\}$

x	−5	−2	0	4
y	?	?	?	?
	−2	1	3	7

3. $\{(x, y) : y = 10x + 1\}$

x	−5	−2	0	3
y	?	?	?	?
	−49	−19	1	31

Compare each rule with $y = ax + b$. Then tell the values of a and b for each function. (P-3)

4. $y = -10x + 1$ $a: -10; b: 1$

5. $y = -3x + 7$ $a: -3; b: 7$

6. $a: -1; b: 5$
6. $y = 5 - x$

7. $y = -x - 3$ $a: -1; b: -3$

8. $y = 10x$ $a: 10; b: 0$

9. $a: -7; b: 0$
9. $y = -7x$

10. $y = -\frac{3}{5}$ $a: 0; b: -\frac{3}{5}$

11. $y = -0.5x + 3.8$ $a: -0.5; b: 3.8$

12. $y = -\frac{2}{3}x - \frac{1}{3}$
12. $a: -\frac{2}{3}; b: -\frac{1}{3}$

WRITTEN EXERCISES

See the Teacher's Manual for the suggested assignments.

Goals: To identify and to graph linear functions

Sample Problems: a. $y = 3x^3$ **b.** $y = -x$

Answers: a. Not linear **b.** Linear; the graph is at the right.

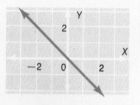

In Ex. 1–10 each graph is a straight line. The coordinates of four points of each line are given.

Graph at least four ordered pairs of each function. Then draw the graph. The domain is {real numbers}. (Examples 1 and 2)

3. (0, –1), (1, 2), (2, 5), (–1, –4)
6. (1, –2), (–1, 2), (0, 0), (2, –4)

1. (3, 0), (0, 3), (1, 2), (–2, 5)
1. $\{(x, y) : y = -x + 3\}$

2. (–2, 0), (0, –2), (–1, –1), (4, –6)
2. $\{(x, y) : y = -x - 2\}$

3. $\{(x, y) : y = 3x - 1\}$

4. (3, 3), (0, –3), (2, 1), (4, 5)
4. $\{(x, y) : y = 2x - 3\}$

5. (–1, –2), (2, 4), (0, 0), (3, 6)
5. $\{(x, y) : y = 2x\}$

6. $\{(x, y) : y = -2x\}$

7. (–3, –2), (0, –2), (1, –2), (2, –2)
7. $\{(x, y) : y = 0 \cdot x - 2\}$

8. $\{(x, y) : y = 0 \cdot x + 3\}$

9. (–1, –2), (3, 0), (5, 1), (–3, –3)
9. $\{(x, y) : y = \frac{1}{2}x - \frac{3}{2}\}$

(–3, 3), (1, 3), (0, 3), (2, 3)
10. $\{(x, y) : y = -\frac{1}{2}x + \frac{1}{2}\}$
(–1, 1), (1, 0), (3, –1), (5, –2)

Write <u>Yes</u> or <u>No</u> to show whether each function is linear. (P-4)

11. $\{(x, y) : y = -4x + 10\}$ Yes

12. $\{(x, y) : y = x^2 + 1)\}$ No

13. $\{(x, y) : y = -\frac{2}{3}x - 5\}$ Yes

14. $\{(x, y) : y = x(x - 1)\}$ No

15. $\{(x, y) : y = 0 \cdot x + 0\}$ Yes

16. $\{(x, y) : y = 0 \cdot x + \frac{1}{3}\}$ Yes

17. $\{(x, y) : y = -2x + 0\}$ Yes

18. $\{(x, y) : y = (x + 1)(x - 1)\}$ No

19. $\{(x, y) : y = x^2 - 2x + 5\}$ No

20. $\{(x, y) : y = x^3 - x^2 + x - 1\}$ No

REVIEW CAPSULE FOR SECTION 11.2

Evaluate each function if x equals 0. (Section 6.5)

1. $y = -8x - 3$ (0, –3)

2. $y = \frac{1}{2}x + \frac{3}{4}$ (0, $\frac{3}{4}$)

3. $y = -x - 10$ (0, –10)

4. $y = -\frac{3}{4}x$ (0, 0)

5. $y = 0.9x + 1.3$ (0, 1.3)

6. $y = 0.6 - 3.7x$ (0, 0.6)

7. $y = x + \sqrt{3}$ (0, $\sqrt{3}$)

8. $y = -\sqrt{2} \cdot x + 5$ (0, 5)

11.2 Y Intercept

OBJECTIVES: To write the Y intercept of a linear function from its rule
To graph a linear function from its given rule using the Y intercept

P-1 **How are the rules for these functions alike?** In each, the value of *b* is 2.

a. $y = \frac{1}{2}x + 2$ **b.** $y = x + 2$ **c.** $y = 2x + 2$

d. $y = -2x + 2$ **e.** $y = -x + 2$ **f.** $y = -\frac{1}{2}x + 2$

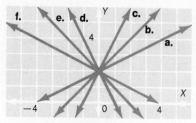

Figure 1

P-2 **What are the coordinates of the common point of the graphs?** (0, 2).

Graphs of the following functions are shown in Figure 2.

1. $y = 3x + 1$
2. $y = 2x - 3$
3. $y = -\frac{1}{2}x + 3$
4. $y = -x - 1$

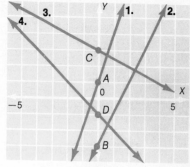

P-3 **What is the x value of each of the points A, B, C, and D? the y value of each point?**

x value: 0; *y* value; 1(*A*), −3(*B*), 3(*C*), −1(*D*)

Figure 2

> The *y* value of the point that a line has in common with the Y axis is the **Y intercept.**

 example 1

Write the Y intercept of the graph of $\{(x, y) : y = 3x - 2\}$.

Some persons call the point itself the Y intercept.

Solution:

$y = 3x - 2$

1 Replace *x* with 0. ────────────▶ $y = 3(0) - 2$

For any point on the Y axis, *x* is zero.

2 Solve for *y*. ────────────▶ $y = -2$

Y intercept

In the rule for the linear function
$y = ax + b$, b represents the Y intercept
of its graph.

$$\{(x, y) : y = -x + \tfrac{1}{2}\}$$
Y intercept $= \tfrac{1}{2}$

P-4 **What is the Y intercept of the graph of each function below?**

a. $\{(x, y) : y = \tfrac{3}{2}x + \tfrac{5}{2}\}$ $\tfrac{5}{2}$ or $2\tfrac{1}{2}$ **b.** $\{(x, y) : y = 4 - x\}$ ^{4}

example 2

Graph $\{(x, y) : y = -2x - 3\}$. Graph at least three
ordered pairs, including one with the Y intercept.

Solution: $y = -2x - 3$

$y = -2(0) - 3 = -3$

$y = -2(-3) - 3 = 3$

$y = -2(2) - 3 = -7$

x	y
0	−3
−3	3
2	−7

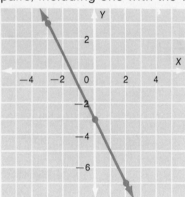

CLASSROOM EXERCISES

Estimate the Y intercept of each graph. (P-3, second part)

1.
1
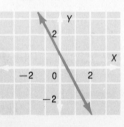

2.
−2
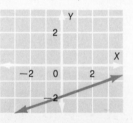

3.
$\tfrac{1}{2}$
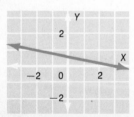

4.
0
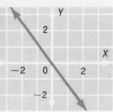

5.
$1\tfrac{1}{2}$
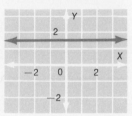

6.
$-\tfrac{3}{4}$
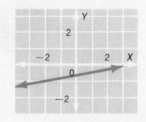

Write each Y intercept. (P-4)

7. $y = 3x + \frac{1}{2}$ $\frac{1}{2}$

8. $y = -2x + 5$ 5

9. $y = \frac{2}{3}x - \frac{1}{3}$ $-\frac{1}{3}$

10. $y = -3x$ 0

11. $y = -x - 1$ −1

12. $y = 3x + \frac{15}{2}$ $\frac{15}{2}$

13. $y = x$ 0

14. $y = 5 - 3x$ 5

15. $y = 2(x + 3)$ 6

WRITTEN EXERCISES

See the Teacher's Manual for the suggested assignments.

Goal: To identify the Y intercept of a linear function and to graph the function

Sample Problem: $y = 3(2 - \frac{1}{3}x)$

Answer: 6   The graph is at the right.

Write each Y intercept. (Example 1)

1. $y = -3x + 7$ 7

2. $y = 5x - 2$ −2

3. $y = -\frac{1}{2}x + \frac{7}{2}$ $\frac{7}{2}$

4. $y = 1.73x + 3.85$ 3.85

5. $y = \frac{2}{3}x - \frac{5}{3}$ $-\frac{5}{3}$

6. $y = -1.17x + 3.14$ 3.14

7. $y = 0.3 - 5x$ 0.3

8. $y = 14 - \frac{1}{2}x$ 14

9. $y = 3(2 - x)$ 6

10. $y = -5(1 - 2x)$ −5

11. $y = -x$ 0

12. $y = \frac{7}{5} + 2x$ $\frac{7}{5}$

Graph each function. Graph at least three ordered pairs including one with the Y intercept. (Example 2)   In Ex. 13-22 each graph is a straight line. The coordinates of two points of each line are given.

13. $\{(x, y) : y = x + 1\}$ (0, 1), (−1, 0)

14. $\{(x, y) : y = -x + 2\}$ (0, 2), (2, 0)

15. $\{(x, y) : y = -2x - 3\}$ (0, −3), (−2, 1)

16. $\{(x, y) : y = 3x - 2\}$ (0, −2), (3, 7)

17. $\{(x, y) : y = \frac{1}{2}x + 5\}$ (0, 5), (4, 7)

18. $\{(x, y) : y = -\frac{1}{2}x + 4\}$ (0, 4), (4, 2)

19. $\{(x, y) : y = -3x\}$ (0, 0), (2, −6)

20. $\{(x, y) : y = 2x\}$ (0, 0), (1, 2)

21. $\{(x, y) : y = \frac{1}{2}x + \frac{3}{2}\}$ (0, $\frac{3}{2}$), (5, 4)

22. $\{(x, y) : y = -2x - \frac{3}{2}\}$ (0, $-\frac{3}{2}$), ($-\frac{3}{2}$, $\frac{3}{2}$)

REVIEW CAPSULE FOR SECTION 11.3

Graph these functions in the same coordinate plane. (Section 10.1)

1. $\{(x, y) : y = \frac{1}{2}x + 5\}$ (0, 5), (2, 6)

2. $\{(x, y) : y = \frac{1}{2}x + 3\}$ (0, 3), (2, 4)

3. $\{(x, y) : y = \frac{1}{2}x + 1\}$ (0, 1), (2, 2)

4. $\{(x, y) : y = \frac{1}{2}x\}$ (0, 0), (2, 1)

5. $\{(x, y) : y = \frac{1}{2}x - 3\}$ (0, −3), (2, −2)

6. $\{(x, y) : y = \frac{1}{2}x - 5\}$ (0, −5), (2, −4)

OBJECTIVES: To write the slope of the graph of a linear function from its rule
To write the slope-intercept form of a linear function given its slope
and its graph

11.3 Slope of a Line

To name the quadrants in which the graph of a linear function will
lie if its rule is given in the form $y = ax$

P-1   **What is the Y intercept for each
graph in Figure 1?**   2

The rules for these linear
functions are listed below.

1. $y = \frac{1}{2}x + 2$ **2.** $y = x + 2$

3. $y = \frac{3}{2}x + 2$ **4.** $y = 2x + 2$

The lines get "steeper" with
respect to the X axis in the order
from **1** to **4**.

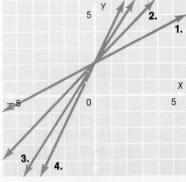

Figure 1

P-2   **What number in the rule $y = ax + b$ affects the "steepness" of
a line?**   a

Compare how the
graph of 1, in Fig.
1 compares with 1
in Fig. 2. Also
compare the graphs
of 2, 3, and 4 in
Fig. 1 with the
graphs of 2, 3, and
4 in Fig. 2,
respectively.

The graphs of four more linear
functions are shown in Figure 2.

1. $y = -\frac{1}{2}x - 1$ **2.** $y = -x - 1$

3. $y = -\frac{3}{2}x - 1$ **4.** $y = -4x - 1$

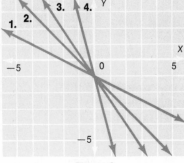

P-3   **In what special way are the rules
for these functions related?**

In all four, the value of b is -1.

The "steepness" of a line is described by a number called **slope**.

Figure 2

> In the rule for the linear function
> $y = ax + b$, **a** represents the **slope** of
> its graph.
>
> $y = -2x + 5$
>
> Slope $= -2$

The rule for a linear function, $y = ax + b$, is called the
slope-intercept form.

P-4   **What is the slope of the graph of the function having each rule
below?   the Y intercept?**

a. $y = -\frac{3}{4}x - 2$ **b.** $y = 5x - \frac{1}{2}$ **c.** $y = \frac{5}{2} - \frac{3}{2}x$

Slope: $-\frac{3}{4}$ Slope: 5   Slope: $-\frac{3}{2}$
                        y intercept: $-\frac{1}{2}$
Y intercept: -2 Y intercept: $\frac{5}{2}$

268 / *Chapter 11*

example 1

Write the slope-intercept form of the rule for the line in the figure. The slope is -2.

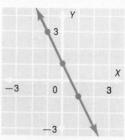

Figure 3

Solution:

$y = ax + b$

$\quad\quad a = -2$
$\quad\quad b = 1$

$y = -2x + 1$

P-5   **In what quadrants does the graph of Figure 3 lie?**   I, II, and IV

example 2

Graph these functions.

1. $y = 2x$ **2.** $y = -\frac{1}{3}x$

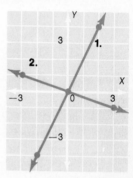

Solutions:

$y = 2x$

x	y
-2	-4
0	0
2	4

$y = -\frac{1}{3}x$

x	y
-3	1
0	0
3	-1

P-6   **In what quadrants does the graph of $y = 2x$ lie?**   **the graph of** $y = -\frac{1}{3}x$**?**   II and IV   I and III

A line such as the graph of $y = 2x$ has a positive slope. It "slopes" upward and to the right. The graph of $y = -\frac{1}{3}x$ has a negative slope. It "slopes" upward and to the left.

CLASSROOM EXERCISES

Find the slope and the Y intercept of the graph of each function. (P-4)

1. $y = 3x + 2$ Slope: 3; Y intercept: 2   **2.** $y = -5x + 1$ Slope: -5; Y intercept: 1   **3.** $y = x + 5$ Slope: 1; Y intercept: 5

4. $y = -x - 1$ Slope: -1; Y intercept: -1 **5.** $y = \frac{1}{3}x - 6$ Slope: $\frac{1}{3}$; Y intercept: -6 **6.** $y = -\frac{1}{2}x + 1$ Slope: $-\frac{1}{2}$; Y intercept: 1

Write the slope-intercept form of the rule for each function. (Example 1)

7. The slope is 5 and the Y intercept is 3.

$y = 5x + 3$

8. The slope is $\frac{1}{4}$ and the Y intercept is $\frac{1}{2}$.

$$y = \frac{1}{4}x + \frac{1}{2}$$

Linear Equations   /   **269**

Tell the slope-intercept form of the rule for each function. (Example 1)

9. The slope is -1 and the Y intercept is 0. $y = -1x + 0$ or $y = -x$

10. The slope is $-\frac{2}{3}$ and the Y intercept
is $\frac{3}{5}$. $y = -\frac{2}{3}x + \frac{3}{5}$

11. The line crosses the Y axis at
$(0, 10)$ and has slope 3. $y = 3x + 10$

12. The line crosses the Y axis at
$(0, -6)$ and has slope -1. $y = -x - 6$

WRITTEN EXERCISES

See the Teacher's Manual for the suggested assignments.

Goal: To write the slope-intercept form of the rule for a linear function
Sample Problem: Slope is $\frac{2}{3}$. See graph below.   **Answer:** $y = \frac{2}{3}x + 2$

Write the slope of the graph of each function. (P-4)

1. $y = x - 5$ 1   **2.** $y = -x + 2$ -1 **3.** $y = -\frac{1}{2}x + 7$ $-\frac{1}{2}$ **4.** $y = \frac{1}{2}x - 6$ $\frac{1}{2}$

5. $y = 2(x - 3)$ 2   **6.** $y = 3(x + 1)$ 3   **7.** $y = 2 - 3x$ -3 **8.** $y = 5 - 7x$ -7

9. $y = \frac{1}{2}(3 - x)$ $-\frac{1}{2}$ **10.** $y = -\frac{1}{3}(5 - x)$ $\frac{1}{3}$ **11.** $y = -\frac{1}{4}(8 + 16x)$ -4 **12.** $y = \frac{1}{5}(10 - 10x)$ -2

*Write the slope-intercept form of the
rule for each function graphed at the
right. The slopes are given below.*
(Example 1)

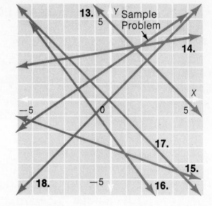

13. Slope is -1.
$y = -x + 5$

14. Slope is $\frac{1}{6}$. $y = \frac{1}{6}x + 3$

15. Slope is $-\frac{1}{3}$.
$y = -\frac{1}{3}x - 3$

16. Slope is $-\frac{4}{3}$. $y = -\frac{4}{3}x - 2$

17. Slope is -1.
$y = -x$

18. Slope is 1. $y = x$

*Name the quadrants in which each
graph would lie.* (P-5, P-6)

19. $y = 5x$ I, III   **20.** $y = 10x$ I, III   **21.** $y = -2x$ II, IV   **22.** $y = -6x$ II, IV

23. $y = -\frac{1}{2}x$ II, IV   **24.** $y = \frac{2}{3}x$ I, III   **25.** $y = \frac{5}{6}x$ I, III   **26.** $y = -\frac{3}{4}x$ II, IV

27. $y = -0.7x$ II, IV   **28.** $y = 0.56x$ I, III   **29.** $y = x$ I, III   **30.** $y = -x$ II, IV

REVIEW CAPSULE FOR SECTION 11.4

Simplify each fraction. (Sections 1.3 and 1.5)

1. $\dfrac{2 - 5}{7 - 2}$ $-\frac{3}{5}$ **2.** $\dfrac{0 - (-3)}{2 - 4}$ $-\frac{3}{2}$ **3.** $\dfrac{(-2) - 3}{4 - 5}$ 5   **4.** $\dfrac{7 - 2}{5 - (-3)}$ $\frac{5}{8}$ **5.** $\dfrac{5 - (-3)}{7 - (-5)}$ $\frac{2}{3}$

11.4 Slope Formula

OBJECTIVES: To write the slope of a line containing two points with their coordinates given
To write the slope-intercept form of a line containing two points with their coordinates given

P-1 **What is the slope of the graph of $y = \frac{3}{2}x + 2$ shown in the figure at the right?** $\frac{3}{2}$

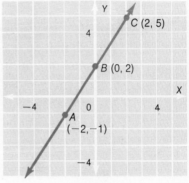

Figure 1

Suppose that you move from B to C in Figure 1 by one vertical and one horizontal motion.

P-2 **How many units and in what direction is the vertical motion? the horizontal motion?** See below.

$$\frac{5 - 2}{2 - 0} = \frac{3}{2}$$ ◀ *Vertical motion: 3* / *Horizontal motion: 2*

Now suppose that you move from A to C by one vertical motion and one horizontal motion.

P-3 **How many units and in what direction is the vertical motion?** 4 units **the horizontal motion?** 6 units

Difference in y coordinates / *Difference in x coordinates* ▶ $$\frac{5 - (-1)}{2 - (-2)} = \frac{5 + 1}{2 + 2}$$

$$= \frac{6}{4} \text{ or } \frac{3}{2}$$ ◀ *Vertical motion* / *Horizontal motion*

A quotient of two numbers such as $\frac{3}{2}$ is called a <u>ratio</u>. The <u>slope</u> of a line is the ratio of the vertical motion to the horizontal motion from one point to another on the line.

You may want to discuss various correct and incorrect ways of substituting in the slope in the Slope Formula.

Slope Formula

If the coordinates of two points on a nonvertical line are (x_1, y_1) and (x_2, y_2), then a, the **slope** of the line, is given by

$$a = \frac{y_2 - y_1}{x_2 - x_1}.$$

◀ *1 and 2 are subscripts. Read x sub 1, x sub 2, etc.*

$(2, -3), (-5, 1)$

$$a = \frac{1 - (-3)}{-5 - 2}$$

$$a = -\frac{4}{7}$$

---

example 1

Write the slope of the line in Figure 2 by using the following ratio:

$$\frac{\text{vertical motion from } A \text{ to } B}{\text{horizontal motion from } A \text{ to } B}$$

Solution:

$$\frac{\text{vertical motion from } A \text{ to } B}{\text{horizontal motion from } A \text{ to } B} = \frac{-5-1}{1-(-3)}$$

$$\text{slope} = \frac{-6}{4} \quad \text{or} \quad -\frac{3}{2}$$

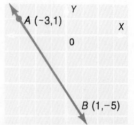

Figure 2

example 2

Write the slope of the line that contains the points $(-2, 5)$ and $(3, -1)$.

Solution:

Method 1

$x_1 = -2, \, x_2 = 3$
$y_1 = 5, \, y_2 = -1$

$$a = \frac{y_2 - y_1}{x_2 - x_1}$$

$$= \frac{-1-5}{3-(-2)}$$

$$= -\frac{6}{5} \quad \blacktriangleleft \text{ Slope of the line}$$

Method 2

$$a = \frac{y_2 - y_1}{x_2 - x_1}$$

$x_1 = 3, \, x_2 = -2$
$y_1 = -1, \, y_2 = 5$

$$= \frac{5-(-1)}{-2-3}$$

$$= -\frac{6}{5} \quad \blacktriangleleft \text{ Slope of the line}$$

example 3

Write the slope-intercept form of the line that contains the points $(0, 3)$ and $(5, 2)$.

Solution:

1. Slope formula

$$\frac{y_2 - y_1}{x_2 - x_1} = \frac{2-3}{5-0}$$

$$= -\frac{1}{5}$$

2. Y intercept → $b = 3$

   If x = 0, the point is on the Y axis.

3. Slope-intercept form → $y = ax + b$

4. Substitute. → $y = -\frac{1}{5}x + 3$

   $a = -\frac{1}{5}$
   $b = 3$

CLASSROOM EXERCISES

Find the value of each ratio. (P-2, P-3)

1. $\dfrac{8-5}{7-2}$ $\;\frac{3}{5}$

2. $\dfrac{3-7}{9-4}$ $\;-\frac{4}{5}$

3. $\dfrac{-1-2}{7-9}$ $\;\frac{3}{2}$

4. $\dfrac{5-(-3)}{2-3}$ $\;-8$

5. $\dfrac{0-(-1)}{-1-2}$ $\;-\frac{1}{3}$

6. $\dfrac{-3-(-2)}{7-(-1)}$ $\;-\frac{1}{8}$

7. $\dfrac{-3-0}{0-(-3)}$ $\;-1$

8. $\dfrac{(-3)-(-3)}{2-7}$ $\;0$

9. $\dfrac{1-2}{4-6}$ $\;\frac{1}{2}$

Write the slope of each line. (Example 1)

10. 1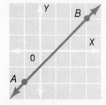

11. -1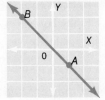

12. 2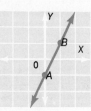

13. 2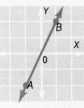

14. -3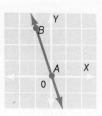

15. $-\dfrac{1}{2}$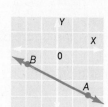

16. 0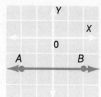

17. 2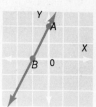

WRITTEN EXERCISES

Goal: To write the slope of a line given coordinates of two points on the line
Sample Problem: $(4, 5)$ and $(-2, -1)$ **Answer:** $a = 1$

Write the slope of each line. (Example 1)

1. 1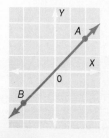

2. $-\dfrac{4}{3}$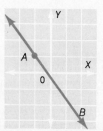

3. 0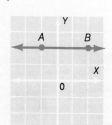

4. $\dfrac{4}{3}$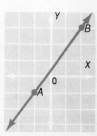

Write the slope of the line that contains the two points. (Example 2)

5. $(-1, 5)$; $(3, 2)$ $-\frac{3}{4}$ **6.** $(4, 6)$; $(-2, 3)$ $\frac{1}{2}$ **7.** $(5, -3)$; $(-1, 4)$ $-\frac{7}{6}$

8. $(2, 3)$; $(-1, -2)$ $\frac{5}{3}$ **9.** $(-3, -4)$; $(-2, -5)$ -1 **10.** $(-1, -5)$; $(-2, -7)$ 2

11. $(3, -5)$; $(-1, -5)$ 0 **12.** $(4, -3)$; $(-1, -3)$ 0 **13.** $(10, -5)$; $(6, -2)$ $-\frac{3}{4}$

14. $(12, 8)$; $(-4, -10)$ $\frac{9}{8}$ **15.** $(3\frac{1}{2}, -5\frac{3}{4})$; $(-\frac{1}{2}, \frac{1}{4})$ $-\frac{3}{2}$ **16.** $(-\frac{3}{2}, -\frac{5}{2})$; $(\frac{1}{2}, \frac{1}{2})$ $\frac{3}{2}$

Write the slope-intercept form of the line that contains the two points.
(Example 3)

17. $(0, 5)$; $(-3, 2)$ $y = x + 5$ **18.** $(0, 1)$; $(5, -3)$ $y = -\frac{4}{5}x + 1$ **19.** $(0, -3)$; $(4, 6)$ $y = \frac{9}{4}x - 3$

20. $(0, -5)$; $(-1, -1)$ $y = -4x - 5$ **21.** $(0, 0)$; $(5, 8)$ $y = \frac{8}{5}x$ **22.** $(0, 0)$; $(-4, 7)$ $y = -\frac{7}{4}x$

23. $(0, -6)$; $(2, -6)$ $y = -6$ **24.** $(0, 10)$; $(-1, 10)$ $y = 10$ **25.** $(0, 5)$; $(5, 0)$ $y = -x + 5$

26. $(0, -2)$; $(-2, 0)$ $y = -x - 2$ **27.** $(0, 6)$; $(3, 8)$ $y = \frac{2}{3}x + 6$ **28.** $(0, 2)$; $(4, 10)$ $y = 2x + 2$

MORE CHALLENGING EXERCISES

Draw the line with the given slope and that contains the given point.

EXAMPLE: $a = -\frac{1}{2}$; $(5, -3)$

SOLUTION: Locate the point as shown in the figure. Call it P.

Use the slope as $\dfrac{\text{vertical motion from } P \text{ to } Q}{\text{horizontal motion from } P \text{ to } Q}$

to locate a second point Q.

$$-\frac{1}{2} = \frac{1 \text{ unit upward } (+)}{2 \text{ units left } (-)}$$

Draw the line containing P and Q.

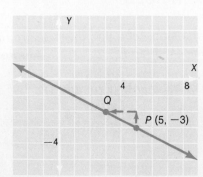

In Ex. 29-34 a second point is given that can be found using the slope. A line can be drawn using the 2 points.

29. $a = 3$; $(0, 0)$ $(1, 3)$ **30.** $a = \frac{1}{2}$; $(1, -1)$ $(3, 0)$ **31.** $a = -\frac{3}{4}$; $(2, -3)$ $(6, -6)$

32. $a = -5$; $(-2, -3)$ $(-3, 2)$ **33.** $a = 0$; $(-5, 3)$ $(0, 3)$ **34.** $a = \frac{5}{3}$; $(1, -5)$ $(4, 0)$

Graph at least four ordered pairs of each function. Then draw the graph. The domain is {real numbers}. (Section 11.1)   In Ex. 1-6 each graph is a straight line.
The coordinates of two points of each line are given.

1. $\{(x, y): y = x - 3\}$ (0, −3), **2.** $\{(x, y): y = -x + 2\}$ (0, 2), **3.** $\{(x, y): y = -2x + 1\}$ (0, 1),
(1, −2)   (−1, 3)   (2, −3)
4. $\{(x, y): y = 3x + 2\}$ **5.** $\{(x, y): y = \frac{1}{2}x - 2\}$ **6.** $\{(x, y): y = -\frac{1}{2}x + 3\}$
(0, 2), (1, 5)   (0, −2), (2, −1)   (0, 3), (−2, 4)

Use the Y intercept and two ordered pairs to graph each function.
(Section 11.2)   In Ex. 7-9 each graph is a straight line. Two points are given. The first is the Y intercept.

7. $\{(x, y): y = -x + 3\}$ **8.** $\{(x, y): y = 2x - 1\}$ **9.** $\{(x, y): y = -\frac{1}{2}x + \frac{5}{2}\}$
(0, 3), (1, 2)   (0, −1), (2, 3)   (0, $\frac{5}{2}$), (1, 2)

Write the slope-intercept form of the rule for each function. (Section 11.3)

10. Slope: −2; Y intercept: 5 **11.** Slope: $-\frac{1}{4}$; Y intercept: −1 **12.** Slope: −1; Y intercept: $\frac{1}{2}$
$y = -2x + 5$ $y = -\frac{1}{4}x - 1$ $y = -x + \frac{1}{2}$

Write the slope of the line that contains the two points. (Section 11.4)

13. (2, 3); (4, 1) $_{-1}$ **14.** (−4, 0); (3, −2) $-\frac{2}{7}$ **15.** (−2, −1); (3, −1) $_0$ **16.** (−7, −4); (−5, −1) $\frac{3}{2}$

━━━━━━━━━━━━━━━━━ *A PAPER CAPER* ━━━━━━━━━━━━━━━━━

Suppose a sheet of paper has a thickness of 0.0015 inch. What would be the thickness of the paper if it could be folded in half several times? A calculator can be used to find the answer.

EXAMPLE   Find the thickness of the folded paper when the number of folds is 15.

SOLUTION	Number of Folds	Number of Thicknesses	Thickness in Inches
	1	$2^1 = 2$	$2 \times 0.0015 = 0.0030$ in
NOTE: To avoid calculator	2	$2^2 = 4$	$4 \times 0.0015 = 0.0060$ in
overload, start with	3	$2^3 = 8$	$8 \times 0.0015 = 0.012$ in
0.000125 ft in Ex.2.	.	.	.
Start Ex. 3 by changing	.	.	.
4194 ft (from Ex. 2)	.	.	.
to 0.7943 miles.	15	$2^{15} = \underline{\ ?\ }$	$\underline{\ ?\ } \times 0.0015 = \underline{\ ?\ }$ in

         `49.152`

 Press "⌐=⌐" 14 times. *About 49 inches thick*

Find the following thicknesses for the sheet of paper in the Example.

1. 16 folds, in inches **2.** 25 folds, in feet **3.** 50 folds, in miles (HINT: $2^{50} = 2^{25} \times 2^{25}$)
About 98 inches thick   About 4194 feet thick   About 27 million miles thick
   (See "NOTE" above.)   (See "NOTE" above.)

OBJECTIVES: Given the rules of two linear functions with equal slopes, to graph the functions in the same coordinate plane
Given the rules of three linear functions with equal slopes, to graph one function using three ordered pairs and to graph the other two functions from the first graph using y intercepts and the meaning of slope
To graph a linear function given its rule in the form $y = b$

11.5 Parallel Lines

example 1

Graph in the same coordinate plane.

1. $y = 2x - 3$　　**2.** $y = 2x + 1$

Solutions:

$y = 2x - 3$

x	y
−1	−5
0	−3
2	1

$y = 2x + 1$

x	y
−2	−3
0	1
2	5

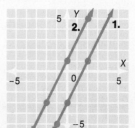

Figure 1

P-1　**What appears to be true about the two lines of Figure 1?**
　　　　　　　　　　　　　　They appear to be parallel.

Lines **1** and **2** of Figure 1 are <u>parallel</u>.

Review the idea that lines are infinite in extent.

> ***Parallel lines*** are two lines in the same plane that do not have a common point.

Lines **1** and **2** also have the same slope.

> If two lines have the same slope, they are parallel.

P-2　**Which functions described below have parallel graphs?**　a. and c.

a. $y = -\frac{1}{2}x - 5$　　**b.** $y = 2x - 5$　　**c.** $y = 4 - \frac{1}{2}x$

example 2

Solution:

Write the slope-intercept form of the function that has its graph parallel to the graph of $y = 2x - 5$ and that contains (0, 3).

$a = 2$
$b = 3$

$y = ax + b$

$y = 2x + 3$　　*Slope-intercept form*

example 3

Graph the three functions. Use three points for the first line. Graph the other two lines using Y intercepts and the meaning of slope.

1. $y = -\frac{1}{2}x + 1$ **2.** $y = -\frac{1}{2}x - 3$ **3.** $y = -\frac{1}{2}x$

Solution:

1. Draw the graph of $y = -\frac{1}{2}x + 1$.

x	−4	0	4
y	3	1	−1

2. Locate (0, −3). Move 1 unit up and 2 units left to locate (−2, −2). Draw the graph of $y = -\frac{1}{2}x - 3$.

3. Locate (0, 0). Move 1 unit up and 2 units left to locate (−2, 1). Draw the graph of $y = -\frac{1}{2}x$.

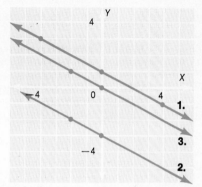

P-3   **What is the value of $0 \cdot x$ for any value of x?** 0

example 4

Graph the three functions.

1. $y = 4$
2. $y = 2$
3. $y = -1$

▶

1. $y = 0 \cdot x + 4$
2. $y = 0 \cdot x + 2$
3. $y = 0 \cdot x - 1$

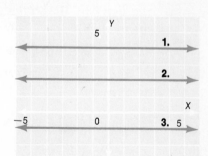

Solution:

All the rules are of the form $y = 0 \cdot x + b$ or simply $y = b$. The three graphs are parallel to the X axis.

CLASSROOM EXERCISES

Write Yes or No to tell whether the graphs of each pair of functions are parallel. (P-1, P-2)

1. $y = \frac{1}{2}x + 2$
$y = 0.5x + 3$ Yes

2. $y = 5 - 2x$
$y = 5x - 2$ No

3. $y = 1$
$y = 3$ Yes

4. $y = \frac{3}{4}x$
$y = -\frac{3}{4}x$ No

Tell the slope-intercept form of each function. (Example 2)

5. Its graph is parallel to the graph of $y = 4x - 3$ and contains (0, 3). $y = 4x + 3$

6. Its graph is parallel to the graph of $y = -5x + 2$ and contains (0, -3). $y = -5x - 3$

7. Its graph is parallel to the graph of $y = \frac{3}{2}x - 1$ and contains (0, 10). $y = \frac{3}{2}x + 10$

8. Its graph is parallel to the graph of $y = -\frac{1}{4}x + \frac{1}{2}$ and contains (0, $\frac{5}{2}$). $y = -\frac{1}{4}x + \frac{5}{2}$

9. Its graph is parallel to the graph of $y = -5.3x + 2.5$ and contains (0, 0.6). $y = -5.3x + 0.6$

WRITTEN EXERCISES See the Teacher's Manual for the suggested assignments.

In Ex. 1-6 each graph is a pair of parallel lines. Two points are given for each line.

Goal: To use slopes to identify and graph parallel lines

Sample Problem: $y = -x$, $y = \frac{1}{2} - x$, $y = -x + 7$

Answer: Each slope: -1; lines are parallel.   Graphs:

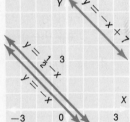

Graph each pair of functions in the same coordinate plane (Example 1)

1. $y = -2x + 3$ (0,3), (1, 1) **2.** $y = x + 4$ (0, 4), (-3, 1) **3.** $y = \frac{3}{2}x - 2$ (0, -2), (4, 4)

$y = -2x - 1$ (0, -1), (-1, 1) $y = x - 3$ (0, -3), (2, -1) $y = \frac{3}{2}x + 1$ (0, 1), (-2, -2)

4. $y = -\frac{1}{2}x$ (0, 0), (-2, 1) **5.** $y = \frac{5}{4}x + 3$ (0, 3), (4, 8) **6.** $y = -\frac{3}{2}x + 2$ (0, 2), (2, -1)

$y = -\frac{1}{2}x - 4$ (0, -4), (-2, -3) $y = \frac{5}{4}x$ (0, 0), (4, 5) $y = -\frac{3}{2}x - 5$ (0, -5), (2, -8)

In Ex. 7-10 the graph is a set of three parallel lines. Two points are given for each line.

Graph the three functions in the same coordinate plane. Use three points for the first line. Graph the other two lines using the Y intercepts and the meaning of slope. (Example 3)

10. (0, 2), (3, -1); (0, -3), (2, -5); (0, 0), (2, -2)

7. $y = 2x - 3$ (0, -3), (2, 1) **8.** $y = 5x + 1$ (0, 1), (1, 6) **9.** $y = x + 3$ (0, 3), (-2, 1) **10.** $y = -x + 2$

$y = 2x + 3$ (0, 3), (-2, -1) $y = 5x - 5$ (0, -5), (1, 0) $y = x - 3$ (0, -3), (2, -1) $y = -x - 3$

$y = 2x$ (0, 0), (2, 4) $y = 5x$ (0, 0), (1, 5) $y = x$ (0, 0), (3, 3) $y = -x$

The graphs of Ex. 11-14 are horizontal lines. One point is given.

Graph the functions in the same coordinate plane. (Example 4)

11. $y = 5$ (0, 5) **12.** $y = -2$ (0, -2) **13.** $y = \frac{3}{2}$ (0, $\frac{3}{2}$) **14.** $y = -\frac{3}{2}$ (0, $-\frac{3}{2}$)

MORE CHALLENGING EXERCISES

Graph all four functions in the same coordinate plane. The graph of $y = -x - 3$ and $y = -x + 2$ is a pair of parallel

The graph of $y = 2x - 2$ and $y = 2x + 3$ is a pair of parallel lines. Similarly for $y = -3x - 5$ and $y = -3x + 4$.

15. $y = 2x - 2$ $y = -3x - 5$ **16.** $y = -x - 3$ $y = -x + 2$ lines. Similarly

$y = 2x + 3$ $y = -3x + 4$ $y = 3x + 5$ $y = 3x - 5$ for $y = 3x + 5$ and $y = 3x - 5$.

REVIEW CAPSULE FOR SECTION 11.6

Solve for x. (Section 3.3)

1. $0 = 3x + 6$ -2 **2.** $0 = \frac{1}{2}x - 1$ 2 **3.** $0 = -\frac{3}{4}x + 9$ 12 **4.** $0 = -3x + \frac{9}{4}$

$\frac{3}{4}$

11.6 *X* Intercept

To graph a linear function given the slope-intercept form of its rule and using only the *x* and *y* intercepts.

To graph a linear function given its rule in the form $x = k$

P-1 **What are the coordinates of the point common to the graph of Figure 1 and the *X* axis?** (−4, 0)

Any point on the *X* axis has a *y* value equal to 0.

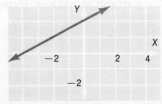

Figure 1

> The *x* value of a point common to the *X* axis and a straight line is called the ***X intercept*** of the line.
>
> In Figure 1, the *X* intercept = −4.

example 1

Write the *X* intercept of the graph of $y = -\frac{1}{2}x + 1$.

Solution:

$$y = -\frac{1}{2}x + 1$$

◀ **Replace *y* with 0.**

$$0 = -\frac{1}{2}x + 1$$

$$-1 = -\frac{1}{2}x$$

◀ **Solve for x.**

$$-2(-1) = -2(-\frac{1}{2}x)$$

$$2 = x$$

◀ **The X intercept is 2.**

P-2 **What is the *X* intercept of the graph of each function below?**

a. $y = x - 5$ 5   **b.** $y = x + \frac{1}{2}$ $-\frac{1}{2}$ **c.** $y = 2x + 8$ −4

example 2

Graph $y = \frac{3}{2}x - 3$ by using the *X* and *Y* intercepts.

Solution:

$$y = \frac{3}{2}x - 3$$

$$0 = \frac{3}{2}x - 3$$

◀ **Let *y* = 0.**

$$3 = \frac{3}{2}x$$

$$\frac{2}{3}(3) = \frac{2}{3}(\frac{3}{2}x)$$

$$2 = x \text{ if } y = 0.$$

The *Y* intercept is −3.

The line is drawn through (2, 0) and (0, −3).

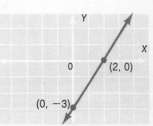

Figure 2

Figure 3 shows the graph of a linear relation that is <u>not</u> a function.

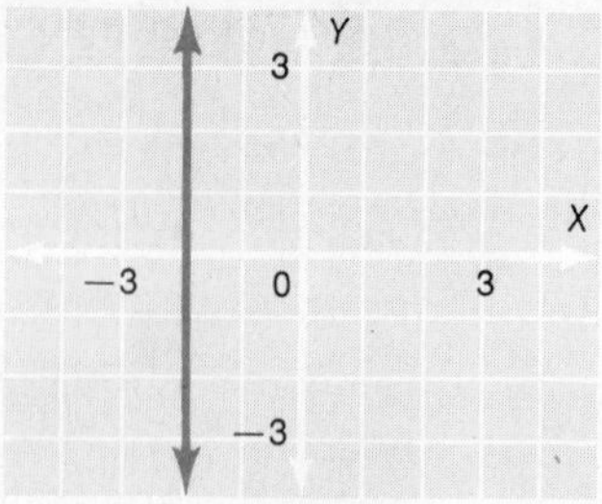

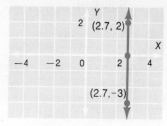

Figure 3

P-3   **What is the domain of the relation?** $\{-2\}$

P-4   **Why is the relation not a function?**
There is more than one y value for the x value, -2.
Let (x, y) represent the coordinates of any point on the vertical line of Figure 3. Then x equals -2 for <u>any</u> value of y.

$x = -2$ ◀ **Rule of the relation**

> The rule of a relation having a vertical line as its graph is $x = k$ in which k is the X intercept of the line.

example 3   Graph $x = 2.7$.

Solution: The rule is of the form $x = k$. The graph is a vertical line 2.7 units to the right of the origin.

Figure 4

The ordered pairs (2.7, 2) and (2.7, −3) are coordinates of two points on the vertical line in Figure 4. Use these points to determine the slope of the line.

$$\frac{y_2 - y_1}{x_2 - x_1} = \frac{-3 - 2}{2.7 - 2.7}$$

$$= \frac{-5}{0}$$

Since you cannot divide by 0, $\frac{-5}{0}$ is not a number.

This is a difficult concept for students to grasp. Remind them that <u>slope</u> is a number.

> A vertical line does not have a slope.

CLASSROOM EXERCISES

Write each X intercept. (Example 1)

1. $y = x + 3$ −3

2. $y = x - 1$ 1

3. $y = 2x - 2$ 1

4. $y = 3x - 5$ $\frac{5}{3}$

5. $y = 2x + 4$ −2

6. $y = x - \frac{1}{2}$ $\frac{1}{2}$

7. $y = 2x - 5$ $\frac{5}{2}$

8. $y = 8x$ 0

9−14. *Write the X intercept of each line in Figure 5. (P-1)*   9. −5; 10. −3; 11. 1; 12. 2; 13. $4\frac{1}{2}$; 14. 7

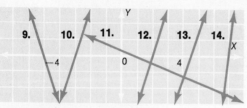 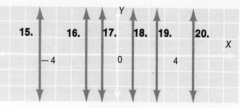

Figure 5   **Figure 6**

15−20. *Give a rule for each relation graphed in Figure 6. (Example 3)*

15. $x = -5$; 16. $x = -2$; 17. $x = -1$; 18. $x = 1$; 19. $x = 2\frac{1}{2}$; 20. $x = 5$

WRITTEN EXERCISES

See the Teacher's Manual for the suggested assignments.

Goal: To graph a linear function using X and Y intercepts

Sample Problem: $y = \frac{3}{2}x - 3$ **Answer:** See Example 2.

Write each X intercept. (Example 1)

1. $y = x + 6$ −6

2. $y = x + 10$ −10

3. $y = x - 3$ 3

4. $y = x - 7$ 7

5. $y = 3x + 6$ −2

6. $y = 2x + 10$ −5

7. $y = 4x - 12$ 3

8. $y = 3x - 15$ 5

9. $y = \frac{1}{2}x - 2$ 4

10. $y = \frac{1}{2}x - 5$ 10

11. $y = \frac{1}{4}x + 1$ −4

12. $y = \frac{1}{4}x + 2$ −8

In Ex. 13-20 each graph is a straight line. Two ordered pairs are given for each line, one using the X intercept, the other using the Y intercept.

Graph each function by using only the X and Y intercepts. (Example 2)

16. (6, 0), (0, −2)

13. $y = 2x - 4$ (2, 0), (0, −4)

14. $y = 3x + 6$ (−2, 0), (0, 6)

15. $y = \frac{1}{2}x - 3$ (6, 0), (0, −3)

16. $y = \frac{1}{3}x - 2$

17. $y = 2x + 6$ (−3, 0), (0, 6)

18. $y = 3x - 3$ (1, 0), (0, −3)

19. $y = 2x - 5$ ($\frac{5}{2}$, 0), (0, −5)

20. $y = 2x + 5$ (−$\frac{5}{2}$, 0), (0, 5)

Graph each linear relation. (Example 3)

In Ex. 21-24 the graphs are vertical lines. One point is given for each line.

21. $x = 5$ (5, 0)

22. $x = -4$ (−4, 0)

23. $x = 2\frac{1}{2}$ ($2\frac{1}{2}$, 0)

24. $x = -3\frac{1}{2}$ (−$3\frac{1}{2}$, 0)

REVIEW CAPSULE FOR SECTION 11.7

For each formula, write the slope and Y intercept. (Section 11.3)

1. $y = 2x + 3$
Slope: 2
Y intercept: 3

2. $F = 1.8C + 32$
Slope: 1.8
Y intercept: 32

3. $c = \pi d$
Slope: π
Y intercept: 0

4. $K = C + 273$
Slope: 1
Y intercept: 273

5. $s = 3 + 2.5t$
Slope: 2.5
Y intercept: 3

Linear Equations / **281**

OBJECTIVES: To graph a linear function representing a practical application
given a description of the application and a rule for the function

11.7 Problem Solving: Linear Functions

To write an approximate value for one coordinate of a point given
a graph of a linear function and the value of the other coordinate
To compute the value of a function given its rule and a number from its domain

Temperature in Fahrenheit degrees is a function of temperature
in Celsius degrees.

$$F = 1.8C + 32$$

*Compare F = 1.8C + 32
with y = 1.8x + 32. The
function is linear.*

example 1   Graph $F = 1.8C + 32$.

Solution: The ordered pairs of this
function are represented by
(C, F).

C	F
−20	−4
0	32
20	68

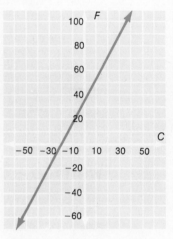

Figure 1

P-1   **What is the approximate value of F from the graph if C = 35?**   **if
C = −40?** −40

95

The distance, d, in meters that a car traveling at r kilometers per hour
will cover in a certain fraction of a second is given by the function
rule $d = 0.28r$.

example 2   Graph $d = 0.28r$.

*Compare with
y = ax + b.
a is 0.28; b is 0.*

Solution: The ordered pairs of this function
are represented by (r, d).

r	10	30	50
d	2.8	8.4	14

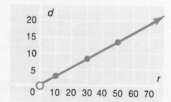

Figure 2

P-2   **What is the approximate value of d from the graph if r equals 60?**

Approximately 17

The circumference of a circle is a function of the length of a diameter.

$$c = \pi d$$

◀ **Compare with**
$y = ax + b$.

example 3

Graph $c = \pi d$. The domain is {positive real numbers}. ($\pi \approx 3.14$)

Solution: The ordered pairs of this function are represented by (d, c).

d	c
1	3.14
2	6.28
3	9.42

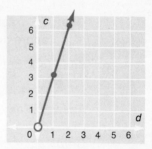

Figure 3

P-3 **What approximate value of d from the graph corresponds to a circumference of 5 centimeters?** 1.6

The simple interest on money in savings for one year at 5% is a function of the principal.

Rule: $i = 0.05p$ ◀ *i = interest*
p = principal

P-4 **What is the simple interest for one year on an investment of $200?** $10

The distance, d, that a coil spring stretches when an object of w kilograms is attached to it is given by the rule below.

Rule: $d = 10w$

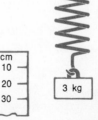

P-5 **How far will the coil spring stretch if 2 kilograms are attached to it?** 20 cm

CLASSROOM EXERCISES

Refer to the graph of Figure 1. Write the approximate Celsius temperature for each Fahrenheit temperature. (P-1)

1. $100°F$ 38°C   **2.** $60°F$ 16°C   **3.** $20°F$ −7°C   **4.** $0°F$ −18°C   **5.** $-20°F$ −29°C   **6.** $-60°F$ −51°C

Refer to the graph of Figure 2. Write the approximate distance traveled at each speed. (P-2)

7. 20 km/hr 6 meters   **8.** 35 km/hr 10 meters   **9.** 25 km/hr 7 meters   **10.** 40 km/hr
11 meters

WRITTEN EXERCISES
See the Teacher's Manual for the suggested assignments.

Goal: To graph linear functions that represent practical applications and to approximate values from the graph

Sample Problem: The circumference of a circle is a function of the length of a diameter. Rule: $c = \pi d$

Answer: See Example 3.

2. The graph is a portion of a line that contains the points (0,0) and (4,2). The graph is in Quadrant I only.

Graph each function as described. Unless otherwise stated the domain is {nonnegative real numbers}. (Examples 1–3)

1. The distance in millimeters that a coil spring stretches when *w* grams are attached is a function with this rule.
Rule: $d = 2w$ See Example 2 on p. 269 ($y = 2x$). This graph is similar except that only the portion in the first quadrant is drawn.

2. The simple interest on money in savings for ten years at 5% is a function of the principal.
Rule: $i = 10(0.05)p$ or $i = 0.5\,p$
See above.

3. The temperature in Kelvin degrees is a function of temperature in Celsius degrees.
Rule: $K = C + 273$
The domain is
{real numbers greater than −273}. The graph is a portion of a line and contains the points (−273,0) and (0,273). The graph is in Quadrants I and II only.

4. In an auto race one racer has a 3 kilometer head start. His speed is 2.5 kilometers per minute. His total distance is a function of the number of minutes he drives.
Rule: $s = 3 + 2.5t$ The graph is a portion of a line and contains the points (0,3) and (6,18). The graph is in Quadrant I only.

Refer to the graph of Figure 1. Write the approximate Fahrenheit temperature for each Celsius temperature. (P-1)

5. 20°C 68°F   **6.** 30°C 86°F   **7.** 40°C 104°F   **8.** −10°C 14°F   **9.** −30°C −22°F   **10.** −50°C
−58°F

Refer to the graph of Figure 2. Write the approximate speed for each distance traveled. (P-2)

11. 5 m 18 km/hr   **12.** 10 m 36 km/hr   **13.** 15 m 54 km/hr   **14.** 20 m
71 km/hr

Use the rule $F = 1.8C + 32$ to compute the Fahrenheit temperature corresponding to each Celsius temperature. (Example 1)

15. 45°C 113°F   **16.** −17°C 1.4°F   **17.** 22.5°C 72.5°F   **18.** 15.6°C
60.08°F

Latitude and Longitude

A special coordinate system is used to describe the position of a point on the earth's surface by **latitude** and **longitude**. The latitude and longitude of New York City to the nearest degree are:

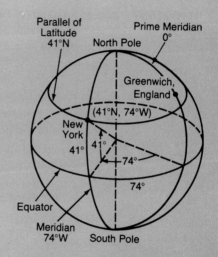

Lat. 41°N   Long. 74°W

This means that New York City is 41° north of the **equator** and 74° west of the **prime meridian.** A point south of the equator has <u>south latitude</u>. A point east of the prime meridian has <u>east longitude</u>.

If you know the latitude and longitude of two cities, then you can determine how the cities are situated with respect to each other.

EXAMPLES: In the table below, find the following.

    a. The northernmost city   **c.** The city directly south of Fargo
    b. The city directly west of Paris

City	Latitude	Longitude	City	Latitude	Longitude
Dallas, Texas	33°N	97°W	Rome, Italy	42°N	13°E
Durham, N.C.	36°N	79°W	Tacoma, Wash.	47°N	122°W
Fargo, N.D.	47°N	97°W	Toledo, Ohio	42°N	84°W
London, England	52°N	0°	Tokyo, Japan	36°N	140°E
Paris, France	49°N	2°E	Vancouver, B.C.	49°N	123°W

SOLUTIONS: **a. London** (greatest latitude, 52°N)
                b. Vancouver (same latitude as Paris, 49°N)
                c. Dallas (same longitude as Fargo, 97°W)

2. Tacoma, Washington
4. Durham, North Carolina
6. Tokyo, Japan

EXERCISES

In Exercises 1–6 use the table to find the following.

Ex. 2, 4, 6: see above.

1. The southernmost city   Dallas, Texas
2. The city directly west of Fargo
3. The city directly west of Rome   Toledo, Ohio
4. The city directly east of Tokyo
5. The city closest to London   Paris, France
6. The city farthest from London

7. Which of the cities in the table is most nearly <u>antipodal to</u> (at the opposite side of the earth from) Buenos Aires (Lat. 35°S Long. 56°W)?   Tokyo, Japan

Special Topic Application

285

CHAPTER SUMMARY

IMPORTANT TERMS	Linear function *(p. 263)* Ratio *(p. 271)*

IMPORTANT TERMS

Linear function *(p. 263)*
Y intercept *(p. 265)*
Slope *(p. 268)*
Slope-intercept form *(p. 268)*

Ratio *(p. 271)*
Parallel lines *(p. 276)*
X intercept *(p. 279)*

IMPORTANT IDEAS

1. The rule for a linear function is $y = ax + b$.

2. In the rule for the linear function $y = ax + b$, b represents the Y intercept of the graph.

3. In the rule for the linear function $y = ax + b$, a represents the slope of its graph.

4. The slope of a line is the ratio of the vertical motion to the horizontal motion from one point to another on the line.

5. *Slope Formula:* If (x_1, y_1) and (x_2, y_2) are coordinates of two points on a nonvertical line, then the slope a equals $\dfrac{y_2 - y_1}{x_2 - x_1}$.

6. If two lines have the same slope, they are parallel.

7. The rule of a relation having a vertical line as its graph is $x = k$ in which k is the X intercept of the line.

8. A vertical line does not have a slope.

CHAPTER REVIEW   NOTE: The Teacher's Resource Book contains two forms of each Chapter Test.

SECTION 11.1

Write Yes or No to show whether each function is linear.

1. $\{(x, y) : y = x^2 + 2x\}$ No

2. $\{(x, y) : y = 5 - 7x\}$ Yes

3. $\{(x, y) : y = -\frac{1}{2}x + \frac{3}{4}\}$ Yes

4. $\{(x, y) : y = |3x| - 2\}$ No

Graph at least four ordered pairs of each function. Then draw the graph with {real numbers} as the domain.   Each graph is a straight line. The coordinates of four points are given for each.

5. $\{(x, y) : y = -2x + 1\}$ (−1, 3), (0, 1), (1, −1), (2, −3)

6. $\{(x, y) : y = \frac{3}{2}x - 3\}$
(−2, −6), (0, −3), (2, 0), (4, 3)

SECTION 11.2

Write each Y intercept.

7. $y = 3x - 10$ −10

8. $y = -4x + 7$ 7

9. $y = -0.7x + 3.8$ ~3.8~

10. $y = 2.4x - 1.3$ ~-1.3~

SECTION 11.3

Write the slope-intercept form of the rule for each function.

11. The slope is 4 and the Y intercept is −1. $y = 4x - 1$

12. The slope is −2 and the Y intercept is 5. $y = -2x + 5$

13. The line crosses the Y axis at (0, 2.9) and has slope −2.8. $y = -2.8x + 2.9$

14. The line crosses the Y axis at (0, −5.3) and has slope 4.9. $y = 4.9x - 5.3$

Name the quadrants in which each graph lies.

15. $y = -7x$ II, IV

16. $y = 4x$ I, III

17. $y = \frac{5}{2}x$ I, III

18. $y = -0.3x$ II, IV

Write the slope of the graph of each function.

19. $y = -\frac{1}{2}x + 2$ $-\frac{1}{2}$

20. $y = \frac{5}{4}x - 3$ $\frac{5}{4}$

21. $y = 0.8x - 1.2$ 0.8

22. $y = -0.3x$ −0.3

SECTION 11.4

Write the slope of the line that contains the two points.

23. (4, −3); (−1, 7) −2

24. (−2, 4); (−1, −2) −6

25. $(-\frac{1}{2}, \frac{5}{2})$; $(\frac{3}{2}, -\frac{7}{2})$ −3

26. $(-\frac{3}{4}, -\frac{1}{4})$; $(\frac{5}{4}, -\frac{3}{4})$ $-\frac{1}{4}$

Write the slope-intercept form of the line that contains the two points.

27. (0, −2); (3, 4) $y = 2x - 2$

28. (0, 3); (−4, −2) $y = \frac{5}{4}x + 3$

29. $(0, -\frac{5}{2})$; $(4, \frac{1}{2})$ $y = \frac{3}{4}x - \frac{5}{2}$

30. $(0, \frac{3}{2})$; $(-2, \frac{1}{2})$ $y = \frac{1}{2}x + \frac{3}{2}$

SECTION 11.5

Ex. 31 and 32, each graph is a set of three parallel lines. Two points are are given for each line.

Graph the three functions in the same coordinate plane.

31. $y = \frac{1}{2}x - 2$ (0, −2), (4, 0)

$y = \frac{1}{2}x + 3$ (0, 3), (4, 5)

$y = \frac{1}{2}x$ (0, 0), (4, 2)

32. $y = x - 5$ (0, −5), (2, −3)

$y = x + 2$ (0, 2), (2, 4)

$y = x$ (0, 0), (3, 3)

Graph the functions in the same coordinate plane. The graphs of Ex. 33-36 are horizontal lines. One point is given.

33. $y = -3$ (0, –3)   **34.** $y = 4$ (0, 4)   **35.** $y = 3.5$ (0, 3.5)   **36.** $y = -\frac{5}{2}$

$(0, -\frac{5}{2})$

SECTION 11.6

Write each X intercept.

37. $y = -2x - 5$ $-2\frac{1}{2}$ **38.** $y = 3x + 8$ $-\frac{8}{3}$

39. $y = -\frac{1}{2}x + 4$ 8   **40.** $y = \frac{1}{4}x - 3$ 12

In Ex. 41-44 each graph is a straight line. Two points are given for each, one using the X intercept, *Graph each function by using only the X and Y intercepts.* the other the Y intercept.

41. $y = x + 1$ (–1, 0), (0, 1)   **42.** $y = -x + 1$ (1, 0), (0, 1)

43. $y = 3x - 6$ (2, 0), (0, –6)   **44.** $y = -2x + 4$ (2, 0), (0, 4)

Graph each linear relation. In Ex. 45-48 the graphs are vertical lines. One point is given for each line.

45. $x = -1$ (–1, 0)   **46.** $x = 2$ (2, 0)   **47.** $x = \frac{7}{2}$ $(\frac{7}{2}, 0)$ **48.** $x = -\frac{3}{2}$

$(-\frac{3}{2}, 0)$

SECTION 11.7

Compute the distance in meters that a car will travel at each given speed. Use $d = 0.28r$. Compare your answer with the approximate answer that you obtain from the graph of Figure 2 on page 282.

49. 70 km/hr 19.6 m   **50.** 32 km/hr 8.96 m   **51.** 45 km/hr 12.6 m   **52.** 28 km/hr

7.84 m

CHAPTER **12** # Systems of Linear Equations

Sections   **12.1**   **Linear Equations**

12.2   **Graphs**

12.3   **Systems of Equations**

12.4   **Substitution Method**

12.5   **Multiplication/Addition Method**

12.6   **2 × 2 Determinants**

12.7   **Solving Systems by Determinants**

Features   *Calculator Exercises:* **Checking a System of Equations**

Career: **Pharmacist**

**Review
and
Testing**

Review Capsules

Mid-Chapter Review

Chapter Summary

Chapter Review

Cumulative Review: **Chapters 7-12**

12.1 Linear Equations

OBJECTIVES: To write a given linear equation in the standard form
$Ax + By + C = 0$
To write a given linear equation in slope-intercept form

An equation such as $y = -2x + 3$ is called a **linear equation** in two variables. A linear equation is often written in standard form.

Note that two choices are available for standard form e.g., $2x - 3y - 7 = 0$ or $-2x + 3y + 7 = 0$.

> The **standard form of a linear equation** is $Ax + By + C = 0$, in which A, B, and C are integers. (A and B cannot both equal 0.)
>
> $5x - y + 4 = 0$
>
> $-x + y - 10 = 0$

P-1 **Which equation below is in standard form?** b.

a. $y = -2x + 7$ b. $2x - 3y - 5 = 0$ c. $-3x + y = 10$

example 1

Write $y = -2x + 3$ in standard form.

Solution:

1. Add $2x$ to each side. ⟶ $2x + y = 2x - 2x + 3$

2. Simplify. ⟶ $2x + y = 3$

3. Subtract 3 from each side. $2x + y - 3 = 3 - 3$

4. Simplify. ⟶ $2x + y - 3 = 0$

example 2

Write $5x + 3 = 2y$ in standard form.

Solution:

1. Add $-2y$ to each side. ⟶ $5x + 3 + (-2y) = 2y + (-2y)$

2. Simplify. ⟶ $5x + 3 + (-2y) = 0$

3. Commutative Property of Addition ⟶ $5x + (-2y) + 3 = 0$

4. Simplify. ⟶ $5x - 2y + 3 = 0$

A linear equation can also be written in slope-intercept form.

example 3

Write $x - 2y + 3 = 0$ in slope-intercept form.

Solution:

1. Add $2y$ to each side. ———————→ $x - 2y + 3 + 2y = 0 + 2y$

2. Simplify. ———————————→ $x + 3 = 2y$

3. Multiply each side by $\frac{1}{2}$. ————→ $\frac{1}{2}(x + 3) = \frac{1}{2}(2y)$

4. Distributive Property ————————→ $\frac{1}{2}x + \frac{3}{2} = y$ or

$$y = \frac{1}{2}x + \frac{3}{2}$$

P-2   **What is the slope-intercept form of each equation below?**

a. $x + y - 2 = 0$ 　　 **b.** $-2x + y + 5 = 0$ 　　 **c.** $4x - y - 10 = 0$
$y = -x + 2$ 　　　　　　　 $y = 2x - 5$ 　　　　　　　　 $y = 4x - 10$

CLASSROOM EXERCISES

Write <u>Yes</u> *or* <u>No</u> *to tell whether each linear equation is in standard form.* (P-1)

1. $2x - 3y + 5 = 0$ Yes 　　　　 **2.** $x - y = 3$ No 　　　　 **3.** $x - y = 0$ Yes

4. $y - x = 0$ No 　　　　　　 **5.** $y - 3x + 2 = 0$ No 　　 **6.** $2x + 1 = 3y$ No

7. $y = -2x + 5$ No 　　　　 **8.** $x - y - 1 = 0$ Yes 　　 **9.** $x + y = 7$ No

10. $3x - 5 = 2y$ No 　　 **11.** $\frac{1}{2}x - y + \frac{1}{3} = 0$ No 　　 **12.** $3x - 2y + 0.5 = 0$ No

In Ex. 13-21 another answer can be given. For example, $-x - y + 5 = 0$, is the other answer to Ex. 13.

Write the standard form of each linear equation. (Examples 1 and 2)

13. $x + y = 5$ $x + y - 5 = 0$ 　　 **14.** $2x = 4 - y$ $2x + y - 4 = 0$ 　　 $3x - y - 1 = 0$
15. $y = 3x - 1$

16. $x - 6 = y$ $x - y - 6 = 0$ 　　 **17.** $2y - 7 = 3x$ $3x - 2y + 7 = 0$ 　　 **18.** $-2y + x = -11$
$x - 2y + 11 = 0$

19. $-12x = 15 - y$ $12x - y + 15 = 0$ 　 **20.** $3x - 2 = \frac{1}{2}y$ $6x - y - 4 = 0$ 　　 **21.** $x = y$ $x - y = 0$

Write the slope-intercept form of each equation. (Example 3)

22. $x + y = 5$ $y = -x + 5$ 　　　　　　　 **23.** $-2x + y - 1 = 0$ $y = 2x + 1$

24. $y + 6 = 5x$ $y = 5x - 6$ 　　　　　　 **25.** $3x - y + 2 = 0$ 　 $y = 3x + 2$

26. $2x = y - 5$ $y = 2x + 5$ 　　　　　　 **27.** $-x + y - 5 = 0$ 　 $y = x + 5$

28. $2x - 4 = 2y$ $y = x - 2$ 　　　　　　 **29.** $x + 2y - 6 = 0$ 　 $y = -\frac{1}{2}x + 3$

WRITTEN EXERCISES

See the Teacher's Manual for the suggested assignments.

Goals: To write the standard and slope-intercept forms of linear equations

Sample Problem: Write $7y = -14x + 21$ in standard form and in slope-intercept form.

Answers: Standard Form: $14x + 7y - 21 = 0$

Slope-Intercept Form: $y = -2x + 3$

In Ex. 1-18 another answer can be written. For example, $-3x + y + 5 = 0$ is the other answer for Ex. 1.

Write each equation in standard form. (Examples 1 and 2)

1. $y = 3x - 5$ $3x - y - 5 = 0$
2. $y = -x + 3$ $x + y - 3 = 0$
3. $2x + 3y = 10$ $2x + 3y - 10 = 0$

4. $5x - 2y = -2$ $5x - 2y + 2 = 0$
5. $y - 3x = -3$ $3x - y - 3 = 0$
6. $y - 5x = 1$ $5x - y + 1 = 0$

7. $-3y = 12 - 4x$ $4x - 3y - 12 = 0$
8. $-5y = -5x - 1$ $5x - 5y + 1 = 0$
9. $6y - 3 = x$ $x - 6y + 3 = 0$

10. $12 - 9y = 4x$ $4x + 9y - 12 = 0$
11. $2y = 3(x - 2)$ $3x - 2y - 6 = 0$
12. $3y = -2(x + 3)$ $2x + 3y + 6 = 0$

13. $2(x + 4) = -3(2y - 1)$ $2x + 6y + 5 = 0$
14. $-5(x - y) = 4(2y + x)$ $9x + 3y = 0$
15. $2x - 3y = 2 + 5x$ $3x + 3y + 2 = 0$

16. $y - 3x = 2 - 5y$ $3x - 6y + 2 = 0$
17. $y - x = 2y + 3x$ $4x + y = 0$
18. $x - 4y = y - x$ $2x - 5y = 0$

Write each equation in slope-intercept form. (Example 3)

19. $x + y - 2 = 0$ $y = -x + 2$
20. $2x + y + 5 = 0$ $y = -2x - 5$
21. $-3x - y + 5 = 0$ $y = -3x + 5$

22. $-5x - y - 2 = 0$ $y = -5x - 2$
23. $x + 2y - 3 = 0$ $y = -\frac{1}{2}x + \frac{3}{2}$
24. $2x + 3y + 1 = 0$ $y = -\frac{2}{3}x - \frac{1}{3}$

25. $5x - 2y + 1 = 0$ $y = \frac{5}{2}x + \frac{1}{2}$
26. $3x - 5y - 10 = 0$ $y = \frac{3}{5}x - 2$
27. $8x - 4y - 12 = 0$ $y = 2x - 3$

28. $9x - 3y - 12 = 0$ $y = 3x - 4$
29. $3x = 2y - 5$ $y = \frac{3}{2}x + \frac{5}{2}$
30. $-2x = 3y - 2$ $y = -\frac{2}{3}x + \frac{2}{3}$

31. $x - 5y = -2$ $y = \frac{1}{5}x + \frac{2}{5}$
32. $2x - 5y = -5$ $y = \frac{2}{5}x + 1$
33. $-y + 0.4x = -1.6x - 6$ $y = 2x + 6$

34. $x - 2.3y = 0.7y + 1$
35. $-5x = 7y$ $y = -\frac{5}{7}x$
36. $11x = -5y$ $y = -\frac{11}{5}x$

$y = \frac{1}{3}x - \frac{1}{3}$

MORE CHALLENGING EXERCISES

Write each equation in slope-intercept form.

37. $x = \frac{2}{3}y - 6$ $y = \frac{3}{2}x + 9$
38. $x = \frac{3}{4}y + 6$ $y = \frac{4}{3}x - 8$
39. $x - \frac{1}{2}y - 2 = 0$ $y = 2x - 4$

40. $2x - \frac{3}{2}y + 5 = 0$ $y = \frac{4}{3}x + \frac{10}{3}$
41. $\frac{4}{3}y - x = 12$ $y = \frac{3}{4}x + 9$
42. $\frac{2}{5}y + \frac{1}{15} = x$ $y = \frac{5}{2}x - \frac{1}{6}$

REVIEW CAPSULE FOR SECTION 12.2

Find the value of y for each given value of x. (Section 6.5)

1. $2x - y - 3 = 0;\ x = 1$ -1
2. $-x + 4y + 2 = 0;\ x = 6$ 1
3. $3x + 2y - 1 = 0;\ x = 4$ $-\frac{11}{2}$

4. $5x - 3y + 1 = 0;\ x = 2$ $\frac{11}{3}$
5. $2x - 4y = -5;\ x = -4$ $-\frac{3}{4}$
6. $-5x - 2y = 12;\ x = -3$ $\frac{3}{2}$

12.2 Graphs

OBJECTIVE: To graph the solution set of a linear equation

When you graph a linear equation, you graph its solution set. The **solution set of a linear equation** is the set of ordered pairs (x, y) that make the equation true.

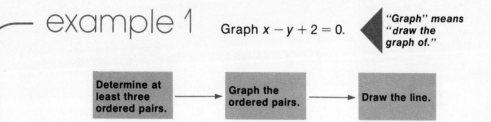

example 1   Graph $x - y + 2 = 0$.

"Graph" means "draw the graph of."

Determine at least three ordered pairs.	→	Graph the ordered pairs.	→	Draw the line.

Solution: It is usually easy to find the value of y when x equals 0. Similarly, it is usually easy to find the value of x when y equals 0.

Let $x = 0$.

$0 - y + 2 = 0$

$y = 2$

Let $y = 0$.

$x - 0 + 2 = 0$

$x = -2$

Let $x = 2$.

$2 - y + 2 = 0$

$y = 4$

x	y
0	2
−2	0
2	4

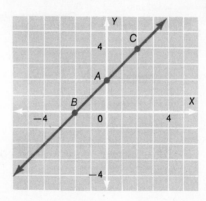

The solution set of $x - y + 2 = 0$ is the set of coordinates of points on the line containing points A, B and C. Thus the solution set is infinite.

P-1   **What is the y value of point A called?   the x value of point B?**

The Y intercept   The X intercept

The intercepts are often used to locate two points on a graph. Other x or y values with small absolute values are then selected.

example 2

Graph $3x + 2y - 5 = 0$.

Solution:

$3(0) + 2y - 5 = 0$ ◀ **Let x = 0.**

$2y - 5 = 0$

$2y = 5$

$y = 2\frac{1}{2}$

$3x + 2(0) - 5 = 0$ ◀ **Let y = 0.**

$3x - 5 = 0$

$3x = 5$

$x = 1\frac{2}{3}$

$3(3) + 2y - 5 = 0$ ◀ **Let x = 3.**

$9 + 2y - 5 = 0$

$2y + 4 = 0$

$2y = -4$

$y = -2$

x	y
0	$2\frac{1}{2}$
$1\frac{2}{3}$	0
3	-2

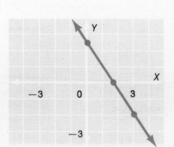

P-2 **What other ordered pair with integral values for x and y can you identify from the graph?** $(3, -2)$

◀ *"Integral values" means "values that are integers."*

example 3

Graph $x - 2y - 3 = 0$. Use the slope-intercept form.

Solution:

$x - 2y - 3 = 0$

$x - 3 = 2y$

$\frac{1}{2}(x - 3) = y$

Slope-intercept form ▶

$\frac{1}{2}x - \frac{3}{2} = y$

$y = \frac{1}{2}x - \frac{3}{2}$

Let x = 0. ▶ $y = \frac{1}{2}(0) - \frac{3}{2}$

$y = -\frac{3}{2}$

Let y = 0. ▶ $0 = \frac{1}{2}x - \frac{3}{2}$

$3 = x$

Let x = -3. ▶ $y = \frac{1}{2}(-3) - \frac{3}{2}$

$y = -3$

x	y
0	$-\frac{3}{2}$
3	0
-3	-3

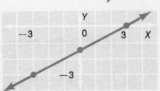

CLASSROOM EXERCISES

Write the unknown values in each table. (Example 1)

1. $x + y - 2 = 0$

x	0	?	4
y	?	0	?

2. $x - y + 1 = 0$

x	0	?	?
y	?	0	3

3. $x - 2y = 0$

x	-2	?	?
y	?	0	1

4. $2x + y - 3 = 0$

x	0	?	-1
y	?	0	?

5. $x - y = 5$

x	0	?	2
y	?	0	?

6. $2x + 3y = 6$

x	0	?	?
y	?	0	-2

7. $x - 3y - 5 = 0$

x	0	?	-4
y	?	0	?

8. $y - 3 = 2x$

x	0	?	-4
y	?	0	?

WRITTEN EXERCISES

See the Teacher's Manual for the suggested assignments.

Goal: To graph the solution sets of linear equations

Sample Problem: $x + 3y + 3 = 0$

Answer: See the graph at the right.

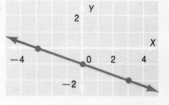

In Ex. 1-8 each graph is a straight line. Three ordered pairs from the Classroom Exercises above are given.

Graph each of the following. Use the tables in the Classroom Exercises. (Examples 1–3)

1. $x + y - 2 = 0$
(0, 2), (2, 0), (4, −2)

2. $x - y + 1 = 0$
(0, 1), (−1, 0), (2, 3)

3. $x - 2y = 0$
• (−2, −1), (0, 0), (2, 1)

4. $2x + y - 3 = 0$
(0, 3), ($\frac{3}{2}$, 0), (−1, 5)

5. $x - y = 5$
(0, −5), (5, 0), (2, −3)

6. $2x + 3y = 6$
(0, 2), (3, 0), (6, −2)

7. $x - 3y - 5 = 0$
(0, $-\frac{5}{3}$), (5, 0), (−4, −3)

8. $y - 3 = 2x$
(0, 3), ($-\frac{3}{2}$, 0), (−4, −5)

Graph each of the following. (Examples 1–3) In Ex. 9-17, each graph is a straight line. Two points are given for each line.

9. $3x - 2y - 5 = 0$ (1, −1), (3, 2)

10. $4x - 2y + 3 = 0$ (−1, $-\frac{1}{2}$), (1, $\frac{7}{2}$)

11. $4y - x = -10$
(−2, −3), (2, −2)

12. $5y - 2x = 3$ (−4, −1), (1, 1)

13. $4x - 5y = 0$ (0, 0), (5, 4)

14. $3y - 5x = 0$
(0, 0), (3, 5)

15. $5x + 5y + 5 = 0$ (−1, 0), (2, −3)

16. $3x - 3y - 3 = 0$ (−2, −3), (3, 2)

17. $y - 3x = -6$
(0, −6), (2, 0)

REVIEW CAPSULE FOR SECTION 12.3

Substitute to find one of the following ordered pairs that is in the solution set of both equations. (Section 6.5)

$$(-3, 14) \quad (-3, -2) \quad (-1, 2) \quad (3, -10) \quad (-1, 1)$$

1. $\begin{cases} 2x - y + 4 = 0 \\ x + y - 1 = 0 \end{cases}$ (−1, 2)

2. $\begin{cases} x + 2y - 1 = 0 \\ x - 2y + 3 = 0 \end{cases}$ (−1, 1)

3. $\begin{cases} 4x + y - 2 = 0 \\ -3x - y + 5 = 0 \end{cases}$ (−3, 14)

12.3 Systems of Equations

OBJECTIVE: To solve a system of two linear equations by graphing

 example 1

Graph both linear equations in the same coordinate plane.

$$\begin{cases} \textbf{1.}\ x - 3y - 3 = 0 \\ \textbf{2.}\ 2x - y + 4 = 0 \end{cases}$$

Solution:

1.

x	y
0	−1
3	0
6	1

2.

x	y
0	4
−2	0
−1	2

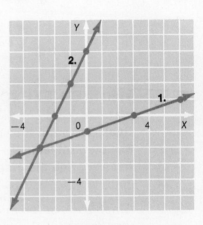

P-1   **What are the coordinates of the common point of the two graphs?**
(−3, −2)

Two equations such as **1** and **2** in Example 1 form a **system of equations.**

The solution set of the system of Example 1 is {(−3, −2)}. This is checked below.

Check: 1. $x - 3y - 3 = 0$

$-3 - 3(-2) - 3$

$-3 + 6 - 3$

0

2. $2x - y + 4 = 0$

$2(-3) - (-2) + 4$

$-6 + 2 + 4$

0

◀ *(−3, −2) makes both equations true.*

> The **solution set of a system of two equations** is the set of ordered pairs that make both equations true.

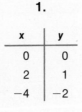example 2   Solve the system below by graphing. Check.

$$\begin{cases} \textbf{1.} & x - 2y = 0 \\ \textbf{2.} & x + y - 3 = 0 \end{cases}$$

Solution:

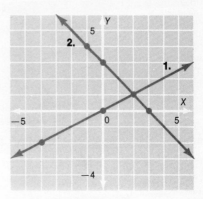

1.

x	y
0	0
2	1
−4	−2

2.

x	y
0	3
3	0
−1	4

Now check the solution set {(2, 1)}.

1. $x - 2y = 0$

$2 - 2(1)$

0

2. $x + y - 3 = 0$

$2 + 1 - 3$

0

example 3   Solve the system below by graphing.

$$\begin{cases} \textbf{1.} & x - 2y + 2 = 0 \\ \textbf{2.} & x - 2y - 4 = 0 \end{cases}$$

Solution:

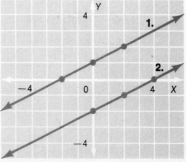

1.

x	y
0	1
−2	0
2	2

2.

x	y
0	−2
4	0
2	−1

The graphs appear to be parallel. If this is true, the solution set of the system is the empty set, ϕ. To check this, write the equations in slope-intercept form.

Each equation is now written in slope-intercept form.

1.

$$x - 2y + 2 = 0$$
$$x + 2 = 2y$$
$$\tfrac{1}{2}(x + 2) = y$$
$$\tfrac{1}{2}x + 1 = y$$
$$y = \tfrac{1}{2}x + 1$$

2.

$$x - 2y - 4 = 0$$
$$x - 4 = 2y$$
$$\tfrac{1}{2}(x - 4) = y$$
$$\tfrac{1}{2}x - 2 = y$$
$$y = \tfrac{1}{2}x - 2$$

◀ The slope of each line is $\tfrac{1}{2}$.

Since the slopes of the lines are equal, the lines are parallel.
The solution set of the system is the empty set, ϕ.

CLASSROOM EXERCISES

Write Yes or No to tell whether each given set is the solution set of the system following it. (Checks of Examples 1 and 2)

1. $\{(1, 1)\}$; $\begin{cases} x + y = 2 \\ x - y = 3 \end{cases}$ No

2. $\{(3, -2)\}$; $\begin{cases} x + y - 1 = 0 \\ x - y + 1 = 0 \end{cases}$ No

3. $\{(0, 0)\}$; $\begin{cases} x + 2y = 0 \\ 2x - y = 0 \end{cases}$ Yes

4. $\{(0, 1)\}$; $\begin{cases} 2x - y + 1 = 0 \\ x + y - 1 = 0 \end{cases}$ Yes

5. $\{(0, 1)\}$; $\begin{cases} x - y - 2 = 0 \\ 3x - y + 1 = 0 \end{cases}$ No

6. $\{(2, -1)\}$; $\begin{cases} x - 2 = 0 \\ y + 1 = 0 \end{cases}$ Yes

7. ϕ; $\begin{cases} y = 2x - 1 \\ y = 2x + 3 \end{cases}$ Yes

8. $\{(-1, 5)\}$; $\begin{cases} x + 1 = 0 \\ y = 5 \end{cases}$ Yes

9. $\{(0, \tfrac{2}{3})\}$; $\begin{cases} 2x + 3y - 2 = 0 \\ 2x - 3y + 2 = 0 \end{cases}$ Yes

10. $\{(50, 50)\}$; $\begin{cases} x + y - 100 = 0 \\ x - y = 0 \end{cases}$ Yes

Write the solution set of each system from its graph. (P-1)

11.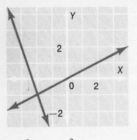

12.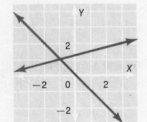

13.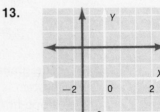

11. $\{(-2, -1)\}$

12. $\{(-1, 1)\}$

13. $\{(-1\tfrac{1}{2}, 2)\}$

WRITTEN EXERCISES

See the Teacher's Manual for the suggested assignments.

Goal: To solve systems of linear equations by graphing

Sample Problem: Solve by graphing and

check: $\begin{cases} \textbf{1.}\ 2x - y = 7 \\ \textbf{2.}\ 5x + 2y = 4 \end{cases}$

Answer: $\{(2, -3)\}$; see the graph at the right.

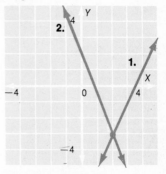

Solve each system by graphing. Check. (Examples 1–3)

1. $\begin{cases} x + y - 4 = 0 \\ x - y + 2 = 0 \end{cases}$ $\{(1, 3)\}$

2. $\begin{cases} x + y + 3 = 0 \\ x - y - 1 = 0 \end{cases}$ $\{(-1, -2)\}$

3. $\begin{cases} 2x + y - 2 = 0 \\ x - y + 5 = 0 \end{cases}$ $\{(-1, 4)\}$

4. $\begin{cases} x - 2y + 3 = 0 \\ 2x + 2y - 6 = 0 \end{cases}$ $\{(1, 2)\}$

5. $\begin{cases} 2x + y = -2 \\ 2x + 3y = 6 \end{cases}$ $\{(-3, 4)\}$

6. $\begin{cases} 2x + y = 1 \\ 4x - 2y = 6 \end{cases}$ $\{(1, -1)\}$

7. $\begin{cases} x - 2y + 3 = 0 \\ 2x - 4y - 1 = 0 \end{cases}$ ϕ

8. $\begin{cases} 2x + y - 1 = 0 \\ 4x + 2y + 1 = 0 \end{cases}$ ϕ

9. $\begin{cases} x = 5 \\ y = -2 \end{cases}$ $\{(5, -2)\}$

10. $\begin{cases} x = -3 \\ y = 4 \end{cases}$ $\{(-3, 4)\}$

11. $\begin{cases} 2x - 3y = 0 \\ 5x + 2y = 0 \end{cases}$ $\{(0, 0)\}$

12. $\begin{cases} y - 3x = 0 \\ -2x - 3y = 0 \end{cases}$ $\{(0, 0)\}$

13. $\begin{cases} x - y = 0 \\ x + y = 0 \end{cases}$ $\{(0, 0)\}$

14. $\begin{cases} 2y - 3x = 0 \\ 3y + 2x = 0 \end{cases}$ $\{(0, 0)\}$

15. $\begin{cases} 2x - y = 5 \\ x - 3y = 10 \end{cases}$ $\{(1, -3)\}$

16. $\begin{cases} 3x - y - 5 = 0 \\ x + y + 1 = 0 \end{cases}$ $\{(1, -2)\}$

17. $\begin{cases} y = -x + 6 \\ y = 5 \end{cases}$ $\{(1, 5)\}$

18. $\begin{cases} 2x - y = 1 \\ x = 4 \end{cases}$ $\{(4, 7)\}$

MORE CHALLENGING EXERCISES

19. $\begin{cases} x + 2y + 4 = 0 \\ -7x + 2y - 4 = 0 \end{cases}$ $\{(-1, -\frac{3}{2})\}$

20. $\begin{cases} x - 3y - 1 = 0 \\ 2x + 3y + 4 = 0 \end{cases}$ $\{(-1, -\frac{2}{3})\}$

21. $\begin{cases} 2x - y = 10 \\ x - 2y = 4 \end{cases}$ $\{(\frac{16}{3}, \frac{2}{3})\}$

REVIEW CAPSULE FOR SECTION 12.4

Solve each equation. (Section 3.4)

1. $2x - 3(x - 5) = 6$ $x = 9$

2. $x + 2(x + 2) = -4$ $x = -\frac{8}{3}$

3. $3x - 2(2x - 1) = 4$ $x = -2$

4. $-3x + 2(-3x + 1) = -7$ $x = 1$

5. $5(-y + 3) - 2y = 8$ $y = 1$

6. $5(-2y + 1) - 2y = 6$

     $y = -\frac{1}{12}$

12.4 Substitution Method

OBJECTIVE: To solve a system of two linear equations by the substitution method

You have often replaced a variable by a number or expression. This process is called <u>substitution</u>. You can solve systems of linear equations by the **substitution method.**

Advise students to look
for a variable whose coefficient
is 1. Then solve for that variable.

 example 1

Solve the system below by the substitution method.

$$\begin{cases} 1.\ y = 2x - 3 \\ 2.\ 2x + 3y = 7 \end{cases}$$

Solution:

$2x + 3y = 7$

1	Substitute $2x - 3$ for y in Equation 2.	⟶	$2x + 3(2x - 3) = 7$
2	Distributive Property	⟶	$2x + 6x - 9 = 7$
3	Add like terms.	⟶	$8x - 9 = 7$
4	Addition Property of Equality	⟶	$8x = 16$
5	Division Property of Equality	⟶	$x = 2$

Substitute 2 for x in either equation. Then solve for y.

$$1.\ y = 2x - 3$$
$$y = 2(2) - 3$$
$$y = 1$$

The solution set of the system is $\{(2, 1)\}$.

Check: 1. $y = 2x - 3$

$$1\ \bigg|\ 2(2) - 3$$
$$\longrightarrow 1$$

2. $2x + 3y = 7$

$$2(2) + 3(1)\ \bigg|\ 7$$
$$4 + 3$$
$$7 \longleftarrow$$

example 2

Solve the system by the substitution method.

$$\begin{cases} 1.\ 2x + 3y - 1 = 0 \\ 2.\ x - 2y + 3 = 0 \end{cases}$$

Solution:

$x - 2y + 3 = 0$

1	Write Equation 2 with x alone on one side.	⟶	$x = 2y - 3$

$$2x + 3y - 1 = 0$$

② Substitute $2y - 3$ for x in **1.** ⟶ $2(2y - 3) + 3y - 1 = 0$

③ Solve for y. ⟶ $4y - 6 + 3y - 1 = 0$

$$7y - 7 = 0$$
$$7y = 7$$
$$y = 1$$

④ Substitute 1 for y in either equation. ⟶ $x - 2y + 3 = 0$

$$x - 2(1) + 3 = 0$$

⑤ Solve for x. ⟶ $x + 1 = 0$

$$x = -1$$

The solution set is $\{(-1, 1)\}$.

Check: 1. 　　$2x + 3y - 1 = 0$　　　　**2.** 　　$x - 2y + 3 = 0$

　　　　　　$2(-1) + 3(1) - 1$　　　　　　　　$-1 - 2(1) + 3$

　　　　　　　$-2 + 3 - 1$　　　　　　　　　　$-1 - 2 + 3$

　　　　　　　　　0 ⟵　　　　　　　　　　　　0 ⟵

P-1 **What expression from $y = 2x - 3$ could be substituted for y in $x = \frac{1}{2}y + 2$?** Solve Equation 1 for y; then $2x - 3$ is the expression.

P-2 **What expression from $x = \frac{1}{2}y + 2$ could be substituted for x in $2x - y = 3$?** $\frac{1}{2}y + 2$

example 3   Solve the system by the substitution method.

$$\begin{cases} \textbf{1.} \ 2x - y = 3 \\ \textbf{2.} \ x = \frac{1}{2}y + 2 \end{cases}$$

Solution: 　　　　　　　　　　　　　　　　$2x - y = 3$

① Substitute $\frac{1}{2}y + 2$ for x in Equation 1. ⟶ $2(\frac{1}{2}y + 2) - y = 3$

② Solve for y. ⟶ $y + 4 - y = 3$

$$4 = 3$$ **False sentence**

The resulting sentence is false. Therefore, the solution set of the system is ϕ.

> **Steps of the Substitution Method**
>
> 1. Change one equation, if necessary, to get one variable by itself on one side of the equation.
> 2. Substitute an expression for that variable in the other equation.
> 3. Solve the resulting equation for one number of the ordered pair.
> 4. Substitute this value in either equation for the other number of the ordered pair.

CLASSROOM EXERCISES

Write an equivalent equation that has a variable with coefficient 1 on one side. (Step 1 of Example 2)   In Ex. 1-6 other answers can also be given.

EXAMPLE: $2x + y = 2$ **ANSWER:** $y = 2 - 2x$ or $y = -2x + 2$

1. $x - 2y = 3$ $\quad x = 2y + 3$
2. $3y + x = -5$ $\quad x = -3y - 5$
3. $x + 3y - 1 = 0$ $\quad x = 1 - 3y$
4. $y + 3 = 5x$ $\quad y = 5x - 3$
5. $x - 3 = -3y$ $\quad x = 3 - 3y$
6. $y - x - 1 = 0$ $\quad y = x + 1$

In Ex. 7-9 other answers can also be given.

Write the equation that results after making a substitution for one of the variables. (Step 1 of Example 1, Step 2 of Example 2)

7. $\begin{cases} y = 2x - 3 \\ x + y - 5 = 0 \end{cases}$ $\quad x + (2x - 3) - 5 = 0$
8. $\begin{cases} x = -3y + 4 \\ x - 2y + 1 = 0 \end{cases}$ $\quad (-3y + 4) - 2y + 1 = 0$
9. $\begin{cases} -2x + 5y - 2 = 0 \\ 3y - x + 1 = 0 \end{cases}$ $\quad -2(3y + 1) + 5y - 2 = 0$

WRITTEN EXERCISES

See the Teacher's Manual for the suggested assignments.

Goal: To solve systems of linear equations by the substitution method

Sample Problem: $\begin{cases} x + y - 5 = 0 \\ 2x - y + 2 = 0 \end{cases}$ **Answer:** $\{(1, 4)\}$ 6. $\{(5, -5)\}$
9. $\{3, -4)\}$

Solve each system by the substitution method. Check. (Examples 1-3)

1. $\begin{cases} y = x - 4 \\ 2x - 5y = 2 \end{cases}$ $\{(6, 2)\}$
2. $\begin{cases} y = -x + 2 \\ 2x - y - 1 = 0 \end{cases}$ $\{(1, 1)\}$
3. $\begin{cases} x - y = 4 \\ 2x - 3y = -2 \end{cases}$ $\{(14, 10)\}$

4. $\begin{cases} x - y = 3 \\ 5x + y = -15 \end{cases}$ $\{(-2, -5)\}$
5. $\begin{cases} x - 2y + 2 = 0 \\ 2x - 3y - 2 = 0 \end{cases}$ $\{(10, 6)\}$
6. $\begin{cases} 2x + y - 5 = 0 \\ 8x - y - 45 = 0 \end{cases}$ See above.

7. $\begin{cases} y = -3x + 4 \\ x = -\frac{1}{3}y + 2 \end{cases}$ ϕ
8. $\begin{cases} x = 2y - 1 \\ y = \frac{1}{2}x - 3 \end{cases}$ ϕ
9. $\begin{cases} 4x - 8 = -y \\ 5x - 3 = -3y \end{cases}$ See above.

10. $\begin{cases} 3x - 16 = -2y \\ 7x - 19 = -y \end{cases}$ $\{(2, 5)\}$
11. $\begin{cases} y = \frac{5}{2}x - 2 \\ 11x - 4y - 8 = 0 \end{cases}$ $\{(0, -2)\}$
12. $\begin{cases} x = -\frac{3}{2}y + 2 \\ 2x + 4y - 4 = 0 \end{cases}$ $\{(2, 0)\}$

MID-CHAPTER REVIEW

NOTE: After completing the Mid-Chapter Review, you may want to administer a quiz covering the same sections. See pages M-32 and M-33 of the Teacher's Manual for the suggested quiz.

Write each equation in standard form. (Section 12.1)

1. $y = -2x + 11$ $2x + y - 11 = 0$

2. $2x - 5y = 17$ $2x - 5y - 17 = 0$

3. $-2y - 5x = 13$
$5x + 2y + 13 = 0$

In Ex. 4-6 each is a graph of a line. Two points on each line are given.

Graph each of the following equations. (Section 12.2)

4. $4x + y - 1 = 0$ (0, 1), (1, −3)

5. $3x - y - 4 = 0$ (0, −4), (2, 2)

6. $3x - 4y + 8 = 0$
(0, 2), (1, $\frac{11}{4}$)

Solve each system by graphing. Check. (Section 12.3)

7. $\begin{cases} 5x - 6y - 8 = 0 \\ 2x - y + 1 = 0 \end{cases}$ $\{(-2, -3)\}$

8. $\begin{cases} x - 3y + 6 = 0 \\ 4x + 3y + 9 = 0 \end{cases}$ $\{(-3, 1)\}$

9. $\begin{cases} x + 2y + 2 = 0 \\ 5x + 2y - 6 = 0 \end{cases}$
$\{(2, -2)\}$

Solve each system by the substitution method. (Section 12.4)

10. $\begin{cases} y = 2x - 3 \\ x - 2y = 9 \end{cases}$ $\{(-1, -5)\}$

11. $\begin{cases} x = -3y + 1 \\ 2x + 3y = 5 \end{cases}$ $\{(4, -1)\}$

12. $\begin{cases} 4x - y - 3 = 0 \\ 2x - y + 3 = 0 \end{cases}$
$\{(3, 9)\}$

 ———— *CHECKING A SYSTEM OF EQUATIONS* ————

You can use a calculator to check whether a given ordered pair is a solution of a system of equations.

EXAMPLE   Check the solution set, $\{(-1, 1)\}$, of Example 2 on page 300.

SOLUTION   **1.** $2x + 3y - 1 = 0$

Pressing MR is the same as if you entered on the keyboard what is stored in memory.

Store "2 · (−1)" in memory before adding it to "3 · (1)."

$\boxed{0.}$

2. $x - 2y + 3 = 0$ This equation is left for you to check.

1-6. Use a calculator to do Exercises 1-6 on page 298.

1. No   2. No   3. Yes   4. Yes   5. No   6. Yes

REVIEW CAPSULE FOR SECTION 12.5

Multiply each side of the first equation by −2 and each side of the second equation by 3. In which exercise does the new system have opposite coefficients for x?   for y?   for neither x nor y? (Section 3.2)

$-6x + 4y + 16 = 0$

1. $\begin{cases} 3x - y = 14 & -6x + 2y = -28 \\ 2x + 4y = 14 & 6x + 12y = 42 \end{cases}$

2. $\begin{cases} 2x + 3y = 22 & -4x - 6y = -44 \\ 5x + 2y = 36 & 15x + 6y = 108 \end{cases}$

3. $\begin{cases} 3x - 2y - 8 = 0 \\ -2x + 3y + 12 = 0 \end{cases}$
$-6x + 9y + 36 = 0$

Opposite coefficients for x: Ex. 1
Opposite coefficients for y: Ex. 2
Neither: Ex. 3

12.5 Multiplication/Addition Method

OBJECTIVE: To solve a system of two linear equations by the Multiplication/Addition Method

Explain that the new equation can be used with either equation in the given system to form a new system that is equivalent to the original system.

Sometimes you can solve a system of equations by adding the corresponding sides of the two equations to obtain a new equation with only one variable. This method is called the **addition method.**

example 1

Solve: $\begin{cases} \textbf{1.} & x - y = -1 \\ \textbf{2.} & x + y = 5 \end{cases}$

Solution:

1	Write the system. ⟶	$\begin{cases} x - y = -1 \\ x + y = 5 \end{cases}$	*Note: The y terms, y and −y, are opposites. −y + y = 0*
2	Add the left and right sides. ⟶	$2x + 0 = 4$	
3	Solve for x. ⟶	$x = 2$	
4	Substitute 2 for x in either equation **1** or **2**. ⟶	$2 + y = 5$	*Equation 2 is used.*
5	Solve for y. ⟶	$y = 3$	

The solution set is $\{(2, 3)\}$.   The check is left for you.

When you add the corresponding sides of the equations of a system you may get an equation that has two variables rather than only one. The following example illustrates how to solve such systems. The procedure is called the **multiplication/addition** method.

example 2

Solve: $\begin{cases} \textbf{1.} & x - y + 1 = 0 \\ \textbf{2.} & 2x - 3y + 1 = 0 \end{cases}$

Solution:

1	Multiply each side of **1** by −2. ⟶	$-2x + 2y - 2 = 0$	*The coefficients of x are now opposites.*
2	Rewrite equation **2**. ⟶	$2x - 3y + 1 = 0$	
3	Add and solve for y. ⟶	$-y - 1 = 0$	
		$y = -1$	
4	Substitute −1 for y in either **1** or **2**. ⟶	$x - (-1) + 1 = 0$	*Equation 1 is used.*
		$x + 1 + 1 = 0$	
		$x + 2 = 0$	
		$x = -2$	

The solution set is $\{(-2, -1)\}$. *The check is left for you.*

P-1 **Multiply each side of equation 1 by a number that will make opposite coefficients for x.** a. Mult. by 3; b. Mult. by −1; c. Mult. by −7.

a. $\begin{cases} \textbf{1. } x + y = 7 \\ \textbf{2. } -3x + 2y = 4 \end{cases}$
b. $\begin{cases} \textbf{1. } x - 6y = -5 \\ \textbf{2. } x + 2y = 11 \end{cases}$
c. $\begin{cases} \textbf{1. } x + 2y = -2 \\ \textbf{2. } 7x - 5y = 43 \end{cases}$

In Example 1, it was necessary to multiply the corresponding sides of only one of the equations to eliminate a variable. It is sometimes necessary to multiply corresponding sides of <u>both</u> equations by numbers that will make opposite coefficients for one variable.

 example 3 Solve: $\begin{cases} \textbf{1. } 2x - 3y = -1 \\ \textbf{2. } -3x + 5y = 2 \end{cases}$

Solution:

1. Multiply each side of **1** by 3. ⟶ $6x - 9y = -3$ ◀ The coefficients of x are now opposites.
2. Multiply each side of **2** by 2. ⟶ $-6x + 10y = 4$
3. Add. ⟶ $y = 1$
4. Substitute 1 for y in either **1** or **2**. ⟶ $2x - 3(1) = -1$ ◀ Equation 1 is used.

$$2x - 3 = -1$$
$$2x = 2$$
$$x = 1$$

The solution set is $\{(1, 1)\}$. ◀ The check is left for you.

Steps for the Multiplication/Addition Method

1. Check for opposite coefficients of one variable. If necessary, multiply each side of either or both equations by numbers that will make opposite coefficients for one variable.

2. Add the corresponding sides to eliminate one of the variables.

3. Solve for the remaining variable.

4. Substitute the value from Step 3 in one of the equations. Solve for the other variable.

P-2 **Multiply each side of both equations by numbers that will make the two coefficients of y into opposites.**

a. $\begin{cases} \textbf{1. } 3x + 8y = -16 \\ \textbf{2. } 4x - 5y = 10 \end{cases}$
Eq. 1: Mult. by 5.
Eq. 2: Mult. by 8.

b. $\begin{cases} \textbf{1. } 2x - 3y = -11 \\ \textbf{2. } 5x + 4y = 30 \end{cases}$
Eq. 1: Mult. by 4.
Eq. 2: Mult. by 3.

c. $\begin{cases} \textbf{1. } 7x + 2y = -36 \\ \textbf{2. } -8x + 3y = 57 \end{cases}$
Eq. 1: Mult. by 3.
Eq. 2: Mult. by −2.

CLASSROOM EXERCISES

Add the corresponding sides of the two equations of each system to eliminate one variable. (Steps 1 and 2 of Example 1)

$3x + 6 = 0$

1. $\begin{cases} x + 2y = 1 \\ x - 2y = -5 \end{cases}$ $2x = -4$

2. $\begin{cases} -3x + y = 1 \\ 3x + 3y = 3 \end{cases}$ $4y = 4$

3. $\begin{cases} x - 5y + 2 = 0 \\ 2x + 5y + 4 = 0 \end{cases}$

4. $\begin{cases} 2x - y + 2 = 0 \\ -2x + 2y - 5 = 0 \end{cases}$ $y - 3 = 0$

5. $\begin{cases} -x - 4y = -3 \\ -3x + 4y = -5 \end{cases}$ $-4x = -8$

6. $\begin{cases} 2x - 3y = -2 \\ -x + 3y = -1 \end{cases}$

$x = -3$

In Exercises 7-12, other answers are possible.

Multiply each side of one equation by a number to eliminate x or y. (Steps 1, 2, and 3 of Example 2)

Eq. 2: Mult. by −2.

7. $\begin{cases} x - 3y + 1 = 0 \\ -2x + y + 3 = 0 \end{cases}$ Eq. 1: Mult. by 2.

8. $\begin{cases} 3x + 5y = 1 \\ 2x - y = -2 \end{cases}$ Eq. 2: Mult. by 5.

9. $\begin{cases} -2x + 4y - 1 = 0 \\ 3x + 2y + 4 = 0 \end{cases}$

Multiply each side of both equations by numbers to eliminate x or y. (Steps 1, 2, and 3 of Example 3)

10. $\begin{cases} 2x - 4y + 1 = 0 \\ 3x - 3y - 2 = 0 \end{cases}$
Eq. 1: Mult. by 3.
Eq. 2: Mult. by −2.

11. $\begin{cases} 4x + 5y = 2 \\ -3x + 2y = 1 \end{cases}$
Eq. 1: Mult. by 3.
Eq. 2: Mult. by 4.

12. $\begin{cases} -6x - 2y + 3 = 0 \\ 4x + 3y - 1 = 0 \end{cases}$
Eq. 1: Mult. by 3.
Eq. 2: Mult. by 2.

WRITTEN EXERCISES

See the Teacher's Manual for the suggested assignment.

Goal: To solve systems of equations by the multiplication/addition method

Sample Problem: $\begin{cases} 5x - 4y = 2 \\ y - x = 1 \end{cases}$ **Answer:** $\{(-2, -3)\}$

Solve each system by the multiplication/addition method. (Examples 1–3)

1. $\begin{cases} 2x + y = 12 \\ x - 2y = 0 \end{cases}$ $\{(\frac{24}{5}, \frac{12}{5})\}$

2. $\begin{cases} 2x - y = 5 \\ x + 2y = 25 \end{cases}$ $\{(7, 9)\}$

3. $\begin{cases} 4x + 3y = 6 \\ 2x - y = -2 \end{cases}$

4. $\begin{cases} 5x + y = 4 \\ x - 2y = 3 \end{cases}$ $\{(1, -1)\}$

5. $\begin{cases} 2x - y = -3 \\ 4x - y = -2 \end{cases}$ $\{(\frac{1}{2}, 4)\}$

6. $\begin{cases} 4x - y = 1 \\ 2x - y = 3 \end{cases}$

7. $\begin{cases} 2x - 3y = 13 \\ 3x + y = 3 \end{cases}$ $\{(2, -3)\}$

8. $\begin{cases} 3x + 4y = 10 \\ 2x - y = -8 \end{cases}$ $\{(-2, 4)\}$

9. $\begin{cases} x + 3y = -3 \\ 2x - y = 4 \end{cases}$

10. $\begin{cases} 2x - 5y = -5 \\ x + 5y = -4 \end{cases}$ $\{(-3, -\frac{1}{5})\}$

11. $\begin{cases} -5x + 3y = 0 \\ x + 2y = 0 \end{cases}$ $\{(0, 0)\}$

12. $\begin{cases} y = 2x - 3 \\ y = -3x + 5 \end{cases}$

13. $\begin{cases} 2x + 5y = 0 \\ 3x - y = 0 \end{cases}$ $\{(0, 0)\}$

14. $\begin{cases} y = 3x + 2 \\ y = -5x - 3 \end{cases}$ $\{(-\frac{5}{8}, \frac{1}{8})\}$

15. $\begin{cases} 3x + 2y - 2 = 0 \\ 2x + 3y + 2 = 0 \end{cases}$

16. $\begin{cases} 5x - 2y - 11 = 0 \\ 3x + 5y - 19 = 0 \end{cases}$ $\{(3, 2)\}$

17. $\begin{cases} 4x - 3y - 5 = 0 \\ 2x + 9y + 1 = 0 \end{cases}$ $\{(1, -\frac{1}{3})\}$

18. $\begin{cases} 6x - 2y + 3 = 0 \\ 2x + 4y - 5 = 0 \end{cases}$

See below

3. $\{(0, 2)\}$ 6. $\{(-1, -5)\}$

9. $\{(\frac{9}{7}, -\frac{10}{7})\}$ 12. $\{(\frac{8}{5}, \frac{1}{5})\}$

15. $\{(2, -2)\}$ 18. $\{(-\frac{1}{14}, \frac{9}{7})\}$

12.6 2 × 2 Determinants

OBJECTIVE: To compute the value of a 2 × 2 determinant
To write the determinant of a system of two linear equations and compute its value

Another method for solving systems of equations uses <u>determinants</u>.

> A **determinant** is a square array of the form $\begin{vmatrix} a & b \\ c & d \end{vmatrix}$ in which a, b, c, and d are real numbers.
>
> $$\begin{vmatrix} -3 & \frac{1}{2} \\ 5 & \sqrt{2} \end{vmatrix}$$

Only 2 × 2 (two-by-two) determinants are used in this book. They have two <u>rows</u> and two <u>columns</u>.

ROWS $\longrightarrow$ $\begin{vmatrix} a & b \\ c & d \end{vmatrix}$ ◀ *Each real number is an <u>element</u> of the determinant.*

COLUMNS

P-1   **What are the elements of the first row of the determinant at the right?   the elements of the second column?**   First row; π, –2; Second column: –2, $-\sqrt{3}$

$$\begin{vmatrix} \pi & -2 \\ 0.6 & -\sqrt{3} \end{vmatrix}$$

> Each 2 × 2 determinant represents a real number.
>
> $$\begin{vmatrix} a & b \\ c & d \end{vmatrix} = ad - bc$$
>
> $$\begin{vmatrix} 2 & 4 \\ 1 & 5 \end{vmatrix} = 2 \cdot 5 - 4 \cdot 1$$
> $$= 6$$

example 1   Compute the value of $\begin{vmatrix} 2 & 4 \\ -3 & 1 \end{vmatrix}$

Solution: 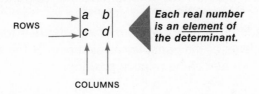$= (2)(1) - (4)(-3)$

$$= 2 - (-12)$$

$$= 2 + 12$$

$$= 14$$

P-2   **What is the value of each determinant below?**

a. $\begin{vmatrix} 2 & 5 \\ 3 & 0 \end{vmatrix}$ −15   b. $\begin{vmatrix} 2 & 3 \\ 2 & 3 \end{vmatrix}$ 0   c. $\begin{vmatrix} 1 & 1 \\ -1 & 1 \end{vmatrix}$ 2

P-3   **What expression represents the value of each determinant?**

a. $\begin{vmatrix} p & q \\ 3 & 2 \end{vmatrix}$ b. $\begin{vmatrix} -x & x \\ 3 & 2 \end{vmatrix}$ −5x   c. $\begin{vmatrix} -s & t \\ -t & -s \end{vmatrix}$ $s^2 + t^2$

$2p - 3q$

The standard form of a system of equations is compared with its **determinant form** below.

Standard form ▶ $\begin{cases} 2x - 3y + 1 = 0 \\ x + y - 5 = 0 \end{cases}$ $\begin{cases} 2x - 3y = -1 \\ x + y = 5 \end{cases}$ ◀ **Determinant form**

P-4   **How is the determinant form different from the standard form?**
In the determinant form the left hand side has only an x term and a y term.

The **determinant of a system of equations** is formed with the coefficients of the variables as elements of the determinant. They are written in their same relative positions.

Determinant form of the system ▶ $\begin{cases} 2x - 3y = -1 \\ x + y = 5 \end{cases}$ $\begin{vmatrix} 2 & -3 \\ 1 & 1 \end{vmatrix}$ ◀ **Determinant of the system**

example 2   Write the system below in determinant form. Then write the determinant of the system and compute its value.

$$\begin{cases} 3x + y - 5 = 0 \\ -2x + y + 3 = 0 \end{cases}$$

Solution: $\begin{cases} 3x + y = 5 \\ -2x + y = -3 \end{cases}$ ◀ **Determinant form**

$\begin{vmatrix} 3 & 1 \\ -2 & 1 \end{vmatrix} = (3)(1) - (1)(-2)$ ◀ **Determinant of the system**

$= 3 - (-2)$

$= 3 + 2$

$= 5$ ◀ **Value of the determinant**

CLASSROOM EXERCISES

Write the value of each determinant. (Example 1)

1. $\begin{vmatrix} 1 & 2 \\ 1 & 4 \end{vmatrix}$ 2

2. $\begin{vmatrix} -2 & 0 \\ 1 & 3 \end{vmatrix}$ −6

3. $\begin{vmatrix} 2 & 3 \\ -1 & 5 \end{vmatrix}$ 13

4. $\begin{vmatrix} -1 & 1 \\ 0 & 1 \end{vmatrix}$ −1

5. $\begin{vmatrix} 0 & 3 \\ 1 & 2 \end{vmatrix}$ −3

6. $\begin{vmatrix} 5 & -1 \\ 2 & -3 \end{vmatrix}$ −13

7. $\begin{vmatrix} 1 & -3 \\ 5 & 2 \end{vmatrix}$ 17

8. $\begin{vmatrix} 1 & -3 \\ 0 & 2 \end{vmatrix}$ 2

9. $\begin{vmatrix} 2 & -3 \\ -1 & 5 \end{vmatrix}$ 7

10. $\begin{vmatrix} -1 & -4 \\ -3 & -2 \end{vmatrix}$ −10

11. $\begin{vmatrix} -5 & 1 \\ 3 & 2 \end{vmatrix}$ −13

12. $\begin{vmatrix} 3 & 6 \\ 2 & 4 \end{vmatrix}$ 0

13. $\begin{vmatrix} -3 & -4 \\ -6 & 8 \end{vmatrix}$ −48

14. $\begin{vmatrix} 2 & -3 \\ 2 & -3 \end{vmatrix}$ 0

15. $\begin{vmatrix} 1 & -5 \\ -1 & 5 \end{vmatrix}$ 0

16. $\begin{vmatrix} \frac{1}{2} & -3 \\ 2 & 4 \end{vmatrix}$ 8

17. $\begin{vmatrix} 1 & 6 \\ -\frac{1}{2} & 3 \end{vmatrix}$ 6

18. $\begin{vmatrix} 1 & 1 \\ -1 & 1 \end{vmatrix}$ 2

19. $\begin{vmatrix} \frac{1}{2} & \frac{1}{2} \\ 2 & -4 \end{vmatrix}$ −3

20. $\begin{vmatrix} -5 & -3 \\ -1 & -2 \end{vmatrix}$ 7

WRITTEN EXERCISES

See the Teacher's Manual for the suggested assignments.

Goals: To write the determinant of a linear system and to compute the value of the determinant

Sample Problem: $\begin{cases} 2x - 3y + 6 = 0 \\ -x + 5y - 1 = 0 \end{cases}$ **Answer:** $\begin{vmatrix} 2 & -3 \\ -1 & 5 \end{vmatrix}$; 7

Compute the value of each determinant. (Example 1)

1. $\begin{vmatrix} -6 & 5 \\ 2 & 3 \end{vmatrix}$ −28

2. $\begin{vmatrix} 5 & 6 \\ 2 & -7 \end{vmatrix}$ −47

3. $\begin{vmatrix} 6 & -12 \\ -3 & 6 \end{vmatrix}$ 0

4. $\begin{vmatrix} -4 & 16 \\ 2 & -8 \end{vmatrix}$ 0

5. $\begin{vmatrix} 1 & 5 \\ 0 & -2 \end{vmatrix}$ −2

6. $\begin{vmatrix} 2 & 0 \\ -10 & -3 \end{vmatrix}$ −6

7. $\begin{vmatrix} \frac{1}{3} & -4 \\ \frac{1}{2} & 6 \end{vmatrix}$ 4

8. $\begin{vmatrix} -\frac{1}{2} & -\frac{1}{3} \\ 9 & 8 \end{vmatrix}$ −1

9. $\begin{vmatrix} -1 & 1 \\ 1 & -1 \end{vmatrix}$ 0

10. $\begin{vmatrix} 5 & 3 \\ 9 & 3 \end{vmatrix}$ −12

11. $\begin{vmatrix} 1 & -15 \\ -15 & 2 \end{vmatrix}$ −223

12. $\begin{vmatrix} -4 & -3 \\ 3 & -4 \end{vmatrix}$ 25

Write each system in determinant form. Then write the determinant of the system and compute its value. (Example 2) In Ex. 13-21 only the determinant and its value are given.

13. $\begin{cases} 2x - y + 3 = 0 \\ x - 3y - 5 = 0 \end{cases}$ $\begin{vmatrix} 2 & -1 \\ 1 & -3 \end{vmatrix}$; −5

14. $\begin{cases} x - 3y + 5 = 0 \\ 5x + 2y - 3 = 0 \end{cases}$ $\begin{vmatrix} 1 & -3 \\ 5 & 2 \end{vmatrix}$; 17

15. $\begin{cases} -2x + 5y - 1 = 0 \\ x - 3y + 8 = 0 \end{cases}$ See below.

16. $\begin{cases} 4x - 3y + 2 = 0 \\ -3x - y - 5 = 0 \end{cases}$ $\begin{vmatrix} 4 & -3 \\ -3 & -1 \end{vmatrix}$; −13

17. $\begin{cases} y = 2x - 5 \\ y = 5x - 2 \end{cases}$ $\begin{vmatrix} 2 & -1 \\ 5 & -1 \end{vmatrix}$; 3

18. $\begin{cases} y = -3x + 7 \\ y = x - 13 \end{cases}$ $\begin{vmatrix} 3 & 1 \\ -1 & 1 \end{vmatrix}$; 4

19. $\begin{cases} 5x - 2 = -3y \\ y - 3x = -2 \end{cases}$ $\begin{vmatrix} 5 & 3 \\ -3 & 1 \end{vmatrix}$; 14

20. $\begin{cases} -3y + 10 = 5x \\ 2x - 8 = -3y \end{cases}$ $\begin{vmatrix} -5 & -3 \\ 2 & 3 \end{vmatrix}$; −9

21. $\begin{cases} 5y - 7 = -4x \\ 5x + 6y = 8 \end{cases}$ $\begin{vmatrix} 4 & 5 \\ 5 & 6 \end{vmatrix}$; −1

15. $\begin{vmatrix} -2 & 5 \\ 1 & -3 \end{vmatrix}$; 1

12.7 Solving Systems by Determinants

OBJECTIVES: To solve a system of two linear equations by determinants
To tell by use of determinants whether or not the graph of a
system of two linear equations is a pair of parallel lines

Systems of equations can be solved by the method of determinants.

$$\begin{cases} 2x - y = 5 \\ x + 3y = -2 \end{cases}$$

Remind students to
make sure the
equations are in
determinant form.

$$x = \frac{\begin{vmatrix} 5 & -1 \\ -2 & 3 \end{vmatrix}}{\begin{vmatrix} 2 & -1 \\ 1 & 3 \end{vmatrix}}$$

◀ First column has constant terms.
Second column has y coefficients.

◀ Determinant
of the system

$$y = \frac{\begin{vmatrix} 2 & 5 \\ 1 & -2 \end{vmatrix}}{\begin{vmatrix} 2 & -1 \\ 1 & 3 \end{vmatrix}}$$

◀ First column has x coefficients.
Second column has constant terms.

◀ Determinant
of the system

P-1 **What is the value of the numerator determinant for x?** ¹³ **the
numerator determinant for y?** ⁻⁹ **the determinant of the system?** ⁷

The values of x and y are computed.

$$x = \frac{13}{7} \qquad\qquad y = \frac{-9}{7}$$

The solution set of the system is $\{(\frac{13}{7}, -\frac{9}{7})\}$.

example 1

Solve the following system by the method of
determinants.

$$\begin{cases} x - 3y + 2 = 0 \\ -2x + 5y - 10 = 0 \end{cases}$$

Solution:

1 Write the system in determinant form.

$$\begin{cases} x - 3y = -2 \\ -2x + 5y = 10 \end{cases}$$

2 Write x and y as quotients of determinants.

$$x = \frac{\begin{vmatrix} -2 & -3 \\ 10 & 5 \end{vmatrix}}{\begin{vmatrix} 1 & -3 \\ -2 & 5 \end{vmatrix}} \qquad\qquad y = \frac{\begin{vmatrix} 1 & -2 \\ -2 & 10 \end{vmatrix}}{\begin{vmatrix} 1 & -3 \\ -2 & 5 \end{vmatrix}}$$

$\boxed{3}$ Solve for x and y.

$$x = \frac{(-2)(5) - (-3)(10)}{(1)(5) - (-3)(-2)} \qquad y = \frac{(1)(10) - (-2)(-2)}{(1)(5) - (-3)(-2)}$$

$$x = \frac{20}{-1} \qquad\qquad\qquad y = \frac{6}{-1}$$

$$x = -20 \qquad\qquad\qquad y = -6$$

The solution set of the system is $\{(-20, -6)\}$. If graphs of the equations are drawn, the lines intersect at the point $(-20, -6)$.

example 2

Solve the following system by the method of determinants.

$$\begin{cases} x - 2y = 5 \\ 2x - 4y = -3 \end{cases} \qquad \blacktriangleleft \begin{array}{l}\textbf{\textit{Determinant}} \\ \textbf{\textit{form}}\end{array}$$

Solution:

$$x = \frac{\begin{vmatrix} 5 & -2 \\ -3 & -4 \end{vmatrix}}{\begin{vmatrix} 1 & -2 \\ 2 & -4 \end{vmatrix}} \qquad y = \frac{\begin{vmatrix} 1 & 5 \\ 2 & -3 \end{vmatrix}}{\begin{vmatrix} 1 & -2 \\ 2 & -4 \end{vmatrix}}$$

$$x = \frac{(5)(-4) - (-2)(-3)}{(1)(-4) - (-2)(2)} \qquad y = \frac{(1)(-3) - (5)(2)}{(1)(-4) - (-2)(2)}$$

$$x = \frac{-26}{0} \qquad\qquad y = \frac{-13}{0} \qquad \blacktriangleleft \begin{array}{l}\textbf{\textit{Division by}} \\ \textbf{\textit{zero is not}} \\ \textbf{\textit{possible.}}\end{array}$$

The two equations are changed to slope-intercept form below.

$$x - 2y = 5 \qquad\qquad 2x - 4y = -3$$

$$y = \tfrac{1}{2}x - \tfrac{5}{2} \qquad\qquad y = \tfrac{2}{4}x + \tfrac{3}{4} \qquad \blacktriangleleft \begin{array}{l}\textbf{\textit{The slopes}} \\ \textbf{\textit{are equal.}}\end{array}$$

The graphs of the two equations are parallel lines. The solution set of the system is ϕ.

If only the determinant of a system of equations equals 0, then the solution set of the system is empty.

CLASSROOM EXERCISES

Tell the missing columns of elements. (Step 2 of Example 1)

1. $\begin{cases} 3x - y = 2 \\ x + 2y = -1 \end{cases}$

$$x = \frac{\begin{vmatrix} 2 & ? & -1 \\ -1 & ? & 2 \end{vmatrix}}{\begin{vmatrix} 3 & -1 \\ 1 & 2 \end{vmatrix}}, \quad y = \frac{\begin{vmatrix} 3 & ? & 2 \\ 1 & ? & -1 \end{vmatrix}}{\begin{vmatrix} 3 & -1 \\ 1 & 2 \end{vmatrix}}$$

2. $\begin{cases} -x + 4y = 6 \\ 2x - 3y = -1 \end{cases}$

$$x = \frac{\begin{vmatrix} 6 & ? & 4 \\ -1 & ? & -3 \end{vmatrix}}{\begin{vmatrix} -1 & ? & 4 \\ 2 & ? & -3 \end{vmatrix}}, \quad y = \frac{\begin{vmatrix} -1 & ? & 6 \\ 2 & ? & -1 \end{vmatrix}}{\begin{vmatrix} -1 & ? & 4 \\ 2 & ? & -3 \end{vmatrix}}$$

3. $\begin{cases} 0.5x - 0.5y = 1.5 \\ -1.5x + 1.5y = -2.5 \end{cases}$

$$x = \frac{\begin{vmatrix} 1.5 & ? & -0.5 & ? \\ -2.5 & ? & 1.5 & ? \end{vmatrix}}{\begin{vmatrix} 0.5 & -0.5 \\ -1.5 & 1.5 \end{vmatrix}}, \quad y = \frac{\begin{vmatrix} 0.5 & ? & 1.5 & ? \\ -1.5 & ? & -2.5 & ? \end{vmatrix}}{\begin{vmatrix} 0.5 & -0.5 \\ -1.5 & 1.5 \end{vmatrix}}$$

4. $\begin{cases} x - 2y + 1 = 0 \\ 2x - y - 2 = 0 \end{cases}$

$$x = \frac{\begin{vmatrix} -1 & ? & -2 \\ 2 & ? & -1 \end{vmatrix}}{\begin{vmatrix} 1 & ? & -2 \\ 2 & ? & -1 \end{vmatrix}}, \quad y = \frac{\begin{vmatrix} 1 & ? & -1 \\ 2 & ? & 2 \end{vmatrix}}{\begin{vmatrix} 1 & ? & -2 \\ 2 & ? & -1 \end{vmatrix}}$$

WRITTEN EXERCISES

See the Teacher's Manual for the suggested assignments.

Goal: To solve systems of linear equations by the method of determinants

Sample Problem: $\begin{cases} 3x + 7y = -4 \\ 2x + 5y = -3 \end{cases}$ **Answer:** $\{(1, -1)\}$

Solve each system by the method of determinants. (Example 1) $\{(-2, 1)\}$

1. $\begin{cases} x + y = 6 \\ x - 2y = 3 \end{cases}$ $\{(5, 1)\}$

2. $\begin{cases} 2x - y = 1 \\ x + y = -2 \end{cases}$ $\{(-\frac{1}{3}, -\frac{5}{3})\}$

3. $\begin{cases} x - 3y = -5 \\ 2x + 5y = 1 \end{cases}$

4. $\begin{cases} 2x - y = 3 \\ x + 3y = 5 \end{cases}$ $\{(2, 1)\}$

5. $\begin{cases} 4x + 3y = -6 \\ 5x - 2y = 3 \end{cases}$ $\{(-\frac{3}{23}, -\frac{42}{23})\}$

6. $\begin{cases} 2x - 5y = 10 \\ x - 6y = 8 \end{cases}$ See below.

7. $\begin{cases} x - 3y + 5 = 0 \\ 5x - 3y - 2 = 0 \end{cases}$ $\{(\frac{7}{4}, \frac{9}{4})\}$

8. $\begin{cases} 3x - 2y - 5 = 0 \\ -x + 5y + 7 = 0 \end{cases}$ $\{(\frac{11}{13}, -\frac{16}{13})\}$

9. $\begin{cases} \frac{1}{3}x - 8y = -4 \\ \frac{3}{4}x + 6y = 3 \end{cases}$

$$\{(0, \tfrac{1}{2})\}$$

Use the method of determinants to tell whether the graphs of the two equations of each system are parallel lines. (Example 2)

10. $\begin{cases} x - 3y = -5 \\ -2x + 6y = 6 \end{cases}$ Yes

11. $\begin{cases} 2x - y = -3 \\ -6x + 3y = 6 \end{cases}$ Yes

12. $\begin{cases} -\frac{1}{4}x + 6y = -6 \\ \frac{1}{2}x - 4y = 12 \end{cases}$ No

13. $\begin{cases} 3x - 2y = 10 \\ -x + \frac{2}{3}y = 7 \end{cases}$ Yes

14. $\begin{cases} \frac{1}{4}x + \frac{1}{6}y = 12 \\ -\frac{1}{2}x + \frac{1}{3}y = -12 \end{cases}$ No

15. $\begin{cases} \frac{1}{2}x + \frac{1}{8}y = 4 \\ x - \frac{1}{4}y = -10 \end{cases}$ No

6. $\{(\frac{20}{7}, -\frac{6}{7})\}$

Pharmacist

Pharmacists prepare drugs and medicines according to doctors' prescriptions. One of their tasks is to prepare solutions of various chemicals as they fill prescriptions. The table below shows the **molecular weights** of some chemicals.

Chemical	Molecular Weight
Boric acid	157.30
Calcium chloride	147.02
Magnesium sulfate	246.47
Potassium chloride	74.56
Sodium bicarbonate	84.01

A **mole** in chemistry is the mass of a substance that equals its molecular weight. A **one molar solution** of boric acid and water would contain 157.3 grams of boric acid in 1 liter of solution.

EXAMPLE: Find the number of grams of boric acid to make 1500 milliliters of a solution with 5% molarity.

SOLUTION: a. Find the number of grams of boric acid to make <u>1 liter</u> (1000 milliliters) of a 5% molarity solution.

$$5\% \text{ of } 157.3 = (0.05)(157.3) \text{ or } 7.9 \text{ grams}$$

b. Find the number of grams of boric acid for 1500 milliliters. Solve the following proportion.

$$\frac{7.9}{1000} = \frac{n}{1500} \qquad n = \frac{(7.9)(1500)}{1000}$$

$$n = 11.85 \text{ or about } \textbf{11.9 grams} \text{ of boric acid}$$

EXERCISES

In Exercises 1–4 find the number of grams needed to make a solution of the given number of milliliters and molarity (%). Round your answer to the nearest tenth of a gram.

1. Magnesium sulfate   29.5 grams
   1200 milliliters; 10% molarity

2. Potassium chloride   0.2 grams
   750 milliliters; 0.3% molarity

3. Sodium bicarbonate   0.5 grams
   380 milliliters; 1.4% molarity

4. Calcium chloride   21.9 grams
   1750 milliliters; 8.5% molarity

CHAPTER SUMMARY

IMPORTANT TERMS	Linear equation *(p. 290)*	Substitution method *(p. 300)*
	Standard form	Multiplication/addition
	of a linear equation *(p. 290)*	method *(p. 304)*
	Solution set	Determinant *(p. 307)*
	of a linear equation *(p. 293)*	Determinant form
	System of equations *(p. 296)*	of a system *(p. 308)*
	Solution set of a system	Determinant
	of two equations *(p. 296)*	of a system *(p. 308)*

IMPORTANT IDEAS

1. To solve a system of linear equations by the *substitution method:*
   a. Change one equation, if necessary, to get one variable by itself on one side of the equation.
   b. Substitute an expression for that variable in the other equation.
   c. Solve the resulting equation for one number of the ordered pair.
   d. Substitute this value in either equation for the other number of the ordered pair.

2. To solve a system of equations by the *multiplication/addition method:*
   a. Check for opposite coefficients of one variable. If necessary, multiply each side of either or both equations by numbers that will make opposite coefficients for one variable.
   b. Add the corresponding sides to eliminate one of the variables.
   c. Solve for the remaining variable.
   d. Substitute the value from step **c** in one of the equations. Solve for the other variable.

3. Each 2×2 determinant represents a real number.
$$\begin{vmatrix} a & b \\ c & d \end{vmatrix} = ad - bc$$

4. The determinant of a system of equations is formed with the coefficients of the variables as elements of the determinant.

5. If only the determinant of a system of equations equals 0, then the solution set of the system is empty.

CHAPTER REVIEW   NOTE: The Teacher's Resource Book contains two forms of each Chapter Test.

SECTION 12.1

Write each equation in standard form.

1. $3y = -2x + 5$ $2x + 3y - 5 = 0$

2. $-5y = 7x - 2$ $7x + 5y - 2 = 0$

3. $2(x - 3) = -3(2y + 1)$ $2x + 6y - 3 = 0$

4. $-5(2x + 4) = 3(y - 5)$ $10x + 3y + 5 = 0$

Write each equation in slope-intercept form.

5. $3x + y - 7 = 0$

6. $-5x + y + 3 = 0$

7. $8x - y = 15$

8. $10x - 2y + 3 = 0$

$y = -3x + 7$

$y = 5x - 3$

$y = 8x - 15$

$y = 5x + \dfrac{3}{2}$

In Ex. 9-14 each graph is a straight line. The coordinates of two points are given for each line.

Graph each of the following.

9. $2x + y - 3 = 0$ (0, 3), (2, –1)   10. $-3x + y + 2 = 0$ (0, –2), (1, 1)   11. $x - 5y + 1 = 0$ (–1, 0), (4, 1)

12. $-x - 3y - 1 = 0$ (–1, 0), (2, –1) 13. $-2x + 3y + 6 = 0$ (0, –2), (3, 0) 14. $4x - 2y + 8 = 0$ (0, 4), (–3, –2)

SECTION 12.3 In Ex. 15-18 each graph is a pair of straight lines.

Solve each system by graphing. Check.

15. $\begin{cases} x + 3y - 3 = 0 \\ 2x + y + 4 = 0 \end{cases}$ $\{(-3, 2)\}$ 16. $\begin{cases} x - 2y - 2 = 0 \\ x + y - 2 = 0 \end{cases}$ $\{(2, 0)\}$

17. $\begin{cases} 2x - y = 0 \\ 2x - 3y + 4 = 0 \end{cases}$ $\{(1, 2)\}$ 18. $\begin{cases} x - 2y - 4 = 0 \\ x + 3y + 1 = 0 \end{cases}$ $\{(2, -1)\}$

SECTION 12.4

Solve each system by the substitution method. Check.

19. $\begin{cases} y = -3x - 6 \\ x + 2y = 3 \end{cases}$ $\{(-3, 3)\}$ 20. $\begin{cases} y = \frac{1}{2}x - \frac{3}{2} \\ 3x - 2y = -3 \end{cases}$ $\{(-3, -3)\}$

21. $\begin{cases} x - 3y = 5 \\ 2y + 3x = 4 \end{cases}$ $\{(2, -1)\}$ 22. $\begin{cases} 6 - x = 5y \\ -3x + 2y - 16 = 0 \end{cases}$ $\{(-4, 2)\}$

SECTION 12.5

Solve each system by the multiplication/addition method. Check.

23. $\begin{cases} x - y = 3 \\ x + y = 1 \end{cases}$ $\{(2, -1)\}$ 24. $\begin{cases} 2x + y = 1 \\ 2x - y = 7 \end{cases}$ $\{(2, -3)\}$ 25. $\begin{cases} -2x + y = 1 \\ 4x + 3y = 23 \end{cases}$ $\{(2, 5)\}$ 26. $\begin{cases} 3x - 4y = 5 \\ 6x - 8y = 3 \end{cases}$ ϕ

SECTION 12.6

Write the value of each determinant.

27. $\begin{vmatrix} 5 & -2 \\ 3 & 7 \end{vmatrix}$ 41   28. $\begin{vmatrix} \frac{1}{2} & 0 \\ -6 & -4 \end{vmatrix}$ -2   29. $\begin{vmatrix} 0 & 1 \\ 1 & 1 \end{vmatrix}$ -1   30. $\begin{vmatrix} 0 & 1 \\ 1 & 0 \end{vmatrix}$ -1

SECTION 12.7

Solve each system by the method of determinants.

31. $\begin{cases} 3x - y = 4 \\ x + 2y = -1 \end{cases}$ $\{(1, -1)\}$ 32. $\begin{cases} 3x + 2y = 13 \\ 2x + 3y = 12 \end{cases}$ $\{(3, 2)\}$ 33. $\begin{cases} x - 3y = 10 \\ 2x + 5y = 1 \end{cases}$ $\{(\frac{53}{11}, -\frac{19}{11})\}$ 34. $\begin{cases} -2x + 5y = 6 \\ 3x - 4y = -2 \end{cases}$ $\{(2, 2)\}$

CUMULATIVE REVIEW: CHAPTERS 7–12

Write each product or quotient as one power. (Sections 7.1–7.3)

1. $8^2 \cdot 8^3$ 8^5

2. $(-13)^4(-13)^5$ $(-13)^9$

3. $r^3 \cdot r^3 \cdot r^2$ r^8

4. $5^x \cdot 5^3$ 5^{x+3}

5. $\dfrac{(13)^8}{(13)^4}$ $(13)^4$

6. $\dfrac{(-2.6)^5}{(-2.6)^3}$ $(-2.6)^2$

7. $(3^{-1})(3^{-4})(3^2)$ 3^{-3}

8. $(t^3)(t^{-7})$ t^{-4}

9. $\dfrac{p^4 \cdot p^{-6}}{p^5}$ p^{-7}

10. $\dfrac{r^2}{r^5}$ r^{-3}

Simplify. (Sections 7.4 and 7.5)

11. $(-7t)^2$ $49t^2$

12. $(-2r)^3$ $-8r^3$

13. $\left(\dfrac{-3}{x}\right)^3$ $-\dfrac{27}{x^3}$

14. $\left(\dfrac{4p}{5q}\right)^2$ $\dfrac{16p^2}{25q^2}$

15. $(2t^{-2})^3$ $\dfrac{8}{t^6}$

16. $(-5n^3)^{-2}$ $\dfrac{1}{25n^6}$

17. $\left(\dfrac{-2ab^3}{c^2}\right)^4$ $\dfrac{16a^4b^{12}}{c^8}$

18. $\left(\dfrac{3p^2}{-q}\right)^3$ $-\dfrac{27p^6}{q^3}$

Write the decimal form of each number. (Section 7.6)

19. 5.8×10^4 58,000

20. 7.34×10^{-2} 0.0734

21. 4.005×10^{-1} 0.4005

22. 8.08×10^3
8080

Simplify. (Sections 8.1–8.4)

23. $-\sqrt{169}$ -13

24. $\sqrt{324}$ 18

25. $\sqrt{2 \cdot 5 \cdot 2 \cdot 5 \cdot 2 \cdot 2}$ 20

26. $-\sqrt{2^2 \cdot 5^2 \cdot 11^4}$ -1210

27. $(-\sqrt{5})(\sqrt{3})$ $-\sqrt{15}$

28. $(-\sqrt{10})(-\sqrt{7})$ $\sqrt{70}$

29. $\sqrt{5} \cdot \sqrt{7} \cdot \sqrt{35}$ 35

30. $\sqrt{2} \cdot \sqrt{10} \cdot \sqrt{5}$ 10

31. $\sqrt{56}$ $2\sqrt{14}$

32. $\sqrt{63}$ $3\sqrt{7}$

33. $\sqrt[3]{32}$ $2\sqrt[3]{4}$

34. $\sqrt[3]{56}$ $2\sqrt[3]{7}$

35. $\sqrt{20t^3}$ $2t\sqrt{5t}$

36. $\sqrt{45r^2s^3}$ $3rs\sqrt{5s}$

37. $\sqrt[3]{y^{15}}$ y^5

38. $\sqrt[3]{n^{21}}$ n^7

Add or subtract. Simplify where necessary. (Section 8.5)

39. $5\sqrt{7} + \sqrt{7}$
$6\sqrt{7}$

40. $3\sqrt{14} - 8\sqrt{14}$
$-5\sqrt{14}$

41. $\sqrt{50} - 7\sqrt{2}$
$-2\sqrt{2}$

42. $3\sqrt{80} + 2\sqrt{5}$
$14\sqrt{5}$

Rationalize each denominator. Then simplify. (Section 8.6)

43. $\dfrac{\sqrt{9a}}{\sqrt{a^3}}$ $\dfrac{3}{a}$

44. $\dfrac{\sqrt{48a^5}}{\sqrt{3a}}$ $4a^2$

45. $\dfrac{\sqrt{2}}{\sqrt{3}}$ $\dfrac{\sqrt{6}}{3}$

46. $\dfrac{\sqrt{10}}{\sqrt{7}}$ $\dfrac{\sqrt{70}}{7}$

Approximate the value of each square root to three decimal places. Use the table of squares and square roots. (Section 8.7)

47. $\sqrt{208}$ 14.424

48. $\sqrt{279}$ 16.704

49. $\sqrt{\dfrac{7}{3}}$ 1.528

50. $\sqrt{\dfrac{5}{12}}$ 0.645

Write Yes or No to show whether each numeral or expression is a monomial over {rational numbers}. (Section 9.1)

51. $-12x^5$ Yes

52. $\dfrac{4}{x^3}$ No

53. $5x^{-3}$ No

54. $-\dfrac{2}{3}x^3$ Yes

Multiply or divide. (Section 9.2)

55. $(-30x^2y)(2xy^3)$
$-60x^3y^4$

56. $(-9m^2n)(\frac{1}{3}n^3)$
$-3m^2n^4$

57. $\dfrac{-45x^5}{9x^3}$ $-5x^2$

58. $\dfrac{8st^3}{-2st}$ $-4t^2$

Evaluate each polynomial. (Section 9.3)

59. $x^2 - 2x + 3$ if $x = -2$ 11

60. $-2x^2 + x - 5$ if $x = 4$ -33

Add or subtract. (Section 9.4)

61. $(-3x^2 + 5x - 4) + (2x^2 - x + 7)$ $-x^2 + 4x + 3$

62. $(4x^2 - 3x + 5) - (-x^2 + 2x - 6)$
$5x^2 - 5x + 11$

63. $(x^3 - 3x + 10) - (2x^3 - 5x^2 + x - 1)$
$-x^3 + 5x^2 - 4x + 11$

64. $(4x^2 - x - 8) + (5x^3 - x^2 + 10)$
$5x^3 + 3x^2 - x + 2$

Multiply. (Section 9.5)

65. $(3x - 5)(4x + 3)$ $12x^2 - 11x - 15$

66. $(5x - 2)(3x - 2)$ $15x^2 - 16x + 4$

67. $(x + 5)(2x^2 - 3x + 4)$ $2x^3 + 7x^2 - 11x + 20$

68. $(2x - 1)(3x^2 + x - 5)$ $6x^3 - x^2 - 11x + 5$

Divide. (Sections 9.6 and 9.7)

69. $4x - 1 \overline{)4x^3 - x^2 - 20x + 5}$ $x^2 - 5$

70. $3x + 2 \overline{)3x^3 - x^2 + 7x + 6}$ $x^2 - x + 3$

71. $5x + 2 \overline{)-10x^2 + 21x + 6}$ $-2x + 5 - \dfrac{4}{5x + 2}$

72. $2x - 1 \overline{)2x^3 - 3x^2 + 3x - 5}$ $x^2 - x + 1 - \dfrac{4}{2x - 1}$

Factor. (Section 10.1)

73. $4x^2 - 2x + 12$ $2(2x^2 - x + 6)$

74. $15x^3 - 9x^2 + 6x$ $3x(5x^2 - 3x + 2)$

Write each trinomial in the form $x^2 + rx + sx + rs$. Then factor. (Section 10.2)

75. $x^2 + 9x + 18$
$x^2 + 3x + 6x + 18$
$(x + 3)(x + 6)$

76. $x^2 + 12x + 35$
$x^2 + 5x + 7x + 35$
$(x + 5)(x + 7)$

Factor. (Sections 10.3–10.6)

77. $x^2 - 2x - 15$
$(x - 5)(x + 3)$

78. $x^2 - 10x + 24$
$(x - 6)(x - 4)$

79. $2x^2 + 3x - 9$
$(2x - 3)(x + 3)$

80. $3x^2 + 7x - 6$
$(3x - 2)(x + 3)$

81. $9x^2 - 25$
$(3x + 5)(3x - 5)$

82. $25x^4 - 16y^2$
$(5x^2 + 4y)(5x^2 - 4y)$

83. $9x^2 - 30x + 25$
$(3x - 5)(3x - 5)$

84. $4x^2 + 28x + 49$
$(2x + 7)(2x + 7)$

Factor. (Section 10.7)

85. $12x^3 + 2x^2 - 4x$ $2x(3x + 2)(2x - 1)$

86. $36x^2y + 39xy + 9y$ $3y(4x + 3)(3x + 1)$

Draw a graph of each function with {real numbers} as the domain.
(Section 11.1) In Ex. 87 and 88 each graph is a straight line. The coordinates of two points are given for each line.

87. $\{(x, y) : y = \frac{1}{2}x - 3\}$ $(0, -3), (4, -1)$

88. $\{(x, y) : y = -\frac{1}{2}x + 1\}$ $(0, 1), (2, 0)$

Write each Y intercept. (Section 11.2)

89. $y = 4x - 5$ −5

90. $y = -3x + 1$ 1

Write the slope of the graph of each function. (Section 11.3)

91. $y = -\frac{2}{3}x + 3$ $-\frac{2}{3}$

92. $y = 0.7x - 5$ 0.7

Write the slope of the line that contains the two points. (Section 11.4)

93. $(-3, 4)$, $(2, -1)$ −1

94. $(2, -5)$, $(-1, -11)$ 2

Write the slope-intercept form of the rule for each function. (Section 11.5)

95. Its graph is parallel to the graph of $y = -2x + 1$ and contains $(0, 5)$. $y = -2x + 5$

96. Its graph is parallel to the graph of $y = \frac{5}{2}x - 6$ and contains $(0, -\frac{1}{2})$. $y = \frac{5}{2}x - \frac{1}{2}$

Write each X intercept. (Section 11.6)

97. $y = -3x + 6$ 2

98. $y = 2x + 7$ $-\frac{7}{2}$

In Ex. 99-102 each graph is a portion of a straight line. Portions not in the first quadrant or on the *y* axis are not included.

Graph each function. The domain is {nonnegative numbers}. (Section 11.7)

Two points are given for each graph.

99. $d = 1.6t$
(0, 0), (3, 4.8)

100. $i = 0.06p$
(0, 0), (400, 24)

101. $R = F + 460$
(0, 460), (200, 660)

102. $s = 2 + 3t$
(0, 2), (1, 5)

Write each equation in slope-intercept form. (Section 12.1)

103. $4x - 2y + 1 = 0$ $y = 2x + \frac{1}{2}$

104. $x + 3y - 6 = 0$ $y = -\frac{1}{3}x + 2$

Graph the solution set of each equation. (Section 12.2) The graphs are straight lines. Two points for each line are given.

105. $x - 2y + 4 = 0$ (0, 2), (4, 4)

106. $2x + y - 3 = 0$
(0, 3), (2, −1)

Solve each system by graphing. Check. (Section 12.3)

107. $\begin{cases} 2x - y - 4 = 0 \\ x - 3y + 3 = 0 \end{cases}$ $\{(3, 2)\}$

108. $\begin{cases} 2x + y + 1 = 0 \\ x - y + 2 = 0 \end{cases}$ $\{(-1, 1)\}$

Solve each system. (Sections 12.4–12.7)

109. $\begin{cases} 2x + y + 1 = 0 \\ 3x + 2y - 1 = 0 \end{cases}$ $\{(-3, 5)\}$

110. $\begin{cases} x - 2y - 2 = 0 \\ 3x - 4y + 4 = 0 \end{cases}$ $\{(-8, -5)\}$

111. $\begin{cases} 4x - 5y + 1 = 0 \\ 2x - 2y - 3 = 0 \end{cases}$ $\{(\frac{17}{2}, 7)\}$

112. $\begin{cases} 3x - 2y - 1 = 0 \\ -4x + 3y + 5 = 0 \end{cases}$ $\{(-7, -11)\}$

113. $\begin{cases} 4x - 3y - 2 = 0 \\ x + y + 1 = 0 \end{cases}$ $\{(-\frac{1}{7}, -\frac{6}{7})\}$

114. $\begin{cases} -2x + 5y + 3 = 0 \\ 3x - y - 4 = 0 \end{cases}$ $\{(\frac{17}{13}, -\frac{1}{13})\}$

CHAPTER

13 Problem Solving: Two Variables

Sections **13.1** **Problem Solving: Number Problems**

13.2 **Problem Solving: Money Problems**

13.3 **Problem Solving: Digit Problems**

13.4 **Problem Solving: Distance / Rate / Time**

13.5 **Problem Solving: Mixture Problems**

Features *Calculator Exercises:* **Objects in Free Fall**

Special Topic Application: **Longitude and Time Zones**

Review and Testing *Review Capsules*

Mid-Chapter Review

Chapter Summary

Chapter Review

13.1 Problem Solving: Number Problems

OBJECTIVE: To solve a word problem involving two unknown numbers by solving a system of two linear equations

example 1

The sum of two numbers is −16. The difference of the two numbers is 30. Find the two numbers.

Discuss how the equation would be written if x represents the smaller number and y represents the greater number.

Solution: Let x = the greater number and y = the smaller number.

1. Write the equation that tells that the sum is −16. ⟶ $x + y = -16$
2. Write the equation that tells that the difference is 30. ⟶ $x - y = 30$
3. Form a system of linear equations. ⟶ $\begin{cases} \textbf{1. } x + y = -16 \\ \textbf{2. } x - y = 30 \end{cases}$

The substitution method will be used.

4. Solve for y in Equation 1. ⟶ $y = -16 - x$
5. Replace y with $(-16 - x)$ in Equation 2. ⟶ $x - (-16 - x) = 30$
6. Simplify. ⟶ $x + 16 + x = 30$
7. Add like terms. ⟶ $2x + 16 = 30$
8. Subtract 16 from each side. ⟶ $2x = 14$
9. Divide each side by 2. ⟶ $x = 7$ **Greater number**

10. Replace x with 7 in Equation 1. ⟶ $7 + y = -16$
11. Subtract 7 from each side. ⟶ $y = -23$ **Smaller number**

Check: The sum of the two numbers is −16.
$7 + (-23) = -16$

The difference of the two numbers is 30.
$7 - (-23) = 30$

example 2

The width of a rectangle is 5 centimeters less than the length. The perimeter is 38 centimeters. Find the length and width.

Solution: Let x = the length and let y = the width.
Then $2x + 2y$ = the perimeter.

1. Write the equation that tells that the width is 5 centimeters less than the length. ⟶ $y = x - 5$
2. Write the equation that tells that the perimeter is 38 centimeters. ⟶ $2x + 2y = 38$

You now have a system of linear equations.

$$\begin{cases} \textbf{1. } y = x - 5 \\ \textbf{2. } 2x + 2y = 38 \end{cases}$$

☐3 Replace y with $(x - 5)$ in Equation 2. Solve for x.   ◀ *The substitution method will be used.*

$$2x + 2y = 38$$
$$2x + 2(x - 5) = 38$$
$$2x + 2x - 10 = 38$$
$$4x - 10 = 38$$
$$x = 12 \quad ◀ \textbf{ Length}$$

☐4 Replace x with 12 in Equation 1. Solve for y.

$$y = x - 5$$
$$y = 12 - 5$$
$$y = 7 \quad ◀ \textbf{Width:} \quad \text{The check is left for you.}$$

Steps in solving problems with two unknowns:

1. Represent the unknowns by two variables.
2. Write a system of two linear equations.
3. Solve the system of equations.

CLASSROOM EXERCISES

Write an equation in two variables that represents each sentence. Write what each variable represents. (Steps 1 and 2 of Examples 1 and 2)

1. The sum of two numbers is 25.
First number: x; second number: y $x + y = 25$

2. The difference of two numbers is -7.
First number: x; second number: y $x - y = -7$

3. The sum of the ages of Jerry and Mary is 25 years. Jerry's age: x; Mary's age: y
$x + y = 25$

4. One number is 12 more than another number. Greater number: x; smaller number: y; $y + 12 = x$

5. Ken is 29 years younger than his mother. Ken's age: x; mother's age: y
$x + 29 = y$

6. The length of a rectangle is 3 meters more than twice the width.
Length: x; width: y $x = 3 + 2y$

7. Half the perimeter of a rectangle is 51. width: x; length: y
$x + y = 51$

8. The perimeter of a rectangle is 93 millimeters. Width: x; length: y
$2x + 2y = 93$

9. Twice one number increased by three times another number is 19.
First number: x; second number: y
$2x + 3y = 19$

10. One number exceeds another number by 24. Smaller number: x; greater number: y $y = x + 24$

4. First: x; second: y; $x + y = -65$; $x - y = 27$; Answer: $-19, -46$

6. Smaller: x; greater: y; $y = 2x - 4$; $2y - 3x = 7$; Answer: $15, 26$

WRITTEN EXERCISES

See the Teacher's Manual for the suggested assignments.

Goal: To solve number problems by systems of linear equations

Sample Problem: The greater of two numbers is 1 more than 3 times the the smaller. If 8 times the smaller is decreased by 2 times the greater, the result is 10. Find the numbers.

Answer: Greater number: 19   Smaller number: 6

For each problem, (a) select two variables for the unknown numbers, (b) write two equations, and (c) solve. (Examples 1 and 2)

2. Larger: x; smaller: y; $x + y = 73$; $x - y = 11$; Answer: $42, 31$

1. The sum of two numbers is 28. The difference of the two numbers is 3. Find the two numbers.
Larger: x; smaller: y; $x + y = 28$; $x - y = 3$; Answer: $15\frac{1}{2}, 12\frac{1}{2}$

2. The sum of two numbers is 73. The difference of the two numbers is 11. Find the two numbers.

3. The sum of two numbers is -12. One number exceeds the other by 42. Find the two numbers.
First: x; second: y; $x + y = -12$; $x - y = 42$; Answer: $15, -27$

4. The sum of two numbers is -65. One number exceeds the other by 27. Find the two numbers. See above.

5. Twice the smaller of two numbers is increased by 2. The result equals the greater number. Three times the smaller number is increased by twice the greater number. The result equals 39. Find the two numbers.
Smaller: x; greater: y; $2x + 2 = y$; $3x + 2y = 39$; Answer: $5, 12$

6. The greater of two numbers is 4 less than twice the smaller number. From twice the greater number, three times the smaller is subtracted. The result equals 7. Find the two numbers. See above.

7. The length of a rectangle is 8 meters more than the width. The perimeter is 34 meters. Find the length and width.
Length: x; width: y; $x = 8 + y$; $2x + 2y = 34$; Answer: $4\frac{1}{2}, 12\frac{1}{2}$

8. The width of a rectangle is 9 decimeters less than the length. The perimeter is 43 decimeters. Find the length and width.   See below.

9. John is seven years younger than his sister Ann. The sum of their ages is 45. Find the ages of both persons.
Ann's age: x; John's age: y
$y + 7 = x$; $x + y = 45$; Answer: $26, 19$

10. Kathy is 31 years younger than her father. The sum of their ages is 47. Find their ages.   Kathy's age: x; father's age: y; $x + 31 = y$; $x + y = 47$ Answer: $8, 39$

REVIEW CAPSULE FOR SECTION 13.2

Write an algebraic expression. (Section 4.1)

1. The value of n nickels in cents $5n$

2. The value of t dollars in cents $100t$

3. The cost of 5 records at w cents $5w$ each

4. The cost of 12 pencils at y cents each $12y$

5. The cost in cents of k tickets at $8.50 each $850k$

6. The cost in cents of n cards at 75 cents each $75n$

8. Length: x; width: y; $y + 9 = x$; $2x + 2y = 43$; Answer: $6\frac{1}{4}, 15\frac{1}{4}$

13.2 Problem Solving: Money Problems

OBJECTIVE: To solve a word problem involving costs by using a system of two linear equations

Word problems that involve the cost of two items can often be solved by systems of two linear equations. One equation usually represents the total number of items. The second equation represents the total cost of the items.

example 1

Jane bought some pencils and felt pens for $1.50. The pencils cost 8 cents each and the pens cost 39 cents each. She bought a total of 11 pencils and pens. How many of each did she buy?

Solution:

Let x = the number of pencils.
Let y = the number of pens.
Then $8x$ = the cost of the pencils in cents,
and $39y$ = the cost of the pens in cents.

The following system of equations must be solved.

$$\begin{cases} \textbf{1. } x + y = 11 \\ \textbf{2. } 8x + 39y = 150 \end{cases}$$

◄ **The cost of the pens and pencils**

The method of determinants is shown. Other methods could also be used.

$$x = \frac{\begin{vmatrix} 11 & 1 \\ 150 & 39 \end{vmatrix}}{\begin{vmatrix} 1 & 1 \\ 8 & 39 \end{vmatrix}} = \frac{429 - 150}{39 - 8} \qquad y = \frac{\begin{vmatrix} 1 & 11 \\ 8 & 150 \end{vmatrix}}{31} = \frac{150 - 88}{31}$$

$$= \frac{279}{31} \qquad\qquad\qquad = \frac{62}{31}$$

$$= 9 \qquad\qquad\qquad\qquad = 2$$

Jane bought 9 pencils and 2 pens.

Check: Jane bought a total of 11 pencils and pens.

$9 + 2 = 11$

The total cost was $1.50 or 150 cents.

The check must involve both conditions of the problem.

$9(8) + 2(39) = 72 + 78$

$= 150$

---

example 2

A school's Ski Club is planning a trip. A large bus will cost $18 per student if it is filled. A smaller bus holding 6 fewer passengers will cost $20 per student. The cost of the large bus is $30 more than the cost of the smaller bus. Find the number of passengers that each bus can carry.

Solution:

	Number of Passengers	Cost Per Passenger	Total Cost
Large bus	x	$18	$18x$
Small bus	y	$20	$20y$

1. Write the equation that tells that the smaller bus carries 6 fewer passengers. ⟶ $y = x - 6$

2. Write the equation that tells that the total cost of the larger bus is $30 more than the cost of the smaller bus. ⟶ $18x - 20y = 30$

$$\begin{cases} \textbf{1. } y = x - 6 \\ \textbf{2. } 18x - 20y = 30 \end{cases}$$ ◀ *System of linear equations*

The substitution method is used.

3. Substitute $(x - 6)$ for y in Equation 2. Solve for x.

$$18x - 20y = 30$$
$$18x - 20(x - 6) = 30$$
$$18x - 20x + 120 = 30$$
$$-2x + 120 = 30$$
$$-2x = -90$$
$$x = 45$$ ◀ *Capacity of large bus*

4. Substitute 45 for x in Equation 1. Solve for y.

$$y = x - 6$$
$$y = 45 - 6$$
$$y = 39$$ ◀ *Capacity of small bus*

CLASSROOM EXERCISES

Write an equation that represents each sentence. (Examples 1 and 2)

1. The total cost of x cans of peas for 44 cents each and y cans of corn for 39 cents each is $3.37. $44x + 39y = 337$

2. The total income from x student tickets at 50 cents each and y adult tickets at 75 cents each is $112.50. $50x + 75y = 11250$

3. The total cost of x shirts at $9.00 each and y ties at $4.50 each is $58.50. $9x + 4.5y = 58.5$

4. The total value in cents of x dimes and y quarters is $5.20. $10x + 25y = 520$

5. The total value in dollars of x one-dollar bills and y five-dollar bills is $235. $x + 5y = 235$

6. The total cost of x hamburgers at 75 cents each and y hot dogs at 55 cents each is $13.40. $75x + 55y = 1340$

7. The total cost of x doughnuts at 15 cents each and y sweet rolls at 25 cents each is $4.20. $15x + 25y = 420$

8. The total amount of club receipts for a month was $4.90. The receipts came from x membership dues at 35 cents each and y fines at 10 cents each. $35x + 10y = 490$

Write two equations for each problem. (Examples 1 and 2)

9. Mike takes 60 coins consisting of x nickels and y dimes to the bank. The total deposit is $6.50. $x + y = 60$; $5x + 10y = 650$

10. The Junior Class sold x boxes of fudge at $1.50 each and y boxes of peanut brittle at $1.25 each. They sold a total of 82 boxes for $110. $x + y = 82$; $1.5x + 1.25y = 110$

11. In a special sale an appliance store sold x color TV sets for $325 each and y black and white TV sets for $135 each. The total receipts from the sale were $11,415 for selling 55 sets. $x + y = 55$; $325x + 135y = 11415$

12. Gina worked x hours at one job for $2.50 an hour and y hours at another job for $3.25 an hour. She worked a total of 55 hours and earned $156.25. $x + y = 55$; $2.5x + 3.25y = 156.25$

13. David sold x boxes of candy at $2.40 a box and y boxes of candy at $3.20 a box. Altogether he sold 20 boxes for $54.40. $x + y = 20$; $2.4x + 3.2y = 54.40$

14. Pat earned $83.80 in one week for 28 hours of work. He worked x hours at $2.75 an hour and y hours at $3.15 an hour. $x + y = 28$; $2.75x + 3.15y = 83.80$

WRITTEN EXERCISES

See the Teacher's Manual for the suggested assignments.

Goal: To solve problems involving costs by systems of linear equations

Sample Problem: Alyx has a total of 20 dimes and quarters worth $3.95 in her purse. How many of each coin does she have?

Answer: She has 7 dimes and 13 quarters.

For each problem, (a) select two variables for the unknown numbers, (b) write two equations, and (c) solve. (Examples 1 and 2)

1. Brad Whitefoot bought 9 records on sale for a total of $20.37. One price was $2.89 per record and one price was $1.95 per record. How many records did he buy at each price? See above.

2. Micky sold two types of calendars for her club. She sold a total of 64 calendars for $140.50. One type of calendar sold for $2.50 each, and the other type sold for $1.75 each. How many calendars of each type did she sell?

   First type: x; Second type: y; $x + y = 64$; 250x + 175y = 14050; Answers: First type: 38; second type: 26

3. The Northeast Riders 4H Club sold orange juice and cocoa at their horse show. The orange juice cost 20 cents per glass and the cocoa 15 cents per cup. They sold 20 more cups of cocoa than glasses of orange juice. How much of each drink did they sell if the total receipts were $11.40? See below.

4. Susie won the ticket selling contest for the school carnival. She sold 82 tickets for total sales of $32.45. The student tickets sold for 35 cents, and the adult tickets for 50 cents. How many tickets of each kind did she sell? 35x + 50y = 3245; Answers: 57 students; 25 adults

   Students: x; Adults: y; $x + y = 82$;

5. Marc's scout troop bought 50 cans of beans and tomatoes for a camping trip at a total cost of $20.30. The tomatoes cost 35 cents per can and the beans 45 cents per can. How many cans of each kind were purchased?

   Tomatoes: x; beans: y; $x + y = 50$; 35x + 45y = 2030; Answers: 22 cans of tomatoes; 28 cans of beans

6. A school lunch stand sold 230 hamburgers and hot dogs in one day for total receipts of $176.50. The hamburgers sold for 80 cents each and the hot dogs for 65 cents each. How many of each were sold? See below.

7. Rafael makes a bank deposit of $675 with 86 five- and ten-dollar bills. How many of each kind of bill are there? Fives: x; tens: y; $x + y = 86$; 5x + 10y = 675; Answers: 37 fives; 49 tens

8. Betty has nickels and dimes in her bank. There are 53 coins worth $3.75. How many coins of each type does she have?

   Nickels: x; dimes: y; $x + y = 53$; 5x + 10y = 375; Answers: 31 nickels; 22 dimes

REVIEW CAPSULE FOR SECTION 13.3

Find the value of (a) 10x + y and (b) xy in each exercise. (Section 1.6)

1.a. 82
 b. 16

1. $x = 8$; $y = 2$ 2. $x = 5$; $y = 9$ a. 59
b. 45   3. $x = 2$; $y = 0$ a. 20
b. 0   4. $x = 6$; $y = 7$
a. 67, b. 42

3. Orange juice: x; cocoa: y; $y = x + 20$; 20x + 15y = 1140; Answers: Orange juice: 24; cocoa: 44

6. Hamburgers: x; hot dogs: y; $x + y = 230$; 80x + 65y = 17650; Answers: 180 hamburgers; 50 hot dogs

13.3 Problem Solving: Digit Problems

OBJECTIVE: To solve a word problem involving two unknown digits by using a system of two linear equations

The ten numerals below are *digits*.

0, 1, 2, 3, 4, 5, 6, 7, 8, 9

Each place that a digit occupies in a whole number has a name. In this section you will work with two-digit numbers.

TEN'S DIGIT   ONE'S DIGIT

78

3, 9, 1, 7, 1

P-1   **What is the ten's digit in each number below? What is the one's digit?**   5, 0, 4, 8, 1

a. 35   **b.** 90   **c.** 14   **d.** 78   **e.** 11

Any two-digit number can be represented as shown below.

Let x = the ten's digit of a two-digit number.
Let y = the one's digit.

It may be helpful to show that a number like 35 can be represented as $10 \cdot 3 + 5$.

Two-digit number: $10x + y$

P-2   **Why is it incorrect to represent such a two-digit number as xy?**

Because xy represents the product of the digits, not the number

example 1

The sum of the digits of a two-digit number is 14. The one's digit is 4 more than the ten's digit. Find the one's and ten's digits and write the number.

Solution: Let x = the ten's digit and y the one's digit.

1. Write the equation that tells that the sum of the digits is 14. ⟶ $x + y = 14$

2. Write the equation that tells that the one's digit is 4 more than the ten's digit. ⟶ $y = x + 4$

$$\begin{cases} \textbf{1. } x + y = 14 \\ \textbf{2. } y = x + 4 \end{cases}$$ 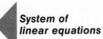 **System of linear equations**

③ Substitute $(x + 4)$ for y in Equation 1. Solve for x.

$$x + y = 14$$
$$x + (x + 4) = 14$$
$$2x + 4 = 14$$
$$2x = 10$$
$$x = 5 \blacktriangleleft \quad \textbf{Ten's digit}$$

④ Substitute 5 for x in Equation 2. Solve for y.

$$y = x + 4$$
$$y = 5 + 4$$
$$y = 9 \blacktriangleleft \quad \textbf{One's digit}$$

⑤ Write the two-digit number.

$$10x + y = 10(5) + 9$$
$$= 50 + 9$$
$$= 59$$

The two-digit number is 59.

Check: $5 + 9 = 14$ $\qquad$ $9 - 5 = 4$

example 2

In a two-digit number, the one's digit is 4 more than the ten's digit. The two-digit number is 2 more than five times the one's digit. Find the ten's and one's digits. Write the number.

Solution: $\qquad$ Let $x =$ the ten's digit and $y =$ the one's digit.

① Write the equation that tells that the one's digit is 4 more than the ten's digit. $\longrightarrow$ $y = x + 4$

② Write the equation that tells that the number is 2 more than five times the one's digit. $\longrightarrow$ $10x + y = 5y + 2$

$$\begin{cases} \textbf{1. } y = x + 4 \\ \textbf{2. } 10x + y = 5y + 2 \end{cases} \blacktriangleleft \quad \textbf{2 more than 5 times the one's digit}$$

$\boxed{3}$ Substitute $(x + 4)$ for y in Equation 2. Solve for x.

$$10x + y = 5y + 2$$
$$10x + (x + 4) = 5(x + 4) + 2$$
$$11x + 4 = 5x + 20 + 2$$
$$6x + 4 = 22$$
$$6x = 18$$
$$x = 3 \quad \blacktriangleleft \textbf{Ten's digit}$$

$\boxed{4}$ Replace x by 3 in Equation 1. Solve for y.

$$y = x + 4$$
$$y = 3 + 4$$
$$y = 7 \quad \blacktriangleleft \textbf{One's digit}$$

The number is 37.

Check: $7 = 3 + 4$ $\qquad\qquad 37 = 5(7) + 2$
$$= 37$$

CLASSROOM EXERCISES

Write an equation for each sentence. Represent each ten's digit by x and each one's digit by y. (Steps 1 and 2 of Examples 1 and 2)

1. The sum of the digits of a two-digit number is 12. $\quad x + y = 12$

2. The ten's digit is 3 greater than the one's digit. $\quad x = y + 3$

3. The one's digit is 5 less than the ten's digit. $\quad y = x - 5$

4. The one's digit equals the ten's digit less 5. $\quad y = x - 5$

5. Five times the ten's digit equals seven times the one's digit. $\quad 5x = 7y$

6. A two-digit number is 9 more than the sum of its digits. $\quad 10x + y = 9 + (x + y)$

7. The sum of the digits of a two-digit number is 1 less than twice the ten's digit. $\quad x + y = 2x - 1$

8. A two-digit number is five times its one's digit. $\quad 10x + y = 5y$

9. The one's digit of a two-digit number diminished by the ten's digit equals -8. $\quad y - x = -8$

10. Twice the one's digit of a two-digit number exceeds the ten's digit by 3. $\quad 2y = x + 3$

WRITTEN EXERCISES

See the Teacher's Manual for the suggested assignments.

Goal: To solve digit problems by systems of linear equations

Sample Problem: The ten's digit of a two-digit number is 1 less than 5 times the unit's digit. The sum of the digits is 11. Write the two-digit number.

Answer: The number is 92.

For each problem, (a) represent the ten's digit by x and the one's digit by y, (b) write two equations, and (c) solve. (Examples 1 and 2)

1. The one's digit of a two-digit number is 2 less than the ten's digit. The sum of the digits is 12. Write the two-digit number. $y = x - 2; x + y = 12;$ Ans.: 75

2. The one's digit of a two-digit number is 7 more than the ten's digit. The sum of the digits is 11. Write the two-digit number. $y = x + 7; x + y = 11;$ Ans.: 29

3. The ten's digit of a two-digit number is twice the one's digit. The ten's digit exceeds the one's digit by 4. Write the two-digit number. $x = 2y;$ $x = y + 4;$ Ans.: 84

4. The one's digit of a two-digit number is three times the ten's digit. The one's digit exceeds the ten's digit by 6. Write the number. $y = 3x;$ $y = x + 6;$ Ans.:39

5. The sum of the digits of a two-digit number is 15. Twice the ten's digit is 5 less than three times the one's digit. Write the two-digit number. $x + y = 15; 2x = 3y - 5;$ Ans.: 87

6. The ten's digit of a two-digit number is 2 less than the one's digit. The one's digit is 4 less than twice the ten's digit. Write the two-digit number. $x = y - 2; y = 2x - 4;$ Ans.: 68

7. The one's digit of a two-digit number exceeds the ten's digit by 1. The number is two more than 8 times the one's digit. Write the two-digit number. $y = x + 1; 10 + y = 8y + 2;$ Ans.: 34

8. Three times the one's digit of a two-digit number is 2 more than the ten's digit. The number is 3 more than 10 times the ten's digit. Write the two-digit number. $3y = x + 2;$ $10x + y = 3 + 10x$ Ans.: 73

9. The ten's digit of a two-digit number decreased by the one's digit equals -4. The number is 3 more than twice the sum of its digits. Write the two-digit number. $x - y = -4;$ $10x + y = 2(x + y) + 3;$ Ans.: 15

10. The one's digit of a two-digit number decreased by the ten's digit equals -5. The number is 8 times the sum of its digits. Write the two-digit number. $y - x = -5; 10x + y = 8(x + y);$ Ans.: 72

MORE CHALLENGING EXERCISES

11. The sum of the digits of a two-digit number is 5. The number formed by reversing the digits is 9 more than the original number. Write the original two-digit number. $x + y = 5;$ $10y + x = 9 + (10x + y);$ Ans.: 23

12. The sum of the digits of a two-digit number is 10. The number formed by reversing the digits is 18 less than the original number. Write the original two-digit number. $x + y = 10; 10y + x = (10x + y) - 18;$ Ans.: 64

NOTE: After completing the Mid-Chapter Review, you may want to administer a quiz covering the same sections. See pages M-34 and M-35 of the Teacher's Manual for the suggested quiz.

MID-CHAPTER REVIEW

For each problem in Exercises 1–6, (a) select two variables for the unknown numbers, (b) write two equations, and (c) solve. (Sections 13.1 through 13.3)

1. The sum of two numbers is −12. The difference of the numbers is 3. Find the two numbers. First: x; second: y; $x + y = −12; x − y = 3;$ Ans.: −4.5 −7.5

2. Juan is 8 years older than his sister Maria. In three years the sum of their ages will be 36. Find the ages of Juan and Maria. Juan's age: x; Maria's age: y; $x = y + 8; x + 3 + y + 3 = 36;$ Ans.: 11, 19

3. A company distributed two home products. Product X sold for $5.95 each and Product Y sold for $8.50 each. The total amount received from the sale of 287 items was $2123.30. Find the number of each product sold. Product X : x; Product Y : y; $x + y = 287;$ $595x + 850y = 212330$; Ans.: 124, 163

4. The paid attendance at an indoor soccer match was 8432. Student tickets cost $6.50 and adult tickets cost $8.75. The total receipts were $71,309.50. Find the number of each kind of ticket sold. See below.

5. A two-digit number is 7 less than 4 times its one's digit. The one's digit is 1 more than 4 times the ten's digit. Write the two-digit number. $10x + y = 4y − 7; y = 1 + 4x;$ Ans.: 29

6. The ten's digit of a two-digit number is 2 more than twice the one's digit. The two-digit number is 11 more than 9 times its ten's digit. Write the two-digit number. 6. $x = 2 + 2y;$ $10x + y = 11 + 9x$ Ans.: 83

4. Student tickets: x; adult tickets: $y; x + y = 8432; 650x + 875y = 7130950$; Ans.: student tickets: 1098; adult tickets: 7334

─────────── *OBJECTS IN FREE FALL* ───────────

The formula at the right is used for freely falling objects.

$d = 16t^2$

d represents distance (feet). t represents time (seconds).

EXAMPLE Show that an object will fall about 6400 feet in 20 seconds.

SOLUTION $d = 16 \cdot 20^2$ or $20^2 \cdot 16$

Evaluate 20^2 before multiplying. See page 19.

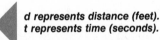

6400.

1–10. Complete the table.

Seconds	1	2	3	4	5	6	7	8	9	10
Feet	? 16	? 64	? 144	? 256	? 400	? 576	? 784	? 1024	? 1296	? 1600

REVIEW CAPSULE FOR SECTION 13.4

Use the formula $d = rt$ to find the distance traveled. (Section 4.5)

1. 470 miles per hour for 5 hours 2350 mi
2. 80 kilometers per hour for 7 hours 560 km
3. 25 meters per second for 42 seconds 1050 m
4. 228 feet per second for 120 seconds 27,360 ft

13.4 Problem Solving: Distance/Rate/Time

OBJECTIVE: To solve a word problem involving distance, rate, and time by a system of two linear equations

The basic formula $d = rt$ relates distance, rate, and time.

example 1

Alexander travels a distance of 360 kilometers in 3 hours by plane and car. The speed of the first part of his trip by plane is 240 kilometers per hour. He completes the journey at a speed of 80 kilometers per hour by car. How long does he travel by plane and how long by car?

Solution:

	Rate	Time	Distance
By plane	240 km/hr	x	$240x$
By car	80 km/hr	y	$80y$

The equations are shown below.

$$\begin{cases} \textbf{1. } x + y = 3 \\ \textbf{2. } 240x + 80y = 360 \end{cases}$$

1 Solve for y in Equation 1.

$$y = -x + 3$$

2 Substitute $(-x + 3)$ for y in Equation 2. Solve for x.

$$240x + 80y = 360$$
$$240x + 80(-x + 3) = 360$$
$$240x - 80x + 240 = 360$$
$$160x = 120$$
$$x = \frac{120}{160}$$
$$x = \frac{3}{4}$$

◄ **Number of hours by plane**

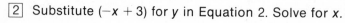

3 Substitute $\frac{3}{4}$ for x in Equation 1. Solve for y.

$$x + y = 3$$
$$\frac{3}{4} + y = 3$$
$$y = 2\frac{1}{4}$$

◄ **Number of hours by car**

example 2

Hisako swims 200 meters against a current in 6 minutes. She returns in 3 minutes swimming with the current. What is the speed of the current and the swimmer's speed in still water?

Solution: Let x = the speed of the swimmer in still water (meters per minute).
Let y = the speed of the current.

The table shows the relationships of the problem.

	Time	Rate	Distance
Against current	6 minutes	$x - y$	200 meters
With current	3 minutes	$x + y$	200 meters

$$\begin{cases} \textbf{1. } 6(x - y) = 200 \\ \textbf{2. } 3(x + y) = 200 \end{cases}$$

Explain why $x - y$ and $x + y$ represent the <u>effective speeds</u> against the current and with the current.

1   Distributive Property

     1. $6(x - y) = 200 \longrightarrow 6x - 6y = 200$

     2. $3(x + y) = 200 \longrightarrow 3x + 3y = 200$

2   Solve. The method of determinants is used.

$$x = \frac{\begin{vmatrix} 200 & -6 \\ 200 & 3 \end{vmatrix}}{\begin{vmatrix} 6 & -6 \\ 3 & 3 \end{vmatrix}} = \frac{600 - (-1200)}{18 - (-18)}$$

$$= \frac{1800}{36}$$

$$= 50$$

$$y = \frac{\begin{vmatrix} 6 & 200 \\ 3 & 200 \end{vmatrix}}{36} = \frac{1200 - 600}{36}$$

$$= \frac{600}{36}$$

$$= 16\frac{2}{3}$$

The speed of the swimmer in still water is 50 meters per minute. The speed of the current is approximately 16.7 meters per minute.

CLASSROOM EXERCISES

Write an algebraic expression for each word phrase. (Examples 1 and 2)

1. The distance traveled in x seconds by an object at a speed of 20 centimeters per second $20x$

2. The distance traveled in 5 hours by an object at a speed of y kilometers per hour $5y$

3. The distance traveled in 10 seconds by an object at a speed of $(x + y)$ meters per second $10(x + y)$

4. The distance traveled in 6 minutes by an object at a speed of $(x - y)$ decimeters per minute $6(x - y)$

5. The speed of a ship against a current of 5 kilometers per hour if the speed of the ship in still water is x kilometers per hour $x - 5$

6. The speed of a boat against a current if its speed in still water is $2x$ kilometers per hour and the speed of the current is y kilometers per hour $2x - y$

7. The speed of a plane with a tailwind of x kilometers per hour if the speed of the plane in still air is y kilometers per hour $y + x$

8. The distance between two planes 2 hours after they take off in opposite directions one at a speed of x kilometers per hour and the other at y kilometers per hour. $2x + 2y$

Tell two equations for each problem. (Examples 1 and 2)

9. A plane's speed in one direction with a tailwind is 300 kilometers per hour. Its speed in the opposite direction against a headwind is 250 kilometers per hour. The plane's speed in still air is x kilometers per hour, and the speed of the wind is y kilometers per hour.

	Speed
With the wind	$x + y$ $x + y = 300$
Against the wind	$x - y$ $x - y = 250$

10. A motor boat goes upstream against the current for a distance of 50 kilometers in 3 hours. It returns with the current the same distance in 2 hours. The speed of the boat in still water is x kilometers per hour, and the speed of the current is y kilometers per hour.

	Time	Speed	Distance
Upstream	3 hr	$(x - y)$ km/hr	50 km
Downstream	2 hr	$(x + y)$ km/hr	50 km

$3(x - y) = 50$
$2(x + y) = 50$

11. A cross country runner runs a distance of 5000 meters against a wind in 18 minutes. He runs the same distance with the wind in 15 minutes. The speed of the runner in still air is x meters per minute, and the speed of the wind is y meters per minute. $18(x - y) = 5000; 15(x + y) = 5000$

	Time	Speed	Distance
Against the wind	18 min	$(x - y)$ m/min	5000 m
With the wind	15 min	$(x + y)$ m/min	5000 m

12. A plane flies 1300 kilometers from Chicago to New York with a tail wind in $1\frac{1}{2}$ hours. Another plane flies from New York to Chicago against a head wind in $1\frac{3}{4}$ hours. The speed of each plane in still air is x kilometers per hour. The speed of the wind is y kilometers per hour. $1\frac{1}{2}(x + y) = 1300; 1\frac{3}{4}(x - y) = 1300$

	Time	Speed	Distance
Chicago to N.Y.	$1\frac{1}{2}$ hr	$(x + y)$ km/hr	1300 km
N.Y. to Chicago	$1\frac{3}{4}$ hr	$(x - y)$ km/hr	1300 km

WRITTEN EXERCISES

See the Teacher's Manual for the suggested assignments.

Goal: To solve motion problems by systems of linear equations

Sample Problem: Two students start walking toward each other at the same time from opposite ends of a field 210 meters long. They meet in 60 seconds. One student's speed is $\frac{3}{4}$ the other student's speed in meters per second. Find the speed of each student.

Answer: Their speeds are 2 meters per second and $1\frac{1}{2}$ meters per second.

For each problem, (a) select two variables for the unknown numbers, (b) write two equations, and (c) solve. (Examples 1 and 2) 1. Speed in still water: x; speed of current: y; $x - y = 8$; $x + y = 10$; Ans.: Speed in still water: 9 km/hr; speed of current: 1 km/hr

1. Three girls paddle a canoe at a speed of 8 kilometers per hour against a current. Their speed with the current is 10 kilometers per hour. Find their speed in still water and the speed of the current.

2. A plane can average 320 kilometers per hour flying with a wind. Its speed is 288 kilometers per hour against the wind. Find the plane's speed in still air and the speed of the wind. Speed in still air: x; speed of wind: y; $x + y = 320$; $x - y = 288$; Ans.: speed in still air: 304 km/hr; wind speed: 16 km/hr

3. Some scouts traveled by bus at a speed of 70 kilometers per hour and then hiked at a speed of 7 kilometers per hour. The total distance traveled was 224 kilometers in 5 hours. How long did they travel by bus and how long did they hike?

	Speed	Time	Distance
By bus	70 km/hr	x hrs	$70x$ km
Hiking	7 km/hr	y hrs	$7y$ km
Total		5 hrs	224 km

$x + y = 5$; $70x + 7y = 224$; Ans.: 3 hours by bus; 2 hours hiking

4. A boy swims part of the way across a lake at a speed of 50 meters per minute. He rides in a boat for the remaining distance at 400 meters per minute. The trip across the lake of 6300 meters takes 42 minutes. How long does he swim and how long does he ride in the boat?

	Speed	Time	Distance
Swimming	50 m/min	x min	$50x$ meters
Riding in boat	400 m/min	y min	$400y$ meters
Total		42 min	6300 meters

$x + y = 42$; $50x + 400y = 6300$; Ans.: swimming: 30 min.; by boat: 12 min

5. Two trains leave the same city in opposite directions. The eastbound train travels 10 hours, and the westbound train travels 5 hours. They are 1300 kilometers apart at their destinations. The westbound train is 20 kilometers per hour faster. What is the speed of each train?

	Time	Speed	Distance
Eastbound train	10 hrs	x km/hr	$10x$ km
Westbound train	5 hrs	y km/hr	$5y$ km
Total			1300 km

$x + 20 = y$; $10x + 5y = 1300$; Ans.: eastbound: 80 km/hr; westbound: 100 km/hr

6. A plane and a carrier 3720 kilometers apart move toward each other and meet in 3 hours. The speed of the plane is 30 times the speed of the carrier in kilometers per hour. Find the speed of the plane and the speed of the carrier.

	Time	Speed	Distance
Plane	3 hrs	x km/hr	$3x$ km
Carrier	3 hrs	y km/hr	$3y$ km
Total			3720 km

$x = 30y$; $3x + 3y = 3720$; Ans.: plane: 1200 km/hr.; carrier: 40 km/hr

REVIEW CAPSULE FOR SECTION 13.5

Solve and check. (Section 3.4 and 3.5)

1. $0.15x - 3.8 = 3.4$ $x = 48$

2. $0.08x + 0.12(200 - x) = 0.10(200)$
   $x = 100$

3. $0.18x + 0.15(450 - x) = 0.16(450)$ $x = 150$

4. $0.06(x - 300) + 0.015(300) = 0.03x$
   $x = 450$

13.5 Problem Solving: Mixture Problems

OBJECTIVE: To solve a word problem involving mixtures by using a system of two linear equations

Per cents are often used to express the strength of a solution or the relative quantity of a specific ingredient in a mixture.

a. 18 grams (g) of salt in 100 grams of a mixture of salt and water is called an 18% solution.

b. 5 decigrams (dg) of acid in 100 decigrams of a mixture of acid and water is a 5% solution.

c. A metal object of 500 grams containing 100 grams of copper is 20% copper.

P-1 **How much sugar is in 80 grams of a 25% solution?** 20 grams

 A 10% salt solution and an 18% salt solution are mixed to obtain 320 grams of a 15% salt solution. How many grams of the 10% solution and of the 18% solution are needed?

Solution:

Solution	Grams of Solution	Grams of Salt
10%	x	$0.10x$
18%	y	$0.18y$
15%	320	$0.15(320)$

1. Write an equation that tells that the mixture of the 10% and 18% solutions totals 320 grams. $\longrightarrow$ $x + y = 320$

2. Write an equation that tells that the total number of grams of salt in the mixture of the 10% and 18% solutions is 0.15(320). $\longrightarrow$ $0.10x + 0.18y = 0.15(320)$

$$\begin{cases} \textbf{1.}\ x + y = 320 \\ \textbf{2.}\ 0.10x + 0.18y = 0.15(320) \end{cases}$$ 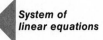 **System of linear equations**

The substitution method is used.

3. Solve for y in Equation 1. $\qquad y = 320 - x$

4 Substitute $(320 - x)$ for y in Equation 2. Solve for x.

$$0.10x + 0.18y = 0.15(320)$$
$$0.10x + 0.18(320 - x) = 0.15(320)$$
$$0.10x + 57.6 - 0.18x = 48$$
$$57.6 - 0.08x = 48$$
$$-0.08x = -9.6$$
$$\frac{-0.08x}{-0.08} = \frac{-9.6}{-0.08}$$
$$x = 120 \quad \blacktriangleleft \quad \textit{Number of grams of 10\% solution}$$

5 Substitute 120 for x in Equation 1. Solve for y.

$$x + y = 320$$
$$120 + y = 320$$
$$y = 200 \quad \blacktriangleleft \quad \textit{Number of grams of 18\% solution}$$

Check: $120 + 200 = 320$ $0.10(120) + 0.18(200) = 0.15(320)$

$12 \quad + \quad 36 \quad = 48$

CLASSROOM EXERCISES

Write how much of each ingredient is in each mixture. (P-1)

1. 800 milliliters of a mixture of concentrated orange juice and water that is 25% orange juice   Orange juice: 200 milliliters; water: 600 milliliters

2. 75 grams of a mixture of brown sugar and white sugar that is 40% brown sugar   Brown sugar: 30 g; white sugar: 45 g

3. A 20% sugar solution (mixture of sugar and water) of 500 grams
   Sugar: 100 g; water: 400 g

4. 300 milligrams of a 5% acid solution (mixture of acid and water)
   Acid: 15 mg; water: 285 mg

5. 500 cubic meters of air (mixture of approximately 20% oxygen and 80% nitrogen)   Oxygen: 100 m³; nitrogen: 400 m³

6. 600 milliliters of a mixture that is 20% chemical A, 30% chemical B, and 50% chemical C Chemical A: 120 milliliters; chemical B: 180 milliliters; chemical C: 300 milliliters

Write the numeral missing from each row of the table for salt solutions.
(Example 1)

	Per Cent Solution	Amount of Mixture	Amount of Salt	
7.	8%	100 grams	?	8
8.	12%	x centigrams	?	0.12x
9.	6%	y milligrams	?	0.06y
10.	15%	(x + 20) decigrams	?	0.15(x + 20)
11.	10%	?	120	12 grams
12.	20%	?	40	8 grams

Write the numeral or numerals missing from each row of the table for acid solutions. (Example 1)

	Per Cent Solution	Amount of Mixture	Amount of Acid	Amount of Water
13.	3%	500 grams	? 15	? 485
14.	10%	x decigrams	? 0.1x	? 0.9x
15.	25%	? 40	10 grams	? 30
16.	20%	? $\frac{x}{0.8}$	? $x - \frac{x}{0.8}$	x centigrams

WRITTEN EXERCISES

See the Teacher's Manual for the suggested assignments.

Goal: To solve mixture problems by systems of linear equations

Sample Problem: A 30% salt solution and a 60% salt solution are mixed to obtain 60 grams of a 50% solution. How many grams of the 30% solution and of the 60% solution are needed?

Answer: 20 grams of the 30% solution and 40 grams of the 60% solution

Write an answer to each question. (Example 1)

1. A certain metal is 75% gold. How many grams of gold are in 12 grams of the metal? 9 grams

2. The sugar content of a solution of sugar and water is 4%. How much sugar is in 800 grams of the solution? 32 grams

3. Twelve decigrams of salt are mixed with water. What per cent describes the solution if there are 240 decigrams of the mixture? 5%

4. 400 grams of fertilizer are mixed with water. What per cent describes the solution if there are 16,000 grams of the mixture? $2\frac{1}{2}\%$

5. 220 grams of water and x grams of acid are mixed. What open phrase describes the amount of the mixture? $220 + x$

6. Five milligrams of a medicine are mixed with water to make a mixture of y milligrams. What open phrase describes the amount of water needed? $y - 5$

7. x grams of a 6% solution and y grams of a 3% solution are mixed. The mixture is 300 grams of a 4% solution. Write two equations to use in solving for x and y.

$x + y = 300;$
$0.06x + 0.03y = 0.04(300)$

8. x grams of a metal that is 80% silver is melted with y grams of a metal that is 60% silver. The result is a 50-gram mixture that is 65% silver. Write two equations to use in solving for x and y. $x + y = 50; 0.8x + 0.6y = 0.65(50)$

For each problem, (a) select two variables for the unknown numbers, (b) write two equations, and (c) solve. (Example 1)

9. A 4% acid solution is mixed with an 8% acid solution. How many **See below.** grams of each solution are used to obtain 400 grams of a 5% solution?

10. A 12% salt solution is mixed with a 20% salt solution. How many kilograms of each solution are used to obtain 24 kilograms of a 15% solution? Kilograms of 12% solution: x $x + y = 24$ **Ans.: 12% solution: 15 kg**
Kilograms of 20% solution: y $0.12x + 0.20y = 0.15(24)$ **20% solution: 9 kg**

11. A 12% salt solution is mixed with 48 grams of a 20% salt solution. The mixture is a 15% salt solution. Find the amounts of the 12% solution and the 15% solution in grams.

Solution	Amount of Solution	Amount of Salt
12%	x	$0.12x$
20%	48	$0.20(48)$
15%	y	$0.15y$

$x + 48 = y$
$0.12x + 0.20(48) = 0.15y$
Ans.: 12% solution: 80 g;
15% solution: 128 g

12. An 8% acid solution is mixed with 200 grams of a 4% acid solution. The mixture is a $5\frac{1}{2}\%$ acid solution. Find the amounts of the 8% solution and the $5\frac{1}{2}\%$ solution in grams.

Solution	Amount of Solution	Amount of Pure Acid
8%	x	$0.08x$
4%	200	$0.04(200)$
$5\frac{1}{2}\%$	y	$0.055y$

$x + 200 = y$
$0.08x + 0.04(200) = 0.055y$
Ans.: 8% solution: 120 g
$5\frac{1}{2}\%$ **solution: 320 g**

9. Grams of 4% solution: x $x + y = 400$ **Ans.: 4% solution: 300 g**
Grams of 8% solution: y $0.04x + 0.08y = 0.05(400)$ **8% solution: 100 g**

Longitude and Time Zones

The longitude (see page 285) of two points on the earth's surface can be used to determine the difference in time between them. The diagram at the right below shows the relation between the longitude of a point and its time zone. Note that a time difference of one hour is equivalent to a difference in longitude of 15 degrees.

The **zone description** (ZD) of a point depends upon its longitude. A zone description of +5 means that the time at Zone 0 is 5 hours later than the time at Zone +5. A zone description of −3 means that the time at Zone 0 is 3 hours earlier than at Zone −3. To find the ZD of a point, first divide its longitude by 15° and round to the nearest whole number. The ZD is positive for West longitude and negative for East longitude.

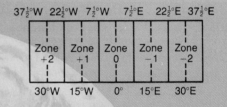

EXAMPLE: At point A with longitude 52.4°E the time is 10:45 a.m. Find the time at point B with longitude 82.7°W.

SOLUTION: Find the ZD of each point.

$$A: \frac{52.4}{15} \approx 3.49 \qquad ZD = -3$$

$$B: \frac{82.7}{15} \approx 5.51 \qquad ZD = +6$$

Point B is 9 zones West of Point A. Thus, the time at B is 9 hours earlier.

$$10:45 - 9 = \textbf{1:45 a.m.}$$

EXERCISES

Find the zone description (ZD) of each city. Then find its time when it is 6:05 p.m. in London (longitude 0°).

1. ZD: −3; 9:05 p.m.
2. ZD: +6; 12:05 p.m.
3. ZD: +8; 10:05 a.m.

1. Moscow (37.7°E)
2. Chicago (87.6°W)
3. Seattle (122.3°W)

See below.

4. Honolulu (157.8°W) See below. 5. New Delhi (77.2°E)
6. Montreal (73.5°W)

6. See below.

7. Buenos Aires (55.8°W)
8. Paris (2.3°E)
9. Rome (12.5°E)

7. ZD: +4; 2:05 p.m.
8. ZD: 0; 6:05 p.m.
9. ZD: −1; 7:05 p.m.

Special Topic Application

4. ZD: +11; 9:05 a.m.

5. ZD: −5; 11:05 p.m.

341

6. ZD: +5; 1:05 p.m.

CHAPTER SUMMARY

IMPORTANT IDEAS

1. Steps for solving a problem with two unknowns by a system of linear equations:
   a. Represent the unknowns by two variables.
   b. Write a system of two linear equations.
   c. Solve the system of equations.

2. Any two-digit number can be represented by $10x + y$, in which x represents the ten's digit and y represents the one's digit.

3. The basic formula $d = rt$ relating distance, rate, and time is often used in motion problems.

4. Sometimes speeds can be added. Thus, if you let x represent the speed of an object in still water and y the speed of the current, then $(x + y)$ will represent the speed of the object with the current and $(x - y)$ the speed against the current.

5. The strength of a solution or the relative quantity of a specific ingredient in a mixture is often expressed by per cents. Thus, ten grams of salt in 100 grams of a mixture of salt and water is called a 10% salt solution.

NOTE: The Teacher's Resource Book contains two forms of each Chapter Test.

CHAPTER REVIEW

2. Greater: x; smaller: y; $x + y = 8$; $4x = 2 + 4y$; Ans.: $3\frac{3}{4}$ and $4\frac{1}{4}$

3. Length: x; width: y; $x = 2y - 3$; $2x + 2y = 24$; Ans.: width: 5 m; length: 7 m

SECTION 13.1

For each problem, (a) select two variables for the unknown numbers, (b) write two equations, and (c) solve.

1. The sum of two numbers is 17. The smaller number is 33 less than the greater number. Find the two numbers. Greater: x; smaller: y; $x + y = 17$; $x = y + 33$; Ans.: 25 and −8

2. The sum of two numbers is 8. Four times the greater number is two See above. more than four times the smaller number. Find the two numbers.

3. The length of a rectangle is three meters less than twice the width. See above. The perimeter is 24 meters. Find the length and width.

4. Three times the width of a rectangle increased by twice the length equals 40. The perimeter is 34 units. Find the number of units in the length and width. Length: x; width: y; $3y + 2x = 40$; $2x + 2y = 34$; Ans.: width: 6; length: 11

For each problem, (a) select two variables for the unknown numbers, (b) write two equations, and (c) solve.

5. The Gymnastics Club sold 204 tickets for their show with total receipts of $215. The adult tickets sold for $1.25 and the student tickets for $0.75. Find the number of each kind of ticket that was sold.

6. Mrs. Bell purchased 96 greeting cards on sale for $10.20. One kind cost 15 cents each and another kind cost 8 cents each. Find the number of each kind she purchased.

SECTION 13.3

7. The ten's digit of a two-digit number is three times the one's digit. The sum of the digits is 12. Write the two-digit number.

8. The one's digit of a two-digit number exceeds the ten's digit by 5. Nine times the ten's digit increased by three times the one's digit equals 39. Write the two-digit number.

9. A two-digit number equals 9 times its one's digit. The sum of the digits is 9. Write the two-digit number.

10. A two-digit number is 2 less than 5 times its one's digit. The one's digit exceeds the ten's digit by 5. Write the two-digit number.

SECTION 13.4

11. A fishing group traveled by plane for 3 hours and then by jeep for 2 hours. The total distance traveled was 1000 kilometers. The speed of the plane in kilometers per hour was six times the speed of the jeep. Find the speed of the plane and the speed of the jeep.

	Time	Speed	Distance
By plane	3 hrs	x km/hr	$3x$ km
By jeep	2 hrs	y km/hr	$2y$ km
Total			1000 km

For each problem, (a) select two variables for the unknown numbers, (b) write two equations, and (c) solve.

12. A tired swimmer and a rescue boat 2600 meters apart move toward each other. They meet in 5 minutes. The speed of the boat in meters per minute is 25 times the speed of the swimmer. Find the speed of the boat and the speed of the swimmer.

	Time	Speed	Distance
Swimmer	5 min	x m/min	$5x$ meters
Boat	5 min	y m/min	$5y$ meters
Total			2600 meters

$5x + 5y = 2600$; $y = 25x$; Ans.: boat: 500 m/min, swimmer: 20m/min

SECTION 13.5

13. A 12% salt solution is mixed with a 20% salt solution to obtain 800 grams of a 17% solution. Find the amount of each solution. See below.

14. A 4% acid solution is mixed with a 1% acid solution. The result is a 90-gram mixture that is $2\frac{1}{2}$% acid. Find the amount of the 4% solution and the amount of the 1% solution.

13. Grams of 12% solution: x
Grams of 20% solution: y
$x + y = 800$
$0.12x + 0.20y = 0.17\,(800)$
Ans.: 12% solution: 300 g
20% solution: 500 g

14. Grams of 4% solution: x
Grams of 1% solution: y
$x + y = 90$
$0.04x + 0.01y = 0.025\,(90)$
Ans.: 4% solution: 45 g
1% solution: 45 g

CHAPTER

14

Products and Quotients of Rational Expressions

Sections   **14.1**   **Rational Expressions**

14.2   **Simplifying Rational Expressions**

14.3   **Multiplying Rational Expressions**

14.4   **Binomial Numerators and Denominators**

14.5   **Trinomial Numerators and Denominators**

14.6   **Dividing Rational Expressions**

14.7   **More Quotients**

Features   *Calculator Exercises:* **Continued Fractions**

Career: **Electrician**

Review and Testing   *Review Capsules*

Mid-Chapter Review

Chapter Summary

Chapter Review

14.1 Rational Expressions

OBJECTIVES: To identify whether or not an expression is a rational expression
To evaluate a rational expression for a given value of its variable
To write the number or numbers that cannot be in the domain of a rational expression

A **rational expression** is one that can be written as the quotient of two polynomials.

$$\frac{x^2 + x - 3}{x^2 - 3x + 5} ; \frac{2}{x} ;$$

$$\frac{4}{3} ; \frac{x^2 - 5}{1}$$

P-1   Write $x^2 + x - 1$ as a quotient. $\frac{x^2 + x - 1}{1}$

Any polynomial is also a rational expression since it can be expressed as a quotient with 1 as divisor.

P-2   **Which of the expressions below are rational expressions?**

a. $\frac{2x}{5}$ Yes   b. $\frac{3x + 7}{x^2 - 3x + 10}$ Yes   c. $\frac{|x^2 + 1|}{5}$ No

d. $\frac{-7}{10}$ Yes   e. $\frac{\sqrt{x - 3}}{\sqrt{x + 3}}$ No   f. 75   Yes

◀ *Remember that both dividend and divisor must be polynomials.*

example 1

Perhaps you would like to discuss how rational expressions could be evaluated by using a calculator. Refer to page 214.

Evaluate the following rational expression if x equals -2.

$$\frac{2x^2 - 3x + 1}{-x^2 + x - 3}$$

Solution:

1. Replace x by -2. ⟶ $\dfrac{2x^2 - 3x + 1}{-x^2 + x - 3} = \dfrac{2(-2)^2 - 3(-2) + 1}{-(-2)^2 + (-2) - 3}$

2. Simplify. ⟶ $= \dfrac{8 + 6 + 1}{-4 - 2 - 3}$

$$= \frac{15}{-9} \quad \text{or} \quad -\frac{15}{9}$$

Any number that will result in a divisor of 0 must be restricted from the domain of the variable in a rational expression.

$$\frac{x+5}{x^2-1}$$

$$x \neq 1; x \neq -1$$

example 2

Write the number or numbers that cannot be in the domain of x in $\dfrac{x-2}{3x+4}$.

Solution: You can see that $3x + 4$ must not equal 0.

| Solve for the number that makes $3x + 4$ equal 0. | → | This number cannot be in the domain. |

$$3x + 4 = 0$$

$$3x + 4 - 4 = 0 - 4$$

$$3x = -4$$

$$\tfrac{1}{3}(3x) = \tfrac{1}{3}(-4)$$

$$x = -\tfrac{4}{3} \qquad \text{The number } -\tfrac{4}{3} \text{ cannot be in the domain.}$$

CLASSROOM EXERCISES

Write <u>Yes</u> or <u>No</u> to tell whether each expression is a rational expression. (P-2)

1. $x^2 - 2x + 1$ Yes

2. $\dfrac{x^2 + 1}{5}$ Yes

3. $\sqrt{x + 1}$ No

4. 15 Yes

5. $\dfrac{2}{5}$ Yes

6. $\dfrac{2}{\sqrt{x}}$ No

7. $\dfrac{x - 3}{x + 1}$ Yes

8. $\dfrac{x(x + 3)}{x^2 + 2x + 1}$ Yes

Write the number or numbers that cannot be in the domain of each variable. (Example 2)

9. $\dfrac{5}{x}$ 0

10. $\dfrac{3}{x + 1}$ −1

11. $\dfrac{x + 3}{x - 3}$ 3

12. $\dfrac{x + 10}{-5x}$ 0

13. $\dfrac{x}{2x - 1}$ $\tfrac{1}{2}$

14. $\dfrac{3x + 1}{2x + 1}$ $-\tfrac{1}{2}$

15. $\dfrac{5}{x^2 - 1}$ 1, −1

16. $\dfrac{x}{(x - 3)(x + 2)}$ 3, −2

WRITTEN EXERCISES

See the Teacher's Manual for the suggested assignments.

Goal: To evaluate rational expressions

Sample Problem: Evaluate $\dfrac{x^2 - 4}{x + 3}$ if x equals 3.

Answer: $\dfrac{5}{6}$

Write Yes or No to show whether each expression is a rational expression. (P-2)

1. $x^2 + 10$ Yes

2. $x^2 - 3x + 5$ Yes

3. $\dfrac{3}{4}$ Yes

4. $-\dfrac{5}{6}$ Yes

5. $\dfrac{x - 2}{x + 2}$ Yes

6. $\dfrac{x^2 - 5}{x^2 + 10}$ Yes

7. $\dfrac{\sqrt{x} - 1}{\sqrt{x} + 1}$ No

8. $\dfrac{x^2 + \sqrt{x}}{x^2 - \sqrt{x}}$ No

9. $\dfrac{|x|}{-x}$ No

10. $\dfrac{x - 3}{|x + 2|}$ No

11. $\dfrac{x^2 - 2x + 3}{3x^2 - 5x + 2}$ Yes

12. $\dfrac{5 - x^2 + x}{x - 6 + 2x^2}$

Yes

Evaluate each rational expression if x equals 1. (Example 1)

13. $\dfrac{5}{-2x}$ $-\dfrac{5}{2}$

14. $\dfrac{-7}{5x}$ $-\dfrac{7}{5}$

15. $\dfrac{x + 3}{x + 2}$ $\dfrac{4}{3}$

16. $\dfrac{x - 2}{x + 2}$ $-\dfrac{1}{3}$

17. $\dfrac{x^2 - 2x + 5}{x^2 + 3x - 1}$ $\dfrac{4}{3}$

18. $\dfrac{x^2 - 1}{x^2 + 1}$ 0

19. $\dfrac{2x^2 - 3x + 1}{x^2 - 5x - 3}$ 0

20. $\dfrac{x^2 - x - 1}{x^2 - 7x + 3}$ $\dfrac{1}{3}$

Write the number or numbers that cannot be in the domain of each variable.
(Example 2)

21. $\dfrac{x^2 + 2}{x}$ 0

22. $\dfrac{x - 5}{-x}$ 0

23. $\dfrac{2x}{x - 10}$ 10

24. $\dfrac{3x}{x + 15}$ -15

25. $\dfrac{x^2 + 3}{5x}$ 0

26. $\dfrac{x^2 - 4}{-3x}$ 0

27. $\dfrac{2}{x^2 - 4}$ $2, -2$

28. $\dfrac{5}{x^2 - 9}$ $3, -3$

29. $\dfrac{2}{3x - 1}$ $\dfrac{1}{3}$

30. $\dfrac{5}{4x + 3}$ $-\dfrac{3}{4}$

31. $\dfrac{3}{(x - 1)(x + 7)}$ $1, -7$

32. $\dfrac{7}{(x + 4)(x - 9)}$

$-4, 9$

REVIEW CAPSULE FOR SECTION 14.2

Write the prime factorization of each polynomial. (Section 10.1) 4. $(c + 9)(c - 9)$

1. $18x^3$
$2 \cdot 3 \cdot 3 \cdot x \cdot x \cdot x$

2. $12ab^2$
$2 \cdot 2 \cdot 3 \cdot a \cdot b \cdot b$

3. $x^2 - 25$ $(x + 5)(x - 5)$

4. $c^2 - 81$

5. $x^2 + 7x$ $x(x + 7)$

6. $a^2 - b^2$ $(a + b)(a - b)$

7. $x^2 - 6x + 9$ $(x - 3)(x - 3)$ 8. $3ab + 3b^2$ See below.

9. $3a^2 + 6ab$
$3a(a + 2b)$

10. $5a^2 - ab$
$a(5a - b)$

11. $x^2 + 4x + 4$
$(x + 2)(x + 2)$

12. $x^2 - y^2$
$(x + y)(x - y)$

8. $3b(a + b)$

14.2 Simplifying Rational Expressions

OBJECTIVES: To simplify rational expressions involving only monomials
To simplify rational expressions involving monomials or trinomials

The Product Rule for Fractions can be applied to rational expressions.

Product Rule for Rational Expressions

If $\dfrac{a}{b}$ and $\dfrac{c}{d}$ are rational expressions,

then $\dfrac{a}{b} \cdot \dfrac{c}{d} = \dfrac{ac}{bd}$. ($b$ and d are not zero.)

$$\frac{x}{x+1} \cdot \frac{x+3}{x-2} =$$

$$\frac{x^2 + 3x}{x^2 - x - 2}$$

You can simplify a rational expression by applying the Product Rule for Rational Expressions.

In working with rational expressions, it will be assumed that no divisor equals 0.

example 1

Simplify $\dfrac{10x}{15x^2}$.

Solution:

1. Write the prime factorizations. $\longrightarrow$ $\dfrac{10x}{15x^2} = \dfrac{2 \cdot 5 \cdot x}{3 \cdot 5 \cdot x \cdot x}$

2. Product Rule for Rational Expressions $\longrightarrow$ $= \dfrac{5x}{5x} \cdot \dfrac{2}{3x}$ $\dfrac{5x}{5x}$ is a name for 1.

3. Multiplication Property of One $\longrightarrow$ $= \dfrac{2}{3x}$ **Simplest form**

example 2

Simplify $\dfrac{x^2 + x}{x^2 + 2x + 1}$.

Solution:

1. $\dfrac{x^2 + x}{x^2 + 2x + 1} = \dfrac{x(x+1)}{(x+1)(x+1)}$

2. $= \dfrac{x+1}{x+1} \cdot \dfrac{x}{x+1}$

3. $= \dfrac{x}{x+1}$ x is **not** a factor of $x + 1$.

P-1   **What are the prime factors of $x^2 - 4$?** $(x + 2), (x - 2)$ **of $x^2 + x - 6$?** $(x + 3), (x - 2)$

example 3   Simplify $\dfrac{x^2 - 4}{x^2 + x - 6}$.

Solution:

$\boxed{1}$ $\dfrac{x^2 - 4}{x^2 + x - 6} = \dfrac{(x + 2)(x - 2)}{(x - 2)(x + 3)}$

$\boxed{2}$ $= \dfrac{x - 2}{x - 2} \cdot \dfrac{x + 2}{x + 3}$

$\boxed{3}$ $= \dfrac{x + 2}{x + 3}$

example 4   Simplify $\dfrac{6x^2y - 3xy^2}{4x^2 - y^2}$.

Solution: The method shown below for identifying a name for 1 is often used to save work.

$$\dfrac{6x^2y - 3xy^2}{4x^2 - y^2} = \dfrac{3xy(2x - y)}{(2x + y)(2x - y)}$$ ◀ **Prime factorization**

$$= \dfrac{3xy(2x \overset{1}{\cancel{-y}})}{(2x + y)(2x \underset{1}{\cancel{-y}})}$$ ◀ **Note how a name for 1 is shown.**

This shortcut method sometimes encourages incorrect "cancellation," e.g. the two "x's" in " $\dfrac{3xy}{2x + y}$ ".

$$= \dfrac{3xy}{2x + y}$$ ◀ **Simplest form**

Steps for simplifying rational expressions:

1. Write the prime factorizations of both polynomials.
2. Form a name for 1 from all factors common to the dividend and divisor.
3. Use this name for 1 and write an indicated product equivalent to the given rational expression.
4. Apply the Multiplication Property of One and write the result in the simplest form.

CLASSROOM EXERCISES

Simplify. No divisor equals 0. (Examples 1–3)

1. $\dfrac{2}{6}$ $\dfrac{1}{3}$

2. $\dfrac{2x}{3x}$ $\dfrac{2}{3}$

3. $\dfrac{x}{x^2}$ $\dfrac{1}{x}$

4. $\dfrac{3x}{3(x-2)}$ $\dfrac{x}{x-2}$

5. $\dfrac{3(x+1)}{x(x+1)}$ $\dfrac{3}{x}$

6. $\dfrac{5(x^2+2)}{x^2+2}$ 5

7. $\dfrac{x+2}{x+3}$ $\dfrac{x+2}{x+3}$

8. $\dfrac{(x+1)(x-2)}{(x+1)}$ $x-2$

9. $\dfrac{x(x+2)}{x^2(x+2)}$ $\dfrac{1}{x}$

10. $\dfrac{x-1}{x^2-1}$ $\dfrac{1}{x+1}$

WRITTEN EXERCISES

See the Teacher's Manual for the suggested assignments.

Goal: To simplify rational expressions

Sample Problem: Simplify $\dfrac{9x^2+18x}{x^2+4x+4}$. **Answer:** $\dfrac{9x}{x+2}$

Simplify. No divisor equals 0. (Examples 1–4)

1. $\dfrac{5x^2}{10x}$ $\dfrac{x}{2}$

2. $\dfrac{18x}{10x^2}$ $\dfrac{9}{5x}$

3. $\dfrac{12x^3}{28x^4}$ $\dfrac{3}{7x}$

4. $\dfrac{20x^3}{50x^2}$ $\dfrac{2x}{5}$

5. $\dfrac{x(x-3)}{5(x-3)}$ $\dfrac{x}{5}$

6. $\dfrac{3(x+10)}{x(x+10)}$ $\dfrac{3}{x}$

7. $\dfrac{2x(x-5)}{3x(x-5)}$ $\dfrac{2}{3}$

8. $\dfrac{5x(x+7)}{4x(x+7)}$ $\dfrac{5}{4}$

9. $\dfrac{(x+2)(x-3)}{(x-3)(x+5)}$ $\dfrac{x+2}{x+5}$

10. $\dfrac{(x-4)(x+2)}{(x+2)(x-1)}$ $\dfrac{x-4}{x-1}$

11. $\dfrac{4x-4}{3x+9}$ $\dfrac{4x-4}{3x+9}$

12. $\dfrac{3x+3}{5x+5}$ $\dfrac{3}{5}$

13. $\dfrac{3x-6}{5x-10}$ $\dfrac{3}{5}$

14. $\dfrac{4x+12}{3x+9}$ $\dfrac{4}{3}$

15. $\dfrac{x^2+3x}{x^2+5x}$ $\dfrac{x+3}{x+5}$

16. $\dfrac{x^2-5x}{x^2+7x}$ $\dfrac{x-5}{x+7}$

17. $\dfrac{x+3}{x^2-9}$ $\dfrac{1}{x-3}$

18. $\dfrac{x-5}{x^2-25}$ $\dfrac{1}{x+5}$

19. $\dfrac{x^2-16}{x(x-4)}$ $\dfrac{x+4}{x}$

20. $\dfrac{x^2-36}{x(x+6)}$ $\dfrac{x-6}{x}$

21. $\dfrac{x^2+2x}{x^2-4}$ $\dfrac{x}{x-2}$

22. $\dfrac{x^2-49}{x^2+7x}$ $\dfrac{x-7}{x}$

23. $\dfrac{x(x-2)}{x^2-4x+4}$ $\dfrac{x}{x-2}$

24. $\dfrac{x^2+6x+9}{x(x+3)}$ $\dfrac{x+3}{x}$

25. $\dfrac{4x^2y}{10xy^2}$ $\dfrac{2x}{5y}$

26. $\dfrac{16a^2b}{12ab^2}$ $\dfrac{4a}{3b}$

27. $\dfrac{2a+2b}{2c}$ $\dfrac{a+b}{c}$

28. $\dfrac{3t}{3x-3y}$ $\dfrac{t}{x-y}$

29. $\dfrac{a^2-b^2}{3a+3b}$ $\dfrac{a-b}{3}$

30. $\dfrac{5x+5y}{x^2-y^2}$ $\dfrac{5}{x-y}$

31. $\dfrac{5a^2-ab}{3a^2+6ab}$ $\dfrac{5a-b}{3a+6b}$

32. $\dfrac{3a^2+3ab}{3ab+3b^2}$ $\dfrac{a}{b}$

REVIEW CAPSULE FOR SECTION 14.3

4. $2 \cdot 2 \cdot 3 \cdot 3 \cdot p \cdot p \cdot p \cdot p \cdot p \cdot p \cdot q \cdot q \cdot r \cdot r \cdot r$

Write the prime factors of each expression. (Section 10.1)

1. $12x^2y^3$
   $2 \cdot 2 \cdot 3 \cdot x \cdot x \cdot y \cdot y \cdot y$

2. $20r^3st^2$
   $2 \cdot 5 \cdot r \cdot r \cdot r \cdot s \cdot t \cdot t$

3. $18a^2b^4c^3$
   $2 \cdot 3 \cdot 3 \cdot a \cdot a \cdot b \cdot b \cdot b \cdot b \cdot c \cdot c \cdot c$

4. $36p^5q^2r^3$

14.3 Multiplying Rational Expressions

OBJECTIVE: To multiply two or more rational expressions with monomial numerators and denominators, writing the product in simplest form

When multiplying fractions, you always simplify the product. This also applies to multiplying rational expressions.

P-1 **Write each product in simplest form.**

a. $\dfrac{10}{3} \cdot \dfrac{12}{5}$ 8   b. $\dfrac{2}{6} \cdot \dfrac{12}{5}$ $\dfrac{4}{5}$ c. $\dfrac{5}{6} \cdot \dfrac{21}{10}$ $1\dfrac{3}{4}$ d. $\dfrac{2}{1} \cdot \dfrac{3}{10} \cdot \dfrac{1}{12}$ $\dfrac{1}{20}$

example 1

Multiply and simplify: $\dfrac{10x}{3} \cdot \dfrac{12}{5x^2}$

Remind students that the Product Rule allows you to write a product as one rational expression or to write one rational expression as a product.

Solution:

1. Product Rule for Rational Expressions ⟶ $\dfrac{10x}{3} \cdot \dfrac{12}{5x^2} = \dfrac{(10x)(12)}{(3)(5x^2)}$

2. Factor. ⟶ $= \dfrac{(2 \cdot 5 \cdot x)(2 \cdot 2 \cdot 3)}{(3)(5 \cdot x \cdot x)}$

3. Product Rule for Rational Expressions ⟶ $= \dfrac{3 \cdot 5 \cdot x}{3 \cdot 5 \cdot x} \cdot \dfrac{2 \cdot 2 \cdot 2}{x}$

4. Multiplication Property of One ⟶ $= \dfrac{2 \cdot 2 \cdot 2}{x}$

5. Simplify. ⟶ $= \dfrac{8}{x}$

Steps can often be saved by identifying common factors first.

example 2

Multiply and simplify: $\dfrac{2x}{6x^2} \cdot \dfrac{12x}{5x^2}$

Solution:

$$\dfrac{2x}{6x^2} \cdot \dfrac{12x}{5x^2} = \dfrac{\overset{1}{2x} \cdot \overset{2 \cdot 1}{12x}}{\underset{1 \cdot x}{6x^2} \cdot \underset{x}{5x^2}}$$ ◀ x, 6, and x are common factors.

$$= \dfrac{4}{5x^2}$$ ◀ Simplest form

352 / Chapter 14

example 3

Multiply and simplify: $\dfrac{5xy}{6a} \cdot \dfrac{21ab}{10y^2}$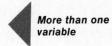

More than one variable

Solution:

$$\dfrac{5xy}{6a} \cdot \dfrac{21ab}{10y^2} = \dfrac{\overset{1 \cdot 1}{\cancel{5xy}}}{\underset{2 \cdot 1}{\cancel{6a}}} \cdot \dfrac{\overset{7 \cdot 1}{\cancel{21ab}}}{\underset{2 \cdot y}{\cancel{10y^2}}}$$

$$= \dfrac{1 \cdot x \cdot 1}{2 \cdot 1} \cdot \dfrac{7 \cdot 1 \cdot b}{2 \cdot y}$$

$$= \dfrac{x}{2} \cdot \dfrac{7b}{2y} = \dfrac{7bx}{4y}$$

example 4

Multiply and simplify: $\dfrac{2}{x} \cdot \dfrac{3x}{10} \cdot \dfrac{x^2}{12}$

Solution:

$$\dfrac{2}{x} \cdot \dfrac{3x}{10} \cdot \dfrac{x^2}{12} = \dfrac{\overset{1}{\cancel{2}}}{\underset{1}{\cancel{x}}} \cdot \dfrac{\overset{1 \cdot 1}{\cancel{3x}}}{\underset{5}{\cancel{10}}} \cdot \dfrac{x^2}{\underset{4}{\cancel{12}}}$$

$$= \dfrac{x^2}{20}$$

P-2 How do you know that $\dfrac{x^2}{20}$ is in simplest form? x^2 and 20 have no common factors.

CLASSROOM EXERCISES

Multiply. Simplify where necessary. (Examples 1 and 2)

1. $\dfrac{2}{x} \cdot \dfrac{x}{5}$ $\dfrac{2}{5}$

2. $\dfrac{y}{3} \cdot \dfrac{2}{y}$ $\dfrac{2}{3}$

3. $\dfrac{x}{5} \cdot \dfrac{5}{x}$ 1

4. $\dfrac{3a}{5} \cdot \dfrac{7}{3a}$ $\dfrac{7}{5}$

5. $\dfrac{2}{3} \cdot \dfrac{x}{y}$ $\dfrac{2x}{3y}$

6. $\dfrac{7}{x} \cdot \dfrac{5}{x}$ $\dfrac{35}{x^2}$

7. $\dfrac{a}{3} \cdot \dfrac{5}{2a}$ $\dfrac{5}{6}$

8. $\dfrac{5x}{7} \cdot \dfrac{6}{x}$ $\dfrac{30}{7}$

9. $\dfrac{3}{a^2} \cdot \dfrac{a}{5}$ $\dfrac{3}{5a}$

10. $-\dfrac{x}{7} \cdot \dfrac{5}{x^2}$ $-\dfrac{5}{7x}$

11. $\dfrac{2}{x} \cdot \dfrac{x}{5}$ $\dfrac{2}{5}$

12. $\dfrac{x}{3} \cdot \dfrac{x^2}{5}$ $\dfrac{x^3}{15}$

Multiply. Simplify where necessary. (Examples 1–4)

13. $\dfrac{2x}{3} \cdot \dfrac{1}{10x}$ $\dfrac{1}{15}$

14. $\dfrac{1}{5x} \cdot 15x$ 3

15. $\dfrac{3a}{b} \cdot 2b^2$ $6ab$

16. $\dfrac{3x^2}{2} \cdot \dfrac{2}{x}$ $3x$

17. $\left(-\dfrac{1}{3}\right)\left(-\dfrac{2}{y}\right)\left(-\dfrac{x}{2}\right)$ $-\dfrac{x}{3y}$

18. $\left(-\dfrac{1}{3}\right)\left(\dfrac{3}{x}\right)\left(-\dfrac{x}{5}\right)$ $\dfrac{1}{5}$

19. $\left(\dfrac{2a}{b}\right)\left(\dfrac{b}{3}\right)\left(\dfrac{3}{2a}\right)$ 1

20. $\dfrac{x}{y^2} \cdot \dfrac{y}{x^2}$ $\dfrac{1}{xy}$

WRITTEN EXERCISES

See the Teacher's Manual for the suggested assignments.

Goal: To multiply rational expressions

Sample Problem: $\dfrac{3x}{4a} \cdot \dfrac{5a^2}{9} \cdot \dfrac{6}{x^2}$ **Answer:** $\dfrac{5a}{2x}$

Multiply. Simplify where necessary. (Examples 1–4)

1. $\dfrac{3}{8} \cdot \dfrac{5}{9}$ $\dfrac{5}{24}$

2. $\dfrac{4}{5} \cdot \dfrac{3}{7}$ $\dfrac{12}{35}$

3. $\dfrac{5}{x} \cdot \dfrac{y}{3}$ $\dfrac{5y}{3x}$

4. $\dfrac{a}{7} \cdot \dfrac{4}{b}$ $\dfrac{4a}{7b}$

5. $\dfrac{2x}{5} \cdot \dfrac{3}{2x}$ $\dfrac{3}{5}$

6. $\dfrac{6}{7x} \cdot \dfrac{7x}{11}$ $\dfrac{6}{11}$

7. $\dfrac{4x}{3} \cdot \dfrac{7}{10x}$ $\dfrac{14}{15}$

8. $\dfrac{5}{12x} \cdot \dfrac{4x}{7}$ $\dfrac{5}{21}$

9. $\left(-\dfrac{x^2}{y}\right)\left(-\dfrac{2y}{x}\right)$ $2x$

10. $\left(-\dfrac{a}{b^2}\right)\left(-\dfrac{2b}{a^2}\right)$ $\dfrac{2}{ab}$

11. $\dfrac{8xy}{3} \cdot \dfrac{15}{2x^2}$ $\dfrac{20y}{x}$

12. $\dfrac{3}{10ab} \cdot \dfrac{14b^2}{15}$ $\dfrac{7b}{25a}$

13. $-\dfrac{21b^2}{a^2} \cdot \dfrac{3ab}{15b}$ $-\dfrac{21b^2}{5a}$

14. $\left(\dfrac{5x^2y}{10x}\right)\left(-\dfrac{6y^2}{21xy}\right)$ $-\dfrac{y^2}{7}$

15. $\dfrac{5y}{12x}(15x^2)$ $\dfrac{25xy}{4}$

16. $(21a^2)\dfrac{5x}{6ab}$ $\dfrac{35ax}{2b}$

17. $\dfrac{36ab^2}{5c} \cdot \dfrac{20ac^2}{24b}$ $6a^2bc$

18. $\dfrac{4x}{18yz^2} \cdot \dfrac{12xyz}{30x^2}$ $\dfrac{4}{45z}$

19. $\dfrac{a}{b} \cdot \dfrac{b}{c} \cdot \dfrac{c}{a}$ 1

20. $\dfrac{x}{y} \cdot \dfrac{z}{x} \cdot \dfrac{y}{z}$ 1

21. $\dfrac{2a^2}{5b} \cdot \dfrac{21b^2}{14c} \cdot \dfrac{11c^2}{10b}$ See below.

22. $\dfrac{4xy}{15z^2} \cdot \dfrac{3y}{10y^2} \cdot \dfrac{25yz}{7x^2}$ $\dfrac{2y}{7xz}$

23. $\dfrac{-5}{a} \cdot \dfrac{3a^2}{-b} \cdot \dfrac{-b^2}{10}$ $-\dfrac{3ab}{2}$

24. $\dfrac{-x}{-y^2} \cdot \dfrac{-3y}{4x} \cdot \dfrac{-8xy}{-z}$ $-\dfrac{6x}{z}$

21. $\dfrac{33a^2c}{50}$

REVIEW CAPSULE FOR SECTION 14.4

Find each product. (Section 9.5)

$x^2 - x - 6$ $x^2 - 10x + 25$

1. $x(x-1)$ $x^2 - x$

2. $(x-5)3$ $3x - 15$

3. $(x-3)(x+2)$

4. $(x-5)^2$

5. $(2a+b)(a+b)$ $2a^2 + 3ab + b^2$

6. $(a-b)(2a+b)$ $2a^2 - ab - b^2$

7. $-1(x-2)$ $-x + 2$

8. $-1(2-a)$ $-2 + a$

14.4 Binomial Numerators and Denominators

OBJECTIVE: To multiply rational expressions that involve binomials, writing the product in simplest form

Binomials such as $x - 2$ and $x - 1$ are prime polynomials. The variable x is <u>not</u> a factor of $x - 2$ and $x - 1$. It is a term of each binomial.

example 1

Multiply and simplify: $\dfrac{x - 2}{x + 3} \cdot \dfrac{x + 3}{x - 1}$

Solution:

1. Product Property $\longrightarrow$ $\dfrac{x - 2}{x + 3} \cdot \dfrac{x + 3}{x - 1} = \dfrac{(x - 2)(x + 3)}{(x + 3)(x - 1)}$

2. Commutative Property of Multiplication $\longrightarrow$ $= \dfrac{(x + 3)(x - 2)}{(x + 3)(x - 1)}$

3. Product Property $\longrightarrow$ $= \dfrac{x + 3}{x + 3} \cdot \dfrac{x - 2}{x - 1}$

4. Multiplication Property of 1 $\longrightarrow$ $= \dfrac{x - 2}{x - 1}$ ◀ *Simplest form*

example 2

Multiply and simplify: $\dfrac{x(x + 3)}{x - 5} \cdot \dfrac{x - 5}{2x}$

Solution:

$$\dfrac{x(x + 3)}{x - 5} \cdot \dfrac{x - 5}{2x} = \dfrac{\overset{1}{x}(x + 3)(\overset{1}{x - 5})}{(\underset{1}{x - 5})\underset{1}{2x}}$$ ◀ *A name for 1 is $\dfrac{x(x - 5)}{(x - 5)x}$.*

$$= \dfrac{x + 3}{2}$$ ◀ *Simplest form*

P-1 **Write $-(a - b)$ without parentheses.** $-a + b$

You can use the Property of the Opposite of a Sum to write $-(a - b)$ without parentheses.

$$-(a - b) = -(a + -b)$$
$$= (-a) + -(-b)$$
$$= (-a) + b$$
$$= b + (-a)$$
$$= b - a$$ ◀ *Thus, $a - b$ and $b - a$ are opposites.*

P-2 Write the opposite of each phrase.

a. $x - 2$ $2 - x$ b. $5 - t$ $t - 5$ c. $r - m$ $m - r$

P-3 What binomial is the opposite of $x - 2$? $2 - x$

example 3

Multiply and simplify: $\dfrac{x + 3}{x - 2} \cdot \dfrac{2 - x}{x - 5}$

In Step $\boxed{1}$, point out that $(2 - x)$ has been replaced by the equivalent $-(x - 2)$. This is a possible source of error.

Solution:

$\boxed{1}$ Property of the Opposite of a Difference $\longrightarrow \dfrac{x + 3}{x - 2} \cdot \dfrac{2 - x}{x - 5} = \dfrac{(x + 3) \cdot -(x - 2)}{(x - 2)(x - 5)}$

$\boxed{2}$ Multiplication Property of -1 $\longrightarrow = \dfrac{(x + 3) \cdot -1(x - 2)}{(x - 2)(x - 5)}$

$\boxed{3}$ Product Rule for Rational Expressions $\longrightarrow = \dfrac{x - 2}{x - 2} \cdot \dfrac{-1(x + 3)}{x - 5}$

$\boxed{4}$ Multiplication Property of 1 $\longrightarrow = \dfrac{-1(x + 3)}{x - 5}$

$\boxed{5}$ Simplest form $\longrightarrow = -\dfrac{x + 3}{x - 5}$

example 4

Multiply: $\dfrac{x + 2}{x - 3} \cdot \dfrac{x + 1}{3}$

Solution: $\dfrac{x + 2}{x - 3} \cdot \dfrac{x + 1}{3} = \dfrac{(x + 2)(x + 1)}{(x - 3)3}$

$= \dfrac{x^2 + 3x + 2}{3x - 9}$

P-4 What is the polynomial form of $(x + 2)(x + 1)$?   of $(x - 3)3$? $3x - 9$

$x^2 + 3x + 2$

CLASSROOM EXERCISES

Multiply. Simplify where necessary. (Examples 1–4) $\dfrac{x^2+4x+3}{x^2+6x+8}$

1. $\dfrac{2}{x-2} \cdot \dfrac{x-2}{3}$ $\dfrac{2}{3}$

2. $\dfrac{x+5}{5x} \cdot \dfrac{3x}{x+5}$ $\dfrac{3}{5}$

3. $\dfrac{x+1}{x+2} \cdot \dfrac{x+3}{x+4}$

4. $\dfrac{2(x-3)}{x+2} \cdot \dfrac{x+2}{6}$ $\dfrac{x-3}{3}$

5. $\dfrac{x+2}{x-1} \cdot \dfrac{x-1}{x+2}$ 1

6. $\dfrac{x+5}{x-2}(x-2)$ $x+5$

7. $\dfrac{1}{x-3} \cdot \dfrac{x-3}{x+2}$ $\dfrac{1}{x+2}$

8. $\dfrac{1}{x+2}(x+2)$ 1

9. $\dfrac{5}{x-5} \cdot \dfrac{5-x}{6}$ $-\dfrac{5}{6}$

10. $\dfrac{2}{-a-2} \cdot \dfrac{a+2}{5}$ $-\dfrac{2}{5}$

11. $\dfrac{x-y}{b-a} \cdot \dfrac{a-b}{y-x}$ 1

12. $\dfrac{2}{a-b} \cdot \dfrac{a+b}{3}$ $\dfrac{2a+2b}{3a-3b}$

13. $\dfrac{3(x+1)}{x-3} \cdot \dfrac{x-3}{3x}$ $\dfrac{x+1}{x}$

14. $\dfrac{y(x+y)}{x-y} \cdot \dfrac{2}{y(x+y)}$ $\dfrac{2}{x-y}$

15. $\dfrac{a-2}{3} \cdot \dfrac{2}{2-a}$ $-\dfrac{2}{3}$

WRITTEN EXERCISES

See the Teacher's Manual for the suggested assignments.

Goal: To multiply rational expressions that involve binomials

Sample Problem: $\dfrac{x-2}{2} \cdot \dfrac{x+5}{2-x}$ **Answer:** $-\dfrac{x+5}{2}$

Multiply. Simplify where necessary. (Examples 1–4)

1. $\dfrac{11}{x-2} \cdot \dfrac{x-2}{12}$ $\dfrac{11}{12}$

2. $\dfrac{x+7}{9} \cdot \dfrac{5}{x+7}$ $\dfrac{5}{9}$

3. $-\dfrac{7}{x+y} \cdot \dfrac{2(x+y)}{15}$ $-\dfrac{14}{15}$

4. $-\dfrac{2(a+b)}{11} \cdot \dfrac{5}{a+b}$ $-\dfrac{10}{11}$

5. $\dfrac{x-3}{x+2} \cdot \dfrac{x+2}{x-1}$ $\dfrac{x-3}{x-1}$

6. $\dfrac{a+7}{a-3} \cdot \dfrac{a-1}{a+7}$ $\dfrac{a-1}{a-3}$

7. $\dfrac{x(x-3)}{y(x+5)} \cdot \dfrac{x+5}{2x}$ $\dfrac{x-3}{2y}$

8. $\dfrac{a+6}{3(a+2)} \cdot \dfrac{12a(a+2)}{4b}$ $\dfrac{a^2+6a}{b}$

9. $\dfrac{x-3}{x+2}(x+2)$ $x-3$

10. $\dfrac{a+7}{a-5}(a-5)$ $a+7$

11. $\dfrac{1}{x-3} \cdot \dfrac{2(x-3)}{x+2}$ $\dfrac{2}{x+2}$

12. $\dfrac{x(x-y)}{x+y} \cdot \dfrac{1}{x}$ $\dfrac{x-y}{x+y}$

13. $\dfrac{x-3}{x+2} \cdot \dfrac{x-2}{x+3}$ $\dfrac{x^2-5x+6}{x^2+5x+6}$

14. $\dfrac{2a+b}{a-b} \cdot \dfrac{a+b}{a+2b}$ $\dfrac{2a^2+3ab+b^2}{a^2+ab-2b^2}$

15. $\dfrac{x-5}{x} \cdot \dfrac{5}{5-x}$ $-\dfrac{5}{x}$

16. $\dfrac{a}{a-7} \cdot \dfrac{7-a}{5}$ $-\dfrac{a}{5}$

17. $\dfrac{a-3}{a+4} \cdot \dfrac{-a-4}{3-a}$ 1

18. $\dfrac{-x-2}{x-3} \cdot \dfrac{3-x}{x+2}$ 1

19. $\dfrac{2(x-y)}{2x-3y} \cdot \dfrac{2x-3y}{6(y-x)}$ $-\dfrac{1}{3}$

20. $\dfrac{-2a-3b}{15(a-b)} \cdot \dfrac{6(b-a)}{2a+3b}$ $\dfrac{2}{5}$

21. $\dfrac{x+2}{(x-1)(x+3)} \cdot \dfrac{x(x-1)}{x+2}$ $\dfrac{x}{x+3}$

22. $\dfrac{(x-5)(x-2)}{x+3} \cdot \dfrac{x+3}{2(x-2)}$ $\dfrac{x-5}{2}$

MID-CHAPTER REVIEW

NOTE: After completing the Mid-Chapter Review, you may want to administer a quiz covering the same sections. See pages M-36 and M-37 of the Teacher's Manual for the suggested quiz.

Evaluate each rational expression if x equals −2. (Section 14.1)

1. $\dfrac{x-5}{x+7}$ $\quad -\dfrac{7}{5}$

2. $\dfrac{x^2+3}{x^2-2}$ $\quad \dfrac{7}{2}$

3. $\dfrac{x^2-x+3}{2x^2+x-1}$ $\quad \dfrac{9}{5}$

4. $\dfrac{-x^2+2x-5}{3x^2-x+2}$ $\quad -\dfrac{13}{16}$

Simplify. No divisor equals 0. (Section 14.2)

5. $\dfrac{3x(x+5)}{6y(x+5)}$ $\quad \dfrac{x}{2y}$

6. $\dfrac{5x-15}{10x+20}$ $\quad \dfrac{x-3}{2x+4}$

7. $\dfrac{x^2-36}{2x^2-12x}$ $\quad \dfrac{x+6}{2x}$

8. $\dfrac{x^2-2x-8}{3x^2-12}$ $\quad \dfrac{x-4}{3x-6}$

Multiply. Simplify where necessary. (Section 14.3)

9. $\dfrac{6x}{35}\cdot\dfrac{14}{9x}$ $\quad \dfrac{4}{15}$

10. $\dfrac{21a}{8bc}\cdot\dfrac{6c^2}{7a^2b}$ $\quad \dfrac{3c}{2ab^2}$

11. $-\dfrac{5r^2}{4st^2}\cdot\dfrac{10s^2}{3r}$ $\quad -\dfrac{25rs}{6t^2}$

12. $\dfrac{mn^2}{6}\cdot\dfrac{4}{-m^2}\cdot\dfrac{-3}{10n}$ $\quad \dfrac{n}{5m}$

Multiply. (Section 14.4)

13. $\dfrac{3(x-5)}{2x}\cdot\dfrac{4x}{5(x-5)}$ $\quad \dfrac{6}{5}$

14. $\dfrac{n+5}{n-2}\cdot\dfrac{n+3}{n+5}$ $\quad \dfrac{n+3}{n-2}$

15. $\dfrac{2r-3}{3r+5}\cdot(3r+5)$ $\quad 2r-3$

16. $\dfrac{m-3}{5m}\cdot\dfrac{10}{3-m}$ $\quad -\dfrac{2}{m}$

 ——————————— *CONTINUED FRACTIONS* ———————————

A fraction such as the one shown at the right is called a **continued fraction.** You can use a calculator to approximate its value.

$$\cfrac{1}{1+\cfrac{1}{1+\cfrac{1}{1+\frac{1}{5}}}}$$

EXAMPLE Find a decimal approximation of the above continued fraction.

SOLUTION Start by finding the reciprocal of 5.

$\boxed{5}\;\boxed{\div}\;\boxed{=}\;\boxed{+}\;\boxed{1}\;\boxed{=}\;\boxed{\div}\;\boxed{=}\;\boxed{+}\;\boxed{1}$

 On some calculators press "÷ = =" to get the reciprocal.

$\boxed{=}\;\boxed{\div}\;\boxed{=}\;\boxed{+}\;\boxed{1}\;\boxed{=}\;\boxed{\div}\;\boxed{=}$

$\boxed{0.6470588}$

Find a decimal approximation.

1. $\cfrac{1}{1+\cfrac{1}{1+\cfrac{1}{1+\frac{1}{7}}}}$ $\quad 0.6521739$

2. $\cfrac{1}{1+\cfrac{1}{1+\cfrac{1}{1+\frac{1}{8}}}}$ $\quad 0.6538461$

3. $\cfrac{1}{1+\cfrac{1}{1+\cfrac{1}{1+\frac{1}{11}}}}$ $\quad 0.6034482$

REVIEW CAPSULE FOR SECTION 14.5

Factor. (Section 10.4)

1. x^2-2x-3
$(x-3)(x+1)$

2. x^2-5x+6
$(x-3)(x-2)$

3. $2x^2+5x-3$
$(2x-1)(x+3)$

4. $4x^2+4x-3$
$(2x+3)(2x-1)$

14.5 Trinomial Numerators and Denominators

OBJECTIVE: To multiply rational expressions that involve trinomials, writing the product in simplest form

Note, in Example 1, that numerators and denominators are factored <u>before</u> multiplying the rational expressions.

example 1   Multiply and simplify: $\dfrac{x^2 - x - 6}{x^2 + 2x + 1} \cdot \dfrac{x + 1}{x + 2}$

Solution:

1. Factor. $\longrightarrow$ $\dfrac{x^2 - x - 6}{x^2 + 2x + 1} \cdot \dfrac{x + 1}{x + 2} = \dfrac{(x - 3)(x + 2)}{(x + 1)(x + 1)} \cdot \dfrac{x + 1}{x + 2}$ **Factor first.**

2. Product Rule for Rational Expressions $\longrightarrow$ $= \dfrac{(x - 3)(x + 2)(x + 1)}{(x + 1)(x + 1)(x + 2)}$

   Students will need to be reminded again and again of the difference between <u>factors</u> and <u>terms</u>.

3. Identify common factors. $\longrightarrow$ $= \dfrac{(x - 3)\overset{1}{\cancel{(x + 2)}}\overset{1}{\cancel{(x + 1)}}}{(x + 1)\underset{1}{\cancel{(x + 1)}}\underset{1}{\cancel{(x + 2)}}}$

4. Simplify. $\longrightarrow$ $= \dfrac{x - 3}{x + 1}$

P-1   **What are the prime factors of $x^2 + 2x$? of $x^2 - 4$?** $x + 2, x - 2$
$x, x + 2$

example 2   Multiply and simplify: $\dfrac{x^2 + 2x}{x^2 - 4} \cdot \dfrac{x - 2}{x + 2}$

Solution: $\dfrac{x^2 + 2x}{x^2 - 4} \cdot \dfrac{x - 2}{x + 2} = \dfrac{x(x + 2)}{(x + 2)(x - 2)} \cdot \dfrac{x - 2}{x + 2}$ **Prime factorization**

$= \dfrac{x\overset{1}{\cancel{(x + 2)}}}{(x + 2)\cancel{(x - 2)}} \cdot \dfrac{\overset{1}{\cancel{x - 2}}}{x + 2}$ **A name for 1 is identified.**

$= \dfrac{x}{x + 2}$ **Simplest form**

P-2 **Write the prime factors of each polynomial below.**

a. $2x^2 + x - 1$ **b.** $x^2 - 36$ **c.** $6x^3 - 4x^2$

$2x - 1, x + 1$ $x + 6, x - 6$ $2x^2, 3x - 2$

It may be helpful to review each of these types of factoring.

$$2x^2 + x - 1 = 2x^2 + rx + sx - 1$$

◄ $r + s = 1$
$r \cdot s = -2$
Let $r = 2$
and $s = -1$.

$$= 2x^2 + 2x - x - 1$$

$$= 2x(x + 1) - 1(x + 1)$$

$$= (2x - 1)(x + 1)$$

$$x^2 - 36 = (x + 6)(x - 6)$$ ◄ **Difference of two squares**

$$6x^3 - 4x^2 = 2x^2(3x - 2)$$ ◄ **Common monomial factor**

P-3 **What are the prime factors of $x^2 - 3x - 10$? of $x^2 - 9$?** $x + 3, x - 3$
of $x^2 + 4x + 4$? $x + 2, x + 2$ $x - 5, x + 2$

example 3   Multiply and simplify: $\dfrac{x^2 - 3x - 10}{x^2 - 9} \cdot \dfrac{x + 3}{x^2 + 4x + 4}$

Solution: $\dfrac{x^2 - 3x - 10}{x^2 - 9} \cdot \dfrac{x + 3}{x^2 + 4x + 4} = \dfrac{(x - 5)(x + 2)}{(x + 3)(x - 3)} \cdot \dfrac{x + 3}{(x + 2)(x + 2)}$

$$= \frac{(x - 5)(x \overset{1}{\cancel{+ 2}})(x \overset{1}{\cancel{+ 3}})}{(x \underset{1}{\cancel{+ 3}})(x - 3)(x \underset{1}{\cancel{+ 2}})(x + 2)}$$

$$= \frac{x - 5}{(x - 3)(x + 2)}$$

> **Steps for multiplying rational expressions:**
>
> 1. Factor all numerators and denominators.
> 2. Apply the Product Rule for Rational Expressions.
> 3. Identify a name for 1.
> 4. Use the Multiplication Property of One and simplify the result.

CLASSROOM EXERCISES

Simplify. (Examples 1–3)

1. $\dfrac{(x-2)(x+3)}{(x+3)(x+4)}$ $\frac{x-2}{x+4}$

2. $\dfrac{(x+5)(x+2)}{(x+5)(x+5)(x+2)}$ $\frac{1}{x+5}$

3. $\dfrac{(x+5)(x-2)}{x^2-4}$ $\frac{x+5}{x+2}$

4. $\dfrac{x-3}{x+7} \cdot \dfrac{x+7}{x+3}$ $\frac{x-3}{x+3}$

5. $\dfrac{x^2-2x+1}{2x} \cdot \dfrac{x}{x-1}$ $\frac{x-1}{2}$

6. $\dfrac{x^2+2x}{x+3} \cdot \dfrac{x+3}{x(x-1)}$ $\frac{x+2}{x-1}$

7. $\dfrac{5x}{x^2-9} \cdot \dfrac{x(x-3)}{x^2-4x+3}$

7. $\dfrac{5x^2}{x^3-x^2-9x+9}$

8. $\dfrac{x^2-x}{2x+4} \cdot \dfrac{x^2-4}{x-1}$ $\frac{x^2-2x}{2}$

9. $\dfrac{x^2-x-2}{x-3} \cdot \dfrac{3x-9}{3x^2-6x}$ $\frac{x+1}{x}$

WRITTEN EXERCISES

See the Teacher's Manual for the suggested assignments.

Goal: To multiply rational expressions that involve trinomials

Sample Problem: $\dfrac{x^2-7x+12}{x^2-16} \cdot \dfrac{x+4}{3x-9}$ **Answer:** $\dfrac{1}{3}$

Multiply and simplify. (Examples 1–3)

1. $\dfrac{3x+6}{x^2+x} \cdot \dfrac{4x+4}{12}$ $\frac{x+2}{x}$

2. $\dfrac{x^2-2x}{15} \cdot \dfrac{3x-9}{2x-4}$ $\frac{x^2-3x}{10}$

3. $\dfrac{x^2-4}{x+2} \cdot \dfrac{5x+10}{3x-6}$ $\frac{5x+10}{3}$

4. $\dfrac{2x-6}{25} \cdot \dfrac{5x+15}{x^2-9}$ $\frac{2}{5}$

5. $\dfrac{x^3-2x^2}{x^2-25} \cdot \dfrac{5x+10}{x^2-2x}$ $\frac{5x^2+10x}{x^2-25}$

6. $\dfrac{9y^2+9}{y^2-1} \cdot \dfrac{2y^3+2y^2}{3y}$ $\frac{6y^3+6y}{y-1}$

7. $\dfrac{x^2-x-2}{10} \cdot \dfrac{2x+4}{x^2-4}$ $\frac{x+1}{5}$

8. $\dfrac{x^2-2x-3}{3x+3} \cdot \dfrac{15}{x^2-9}$ $\frac{5}{x+3}$

9. $\dfrac{x^2+8x+16}{12} \cdot \dfrac{3x+3}{x^2+5x+4}$ $\frac{x+4}{4}$

10. $\dfrac{x^2-5x+6}{5x-10} \cdot \dfrac{15}{x^2-6x+9}$ $\frac{3}{x-3}$

11. $\dfrac{x^2-16}{2x} \cdot \dfrac{3x^2-6x}{16-x^2}$ $\frac{-3x+6}{2}$ or $\frac{6-3x}{2}$

12. $\dfrac{5a}{a^2-9} \cdot \dfrac{9-a^2}{5a^2-a}$ $\frac{5}{1-5a}$

MORE CHALLENGING EXERCISES

13. $\dfrac{2x^2-5x-3}{4x^2-1} \cdot \dfrac{3}{x^2+2x-15}$ $\frac{3}{2x^2+9x-5}$

14. $\dfrac{3x^2-14x-5}{9x^2-1} \cdot \dfrac{1}{x^2-6x+5}$ $\frac{1}{3x^2-4x+1}$

15. $\dfrac{2x^2-4x+8}{6x^2+7x-3}(2x^2+x-3)$ $\frac{2x^3-6x^2+12x-8}{3x-1}$

16. $\dfrac{3x^2+15x-3}{3x^2-27}(3x^2-7x-6)$ $\frac{3x^3+17x^2+7x-2}{x+3}$

REVIEW CAPSULE FOR SECTION 14.6

Write the reciprocal of each expression. (Section 1.5)

1. $\dfrac{2}{x-3}$ $\frac{x-3}{2}$

2. $\dfrac{3x-1}{2x}$ $\frac{2x}{3x-1}$

3. $\dfrac{1}{x+4}$ $\frac{x+4}{1}$

4. $\dfrac{4x+3}{2x-5}$ $\frac{2x-5}{4x+3}$

14.6 Dividing Rational Expressions

OBJECTIVES: To divide two rational expressions involving only monomials, writing the quotient in simplest form
To divide two rational expressions involving monomials and binomials, writing the quotient in simplest form

The Quotient Rule for Fractions can be applied to rational expressions.

Quotient Rule for Rational Expressions

If $\dfrac{a}{b}$ and $\dfrac{c}{d}$ are rational expressions,

then $\dfrac{a}{b} \div \dfrac{c}{d} = \dfrac{a}{b} \cdot \dfrac{d}{c}$. ($b$, c, and d are not zero.)

▲ *Dividing by a rational expression is the same as multiplying by its reciprocal.*

$$\frac{x}{x+2} \div \frac{x-1}{x}$$

$$\frac{x}{x+2} \cdot \frac{x}{x-1}$$

$$\frac{x^2}{(x+2)(x-1)}$$

Expressions such as $\dfrac{x}{x+1}$ and $\dfrac{x+1}{x}$ are reciprocals. The product of a rational expression and its reciprocal is 1.

P-1   **Write each quotient below as a product.**

a. $\dfrac{x-3}{x+2} \div \dfrac{x}{x-2}$

$\dfrac{x-3}{x+2} \cdot \dfrac{x-2}{x}$

b. $\dfrac{3x}{5} \div \dfrac{4}{9x}$

$\dfrac{3x}{5} \cdot \dfrac{9x}{4}$

c. $\dfrac{2x^2}{5} \div (x+1)$

$\dfrac{2x^2}{5} \cdot \dfrac{1}{x+1}$

example 1

Divide and simplify: $\dfrac{2x}{3} \div \dfrac{5x}{6}$

Solution:

$$\frac{2x}{3} \div \frac{5x}{6} = \frac{2x}{3} \cdot \frac{6}{5x}$$

Remind students that this shortcut is a way of identifying common factors (or a name for 1).

$\dfrac{3x}{3x} \cdot \dfrac{2 \cdot 2}{5} = 1 \cdot \dfrac{4}{5}$

$= \dfrac{4}{5}$

$$= \frac{\overset{1}{\cancel{2x}}}{\underset{1}{\cancel{3}}} \cdot \frac{\overset{2}{\cancel{6}}}{\underset{1}{\cancel{5x}}}$$

$$= \frac{4}{5} \quad ◀ \textit{ Simplest form}$$

P-2 Write $\dfrac{x-2}{x} \div \dfrac{x-2}{5}$ **as a product.** $\dfrac{x-2}{x} \cdot \dfrac{5}{x-2}$

example 2

Divide and simplify: $\dfrac{x-2}{x} \div \dfrac{x-2}{5}$

Solution:

$$\frac{x-2}{x} \div \frac{x-2}{5} = \frac{x-2}{x} \cdot \frac{5}{x-2}$$

$$= \frac{5(\overset{1}{\cancel{x-2}})}{x(\underset{1}{\cancel{x-2}})}$$

$$= \frac{5}{x}$$

P-3 **What is the reciprocal of** $\dfrac{9pq}{4(r-3)}$**?** $\dfrac{4(r-3)}{9pq}$

example 3

Divide and simplify: $\dfrac{3p^2q}{2r(r-3)} \div \dfrac{9pq}{4(r-3)}$

Solution:

$$\frac{3p^2q}{2r(r-3)} \div \frac{9pq}{4(r-3)} = \frac{3p^2q}{2r(r-3)} \cdot \frac{4(r-3)}{9pq}$$

$$= \frac{\overset{1 \cdot p \cdot 1 \quad 2}{\cancel{3p^2q} \cdot \cancel{4(r-3)}}}{\underset{1 \quad 1 \quad 3 \cdot 1 \cdot 1}{\cancel{2r(r-3)} \cdot \cancel{9pq}}}$$

$$= \frac{2p}{3r}$$

CLASSROOM EXERCISES

Write each quotient as an equivalent product. (P-1, P-2)

1. $\dfrac{2}{3} \div \dfrac{5}{6}$ $\dfrac{2}{3} \cdot \dfrac{6}{5}$

2. $\dfrac{x}{5} \div \dfrac{3}{x}$ $\dfrac{x}{5} \cdot \dfrac{x}{3}$

3. $\dfrac{2x}{6} \div \dfrac{x}{3}$ $\dfrac{2x}{6} \cdot \dfrac{3}{x}$

4. $\dfrac{x}{3y} \div \dfrac{3x}{y}$

   $\dfrac{x}{3y} \cdot \dfrac{y}{3x}$

5. $\dfrac{2}{x-2} \div \dfrac{x}{5}$ $\dfrac{2}{x-2} \cdot \dfrac{5}{x}$

6. $\dfrac{x+1}{2} \div \dfrac{3}{5}$ $\dfrac{x+1}{2} \cdot \dfrac{5}{3}$

7. $\dfrac{x-7}{5x} \cdot \dfrac{4}{x+1}$
$\dfrac{x-7}{5x} \div \dfrac{x+1}{4}$

8. $\dfrac{x+3}{x} \div \dfrac{x-5}{2x}$ $\dfrac{x+3}{x} \cdot \dfrac{2x}{x-5}$

9. $\dfrac{1}{x+2} \div (x-3)$ $\dfrac{1}{x+2} \cdot \dfrac{1}{x-3}$

10. $(x+3) \div \dfrac{1}{x+5}$
$(x+3)(x+5)$

11. $\dfrac{x+1}{x} \div \dfrac{x-10}{2x}$ $\dfrac{x+1}{x} \cdot \dfrac{2x}{x-10}$

12. $\dfrac{x+3}{x-4} \div \dfrac{x+7}{x-5}$ $\dfrac{x+3}{x-4} \cdot \dfrac{x-5}{x+7}$

13. $\dfrac{x+8}{x-5} \div \dfrac{x+2}{x-10}$
$\dfrac{x+8}{x-5} \cdot \dfrac{x-10}{x+2}$

WRITTEN EXERCISES

See the Teacher's Manual for the suggested assignments.

Goal: To divide rational expressions

Sample Problem: $\dfrac{5a^2b^2}{a(1-b)} \div \dfrac{25ab^2}{b(1-b)}$ **Answer:** $\dfrac{b}{5}$

Divide and simplify. (Examples 1–3)

1. $\dfrac{2}{5} \div \dfrac{3}{5}$ $\dfrac{2}{3}$

2. $\dfrac{5}{8} \div \dfrac{3}{16}$ $\dfrac{10}{3}$

3. $\dfrac{3}{x} \div \dfrac{1}{2x}$ 6

4. $\dfrac{x}{5} \div \dfrac{3x}{10}$ $\dfrac{2}{3}$

5. $\dfrac{a^2}{3} \div \dfrac{5a}{9}$ $\dfrac{3a}{5}$

6. $\dfrac{2}{b^2} \div \dfrac{4}{3b}$ $\dfrac{3}{2b}$

7. $\dfrac{3}{x-5} \div \dfrac{6}{x-5}$ $\dfrac{1}{2}$

8. $\dfrac{x+2}{5} \div \dfrac{x+2}{3}$ $\dfrac{3}{5}$

9. $\dfrac{x^2y}{7} \div \dfrac{3x}{14}$ $\dfrac{2xy}{3}$

10. $\dfrac{5}{2a^2b} \div \dfrac{15}{ab}$ $\dfrac{1}{6a}$

11. $\dfrac{2}{x^2y^2} \div \dfrac{4}{5xy}$ $\dfrac{5}{2xy}$

12. $\dfrac{5xy}{3z} \div \dfrac{10x^2}{9z^2}$ $\dfrac{3yz}{2x}$

13. $\dfrac{x-5}{x+2} \div \dfrac{5}{x+2}$ $\dfrac{x-5}{5}$

14. $\dfrac{3}{a+b} \div \dfrac{a+3}{a+b}$ $\dfrac{3}{a+3}$

15. $\dfrac{x^2+2}{5} \div \dfrac{x^2}{10}$ $\dfrac{2x^2+4}{x^2}$

16. $\dfrac{3}{x+6} \div \dfrac{9}{x}$ $\dfrac{x}{3x+18}$

17. $\dfrac{x-6}{x+5} \div 2(x-6)$ $\dfrac{1}{2x+10}$

18. $\dfrac{x+3}{x-10} \div 5(x+3)$ $\dfrac{1}{5x-50}$

19. $x(x^2+3) \div \dfrac{3x}{x^2+3}$ $\dfrac{x^4+6x^2+9}{3}$

20. $3a(a^2+2) \div \dfrac{a^2}{a-2}$ $\dfrac{3a^3-6a^2+6a-12}{a}$

MORE CHALLENGING EXERCISES

21. $\dfrac{5}{x} \div \dfrac{3}{5x} \div \dfrac{10}{3x}$ $\dfrac{5x}{2}$

22. $\dfrac{a}{3} \div \dfrac{a^2}{2} \div \dfrac{7}{3a}$ $\dfrac{2}{7}$

23. $\dfrac{x+1}{x+3} \div \dfrac{x-1}{2(x+3)} \div \dfrac{3(x-1)}{x+1}$
$\dfrac{2x^2+4x+2}{3x^2-6x+3}$

REVIEW CAPSULE FOR SECTION 14.7

Find a common multiple of the given numbers.

EXAMPLE: 3, 5, and 11   **SOLUTION:** $3 \cdot 5 \cdot 11 = 165$

1. 2, 3, and 7 42

2. 8 and 13 104

3. 2, 5, and 6 30

4. 8, 12, and 15
120

14.7 More Quotients

OBJECTIVES: To divide two rational expressions involving monomials, binomials, or trinomials as numerators, or denominators, writing the quotient in simplest form
To simplify a complex fraction having a variable in one or more of the numerators

P-1   **What is the reciprocal of $(x^2 - 25)$?** $\dfrac{1}{x^2 - 25}$

example 1

Divide and simplify: $\dfrac{x^2 + 4x - 5}{3x - 3} \div (x^2 - 25)$

Solution:

1. Factor. ⟶ $\dfrac{x^2 + 4x - 5}{3x - 3} \div (x^2 - 25) = \dfrac{(x + 5)(x - 1)}{3(x - 1)} \div (x + 5)(x - 5)$

2. Quotient Property of Rational Expressions ⟶ $= \dfrac{(x + 5)(x - 1)}{3(x - 1)} \cdot \dfrac{1}{(x + 5)(x - 5)}$

3. Identify common factors. ⟶ $= \dfrac{\overset{1}{(\cancel{x + 5})}\overset{1}{(\cancel{x - 1})}}{3\underset{1}{(\cancel{x - 1})}} \cdot \dfrac{1}{\underset{1}{(\cancel{x + 5})}(x - 5)}$

4. Simplify. ⟶ $= \dfrac{1}{3(x - 5)}$

example 2

Divide and simplify: $\dfrac{x^2 - 3x - 4}{6} \div \dfrac{x^2 - 1}{2x - 2}$

Solution:

$$\dfrac{x^2 - 3x - 4}{6} \div \dfrac{x^2 - 1}{2x - 2} = \dfrac{(x - 4)(x + 1)}{6} \div \dfrac{(x + 1)(x - 1)}{2(x - 1)}$$

$$= \dfrac{(x - 4)(\overset{1}{\cancel{x + 1}})}{\underset{3}{\cancel{6}}} \cdot \dfrac{\overset{1 \cdot 1}{\cancel{2}(\cancel{x - 1})}}{\underset{1}{(\cancel{x + 1})}\underset{1}{(\cancel{x - 1})}}$$

$$= \dfrac{x - 4}{3}$$

A quotient such as $\left(\dfrac{x^2}{2} + \dfrac{x}{3}\right) \div \dfrac{x}{6}$ is often written as a fraction.

$$\left(\dfrac{x^2}{2} + \dfrac{x}{3}\right) \div \dfrac{x}{6} = \dfrac{\dfrac{x^2}{2} + \dfrac{x}{3}}{\dfrac{x}{6}}$$

◄ *Such fractions are called* **complex fractions.**

example 3

Simplify $\dfrac{\dfrac{x^2}{2}+\dfrac{x}{3}}{\dfrac{x}{6}}$

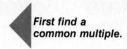
First find a common multiple.

Solution: You may want to compare this method with the method used in Examples 1 and 2.

1. Multiplication Property of One ⟶ $\dfrac{\dfrac{x^2}{2}+\dfrac{x}{3}}{\dfrac{x}{6}}=\dfrac{6}{6}\cdot\dfrac{\dfrac{x^2}{2}+\dfrac{x}{3}}{\dfrac{x}{6}}$

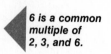
6 is a common multiple of 2, 3, and 6.

2. Product Property of Rational Expressions ⟶ $=\dfrac{6\left(\dfrac{x^2}{2}+\dfrac{x}{3}\right)}{6\left(\dfrac{x}{6}\right)}$

3. Distributive Property ⟶ $=\dfrac{6\left(\dfrac{x^2}{2}\right)+6\left(\dfrac{x}{3}\right)}{6\left(\dfrac{x}{6}\right)}$

4. Multiply. ⟶ $=\dfrac{3x^2+2x}{x}$

5. Factor. ⟶ $=\dfrac{x(3x+2)}{x}$

6. Simplify. ⟶ $=3x+2$

Steps for simplifying a complex fraction:

1. Determine m, a common multiple of all the denominators.

2. Multiply the complex fraction by $\dfrac{m}{m}$.

3. Simplify the result.

CLASSROOM EXERCISES

Write the prime factors of each polynomial. (Step 1 of Examples 1 and 2)

1. $2x-6$ $2, x-3$ 2. x^2-9 $x+3, x-3$ 3. $3x^2-x$ $x, 3x-1$ 4. $5x+10$ $5, x+2$ 5. x^2-4 $x+2, x-2$

6. x^2-81 7. $4x-16$ $4, x-4$ 8. x^2+4x $x, x+4$ 9. $3x-21$ $3, x-7$ 10. x^2-49

    $x+9, x-9$ $x+7, x-7$

11. $x^2 - 7x$ $x, x - 7$

12. $x^2 + x$ $x, x + 1$

13. $2x^2 - 10x$
      $2x, x - 5$

14. $x^2 - 10x + 25$ $x - 5, x - 5$

15. $x^2 - 16$ $x + 4, x - 4$

16. $5x - 20$
      $5, x - 4$

17. $3x^2 - 15x$ $3x, x - 5$

18. $x^2 + 2x - 15$ $x + 5, x - 3$

19. $5x^2 + 15x$
      $5x, x + 3$

WRITTEN EXERCISES

See the Teacher's Manual for the suggested assignments.

Goal: To simplify complex fractions

Sample Problem: $\dfrac{\dfrac{a}{2} - \dfrac{a}{4}}{\dfrac{a}{6}}$ **Answer:** $\dfrac{3}{2}$

Divide and simplify. (Examples 1 and 2)

1. $\dfrac{2x - 6}{5x^2} \div \dfrac{x^2 - 9}{x}$ $\dfrac{2}{5x^2 + 15x}$

2. $\dfrac{3x^2 - x}{5x + 10} \div \dfrac{3x}{x^2 - 4}$ $\dfrac{3x^2 - 7x + 2}{15}$

3. $\dfrac{x^2 - 16}{4x - 16} \div \dfrac{x^2 + 4x}{2x}$ $\dfrac{1}{2}$

4. $\dfrac{3x - 21}{x^2 - 49} \div \dfrac{3x}{x^2 - 7x}$ $\dfrac{x - 7}{x + 7}$

5. $\dfrac{x^2 - 10x + 25}{x + 1} \div \dfrac{2x^2 - 10x}{x^2 + x}$ $\dfrac{x - 5}{2}$

6. $\dfrac{x^2 - 16}{6x} \div \dfrac{5x - 20}{3x^2 - 15x}$ $\dfrac{x^2 - x - 20}{10}$

7. $\dfrac{x^2 + 2x - 15}{x + 3} \div \dfrac{x^2 + 7x + 10}{x - 2}$ $\dfrac{x^2 - 5x + 6}{x^2 + 5x + 6}$

8. $\dfrac{x - 5}{x^2 + 3x - 10} \div \dfrac{9x^2}{3x^2 - 6x}$ $\dfrac{x - 5}{3x^2 + 15x}$

9. $\dfrac{x^2 + 10x + 24}{3x^2 - 12x} \div (x^2 - 3x - 18)$
    $\dfrac{x^2 + 10x + 24}{3x^4 - 21x^3 - 18x^2 + 216x}$

10. $\dfrac{x^2 - 2x - 15}{5x^2 + 15x} \div (x^2 - 6x + 5)$ $\dfrac{1}{5x^2 - 5x}$

11. $\dfrac{x^2 - y^2}{6x} \div \dfrac{x^2y + xy^2}{3x^2y^2}$ $\dfrac{xy - y^2}{2}$

12. $\dfrac{4x^2 - 25y^2}{2x^2y + 5xy^2} \div \dfrac{6x^2 - 15xy}{9x^2y^2}$ $3y$

Simplify. (Example 3)

13. $\dfrac{\dfrac{x}{5}}{\dfrac{x}{2} + \dfrac{x}{5}}$ $\dfrac{2}{7}$

14. $\dfrac{\dfrac{y}{3} + \dfrac{y}{5}}{\dfrac{y}{5}}$ $\dfrac{8}{3}$

15. $\dfrac{\dfrac{a}{6} + \dfrac{3}{5}}{\dfrac{2}{5}}$ $\dfrac{5a + 18}{12}$

16. $\dfrac{\dfrac{b}{8} + \dfrac{1}{3}}{\dfrac{5}{3}}$ $\dfrac{3b + 8}{40}$

17. $\dfrac{\dfrac{a}{10} + \dfrac{b}{5}}{\dfrac{a}{3} + \dfrac{b}{6}}$ $\dfrac{3a + 6b}{10a + 5b}$

18. $\dfrac{\dfrac{x}{6} + \dfrac{y}{8}}{\dfrac{x}{2} + \dfrac{y}{4}}$ $\dfrac{4x + 3y}{12x + 6y}$

MORE CHALLENGING EXERCISES

Divide and simplify.

19. $\dfrac{6x^2 - 7x - 3}{10x - 15} \div \dfrac{3x^2 - 14x - 5}{5x - 25}$ 1

20. $\dfrac{10x^2 - 13x - 3}{15x + 3} \div \dfrac{2x^2 + 7x - 15}{3x^2 + 15x}$ x

21. $\dfrac{10x + 15}{2x^2 - 3x - 9} \div \dfrac{x^2 + 6x + 9}{9 - x^2}$ $-\dfrac{5}{x + 3}$

22. $\dfrac{3x^2 - 15x}{2x^2 + x} \div \dfrac{25 - x^2}{2x^2 + 7x + 5}$ $\dfrac{-6x^2 - 21x - 15}{2x^2 + 11x + 5}$

Career Electrician

Electricians keep electric equipment in working order. An important example of such equipment is the <u>transformer</u>.

The main parts of a transformer are the core, the primary coil to which the input power is supplied, and the secondary coil from which output power is delivered. The following **direct proportion** relates the input (V_P) and output (V_S) <u>voltages</u> and the number of turns on the primary $\overline{(N_P)}$ and the secondary (N_S) coils.

$$\frac{V_S}{V_P} = \frac{N_S}{N_P}$$

◄ The ratio $\frac{N_S}{N_P}$ is called the <u>turns ratio.</u>

The following **inverse proportion** relates the input (I_P) and output (I_S) <u>amperages</u> and the number of turns on the coils.

$$\frac{I_S}{I_P} = \frac{N_P}{N_S}$$

◄ Note that the turns ratio is inverted.

Power Input

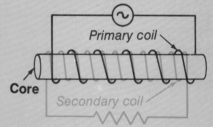

Primary coil

Core   *Secondary coil*

Power Output

EXAMPLE: The number of turns on the primary coil of a transformer is 200. The number of turns on the secondary coil is 800. The input voltage is 110 volts. The input current is 1.2 amperes. Find **a.** the output voltage in volts and **b.** the output current in amperes.

SOLUTION: a. $\dfrac{V_S}{V_P} = \dfrac{N_S}{N_P}$ $\dfrac{V_S}{100} = \dfrac{800}{200}$ **b.** $\dfrac{I_S}{I_P} = \dfrac{N_P}{N_S}$ $\dfrac{I_S}{1.2} = \dfrac{200}{800}$

$$V_S = \frac{(110)(800)}{200}$$ $$I_S = \frac{(1.2)(200)}{800}$$

$$V_S = \textbf{440 volts}$$ $$I_S = \textbf{0.3 amperes}$$

EXERCISES

Find the output voltage (V_S) in volts of each transformer.

1. Turns ratio: $\frac{20}{1}$ 2300 volts
   Input voltage: 115 volts

2. Turns Ratio: $\frac{1}{3}$ 230 volts
   Input voltage: 690 volts

Find the output current (I_S) in amperes for each transformer.

3. Turns Ratio: $\frac{4}{5}$ 1.625 amperes
   Input current: 1.3 amperes

4. Turns Ratio: $\frac{25}{3}$ 1.44 amperes
   Input current: 12 amperes

CHAPTER SUMMARY

NOTE: You may wish to administer a quiz covering Sections 14.5 through 14.7. See page M-37 of the Teacher's Manual for the suggested quiz.

IMPORTANT TERMS	Rational expression *(p. 346)* Complex fraction *(p. 365)*

IMPORTANT IDEAS

1. Any polynomial is also a rational expression.

2. Any number that will result in a divisor of 0 must be restricted from the domain of the variable in a rational expression.

3. Product Rule of Rational Expressions: If $\frac{a}{b}$ and $\frac{c}{d}$ are rational expressions, then $\frac{a}{b} \cdot \frac{c}{d} = \frac{ac}{bd}$. (*b* and *d* are not zero.)

4. Property of the Opposite of a Difference: If *a* and *b* are any real numbers, then $-(a - b) = b - a$.

5. Quotient Rule for Rational Expressions: If $\frac{a}{b}$ and $\frac{c}{d}$ are rational expressions, then $\frac{a}{b} \div \frac{c}{d} = \frac{a}{b} \cdot \frac{d}{c}$. (*b*, *c*, and *d* are not zero.)

CHAPTER REVIEW

NOTE: The Teacher's Resource Book contains two forms of each Chapter Test.

SECTION 14.1

Write __Yes__ or __No__ to show whether each expression is a rational expression.

1. $\dfrac{2x^2 - 5x + 3}{x^2 + 7}$ Yes **2.** $-5x^3 - 2x$ Yes **3.** $3x^{-2} + 4x^{-1} + 10$ No **4.** $\dfrac{\sqrt{x + 1}}{|x - 3|}$ No

Write the number or numbers that cannot be in the domain of each variable.

5. $\dfrac{x + 1}{x + 3}$ -3 **6.** $\dfrac{x - 3}{x - 2}$ 2 **7.** $\dfrac{x + 3}{2x - 1}$ $\frac{1}{2}$ **8.** $\dfrac{x + 6}{3x + 2}$ $-\frac{2}{3}$

SECTION 14.2

Simplify. No divisor equals 0.

9. $\dfrac{10x^2y}{12xy}$ $\frac{5x}{6}$ **10.** $\dfrac{8ab^2c}{20a^2bc}$ $\frac{2b}{5a}$ **11.** $\dfrac{x^2 - 100}{3x^2 - 300}$ $\frac{1}{3}$ **12.** $\dfrac{-3x^2 - 36x}{x^2 - 144}$

$\frac{-3x}{x - 12}$

SECTION 14.3

Multiply and simplify.

13. $\dfrac{12x}{5} \cdot \dfrac{15}{18x^2}$ $\dfrac{2}{x}$

14. $\dfrac{9}{14x} \cdot \dfrac{8x^3}{30}$ $\dfrac{6x^2}{35}$

15. $\dfrac{3xy^2}{5a^2b} \cdot \dfrac{10a}{9by}$ $\dfrac{2xy}{3ab^2}$

16. $\dfrac{5ab}{18xy} \cdot \dfrac{8x^2y}{15a^2b^2}$ $\dfrac{4x}{27ab}$

SECTION 14.4

Multiply and simplify.

17. $\dfrac{ax}{x^2-a^2} \cdot \dfrac{x^2+xa}{a^2x^2}$ $\dfrac{1}{ax-a^2}$

18. $\dfrac{5x}{x^2-25} \cdot \dfrac{x^2+5x}{2x^2y}$ $\dfrac{5}{2xy-10y}$

19. $\dfrac{x^2-4}{14} \cdot \dfrac{6x^2}{3x^2+6x}$ $\dfrac{x^2-2x}{7}$

20. $\dfrac{5r^2-15r}{22} \cdot \dfrac{2r+6}{r^2-9}$ $\dfrac{5r}{11}$

21. $\dfrac{3-x}{6} \cdot \dfrac{15}{3x-9}$ $-\dfrac{5}{6}$

22. $\dfrac{2y-4}{21} \cdot \dfrac{7y}{6-3y}$ $-\dfrac{2y}{9}$

SECTION 14.5

Multiply and simplify.

23. $\dfrac{x^2+2x-15}{x^2-6x+9} \cdot \dfrac{x^2-2x-3}{x^2+7x+10}$ $\dfrac{x+1}{x+2}$

24. $\dfrac{x^2+6x+8}{x^2+8x+16} \cdot \dfrac{x^2-x-20}{x^2+4x+4}$ $\dfrac{x-5}{x+2}$

25. $\dfrac{x^2+4x+4}{x^2-x-6} \cdot \dfrac{x^2-5x+6}{x^2-4}$ 1

26. $\dfrac{x^2-1}{x^2-6x+5} \cdot \dfrac{x^2-10x+25}{x^2-4x-5}$ 1

SECTION 14.6

Divide and simplify.

27. $\dfrac{-10abc}{21xy} \div \dfrac{-2a^2bc}{-14x^2y}$ $-\dfrac{10x}{3a}$

28. $\dfrac{49xy^2}{24c^2d^2} \div \dfrac{21x^2y}{-8cd}$ $-\dfrac{7y}{9cdx}$

29. $\dfrac{x-2}{x(x+3)} \div \dfrac{x+2}{2(x+3)}$ $\dfrac{2x-4}{x^2+2x}$

30. $\dfrac{2x+1}{x+7} \div \dfrac{5(2x-1)}{x(x+7)}$ $\dfrac{2x^2+x}{10x-5}$

SECTION 14.7

Divide and simplify.

31. $\dfrac{2x^3-6x^2+4x}{x-2} \div \dfrac{3x^3-3x^2}{x^2+4}$ $\dfrac{2x^2+8}{3x}$

32. $\dfrac{x^3+2x^2-3x}{x^2-5} \div \dfrac{x^2-4x-12}{2x^2}$ $\dfrac{2x^5+4x^4-6x^3}{x^4-4x^3-17x^2+20x+60}$

Simplify.

33. $\dfrac{\frac{a}{10}+\frac{a}{3}}{\frac{5}{6}}$ $\dfrac{13a}{25}$

34. $\dfrac{\frac{x}{12}}{\frac{3}{4}-\frac{x}{8}}$ $\dfrac{2x}{18-3x}$

35. $\dfrac{\frac{a}{6}-\frac{b}{5}}{\frac{a}{12}+\frac{b}{20}}$ $\dfrac{10a-12b}{5a+3b}$

36. $\dfrac{\frac{x}{7}+\frac{x}{5}}{\frac{y}{2}-\frac{y}{3}}$ $\dfrac{72x}{35y}$

CHAPTER

15 Sums and Differences of Rational Expressions

Sections

15.1 Sums/Differences: Like Denominators

15.2 More Sums and Differences

15.3 Least Common Multiple of Polynomials

15.4 Unlike Monomial Denominators

15.5 Sum/Differences: Unlike Denominators

15.6 More Sums and Differences

15.7 Equations with Rational Expressions

Features

Calculator Exercises: Adding or Subtracting Fractions

Special Topic Application: Rate of Work

Review and Testing

Review Capsules

Mid-Chapter Review

Chapter Summary

Chapter Review

15.1 Sums/Differences: Like Denominators

OBJECTIVE: To add or subtract with two or more rational expressions having monomial numerators and like monomial or binomial denominators

P-1   **Add or subtract:**   a. $\frac{3}{7} + \frac{2}{7}$ $\frac{5}{7}$ b. $\frac{5}{12} - \frac{11}{12}$ $-\frac{1}{2}$

The Sum and Difference Rules for Fractions also apply to rational expressions.

Sum and Difference Rules for Rational Expressions

If $\dfrac{a}{c}$ and $\dfrac{b}{c}$ are rational expressions, then $\dfrac{3}{x+1} + \dfrac{2}{x+1} = \dfrac{5}{x+1}$

1. $\dfrac{a}{c} + \dfrac{b}{c} = \dfrac{a+b}{c}$ 2. $\dfrac{a}{c} - \dfrac{b}{c} = \dfrac{a-b}{c}$.

(*c* is not zero.) $\dfrac{3x+2}{11x} - \dfrac{4}{11x} = \dfrac{3x-2}{11x}$

P-2   **Add or subtract.**

a. $\dfrac{4}{x} + \dfrac{5}{x}$ $\dfrac{9}{x}$ b. $\dfrac{10}{a} - \dfrac{3}{a}$ $\dfrac{7}{a}$ c. $\dfrac{x}{3y} + \dfrac{2x}{3y}$ $\dfrac{x}{y}$

P-3   In $\dfrac{2}{x-3}$, what number must be restricted from the domain of x?   3

In Examples 1 and 2 you might ask students to identify what a, b, and c of the Sum and Difference Rules represent.

example 1   Add: $\dfrac{2}{x-3} + \dfrac{12}{x-3}$

Solution:

1. Sum Rule for Rational Expressions ⟶ $\dfrac{2}{x-3} + \dfrac{12}{x-3} = \dfrac{2+12}{x-3}$

2. Simplify. ⟶ $= \dfrac{14}{x-3}$

example 2   Subtract: $\dfrac{x}{x+y} - \dfrac{y}{x+y}$

Solution: $\dfrac{x}{x+y} - \dfrac{y}{x+y} = \dfrac{x-y}{x+y}$ ◀ *Simplest form*

example 3

Subtract: $\dfrac{3x}{x+5} - \dfrac{10x}{x+5}$

Solution:

① Difference Rule for Rational Expressions $\longrightarrow$ $\dfrac{3x}{x+5} - \dfrac{10x}{x+5} = \dfrac{3x-10x}{x+5}$

② Subtract like terms. $\longrightarrow$ $= \dfrac{-7x}{x+5}$

③ Simplify. $\longrightarrow$ $= -\dfrac{7x}{x+5}$

example 4

Subtract: $\dfrac{3x}{5y} - \dfrac{x}{5y} - \dfrac{4x}{5y}$

Solution: Remember that addition and subtraction in an expression are performed from left to right.

$$\dfrac{3x}{5y} - \dfrac{x}{5y} - \dfrac{4x}{5y} = \dfrac{3x-x-4x}{5y} \quad \blacktriangleleft \textbf{\textit{Difference rule}}$$

$$= \dfrac{-2x}{5y} \quad \blacktriangleleft \textbf{Like terms are combined.}$$

$$= -\dfrac{2x}{5y}$$

CLASSROOM EXERCISES

Add or subtract. Simplify where necessary. (Examples 1–3)

1. $\dfrac{1}{5} + \dfrac{2}{5}$ $\dfrac{3}{5}$

2. $\dfrac{2}{9} + \dfrac{5}{9}$ $\dfrac{7}{9}$

3. $\dfrac{5}{12} - \dfrac{3}{12}$ $\dfrac{1}{6}$

4. $\dfrac{8}{15} - \dfrac{11}{15}$ $-\dfrac{1}{5}$

5. $\dfrac{2}{x} + \dfrac{1}{x}$ $\dfrac{3}{x}$

6. $\dfrac{8}{a} - \dfrac{5}{a}$ $\dfrac{3}{a}$

7. $\dfrac{5}{3x} + \dfrac{2}{3x}$ $\dfrac{7}{3x}$

8. $\dfrac{7}{5a} - \dfrac{4}{5a}$ $\dfrac{3}{5a}$

9. $\dfrac{5}{x+1} + \dfrac{6}{x+1}$ $\dfrac{11}{x+1}$

10. $\dfrac{10}{x-2} - \dfrac{3}{x-2}$ $\dfrac{7}{x-2}$

11. $\dfrac{x}{x+3} + \dfrac{2x}{x+3}$ $\dfrac{3x}{x+3}$

12. $\dfrac{3y}{y-2} - \dfrac{y}{y-2}$ $\dfrac{2y}{y-2}$

13. $\dfrac{a}{a+1} - \dfrac{5a}{a+1}$ $-\dfrac{4a}{a+1}$

14. $\dfrac{3x}{x-5} - \dfrac{3x}{x-5}$ 0

15. $\dfrac{2x}{x+y} + \dfrac{3y}{x+y}$ $\dfrac{2x+3y}{x+y}$

16. $\dfrac{2a}{2a+3b} - \dfrac{3b}{2a+3b}$ $\dfrac{2a-3b}{2a+3b}$

Add or subtract. (Example 4)

17. $\dfrac{x}{11} - \dfrac{3x}{11} + \dfrac{5x}{11}$ $\dfrac{3x}{11}$

18. $\dfrac{4}{a} + \dfrac{9}{a} - \dfrac{6}{a}$ $\dfrac{7}{a}$

19. $\dfrac{3x}{y+1} + \dfrac{5}{y+1} - \dfrac{x}{y+1}$

$\dfrac{2x+5}{y+1}$

WRITTEN EXERCISES
See the Teacher's Manual for the suggested assignments.

Goal: To add or subtract rational expressions with equal denominators

Sample Problems: a. $\dfrac{6}{x-4} + \dfrac{x}{x-4}$ **b.** $\dfrac{6}{x-4} - \dfrac{x}{x-4}$

Answers: a. $\dfrac{6+x}{x-4}$ **b.** $\dfrac{6-x}{x-4}$

Add or subtract. (Examples 1–4)

1. $\dfrac{5}{13} + \dfrac{6}{13}$ $\dfrac{11}{13}$

2. $\dfrac{2}{11} + \dfrac{8}{11}$ $\dfrac{10}{11}$

3. $\dfrac{3}{17} - \dfrac{8}{17}$ $-\dfrac{5}{17}$

4. $\dfrac{3}{7} - \dfrac{5}{7}$ $-\dfrac{2}{7}$

5. $\dfrac{5}{a} + \dfrac{11}{a}$ $\dfrac{16}{a}$

6. $\dfrac{2}{b} + \dfrac{13}{b}$ $\dfrac{15}{b}$

7. $\dfrac{8}{y} - \dfrac{13}{y}$ $-\dfrac{5}{y}$

8. $\dfrac{12}{x} - \dfrac{27}{x}$ $-\dfrac{15}{x}$

9. $\dfrac{5}{x+3} + \dfrac{7}{x+3}$ $\dfrac{12}{x+3}$

10. $\dfrac{3}{y+2} + \dfrac{7}{y+2}$ $\dfrac{10}{y+2}$

11. $\dfrac{3}{a-3} - \dfrac{4}{a-3}$ $-\dfrac{1}{a-3}$

12. $\dfrac{10}{b+7} - \dfrac{11}{b+7}$ $\dfrac{-1}{b+7}$

13. $\dfrac{2x}{x+2} + \dfrac{5x}{x+2}$ $\dfrac{7x}{x+2}$

14. $\dfrac{y}{y-1} + \dfrac{4y}{y-1}$ $\dfrac{5y}{y-1}$

15. $\dfrac{a}{a+1} - \dfrac{5a}{a+1}$ $\dfrac{-4a}{a+1}$

16. $\dfrac{2r}{r-6} - \dfrac{3r}{r-6}$ $-\dfrac{r}{r-6}$

17. $\dfrac{a}{2a+b} + \dfrac{b}{2a+b}$ See below

18. $\dfrac{x}{x-3y} + \dfrac{y}{x-3y}$ $\dfrac{x+y}{x-3y}$

19. $\dfrac{3r}{r-2s} - \dfrac{5s}{r-2s}$ $\dfrac{3r-5s}{r-2s}$

20. $\dfrac{c}{c-d} - \dfrac{2d}{c-d}$ $\dfrac{c-2d}{c-d}$

21. $\dfrac{3y}{19} - \dfrac{8y}{19} + \dfrac{y}{19}$ $-\dfrac{4y}{19}$

22. $\dfrac{t}{8} + \dfrac{4t}{8} - \dfrac{10t}{8}$ $-\dfrac{5t}{8}$

23. $\dfrac{4x}{3y} - \dfrac{x}{3y} - \dfrac{5x}{3y}$ $-\dfrac{2x}{3y}$

24. $\dfrac{3p}{10q} - \dfrac{2p}{10q} - \dfrac{8p}{10q}$ $-\dfrac{7p}{10q}$

25. $\dfrac{5}{9t} - \dfrac{12}{9t} + \dfrac{3}{9t}$ $-\dfrac{4}{9t}$

26. $\dfrac{4}{7y} - \dfrac{9}{7y} + \dfrac{1}{7y}$ $-\dfrac{4}{7y}$

17. $\dfrac{a+b}{2a+b}$

REVIEW CAPSULE FOR SECTION 15.2

Subtract. Then combine like terms. (Section 9.4) $4m-16$

1. $(4x-2) - (3x+1)$ $x-3$ **2.** $(5t+1) - (6t-5)$ $-t+6$ **3.** $(3m-6) - (-m+10)$

4. $(r^2-r) - (3r+2)$ r^2-4r-2 **5.** $(3n^2+n) - (12-n)$ **6.** $(s^2-3s) - (3s^2-5s+3)$

$3n^2 + 2n - 12$

$-2s^2 + 2s - 3$

15.2 More Sums and Differences

OBJECTIVES: To add or subtract with two rational expressions having monomial or binomial numerators and like binomial denominators

In many of the examples and exercises of this section, it will be necessary to simplify the result after applying the Sum or Difference Rule.

P-1   In $\dfrac{a}{a-b}$, what values cannot be assigned to *a* and *b*?   Their values cannot be the same.

example 1

Subtract and simplify: $\dfrac{a}{a-b} - \dfrac{b}{a-b}$

Solution:

1. Difference Rule for Rational Expressions $\longrightarrow$ $\dfrac{a}{a-b} - \dfrac{b}{a-b} = \dfrac{a-b}{a-b}$

2. Simplify. $\longrightarrow$ $= 1$

example 2

Add: $\dfrac{2x+3}{x} + \dfrac{x-5}{x}$

Solution:

1. Sum Rule for Rational Expressions $\longrightarrow$ $\dfrac{2x+3}{x} + \dfrac{x-5}{x} = \dfrac{(2x+3)+(x-5)}{x}$

2. Add binomials in the numerator. $\longrightarrow$ $= \dfrac{3x-2}{x}$

P-2   How do you know that $\dfrac{3x-2}{x}$ in Example 2 cannot be simplified?

The numerator and denominator have no common factors.

Recall how to subtract binomials.

Vertical Method

$$4x - 3$$
$$(-)\ \underline{x + 1}$$
$$3x - 4$$

Horizontal Method

$(4x - 3) - (x + 1) = (4x - 3) + -(x + 1)$

$= (4x - 3) + (-x - 1)$

$= 3x - 4$

◀ *The binomial x + 1 is subtracted by adding its opposite (−x − 1).*

example 3

Subtract: $\dfrac{5x - 2}{x - 3} - \dfrac{2x + 3}{x - 3}$

Special attention will have to be given to Step $\boxed{2}$ in both Examples 3 and 4. This concept causes much difficulty

Solution:

$\boxed{1}$ Difference Rule $\longrightarrow \dfrac{5x - 2}{x - 3} - \dfrac{2x + 3}{x - 3} = \dfrac{(5x - 2) - (2x + 3)}{x - 3}$

$\boxed{2}$ Meaning of subtraction $\longrightarrow = \dfrac{(5x - 2) + (-2x - 3)}{x - 3}$

◀ 2x + 3 is subtracted by adding its opposite.

$\boxed{3}$ Combine like terms. $\longrightarrow = \dfrac{3x - 5}{x - 3}$

example 4

Subtract and simplify: $\dfrac{3x + 2}{x + 2} - \dfrac{x - 2}{x + 2}$

Solution:

$\boxed{1}$ Difference Rule $\longrightarrow \dfrac{3x + 2}{x + 2} - \dfrac{x - 2}{x + 2} = \dfrac{(3x + 2) - (x - 2)}{x + 2}$

$\boxed{2}$ Meaning of subtraction $\longrightarrow = \dfrac{(3x + 2) + (-x + 2)}{x + 2}$

$\boxed{3}$ Combine like terms. $\longrightarrow = \dfrac{2x + 4}{x + 2}$

$\boxed{4}$ Factor the numerator. $\longrightarrow = \dfrac{2(x + 2)}{x + 2}$

$\boxed{5}$ Identify a name for 1. $\longrightarrow = \dfrac{(x + 2)}{(x + 2)} \cdot \dfrac{2}{1}$

◀ Simplifying a fraction is also called <u>reducing</u> the fraction.

$\boxed{6}$ Simplify. $\longrightarrow = 2$

CLASSROOM EXERCISES

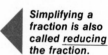

2. $\frac{5a + 3}{a - 5}$ 3. $\frac{3y + 3}{y + 3}$ 4. $\frac{2x - 4}{x + 1}$

5. $\frac{4b + 1}{b + 2}$ 6. $\frac{3r - 2}{r - 4}$

Add or subtract. Simplify where necessary. (Examples 1–4)

1. $\dfrac{x + 3}{x + 2} + \dfrac{2}{x + 2}$ $\frac{x + 5}{x + 2}$ 2. $\dfrac{3a}{a - 5} + \dfrac{2a + 3}{a - 5}$ See above.   3. $\dfrac{3y + 5}{y + 3} - \dfrac{2}{y + 3}$ See above.   4. $\dfrac{2x - 3}{x + 1} - \dfrac{1}{x + 1}$ See above.

5. $\dfrac{3b + 1}{b + 2} + \dfrac{b}{b + 2}$ See above.   6. $\dfrac{5r - 2}{r - 4} - \dfrac{2r}{r - 4}$ See above.   7. $\dfrac{2a + b}{a + b} - \dfrac{a}{a + b}$ 1   8. $\dfrac{x + y}{2x + y} + \dfrac{x}{2x + y}$ 1

9. $\dfrac{x + 2}{x - 3} + \dfrac{x + 3}{x - 3}$ 10. $\dfrac{x + 5}{x + 1} + \dfrac{3 - x}{x + 1}$ $\frac{8}{x + 1}$ 11. $\dfrac{3x + 3}{x + y} - \dfrac{x + 1}{x + y}$ 12. $\dfrac{3x + 1}{x + 4} - \dfrac{x + 4}{x + 4}$

$\frac{2x + 5}{x - 3}$

$\frac{2x + 2}{x + y}$

$\frac{2x - 3}{x + 4}$

WRITTEN EXERCISES

See the Teacher's Manual for the suggested assignments.

Goal: To add or subtract rational expressions

Sample Problem: $\dfrac{4x + 13}{x + 4} - \dfrac{x + 1}{x + 4}$

Answer: 3

Add or subtract. Simplify where necessary. (Examples 1–4) $\dfrac{6r - 1}{r + s}$

1. $\dfrac{2x + 1}{x + y} + \dfrac{4}{x + y}$ $\dfrac{2x + 5}{x + y}$

2. $\dfrac{2}{a - b} + \dfrac{3a + 5}{a - b}$ $\dfrac{3a + 7}{a - b}$

3. $\dfrac{6r + 3}{r + s} - \dfrac{4}{r + s}$

4. $\dfrac{5d + 1}{c + d} - \dfrac{3}{c + d}$ $\dfrac{5d - 2}{c + d}$

5. $\dfrac{3x - 5}{x + 2} + \dfrac{x - 2}{x + 2}$ $\dfrac{4x - 7}{x + 2}$

6. $\dfrac{5y - 1}{y - 3} + \dfrac{2y - 7}{y - 3}$ See below.

7. $\dfrac{5a - 2}{a + b} - \dfrac{a + 3}{a + b}$ $\dfrac{4a - 5}{a + b}$

8. $\dfrac{7c - 1}{c - d} - \dfrac{2c + 3}{c - d}$ $\dfrac{5c - 4}{c - d}$

9. $\dfrac{5x - 7}{2x - 3} + \dfrac{4 - 3x}{2x - 3}$ 1

10. $\dfrac{10 - 3y}{5y + 1} + \dfrac{8y - 9}{5y + 1}$ 1

11. $\dfrac{5a + 1}{a + 2} - \dfrac{3a - 3}{a + 2}$ 2

12. $\dfrac{4b - 9}{b - 1} - \dfrac{2b - 7}{b - 1}$ 2

13. $\dfrac{x^2 + 3x}{4x + 3} + \dfrac{3x^2}{4x + 3}$ x

14. $\dfrac{4y^2}{y - 1} + \dfrac{y^2 - 5y}{y - 1}$ $5y$

6. $\dfrac{7y - 8}{y - 3}$

15. $\dfrac{9a - 2a^2}{a + 2} - \dfrac{3a - 5a^2}{a + 2}$ $3a$

16. $\dfrac{b^2 + 5b}{b + 2} - \dfrac{-5b - 4b^2}{b + 2}$ $5b$

17. $\dfrac{x^2 + 3x}{x + 4} - \dfrac{16 + 3x}{x + 4}$ $x - 4$

18. $\dfrac{2a^2 + 2x}{a + 3} - \dfrac{a^2 + 2x + 9}{a + 3}$ $a - 3$

19. $\dfrac{y^2 - 3y}{y - 4} + \dfrac{16 - 5y}{y - 4}$ $y - 4$

20. $\dfrac{25 - 8b}{b - 5} + \dfrac{b^2 - 2b}{b - 5}$ $b - 5$

MORE CHALLENGING EXERCISES

21. $\dfrac{3x + 2}{x - 3} - \dfrac{x + 7}{x - 3} + \dfrac{2x - 7}{x - 3}$ 4

22. $\dfrac{x + 3}{2x - 1} + \dfrac{3x - 5}{2x - 1} - \dfrac{1 - 2x}{2x - 1}$ 3

23. $\dfrac{x - 5}{x + 5} - \dfrac{2x}{x + 5} - \dfrac{1 - x}{x + 5}$ $\dfrac{-6}{x + 5}$

24. $\dfrac{a^2 + a}{a + 4} + \dfrac{a}{a + 4} - \dfrac{a^2 + 2a}{a + 4}$ 0

REVIEW CAPSULE FOR SECTION 15.3

Write the prime factors of each polynomial. (Section 10.7)

1. $24x^3y^2$ $2, 2, 2, 3, x, x, x, y, y$

2. $56r^2s^4t^3$ $2, 2, 2, 7, r, r, s, s, s, s, t, t, t$

3. $4m^2 - 36$ $2, 2, (m - 3), (m + 3)$

4. $x^2 - 6x + 5$ $(x - 5), (x - 1)$

5. $6x^2 + 6x - 72$ $3, 2, (x + 4), (x - 3)$

6. $(a^2 - 4)(4a^2 - 4a - 8)$ $2, 2, (a + 2), (a - 2), (a - 2), (a + 1)$

15.3 Least Common Multiple of Polynomials

OBJECTIVE: To write the least common multiple of two or more polynomials in factored form

It is important to have students follow the steps as shown in Example 1 and summarized on page 380.

> The **least common multiple** (*LCM*) of two or more counting numbers is the smallest counting number that is divisible by the given numbers.
>
> 12 is the *LCM* of 4 and 6.

example 1   Find the *LCM* of 12, 30, and 45.

Solution:

$\boxed{1}$ Write the prime factorization of each number. $\longrightarrow$ $12 = 2^2 \cdot 3$

$$30 = 2 \cdot 3 \cdot 5$$

$$45 = 3^2 \cdot 5$$

$\boxed{2}$ Write a product using each prime factor only once. $\longrightarrow$ $2 \cdot 3 \cdot 5$

$\boxed{3}$ For each factor, write the greatest exponent used in any of the prime factorizations. $\longrightarrow$ $2^2 \cdot 3^2 \cdot 5$

$\boxed{4}$ Multiply. $\longrightarrow$ $4 \cdot 9 \cdot 5 = 180$

The method of Example 1 can also be used with polynomials.

example 2   Find the *LCM* of $10x^2$, $4xy$, and $15x^2y$.

Solution: $\boxed{1}$ $10x^2 = 2 \cdot 5 \cdot x^2$

$$4xy = 2^2 \cdot x \cdot y$$

$$15x^2y = 3 \cdot 5 \cdot x^2 \cdot y$$

$\boxed{2}$ $2 \cdot 3 \cdot 5 \cdot x \cdot y$

$\boxed{3}$ $2^2 \cdot 3 \cdot 5 \cdot x^2 \cdot y$

$\boxed{4}$ $60x^2y$

You can write the *LCM* in factored form if one or more of the factors is a binomial.

example 3   Find the *LCM* of $(2x - 4)$ and $(x^2 - 4)$.

Solution:

1 Factor. ─────────────────────────────→ $2x - 4 = 2(x - 2)$

$x^2 - 4 = (x + 2)(x - 2)$

2 Write a product using each factor only once. ──→ $2(x + 2)(x - 2)$

3 Write the greatest exponent for each factor. ──→ $2(x + 2)(x - 2)$ ◀ **Factored form**

example 4   Find the *LCM* of $(x - 3)$ and $(x + 5)$.

Solution: Both of the binomials are prime.

$$LCM = (x - 3)(x + 5)$$ ◀ *Since the factors are prime, the LCM is their product.*

The least common multiple of prime polynomials is their product.

P-1   What is the *LCM* of the polynomials below? $(x - y)(x + y)3xy$

$(x - y)$ $(x + y)$ $3xy$

example 5   Find the *LCM* of $x^2 - 9$, $5x^2 + 5x - 30$, and $x^2 - 4x + 4$.

Solution:

1 Factor. ───────────────────→ $\begin{cases} x^2 - 9 = (x + 3)(x - 3) \\ 5x^2 + 5x - 30 = 5(x^2 + x - 6) \\ \qquad\qquad\qquad = 5(x + 3)(x - 2) \\ x^2 - 4x + 4 = (x - 2)(x - 2) \end{cases}$ ◀ **Prime factorizations**

2 Write a product using each factor only once. ──→ $5(x + 3)(x - 3)(x - 2)$

3 Write the greatest exponent for each factor. ──→ $5(x + 3)(x - 3)(x - 2)^2$

> **Steps in finding the LCM of two or more polynomials:**
>
> 1. Write the prime factorization of each polynomial.
> 2. Write a product using each prime factor only once.
> 3. For each factor, write the greatest exponent used in any prime factorization.
> 4. Multiply where necessary.

CLASSROOM EXERCISES

3. $2 \cdot 3 \cdot x \cdot x \cdot y$ 14. $(5x - 3)(x + 2)(x - 4)$
8. $(2x + 3)(3x - 5)$ 17. $3 \cdot 5(a + b)(a - b)$
13. $(2x - y)(x + 2y)$

Tell the factored form of each LCM. (Examples 1–4)

$2 \cdot 3 \cdot 5 \cdot a \cdot b \cdot c$

1. 3; 7 $3 \cdot 7$ **2.** $2x$; y $2xy$ **3.** $3x^2$; $2y$ See above. **4.** 2; 3; 5 $2 \cdot 3 \cdot 5$ **5.** $2a$; $3b$; $5c$

6. $5x$; $7y$; $2z$ $2 \cdot 5 \cdot 7 \cdot x \cdot y \cdot z$ **7.** $(x - 3)$; $(x - 5)$ $(x-3)(x-5)$ **8.** $(2x + 3)$; $(3x - 5)$ See above.

9. $(a + b)$; $(a - b)$ $(a+b)(a-b)$ **10.** $12x^2y$; $3xy$ $2 \cdot 2 \cdot 3 \cdot x \cdot x \cdot y$ **11.** $3(a - b)$; $(a - b)$ $3(a-b)$

12. $2x$; $3x$ $2 \cdot 3 \cdot x$ **13.** $(2x - y)$; $(x + 2y)$ See above.   **14.** $(5x - 3)$; $(x + 2)$; $(x - 4)$ See above.

15. $5xy$; $3xy$ $3 \cdot 5 \cdot x \cdot y$ **16.** $2(x + y)$; $3(x + y)$ $2 \cdot 3(x+y)$ **17.** $5(a + b)$; $3(a - b)$ See above.

WRITTEN EXERCISES

18. $(x + 6)^2(x - 3)$ 24. $(3x - 1)(x - 4)(2x + 3)$
20. $(x - 4)(x + 2)(x - 2)$ 25. $5(3x - 2)(2x - 1)(2x + 1)$
23. $(2x - 3)(x + 1)(3x + 2)$ 26. $4(3x + 1)(3x + 5)(3x - 1)$

See the Teacher's Manual for the suggested assignments.

Goal: To find the least common multiple of two or more polynomials

Sample Problem: $2x + 2y$; $x^2 - y^2$; $x^2 + xy$ **Answer:** $2x(x + y)(x - y)$

Find each LCM. (Examples 1–5)

1. 10; 6 30   **2.** 12; 30 60   **3.** $4x^2$; $6xy$ $12x^2y$

4. $2ab^2$; $8a^2b$ $8a^2b^2$ **5.** $12a^2b$; $3ab$; $10a^2b$ $60a^2b$ **6.** $4xy$; $6xy^2$; $15x^2$ $60x^2y^2$

7. $(x^2 - 9)$; $(x + 3)$ See below. **8.** $(a - 5)$; $(a^2 - 25)$ See below.   **9.** $x^2 - y^2$; $3x - 3y$ See below.

10. $5a + 5b$; $a^2 - b^2$ See below.   **11.** $3b^2 + 15b$; $2b^2 - 12b$ See below.   **12.** $5r^2 - 15r$; $2r^2 + 6r$ See below.

13. $x^2 - 5x$; $x^2 - 25$; $x^3 + 5x^2$ $x^2(x - 5)(x + 5)$ **14.** $a^2 - 36$; $2a^2 + 12a$; $a^3 - 6a^2$ See below.

15. $x^2 + 4x + 4$; $5x + 10$ $5(x + 2)^2$ **16.** $x^2 - 6x + 9$; $4x - 12$ $4(x - 3)^2$

17. $x^2 - 8x + 16$; $x^2 - 2x - 8$ $(x - 4)^2(x + 2)$ **18.** $x^2 + 12x + 36$; $x^2 + 3x - 18$ See above.

19. $x^2 - 5x + 6$; $x^2 + x - 6$ $(x - 2)(x - 3)(x + 3)$ **20.** $x^2 - 2x - 8$; $x^2 - 6x + 8$ See above.

MORE CHALLENGING EXERCISES

7. $(x + 3)(x - 3)$ 9. $3(x - y)(x + y)$
8. $(a + 5)(a - 5)$

21. $4x^2 - 9y^2$; $4x + 6y$ $2(2x - 3y)(2x + 3y)$ **22.** $a^2 - 25b^2$; $3a - 15b$ $3(a - 5b)(a + 5b)$

23. $2x^2 - x - 3$; $3x^2 + 5x + 2$ See above.   **24.** $3x^2 - 13x + 4$; $2x^2 - 5x - 12$ See above.

25. $6x^2 - 7x + 2$; $15x - 10$; $4x^2 - 1$ See above.   **26.** $9x^2 + 18x + 5$; $12x + 20$; $9x^2 - 1$ See above.

10. $5(a - b)(a + b)$ 11. $6b(b + 5)(b - 6)$ 12. $10r(r - 3)(r + 3)$ 14. $2a^2(a - 6)(a + 6)$

15.4 Unlike Monomial Denominators

OBJECTIVE: To add or subtract with rational expressions having monomial numerators and unlike monomial denominators

example 1 Add: $\dfrac{2}{a} + \dfrac{3}{b}$

Solution:

1. Find the *LCM* of *a* and *b*. ⟶ ab

2. Multiplication Property of One ⟶ $\dfrac{2}{a} = \dfrac{2}{a} \cdot \dfrac{b}{b}; \dfrac{3}{b} = \dfrac{3}{b} \cdot \dfrac{a}{a}$

   ◀ **You must get ab as the common denominator.**

3. Substitute. ⟶ $\dfrac{2}{a} + \dfrac{3}{b} = \dfrac{2}{a} \cdot \dfrac{b}{b} + \dfrac{3}{b} \cdot \dfrac{a}{a}$

4. Product Rule ⟶ $= \dfrac{2b}{ab} + \dfrac{3a}{ab}$

5. Sum Rule ⟶ $= \dfrac{2b + 3a}{ab}$

   ◀ **Simplest form**

example 2 Subtract: $\dfrac{5}{2x} - \dfrac{2}{3x}$

Solution:

1. Find the *LCM* of $2x$ and $3x$. ⟶ $6x$

2. Multiplication Property of One ⟶ $\dfrac{5}{2x} = \dfrac{5}{2x} \cdot \dfrac{3}{3}; \dfrac{2}{3x} = \dfrac{2}{3x} \cdot \dfrac{2}{2}$

3. Substitute. ⟶ $\dfrac{5}{2x} - \dfrac{2}{3x} = \dfrac{5}{2x} \cdot \dfrac{3}{3} - \dfrac{2}{3x} \cdot \dfrac{2}{2}$

   Students will probably need some special help on choosing the names for 1 that will convert each denominator to the LCM.

4. Product Rule ⟶ $= \dfrac{15}{6x} - \dfrac{4}{6x}$

5. Difference Rule ⟶ $= \dfrac{15 - 4}{6x}$

6. Simplify. ⟶ $= \dfrac{11}{6x}$

P-1   In Step 2 of Example 2, how were $\dfrac{3}{3}$ and $\dfrac{2}{2}$ chosen as names for 1?

Multiplying by these numbers gives the LCM, $6x$, as the denominator for both fractions.

P-2
P-2   **What is the *LCM* of 10x²y and 8xy?** $40x^2y$

example 3   Add: $\dfrac{3}{10x^2y} + \dfrac{5}{8xy}$

Solution: $\dfrac{3}{10x^2y} + \dfrac{5}{8xy} = \dfrac{3}{10x^2y}\left(\dfrac{4}{4}\right) + \dfrac{5}{8xy}\left(\dfrac{5x}{5x}\right)$

$10x^2y = 2 \cdot 5 \cdot x^2 \cdot y$
$8xy = 2^3 \cdot x \cdot y$
$LCM = 2^3 \cdot 5 \cdot x^2 \cdot y \text{ or } 40x^2y$

$$= \dfrac{12}{40x^2y} + \dfrac{25x}{40x^2y}$$

$$= \dfrac{12 + 25x}{40x^2y}$$

P-3   **How do you know that $\dfrac{12 + 25x}{40x^2y}$ in Example 3 is in simplest form?**

There is no common factor.

P-4   **How can 5r be written as a fraction?** $\dfrac{5r}{1}$

example 4   Subtract: $5r - \dfrac{3r}{8t}$

Solution: $\dfrac{5r}{1} - \dfrac{3r}{8t} = \dfrac{5r}{1}\left(\dfrac{8t}{8t}\right) - \dfrac{3r}{8t}$

$$= \dfrac{40rt}{8t} - \dfrac{3r}{8t}$$

$$= \dfrac{40rt - 3r}{8t}$$

CLASSROOM EXERCISES

Write the missing name for 1.

1. $\dfrac{2}{x}\left(\dfrac{?}{?}\right) = \dfrac{2x}{x^2}$ $\frac{x}{x}$
2. $\dfrac{3}{ab}\left(\dfrac{?}{?}\right) = \dfrac{15}{5ab}$ $\frac{5}{5}$
3. $\dfrac{2}{5y}\left(\dfrac{?}{?}\right) = \dfrac{4}{10y}$ $\frac{2}{2}$
4. $\dfrac{3}{a^2b}\left(\dfrac{?}{?}\right) = \dfrac{3b}{a^2b^2}$ $\frac{b}{b}$

5. $\dfrac{5}{6xy}\left(\dfrac{?}{?}\right) = \dfrac{10x}{12x^2y}$ $\frac{2x}{2x}$
6. $\dfrac{3a}{2b}\left(\dfrac{?}{?}\right) = \dfrac{18a^2b}{12ab^2}$ $\frac{6ab}{6ab}$
7. $\dfrac{2}{5r}\left(\dfrac{?}{?}\right) = \dfrac{6s}{15rs}$ $\frac{3s}{3s}$
8. $\dfrac{5}{12xy}\left(\dfrac{?}{?}\right) = \dfrac{15xy}{36x^2y^2}$

$\frac{3xy}{3xy}$

Write the missing polynomials in each exercise. (Step 2 of Examples 1 and 2)

9. $\dfrac{2}{3ab}\left(\dfrac{?}{?}\right) = \dfrac{?}{9a^2b^2}$ $\dfrac{3ab}{3ab}$; 6ab

10. $\dfrac{9s}{5r^2}\left(\dfrac{?}{?}\right) = \dfrac{?}{15r^2s}$ $\dfrac{3s}{3s}$; 27s²

11. $\dfrac{?}{5y}\left(\dfrac{2x}{2x}\right) = \dfrac{6ax}{?}$ 3a; 10xy

12. $\dfrac{3b}{?}\left(\dfrac{10b}{10b}\right) = \dfrac{?}{40a^2b}$ 4a² , 30b²

13. $\dfrac{15x}{22y}\left(\dfrac{?}{?}\right) = \dfrac{?}{66xy}$ $\dfrac{3x}{3x}$; 45x²

14. $\dfrac{7s}{5r}\left(\dfrac{3rs}{3rs}\right) = \dfrac{?}{?}$ $\dfrac{21rs^2}{15r^2s}$

15. $\dfrac{2}{3x} + \dfrac{5}{2y} = \dfrac{2}{3x}\left(\dfrac{?}{?}\right) + \dfrac{5}{2y}\left(\dfrac{?}{?}\right)$ $\dfrac{2y}{2y}$; $\dfrac{3x}{3x}$

$= \dfrac{?}{6xy} + \dfrac{15x}{6xy}$ 4y

$= \dfrac{?}{6xy}$ 4y + 15x

16. $\dfrac{3}{a^2b} - \dfrac{5}{2ab} = \dfrac{3}{a^2b}\left(\dfrac{2}{2}\right) - \dfrac{5}{2ab}\left(\dfrac{?}{?}\right)$ $\dfrac{a}{a}$

$= \dfrac{?}{?} - \dfrac{5a}{2a^2b}$ $\dfrac{6}{2a^2b}$

$= \dfrac{?}{2a^2b}$ 6 − 5a

WRITTEN EXERCISES

See the Teacher's Manual for the suggested assignments.

Goal: To add or subtract rational expressions that have unlike monomial denominators

Sample Problem: $\dfrac{7}{4x^2} + \dfrac{5}{6xy}$ **Answer:** $\dfrac{21y + 10x}{12x^2y}$

Add or subtract. (Examples 1–4)

1. $\dfrac{3}{7} + \dfrac{2}{5}$ $\dfrac{29}{35}$

2. $\dfrac{2}{3} + \dfrac{5}{11}$ $\dfrac{37}{33}$

3. $\dfrac{5}{a} + \dfrac{7}{b}$ $\dfrac{5b + 7a}{ab}$

4. $\dfrac{1}{x} + \dfrac{4}{y}$ $\dfrac{y + 4x}{xy}$

5. $\dfrac{3}{2x} - \dfrac{5}{x}$ $-\dfrac{7}{2x}$

6. $\dfrac{3}{y} - \dfrac{4}{3y}$ $\dfrac{5}{3y}$

7. $\dfrac{2}{5x} + \dfrac{3}{10x}$ $\dfrac{7}{10x}$

8. $\dfrac{5}{3a} + \dfrac{2}{15a}$ $\dfrac{27}{15a}$

9. $\dfrac{5}{4a} - \dfrac{5}{12b}$ $\dfrac{15b - 5a}{12ab}$

10. $\dfrac{5}{6x} - \dfrac{3}{24y}$ $\dfrac{20y - 3x}{24xy}$

11. $\dfrac{2}{a^2b} + \dfrac{3}{ab^2}$ $\dfrac{2b + 3a}{a^2b^2}$

12. $\dfrac{5}{xy} + \dfrac{3}{xy^2}$ See below.

13. $\dfrac{5}{2a^2} - \dfrac{1}{6b^2}$ $\dfrac{15b^2 - a^2}{6a^2b^2}$

14. $\dfrac{2}{5xy} - \dfrac{7}{10y^2}$ $\dfrac{4y - 7x}{10xy^2}$

15. $\dfrac{2a}{bc} + \dfrac{3b}{ac}$ $\dfrac{2a^2 + 3b^2}{abc}$

16. $\dfrac{t}{2rs} + \dfrac{3s}{rt}$ See below.

17. $\dfrac{2}{3a^2b} + 5a$ $\dfrac{2 + 15a^3b}{3a^2b}$

18. $\dfrac{5}{7xy} + 4y$ $\dfrac{5 + 28xy^2}{7xy}$

19. $5cd - \dfrac{3d}{8c}$ $\dfrac{40c^2d - 3d}{8c}$

20. $10rt - \dfrac{4r}{9t}$ $\dfrac{90rt^2 - 4r}{9t}$

MORE CHALLENGING EXERCISES

21. $\dfrac{3}{x} + \dfrac{5}{2x} + \dfrac{1}{3x}$ $\dfrac{35}{6x}$

22. $\dfrac{7}{2a} + \dfrac{5}{a} + \dfrac{3}{5a}$ $\dfrac{91}{10a}$

23. $\dfrac{1}{ab^2} + \dfrac{2}{3ab} - \dfrac{5}{2a}$ See above.

24. $\dfrac{1}{x^2} + \dfrac{7}{xy} - \dfrac{3}{5y}$ $\dfrac{5y + 35x - 3x^2}{5x^2y}$

25. $\dfrac{a}{xy} + \dfrac{b}{xz} + \dfrac{c}{yz}$ $\dfrac{az + by + cx}{xyz}$

26. $\dfrac{r}{ab} + \dfrac{s}{ac} + \dfrac{t}{bc}$ $\dfrac{rc + bs + at}{abc}$

12. $\dfrac{5y + 3}{xy^2}$

16. $\dfrac{t^2 + 6s^2}{2rst}$

23. $\dfrac{6 + 4b - 15b^2}{6ab^2}$

MID-CHAPTER REVIEW

NOTE: After completing the Mid-Chapter Review, you may want to administer a quiz covering the same sections. See pages M-38 and M-39 of the Teacher's Manual for the suggested quiz.

Add or subtract. (Section 15.1)

1. $\dfrac{5}{t} - \dfrac{9}{t}$ $-\dfrac{4}{t}$

2. $\dfrac{3}{5t} + \dfrac{1}{5t}$ $\dfrac{4}{5t}$

3. $\dfrac{3m}{m+8} + \dfrac{5m}{m+8}$ $\dfrac{8m}{m+8}$

4. $\dfrac{6r}{r-3} - \dfrac{r}{r-3}$ $\dfrac{5r}{r-3}$

Add or subtract. Simplify where necessary. (Section 15.2)

5. $\dfrac{3a-1}{a+1} - \dfrac{2}{a+1}$ $\dfrac{3a-3}{a+1}$

6. $\dfrac{4r+8}{r+5} + \dfrac{r+7}{r+5}$ $\dfrac{5r+15}{r+5}$

7. $\dfrac{m^2-3}{m+4} - \dfrac{5-2m}{m+4}$ $m-2$

Find each LCM. (Section 15.3)

8. $10a^2b$; $12abc$ $60a^2bc$

9. $2t^2 - 18$; $3t^2 - 9t$ $6t(t-3)(t+3)$

10. $x^2 + x - 2$; $x^2 - x - 6$ $(x-1)(x+2)(x-3)$

Add or subtract. (Section 15.4)

11. $\dfrac{2}{5a} - \dfrac{3}{b}$ $\dfrac{2b-15a}{5ab}$

12. $\dfrac{4}{3t} + \dfrac{7}{12t}$ $\dfrac{23}{12t}$

13. $\dfrac{c}{6d} + \dfrac{d}{3c}$ $\dfrac{c^2+2d^2}{6cd}$

14. $\dfrac{2m}{6np} - \dfrac{5n}{8mp}$ $\dfrac{8m^2-15n^2}{24mnp}$

——— ADDING OR SUBTRACTING FRACTIONS ———

You can add or subtract fractions using the calculator. However, it is helpful to rewrite the addition or subtraction into a form that is easier for the calculator to handle.

EXAMPLE $\dfrac{2}{3} + \dfrac{5}{8}$

SOLUTION $\dfrac{2}{3} + \dfrac{5}{8} = 8(\dfrac{2}{3} + \dfrac{5}{8}) \div 8$

Multiply by 8 and divide by 8.
$8 \div 8 = 1$

$= [8(\tfrac{2}{3}) + 8(\tfrac{5}{8})] \div 8$

$= [8 \times 2 \div 3 + 5] \div 8$

$\boxed{1.2916666}$

Add or subtract.

1. $\tfrac{1}{2} + \tfrac{3}{4}$ 1.2500000

2. $\tfrac{3}{4} + \tfrac{5}{6}$ 1.5833333

3. $\tfrac{7}{8} + \tfrac{4}{9}$ 1.3194444

4. $\tfrac{11}{12} - \tfrac{3}{14}$ .7023809

5. $\tfrac{15}{8} - \tfrac{5}{12}$ 1.4583333

REVIEW CAPSULE FOR SECTION 15.5

Simplify. (Section 14.2)

1. $\dfrac{x^2+3x-10}{(x+5)(x-1)}$ $\dfrac{x-2}{x-1}$

2. $\dfrac{5x^2-15x}{(x-3)(x-3)}$ $\dfrac{5x}{x-3}$

3. $\dfrac{2x^2-2x-4}{(x-4)(x-2)}$ $\dfrac{2(x+1)}{x-4}$

4. $\dfrac{4x^3-2x^2}{3x(2x-1)}$ $\dfrac{2x}{3}$

15.5 Sums/Differences: Unlike Denominators

OBJECTIVE: To add or subtract with rational expressions having monomials or binomial numerators and unlike monomial or binomial denominators

example 1

Add: $\dfrac{3}{x} + \dfrac{2}{x-2}$

1. Find the *LCM* of x and $x - 2$. $\longrightarrow x(x-2)$

2. Multiplication Property of One $\longrightarrow \dfrac{3}{x} = \dfrac{3}{x}\left(\dfrac{x-2}{x-2}\right); \dfrac{2}{x-2} = \dfrac{2}{x-2}\left(\dfrac{x}{x}\right)$

3. Substitute. $\longrightarrow \dfrac{3}{x} + \dfrac{2}{x-2} = \dfrac{3}{x}\left(\dfrac{x-2}{x-2}\right) + \dfrac{2}{x-2}\left(\dfrac{x}{x}\right)$

4. Product Rule $\longrightarrow = \dfrac{3(x-2)}{x(x-2)} + \dfrac{2x}{x(x-2)}$

5. Sum Rule $\longrightarrow = \dfrac{3(x-2) + 2x}{x(x-2)}$

6. Distributive Property $\longrightarrow = \dfrac{3x - 6 + 2x}{x(x-2)}$

7. Combine like terms. $\longrightarrow = \dfrac{5x - 6}{x(x-2)}$

Explain that the denominators are usually left in factored form.

example 2

Subtract: $\dfrac{5}{x+3} - \dfrac{4}{x-1}$

Solution:

1. Find the *LCM* of $x + 3$ and $x - 1$. $\longrightarrow (x+3)(x-1)$

2. Multiplication Property of One $\longrightarrow \dfrac{5}{x+3} = \dfrac{5}{x+3}\left(\dfrac{x-1}{x-1}\right); \dfrac{4}{x-1} = \dfrac{4}{x-1}\left(\dfrac{x+3}{x+3}\right)$

3. Substitute. $\longrightarrow \dfrac{5}{x+3} - \dfrac{4}{x-1} = \dfrac{5}{x+3}\left(\dfrac{x-1}{x-1}\right) - \dfrac{4}{x-1}\left(\dfrac{x+3}{x+3}\right)$

4. Product Rule $\longrightarrow = \dfrac{5(x-1)}{(x+3)(x-1)} - \dfrac{4(x+3)}{(x+3)(x-1)}$

5. Difference Rule $\longrightarrow = \dfrac{5(x-1) - 4(x+3)}{(x+3)(x-1)}$

6. Distributive Property $\longrightarrow = \dfrac{5x - 5 - 4x - 12}{(x+3)(x+1)}$

7. Combine like terms. $\longrightarrow = \dfrac{x - 17}{(x+3)(x+1)}$

P-1 **What names for 1 are needed as suggested below?**

$$\frac{x+4}{x+4}\quad \frac{x+1}{x-1}\left(\frac{?}{?}\right)=\frac{?}{(x-1)(x+4)}\qquad \frac{x+3}{x+4}\left(\frac{?}{?}\right)=\frac{?}{(x-1)(x+4)}$$
$$\frac{x-1}{x-1}$$

example 3   Add: $\dfrac{x+1}{x-1}+\dfrac{x+3}{x+4}$

Solution:

1   Multiplication Property of 1 $\longrightarrow$ $\dfrac{x+1}{x-1}+\dfrac{x+3}{x+4}=\dfrac{x+1}{x-1}\left(\dfrac{x+4}{x+4}\right)+\dfrac{x+3}{x+4}\left(\dfrac{x-1}{x-1}\right)$

2   Product Rule $\longrightarrow$ $=\dfrac{(x+1)(x+4)}{(x-1)(x+4)}+\dfrac{(x+3)(x-1)}{(x+4)(x-1)}$

3   Sum Rule $\longrightarrow$ $=\dfrac{(x+1)(x+4)+(x+3)(x-1)}{(x-1)(x+4)}$

4   Distributive Property $\longrightarrow$ $=\dfrac{x^2+5x+4+x^2+2x-3}{(x-1)(x+4)}$

5   Add like terms. $\longrightarrow$ $=\dfrac{2x^2+7x+1}{(x-1)(x+4)}$

Check: Test to see whether the result in Step 5 is in simplest form.
Try to factor $2x^2+7x+1$.

Explain also that neither $(x-1)$ or $(x+4)$ can be a factor of $2x^2+7x+1$ because $(-1)(4)$ does not equal 1, the last term.

$$2x^2+rx+sx+1$$
$$r+s=7\qquad r\cdot s=2$$

There are no integers for r and s that meet both of these conditions.
The polynomial $2x^2+7x+1$ is prime.

$$\dfrac{2x^2+7x+1}{(x-1)(x+4)}$$ **Simplest form**

CLASSROOM EXERCISES

Tell the LCM. (Step 1 of Examples 1 and 2)

1. x and $(x+1)$ $x(x+1)$

2. b and $(b-1)$ $b(b-1)$

3. $(x+5)$ and $(x-3)$ $(x+5)(x-3)$

4. $(y-2)$ and $(y+2)$ $(y-2)(y+2)$

5. r and $(r+4)$ $r(r+4)$

6. $(a+b)$ and $(a-b)$ $(a+b)(a-b)$

7. $(2x-1)$ and $(x+3)$ $(2x-1)(x+3)$

8. $(3x+2)$ and $(2x+3)$ $(3x+2)(2x+3)$

9. $x(x-1)$ and $(x-1)$ $x(x-1)$

Tell the missing name for 1. Then tell the numerator of the expression on the right. (Step 2 of Examples 1 and 2)

10. $\dfrac{5}{x-2}\left(\dfrac{?}{?}\right)^{\tfrac{x}{x}} = \dfrac{?}{x(x-2)}$ $5x$

11. $\dfrac{3}{a}\left(\dfrac{?}{?}\right)^{\tfrac{a+3}{a+3}} = \dfrac{?}{a(a+3)}$ $3a+9$

12. $\dfrac{x}{x+5}\left(\dfrac{?}{?}\right)^{\tfrac{x}{x}} = \dfrac{?}{x(x+5)}$ x^2

13. $\dfrac{2}{y+2}\left(\dfrac{?}{?}\right)^{\tfrac{y-2}{y-2}} = \dfrac{?}{(y+2)(y-2)}$ $2y-4$

14. $\dfrac{a}{a+b}\left(\dfrac{?}{?}\right)^{\tfrac{a-b}{a-b}} = \dfrac{?}{(a+b)(a-b)}$ a^2-ab

15. $\dfrac{x-1}{x+3}\left(\dfrac{?}{?}\right)^{\tfrac{x-2}{x-2}} = \dfrac{?}{(x-2)(x+3)}$ x^2-3x+2

16. $\dfrac{b+5}{b-7}\left(\dfrac{?}{?}\right)^{\tfrac{b+1}{b+1}} = \dfrac{?}{(b-7)(b+1)}$ b^2+6b+5

17. $\dfrac{x+5}{2(x+3)}\left(\dfrac{?}{?}\right)^{\tfrac{x-2}{x-2}} = \dfrac{?}{2(x+3)(x-2)}$ $x^2+3x-10$

WRITTEN EXERCISES

See the Teacher's Manual for the suggested assignments.

Goal: To add or subtract rational expressions that have binomial denominators

Sample Problem: $\dfrac{7}{x-4} - \dfrac{3}{x+1}$ **Answer:** $\dfrac{4x+19}{(x-4)(x+1)}$

Add or subtract. (Examples 1–3)   5. $\dfrac{x^2+2x+25}{(x+5)(x-3)}$ 6. $\dfrac{y^2+y+6}{(y-2)(y+2)}$

1. $\dfrac{1}{x+1} + \dfrac{2}{x}$ $\dfrac{3x+2}{x(x+1)}$

2. $\dfrac{3}{x-1} + \dfrac{5}{x}$ $\dfrac{8x-5}{x(x-1)}$

3. $\dfrac{4}{a} - \dfrac{2}{a+2}$ $\dfrac{2a+8}{a(a+2)}$

4. $\dfrac{2}{b} - \dfrac{3}{b-1}$ $\dfrac{-b-2}{b(b-1)}$

5. $\dfrac{x}{x+5} + \dfrac{5}{x-3}$ See above.

6. $\dfrac{3}{y-2} + \dfrac{y}{y+2}$ See above.

7. $\dfrac{a}{a-5} - \dfrac{2}{a}$ $\dfrac{a^2-2a+10}{a(a-5)}$

8. $\dfrac{r}{r+4} - \dfrac{1}{r}$ $\dfrac{r^2-r-4}{r(r+4)}$

9. $\dfrac{a}{a+b} + \dfrac{b}{a-b}$ See below.

10. $\dfrac{r}{r-s} - \dfrac{s}{r+s}$ See below.

11. $\dfrac{a+1}{a-3} + \dfrac{3}{a+2}$ See below.

12. $\dfrac{y-2}{y+1} + \dfrac{5}{y+3}$ See below.

13. $\dfrac{3}{2x-1} - \dfrac{5}{x+3}$ See below.

14. $\dfrac{2}{3x+2} - \dfrac{1}{2x+3}$ See below.

15. $\dfrac{x+3}{x-1} + \dfrac{x+4}{x-2}$ $\dfrac{2(x^2+2x-5)}{(x-1)(x-2)}$

16. $\dfrac{y+5}{y+2} + \dfrac{y-3}{y-1}$ $\dfrac{2y^2+3y-11}{(y+2)(y-1)}$

MORE CHALLENGING EXERCISES

17. $\dfrac{b+2}{b-1} - \dfrac{b+5}{b-2}$ $\dfrac{-4b+1}{(b-1)(b-2)}$

18. $\dfrac{t+2}{t-4} - \dfrac{t+1}{t+2}$ $\dfrac{7t+8}{(t-4)(t+2)}$

19. $\dfrac{x+1}{x(x-1)} + \dfrac{5}{x-1}$ $\dfrac{6x+1}{x(x-1)}$

9. $\dfrac{a^2+b^2}{(a+b)(a-b)}$ **10.** $\dfrac{r^2+s^2}{(r+s)(r-s)}$ **11.** $\dfrac{a^2+6a-7}{(a-3)(a+2)}$ **12.** $\dfrac{y^2+6y-1}{(y+1)(y+3)}$ **13.** $\dfrac{-7x+14}{(2x-1)(x+3)}$ **14.** $\dfrac{x+4}{(3x+2)(2x+3)}$

REVIEW CAPSULE FOR SECTION 15.6

Find the LCM. (Section 15.3)

1. $4x-2$ and $6x-3$ $6(2x-1)$

2. $5x+15$ and x^2-9 $5(x+3)(x-3)$

3. x^2-2x and $x^2+3x-10$ $x(x-2)(x+5)$

15.6 More Sums and Differences

OBJECTIVE: To add or subtract with rational expressions having monomial or binomial numerators and unlike binomial or trinomial denominators

Students may need special help with Step $\boxed{3}$ in all the Examples.

P-1 **What are the factors of $2x + 4$? of $3x + 6$?**

$$2(x + 2) \qquad 3(x + 2)$$

example 1   Add: $\dfrac{3}{2x + 4} + \dfrac{2}{3x + 6}$

Solution:

$\boxed{1}$ Factor the denominators. $\longrightarrow$ $2x + 4 = 2(x + 2)$; $3x + 6 = 3(x + 2)$

$\boxed{2}$ Use the factors to write the *LCM*. $\longrightarrow$ $2 \cdot 3(x + 2)$ or $6(x + 2)$

$\boxed{3}$ Multiplication Property of 1 $\longrightarrow$ $\dfrac{3}{2(x + 2)} + \dfrac{2}{3(x + 2)} = \dfrac{3}{2(x + 2)}\left(\dfrac{3}{3}\right) + \dfrac{2}{3(x + 2)}\left(\dfrac{2}{2}\right)$

$\boxed{4}$ Product Rule for Rational Expressions $\longrightarrow$ $= \dfrac{9}{6(x + 2)} + \dfrac{4}{6(x + 2)}$

$\boxed{5}$ Sum Rule for Rational Expressions $\longrightarrow$ $= \dfrac{13}{6(x + 2)}$ ◀ **Simplest form**

example 2   Subtract: $\dfrac{3}{5x - 10} - \dfrac{2}{x^2 - 4}$

Solution:

$\boxed{1}$ Factor the denominators. $\longrightarrow$ $5x - 10 = 5(x - 2)$; $x^2 - 4 = (x - 2)(x + 2)$

$\boxed{2}$ Use the factors to write the *LCM*. $\longrightarrow$ $5 \cdot (x - 2)(x + 2)$

$\boxed{3}$ Multiplication Property of 1 $\longrightarrow$ $\dfrac{3}{5x - 10} - \dfrac{2}{x^2 - 4} = \dfrac{3}{5(x - 2)}\left(\dfrac{x + 2}{x + 2}\right) - \dfrac{2}{(x - 2)(x + 2)}\left(\dfrac{5}{5}\right)$

$\boxed{4}$ Product Rule $\longrightarrow$ $= \dfrac{3(x + 2)}{5(x - 2)(x + 2)} - \dfrac{2(5)}{5(x - 2)(x + 2)}$

$\boxed{5}$ Distributive Property and the Difference Rule $\longrightarrow$ $= \dfrac{3x + 6 - 10}{5(x - 2)(x + 2)}$

$\boxed{6}$ Combine like terms. $\longrightarrow$ $= \dfrac{3x - 4}{5(x - 2)(x + 2)}$

P-2 How do you know that $\dfrac{3x-4}{5(x-2)(x+2)}$ in Example 2 is in simplest form? There are no common factors.

P-3 What are the prime factors of x^2+x? $x, x+1$

P-4 What are the prime factors of x^2+3x+2? $x+1, x+2$

P-5 What is the *LCM* of $x(x+1)$ and $(x+1)(x+2)$? $x(x+1)(x+2)$

example 3

Add: $\dfrac{4}{x^2+x} + \dfrac{1}{x^2+3x+2}$

Solution:

1. Factor the denominators. $\longrightarrow$ $x^2+x = x(x+1);\ (x^2+3x+2) = (x+2)(x+1)$

2. Use the factors to write the *LCM*. $\longrightarrow$ $x(x+1)(x+2)$

3. Multiplication Property of 1 $\longrightarrow$ $\dfrac{4}{x^2+x} + \dfrac{1}{x^2+3x+2} = \dfrac{4}{x(x+1)}\left(\dfrac{x+2}{x+2}\right) + \dfrac{1}{(x+1)(x+2)}\left(\dfrac{x}{x}\right)$

4. Product Rule $\longrightarrow$ $= \dfrac{4(x+2)}{x(x+1)(x+2)} + \dfrac{x}{(x+1)(x+2)x}$

5. Sum Rule $\longrightarrow$ $= \dfrac{4(x+2)+x}{x(x+1)(x+2)}$

6. Distributive Property $\longrightarrow$ $= \dfrac{4x+8+x}{x(x+1)(x+2)}$

7. Combine like terms. $\longrightarrow$ $= \dfrac{5x+8}{x(x+1)(x+2)}$

The steps of Examples 1–3 are summarized.

> **Steps in adding or subtracting rational expressions:**
>
> 1. Factor the denominators.
> 2. Determine the *LCM*.
> 3. Change the rational expressions to equivalent expressions with the *LCM* as the denominator of each.
> 4. Add or subtract.
> 5. Simplify.

CLASSROOM EXERCISES

Write the LCM. (Step 2 of Examples 1–3)

1. $x(x-1)$; $(x-1)(x+1)$ $x(x-1)(x+1)$ **2.** $2(x+2)$; $3(x+2)$ $6(x+2)$

3. $(x+3)(x+3)$; $(x-2)(x+3)$ $(x+3)^2(x-2)$ **4.** $a(a-1)$; $a(a+1)$ $a(a-1)(a+1)$

5. $(y+2)(y-3)$; $(y+2)(y+1)$ $(y+2)(y-3)(y+1)$ **6.** $10(x-5)$; $2(x-2)$ $10(x-5)(x-2)$

7. $2(x+1)(x-2)$; $(x-2)(x-2)$ $2(x+1)(x-2)^2$ **8.** $3(a+2)$; $(a-2)(a-2)$ $3(a+2)(a-2)^2$

Write the prime factors. (P-3, P-4)

9. $2x-6$ $2, x-3$ **10.** $6x+6$ $6, x+1$ **11.** $4x+12$ $4, x+3$ **12.** $8x-8$ $8, x-1$

13. x^2+x-2 **14.** x^2-x-6 **15.** $a^2+3a-10$ **16.** $a^2+2a-15$

     $x+2, x-1$ $x-3, x+2$ $a+5, a-2$ $a+5, a-3$

WRITTEN EXERCISES

See the Teacher's Manual for the suggested assignments.

Goal: To add or subtract rational expressions that have binomial or trinomial denominators

Sample Problem: $\dfrac{5}{4x-12}+\dfrac{1}{x^2-6x+9}$ **Answer:** $\dfrac{5x-11}{4(x-3)(x-3)}$

Copy each exercise. Replace each question mark with the correct polynomial. (Examples 1 and 2)

1. $\dfrac{3}{2x+2}+\dfrac{1}{x^2-1}=\dfrac{3}{2(?)}+\dfrac{1}{(x-1)(?)}$ $x+1, x+1$

$$=\dfrac{3}{2(?)}\left(\dfrac{?}{?}\right)+\dfrac{1}{(x-1)(?)}\left(\dfrac{?}{?}\right) \quad x+1, \dfrac{x-1}{x-1}, x+1, \dfrac{2}{2}$$

$$=\dfrac{3(?)}{2(x+1)(x-1)}\overset{x-1}{}+\dfrac{1(?)}{2(x+1)(x-1)}\overset{2}{}=\dfrac{?}{2(x+1)(x-1)}\overset{3x-1}{}$$

2. $\dfrac{2}{x^2-25}+\dfrac{4}{3x-15}=\dfrac{2}{(x-5)(?)}+\dfrac{4}{3(?)}$ $x+5, x-5$

$$=\dfrac{2}{(x-5)(?)}\left(\dfrac{?}{?}\right)+\dfrac{4}{3(?)}\left(\dfrac{?}{?}\right) \quad x+5, \dfrac{3}{3}, x-5, \dfrac{x+5}{x+5}$$

$$=\dfrac{2(?)}{3(x-5)(x+5)}\overset{3}{}+\dfrac{4(?)}{3(x-5)(x+5)}\overset{x+5}{}=\dfrac{?}{3(x-5)(x+5)}\overset{26+4x}{}$$

Copy each exercise. Replace each question mark with the correct polynomial.
(Example 3)

3. $\dfrac{1}{x^2 + x - 6} - \dfrac{2}{x^2 - 2x} = \dfrac{1}{(x-2)(?)} - \dfrac{2}{x(?)}$ $\quad x+3, x-2$

$\qquad = \dfrac{1}{(x-2)(?)}\left(\dfrac{?}{?}\right) - \dfrac{2}{x(?)}\left(\dfrac{?}{?}\right)$ $\quad x+3, \frac{x}{x}, x-2, \frac{x+3}{x+3}$

$\qquad = \dfrac{1(?)}{x(x+3)(x-2)} \dfrac{x}{} - \dfrac{2(?)}{x(x+3)(x-2)} \dfrac{x+3}{} = \dfrac{?}{x(x+3)(x-2)} \dfrac{-x-6}{}$

4. $\dfrac{2}{x^2 + 4x} - \dfrac{3}{x^2 + 3x - 4} = \dfrac{2}{x(?)} - \dfrac{3}{(x-1)(?)}$ $\quad x+4, x+4$

$\qquad = \dfrac{2}{x(?)}\left(\dfrac{?}{?}\right) - \dfrac{3}{(x-1)(?)}\left(\dfrac{?}{?}\right)$ $\quad x+4, \frac{x-1}{x-1}, x+4, \frac{x}{x}$

$\qquad = \dfrac{2(?)}{x(x+4)(x-1)} \dfrac{x-1}{} - \dfrac{3(?)}{x(x+4)(x-1)} \dfrac{x}{} = \dfrac{?}{x(x+4)(x-1)} \dfrac{-x-2}{}$

5. $\dfrac{2x-3}{3(x-3)(x-1)}$

Add or subtract. (Examples 1–3)   **6.** $\dfrac{3x+1}{8(x+3)(x-1)}$ **7.** $\dfrac{x-7}{(x+2)(x-1)(x-3)}$

5. $\dfrac{1}{2x-6} + \dfrac{1}{6x-6}$ See above.   **6.** $\dfrac{1}{4x+12} + \dfrac{1}{8x-8}$ **7.** $\dfrac{3}{x^2+x-2} - \dfrac{2}{x^2-x-6}$

8. $\dfrac{2}{x^2-9} + \dfrac{1}{2x+6}$ See below.   **9.** $\dfrac{7}{10x-50} - \dfrac{3}{x^2-25}$ See below.   **10.** $\dfrac{4}{a^2+3a-10} - \dfrac{5}{a^2+2a-15}$ See below.

11. $\dfrac{x}{2x-4} + \dfrac{x-1}{x^2-4}$ $\dfrac{x^2+4x-2}{2(x-2)(x+2)}$ **12.** $\dfrac{5a}{a^2+2a-15} + \dfrac{a+3}{a^2+6a+5}$ $\dfrac{6a^2+5a-9}{(a+5)(a-3)(a+1)}$

13. $\dfrac{a+7}{a^2-a-6} - \dfrac{a}{a^2-10a+21}$ $\dfrac{-2a-49}{(a-3)(a+2)(a-7)}$ **14.** $\dfrac{2x+1}{x^2-81} - \dfrac{x}{x^2-10x+9}$ $\dfrac{x^2-10x-1}{(x-9)(x+9)(x-1)}$

15. $\dfrac{x-2}{x^2-1} + \dfrac{x}{x^2+2x-3}$ $\dfrac{2(x^2+x-3)}{(x+1)(x-1)(x+3)}$ **16.** $\dfrac{y}{y^2+2y-8} + \dfrac{y+3}{y^2-16}$ $\dfrac{2y^2-3y-6}{(y+4)(y-2)(y-4)}$

17. $\dfrac{2a-1}{2a^2-5a-3} - \dfrac{3a+1}{2a^2-a-1}$ $\dfrac{-a^2+5a+4}{(2a+1)(a-3)(a-1)}$ **18.** $\dfrac{2x+1}{3x^2+8x-3} - \dfrac{x-5}{3x^2+2x-1}$

8. $\dfrac{x+1}{2(x-3)(x+3)}$ **9.** $\dfrac{7x+5}{10(x-5)(x+5)}$ **10.** $\dfrac{-a-2}{(a+5)(a-2)(a-3)}$ $\dfrac{x^2+5x+16}{(3x-1)(x+3)(x+1)}$

REVIEW CAPSULE FOR SECTION 15.7

Multiply. (Sections 14.3 and 14.4)

1. $6r^2s \cdot \dfrac{3}{2rs}$ $9r$ **2.** $(t+1)(t-1) \cdot \dfrac{t}{t+1}$ $t(t-1)$ **3.** $3q(q+2)\left(\dfrac{3}{q} - \dfrac{5}{3q}\right)$ $4(q+2)$

15.7 Equations with Rational Expressions

OBJECTIVE: To solve and check an equation containing one or more rational expressions

Recall that numbers that will make zero divisors are excluded from the domains of rational expressions.

example 1

Solve $\dfrac{3}{x-3} = 5$.

Solution:

1. Multiply each side by $x - 3$. $\longrightarrow$ $\dfrac{3}{x-3}(x-3) = 5(x-3)$

2. Simplify the left side. $\longrightarrow$ $3 = 5(x-3)$

3. Distributive Property $\longrightarrow$ $3 = 5x - 15$

4. Addition Property of Equality $\longrightarrow$ $18 = 5x$

5. Division Property of Equality $\longrightarrow$ $\dfrac{18}{5} = x$

To check the solution set of Example 1, replace x in $\dfrac{3}{x-3} = 5$ with $\dfrac{18}{5}$.

example 2

Solve $\dfrac{2}{x-1} = \dfrac{3}{x+1}$.

In step 1, each side is multiplied by the LCM of the denominators.

Solution:

1. Multiply each side by $(x-1)(x+1)$. $\longrightarrow$ $\dfrac{2}{x-1}(x-1)(x+1) = \dfrac{3}{x+1}(x-1)(x+1)$

2. Simplify each side. $\longrightarrow$ $\dfrac{2}{\cancel{x-1}} \cdot \dfrac{\cancel{(x-1)}(x+1)}{1} = \dfrac{3}{\cancel{x+1}} \cdot \dfrac{(x-1)\cancel{(x+1)}}{1}$

$$2(x+1) = 3(x-1)$$

3. Distributive Property $\longrightarrow$ $2x + 2 = 3x - 3$

4. Subtract $2x$ from each side. $\longrightarrow$ $2 = x - 3$

5. Add 3 to each side. $\longrightarrow$ $5 = x$

Check:

$$\dfrac{2}{x-1} = \dfrac{3}{x+1}$$

$$\dfrac{2}{5-1} \quad \Big| \quad \dfrac{3}{5+1}$$

$$\dfrac{2}{4} \quad \Big| \quad \dfrac{3}{6}$$

$$\dfrac{1}{2} \quad \Big| \quad \dfrac{1}{2}$$

P-1 **What is the *LCM* of x, 3x, and x + 2?** $3x(x + 2)$

example 3 Solve $\dfrac{1}{x} + \dfrac{1}{3x} = \dfrac{2}{x + 2}$.

Solution:

1. Multiply each side by 3x(x + 2). $\longrightarrow$ $3x(x + 2)\left(\dfrac{1}{x} + \dfrac{1}{3x}\right) = 3x(x + 2) \cdot \dfrac{2}{x + 2}$

2. Distributive Property $\longrightarrow$ $3x(x + 2) \cdot \dfrac{1}{x} + 3x(x + 2) \cdot \dfrac{1}{3x} = 3x(x + 2) \cdot \dfrac{2}{x + 2}$

3. Simplify each side. $\longrightarrow$ $3x + 6 + x + 2 = 6x$

4. Combine like terms. $\longrightarrow$ $4x + 8 = 6x$

5. Subtract 4x from each side. $\longrightarrow$ $8 = 2x$

6. Divide each side by 2. $\longrightarrow$ $4 = x$

Check: $\dfrac{1}{x} + \dfrac{1}{3x} \;\Big|\; \dfrac{2}{x + 2}$

$\dfrac{1}{4} + \dfrac{1}{12} \;\Big|\; \dfrac{2}{4 + 2}$

$\dfrac{3}{12} + \dfrac{1}{12} \;\Big|\; \dfrac{2}{6}$

$\dfrac{4}{12} \;\Big|\; \dfrac{1}{3}$

$\dfrac{1}{3}$

The steps of Examples 1–3 are summarized.

> **Steps in solving equations with rational expressions:**
>
> 1. Exclude numbers that will make zero divisors.
> 2. Multiply each side by the *LCM* of the denominators.
> 3. Solve the resulting equation.

CLASSROOM EXERCISES

Write the real number or numbers that must be restricted from each domain.

1. $\dfrac{2}{x} = \dfrac{5}{x-3}$ 0, 3

2. $\dfrac{3}{x+2} = \dfrac{1}{x-5}$ −2, 5

3. $\dfrac{4}{3x} = \dfrac{2}{x(x+1)}$ 0, −1

4. $\dfrac{x}{x+7} = 12$ −7

5. $\dfrac{3x}{2x+1} = 5$ $-\dfrac{1}{2}$

6. $\dfrac{5}{3x+1} = \dfrac{4}{2x-1}$ $-\dfrac{1}{3}, \dfrac{1}{2}$

Write the LCM of the denominators. (P-1)

7. $\dfrac{x}{x-3} = \dfrac{3}{4}$ $4(x-3)$

8. $\dfrac{6}{x} = \dfrac{8}{x-5}$ $x(x-5)$

9. $\dfrac{3}{2x} = \dfrac{6}{5x-1}$ $2x(5x-1)$

10. $\dfrac{5}{3} = \dfrac{2}{6(x-1)} + 3$ $6(x-1)$

11. $\dfrac{5}{2x} = \dfrac{1}{x+3}$ $2x(x+3)$

12. $\dfrac{10}{7x} = \dfrac{3}{7(2x+1)}$ $7x(2x+1)$

WRITTEN EXERCISES

See the Teacher's Manual for the suggested assignments.

Goal: To solve equations that have rational expressions

Sample Problem: $\dfrac{1}{2x} + \dfrac{1}{x-1} = \dfrac{1}{x}$

Answer: −1

Solve and check each equation. (Examples 1–3)

1. $\dfrac{12}{x} = 3$ {4}

2. $\dfrac{18}{x} = 6$ {3}

3. $\dfrac{6}{x+2} = 3$ {0}

4. $\dfrac{4}{x+5} = 2$ {−3}

5. $\dfrac{3}{4} = \dfrac{12}{x}$ {16}

6. $\dfrac{9}{x} = \dfrac{3}{8}$ {24}

7. $\dfrac{2}{x-1} = \dfrac{3}{x-1}$ ϕ

8. $\dfrac{6}{x+3} = \dfrac{5}{x+3}$ ϕ

9. $\dfrac{5}{x} = \dfrac{4}{x-3}$ {15}

10. $\dfrac{2}{x-7} = \dfrac{3}{x}$ {21}

11. $\dfrac{7}{x+1} = \dfrac{3}{x+5}$ {−8}

12. $\dfrac{2}{x+4} = \dfrac{3}{x-3}$ {−18}

13. $\dfrac{2}{3} + \dfrac{3}{x} = \dfrac{5}{2x}$ $\left\{-\dfrac{3}{4}\right\}$

14. $\dfrac{1}{3x} + \dfrac{2}{5} = \dfrac{5}{x}$ $\left\{\dfrac{35}{3}\right\}$

15. $\dfrac{1}{x} + \dfrac{2}{x-2} = \dfrac{1}{2x}$ $\left\{\dfrac{2}{5}\right\}$

16. $\dfrac{1}{x-4} + \dfrac{1}{3x} = \dfrac{1}{x}$ {−8}

MORE CHALLENGING EXERCISES

17. $\dfrac{2}{2x+1} = \dfrac{3}{2x+1} + \dfrac{1}{2x}$ $\left\{-\dfrac{1}{4}\right\}$

18. $\dfrac{3}{2x} + \dfrac{1}{3x-1} = \dfrac{1}{3x-1}$ ϕ

19. $\dfrac{x}{x-2} = \dfrac{x}{x-3}$ {0}

20. $\dfrac{2x}{2x-1} = \dfrac{x}{x+2}$ {0}

Rate of Work

Rate of work on a job is the fraction of the job that can be completed in one unit of time.

$\frac{1}{5}$ is the rate of work on a job requiring 5 hours.

$\frac{1}{5}$ means "one-fifth of the job per hour."

In two hours, $2(\frac{1}{5})$ or $\frac{2}{5}$ of the job can be completed.

In three hours, $3(\frac{1}{5})$ or $\frac{3}{5}$ of the job can be completed.

$$\frac{2}{5} + \frac{3}{5} = 1 \quad \blacktriangleleft \quad \textit{The entire job is represented by 1.}$$

EXAMPLE 1: Two architects are working on the plans for a building. Jane estimates she could prepare the plans by herself in 100 hours. Melanie estimates she would need 120 hours for the entire job working alone. How many hours would the two need to prepare the plans working together? Round to the nearest whole hour.

SOLUTION:

Architect	Number of Hours Together on Job	Rate of Work	Part of Job Done
Jane	x	$\frac{1}{100}$	$x(\frac{1}{100})$ or, $\frac{x}{100}$
Melanie	x	$\frac{1}{120}$	$x(\frac{1}{120})$ or, $\frac{x}{120}$

Write an equation. $\longrightarrow$ $\frac{x}{100} + \frac{x}{120} = 1$ $\quad \blacktriangleleft \quad$ *The entire job is represented by 1.*

Solve. $\longrightarrow$
$$600(\frac{x}{100} + \frac{x}{120}) = 600(1)$$
$$6x + 5x = 600$$
$$11x = 600$$
$$x = 54\tfrac{6}{11} \text{ or about } \textbf{55 hours}$$

EXAMPLE 2: A diesel–powered pump can drain a lake in 24 hours. After operating for 10 hours, the pump broke down. A smaller electric–powered pump, capable of doing the whole job in 36 hours, was substituted. How long did it take the smaller pump to complete the job?

SOLUTION:

Pump	Number of Hours on Job	Rate of Work	Part of Job Done
Diesel	10	$\frac{1}{24}$	$10\left(\frac{1}{24}\right)$ or, $\frac{10}{24}$
Electric	x	$\frac{1}{36}$	$x\left(\frac{1}{36}\right)$ or, $\frac{x}{36}$

Write an equation. ⟶ $\frac{10}{24} + \frac{x}{36} = 1$

Solve. ⟶ $72\left(\frac{10}{24} + \frac{x}{36}\right) = 72(1)$

$$30 + 2x = 72$$
$$2x = 42$$
$$x = \textbf{21 hours}$$

EXERCISES

1. An experienced roofer can roof a building alone in 20 hours. An apprentice roofer would need 30 hours working alone. How long would it take the two working together to do the job?

   12 hours

2. Two printers are used to print mailing labels. The faster printer could do the job alone in 15 hours. The slower printer would require 35 hours working alone. How long would it take for both printers together to do the job? $10\frac{1}{2}$ hours

3. It takes 1000 hours for a worker to enter names and addresses into a computer disk. After 450 hours this worker was replaced by a second worker who could do the entire job in 800 hours. How long did the second worker take to finish the job?   440 hours

4. A gravity drain can drain the city pool in 5 hours. A pump could drain the pool in 3 hours. Both methods were used together for one hour until the pump broke. How many hours were needed for the gravity drain to complete the job? $2\frac{1}{3}$ more hours

   $(3\frac{1}{3}$ hours in all)

396

CHAPTER SUMMARY

IMPORTANT TERMS	Least common multiple of counting numbers *(p. 378)* Least common multiple of polynomials *(p. 378)*

IMPORTANT IDEAS

1. Sum and Difference Rules for Rational Expressions:

If $\dfrac{a}{c}$ and $\dfrac{b}{c}$ are rational expressions, then

$$\frac{a}{c} + \frac{b}{c} = \frac{a+b}{c} \quad \text{and} \quad \frac{a}{c} - \frac{b}{c} = \frac{a-b}{c}. \ (c \neq 0)$$

2. The least common multiple of prime polynomials is their product.

3. Steps in finding the *LCM* of two or more polynomials:
   a. Write the prime factorization of each polynomial.
   b. Write a product using each prime factorization only once.
   c. For each factor, write the greatest exponent used in any prime factorization.
   d. Multiply.

4. Steps in adding or subtracting rational expressions:
   a. Factor the denominators.
   b. Determine the *LCM*.
   c. Change the rational expressions to equivalent expressions with the *LCM* as the denominator of each.
   d. Add or subtract.
   e. Simplify.

5. Steps in solving an equation with rational expressions:
   a. Exclude numbers from the domain that will make zero divisors.
   b. Multiply each side by the *LCM* of the denominators.
   c. Solve the resulting equation.

CHAPTER REVIEW

NOTE: The Teacher's Resource Book contains two forms of each Chapter Test.

SECTION 15.1

Add or subtract.

1. $\dfrac{13}{3x} - \dfrac{5}{3x}$ $\tfrac{8}{3x}$

2. $\dfrac{3}{5a} + \dfrac{1}{5a}$ $\tfrac{4}{5a}$

3. $\dfrac{2a}{a+5} - \dfrac{a}{a+5}$ $\tfrac{a}{a+5}$

4. $\dfrac{b}{b+2} + \dfrac{-3b}{b+2}$

$\tfrac{-2b}{b+2}$

SECTION 15.2

Add or subtract. Simplify where necessary.

5. $\dfrac{x+1}{2x+3} + \dfrac{x+2}{2x+3}$ 1

6. $\dfrac{3x+1}{x-1} - \dfrac{x+3}{x-1}$ 2

7. $\dfrac{3a+1}{5a-1} - \dfrac{a-3}{5a-1}$

$\tfrac{2(a+2)}{5a-1}$

8. $\dfrac{a-5}{3a+2}+\dfrac{5a+2}{3a+2}$ $\dfrac{6a-3}{3a+2}$ **9.** $\dfrac{5x-4}{2x-3}-\dfrac{x+2}{2x-3}$ 2   **10.** $\dfrac{8x+3}{5x-1}-\dfrac{-2x+5}{5x-1}$ 2

SECTION 15.3

Find each LCM.

11. $2x;\ 3x\ ;\ x-2$ $6x(x-2)$ **12.** $5a;\ 10a^2;\ a+5$ $10a^2(a+5)$ $y^2(y-2)(y-3)$
13. $y-2;\ y-3;\ y^2$

14. $b+2;\ b+5;\ 3b$ **15.** $y^2-4;\ y+2;\ 2$ $2(y+2)(y-2)$ **16.** $a^2-9;\ a-3;\ 3a$
$3b(b+2)(b+5)$ $3a(a+3)(a-3)$

SECTION 15.4

Add or subtract.

17. $\dfrac{1}{2a}+\dfrac{1}{3a}$ $\dfrac{5}{6a}$ **18.** $\dfrac{5}{4x}+\dfrac{3}{10x}$ $\dfrac{31}{20x}$ **19.** $\dfrac{3}{4x}-\dfrac{5}{6y}$ $\dfrac{9y-10x}{12xy}$ **20.** $\dfrac{5}{8a}-\dfrac{7}{12b}$
$\dfrac{15b-14a}{24ab}$

SECTION 15.5

Add or subtract.

$\dfrac{4a^2-23a+3}{(a+7)(a-3)}$

21. $\dfrac{1}{a+b}+\dfrac{a}{a-b}$ $\dfrac{a^2+ab+a-b}{(a+b)(a-b)}$ **22.** $\dfrac{1}{2x+3}+\dfrac{3}{x-1}$ $\dfrac{7x+8}{(2x+3)(x-1)}$ **23.** $\dfrac{5a-1}{a+7}-\dfrac{a}{a-3}$

24. $\dfrac{y+1}{y-1}-\dfrac{1}{y+3}$ $\dfrac{y^2+3y+4}{(y-1)(y+3)}$ **25.** $\dfrac{x-2}{x+1}+\dfrac{x-3}{x+2}$ $\dfrac{2x^2-2x-7}{(x+1)(x+2)}$ **26.** $\dfrac{x+4}{x+2}+\dfrac{x-5}{x-4}$

$\dfrac{2x^2-3x-26}{(x+2)(x-4)}$

SECTION 15.6

Add or subtract.

$\dfrac{-9x+16}{(2x+3)(2x-3)}$

27. $\dfrac{1}{3x+6}+\dfrac{x-1}{x+2}$ $\dfrac{3x-2}{3(x+2)}$ **28.** $\dfrac{2}{x-3}+\dfrac{x+1}{x^2-3x}$ $\dfrac{3x+1}{x(x-3)}$ **29.** $\dfrac{x+1}{4x^2-9}-\dfrac{5}{2x+3}$

30. $\dfrac{3}{x+y}-\dfrac{2x+y}{x^2-y^2}$ **31.** $\dfrac{2}{x^2-2x+1}+\dfrac{3}{x^2+x}$ **32.** $\dfrac{4}{x^2-x-2}+\dfrac{1}{x^2-2x}$

30. $\dfrac{x-4y}{(x+y)(x-y)}$ $\dfrac{5x^2-4x+3}{x(x-1)(x-1)(x+1)}$ $\dfrac{5x+1}{x(x-2)(x+1)}$

SECTION 15.7

Solve and check each equation.

33. $\dfrac{2}{x-3}=3$ $\left\{\dfrac{11}{3}\right\}$ **34.** $\dfrac{10}{2x-1}=2$ $\{3\}$ **35.** $\dfrac{3}{x}=\dfrac{1}{x+5}$ $\left\{-\dfrac{15}{2}\right\}$

36. $\dfrac{4}{3x}=\dfrac{2}{x+1}$ $\{2\}$ **37.** $\dfrac{5}{x+2}=\dfrac{6}{x+2}$ ϕ **38.** $\dfrac{1}{x-5}=\dfrac{2}{x-5}$ ϕ

Systems of Inequalities

Sections   **16.1**   Inequalities in Two Variables

16.2   Graphs of Inequalities with < and >

16.3   Graphs of Inequalities with ≤ and ≥

16.4   Graphs of Systems of Inequalities

16.5   Systems of Three or More Inequalities

Features   *Calculator Exercises:* Checking Inequalities

Career: Production Planner

Review and Testing   *Review Capsules*

Mid-Chapter Review

Chapter Summary

Chapter Review

16.1 Inequalities in Two Variables

OBJECTIVES: To write ordered pairs that are in the solution set of a given inequality
To write the slope-intercept form of a given inequality

These three inequalities are examples of **linear inequalities**.

a. $y < 2x - 5$ **b.** $x - 3y + 2 > 0$ **c.** $-x + 2y + 1 \leq 0$

You can see that if you replace each inequality symbol by "=", you obtain three linear equations.

> The **solution set of a linear inequality** is the set of ordered pairs (x, y) that make the inequality true.

A linear inequality is the rule for a relation. ◀ *A relation is a set of ordered pairs.*

P-1 **What is one ordered pair in the solution set of $y < 2x - 5$?**

Many answers are possible, $(2, -1\frac{1}{2})$ is one answer.

example 1

Write three ordered pairs having different x values for $-2x + y - 1 \leq 0$.

Solution:

1. Let $x = 0.$ ⟶ $-2(0) + y - 1 \leq 0$

   $y - 1 \leq 0$

   $y \leq 1$ ◀ *Infinitely many y values*

   Choose a value for y that is less than or equal to 1. ◀ *The first ordered pair can be (0, 1), (0, 0.3), (0, -2), etc.*

2. Let $x = 2.7.$ ⟶ $-2(2.7) + y - 1 \leq 0$

   $-5.4 + y - 1 \leq 0$

   $y - 6.4 \leq 0$

   $y \leq 6.4$

   Choose a value for y that is less than or equal to 6.4. ◀ *The second ordered pair can be (2.7, 6.2), (2.7, 0), (2.7, -1), etc.*

3. Let $x = -3\frac{1}{2}.$ ⟶ $-2(-3\frac{1}{2}) + y - 1 \leq 0$

   $7 + y - 1 \leq 0$

   $y \leq -6$

   Choose a value for y that is less than or equal to -6. ◀ *The third ordered pair can be $(-3\frac{1}{2}, -6)$, $(-3\frac{1}{2}, -7)$, etc.*

A linear inequality can be written in <u>slope-intercept form</u>.

> The **slope-intercept form** of a linear inequality is one of the following:
>
> $$y < ax + b \qquad y > ax + b$$
> $$y \leq ax + b \qquad y \geq ax + b$$
>
> $$y \leq -2x + 7$$
> $$y > \tfrac{1}{2}x - \tfrac{5}{2}$$

example 2

Write the slope-intercept form of $2x + y < 5$.

Solution: $\qquad\qquad\qquad\qquad 2x + y < 5$

1. Addition Property of Order $\longrightarrow 2x + y + (-2x) < 5 + (-2x)$
2. Simplify. $\longrightarrow y < 5 + (-2x)$
3. Commutative Property of Addition $\longrightarrow y < -2x + 5$ ◀ **Slope-intercept form**

example 3

Write the slope-intercept form of $-3x - 5y + 2 \geq 0$.

Solution: $\qquad\qquad\qquad\qquad -3x - 5y + 2 \geq 0$

1. Add $3x$ to each side. $\longrightarrow -3x - 5y + 2 + 3x \geq 0 + 3x$
2. Simplify. $\longrightarrow -5y + 2 \geq 3x$
3. Subtract 2 from each side. $\longrightarrow -5y + 2 - 2 \geq 3x - 2$
4. Simplify. $\longrightarrow -5y \geq 3x - 2$
5. Multiply each side by $-\tfrac{1}{5}$. $\longrightarrow -\tfrac{1}{5}(-5y) \leq -\tfrac{1}{5}(3x - 2)$
6. Simplify. $\longrightarrow y \leq -\tfrac{3}{5}x + \tfrac{2}{5}$

◀ Discuss other possible steps, e.g. add $5y$ to each side as the first step. **The direction is reversed.**

CLASSROOM EXERCISES

Write three ordered pairs having different x values for each inequality.
(Example 1) In Ex. 1-8 many other answers are possible.

1. $y < x + 1$ $(-2, -3),$

2. $y < 2x - 1$ $(1, 0), (3, 1),$ $(4, 6)$

3. $y < -x + 2$ $(-3, 4), (0, \tfrac{1}{2}),$ $(1, 0)$

4. $y < x$ $(3, -1), (-2, -4),$ $(0, -\tfrac{1}{2})$

5. $y < -x$ $(0, \tfrac{1}{2}), (2, -3),$ $(-2, 1), (0, -\tfrac{1}{3}), (2, -3)$

6. $y > 3x + 5$ $(-1, 4), (0, 7), (2, 18)$

7. $y > \tfrac{1}{2}x + 3$ $(-2, 4), (1, 4), (2, 4\tfrac{1}{2})$

8. $y \leq \tfrac{1}{3}x + 1$ $(-2, 0), (3, 2), (6, 3)$

Tell the slope-intercept form of each inequality. (Examples 2 and 3)

9. $-2x + y - 1 < 0$ $y < 2x + 1$ **10.** $3x + y > 2$ $y > -3x + 2$ **11.** $-3x + y - 2 \le 0$ $y \le 3x + 2$

12. $y + 5 \ge \frac{1}{2}x$ $y \ge \frac{1}{2}x - 5$ **13.** $-y - x > 10$ $y < -x - 10$ **14.** $2y < 2x + 4$ $y < x + 2$

WRITTEN EXERCISES

See the Teacher's Manual for the suggested assignments.

Goals: To write ordered pairs in the solution set of a given inequality and to write the slope-intercept form of the inequality

Sample Problems: a. Write three ordered pairs in the solution set of $-2x + 3y + 5 > 0$.

   b. Write the slope-intercept form of $-2x + 3y + 5 > 0$.

Answers: a. $(0, 0)$, $(\frac{5}{2}, 3)$, $(-1, -2)$, etc.   **b.** $y > \frac{2}{3}x - \frac{5}{3}$

6. $(-4, 3)$, $(-2, 3)$, $(0, 3\frac{1}{2})$, $(3, 5)$, $(-1, 4\frac{1}{2})$

9. $(2, 25)$, $(-2, -18)$, $(-1, -6)$, $(0, 2)$, $(1, 12)$

Write five ordered pairs having different x values for each inequality.
(Example 1)   In Ex. 1-12 many other answers are possible.

3. $(-2, 7)$, $(-1, 5)$, $(0, 2)$, $(1, -1)$, $(3, -8)$

1. $y < 2x$ $(-1, -3)$, $(0, -2)$, $(1, 1)$, $(2, 1)$, $(3, 4)$ **2.** $y < -5x$ $(-2, 8)$, $(0, -\frac{1}{2})$, $(1, -7)$, $(2, -15)$, $(3, -16)$ **3.** $y \ge -3x + 1$

4. $y \ge 2x - 5$ $(-3, -10)$, $(-2, -9)$, $(0, -3)$, $(1, -1)$, $(2, -1)$ **5.** $y < \frac{1}{2}x - 3$ See below.   **6.** $y > \frac{1}{3}x + 3$ See above.

7. $x + y \ge -2$ $(-3, 2)$, $(-1, -1)$, $(0, -1)$, $(2, -3)$, $(3, 2)$ **8.** $x - y \le 4$ $(-2, 0)$, $(-1, -3)$, $(0, -4)$, $(1, 0)$, $(2, 1)$ **9.** $y \ge 10x + 2$ See above.

10. $x + y \le 3$ $(-4, 5)$, $(-2, 5)$, $(0, 3)$, $(1, 2)$, $(2, 1)$ **11.** $-2x + 3y - 5 > 0$ $(-3, 0)$, $(0, 2)$, $(1, 3)$, $(3, 4)$, $(4, 10)$ **12.** $4x - y + 3 < 0$ $(-3, -8)$, $(-2, -1)$, $(0, 3\frac{1}{2})$, $(1, 10)$, $(2, 12)$

Write the slope-intercept form of each inequality. (Examples 2 and 3)

13. $-3x + y - 5 > 0$ $y > 3x + 5$ **14.** $2x + y + 3 < 0$ $y < -2x - 3$ **15.** $4x + y \le 6$ $y \le -4x + 6$

16. $-5x + y \ge -2$ $y \ge 5x - 2$ **17.** $x - y < -3$ $y > x + 3$ **18.** $3x - y > 7$

19. $\frac{1}{3}y > x - 5$ $y > 3x - 15$ **20.** $-\frac{1}{5}y \le -x + 2$ $y \ge 5x - 10$ **21.** $2x + 3y - 6 \ge 0$

22. $-5x + 2y + 3 \le 0$ $y \le \frac{5}{2}x - \frac{3}{2}$ **23.** $4x - 2y < 5$ $y > 2x - \frac{5}{2}$ **24.** $6x - 3y + 2 > 0$

25. $-7x + 14y - 3 \ge 0$ $y \ge \frac{1}{2}x + \frac{3}{14}$ **26.** $-9x + 27y > 3$ $y > \frac{1}{3}x + \frac{1}{9}$ **27.** $3y + 5x - 1 < 0$ $y < -\frac{5}{3}x + \frac{1}{3}$

> See below

5. $(-2, -5)$, $(-1, -4)$, $(0, -6)$, $(1, -3)$, $(4, -2)$

REVIEW CAPSULE FOR SECTION 16.2

In Ex. 1-8, each graph is a straight line. Two points of each line are given.

Graph each equation. (Section 12.2)

1. $y = -x + 2$ $(0, 2)$, $(1, 1)$ **2.** $y = 2x - 1$ $(0, -1)$, $(2, 3)$ **3.** $y = \frac{3}{2}x - 3$ $(0, -3)$, $(2, 0)$ **4.** $y = \frac{5}{4}x + 2$ $(0, 2)$, $(4, 7)$

5. $y = \frac{1}{2}x + \frac{3}{2}$ $(0, \frac{3}{2})$, $(1, 2)$ **6.** $y = -3x - 1$ $(0, -1)$, $(-2, 5)$ **7.** $y = -2$ $(0, -2)$, $(-3, -2)$ **8.** $x = -3$ $(-3, 0)$, $(-3, 4)$

18. $y < 3x - 7$ 21. $y \ge -\frac{2}{3}x + 2$ 24. $y < 2x + \frac{2}{3}$

16.2 Graphs of Inequalities with < and >

OBJECTIVES: To graph an inequality involving $\leq$
To graph an inequality involving $>$

Every linear inequality has a related linear equation.

Inequality: $y < 2x - 1$ **Related Equation:** $y = 2x - 1$

The graph of $y = 2x - 1$ is shown
in Figure 1. The line separates
the coordinate plane into three
sets of points or **regions**.

a. One region is one side of the line.
b. One region is the other side of the
line.
c. One region is the line itself.

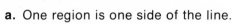

The region in which $y > 2x - 1$ **Figure 1**

P-1   **In which region is the point with coordinates (0, 0)?   the point with
coordinates (2, 3)?   the point with coordinates (5, −3)?**

The line $y = 2x - 1$ The region in which $y < 2x - 1$

(2, 3) is in the solution set of $y = 2x - 1$.
(0, 0) is in the solution set of $y > 2x - 1$.
(5, −3) is in the solution set of $y < 2x - 1$.

In Figure 1, the region above, and to the left of, the line is the
graph of $y > 2x - 1$. The region below, and to the right of, the
line is the graph of $y < 2x - 1$.

In graphing inequalities that contain > or <, you must remember that
the line is <u>not</u> part of the graph. Therefore, the graph of the related
equation is drawn as a <u>dashed line</u>.

The shaded region contains
all points and only those
points with ordered pairs
that are in the solution set

example 1   Graph $y < 2x - 1$.   ◄ *"To graph"* of the inequality.
means *"to graph
the solution set of."*

Solution:

☐1 Graph the related equation
$y = 2x - 1$. Use a dashed line.

☐2 Shade the region of the plane
to the right of the dashed line.

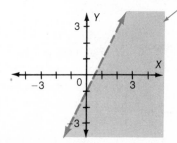

Systems of Inequalities / **403**

example 2

Graph $x + y - 1 > 0$.

Solution:

1. Write the slope-intercept form. ⟶ $y > -x + 1$

2. Graph the related equation $y = -x + 1$ as a dashed line as in Figure 2.

3. Choose a point not on the line. Check whether its coordinates make the inequality true or false.

$y > -x + 1$　◀ **Try the origin, (0, 0).**

$0 > -0 + 1$

$0 > 1$　◀ **False sentence**

The origin is not in the graph.

4. Shade the region on the side of the line not containing the origin as in Figure 3.

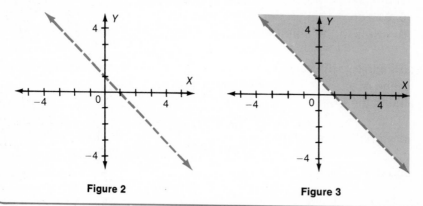

Figure 2　　　　Figure 3

Steps for graphing the relations $y < ax + b$ and $y > ax + b$:

1. Draw the graph of $y = ax + b$.
2. Select a point not on the line and substitute its coordinates in the inequality.
3. Shade the region of the plane containing this point if its coordinates make the inequality true.
4. Shade the region on the other side of the line from this point if its coordinates make the inequality false.

CLASSROOM EXERCISES

Say <u>Yes</u> *or* <u>No</u> *to tell whether (0, 0) is in each solution set.* (P-1)

1. $y < 2x + 5$ Yes

2. $y > x - 1$ Yes

3. $y < -2x - 3$ No

4. $y < 3x$ No

5. $y = 5x$ Yes

6. $y > -\frac{1}{2}x - \frac{2}{3}$ Yes

7. $y > 3$ No

8. $x < -2$ No

Tell an inequality for each graph. The equation of each dashed line is given.

9.

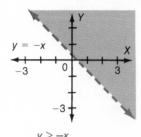

$y = -x$

$y > -x$

10.

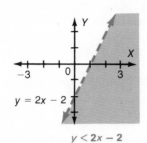

$y = 2x - 2$

$y < 2x - 2$

11.

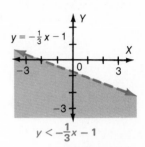

$y = -\frac{1}{3}x - 1$

$y < -\frac{1}{3}x - 1$

WRITTEN EXERCISES

See the Teacher's Manual for the suggested assignments.

Goal: To graph linear inequalities that use $>$ or $<$

Sample Problem: $x + y - 3 > 0$

Answer: See the graph at the right.

In Ex. 1-18, each graph is a region that does not include the linear boundary.

Graph each inequality. (Examples 1 and 2)

1. $y < 3x - 1$ The region is at the right of the boundary.

2. $y < -2x + 2$ left of the boundary

3. $y > -x + 3$ right of the boundary

4. $y > x - 3$ left of the boundary

5. $y < \frac{1}{2}x - 3$ right of the boundary

6. $y < -\frac{1}{2}x - 1$ left of the boundary

7. $y < x$ right of the boundary

8. $y > -x$ right of the boundary

9. $y > -3$ above the boundary

10. $y < -2$ below the boundary

11. $3x + y - 2 < 0$ left of the boundary

12. $-2x + y + 3 < 0$ right of the boundary

13. $x < -2$ left of the boundary

14. $x > -3$ right of the boundary

15. $-3x + 2y - 2 > 0$ left of the boundary

16. $4x + 2y - 3 > 0$ right of the boundary

17. $3x - 4y - 12 < 0$ left of the boundary

18. $2x - y + 4 > 0$ right of the boundary

REVIEW CAPSULE FOR SECTION 16.3

Write as one inequality using $\leq$ *or* $\geq$. (Section 5.1)

1. $y < 2$ <u>or</u> $y = 2$ $y \leq 2$

2. $y < x - 5$ <u>or</u> $y = x - 5$ $y \leq x - 5$

3. $y > 2x$ <u>or</u> $y = 2x$ $y \geq 2x$

4. $y = \frac{1}{2} - 3x$ <u>or</u> $y > \frac{1}{2} - 3x$ $y \geq \frac{1}{2} - 3x$

5. $y = -x + 1$ <u>or</u> $y < -x + 1$ $y \leq -x + 1$

6. $y > 2 - x$ <u>or</u> $y = 2 - x$ $y \geq 2 - x$

16.3 Graphs of Inequalities with ≤ and ≥

Mathematical sentences can be classified as <u>simple</u> or <u>compound</u>. An important example of a compound sentence is the *or* sentence.

Simple Sentences	Compound *Or* Sentences
$x > 9$	$x > 1$ *or* $x = -5$
$x = -2$	$x < 4$ *or* $x = 6$
$x < 6$	$x > -3$ *or* $x = -3$

◀ *This can also be shown as $x \geq -3$.*

P-1   **What are some numbers in the solution set of $x > -3$?**

−2.9, −1, 12, 473, etc.

$\{x : x > -3\}$

$$\xleftarrow{\quad}\overset{\circ}{\underset{-4\ -3\ -2\ -1\ \ 0\ \ 1\ \ 2\ \ 3\ \ 4}{\vphantom{|}}}\xrightarrow{\quad}$$

P-2   **Find the only number in the solution set of $x = -3$.**   −3

$\{x : x = -3\}$

$$\xleftarrow{\quad}\overset{\bullet}{\underset{-4\ -3\ -2\ -1\ \ 0\ \ 1\ \ 2\ \ 3\ \ 4}{\vphantom{|}}}\xrightarrow{\quad}$$

The **union of two sets** is the set of elements in either one of the two sets or in both of them.

$$\{1, 3, 5\} \cup \{2, 3, 4\} = \{1, 2, 3, 4, 5\}$$

◀ *$A \cup B$ means "the union of A and B."*

The **solution set of a compound <u>or</u> sentence** is the union of the solution sets of its two simple sentences.

P-3   **What are some numbers in the solution set of the compound *or* sentence "$x > -3$ *or* $x = -3$"?**   −3, −2.7, 0, 5, etc.

$\{x : x > -3$ *or* $x = -3\}$

$$\xleftarrow{\quad}\underset{-4\ -3\ -2\ -1\ \ 0\ \ 1\ \ 2\ \ 3\ \ 4}{\vphantom{|}}\xrightarrow{\quad}$$

When a compound *or* sentence has *two* variables its graph is drawn in a coordinate plane.

(−2, 4), (−1, 3), (0, 2), (1, 1), etc.

P-4   **What are some ordered pairs in the solution set of $x + y = 2$? of $x + y < 2$?**   (−2, 3), (−1, 2), (0, 1), (1, 0), etc.

Emphasize this distinction between graphs of inequalities containing < or >.

In graphing inequalities that contain ≥ or ≤, you must remember that the line <u>is</u> part of the graph. Therefore, the graph of the related equation is drawn as a <u>solid line</u>.

example 1

Graph $x + y \leq 2$.

$$\begin{array}{c} x + y < 2 \\ \textit{or} \\ x + y = 2 \end{array}$$

Solution:

1. Write the slope-intercept form. $\longrightarrow$ $y \leq -x + 2$

2. Graph $y = -x + 2$.

3. Choose a point not on the line such as the origin, $(0, 0)$. Check whether its coordinates make $y < -x + 2$ true or false.

    $y < -x + 2$

    $0 < -0 + 2$

    $0 < 2$ **True sentence**

4. Shade the region on the side of the line containing the origin.

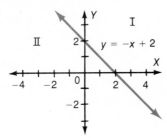 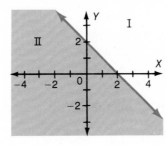

The graph is the union of the solid line and Region II.

---

example 2

Graph $x + 2y - 2 \geq 0$.

$$\begin{array}{c} x + 2y - 2 > 0 \\ \textit{or} \\ x + 2y - 2 = 0 \end{array}$$

Solution:

1. Write the slope-intercept form. $\longrightarrow$ $y \geq -\frac{1}{2}x + 1$

2. Graph $y = -\frac{1}{2}x + 1$.

3. Choose a point not on the line such as the origin, $(0, 0)$. Check whether its coordinates make $y > -\frac{1}{2}x + 1$ true or false.

    $y > -\frac{1}{2}x + 1$

    $0 > -\frac{1}{2}(0) + 1$

    $0 > 1$ **False sentence**

4. Shade Region I above the line. It does not contain the origin.

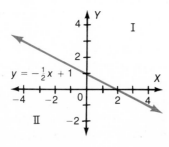 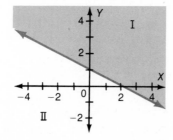

The graph is the union of the solid line and Region I.

example 3

Write the slope-intercept form of the inequality that is graphed below. The slope a of the line is $\frac{1}{2}$.

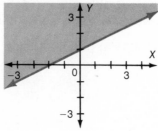

Solution:

It is clear from the graph that the point with the coordinates (0, 2), for example, is in the graph.

The Y intercept of the line is 1 as shown on the graph.

Equation of the line: $y = ax + b$

$$y = \tfrac{1}{2}x + 1$$

Inequality: $y \geq \tfrac{1}{2}x + 1$ ◀ **The region above the line is shaded.**

Note, as a check, that the point with coordinates (0, 2) makes the inequality true.

CLASSROOM EXERCISES

Write Yes or No to indicate whether (0, 0) is in each solution set. (Step 3 of Example 1)

1. $y \leq x + 1$ Yes

2. $y \leq -x - 1$ No

3. $y \leq 2x + 3$ Yes

4. $y \leq -5x + 1$ Yes

5. $y \geq x$ Yes

6. $y \leq -x$ Yes

7. $x + 2y - 5 \leq 0$ Yes

8. $-2x + 3y - 1 \geq 0$ No

9. $x + y \geq -2$ Yes

Write the slope-intercept form for each graph. The slope, a, of each line is given. (Example 3)

10. $a = 1$ $y \leq x$

11. $a = -1$ $y \geq -x$

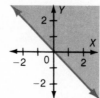

12. $a = -\frac{1}{2}$ $y \leq -\frac{1}{2}x$

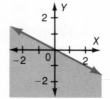

13. $a = \frac{1}{2}$ $y \leq \frac{1}{2}x + 1$

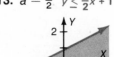

WRITTEN EXERCISES

See the Teacher's Manual for the suggested assignments.

Goal: To graph inequalities in two variables that use $\geq$ or $\leq$

Sample Problem: $x + y \leq 3$

Answer: See the graph at the right.

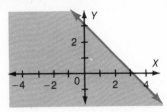

In Ex. 1-18, each graph is a region that has a straight line as its boundary. The boundary is included in Ex. 1-16, but not in the graphs of Ex. 17 and Ex. 18.

Graph each inequality. (Examples 1 and 2)

1. $y \leq x + 1$ The region is at the right of the boundary.

2. $y \leq -x + 1$ The region is at the left of the boundary.

3. $y \leq 2x - 3$ right of the boundary

4. $y \leq 3x - 2$ right of the boundary

5. $y \geq -2x + 1$ right of the boundary

6. $y \geq -3x - 1$ right of the boundary

7. $-\frac{1}{2}x + y - 1 \leq 0$ right of the boundary

8. $\frac{1}{2}x + y + 2 \leq 0$ left of the boundary

9. $2x + 2y - 3 \geq 0$ right of the boundary

10. $3x + 3y - 6 \geq 0$ right of the boundary

11. $-\frac{1}{3}x + y \leq 1$ right of the boundary

12. $-\frac{1}{4}x + y \leq -2$ right of the boundary

13. $y \geq -1$ above boundary

14. $y \leq -2$ below boundary

15. $x \leq 3$ left of boundary

16. $x \geq -3$ right of boundary

17. $x > -y + 2$ right of boundary

18. $x < -y - 3$ left of boundary

Write the slope-intercept form of an inequality for each graph. The slope, a, of each line is given. (Example 3)

19. $a = 1$ $y \leq x + 1$

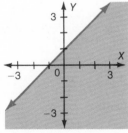

20. $a = -1$ $y \geq -x - 1$

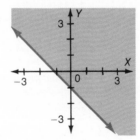

21. $a = -2$ $y \geq -2x - 2$

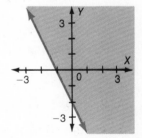

22. $a \cdot = 2$ $y \leq 2x + 2$

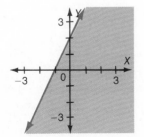

23. $a = -\frac{1}{3}$ $y \leq -\frac{1}{3}x + 1$

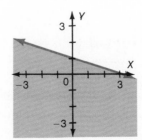

24. $a = \frac{1}{2}$ $y \geq \frac{1}{2}x + 1$

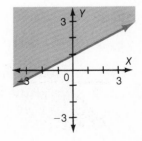

MID-CHAPTER REVIEW

NOTE: After completing the Mid-Chapter Review you may want to administer a quiz covering the same sections. See pages M-40 and M-41 of the Teacher's Manual for the suggested quiz

Write the slope-intercept form of each inequality. (Section 16.1) $y < \frac{3}{2}x + \frac{5}{2}$

1. $5x + y - 2 < 0$ $y < -5x + 2$ **2.** $-2x + y + 6 > 0$ $y > 2x - 6$ **3.** $3x - 2y > -5$

4. $-5x + 3y < 8$ $y < \frac{5}{3}x + \frac{8}{3}$ **5.** $-3 > -8x + 6y$ $y < \frac{4}{3}x - \frac{1}{2}$ **6.** $12 < 20x - 8y$
$y < \frac{5}{2}x - \frac{3}{2}$

Graph each inequality. (Section 16.2)   In Ex. 7-12, each graph is a region that does not include its linear boundary.

7. $y > 2x + 3$ The region is to the left of the boundary.   **8.** $y < 3x - 2$ right of the boundary   **9.** $y < \frac{1}{2}x - 2$ right of the boundary

10. $y > -\frac{1}{3}x + 1$ right of the boundary   **11.** $2x - y + 5 < 0$ left of the boundary   **12.** $-3x + y - 3 > 0$ left of the boundary

Graph each inequality. (Section 16.3)   In Ex. 13-18, each graph is a region that does include its linear boundary.

13. $y \geq \frac{3}{2}x - 3$ The region is to the left of the boundary.   **14.** $y \leq -\frac{7}{4}x + 2$ left of the boundary   **15.** $y \leq -x + \frac{5}{2}$ right of the boundary

16. $y \geq -x - \frac{9}{4}$ right of the boundary   **17.** $3x - 2y + 6 \geq 0$ right of the boundary   **18.** $-4x + 2y - 5 \leq 0$ right of the boundary

 ──────── *CHECKING INEQUALITIES* ────────

You can use a calculator to check whether an ordered pair is in the solution set of an inequality. First, substitute the ordered pair in the inequality. Then compare the two sides of the inequality.

EXAMPLE   Is $(-2, 5)$ in the solution set of $6x - y > 1 + 3y$?

SOLUTION   Left side: $-17.$

Think of the right side as $3y + 1$ for easier calculation.   Right side: $16.$

 Note: Multiply before adding. See page 17.

Since "$-17 > 16$" is <u>false</u>, $(-2, 5)$ is not in the solution set.

Check whether the given ordered pair is in the solution set of the inequality.

1. $3x - 5 < 5y + 2; (3, 2)$ Yes   **2.** $4x + y > 2x - 4; (3, -7)$ Yes   **3.** $(x + 2)5 \leq x + 2y; (-5, 6)$
Yes

REVIEW CAPSULE FOR SECTION 16.4

Which of the following are in the solution sets of <u>both</u> inequalities? {$(-2, 3)$, $(0, -1)$, $(3, 5)$, $(2, -4)$, $(-4, 3)$} (Section 16.1)

1. $\begin{cases} y > 2x - 1 \\ y > \frac{1}{2}x + 3 \end{cases}$ (-2, 3), (-4, 3)   **2.** $\begin{cases} y < 4x + 3 \\ y > x - 5 \end{cases}$ (0, -1), (3, 5)   **3.** $\begin{cases} y \leq -x + 3 \\ y > -3x - 1 \end{cases}$ (2, -4)   **4.** $\begin{cases} y \geq x + 5 \\ y \leq -2x - 4 \end{cases}$ (-4, 3)

16.4 Graphs of Systems of Inequalities

OBJECTIVES: To graph a system of two linear sentences involving $<, >, \leq, \geq$, or $=$
To write a system of two linear sentences that corresponds to a given graph

P-1 **What are some numbers in the solution set of $x < 4$?** 3.8, 2, −7, etc.

$\{x : x < 4\}$

P-2 **What are some numbers in the solution set of $x > -2$?** −1.9, 0, 13, etc.

$\{x : x > -2\}$

The *intersection of two sets* is the set of elements they have in common.

$$\{1, 5, 8\} \cap \{0, 5, 10\} = \{5\}$$

◄ $A \cap B$ *means*
"the intersection
of A and B."

The *solution set of a compound **and** sentence* is the intersection of the solution sets of its simple sentences.

P-3 **What are some numbers in the solution set of the compound *and* sentence "$x < 4$ *and* $x > -2$"?** −1.9, 0, 2, 3.8, etc.

$\{x : x < 4 \text{ and } x > -2\}$

When a compound *and* sentence has two variables, its graph is drawn in a coordinate plane. A compound *and* sentence in two variables is often written as a *system of linear sentences* or, simply, as a linear system.

$$\begin{cases} 1.\ y < -x + 3 \\ 2.\ y > 3x - 1 \end{cases}$$

◄ $y < -x + 3$
and
$y > 3x - 1$

The *solution set of a system of linear sentences* is the intersection of the solution sets of the sentences.

> The *graph of the solution set of a system of sentences* is the intersection of the graphs of the sentences.

example 1

Graph the following linear system.

$$\begin{cases} \textbf{1. } y < 2x + 1 \\ \textbf{2. } y < -\tfrac{1}{2}x - 2 \end{cases}$$

$y < 2x + 1$
$\underline{\textit{and}}$
$y < -\tfrac{1}{2}x - 2$

Solution:

1. Graph $y = 2x + 1$ as the dashed line in Figure 1.

2. Shade the region below the dashed line to represent the solution set of $y < 2x + 1$.

3. Graph $y = -\tfrac{1}{2}x - 2$ as the dashed line in Figure 2.

4. Shade the region below the dashed line to represent the solution set of $y < -\tfrac{1}{2}x - 2$.

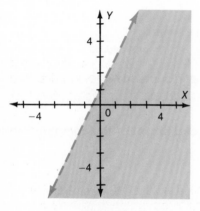

Figure 1

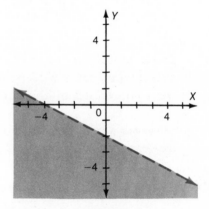

Figure 2

The graph of the solution set of the system of Example 1 is the intersection of the two graphs in Figures 1 and 2. The intersection is shown by the darkest region in Figure 3.

Discuss whether or not the point of intersection of the two dashed lines is in the graph of the system.

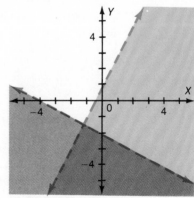

Figure 3

example 2

Graph the following linear system.

$$\begin{cases} \textbf{1. } y > 5x - 2 \\ \textbf{2. } y \geq \frac{1}{3}x \end{cases}$$

Solution:

1️⃣ Graph $y > 5x - 2$ in the coordinate plane of Figure 4.

2️⃣ Graph $y \geq \frac{1}{3}x$.

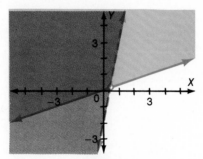

Figure 4

The graph of the solution set of the system is the region showing the darkest shading in Figure 4. A circle is drawn to emphasize that the point of intersection of the lines is not in the solution set of the system.

example 3

Write a system of linear sentences that corresponds to the graph of Figure 5.

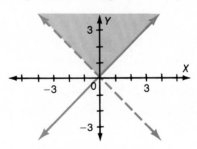

Figure 5

Solution: Inequality for points on and above the graph of $y = x$: $y \geq x$

Inequality for points above the graph of $y = -x$: $y > -x$

Discuss whether or not the origin is in the graph of the system.

System: $\begin{cases} \textbf{1. } y \geq x \\ \textbf{2. } y > -x \end{cases}$

CLASSROOM EXERCISES

Write the region that is the graph of each system.

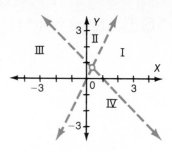

1. $\begin{cases} y < -x + 1 \\ y < 2x \end{cases}$ IV

5. $\begin{cases} y < x \\ y > -x \end{cases}$ **6.** $\begin{cases} y < x \\ y \le -x \end{cases}$

2. $\begin{cases} y > -x + 1 \\ y < 2x \end{cases}$ I

3. $\begin{cases} y > -x + 1 \\ y > 2x \end{cases}$ II

7. $\begin{cases} y \le x \\ y \ge -x \end{cases}$ **8.** $\begin{cases} y \le x \\ y < -x \end{cases}$

4. $\begin{cases} y < -x + 1 \\ y > 2x \end{cases}$ III

Write a system of linear sentences that corresponds to each graph. The equations of the lines are $y = x$ and $y = -x$. (Example 3)

5. See above.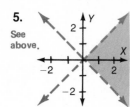

6. See above.

7. See above.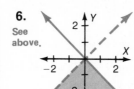

8. See above.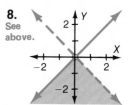

In Ex. 1-12 below, each region has two straight lines as boundaries.
Abbreviations are: Quadrants: Q; Left boundary: L; Right boundary: R; Top boundary: T; Bottom boundary: B

WRITTEN EXERCISES

See the Teacher's Manual for the suggested assignments.

Goal: To graph systems of linear sentences

Sample Problem: $\begin{cases} \text{1. } y \ge 2x + 5 \\ \text{2. } y \le -x \end{cases}$

Answer: See the graph at the right.

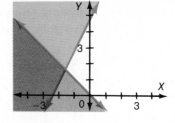

Graph each linear system. (Examples 1 and 2)

1. $\begin{cases} y < x + 1 \\ y < -x - 1 \end{cases}$ Q: III, IV; L: $y = x + 1$; R: $y = -x - 1$; Boundaries not included

2. $\begin{cases} y > -x + 1 \\ y > x - 1 \end{cases}$ Q: II, III; L: $y = -x + 1$; R: $y = x - 1$; Boundaries not included

3. $\begin{cases} y \ge 2x + 1 \\ y < -x + 2 \end{cases}$ Q: I, II, III; R: $y = 2x + 1$; B: $y = -x + 2$; Right boundary included

4. $\begin{cases} y \le \frac{1}{2}x + 2 \\ y < 3x - 1 \end{cases}$ See below.

5. $\begin{cases} x + 2y \le 4 \\ x - 2y \le -4 \end{cases}$ Q: II, III; B: $x - 2y = -4$; T: $x + 2y = 4$; Boundaries included

6. $\begin{cases} 2x + y \ge -1 \\ x - 2y \ge 2 \end{cases}$ Q: I, IV; L: $2x + y = -1$; B: $x - 2y = 2$; Boundaries included

7. $\begin{cases} x - 3y = 3 \\ 2x + y \le -1 \end{cases}$ See below.

8. $\begin{cases} 2x + y = 4 \\ x - y \le 3 \end{cases}$ See below.

9. $\begin{cases} y \le 2 \\ x < -1 \end{cases}$ Q: II, III; R: $x = -1$; B: $y = 2$; Bottom boundary included

10. $\begin{cases} y > -2 \\ x \le -3 \end{cases}$ Q: II, III; B: $y = -2$; R: $x = -3$; Right boundary included

11. $\begin{cases} y \le 3x \\ x > -1 \end{cases}$ Q: I, III, IV; L: $x = -1$; B: $y = 3x$; Bottom boundary included

12. $\begin{cases} y > -2x \\ x \le 3 \end{cases}$ See below.

4. Q: II, III, IV; B: $y = \frac{1}{2}x + 2$; L: $y = 3x - 1$; Bottom boundary included

REVIEW CAPSULE FOR SECTION 16.5

Determine whether (0, 0) is in the solution set of all three inequalities. (Section 16.1)

1. $y < x + 2$ Yes
$y > -x - 3$
$y \le -2x$

2. $y > -\frac{1}{2}x + 1$ No
$y \le \frac{3}{2}x + 3$
$y \ge -2$

3. $y \le 4$ Yes
$y \ge -\frac{1}{3}x - \frac{4}{3}$
$y \ge \frac{3}{4}x - 10$

4. $y > 1$ No
$y \le -x$
$y \ge -3x$

7. The portion of the line $x - 3y = 3$ that is in Quadrant III and on the Y axis

8. The portion of the line $2x + y = 4$ above and to the left of the point $(\frac{7}{3}, -\frac{2}{3})$; The point is included.

12. Q: I, II, IV; R: $x = 3$; L: $y = -2x$; Right boundary included

16.5 Systems of Three or More Inequalities

To find the maximum and minimum values of an expression of the form $ax + by$ in which (x, y) represents a given set of ordered pairs that are in the solution set of a system of sentences

example 1　Graph the following linear system: $\begin{cases} \textbf{1. } x \geq 0 \\ \textbf{2. } y \geq 0 \\ \textbf{3. } x + y \leq 4 \end{cases}$

Solution:　The graph of $x \geq 0$ is the X axis and all points above the X axis. The graph $y \geq 0$ is the Y axis and all points to the right of the Y axis. The graph of $x \geq 0$ and $y \geq 0$ is the first quadrant (Figure 1).

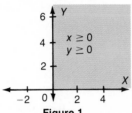
Figure 1

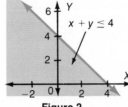
Figure 2

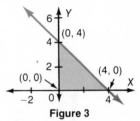
Figure 3

The solution set of the system is shown in Figure 3. Note that three lines meet to form the corners or **vertices** (singular: **vertex**) of a triangle. The solution set is the triangle with vertices (0, 0), (0, 4), and (4, 0) together with its interior.

Example 2 is preparation for doing the Career lesson on Production Planner, pages 417 and 418.

A method called **linear programming** has been developed to solve certain industrial problems. It is used to find the maximum or minimum value of an expression such as $5x + y$, where (x, y) is in the solution set of a system of inequalities.

example 2

Find the maximum and minimum values of k in $k = 5x + y$, where (x, y) is in the solution set of the system shown at the right. $\begin{cases} x \geq 0 \\ y \geq 0 \\ y - x \leq 3 \\ y - 6x \geq -12 \end{cases}$

Solution:　The graph of the system is shown at the left below. Identify the four vertices of the shaded region: (0, 0), (0, 3), (3, 6), (2, 0).

Next, check each of the coordinates in $k = 5x + y$ to find the maximum and minimum values.

Vertex	$k = 5x + y$	Value
(0, 0)	$k = 5(0) + 0$	0
(0, 3)	$k = 5(0) + 3$	3
(3, 6)	$k = 5(3) + 6$	21
(2, 0)	$k = 5(2) + 0$	10

Maximum value: 21, when $x = 3$, $y = 6$
Minimum value: 0, when $x = 0$, $y = 0$

Systems of Inequalities / 415

CLASSROOM EXERCISES

In each of Exercises 1–4 match one of the graphs in Figures A–C with the exercise or write "No Graph."

1. $\begin{cases} x \le -1 \\ y \le -1 \\ y \le -x - 2 \end{cases}$ B

2. $\begin{cases} x \ge 0 \\ y \ge 0 \\ y \le -x + 2 \end{cases}$ A

3. $\begin{cases} x \le 2 \\ y \ge 2 \\ x \le -2 \\ y \le -2 \end{cases}$ No graph

4. $\begin{cases} x < 1 \\ y < 1 \\ x > -1 \\ y > -1 \end{cases}$ C

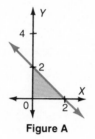

Figure A

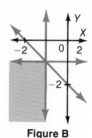

Figure B

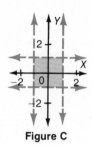

Figure C

4. Triangle
   Vertices: $(-5, 3)$, $(3, 2)$, $(3, -5)$

8. Trapezoid
   Vertices: $(5, 0)$, $(5, 1)$, $(-2, 8)$, $(2, 0)$

WRITTEN EXERCISES

See the Teacher's Manual for the suggested assignments.

Goal: To graph the solution set of a system of three or more linear inequalities

Sample Problem: $\begin{cases} x \ge 0 \\ y \ge 0 \\ x \le 3 \\ y \le 2 \end{cases}$ **Answer:** See graph at the right.

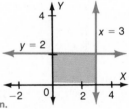

In Ex. 1-8, the name of the polygon formed by the linear system is given. The coordinates of the vertices are also given. All lines are included in the region.

Graph each linear system. (Example 1)

1. $\begin{cases} x \ge 0 \\ y \ge 0 \\ x + y \le 5 \end{cases}$ Triangle Vertices: $(0, 0)$, $(5, 0)$, $(0, 5)$

2. $\begin{cases} x \ge 0 \\ y \ge 0 \\ y \le 3 - x \end{cases}$ Triangle Vertices: $(0, 0)$, $(3, 0)$, $(0, 3)$

3. $\begin{cases} y \le 2 \\ y \ge -x - 1 \\ x \le 2 \end{cases}$ Triangle Vertices: $(2, 2)$, $(2, -3)$, $(-3, 2)$

4. $\begin{cases} y \ge -x - 2 \\ y \le 2 \\ x \le 3 \end{cases}$ See above.

5. $\begin{cases} x \le 2 \\ y \ge -3 \\ x \ge -3 \\ y \le 1 \end{cases}$ Rectangle Vertices: $(2, -3)$, $(-3, -3)$, $(-3, 1)$, $(2, 1)$

6. $\begin{cases} y \ge -3 \\ y \le 2 \\ x \le 1 \\ x \ge -3 \end{cases}$ Rectangle Vertices: $(1, -3)$, $(1, 2)$, $(-3, 2)$, $(-3, -3)$

7. $\begin{cases} y \ge -2 \\ y \le x + 2 \\ y \le 2 \\ y \le -x + 4 \end{cases}$ Trapezoid Vertices: $(0, 2)$, $(2, 2)$, $(-4, -2)$, $(6, -2)$

8. $\begin{cases} x \le 5 \\ y \ge 0 \\ x + y \le 6 \\ 2x + y \ge 4 \end{cases}$ See above.

In Exercises 9–12, the vertices of a shaded region are given. Find the maximum and minimum values of k for each given expression involving x and y. (Example 2)

9. Vertices: $(0, 0)$, $(0, 5)$, $(6, 0)$; $k = 4x + y$ Max: 24, when $x = 6$, $y = 0$; min: 0, when $x = 0$, $y = 0$

10. Vertices: $(0, 0)$, $(0, 6)$, $(4, 8)$, $(2, 0)$; $k = 4x + y$ Max: 24, when $x = 4$, $y = 8$; min: 0, when $x = 0$, $y = 0$

11. Vertices: $(1, -1)$ $(0, 2)$, $(3, 0)$; $y = 2x + 3k$ Max: $\frac{2}{3}$, when $x = 0$, $y = 2$; min: -2, when $x = 3$, $y = 0$

12. Vertices: $(1, 1)$, $(0, 4)$, $(4, 5)$, $(3, 0)$; $y = -x + k$ Max: 9, when $x = 4$, $y = 5$; min: 2, when $x = 1$, $y = 1$

Production Planner

In large manufacturing companies there may be <u>production planners</u> or <u>industrial</u> or <u>production technicians</u> who plan the layout of machinery and movement of materials in order to obtain the most efficient way of operating.

A method called <u>linear programming</u> (see page 415) has been developed for solving some of these problems. It is based on the solution of systems of linear inequalities.

EXAMPLE: A cement mixing company has two plants. There are 5 trucks at Plant I and 10 trucks at Plant II. The company must supply mixed cement for two building sites A and B. Site A can handle 8 trucks, and Site B can handle 4. The company's production planner must decide how many trucks to send from each plant to each building site in order to make transportation costs as small as possible. How many trucks should be sent from each plant to each site?

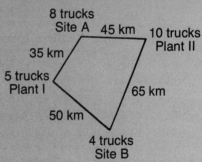

SOLUTION: Prepare a table showing the facts of the problem with the unknowns represented by two variables.

From Plant	To Site	Distance	Number of Trucks	Total Distance
I	A	35 km	x	$35x$
I	B	50 km	y	$50y$
II	A	45 km	$8 - x$	$45(8 - x)$
II	B	65 km	$4 - y$	$65(4 - y)$

Next, write a system of inequalities for the problem. Graph the system. In each case the number of trucks used must be greater than or equal to zero. Thus, six inequalities can be written.

1. $x \geq 0$
2. $y \geq 0$
3. $8 - x \geq 0$
   or, $x \leq 8$
4. $4 - y \geq 0$
   or, $y \leq 4$
5. $x + y \leq 5$
6. $(8 - x) + (4 - y) \leq 10$
   or, $x + y \geq 2$

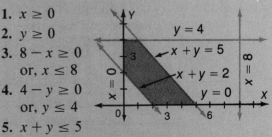

Represent the total distance by an algebraic expression.

Total Distance $= 35x + 50y + 45(8 - x) + 65(4 - y)$
$$= 620 - 10x - 15y$$

This distance must have a minimum value. Find the minimum value by substituting the x and y values of the five vertices of the polygon shown in the graph.

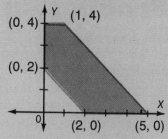

Vertex	Total Distance
(2, 0)	$620 - 10(2) - 15(0) = 600$ kilometers
(5, 0)	$620 - 10(5) - 15(0) = 605$ kilometers
(1, 4)	$620 - 10(1) - 15(4) = 550$ kilometers
(0, 4)	$620 - 10(0) - 15(4) = 560$ kilometers
(0, 2)	$620 - 10(0) - 15(2) = 590$ kilometers

The least value for the total distance is **550 kilometers.** This occurs when $x = 1$ and $y = 4$. Now the problem can be solved.

Since $x = 1$, send 1 truck from Plant I to Site A.
Since $y = 4$, send 4 trucks from Plant I to Site B.
Since $8 - x = 7$, send 7 trucks from Plant II to Site A.
Since $4 - y = 0$, send 0 trucks from Plant II to Site B.

For more information concerning practical applications of linear programming, see "The Allocation of Resources by Linear Programming," by Robert G. Bland, *Scientific American*, June, 1981, pp. 126-144.

EXERCISE

An electronics company has two plants that manufacture calculators. A special order of 10,000 calculators requires delivery within two weeks. To meet that deadline, the calculators must be produced in 5 or fewer working days (120 hours). Plant A can produce the calculators at a cost of $1.30 each and at a rate of 60 units per hour. Plant B can produce the calculators at a cost of $1.35 each and at a rate of 40 units per hour. On an order of 10,000 units, the quality control engineer recommends that 200 extra units be produced to assure at least 10,000 units of acceptable quality. Find how many calculators should be produced by each plant if the production cost is to be kept to a minimum. Complete the following table as the first step.

Plant A should produce 7200 calculators and Plant B should produce 3000 calculators. The cost would be $13,410.00.

Plant	Number of Units	Hours Needed	Production Cost
A	x	? $\frac{x}{60}$	? 1.30x
B	y	$\frac{y}{40}$?	1.35y ?

CHAPTER SUMMARY

IMPORTANT TERMS	
	Linear inequality *(p. 400)*
	Solution set of a linear inequality *(p. 400)*
	Slope-intercept form of a linear inequality *(p. 401)*
	Region *(p. 403)*
	Compound sentence *(p. 406)*
	Union of two sets *(p. 406)*
	Solution set of a compound *or* sentence *(p. 406)*
	Intersection of two sets *(p. 411)*
	Solution set of a compound *and* sentence *(p. 411)*
	System of linear sentences *(p. 411)*
	Solution set of a system of linear sentences *(p. 411)*

IMPORTANT IDEAS

1. The graph of a linear equation separates a coordinate plane into three regions: the points on the line and the points of the plane on each side of the line.

2. Steps for drawing the graph of the relations $y < ax + b$ and $y > ax + b$:
   a. Draw the graph of $y = ax + b$.
   b. Select a point, not on the line, and substitute its coordinates in the inequality.
   c. Shade the region of the plane containing this point if its coordinates make the inequality true.
   d. Shade the region on the other side of the line from this point if its coordinates make the inequality false.

3. The graph of the solution set of a system of sentences is the intersection of the graphs of the sentences.

CHAPTER REVIEW NOTE: The Teacher's Resource Book contains two forms of each Chapter Test.

SECTION 16.1
In Ex. 1-4, many other answers are possible.

Write five ordered pairs having different x values for each inequality.

1. $y > -2x - 3$ (1, −4), (2, −4), (−2, 2), (−1, 2), (0, −2)

2. $y < 4x - 6$ (−3, −19), (−2, −15), (0, −7), (1, 0), (2, 1)

3. $y \le \frac{5}{2}x + 1$
(−2, −4), (−1, −3), (0, 0), (1, 2), (2, 6)

4. $y \ge -2.3x + 1.9$ (−1, 10), (0, 2), (1, 0), (2, −2.6), (3, 0)

Write the slope-intercept form of each inequality.

5. $-3x + y + 2 \ge 0$ $y \ge 3x - 2$

6. $5x - y + 4 > 0$ $y < 5x + 4$

7. $x - 3y + 5 < 0$ $y > \frac{1}{3}x + \frac{5}{3}$

8. $2x + 3y - 1 \le 0$ $y \le -\frac{2}{3}x + \frac{1}{3}$

SECTION 16.2 In Ex. 9-14, each graph is a region with a linear boundary that is not part of the graph.

Graph each inequality.

left of the boundary

9. $y > \frac{1}{2}x + 3$ The region is above the boundary.　　**10.** $y < -x + 2$ below the boundary　　**11.** $y < -2x - 1$

12. $y > 2x - 3$ left of the boundary　　**13.** $y < -x$ below the boundary　　**14.** $y > x$

above the boundary

SECTION 16.3 In Ex. 15-20, each graph is a region with a linear boundary that is also part of the graph.

Graph each inequality.

above the boundary

15. $y \geq -x + 3$ The region is above the boundary.　　**16.** $y \leq -\frac{1}{2}x + 1$ below the boundary　　**17.** $x - 2y + 4 \leq 0$

18. $3x - 4y + 8 \geq 0$ below the boundary　　**19.** $y \geq -4.5$ above the boundary　　**20.** $x \leq -1.5$

left of the boundary

SECTION 16.4 In Ex. 21-26, each graph is a region with two boundaries that are straight lines. The quadrants that contain the region are indicated, as are the equations of the boundaries.

Graph each linear system.

21. $\begin{cases} y < \frac{1}{2}x + 2 \\ y < -x - 1 \end{cases}$ Quadrants: II, III, IV; Boundaries: Below: $y = -x - 1$, Below: $y = \frac{1}{2}x + 2$; Boundaries not included

22. $\begin{cases} y < -2x + 3 \\ y > \frac{1}{3}x - 2 \end{cases}$ Quadrants: All; Boundaries: Above: $y = \frac{1}{3}x - 2$, Right: $y = -2x + 3$; Boundaries not included

23. $\begin{cases} 2x + y \leq -3 \\ x + y > 2 \end{cases}$ See below.

24. $\begin{cases} -3x + y < -1 \\ x + 2y \geq 4 \end{cases}$

25. $\begin{cases} y \geq -3 \\ x < 2 \end{cases}$

26. $\begin{cases} y < 2 \\ x \geq -4 \end{cases}$ See below.

Quadrants: I, IV; Boundaries: Above: $x + 2y = 4$; Left: $-3x + y = -1$; Top boundary included

Quadrants: All; Boundaries: Above: $y = -3$, Right: $x = 2$; Top boundary included

SECTION 16.5 included

Graph each linear system.

27. $\begin{cases} x \geq 0 \\ y \geq 0 \\ x + y \leq 3 \end{cases}$ Triangle; Vertices: (0, 0), (3, 0), (0, 3)

28. $\begin{cases} x \geq 0 \\ y \geq 0 \\ y \leq x + 6 \end{cases}$ Quadrant: I; Boundaries: Above: $y = x + 6$; Left: $x = 0$; Below: $y = 0$; Boundaries included

29. $\begin{cases} x \geq -1 \\ y \leq 4 \\ x \leq 7 \\ y \geq -2 \end{cases}$ Rectangle; Vertices: (−1, 4), (7, 4), (−1, −2), (7, −2)

30. $\begin{cases} x \leq 5 \\ y \leq -2 \\ y \geq x - 3 \\ x \geq y - 2 \end{cases}$ See below.

In Exercises 31–32, the vertices of a shaded region are given. Find the maximum and minimum values of k for each given expression involving x and y.

Maximum: 15, when $x = 5$, $y = 0$; minimum: −15, when $x = -5$, $y = 0$

31. Vertices: (−5, 0), (0, 2), (5, 0); $k = 3x + y$

32. Vertices: (0, 0), (1, 3), (3, 4), (4, 0); $k = 2x - y$

Maximum: 8, when $x = 4$, $y = 0$; minimum: −1, when $x = 1$, $y = 3$

23. Quadrant: II; Boundaries: Left: $x + y = 2$; Right: $2x + y = -3$; Right boundary included

26. Quadrants: All; Boundaries: Left: $x = -4$; Below: $y = 2$; Left boundary included

30. Quadrants: III, IV; Boundaries: Left: $x = y - 2$; Above: $y = -2$; Right: $y = x - 3$; Boundaries included

CHAPTER **17** Quadratic Functions

Sections **17.1** Quadratic Functions

17.2 Graphs of Quadratic Functions

17.3 Functions Defined by $y = ax^2$

17.4 Functions Defined by $y = a(x - h)^2$

17.5 Functions Defined by $y = a(x - h)^2 + k$

17.6 Standard Form of Quadratic Polynomials

17.7 Vertex and Axis of a Parabola

Features *Calculator Exercises:* Least Value of a Quadratic Function

Special Topic Application: Gravity

Review and Testing *Review Capsules*

Mid-Chapter Review

Chapter Summary

Chapter Review

17.1 Quadratic Functions

OBJECTIVES: To identify whether or not a given rule describes a quadratic function

To write ordered pairs of a quadratic function by using a rule for the function

To compute values of a quadratic function corresponding to given real numbers of the domain

Quadratic trinomials such as $ax^2 + bx + c$ are used to form rules for quadratic functions.

> A **quadratic function** is a function described by the rule $y = ax^2 + bx + c$, in which a, b, and c are rational numbers with $a \neq 0$.
>
> $\{(x, y) : y = 2x^2 - 3x + 5\}$
>
> $\{(x, y) : y = 0.5x^2 + 1.2x - 4.8\}$

P-1 **Which functions below are quadratic?** a, d

a. $\{(x, y) : y = 5x^2\}$ **b.** $\{(x, y) : y = 2x + 5\}$

c. $\{(x, y) : y = x^3 - 5x\}$ **d.** $\{(x, y) : y = 3 - 2x^2\}$

example 1

Write three ordered pairs of $\{(x, y) : y = -3x^2 + x - 2\}$.

Solution: Let the x values equal -2, 0, and 2.

$y = -3(-2)^2 + (-2) - 2$ Let $x = -2$.

$y = -3(4) - 2 - 2$

$y = -12 - 2 - 2$

$y = -16$ The first ordered pair is $(-2, -16)$.

$y = -3(0)^2 + 0 - 2$ Let $x = 0$.

$y = -3(0) + 0 - 2$

$y = 0 + 0 - 2$

$y = -2$ The second ordered pair is $(0, -2)$.

$y = -3(2)^2 + 2 - 2$ Let $x = 2$.

$y = -3(4) + 2 - 2$

$y = -12 + 2 - 2$

$y = -12$ The third ordered pair is $(2, -12)$.

Suppose that the function in Example 1 is called f. There is a

Careful explanation will be needed for this unfamiliar notation. Warn students that $f(-2)$ **does not refer to the product of** f **and** -2**.**

special way of referring to the y values. This is shown below.

$$f(-2) = -16 \qquad f(0) = -2 \qquad f(2) = -12$$

You may read "f(−2)" as "f of −2" and similarly for f(0), f(2), and other y values. The "y values of a function" are often referred to simply as the "values of the function."

example 2

Suppose that $g = \{(x, y) : y = x^2 - x + 1\}$.
Compute the following values.

1. g(3) **2.** g(−2)  **You may use any letter to name a function.**

Solutions: 1.
$$y = x^2 - x + 1$$
$$g(3) = 3^2 - 3 + 1$$ **Replace x with 3.**
$$= 9 - 3 + 1$$
$$= 7$$

2.
$$g(-2) = (-2)^2 - (-2) + 1$$ **Replace x with −2.**
$$= 4 + 2 + 1$$
$$= 7$$

As with other functions, you can limit the domain of a quadratic function. Unless indicated otherwise, however, the domain will be {real numbers}.

CLASSROOM EXERCISES

Write Yes or No to indicate if each rule describes a quadratic function. (P-1)

1. $y = 5x^2 - 10x + 2$ Yes

2. $y = 3x - 10$ No

3. $y = x^3 + x^2 - 2x + 5$ No

4. $y = -3x^2$ Yes

5. $y = \dfrac{1}{x^2} + \dfrac{2}{x} + 3$ No

6. $y = x^2 - 3x$ Yes

7. $y = -2x + 1$ No

8. $y = \frac{3}{4}x^2 - \frac{1}{2}$ Yes

9. $y = \sqrt{x^2}$ No

10. $y = \sqrt{3}x^2 + \sqrt{2}x + \sqrt{5}$ No

11. $y = 2 - 3x^2 - 5x$ Yes

12. $y = (x + 1)^2$ Yes

13. $y = (x - 2)(x + 3)$ Yes

14. $y = x^{-2} + 3x^{-1} + 5$ No

15. $y = 3^2$ No

WRITTEN EXERCISES

See the Teacher's Manual for the suggested assignments.

Goal: To compute values of quadratic functions
Sample Problem: Suppose that $g = \{(x, y) : y = -x^2 + x - 7\}$.
Compute $g(0)$ and $g(-1)$.   **Answer:** $g(0) = -7$; $g(-1) = -9$

Write Yes or No to show whether each rule describes a quadratic function.
(P-1)

1. $y = 2x - 5$ No

2. $y = -x + 3$ No

3. $y = -3x^2$ Yes

4. $y = 5x^2$ Yes

5. $y = x^3 + 2x - 6$ No

6. $y = x^4 - 2x - 3$ No

7. $y = (x - 2)^2$ Yes

8. $y = (2x - 3)(x + 1)$ Yes

9. $y = \dfrac{1}{x^2 + x - 5}$ No

10. $y = \sqrt{x^2 - 2x - 3}$ No

11. $y = 0.5x^2 + 0.7x - 0.3$ Yes

12. $y = -1.7x^2 - 3.1x + 2.7$ Yes

Write three ordered pairs of each function. Let the x values equal −3, −1, and 2. (Example 1)

13. $\{(x, y) : y = -x^2\}$ $(-3, -9), (-1, -1), (2, -4)$

14. $\{(x, y) : y = -x^2 + 1\}$
$(-3, -8), (-1, 0), (2, -3)$

15. $\{(x, y) : y = x^2 + 2x + 1\}$ $(-3, 4), (-1, 0), (2, 9)$

16. $\{(x, y) : y = x^2 - x + 1\}$
$(-3, 13), (-1, 3), (2, 3)$

17. $\{(x, y) : y = x^2 - 3\}$ $(-3, 6), (-1, -2), (2, 1)$

18. $\{(x, y) : y = x^2 - 4\}$
$(-3, 5), (-1, -3), (2, 0)$

19. $\{(x, y) : y = -2x^2 - 3x\}$ $(-3, -9), (-1, 1), (2, -14)$

20. $\{(x, y) : y = -3x^2 - 1\}$
$(-3, -28), (-1, -4), (2, -13)$

Compute g(−2), g(0), and g(3) for each function g below. (Example 2)

21. $g = \{(x, y) : y = 2x^2 - x - 3\}$ $7; -3; 12$

22. $g = \{(x, y) : y = -3x^2 + 2x - 1\}$
$-17; -1; -22$

23. $g = \{(x, y) : y = (x - 2)^2\}$ $16; 4; 1$

24. $g = \{(x, y) : y = (x + 1)^2\}$
$1; 1; 16$

25. $g = \{(x, y) : y = (x - 1)(x + 3)\}$ $-3; -3; 12$

26. $g = \{(x, y) : y = (x + 5)(x - 3)\}$
$-15; -15; 0$

REVIEW CAPSULE FOR SECTION 17.2

Complete each table. (Section 6.5)

1. $y = x^2 - 3$

x	−2	−1	0	1	2
y	?	?	?	?	?

1   −2   −3 −2   1

2. $y = -x^2 + 2$

x	−2	−1	0	1	2
y	?	?	?	?	?

−2   1   2   1 −2

3. $y = \frac{1}{2}x^2 - x$

x	−2	−1	0	1	2
y	?	?	?	?	?

4   $\frac{3}{2}$ 0 $-\frac{1}{2}$ 0

OBJECTIVES: To graph a quadratic function with {real numbers} as the domain, given a table
of ordered pairs of the function
To graph a quadratic function with {real numbers} as the domain, give a rule for the function

17.2 Graphs of Quadratic Functions

You have already seen the graph of a quadratic function. It is a smooth curved line.

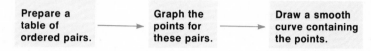 example 1   Graph $\{(x, y) : y = x^2 - 2x - 3\}$.

| Prepare a table of ordered pairs. | → | Graph the points for these pairs. | → | Draw a smooth curve containing the points. |

Solution:

$y = x^2 - 2x - 3$

$y = (-2)^2 - 2(-2) - 3 = 5$

$y = (-1)^2 - 2(-1) - 3 = 0$

$y = (0)^2 - 2(0) - 3 = -3$

$y = (1)^2 - 2(1) - 3 = -4$

$y = (2)^2 - 2(2) - 3 = \underline{\quad?\quad}$ -3

$y = (3)^2 - 2(3) - 3 = \underline{\quad?\quad}$ 0

$y = (4)^2 - 2(4) - 3 = \underline{\quad?\quad}$ 5

x	y	
-2	5	
-1	0	
0	-3	
1	-4	
2	?	-3
3	?	0
4	?	5

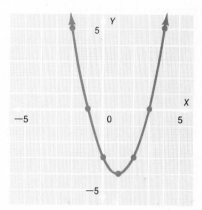

Figure 1

The points corresponding to these ordered pairs are graphed in Figure 1. A smooth curve containing the points is drawn.

The curve of Example 1 is called a **parabola.**

P-1   **Based on the graph, what is an estimate of each unknown y value?**

   a. $(2\frac{1}{2}, \underline{\quad?\quad})$ $-1\frac{3}{4}$ **b.** $(-1\frac{1}{2}, \underline{\quad?\quad})$ $2\frac{1}{4}$ **c.** $(\frac{1}{2}, \underline{\quad?\quad})$ $-3\frac{3}{4}$

The two arrows on the graph of Figure 1 indicate that the parabola extends upward infinitely. The curve widens as it extends upward.

P-2   **Based on the graph, what is the range of the function?** $\{y : y \geqslant -4\}$

There is no y value less than −4. The range is $\{y : y \geq -4\}$.

example 2

Graph $\{(x, y) : y = -x^2 + 3x\}$.

Solution:

$y = -x^2 + 3x$

$y = -(-1)^2 + 3(-1) = -4$

$y = -(0)^2 + 3(0) = 0$

$y = -(1)^2 + 3(1) = 2$

$y = -(2)^2 + 3(2) = 2$

$y = -(3)^2 + 3(3) = 0$

$y = -(4)^2 + 3(4) = -4$

x	y
−1	−4
0	0
1	2
2	2
3	0
4	−4

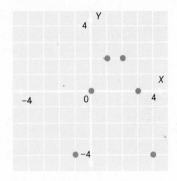

It is also helpful to locate the point at which the parabola "turns" or changes direction.

$y = -x^2 + 3x$

Let $x = \frac{3}{2}$.

$y = -\left(\frac{3}{2}\right)^2 + 3\left(\frac{3}{2}\right)$

For this parabola, you can "see" that the x value of the turning point is $\frac{3}{2}$. Discuss the range of this function based on its graph.

Solve for y.

$y = -\frac{9}{4} + \frac{9}{2}$

Compare the parabola in Example 2 with the parabola in Example 1

$y = -\frac{9}{4} + \frac{18}{4}$

$y = \frac{9}{4}$

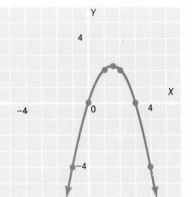

The point, $(\frac{3}{2}, \frac{9}{4})$, is located.

CLASSROOM EXERCISES

Write the unknown y values in each table. (Example 1)

1. $y = x^2$

x	y
−2	? 4
−1	? 1
0	? 0
1	? 1
2	? 4

2. $y = -x^2$

x	y
−2	? −4
−1	? −1
0	? 0
1	? −1
2	? −4

3. $y = x^2 + 2$

x	y
−2	? 6
−1	? 3
0	? 2
1	? 3
2	? 6

4. $y = x^2 + x + 1$

x	−2	−1	0	1	2
y	? 3	? 1	? 1	? 3	? 7

5. $y = 2x^2 + x$

x	−2	−1	0	1	2
y	? 6	? 1	? 0	? 3	? 10

6. $y = -x^2 + 2x - 3$

x	−2	−1	0	1	2
y	? −11	? −6	? −3	? −2	? −3

Refer to the graph at the right. Estimate one value for y and two values for x. (P-1)

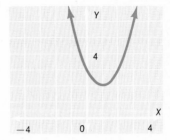

7. $(1, y)$ 2

8. $(2, y)$ 3

9. $(\frac{1}{2}, y)$ $2\frac{1}{4}$

10. $(-\frac{1}{2}, y)$ $4\frac{1}{4}$

11. $(x, 3)$ 0, 2

12. $(x, 6)$ −1, 3

13. $(x, 2\frac{1}{4})$ $\frac{1}{2}, 1\frac{1}{2}$

14. $(x, 5)$ $-\frac{3}{4}, 2\frac{3}{4}$

WRITTEN EXERCISES
See the Teacher's Manual for the suggested assignments.

Goal: To graph quadratic functions

Sample Problem: Graph $\{(x, y) : y = -x^2 + 3x\}$.   **Answer:** See Example 2.

In Ex. 1-6, each parabola turns at a high point (maximum), or a low point (minimum). This point is given for each exercise.

Graph the ordered pairs of each table. Draw a parabola that contains the points. (Examples 1 and 2)

1. Turns at (0, 1); low point

x	−2	−1	0	1	2
y	5	2	1	2	5

2. Turns at (0, −1); low point

x	−2	−1	0	1	2
y	3	0	−1	0	3

3. Turns at (1, 4); high point

x	−2	−1	0	1	2	3
y	−5	0	3	4	3	0

4. Turns at (−1, 1); high point

x	−3	−2	−1	0	1
y	−3	0	1	0	−3

5. Turns at (1, 2); low point

x	−1	0	1	2	3
y	6	3	2	3	6

6. Turns at $(\frac{1}{2}, -2\frac{1}{4})$; low point

x	−2	−1	0	1	2	3
y	4	0	−2	−2	0	4

In Ex. 7-12, the high or low point and three points on the parabola are given.

Graph each function. (Examples 1 and 2)

7. $\{(x, y) : y = x^2 - 2\}$ (−1, −1), (0, −2), (1, −1); Turns at (0, −2); low point

8. $\{(x, y) : y = -x^2 + 3\}$ (−1, 2); (0, 3); (1, 2); Turns at (0, 3); high point

9. $\{(x, y) : y = -x^2 - x\}$ (−1, 0); $(-\frac{1}{2}, \frac{1}{4})$; (0,0); Turns at $(-\frac{1}{2}, \frac{1}{4})$; high point

10. $\{(x, y) : y = 2x^2 + x\}$ (−1, 1); $(-\frac{1}{4}, -\frac{1}{8})$, (0, 0); Turns at $(-\frac{1}{4}, -\frac{1}{8})$; low point

11. $\{ x, y) : y = x^2 - 6x + 10\}$ (2, 2); (3, 1); (4, 2); Turns at (3, 1); low point

12. $\{(x, y) : y = -x^2 - 2x + 1\}$ (−2, 1); (−1, 2); (0, 1); Turns at (−1, 2); high point

REVIEW CAPSULE FOR SECTION 17.3

Compare each rule with $y = ax^2 + bx + c$. Then give the value of a, b, and c for each rule. (Section 17.1)

1. $y = -x^2 + 2x - 5$

$a = -1; b = 2; c = -5$

2. $y = 2x^2 - 3x + 1$

$a = 2; b = -3; c = 1$

3. $y = \frac{1}{2}x^2 - 3x + 7$

$a = \frac{1}{2}; b = -3; c = 7$

4. $y = -4x^2 - 1$

$a = -4; b = 0; c = -1$

17.3 Functions Defined by $y = ax^2$

OBJECTIVES: To graph two functions of the form $y = ax^2$ in the same coordinate plane
To graph a relation of the form $x = ay^2$

You have learned that any quadratic function has a rule of the form $y = ax^2 + bx + c$.

P-1 **Find the values of a, b, and c in each rule below.**

1. $y = -\frac{5}{2}x^2$
$a = -\frac{5}{2}, b = 0, c = 0$

2. $y = 3x^2 - 4x - 1$
$a = 3, b = -4, c = -1$

3. $y = x^2 + 3x$
$a = 1, b = 3, c = 0$

example 1

Graph in the same coordinate plane.

1. $y = 2x^2$ **2.** $y = x^2$ **3.** $y = \frac{1}{2}x^2$

Solutions:

1.

x	y
-2	8
-1	2
0	0
1	2
2	8

2.

x	y
-2	4
-1	1
0	0
1	1
2	4

3.

x	y
-4	8
-2	2
0	0
2	2
4	8

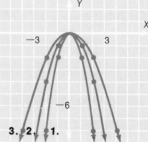

If $a > 0$, the parabola opens upward.

P-2 **Which function in Example 1 has the "widest" graph? the next widest? the least wide?** $y = \frac{1}{2}x^2$ $y = 2x^2$ $y = x^2$

example 2

Graph in the same coordinate plane.

1. $y = -2x^2$ **2.** $y = -x^2$ **3.** $y = -\frac{1}{2}x^2$

Solutions:

1.

x	y
-2	-8
-1	-2
0	0
1	-2
2	-8

2.

x	y
-2	-4
-1	-1
0	0
1	-1
2	-4

3.

x	y
-4	-8
-2	-2
0	0
2	-2
4	-8

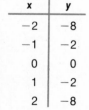

If $a < 0$, the parabola opens downward.

$$y = -\tfrac{1}{2}x^2$$

P-3 Which function in Example 2 has the widest graph? the next
$y = -x^2$ widest? the least wide? $y = -2x^2$

Examples 1 and 2 show that as *a* gets smaller in absolute value,
the corresponding parabola gets wider.

Urge students
to learn these
facts because
they will be
referred to in
succeeding sections.

Effect of *a* on the graph of $y = ax^2 + bx + c$:

1. If *a* is positive, the parabola opens upward.
2. If *a* is negative, the parabola opens downward.
3. As $|a|$ decreases, the parabola becomes wider.

A relation defined by a rule of the form $x = ay^2$ also has a parabola
for its graph.

example 3

Graph the parabola defined by $x = -\tfrac{1}{2}y^2$.

Solution: Choose values for *y* and compute corresponding values for *x*.

$x = -\tfrac{1}{2}y^2$

$x = -\tfrac{1}{2}(-2)^2 = -2$

$x = -\tfrac{1}{2}(-1)^2 = -\tfrac{1}{2}$

$x = -\tfrac{1}{2}(0)^2 = 0$

$x = -\tfrac{1}{2}(1)^2 = -\tfrac{1}{2}$

$x = -\tfrac{1}{2}(2)^2 = -2$

x	y
-2	-2
$-\tfrac{1}{2}$	-1
0	0
$-\tfrac{1}{2}$	1
-2	2

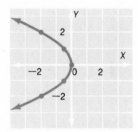

You can see that $x = -\tfrac{1}{2}y^2$ does not define a function. There are many
ordered pairs that have the same *x* values.

CLASSROOM EXERCISES

Refer to the graphs of Examples 1 and 2.

1. What point is in all six graphs? The point with coordinates (0, 0)

2. How do the graphs of $y = x^2$ and $y = -x^2$ compare? They are mirror images in the X axis.

3. Does the graph of $y = -2x^2$ open upward or downward? Downward

Quadratic Functions / **429**

4. Which parabola is wider, $y = -x^2$ or $y = 2x^2$? $y = -x^2$

5. What is the range of the function defined by $y = 2x^2$? $\{y : y \geq 0\}$

6. What is the range of the function defined by $y = -2x^2$? $\{y : y \leq 0\}$

Indicate if the graph of each function opens upward or downward.
(Examples 1 and 2)

7. $y = -10x^2$ Downward **8.** $y = 0.3x^2$ Upward **9.** $y = 4 - \frac{5}{2}x^2$ Downward **10.** $y = (2x - 1)^2$
Upward

Indicate which of the two functions in each exercise has the wider graph.
(P-2, P-3)

11. $y = 5x^2$ $y = 3x^2$ $y = 3x^2$ **12.** $y = \frac{1}{2}x^2$ $y = \frac{1}{2}x^2$ $y = \frac{3}{2}x^2$ **13.** $y = 0.15x^2$ $y = 0.09x^3$ $y = 0.09x^2$ **14.** $y = x^2 - 5x + 1$
$y = -2x^2 + x - 3$
$y = x^2 - 5x + 1$

WRITTEN EXERCISES
See the Teacher's Manual for the suggested assignments.

Goal: To use a in the rule $y = ax^2 + bx + c$ to compare the graphs of
quadratic functions
Sample Problem: Graph in the same coordinate plane: $y = 2x^2$, $y = \frac{1}{2}x^2$,
$y = x^2$, $y = -2x^2$, $y = -\frac{1}{2}x^2$, $y = -x^2$.
Answer: See Examples 1 and 2.
In Ex. 1-10, the graphs are all parabolas that open upward or downward.

Complete each table. Graph the two functions in the same coordinate plane.
(Examples 1 and 2)

1. $y = x^2$ Opens upward at (0, 0) $y = \frac{1}{4}x^2$ Opens upward at (0, 0)

x	y		x	y
−2	? 4		−4	? 4
−1	? 1		−2	? 1
0	? 0		0	? 0
1	? 1		2	? 1
2	? 4		4	? 4

2. $y = -x^2$ Opens downward at (0, 0) $y = -\frac{1}{4}x^2$ Opens downward at (0, 0)

x	y		x	y
−2	? −4		−4	? −4
−1	? −1		−2	? −1
0	? 0		0	? 0
1	? −1		2	? −1
2	? −4		4	? −4

3. $y = -\frac{1}{2}x^2$ Opens downward at (0, 0) $y = -\frac{3}{2}x^2$ Opens downward at (0, 0)

x	y		x	y
−3	? $-\frac{9}{2}$		−2	? −6
−2	? −2		−1	? $-\frac{3}{2}$
0	? 0		0	? 0
2	? −2		1	? $-\frac{3}{2}$
3	? $-\frac{9}{2}$		2	? −6

4. $y = \frac{1}{2}x^2$ Opens upward at (0, 0) $y = \frac{3}{2}x^2$ Opens upward at (0, 0)

x	y		x	y
−3	? $\frac{9}{2}$		−2	? 6
−2	? 2		−1	? $\frac{3}{2}$
0	? 0		0	? 0
2	? 2		1	? $\frac{3}{2}$
3	? $\frac{9}{2}$		2	? 6

5. $y = -2x^2$ Opens downward at (0, 0) $y = \frac{3}{2}x^2$ Opens upward at (0, 0)

x	y	x	y
−2	? −8	−2	? 6
−1	? −2	−1	? $\frac{3}{2}$
0	? 0	0	? 0
1	? −2	1	? $\frac{3}{2}$
2	? −8	2	? 6

6. $y = 2x^2$ Opens upward at (0,0) $y = -\frac{3}{2}x^2$ Opens downward at (0, 0)

x	y	x	y
−2	? 8	−2	? −6
−1	? 2	−1	? $-\frac{3}{2}$
0	? 0	0	? 0
1	? 2	1	? $-\frac{3}{2}$
2	? 8	2	? −6

7. $y = \frac{1}{2}x^2$ Opens upward at (0, 0) $y = \frac{1}{2}x^2 - 2$ Opens upward at (0, −2)

x	y	x	y
−2	? 2	−2	? 0
−1	? $\frac{1}{2}$	−1	? $-\frac{3}{2}$
0	? 0	0	? −2
1	? $\frac{1}{2}$	1	? $-\frac{3}{2}$
2	? 2	2	? 0

8. $y = -\frac{1}{4}x^2$ Opens downward at (0, 0) $y = -\frac{1}{4}x^2 + 3$ Opens downward at (0, 3)

x	y	x	y
−4	? −4	−4	? −1
−2	? −1	−2	? 2
0	? 0	0	? 3
2	? −1	2	? 2
4	? −4	4	? −1

9. $y = -\frac{3}{4}x^2$ Opens downward at (0,0) $y = -\frac{3}{4}x^2 + 1$ Opens downward at (0, 1)

x	y	x	y
−4	? −12	−4	? −11
−2	? −3	−2	? −2
0	? 0	0	? 1
2	? −3	2	? −2
4	? −12	4	? −11

10. $y = \frac{3}{8}x^2$ Opens upward at (0,0) $y = \frac{3}{8}x^2 - 2$ Opens upward at (0, −2)

x	y	x	y
−4	? 6	−4	? 4
−2	? $\frac{3}{2}$	−2	? $-\frac{1}{2}$
0	? 0	0	? −2
2	? $\frac{3}{2}$	2	? $-\frac{1}{2}$
4	? 6	4	? 4

In Ex. 11-14, the parabolas open at the origin to the right or to the left of the Y axis.

Complete each table. Then graph each parabola. (Example 3)

11. $x = y^2$ Opens to the right

x	y
1	? 1
1	? −1
0	? 0
4	? 2
4	? −2

12. $x = -y^2$ Opent to the left

x	y
−1	? 1
−1	? −1
0	? 0
−4	? 2
−4	? −2

13. $x = 2y^2$ Opens to the right

x	y
2	? 1
2	? −1
0	? 0
8	? 2
8	? −2

14. $x = -2y^2$ Opens to the left

x	y
−2	? 1
−2	? −1
0	? 0
−8	? 2
−8	? −2

REVIEW CAPSULE FOR SECTION 17.4

Multiply and simplify. (Section 9.5)

1. $(x - 2)(x - 2)$ $x^2 - 4x + 4$

2. $(x + 3)(x + 3)$ $x^2 + 6x + 9$

3. $(x - 5)(x - 5)$ $x^2 - 10x + 25$

4. $(x + 6)(x + 6)$ $x^2 + 12x + 36$

5. $(x + 2.1)(x + 2.1)$ $x^2 + 4.2x + 4.41$

6. $(x - 2.7)(x - 2.7)$ $x^2 - 5.4x + 7.29$

OBJECTIVES: To write the number of units and the direction which the graph of a
function $y = a(x - h)^2$ is from the graph of a function $y = ax^2$ in the same
coordinate plane

17.4 Functions Defined by $y = a(x - h)^2$

To graph a function $y = ax^2$ by using several ordered pairs and then to
graph $y = a(x - h)^2$ by using the effect that h has on the first graph

The equation $y = \frac{1}{2}(x - 2)^2$ is a rule for a quadratic function.

$$\frac{1}{2}(x - 2)^2 = \frac{1}{2}(x - 2)(x - 2)$$

Explain that in a rule,
such as $y = 3x^2 - 5x + 4$ it
is not at once apparent what
the value of h is. This will
be learned in
Section 17.6.

$$= \frac{1}{2}(x^2 - 4x + 4)$$

$$= \frac{1}{2}x^2 - 2x + 2 \quad \blacktriangleleft \quad \text{In the form}\ ax^2 + bx + c$$

P-1 **What are the values of a, b, and c?** $a = \frac{1}{2}, b = -2, c = 2$

Replace $(x - 2)$ by A in $y = \frac{1}{2}(x - 2)^2$: $\longrightarrow$ $y = \frac{1}{2}A^2$

This form suggests that the graph of $y = \frac{1}{2}(x - 2)^2$ is related to the
graph of $y = \frac{1}{2}x^2$.

example 1

Graph the parabolas $y = \frac{1}{2}x^2$ and $y = \frac{1}{2}(x - 2)^2$ in
the same coordinate plane.

Solutions:

$y = \frac{1}{2}x^2$

x	y
-3	$4\frac{1}{2}$
-2	2
-1	$\frac{1}{2}$
0	0
1	$\frac{1}{2}$
2	2
3	$4\frac{1}{2}$

$y = \frac{1}{2}(x - 2)^2$

x	y
-1	$4\frac{1}{2}$
0	2
1	$\frac{1}{2}$
2	0
3	$\frac{1}{2}$
4	2
5	$4\frac{1}{2}$

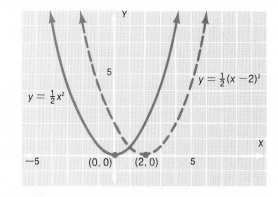

$\blacktriangle$ **The parabolas have the same shape.**

Note that the graph of $y = \frac{1}{2}x^2$ can be moved **two** units to the **right**
to obtain the graph of $y = \frac{1}{2}(x - 2)^2$.

example 2

Graph in the same coordinate plane.

1. $y = -\frac{1}{2}x^2$ 2. $y = -\frac{1}{2}(x + 3)^2$

Explain that $y = -\frac{1}{2}(x + 3)^2$ can be expressed as $y = -\frac{1}{2}(x - (-3))^2$;
thus, h has the value -3.

Solutions:

$y = -\frac{1}{2}x^2$

x	y
−3	$-4\frac{1}{2}$
−2	−2
−1	$-\frac{1}{2}$
0	0
1	$-\frac{1}{2}$
2	−2
3	$-4\frac{1}{2}$

$y = -\frac{1}{2}(x + 3)^2$

x	y
−6	$-4\frac{1}{2}$
−5	−2
−4	$-\frac{1}{2}$
−3	0
−2	$-\frac{1}{2}$
−1	−2
0	$-4\frac{1}{2}$

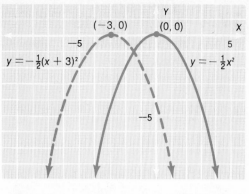

The parabolas have the same shape.

Note that the graph of $y = -\frac{1}{2}x^2$ can be moved **three** units to the **left** to obtain the graph of $y = -\frac{1}{2}(x + 3)^2$.

> ### Graphs of $y = ax^2$ and $y = a(x - h)^2$
>
> The graph of $y = ax^2$ can be moved horizontally $|h|$ units to obtain the graph of $y = a(x - h)^2$. If h is negative, the motion is to the left. If h is positive, the motion is to the right.

example 3

Graph the parabola $y = (x + 4)^2$ in the same plane as the parabola $y = x^2$ shown in Figure 1. Locate points of $y = (x + 4)^2$ that correspond to points A, B, C, D, and E.

Solution:

1. Locate points A', B', C', D', and E' in Figure 2 that are 4 units to the left of the corresponding points of Figure 1.

Ask what the value of h is in $y = (x + 4)^2$ as it is compared with $y = a(x - h)^2$. Also ask what the value of a is.

2. Draw the parabola.

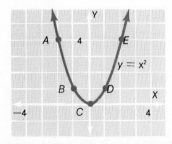

Figure 1

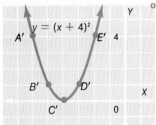

Figure 2

CLASSROOM EXERCISES

For each exercise, indicate how to move the graph of the first function to obtain the graph of the second function.

1. $y = x^2$; $y = (x - 2)^2$ 2 units right

2. $y = x^2$; $y = (x + 2)^2$ 2 units left

3. $y = 5x^2$; $y = 5(x - 1)^2$ 1 unit right

4. $y = 5x^2$; $y = 5(x + 4)^2$ 4 units left

5. $y = -3x^2$; $y = -3(x + 2)^2$ 2 units left

6. $y = -3x^2$; $y = -3(x - 1)^2$ 1 unit right

7. $y = \frac{1}{3}x^2$; $y = \frac{1}{3}(x + 10)^2$ 10 units left

8. $y = \frac{1}{3}x^2$; $y = \frac{1}{3}(x - 5)^2$ 5 units right

9. $y = \frac{3}{4}x^2$; $y = \frac{3}{4}(x - 7)^2$ 7 units right

10. $y = \frac{3}{4}x^2$; $y = \frac{3}{4}(x + 6)^2$ 6 units left

11. $y = 2(x - 3)^2$; $y = 2(x + 3)^2$ 6 units left

12. $y = 2(x - 1)^2$; $y = 2(x + 2)^2$ 3 units left

WRITTEN EXERCISES

See the Teacher's Manual for the suggested assignments.

Goal: To use a graph of $y = ax^2$ to draw a graph of the form $y = a(x - h)^2$

Sample Problem: Graph $y = (x - 4)^2$ and $y = (x + 4)^2$.

Answer: See Example 3.

Write the number of units and the direction the graph of the first function can be moved to obtain the graph of the second function.

EXAMPLE: $y = 5x^2$; $y = 5(x + 6)^2$ **ANSWER:** 6 units left

1. $y = -3x^2$; $y = -3(x - 5)^2$ 5 units right

2. $y = 4x^2$; $y = 4(x - 10)^2$ 10 units right

3. $y = \frac{5}{2}x^2$; $y = \frac{5}{2}(x + 8)^2$ 8 units left

4. $y = -\frac{7}{2}x^2$; $y = -\frac{7}{2}(x + 6)^2$ 6 units left

5. $y = -x^2$; $y = -(x + 3\frac{1}{2})^2$ $3\frac{1}{2}$ units left

6. $y = x^2$; $y = (x - 2\frac{1}{4})^2$ $2\frac{1}{4}$ units right

7. $y = 1.4x^2$; $y = 1.4(x - 2.7)^2$ 2.7 units right

8. $y = -3.6x^2$; $y = -3.6(x + 2.1)^2$
2.1 units left

Graph the first parabola in each exercise using the x values -2, -1, 0, 1, and 2. Then graph the second parabola. (Examples 1–3)

9. $y = 2x^2$; $y = 2(x + 2)^2$ Second parabola is 2 units to left of first.

10. $y = -2x^2$; $y = -2(x - 2)^2$ Second parabola is 2 units to right of first.

11. $y = -\frac{1}{2}x^2$; $y = -\frac{1}{2}(x - 3)^2$ Second parabola is 3 units to right of first.

12. $y = \frac{1}{2}x^2$; $y = \frac{1}{2}(x + 3)^2$ Second parabola is 3 units to left of first.

13. $y = -x^2$; $y = -(x + \frac{3}{2})^2$ Second parabola is $\frac{3}{2}$ units to left of first.

14. $y = x^2$; $y = (x - \frac{5}{2})^2$ Second parabola is $\frac{5}{2}$ units to right of first.

15. $y = \frac{3}{2}x^2$; $y = \frac{3}{2}(x - 2)^2$ Second parabola is 2 units to right of first.

16. $y = -\frac{3}{2}x^2$; $y = -\frac{3}{2}(x + 2)^2$ Second parabola is 2 units to left of first

17. $y = -3x^2$; $y = -3(x + 1)^2$
Second parabola is 1 unit to left of first.

18. $y = 3x^2$; $y = 3(x - 1)^2$
Second parabola is 1 unit to right of first.

See page 533 for the answers to the odd-numbered Mid-Chapter Review Exercises.

MID-CHAPTER REVIEW

NOTE: After completing the Mid-Chapter Review, you may want to administer a quiz covering the same sections. See pages M-42 and M-43 of the Teacher's Manual for the suggested quiz.

Compute f(−2), f(−1), f(0), f(1), and f(2) for each function. (Section 17.1)

1. $f = \{(x, y): y = -\frac{1}{2}x^2 - 3x\}$

2. $f = \{(x, y): y = 5x^2 - 2\}$

3. $f = \{(x, y): y = x^2 + x - 3\}$

18; 3; −2; 3; 18

Graph each function. (Section 17.2)

In Ex. 4 and 6, the high or low point and three points of the graph (parabola) are given.

4. $\{(x, y): y = \frac{1}{2}x^2 - 3)\}$

5. $\{(x, y): y = -\frac{1}{2}x^2 + 2\}$

6. $\{(x, y): y = x^2 - 4x + 2\}$

Low point: (0, −3); (−1, −2½), (0, −3), (1, −2½)

Low point: (2, −2); (1, −1), (3, −1), (2, −2)

Graph the two functions in the same coordinate plane. (Section 17.3)

Ex. 8, 10: Three points are given for each curve (a parabola).

7. $y = \frac{3}{4}x^2$

8. $y = \frac{5}{2}x^2$

9. $y = 2x^2$

10. $y = -\frac{3}{2}x^2$

11. $y = -2x^2 - 2$

$y = -\frac{3}{4}x^2$

$y = -\frac{5}{2}x^2$

$y = \frac{1}{2}x^2$

$y = -\frac{3}{4}x^2$

$y = \frac{1}{2}x^2 + 1$

(0, 0), (1, $\frac{5}{2}$), (−1, $\frac{5}{2}$); (0, 0), (1, $-\frac{5}{2}$)

(0, 0), (1, $-\frac{3}{4}$), (−1, $-\frac{3}{4}$); (0, 0), (1, $-\frac{3}{2}$), (−1, $-\frac{3}{2}$)

Write the number of units and the direction the graph of the first function can be moved to obtain the graph of the second function. (Section 17.4)

12. $y = \frac{1}{4}x^2$

13. $y = -3x^2$

14. $y = -\frac{5}{2}x^2$

15. $y = 5x^2$

$y = \frac{1}{4}(x - 3)^2$

$y = -3(x - 5)^2$

$y = -\frac{5}{2}(x + \frac{3}{2})^2$

$y = 5(x + 4)^2$

Second is 3 units to the right of the first.

Second is $\frac{3}{2}$ units to the left of the first.

— LEAST VALUE OF A QUADRATIC FUNCTION —

The expression $c - \frac{b^2}{4a}$ represents the <u>least</u> value of the quadratic function $y = ax^2 + bx + c$, when $a > 0$.

EXAMPLE Find the approximate least value of $y = 21x^2 + 9x + 52$.

See if any students can work this Example by using the $\boxed{+/-}$ key but not the memory.

SOLUTION $a = 21, b = 9, c = 52$ $c - \frac{b^2}{4a} = 52 - \frac{9^2}{(4)(21)}$

$\boxed{9}$ $\boxed{\times}$ $\boxed{=}$ $\boxed{\div}$ $\boxed{4}$ $\boxed{\div}$ $\boxed{2}$ $\boxed{1}$

$\boxed{=}$ $\boxed{M+}$ $\boxed{5}$ $\boxed{2}$ $\boxed{-}$ $\boxed{MR}$ $\boxed{=}$ $\boxed{51.035715}$ **Least value**

Find the least value.

1. $y = 34x^2 + 68x + 109$ 75

2. $y = 176x^2 + 465x + 239$

−68.13778

3. $y = 1084x^2 + 1296x + 238$

−149.36531

REVIEW CAPSULE FOR SECTION 17.5

Compute g(−2), g(0), and g(2) for each function below. (Section 17.1)

1. $g = \{(x, y): y = \frac{1}{2}(x - 2)^2 + 1\}$ 9; 3; 1

2. $g = \{(x, y): y = -2(x + 1)^2 - 3\}$

−5; −5; −21

17.5 Functions Defined by $y = a(x - h)^2 + k$

OBJECTIVES: To graph a function $y = ax^2$ using several ordered pairs and then to graph $y = a(x - h)^2 + k$ by using the effect that h and k have on the first graph
To write an equation for a function obtained by moving the graph of $y = ax^2$ according to stated horizontal and vertical motions

The expression $\frac{1}{2}(x - 3)^2 + 2$ can be changed to the form $ax^2 + bx + c$.

$$\frac{1}{2}(x - 3)^2 + 2 = \frac{1}{2}(x^2 - 6x + 9) + 2$$

$$= \frac{1}{2}x^2 - 3x + \frac{9}{2} + 2$$

$$= \frac{1}{2}x^2 - 3x + \frac{13}{2} \quad \blacktriangleleft \quad \text{In the form } ax^2 + bx + c$$

P-1 **What kind of function does $y = \frac{1}{2}(x - 3)^2 + 2$ represent?** Quadratic

example 1

Graph the following functions in the same coordinate plane.

1. $y = \frac{1}{2}x^2$ **2.** $y = \frac{1}{2}(x - 3)^2$ **3.** $y = \frac{1}{2}(x - 3)^2 + 2$

Solutions:

1.

x	y
−3	$4\frac{1}{2}$
−2	2
−1	$\frac{1}{2}$
0	0
1	$\frac{1}{2}$
2	2
3	$4\frac{1}{2}$

2.

x	y
0	$4\frac{1}{2}$
1	2
2	$\frac{1}{2}$
3	0
4	$\frac{1}{2}$
5	2
6	$4\frac{1}{2}$

3.

x	y
0	$6\frac{1}{2}$
1	4
2	$2\frac{1}{2}$
3	2
4	$2\frac{1}{2}$
5	4
6	$6\frac{1}{2}$

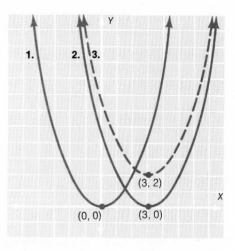

$\blacktriangleright$ *The parabolas have same shape.*

P-2 **How could the graph of $y = \frac{1}{2}(x - 3)^2$ be moved to make it coincide with the graph of $y = \frac{1}{2}(x - 3)^2 + 2$?** 2 units up

P-3 **How could the graph of $y = \frac{1}{2}x^2$ be moved in two steps to make it coincide with the graph of $y = \frac{1}{2}(x - 3)^2 + 2$?** Move 3 units right and 2 units up.

example 2

Graph the following functions in the same coordinate plane.

1. $y = -2x^2$ **2.** $y = -2(x + 4)^2$

3. $y = -2(x + 4)^2 - 3$

Remind students that equations 2 and 3 can be written as $y = -2(x - (-4))^2$ and $y = -2(x - (-4))^2 - 3$.

Solutions:

1.

x	y
−2	−8
−1	−2
0	0
1	−2
2	−8

2.

x	y
−6	−8
−5	−2
−4	0
−3	−2
−2	−8

3.

x	y
−6	−11
−5	−5
−4	−3
−3	−5
−2	−11

▲ *The parabolas have same shape.*

P-4 **How could the graph of $y = -2(x + 4)^2$ be moved to make it coincide with the graph of $y = -2(x + 4)^2 - 3$?** 3 units down

P-5 **How could the graph of $y = -2x^2$ be moved in two steps to make it coincide with the graph of $y = -2(x + 4)^2 - 3$?** Move 4 units left and 3 units down.

Graphs of $y = ax^2$ and $y = a(x - h)^2 + k$

1. The graph of $y = a(x - h)^2 + k$ has the same shape as the graph of $y = ax^2$.
2. The graph of $y = a(x - h)^2 + k$ is $|h|$ units to the right or to the left of the graph of $y = ax^2$.
3. The graph of $y = a(x - h)^2 + k$ is $|k|$ units above or below the graph of $y = ax^2$.

P-6 **How do you know whether the graph of $y = a(x - h)^2 + k$ is to the right or to the left of the graph of $y = ax^2$?** If h is positive, it is to the right. If h is negative, it is to the left.

Quadratic Functions / **437**

P-7 **How do you know whether the graph of $y = a(x - h)^2 + k$ is above or below the graph of $y = ax^2$?** If k is positive, it is above. If k is negative, it is below.

example 3

Write an equation of a function for which the graph is obtained as described below.

"The graph of $y = -\frac{3}{2}x^2$ is moved 4 units to the left and 3 units upward."

Solution: Let $h = -4$, $k = 3$, $a = -\frac{3}{2}$. ◄ The graph is 4 units to the left, 3 units upward, and has the same shape as $y = -\frac{3}{2}x^2$.

$$y = a(x - h)^2 + k$$

$$y = -\frac{3}{2}(x - (-4))^2 + 3$$

$$y = -\frac{3}{2}(x + 4)^2 + 3$$ ◄ Equation of the function

CLASSROOM EXERCISES

Write <u>Yes</u> or <u>No</u> to indicate if the graph of each function below has the same shape as the graph of $y = \frac{1}{2}(x - 3)^2 + 5$.

1. $y = \frac{1}{2}x^2$ Yes

2. $y = 2x^2$ No

3. $y = 3(x - 3)^2 + 5$ No / Yes

4. $y = \frac{1}{2}(x + 3)^2 - 5$ Yes

5. $y = -\frac{1}{2}x^2$ No

6. $y = \frac{1}{2}(x - 4)^2 + 3$

7. What variable in $a(x - h)^2 + k$ represents a number that determines the shape of the parabola? a

8. What variable in $a(x - h)^2 + k$ represents a number that determines the horizontal position of the parabola? h

9. What variable in $a(x - h)^2 + k$ represents a number that determines the vertical position of the parabola? k

Write the two motions needed to make the graph of the first function coincide with the graph of the second function. (P-3, P-5)

10. $y = x^2$ 2 units right, 3 units up
$y = (x - 2)^2 + 3$

11. $y = 3x^2$ 5 units right, 2 units down
$y = 3(x - 5)^2 - 2$

12. $y = \frac{1}{3}x^2$ 3 units left, 5 units up
$y = \frac{1}{3}(x + 3)^2 + 5$

13. $y = -\frac{1}{2}x^2$ 2 units left, 3 units down
$y = -\frac{1}{2}(x + 2)^2 - 3$

14. $y = -x^2$ 2 units right, 1 unit up
$y = -(x - 2)^2 + 1$

15. $y = \frac{3}{4}x^2$
$y = \frac{3}{4}(x + 1)^2 - 1$
1 unit left, 1 unit down

WRITTEN EXERCISES

See the Teacher's Manual for the suggested assignments.

Goal: To use a graph of $y = ax^2$ to graph a function of the form
$$y = a(x - h)^2 + k$$

Sample Problem: Graph in the same coordinate plane: $y = -2x^2$,
$$y = -2(x + 1)^2 + 5, \quad y = -2(x + 1)^2 - 5.$$

Answer: See Examples 1 and 2. In Ex. 1-8, the relationship between the first and second parabola is given.

Graph the first function using the x values $-2, -1, 0, 1,$ *and* 2. *Then graph the second function. (Examples 1 and 2)*

2. Moves 2 units up, 5 units right.

1. $y = \frac{1}{2}x^2$; $y = \frac{1}{2}(x - 2)^2 + 3$ Moves 3 units up, 2 units right.

2. $y = -\frac{1}{2}x^2$; $y = -\frac{1}{2}(x - 5)^2 + 2$

4. Moves 4 units up, 2 units left.

3. $y = -x^2$; $y = -(x + 3)^2 + 2$ Moves 2 units up, 3 units left.

4. $y = x^2$; $y = (x + 2)^2 + 4$

6. Moves 3 units down, 3 units right.

5. $y = 2x^2$; $y = 2(x + 1)^2 - 3$ Moves 3 units down, 1 unit left.

6. $y = -2x^2$; $y = -2(x - 3)^2 - 3$

7. $y = -\frac{3}{2}x^2$; $y = -\frac{3}{2}(x - 3\frac{1}{2})^2 + 2\frac{1}{2}$ Moves $2\frac{1}{2}$ units up, $3\frac{1}{2}$ units right.

8. $y = \frac{3}{2}x^2$; $y = \frac{3}{2}(x + 2\frac{1}{2})^2 - 3\frac{1}{2}$ Moves $3\frac{1}{2}$ units down, $2\frac{1}{2}$ units left.

Write an equation of a function for which the graph is obtained as described in each exercise. (Example 3)

9. The graph of $y = 2x^2$ is moved three units to the right. $y = 2(x - 3)^2$

10. The graph of $y = -3x^2$ is moved five units to the right. $y = -3(x - 5)^2$

11. The graph of $y = \frac{1}{2}x^2$ is moved two units to the left and five units upward. $y = \frac{1}{2}(x + 2)^2 + 5$

12. The graph of $y = 5x^2$ is moved three units to the left and two units upward. $y = 5(x + 3)^2 + 2$

13. The graph of $y = \frac{1}{3}(x + 1)^2$ is moved five units downward. $y = \frac{1}{3}(x + 1)^2 - 5$

14. The graph of $y = -3(x - 5)^2$ is moved four units downward. $y = -3(x - 5)^2 - 4$

15. The graph of $y = -x^2$ is moved three units to the right and two units downward. $y = -(x - 3)^2 - 2$

16. The graph of $y = \frac{1}{2}x^2$ is moved five units to the right and six units downward. $y = \frac{1}{2}(x - 5)^2 - 6$

17. The graph of $y = 3x^2$ is moved five units downward. $y = 3x^2 - 5$

18. The graph of $y = -\frac{1}{2}x^2$ is moved three units downward. $y = \frac{1}{2}x^2 - 3$

REVIEW CAPSULE FOR SECTION 17.6

Find the missing term to form a trinomial square (take $\frac{1}{2}$ the coefficient of x and square it). Then factor the trinomial. (Section 10.6) $(x + \frac{1}{2})(x + \frac{1}{2})$ $(x - \frac{3}{2})(x - \frac{3}{2})$

$(x - 2)(x - 2)$ $(x + 3)(x + 3)$

1. $x^2 - 4x + \underline{?}$ 4 **2.** $x^2 + 6x + \underline{?}$ 9 **3.** $x^2 + x + \underline{?}$ $\frac{1}{4}$ **4.** $x^2 - 3x + \underline{?}$ $\frac{9}{4}$

5. $x^2 + 10x + \underline{?}$ 25 **6.** $x^2 + 18x + \underline{?}$ 81 **7.** $x^2 - 5x + \underline{?}$ $\frac{25}{4}$ **8.** $x^2 - 7x + \underline{?}$ $\frac{49}{4}$

$(x + 5)(x + 5)$ $(x + 9)(x + 9)$ $(x - \frac{5}{2})(x - \frac{5}{2})$ $(x - \frac{7}{2})(x - \frac{7}{2})$

17.6 Standard Form of Quadratic Polynomials

OBJECTIVES: To change an expression from the form $a(x - h)^2 + k$ to the form $ax^2 + bx + c$
To change a polynomial from the form $ax^2 + bx + c$ to the form $a(x - h)^2 + k$

P-1 **What are the values of a, h, and k in each expression below?**

a. $-(x + 3)^2 - \frac{3}{4}$ **b.** $\frac{3}{2}(x - \frac{1}{4})^2 + \frac{5}{4}$ $a = \frac{3}{2}, h = \frac{1}{4}, k = \frac{5}{4}$
$a = -1, h = -3, k = -\frac{3}{4}$

example 1   Change $2(x - 3)^2 + 5$ to the form $ax^2 + bx + c$.

Solution: $2(x - 3)^2 + 5 = 2(x^2 - 6x + 9) + 5$ ◄ $x^2 - 6x + 9$ is a **trinomial square**.

$= 2x^2 - 12x + 18 + 5$

$= 2x^2 - 12x + 23$

Every quadratic polynomial can be changed from the form $ax^2 + bx + c$ to the **standard form** $a(x - h)^2 + k$.

example 2   Change $x^2 + 2x + 5$ to standard form.

Solution:

1. Group terms to form a trinomial square. ⟶ $(x^2 + 2x + \underline{}) + 5 + \underline{}$

2. Multiply the coefficient of x by $\frac{1}{2}$. Square. ⟶ $\frac{1}{2}(2) = 1$; $(1)^2 = 1$

3. Add 1 to make a trinomial square.
   Then add -1. ⟶ $(x^2 + 2x + 1) + 5 + (-1)$

4. Factor and simplify. ⟶ $(x + 1)^2 + 4$

5. Write the standard form. ⟶ $(x - (-1))^2 + 4$ ◄ $a = 1$
                                                          $h = -1$
                                                          $k = 4$

example 3   Change $x^2 - 6x - 2$ to standard form.

Solution:

1. Group terms. ⟶ $(x^2 - 6x + \underline{}) - 2 + \underline{}$

2. Multiply the coefficient of x by $\frac{1}{2}$. Square. ⟶ $\frac{1}{2}(6) = 3$; $3^2 = 9$

3. Add 9 to make a trinomial square.
   Then add -9. ⟶ $(x^2 - 6x + 9) - 2 + (-9)$ ◄ $9 + (-9) = 0$

4. Factor and simplify. ⟶ $(x - 3)^2 - 11$

example 4

Change $x^2 + 5x + 1$ to standard form.

Solution:

1. Group terms. $\longrightarrow$ $(x^2 + 5x + \underline{\ ?\ }) + 1 + \underline{\ ?\ }$

2. Multiply the coefficient of x by $\frac{1}{2}$. Square. $\longrightarrow$ $\frac{1}{2}(5) = \frac{5}{2};\ (\frac{5}{2})^2 = \frac{25}{4}$

3. Add $\frac{25}{4}$. Then add its opposite. $\rightarrow$ $(x^2 + 5x + \frac{25}{4}) + 1 + (-\frac{25}{4})$ $\frac{25}{4} + (-\frac{25}{4}) = 0$

4. Factor and simplify. $\longrightarrow$ $(x + \frac{5}{2})^2 - \frac{21}{4}$

5. Write the standard form. $\longrightarrow$ $(x - (-\frac{5}{2}))^2 - \frac{21}{4}$

CLASSROOM EXERCISES

Tell the form $(x - h)^2$ for each trinomial.

1. $x^2 + 2x + 1$ $(x + 1)^2$ **2.** $x^2 + 4x + 4$ $(x + 2)^2$ **3.** $x^2 - 6x + 9$ $(x - 3)^2$ **4.** $x^2 - 8x + 16$ $(x - 4)^2$

5. $x^2 + x + \frac{1}{4}$ $(x + \frac{1}{2})^2$ **6.** $x^2 - x + \frac{1}{4}$ $(x - \frac{1}{2})^2$ **7.** $x^2 - 5x + \frac{25}{4}$ $(x - \frac{5}{2})^2$ **8.** $x^2 - 3x + \frac{9}{4}$ $(x - \frac{3}{2})^2$

WRITTEN EXERCISES

See the Teacher's Manual for the suggested assignments.

Goal: To write a quadratic polynomial in standard form

Sample Problem: $x^2 - 7x + 10$ **Answer:** $(x - \frac{7}{2})^2 - \frac{9}{4}$

13. $(x - (-3))^2 - 14$
14. $(x - 3)^2 + 1$
15. $(x - 5)^2 - 26$
16. $(x - (-6))^2 - 33$

Change each expression to the form $ax^2 + bx + c$. (Example 1)

1. $(x - 3)^2 + 2$ **2.** $(x - 2)^2 + 5$ **3.** $2(x - 1)^2 - 7$ **4.** $-2(x + 1)^2 - 5$
$x^2 - 6x + 11$ $x^2 - 4x + 9$ $2x^2 - 4x - 5$ $-2x^2 - 4x - 7$

5. $3(x + 2)^2 + 3$ **6.** $5(x - 5)^2 + 3$ **7.** $\frac{1}{2}(x - 2)^2 + 6$ **8.** $-\frac{1}{2}(x + 2)^2 - 3$
$3x^2 + 12x + 15$ $5x^2 - 50x + 128$ $\frac{1}{2}x^2 - 2x + 8$ $-\frac{1}{2}x^2 - 2x - 5$

Change each polynomial to standard form. (Examples 2–4)

9. $x^2 + 2x + 3$ **10.** $x^2 - 2x - 5$ **11.** $x^2 - 4x + 1$ **12.** $x^2 + 4x + 3$
$(x - (-1))^2 + 2$ $(x - 1)^2 - 6$ $(x - 2)^2 - 3$ $(x - (-2))^2 - 1$

13. $x^2 + 6x - 5$ See above.   **14.** $x^2 - 6x + 10$ See above.   **15.** $x^2 - 10x - 1$ See above.   **16.** $x^2 + 12x + 3$ See above.

17. $x^2 - x + 5$ **18.** $x^2 + x - 2$ **19.** $x^2 + 3x - 4$ **20.** $x^2 - 5x - 3$
$(x - \frac{1}{2})^2 + \frac{19}{4}$ $(x - (-\frac{1}{2}))^2 - \frac{9}{4}$ $(x - (-\frac{3}{2}))^2 - \frac{25}{4}$ $(x - \frac{5}{2})^2 - \frac{37}{4}$

REVIEW CAPSULE FOR SECTION 17.7

Identify the values of a, h, and k in each function. (Section 17.5)

1. $y = 3(x - 2)^2 + 1$
$a = 3, h = 2, k = 1$

2. $y = 4(x - 5)^2 - 2$
$a = 4, h = 5, k = -2$

3. $y = \frac{1}{2}(x + \frac{3}{2})^2 - 5$
$a = \frac{1}{2}, h = -\frac{3}{2}, k = -5$

17.7 Vertex and Axis of a Parabola

To write an equation for the axis of the parabola that is the graph of a given function having the rule $y = a(x - h)^2 + k$

You have seen how the values of a, h, and k in $y = a(x - h)^2 + k$ affect the shape and position of the graph. There are other facts about the graph that the standard form can provide.

example 1

The graph of $y = \frac{1}{2}(x - 2)^2 + 3$ is drawn. Write the coordinates of its lowest point.

Solution:

$$y = \frac{1}{2}(x - 2)^2 + 3$$

x	y
0	5
1	$3\frac{1}{2}$
2	3
3	$3\frac{1}{2}$
4	5

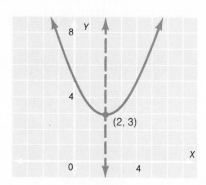

Figure 1

The coordinates of the lowest point of the graph are (2, 3).

Point out that a parabola opening upwards has a lowest point (the vertex). A parabola opening downward has a highest point (also the vertex).

The point with coordinates (2, 3) is called the **vertex of the parabola.** The vertex of a parabola that is a graph of a quadratic function is either the lowest point or the highest point of the graph.

P-1 **Is the vertex in Figure 1 the highest point or the lowest point of the graph?** Lowest point

Compare $\frac{1}{2}(x - 2)^2 + 3$ with the standard form $y = a(x - h)^2 + k$.

P-2 **What is the value of a?** $\frac{1}{2}$ **of h?** 2 **of k?** 3

The coordinates of the vertex of the parabola in Figure 1 are (2, 3). They correspond to (h, k).

> The vertex of a parabola with a rule of the form $y = a(x - h)^2 + k$ has coordinates (h, k).
>
> $y = -2(x - (-5))^2 - 1$
>
> Vertex: $(-5, -1)$

P-3 What are the coordinates of the vertex of the graph of each function below?

a. $y = (x - \frac{1}{2})^2 + \frac{5}{2}$ $(\frac{1}{2}, \frac{5}{2})$ b. $y = (x + 3)^2 - 7$ $(-3, -7)$

A vertical line that contains the vertex of a parabola is called the *axis* of the parabola. The dashed line in Figure 1 is the axis.

P-4 What is an equation for the axis in Figure 1? $x = 2$

> If a parabola has the rule $y = a(x - h)^2 + k$, its axis has the equation $x = h$.
>
> $y = 5(x - 2)^2 + 3$
>
> Equation of axis: $x = 2$

P-5 What is the value of h if you compare each of the following with $y = a(x - h)^2 + k$?

a. $y = -3(x - 5)^2 + 2$ $h = 5$ b. $y = -(x + 3)^2 - 2$ $h = -3$

c. $y = \frac{1}{2}(x - \frac{1}{4})^2 + 1$ $h = \frac{1}{4}$ d. $y = -2(x + \frac{4}{3})^2 - 5$ $h = -\frac{4}{3}$

example 2

Write an equation for the axis of the graph of $y = -(x + 3)^2 - 2$.

Solution: Since $h = -3$,
$x = -3$. ◀ *Equation of the axis*

P-6 What are the coordinates of the vertex of the parabola in Example 2? $(-3, -2)$

CLASSROOM EXERCISES

Write the coordinates of the vertex of each graph. (P-3)

1. $y = 2(x - 5)^2 + 2$ $(5, 2)$

2. $y = 3(x - 1)^2 - 4$ $(1, -4)$

3. $y = -\frac{1}{2}(x + 2)^2 + 6$ $(-2, 6)$

4. $y = (x + 1)^2 - 6$ $(-1, -6)$

5. $y = x^2$ (0, 0)

6. $y = x^2 + 1$ (0, 1)

7. $y = -(x - \frac{1}{2})^2 + \frac{3}{4}$ $(\frac{1}{2}, \frac{3}{4})$

8. $y = 2.5(x + 0.3)^2 - 1.2$
(−0.3, −1.2)

9. $y = (x - 5)^2$ (5, 0)

10. $y = -(x + 4)^2$
(−4, 0)

Write an equation for the axis of each graph. (Example 2)

11. $y = \frac{1}{2}(x + 1)^2 - 2$ $x = -1$

12. $y = -2(x - 3)^2 + 4$ $x = 3$

13. $y = -3(x - \frac{1}{2})^2 + \frac{3}{2}$ $x = \frac{1}{2}$

14. $y = (x + 4.5)^2 - 2.5$ $x = -4.5$

15. $y = -\frac{1}{2}x^2$ $x = 0$

16. $y = \frac{4}{3}x^2$ $x = 0$

17. $y = 2x^2 + 3$ $x = 0$

18. $y = -3(x + 5)^2$ $x = -5$

WRITTEN EXERCISES

See the Teacher's Manual for the suggested assignments.

Goals: To write the coordinates of the vertex and the equation of the
axis of the graph of a parabola

Sample Problem: $y = -3(x + 5)^2 - 2$

Answer: Vertex: $(-5, -2)$;   Equation of axis: $x = -5$

Write the coordinates of the vertex of each graph. (Example 1, P-3)

1. $y = 3(x - 1)^2 + 10$ (1, 10)

2. $y = \frac{1}{2}(x - 5)^2 + 2$ (5, 2)

3. $y = -5(x - 7)^2 - 2$ (7, −2)

4. $y = -3(x - 3)^2 - 5$ (3, −5)

5. $y = -(x + 2)^2 + 3$ (−2, 3)

6. $y = 2(x + 5)^2 + 7$ (−5, 7)

7. $y = \frac{2}{3}(x + 1)^2 - 8$ (−1, −8)

8. $y = -\frac{1}{2}(x + 4)^2 - 3$ (−4, −3)

9. $y = \frac{3}{4}(x - \frac{1}{2})^2 - \frac{2}{3}$ $(\frac{1}{2}, -\frac{2}{3})$

10. $y = \frac{2}{3}(x - \frac{1}{3})^2 - \frac{3}{4}$ $(\frac{1}{3}, -\frac{3}{4})$

Write an equation for the axis of each graph. (Example 2)

11. $y = 3(x - 5)^2 + 2$ $x = 5$

12. $y = -3(x - 2)^2 + 1$ $x = 2$

13. $y = -2(x - 3)^2 + 5$ $x = 3$

14. $y = \frac{1}{2}(x - 1)^2 + 5$ $x = 1$

15. $y = -(x + 1)^2 - 5$ $x = -1$

16. $y = (x + 2)^2 - 6$ $x = -2$

17. $y = 3x^2 - 2x + 3$ $x = \frac{1}{3}$

18. $y = 2x^2 + 3x - 5$ $x = -\frac{3}{4}$

19. $y = -x^2 - 7x + 2$ $x = -\frac{7}{2}$

20. $y = -3x^2 - x + 7$ $x = -\frac{1}{6}$

21. $y = -5x^2 - x + 3$ $x = -\frac{1}{10}$

22. $y = -x^2 - 9x + 1$ $x = -\frac{9}{2}$

Gravity

All objects in the universe are attracted to one another by a force called the <u>force of gravity</u>. Gravity is the force that causes an object to fall when it is released above the ground.

The speed of a falling object starting from rest increases as the object falls. The table at the right shows the object's speed in meters per second after each of the first five seconds. This increase in speed, or <u>acceleration</u>, is due to gravity. The **acceleration due to gravity**, represented by "g," is constant on and near the earth. It has a value of 9.8 meters per second per second.

Time (seconds)	Speed (meters/second)
1	9.8
2	19.6
3	29.4
4	39.2
5	49.0

The following formula computes the distance s that a falling object, starting from rest, travels in a length of time t, with acceleration g.

$$s = \tfrac{1}{2}gt^2$$

EXAMPLE: Find the approximate distance in meters a parachutist would fall after jumping from a plane and free-falling for 12 seconds before opening the chute.

SOLUTION: $s = \tfrac{1}{2}gt^2$ $g = 9.8$
$t = 12$

$s = \tfrac{1}{2}(9.8)(12)^2$

$\quad = 4.9(144)$

$\quad = 705.6$ or about **706 meters**

EXERCISES

1. A plane releases its auxiliary fuel tanks at a low altitude. The tanks take 15 seconds to reach the ground. At what altitude were they released?   1102.5 meters

2. A helicopter drops bales of hay to feed snowbound cattle. Each bale takes 5 seconds to reach the ground. At what height were the bales of hay released?   122.5 meters

3. A rock dropped from the Royal Gorge Bridge in Colorado takes about 8 seconds to reach the river below. Find the approximate height of the bridge above the river to the nearest meter.   314 meters

4. A ball dropped from the observation level of the Washington Monument reaches the ground in about $5\tfrac{1}{2}$ seconds. Find the height to the nearest meter.   148 meters

CHAPTER SUMMARY

NOTE: You may wish to administer a quiz covering Sections 17.5 through 17.7. See page M-43 of the Teacher's Manual for the suggested quiz.

IMPORTANT TERMS

Quadratic function *(p. 422)*
Parabola *(p. 425)*
Standard form of a quadratic polynomial *(p. 440)*
Vertex of a parabola *(p. 442)*
Axis of a parabola *(p. 443)*

IMPORTANT IDEAS

1. *Effect of a on the graph of $y = ax^2 + bx + c$:*
   a. If a is positive, the parabola opens upward.
   b. If a is negative, the parabola opens downward.
   c. If $|a|$ decreases, the parabola becomes wider.

2. The graph of $y = ax^2$ can be moved horizontally $|h|$ units to obtain the graph of $y = a(x - h)^2$. If h is negative, the motion is to the left. If h is positive, the motion is to the right.

3. The graph of $y = a(x - h)^2 + k$ has the same shape as the graph of $y = ax^2$.

4. The graph of $y = a(x - h)^2 + k$ is $|h|$ units to the right or to the left of the graph of $y = ax^2$.

5. The graph of $y = a(x - h)^2 + k$ is $|k|$ units above or below the graph of $y = ax^2$.

6. Every quadratic polynomial can be changed from the form $ax^2 + bx + c$ to the standard form $a(x - h)^2 + k$.

7. The vertex of a parabola with a rule of the form $y = a(x - h)^2 + k$ has coordinates (h, k).

8. If a parabola has the rule $y = a(x - h)^2 + k$, its axis has the equation $x = h$.

CHAPTER REVIEW

NOTE: The Teacher's Resource Book contains two forms of each Chapter Test.

SECTION 17.1

Write Yes or No to show whether each rule describes a quadratic function.

1. $y = -5x + 1$ No

2. $y = -x^2 + 3x - 5$ Yes

Compute $f(-1)$, $f(0)$, and $f(2)$ for each function f below.

3. $y = -3x^2 + x - 1$ $-5; -1; -11$

4. $y = (2x - 1)^2$ $9; 1; 9$

SECTION 17.2 In Ex. 5-10 the high or low point and three points on the parabola are given.

Graph each function.

5. $y = x^2 - 1$ Turns at $(0, -1)$; low point; $(-1, 0), (0, -1), (1, 0)$

6. $y = -x^2 + 2$ Turns at $(0, 2)$; high point; $(-1, 1), (0, 2), (1, 1)$

7. $y = -\frac{1}{2}x^2 + x$ Turns at $(1, \frac{1}{2})$; high point; $(0, 0), (1, \frac{1}{2})$; $(2, 0)$

8. $y = \frac{1}{2}x^2 - 2x$ Turns at $(2, -2)$; low point; $(1, -\frac{3}{2}), (2, -2), (3, -\frac{3}{2})$

9. $y = x^2 + 2x - 3$ Turns at $(-1, -4)$; low point; $(-2, -3), (-1, -4), (0, -3)$

10. $y = -x^2 + 4x + 5$ Turns at $(2, 9)$; high point; $(0, 5), (2, 9), (4, 5)$

SECTION 17.3 In Ex. 11-18, three points are given for each parabola. The point at which it opens is also given.

Graph the two functions in the same coordinate plane.

11. $y = -\frac{1}{2}x^2$; $y = -2x^2$ $(-1, -\frac{1}{2}), (0, 0), (1, -\frac{1}{2})$; $(-1, -2), (0, 0), (1, -2)$; parabolas open downward at $(0, 0)$.

12. $y = -x^2$; $y = -\frac{3}{2}x^2$ $(-1, -1), (0, 0), (1, -1)$; $(-1, -\frac{3}{2}), (0, 0), (1, -\frac{3}{2})$; parabolas open downward at $(0, 0)$.

13. $y = \frac{5}{2}x^2$; $y = -\frac{5}{2}x^2$ $(-1, \frac{5}{2}), (0, 0), (1, \frac{5}{2})$; opens upward at $(0, 0)$. $(-1, -\frac{5}{2}), (0, 0), (1, -\frac{5}{2})$; opens downward at $(0,0)$.

14. $y = -\frac{1}{2}x^2$; $y = \frac{1}{2}x^2$ $(-1, \frac{1}{2}), (0, 0), (1, \frac{1}{2})$; opens upward at $(0, 0)$. $(-1, -\frac{1}{2}), (0, 0), (1, -\frac{1}{2})$; opens downward at $(0, 0)$.

Graph each parabola.

15. $x = \frac{1}{2}y^2$ $(\frac{1}{2}, -1), (0, 0),$ $(\frac{1}{2}, 1)$; turns right at $(0, 0)$.

16. $x = \frac{3}{2}y^2$ $(\frac{3}{2}, -1), (0, 0),$ $(\frac{3}{2}, 1)$; turns right at $(0, 0)$.

17. $x = -y^2$ $(-1, -1), (0, 0),$ $(-1, 1)$; turns left $(0, 0)$.

18. $x = -2y^2$ $(-2, -1),$ $(-2, 1)$; turns left at $(0, 0)$.

SECTION 17.4

Write the number of units and the direction the graph of the first function can be moved to obtain the graph of the second function.

19. $y = 2x^2$; $y = 2(x + 3)^2$ 3 units left

20. $y = -\frac{1}{2}x^2$; $y = -\frac{1}{2}(x - 5)^2$ 5 units right

21. $y = -x^2$; $y = -(x - \frac{5}{2})^2$ $\frac{5}{2}$ units right

22. $y = x^2$; $y = (x + 12)^2$ 12 units left

SECTION 17.5 In Ex. 23-26, the relationship between the first and second parabola is given.

Graph the first function using the x values $-2, -1, 0, 1,$ and 2. Then graph the second function.

23. $y = x^2$
$y = (x - 3)^2 - 2$ Moves 2 units down, 3 units right.

24. $y = -x^2$
$y = -(x + 2)^2 - 3$ Moves 3 units down, 2 units left.

25. $y = -\frac{1}{2}x^2$
$y = -\frac{1}{2}(x + 1)^2 + 3$ Moves 3 units up, 1 unit left.

26. $y = \frac{3}{2}x^2$
$y = \frac{3}{2}(x - 3)^2 + 1$ Moves 1 unit up, 3 units right.

Write an equation of a function for which the graph is obtained as described in each exercise.

27. The graph of $y = -10x^2$ is moved 5 units to the left. $y = -10(x + 5)^2$

28. The graph of $y = 4x^2$ is moved 8 units to the right. $y = 4(x - 8)^2$

Write an equation of a function for which the graph is obtained as described in each exercise.

$$y = \frac{5}{2}(x - 2)^2 - 3$$

29. The graph of $\frac{5}{2}x^2$ is moved 2 units to the right and 3 units downward.

30. The graph of $-3.7x^2$ is moved 4 units to the left and 2 units upward.

$$y = -3.7(x + 4)^2 + 2$$

SECTION 17.6

Change each expression to the form $ax^2 + bx + c$.

31. $(x + 1)^2 - 5$ $x^2 + 2x - 4$

32. $(x - 3)^2 + 4$ $x^2 - 6x + 13$

$-3x^2 + 12x - 11$
33. $-3(x - 2)^2 + 1$

34. $4(x + 1)^2 - 6$ $4x^2 + 8x - 2$

35. $\frac{1}{2}(x + 4)^2 - 8$ $\frac{1}{2}x^2 + 4x$

36. $-\frac{1}{2}(x - 2)^2 + 3$
$-\frac{1}{2}x^2 + 2x + 1$

Change each polynomial to the form $(x - h)^2 + k$.

37. $x^2 - 6x + 2$ $(x - 3)^2 - 7$

38. $x^2 + 4x - 5$ $(x - (-2))^2 - 9$

39. $x^2 + 3x - \frac{1}{4}$

40. $x^2 - 5x + \frac{3}{4}$ $\left(x - \frac{5}{2}\right)^2 - \frac{11}{2}$

41. $x^2 - 2x + \frac{1}{2}$ $(x - 1)^2 - \frac{1}{2}$

42. $x^2 + 7x + \frac{5}{4}$

$$\left(x - \left(-\frac{7}{2}\right)\right)^2 - 11$$

SECTION 17.7

Write the coordinates of the vertex of each graph.

39. $\left(x - \left(\frac{3}{2}\right)\right)^2 - \frac{5}{2}$

43. $y = \frac{1}{2}(x - 10)^2 + 5$ (10, 5)

44. $y = -2(x + 8)^2 - 3$ (−8, −3)

45. $y = 3(x - 6)^2$ (6, 0)

46. $y = -4(x + 5)^2$ (−5, 0)

Write an equation for the axis of each graph.

47. $y = \frac{3}{2}(x - 2)^2 + 5$ $x = 2$

48. $y = -5(x + 1)^2 - 6$ $x = -1$

49. $y = -\left(x + \frac{9}{2}\right)^2 - \frac{7}{2}$ $x = -\frac{9}{2}$

50. $y = \left(x - \frac{4}{3}\right)^2 + \frac{5}{3}$ $x = \frac{4}{3}$

CHAPTER

18 Quadratic Equations

Sections 18.1 Quadratic Equations and Graphs

18.2 Solving by Factoring

18.3 Special Quadratic Equations

18.4 Completing the Square

18.5 The Quadratic Formula

18.6 The Discriminant

18.7 Problem Solving with Quadratic Equations

Features *Calculator Exercises:* Radicals within Radicals

Career: Industrial Production Technician

Review
and
Testing
Review Capsules

Mid-Chapter Review

Chapter Summary

Chapter Review

Cumulative Review: Chapters 13-18

18.1 Quadratic Equations and Graphs

To graph a function defined by $y = ax^2 + bx + c$ and then write the approximate solutions of an equation $ax^2 + bx + c = k$ where a, b, and c have the same values as in $y = ax^2 + bx + c$ and where k is a rational number

The equation $ax^2 + bx + c = 0$ can be obtained from the rule of the function $y = ax^2 + bx + c$ if y is replaced with 0.

> A **quadratic equation** is an equation of the form $ax^2 + bx + c = 0$, ($a \neq 0$). (a, b, and c represent rational numbers in this course.)
>
> $2x^2 - 3x + 1 = 0$
>
> $-\frac{1}{2}x^2 + \frac{3}{2}x + \frac{1}{4} = 0$

example 1

Change $x^2 - 3x - 5 = 2$ to the form $ax^2 + bx + c = 0$.

Solution:

1. Subtract 2 from each side. ⟶ $x^2 - 3x - 5 - 2 = 2 - 2$

2. Simplify. ⟶ $x^2 - 3x - 7 = 0$ ◀ **In the form** $ax^2 + bx + c = 0$

A graph of the function $y = x^2 - x - 2$ is shown in Figure 1.

The standard form of $y = x^2 - x - 2$ is $y = (x - \frac{1}{2})^2 - \frac{9}{4}$. You can see that the coordinates of the vertex are $(\frac{1}{2}, -2\frac{1}{4})$,

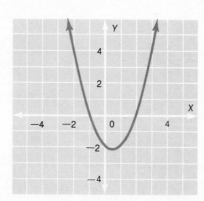

Figure 1

P-1   **What are the x values of the points which the parabola and the X axis have in common?** $-1, 2$

The numbers -1 and 2 are **zeros of the function** $y = x^2 - x - 2$. They are values of x which make the value of the function 0. They are also the **solutions** of $x^2 - x - 2 = 0$.

example 2

Use the graph of $y = x^2 - x - 2$ to estimate the solutions of $x^2 - x - 2 = 4$.

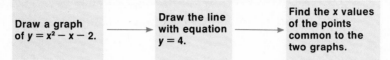

| Draw a graph of $y = x^2 - x - 2$. | → | Draw the line with equation $y = 4$. | → | Find the x values of the points common to the two graphs. |

Solution: Notice the x values of points A and B in Figure 2.

The numbers -2 and 3 are the solutions of $x^2 - x - 2 = 4$.

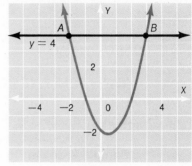

Figure 2

You can estimate the solutions of other equations from the same graph. Note the horizontal lines and their equations.

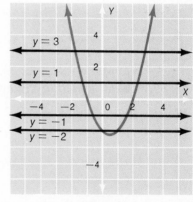

Figure 3

Equation	Estimated Solutions
$x^2 - x - 2 = 3$	$-1.8, 2.8$
$x^2 - x - 2 = -1$	$-0.6, 1.6$
$x^2 - x - 2 = 1$	$-1.3, 2.3$
$x^2 - x - 2 = -2$	$0, 1$

The line with equation $y = -3$ does not intersect the parabola. There are no real solutions for $x^2 - x - 2 = -3$.

CLASSROOM EXERCISES

Change each equation to the form $ax^2 + bx + c = 0$. (Example 1)

1. $x^2 - 2x - 1 = 2$ $x^2 - 2x - 3 = 0$ **2.** $2x^2 - 3x + 5 = 1$ $2x^2 - 3x + 4 = 0$ **3.** $-3x^2 + 5x = 6$

$3x^2 - 5x + 6 = 0$

4. $5x - x^2 + 3 = 0$ $x^2 - 5x - 3 = 0$ **5.** $4 + x^2 + 2x = 0$ $x^2 + 2x + 4 = 0$ **6.** $x^2 = 2x$

$x^2 - 2x = 0$

The graph of $y = x^2 - 4x + 3$ is shown at the right. Estimate the solutions of each equation from the graph. (Example 2)

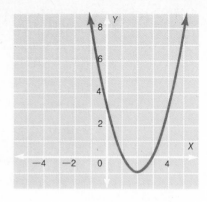

7. $x^2 - 4x + 3 = 0$ 1, 3

8. $x^2 - 4x + 3 = 1$ 0.5, 3.5

9. $x^2 - 4x + 3 = 3$ 0, 4

10. $x^2 - 4x + 3 = 5$ $-\frac{1}{4}, 4\frac{1}{4}$

11. $x^2 - 4x + 3 = -1$ 2

12. $x^2 - 4x + 3 = -2$ No real solutions

WRITTEN EXERCISES

See the Teacher's Manual for the suggested assignments.

Goal: To estimate the solutions of a quadratic equation from the graph of a related function

Sample Problem: $x^2 - x - 2 = 2$ (Refer to Figure 2.)

Answer: The solutions are approximately 2.6 and -1.6.

Change each equation to the form $ax^2 + bx + c = 0$. (Example 1)

1. $x^2 = 5x - 3$ $x^2 - 5x + 3 = 0$

2. $x^2 = 5 - 3x$ $x^2 + 3x - 5 = 0$

3. $5x - 2x^2 = 10$ $2x^2 - 5x + 10 = 0$

4. $3x - x^2 = -5$ $x^2 - 3x - 5 = 0$

5. $x^2 = 9$ $x^2 - 9 = 0$

6. $x^2 = 3x$ $x^2 - 3x = 0$

Graph $y = x^2 + 2x - 3$. Refer to this graph to estimate the solutions of each equation. (Example 2)

7. $x^2 + 2x - 3 = 0$ $-3, 1$

8. $x^2 + 2x - 3 = 1$ $-3.2, 1.2$

9. $x^2 + 2x - 3 = 2$ $-3.4, 1.4$

10. $x^2 + 2x - 3 = 4$ $-3.8, 1.8$

11. $x^2 + 2x - 3 = -5$ No real solutions

12. $x^2 + 2x - 3 = -6$ No real solutions

Graph $y = -x^2 + 4x - 5$. Estimate the solutions of each equation. (Example 2)

13. $-x^2 + 4x - 5 = 0$ No real solutions

14. $-x^2 + 4x - 5 = 1$ No real solutions

15. $-x^2 + 4x - 5 = -1$ 2

16. $-x^2 + 4x - 5 = -2$ 1, 3

17. $-x^2 + 4x - 5 = -3$ 0.6, 3.4

18. $-x^2 + 4x - 5 = -4$ 0.3, 3.7

REVIEW CAPSULE FOR SECTION 18.2

Factor each trinomial. (Section. 10.4)

1. $x^2 - 4x - 12$ $(x - 6)(x + 2)$

2. $x^2 - 7x + 10$ $(x - 5)(x - 2)$

3. $x^2 - 2x - 24$ $(x - 6)(x + 4)$

4. $x^2 + x - 56$ $(x - 7)(x + 8)$

5. $2x^2 + 7x - 4$ $(2x - 1)(x + 4)$

6. $3x^2 - 5x + 2$ $(3x - 2)(x - 1)$

7. $7 - x^2 - 6x$ $(x - 1)(x + 7)$

8. $9x^2 + 14 - 65x$ $(x - 7)(9x - 2)$

18.2 Solving by Factoring

OBJECTIVE: To solve a quadratic equation by using the Factors of Zero Property

In this course, polynomials represent real numbers. Therefore, the **Factors of Zero Property** applies to polynomials.

> **Factors of Zero Property**
>
> If a and b are real numbers and $ab = 0$, then $a = 0$ or $b = 0$.

P-1 **What is the value of x in the equation $x + 5 = 0$?** −5
in the equation $x - 2 = 0$? 2

example 1 — Solve $(x + 5)(x - 2) = 0$.

Solution:

$$(x + 5)(x - 2) = 0$$

1. Factors of Zero Property $\longrightarrow$ $x + 5 = 0$ *or* $x - 2 = 0$

2. Solve both equations. $\longrightarrow$ $x = -5$ $\qquad x = 2$

You may want to demonstrate checks of the solution in all the Examples.

The solution set is $\{-5, 2\}$.

example 2 — Solve $x^2 - 2x - 3 = 0$.

Factor the left side.	$\longrightarrow$	Apply the Factors of Zero Property.	$\longrightarrow$	Solve for values of x.

Solution:

$$x^2 - 2x - 3 = 0$$

◀ *In the form* $ax^2 + bx + c = 0$

1. Factor. $\longrightarrow$ $(x - 3)(x + 1) = 0$

2. Factors of Zero Property $\longrightarrow$ $x - 3 = 0$ *or* $x + 1 = 0$

3. Solve both equations. $\longrightarrow$ $x = 3$ $\qquad x = -1$

The solution set is $\{3, -1\}$.

example 3   Solve $x^2 - 6x + 9 = 0$.

Solution: $x^2 - 6x + 9 = 0$

$(x - 3)(x - 3) = 0$

$x - 3 = 0$ *or* $x - 3 = 0$

Both equations have the same solution, 3.
Solution set: $\{3\}$

Before solving a quadratic equation, be sure that it is in the form $ax^2 + bx + c = 0$.

example 4   Solve $x^2 = 5x$.

Solution: $x^2 = 5x$

1. Subtract $5x$ from each side. ⟶ $x^2 - 5x = 0$ 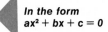 *In the form* $ax^2 + bx + c = 0$

2. Factor. ⟶ $x(x - 5) = 0$

3. Factors of Zero Property ⟶ $x = 0$ *or* $x - 5 = 0$

4. Solve both equations. ⟶ $x = 0$ $x = 5$

Solution set: $\{0, 5\}$

example 5   Solve $2x^2 + x = 6$.

Solution: $2x^2 + x = 6$

1. Subtract 6 from each side. ⟶ $2x^2 + x - 6 = 0$

2. Factor. ⟶ $(2x - 3)(x + 2) = 0$

3. Factors of Zero Property ⟶ $2x - 3 = 0$ *or* $x + 2 = 0$

4. Solve both equations. ⟶ $2x - 3 + 3 = 0 + 3$ $x + 2 - 2 = 0 - 2$

$2x = 3$ $x = -2$

$\frac{1}{2}(2x) = \frac{1}{2}(3)$

$x = \frac{3}{2}$ Solution set: $\{\frac{3}{2}, -2\}$

CLASSROOM EXERCISES

Solve. (Example 1)

1. $(x - 3)(x + 5) = 0$ 3, –5

2. $x(x - 1) = 0$ 0, 1

3. $(x - 6)(x + 6) = 0$ 6, –6

4. $(x - 2)(x - 7) = 0$ 2, 7

5. $(x + 4)(x + 7) = 0$ –4, –7

6. $(x - 3)(x - 3) = 0$ 3

7. $(2x - 1)(x + 5) = 0$ $\frac{1}{2}$, –5

8. $(x - 1)(2x + 1) = 0$ 1, $-\frac{1}{2}$

9. $(2x + 3)(x + 1) = 0$ $-\frac{3}{2}$, –1

10. $(4x - 1)(3x + 2) = 0$ $\frac{1}{4}$, $-\frac{2}{3}$

WRITTEN EXERCISES

See the Teacher's Manual for the suggested assignments.

Goal: To use the Factors of Zero Property to solve quadratic equations

Sample Problem: $x^2 - 56 = -x$

Answer: $\{7, -8\}$

Solve. (Examples 2–4)

1. $x^2 + 3x = 0$ 0, –3

2. $x^2 - 4x = 0$ 0, 4

3. $x^2 - 25 = 0$ 5, –5

4. $x^2 - 49 = 0$ 7, –7

5. $x^2 = 10x$ 0, 10

6. $x^2 = -8x$ 0, –8

7. $x^2 = 100$ 10, –10

8. $x^2 = 81$ 9, –9

9. $x^2 + 4x - 5 = 0$ –5, 1

10. $x^2 - 5x + 6 = 0$ 2, 3

11. $x^2 + 3x = 4$ –4, 1

12. $x^2 - 3x = 10$ –2, 5

13. $x^2 + 8x + 16 = 0$ –4

14. $x^2 - 12x + 36 = 0$ 6

15. $x^2 + 4 = 4x$ 2

16. $x^2 + 9 = -6x$ –3

17. $8x - 12 = x^2$ 2, 6

18. $2x + x^2 = 24$ –6, 4

19. $x^2 + 24 = 11x$ 3, 8

20. $x^2 + 15 = 8x$ 3, 5

21. $x^2 + 18x = -81$ –9

22. $x^2 + 100 = 20x$ 10

23. $x^2 = x + 72$ –8, 9

24. $7 = x^2 + 6x$ –7, 1

Solve. (Example 5)

25. $3x^2 + 8x - 3 = 0$ –3, $\frac{1}{3}$

26. $2x^2 - 9x + 7 = 0$ 1, $\frac{7}{2}$

27. $6x^2 + x - 2 = 0$ $-\frac{2}{3}$, $\frac{1}{2}$

28. $9x^2 - 9x + 2 = 0$ $\frac{1}{3}$, $\frac{2}{3}$

29. $4 - 12x^2 = 13x$ $-\frac{4}{3}$, $\frac{1}{4}$

30. $10 - 15x^2 = 19x$ $-\frac{5}{3}$, $\frac{2}{5}$

31. $8x^2 - 5 + 6x = 0$ $-\frac{5}{4}$, $\frac{1}{2}$

32. $6x^2 - 7x - 5 = 0$ $-\frac{1}{2}$, $\frac{5}{3}$

33. $2x^2 - 13x = 45$ $-\frac{5}{2}$, 9

34. $9x^2 + 14 = 65x$ $\frac{2}{9}$, 7

35. $4x^2 + x - 3 = 0$ –1, $\frac{3}{4}$

36. $25x^2 + 9 - 30x = 0$ $\frac{3}{5}$

OBJECTIVES: To solve an equation of the form $x^2 = k$, where k is a nonnegative rational number
To write an equivalent compound *or* sentence for a quadratic equation of the form $(x - a)^2 = k$,
where a and k are
rational numbers, $k \geqslant 0$

18.3 Special Quadratic Equations

To solve a quadratic equation of the form $(x - a)^2 = k$, where a and k are rational numbers, $k \geqslant 0$
To solve a quadratic equation of the form $x^2 + bx + c = k$, where $x^2 + bx + c$ is a trinomial square and $k \geqslant 0$

P-1 **Solve each equation below.**

a. $x^2 = 16$ **b.** $x^2 = 49$ **c.** $x^2 = 100$
4, −4   7, −7   10, −10

If the left side of an equation is the square of a binomial, the equation can be solved in the same way you solved P-1.

example 1

Solve $(x - 3)^2 = 25$.

Solution:

☐1 Write the equivalent compound *or* sentence. ⟶ $x - 3 = 5$ *or* $x - 3 = -5$

☐2 Solve both equations. ⟶ $x = 8$ $x = -2$

Solution set: $\{8, -2\}$

Check: $(x - 3)^2 = 25$ $(x - 3)^2 = 25$

$(8 - 3)^2$ $(-2 - 3)^2$

5^2 $(-5)^2$

25 25

This rule will be useful in the sections that follow.

Any quadratic equation of the form $(x + r)^2 = s$ in which r and s are rational numbers, $s \geq 0$, is equivalent to "$x + r = \sqrt{s}$ *or* $x + r = -\sqrt{s}$."

"$(x + 1)^2 = 5$"
is equivalent to
"$x + 1 = \sqrt{5}$ *or* $x + 1 = -\sqrt{5}$."

P-2 **What is the value of r if you compare $(x - 5)^2 = 81$ with $(x + r)^2 = s$?**
−5

example 2

Solve $(x - 5)^2 = 81$.

Solution: $(x - 5)^2 = 81$

$x - 5 = 9$ *or* $x - 5 = -9$

$x = 14$ $x = -4$

Solution set: $\{14, -4\}$

The check is left for you.

You have learned to tell whether a quadratic trinomial of the form $ax^2 + bx + c$ is a trinomial square.

1. The leading coefficient a must be a perfect square.
2. The constant term c must be a perfect square.
3. The sentence $(\frac{1}{2}b)^2 = ac$ must be true.

P-3 **What is the value of a in $x^2 - 8x + 16$? of c? of $(\frac{1}{2}b)^2$? of ac?**
　　　　　　　　　　　　　　　　　　　1　　　　16　　　　16　　　16

example 3 Solve $x^2 - 8x + 16 = 36$.

Solution:　　　$x^2 - 8x + 16 = 36$　◀ $x^2 - 8x + 16$ *is a trinomial square.*

$$(x - 4)^2 = 36$$

$$x - 4 = 6 \quad or \quad x - 4 = -6$$

$$x = 10 \qquad\qquad x = -2$$　◀ *The check is left for you.*

Solution set: $\{10, -2\}$

example 4 Solve $x^2 + 3x + \frac{9}{4} = 5$.

Solution: $x^2 + 3x + \frac{9}{4}$ is a trinomial square over {rational numbers}.

$$a = 1 \qquad b = 3 \qquad c = \frac{9}{4} \qquad ◀ \text{ } a \text{ and } c \text{ are perfect squares.}$$

$$(\tfrac{1}{2}b) = \tfrac{3}{2}$$

$$(\tfrac{1}{2}b)^2 = \tfrac{9}{4} \qquad ac = \tfrac{9}{4} \qquad ◀ (\tfrac{1}{2}b)^2 = ac$$

$$x^2 + 3x + \tfrac{9}{4} = 5$$

$$(x + \tfrac{3}{2})^2 = 5$$

$$x + \tfrac{3}{2} = \sqrt{5} \quad or \quad x + \tfrac{3}{2} = -\sqrt{5}$$

$$x = -\tfrac{3}{2} + \sqrt{5} \qquad x = -\tfrac{3}{2} - \sqrt{5}$$

Solution set: $\{-\tfrac{3}{2} + \sqrt{5}, -\tfrac{3}{2} - \sqrt{5}\}$

CLASSROOM EXERCISES

Solve. (P-1)

1. $x^2 = 1$ $1, -1$　　　**2.** $x^2 = 5$ $\sqrt{5}, -\sqrt{5}$　　　**3.** $x^2 = 121$ $11, -11$　　　**4.** $x^2 = 3$ $\sqrt{3}, -\sqrt{3}$

Write an equivalent compound <u>or</u> sentence. (Step 1 of Example 1)

5. $(x-6)^2 = 36$ $x-6=6$ or $x-6=-6$ **6.** $(x+3)^2 = 49$ $x+3=7$ or $x+3=-7$ **7.** $(x-\frac{1}{2})^2 = 16$

$$x - \frac{1}{2} = 4 \text{ or } x - \frac{1}{2} = -4$$

Write the values of $(\frac{1}{2}b)^2$ and ac for each trinomial. Write <u>Yes</u> or <u>No</u> to indicate if each trinomial is a trinomial square. (P-3)

36; 36; Yes

8. $x^2 + 2x + 2$ 1; 2; No   **9.** $x^2 - 4x + 2$ 4; 2; No   **10.** $x^2 - 12x + 36$

11. $x^2 + 10x + 25$ 25; 25; Yes   **12.** $x^2 + x + \frac{1}{4}$ $\frac{1}{4}$; $\frac{1}{4}$; Yes   **13.** $x^2 - 3x + \frac{3}{4}$

$$\frac{9}{4}; \frac{3}{4}; \text{No}$$

Write two equal factors of each trinomial square over {rational numbers}.

See below.

14. $x^2 - 8x + 16$ $x-4, x-4$ **15.** $x^2 + 20x + 100$ $x+10, x+10$ **16.** $x^2 + x + \frac{1}{4}$

17. $x^2 - \frac{1}{2}x + \frac{1}{16}$ $x - \frac{1}{4}, x - \frac{1}{4}$ **18.** $x^2 + 5x + \frac{25}{4}$ $x + \frac{5}{2}, x + \frac{5}{2}$ **19.** $x^2 - 3x + \frac{9}{4}$

$$x - \frac{3}{2}, x - \frac{3}{2}$$

WRITTEN EXERCISES

16. $x + \frac{1}{2}, x + \frac{1}{2}$

See the Teacher's Manual for the suggested assignments.

Goal: To solve quadratic equations of the form $(x + r)^2 = s$

Sample Problem: Solve $x^2 + x + \frac{1}{4} = 9$.   **Answer:** $\{\frac{5}{2}, -\frac{7}{2}\}$

Solve each equation. (P-1)

15, −15

1. $x^2 = 9$ 3, −3   **2.** $x^2 = 16$ 4, −4   **3.** $x^2 = 169$ 13, −13   **4.** $x^2 = 225$

5. $x^2 = 7$ $\sqrt{7}, -\sqrt{7}$ **6.** $x^2 = 10$ $\sqrt{10}, -\sqrt{10}$ **7.** $x^2 = 75$ $5\sqrt{3}, -5\sqrt{3}$ **8.** $x^2 = 48$

$$4\sqrt{3}, -4\sqrt{3}$$

Write an equivalent compound <u>or</u> sentence. (Step 1 of Example 1)

$x + 6 = 5$ or $x + 6 = -5$

9. $(x-5)^2 = 36$ $x-5=6$ or $x-5=-6$ **10.** $(x-4)^2 = 49$ $x-4=7$ or $x-4=-7$ **11.** $(x+6)^2 = 25$

12. $(x-1)^2 = 5$ $x-1=\sqrt{5}$ or $x-1=-\sqrt{5}$ **13.** $(x+\frac{1}{2})^2 = \frac{1}{4}$ $x+\frac{1}{2}=\frac{1}{2}$ or $x+\frac{1}{2}=-\frac{1}{2}$ **14.** $(x+\frac{2}{3})^2 = \frac{4}{9}$

$$x + \frac{2}{3} = \frac{2}{3} \text{ or } x + \frac{2}{3} = -\frac{2}{3}$$

Solve. (Examples 1–4)

$3 + \sqrt{5}, 3 - \sqrt{5}$

15. $(x+1)^2 = 121$ −12, 10   **16.** $(x+2)^2 = 169$ −15, 11   **17.** $(x-3)^2 = 5$

18. $(x-5)^2 = 3$ $5+\sqrt{3}, 5-\sqrt{3}$ **19.** $(x-\frac{1}{2})^2 = \frac{1}{4}$ 0, 1   **20.** $(x-\frac{3}{4})^2 = \frac{1}{16}$ $\frac{1}{2}$, 1

21. $(x+\frac{2}{3})^2 = \frac{5}{9}$ $-\frac{2}{3} + \frac{\sqrt{5}}{3}, -\frac{2}{3} - \frac{\sqrt{5}}{3}$ **22.** $(x+\frac{1}{3})^2 = \frac{2}{9}$ $-\frac{1}{3} + \frac{\sqrt{2}}{3}, -\frac{1}{3} - \frac{\sqrt{2}}{3}$ **23.** $x^2 + 8x + 16 = 0$ −4

24. $x^2 + 12x + 36 = 0$ −6   **25.** $x^2 - 10x + 25 = 0$ 5   **26.** $x^2 - 6x + 9 = 0$ 3

27. $x^2 - \frac{1}{2}x + \frac{1}{16} = 0$ $\frac{1}{4}$ **28.** $x^2 - 3x + \frac{9}{4} = 0$ $\frac{3}{2}$ **29.** $x^2 - \frac{4}{5}x + \frac{4}{25} = 0$ $\frac{2}{5}$

MORE CHALLENGING EXERCISES

Write the missing numeral in each trinomial square.

30. $x^2 + 8x + \underline{\ ?\ }$ 16   **31.** $x^2 - 10x + \underline{\ ?\ }$ 25   **32.** $x^2 - 20x + \underline{\ ?\ }$ 100

33. $x^2 + \underline{\ ?\ }x + 64$ 16   **34.** $x^2 - \underline{\ ?\ }x + \frac{1}{4}$ 1   **35.** $x^2 - \underline{\ ?\ }x + \frac{9}{4}$ 3

MID-CHAPTER REVIEW

NOTE: After completing the Mid-Chapter Review, you may want to administer a quiz covering the same sections. See pages M-44 and M-45 of the Teacher's Manual for the suggested quiz.

Graph $y = x^2 + 3x - 4$. Estimate the solutions in each equation.
(Section 18.1)

1. $x^2 + 3x - 4 = 0$ $\quad$ $-4, 1$ $\qquad$ **2.** $x^2 + 3x - 4 = 1$ $\;$ $2.1, -4.1$ $\qquad$ **3.** $x^2 + 3x - 4 = 2$ $\quad$ $1.3, -4.3$

4. $x^2 + 3x - 4 = -1$ $\;$ $-3.8, 0.8$ $\qquad$ **5.** $x^2 + 3x - 4 = -2$ $\;$ $0.6, -3.8$ $\qquad$ **6.** $x^2 + 3x - 4 = -3$ $\quad$ $0.3, -3.3$

Solve. (Section 18.2)

7. $2x^2 + 9x - 5 = 0$ $\;$ $\frac{1}{2}, -5$ $\qquad$ **8.** $2x^2 - 5x - 3 = 0$ $\;$ $3, -\frac{1}{2}$ $\qquad$ **9.** $3x^2 - 2x - 1 = 0$ $\quad$ $1, -\frac{1}{3}$

10. $4x^2 - 5x + 1 = 0$ $\;$ $1, \frac{1}{4}$ $\qquad$ **11.** $6x^2 + 5x + 1 = 0$ $\quad$ $-\frac{1}{2}, -\frac{1}{3}$ $\qquad$ **12.** $4x^2 + 4x - 3 = 0$ $\quad$ $-\frac{3}{2}, \frac{1}{2}$

Solve. (Section 18.3)

13. $(x - 3)^2 = 144$ $\;$ $15, -9$ $\qquad$ **14.** $(x + 5)^2 = 81$ $\;$ $4, -14$ $\qquad$ **15.** $x^2 - x + \frac{1}{4} = \frac{9}{4}$ $\;$ $2, -1$

16. $x^2 + x + \frac{1}{4} = \frac{9}{16}$ $\;$ $\frac{1}{4}, -\frac{5}{4}$ $\qquad$ **17.** $x^2 + 10x + 25 = 9$ $\;$ $-8, -2$ $\qquad$ **18.** $x^2 + 14x + 49 = 121$ $\;$ $4, -18$

RADICALS WITHIN RADICALS

You can use a calculator to evaluate an expression such as the following that involves several radicals.

$$\sqrt{x + \sqrt{x + \sqrt{x + \sqrt{x}}}}$$

Suggest that students extend the number of radicals and conjecture what happens to the approximate values obtained. Hint: In this Example the result approaches 2.

EXAMPLE $\quad$ Evaluate the above expression for $x = 2$.

SOLUTION $\quad$ Start with 2 at the extreme right. Then work to the left.

$$1.9903694$$

Evaluate the radical expression shown above for each given value of x.

1. $x = 4$ $\;$ 2.5572611 $\qquad$ **2.** $x = 3$ $\;$ 2.2967225 $\qquad$ **3.** $x = 10$ $\;$ 3.7002175 $\qquad$ **4.** $x = 16$ $\;$ 4.5304099

5. $x = 5.2$ $\;$ 2.8314161 $\qquad$ **6.** $x = 0.67$ $\;$ 1.4299625 $\qquad$ **7.** $x = 100$ $\;$ 10.512436 $\qquad$ **8.** $x = 359$ $\;$ 19.453882

REVIEW CAPSULE FOR SECTION 18.4

Write each equation in the form $x^2 + bx = -c$. (Sections 3.1 and 3.2)

1. $x^2 - 6x + 3 = 0$ $\;$ $x^2 - 6x = -3$ $\qquad$ **2.** $x^2 + 5x - 4 = 0$ $\;$ $x^2 + 5x = 4$ $\qquad$ **3.** $x^2 = 4x - 10$ $\;$ $x^2 - 4x = -10$

4. $x^2 - \frac{1}{2}x + \frac{3}{2} = 0$ $\;$ $2x^2 - x = -3$ $\qquad$ **5.** $2x^2 - 4x + 5 = 0$ $\;$ $2x^2 - 4x = -5$ $\qquad$ **6.** $2x^2 + 3x - 10 = 0$ $\;$ $2x^2 + 3x = 10$

18.4 Completing the Square

OBJECTIVE: To solve a quadratic equation by completing the square

Lead students through the steps of these examples carefully.

It is possible to write any quadratic equation in a form that makes the left side a trinomial square. This is called **completing the square**.

example 1

Solve by completing the square: $x^2 - 8x - 9 = 0$

Solution:

1. Add 9 to each side. $\longrightarrow$ $x^2 - 8x = 9$

2. Multiply the coefficient of x by $\frac{1}{2}$. $\longrightarrow$ $\frac{1}{2}(-8) = -4$

3. Square (-4). $\longrightarrow$ $(-4)^2 = 16$

4. Add 16 to each side. $\longrightarrow$ $x^2 - 8x + 16 = 9 + 16$ ◄ $x^2 - 8x + 16$ *is a trinomial square.*

5. Factor and simplify. $\longrightarrow$ $(x - 4)^2 = 25$

6. Write the equivalent compound *or* sentence. $\longrightarrow$ $x - 4 = 5$ *or* $x - 4 = -5$

7. Solve both equations. $\longrightarrow$ $x = 9$ $\qquad$ $x = -1$

Solution set: $\{9, -1\}$

example 2

Solve $x^2 - x - 1 = 0$.

Solution:

1. Add 1 to each side. $\longrightarrow$ $x^2 - x = 1$

2. Multiply the coefficient of x by $\frac{1}{2}$. $\longrightarrow$ $\frac{1}{2}(-1) = -\frac{1}{2}$

3. Square $(-\frac{1}{2})$. $\longrightarrow$ $(-\frac{1}{2})^2 = \frac{1}{4}$

4. Add $\frac{1}{4}$ to each side. $\longrightarrow$ $x^2 - x + \frac{1}{4} = 1 + \frac{1}{4}$

5. Factor and simplify. $\longrightarrow$ $(x - \frac{1}{2})^2 = \frac{5}{4}$

6. Write the equivalent compound *or* sentence. $\longrightarrow$ $x - \frac{1}{2} = \sqrt{\frac{5}{4}}$ *or* $x - \frac{1}{2} = -\sqrt{\frac{5}{4}}$

7. Simplify the radicals. $\longrightarrow$ $x - \frac{1}{2} = \frac{\sqrt{5}}{2}$ $\qquad$ $x - \frac{1}{2} = -\frac{\sqrt{5}}{2}$

8. Solve both equations. $\longrightarrow$ $x = \frac{1}{2} + \frac{\sqrt{5}}{2}$ $\qquad$ $x = \frac{1}{2} - \frac{\sqrt{5}}{2}$

Solution set: $\left\{ \dfrac{1 + \sqrt{5}}{2}, \dfrac{1 - \sqrt{5}}{2} \right\}$

It might prove helpful to approximate these solutions. A calculator makes it easy!

example 3   Solve $2x^2 + 3x - 5 = 0$.

Solution:

1. Add 5 to each side. $\longrightarrow$ $2x^2 + 3x = 5$

2. Multiply each side by $\frac{1}{2}$. $\longrightarrow$ $x^2 + \frac{3}{2}x = \frac{5}{2}$

3. Multiply the coefficient of x by $\frac{1}{2}$. $\longrightarrow$ $\frac{1}{2}(\frac{3}{2}) = \frac{3}{4}$

4. Square $\frac{3}{4}$. $\longrightarrow$ $(\frac{3}{4})^2 = \frac{9}{16}$

5. Add $\frac{9}{16}$ to each side. $\longrightarrow$ $x^2 + \frac{3}{2}x + \frac{9}{16} = \frac{5}{2} + \frac{9}{16}$

6. Factor and simplify. $\longrightarrow$ $(x + \frac{3}{4})^2 = \frac{49}{16}$

7. Write the equivalent compound *or* sentence. $\longrightarrow$ $x + \frac{3}{4} = \sqrt{\frac{49}{16}}$ *or* $x + \frac{3}{4} = -\sqrt{\frac{49}{16}}$

8. Simplify the radicals. $\longrightarrow$ $x + \frac{3}{4} = \frac{7}{4}$ $x + \frac{3}{4} = -\frac{7}{4}$

9. Solve both equations. $\longrightarrow$ $x = -\frac{3}{4} + \frac{7}{4}$ $x = -\frac{3}{4} - \frac{7}{4}$

10. Simplify. $\longrightarrow$ $x = 1$ $x = -2\frac{1}{2}$

Solution set: $\{1, -2\frac{1}{2}\}$

The solutions of the equations of Examples 1–3 can be checked by replacing x in the original equation with each number from the solution set.

Steps for solving $ax^2 + bx + c = 0$ by completing the square:

1. Add $-c$ to each side.

2. Multiply each side by $\frac{1}{a}$.

3. Compute $\left(\frac{1}{2} \cdot \frac{b}{a}\right)$.

4. Compute $\left(\frac{1}{2} \cdot \frac{b}{a}\right)^2$.

5. Add $\left(\frac{1}{2} \cdot \frac{b}{a}\right)^2$ to each side.

6. Factor the left side.

7. Write the equivalent compound *or* sentence.

8. Solve.

CLASSROOM EXERCISES

Write the number that you should add to each side to form a trinomial square in the left side. (Examples 1 and 2)

1. $x^2 + 4x = 1$ 4   **2.** $x^2 - 6x = 5$ 9   **3.** $x^2 - 2x = 3$ 1   **4.** $x^2 + 10x = 12$ 25

5. $x^2 - x = 2$ $\frac{1}{4}$ **6.** $x^2 + 3x = 5$ $\frac{9}{4}$ **7.** $x^2 + \frac{1}{3}x = 3$ $\frac{1}{36}$ **8.** $x^2 - \frac{2}{3}x = 4$ $\frac{1}{9}$

Solve each equation.

14. $3 + \frac{\sqrt{13}}{5}, 3 - \frac{\sqrt{13}}{5}$

9. $x^2 = \frac{3}{4}$ $\frac{\sqrt{3}}{2}, -\frac{\sqrt{3}}{2}$ **10.** $x^2 = \frac{5}{9}$ $\frac{\sqrt{5}}{3}, -\frac{\sqrt{5}}{3}$ **11.** $x^2 = \frac{1}{2} + \frac{3}{4}$ $\frac{\sqrt{5}}{2}, -\frac{\sqrt{5}}{2}$

12. $x^2 = \frac{3}{2} + \frac{5}{16}$ $\frac{\sqrt{29}}{4}, -\frac{\sqrt{29}}{4}$ **13.** $(x - \frac{1}{2})^2 = \frac{3}{4}$ $\frac{1}{2} + \frac{\sqrt{3}}{2}, \frac{1}{2} - \frac{\sqrt{3}}{2}$ **14.** $(x - 3)^2 = \frac{13}{25}$ See above.

Write the factors of each trinomial square over {rational numbers}.

$x + \frac{3}{2}, x + \frac{3}{2}$

15. $x^2 + 18x + 81$ $x + 9, x + 9$ **16.** $x^2 - 14x + 49$ $x - 7, x - 7$ **17.** $x^2 + 3x + \frac{9}{4}$

18. $x^2 + 5x + \frac{25}{4}$ $x + \frac{5}{2}, x + \frac{5}{2}$ **19.** $x^2 - \frac{2}{5}x + \frac{1}{25}$ $x - \frac{1}{5}, x - \frac{1}{5}$ **20.** $x^2 + \frac{3}{2}x + \frac{9}{16}$ $x + \frac{3}{4}, x + \frac{3}{4}$

15. $\frac{3}{2} + \frac{\sqrt{13}}{2}, \frac{3}{2} - \frac{\sqrt{13}}{2}$

WRITTEN EXERCISES

See the Teacher's Manual for the suggested assignments.

16. $\frac{5}{2} + \frac{\sqrt{37}}{2}, \frac{5}{2} - \frac{\sqrt{37}}{2}$

Goal: To solve quadratic equations by completing the square

17. $-\frac{3}{2} + \frac{\sqrt{29}}{2},$

Sample Problem: Solve $2x^2 - 5x - 7 = 0$.   **Answer:** $\{\frac{7}{2}, -1\}$ $-\frac{3}{2} - \frac{\sqrt{29}}{2}$

Solve by completing the square. (Examples 1–3)   **18.** $-\frac{1}{3} + \frac{\sqrt{7}}{3}, -\frac{1}{3} - \frac{\sqrt{7}}{3}$

1. $x^2 - 2x - 15 = 0$ $-3, 5$ **2.** $x^2 + 2x - 8 = 0$ $-4, 2$ **3.** $x^2 + 4x - 5 = 0$ $-5, 1$

4. $x^2 - 4x - 12 = 0$ $-2, 6$ **5.** $x^2 + x - 6 = 0$ $-3, 2$ **6.** $x^2 - x - 20 = 0$ $-4, 5$

7. $x^2 + 2x - 5 = 0$ $-1 + \sqrt{6},$ **8.** $x^2 + 4x - 1 = 0$ $-2 + \sqrt{5}, -2 - \sqrt{5}$ **9.** $x^2 - 4x + 7 = 0$ ϕ
       $-1 - \sqrt{6}$

10. $x^2 + 10x + 2 = 0$ See above.   **11.** $x^2 - 6x - 5 = 0$ See above.   **12.** $x^2 - 4x - 10 = 0$ See above.

13. $x^2 + 8x + 13 = 0$ $\begin{array}{l}-4 + \sqrt{3},\\ -4 - \sqrt{3}\end{array}$ **14.** $x^2 - x - 3 = 0$ $\frac{1}{2} + \frac{\sqrt{13}}{2}, \frac{1}{2} - \frac{\sqrt{13}}{2}$ **15.** $x^2 - 3x - 1 = 0$ See above.

16. $x^2 - 5x - 3 = 0$ See above.   **17.** $x^2 + 3x - 5 = 0$ See above.   **18.** $x^2 + \frac{2}{3}x - \frac{2}{3} = 0$ See above.

19. $x^2 + \frac{2}{5}x - \frac{1}{5} = 0$ See below.   **20.** $2x^2 + 5x - 3 = 0$ $-3, \frac{1}{2}$ **21.** $2x^2 + x - 3 = 0$ $-\frac{3}{2}, 1$

22. $3x^2 + 8x - 3 = 0$ $-3, \frac{1}{3}$ **23.** $3x^2 - 5x - 2 = 0$ $-\frac{1}{3}, 2$ **24.** $2x^2 - 4x - 3 = 0$ See below.

25. $3x^2 - 6x + 2 = 0$ **26.** $2x^2 + 4x - 5 = 0$ **27.** $-2x + 4x^2 - 10 = 0$
$1 + \frac{\sqrt{3}}{3}, 1 - \frac{\sqrt{3}}{3}$ $-1 + \frac{\sqrt{14}}{2}, -1 - \frac{\sqrt{14}}{2}$ $\frac{1}{4} + \frac{\sqrt{41}}{4}, \frac{1}{4} - \frac{\sqrt{41}}{4}$

REVIEW CAPSULE FOR SECTION 18.5

Simplify. (Sections 8.3 and 8.5) $\frac{1}{2} + \frac{\sqrt{6}}{4}, \frac{1}{2} - \frac{\sqrt{6}}{4}$

1. $\frac{3 + \sqrt{49}}{4}; \frac{3 - \sqrt{49}}{4}$ $\frac{5}{2}, -1$ **2.** $\frac{-2 + \sqrt{36}}{2}; \frac{-2 - \sqrt{36}}{2}$ $2, -4$ **3.** $\frac{4 + \sqrt{24}}{8}; \frac{4 - \sqrt{24}}{8}$

19. $-\frac{1}{5} + \frac{\sqrt{6}}{5}, -\frac{1}{5} - \frac{\sqrt{6}}{5}$ **24.** $1 + \frac{\sqrt{10}}{2}, 1 - \frac{\sqrt{10}}{2}$

18.5 The Quadratic Formula

OBJECTIVE: To solve a quadratic equation by using the quadratic formula

A special formula called the **quadratic formula** can be used to solve <u>any</u> quadratic equation.

example 1

Solve $ax^2 + bx + c = 0$ for x.

Solution:

| 1 | Add $-c$ to each side. ───────────────→ | $ax^2 + bx = -c$ |

| 2 | Multiply each side by $\dfrac{1}{a}$. ───────→ | $x^2 + \dfrac{b}{a}x = \dfrac{-c}{a}$ |

| 3 | Add $\left(\dfrac{1}{2} \cdot \dfrac{b}{a}\right)^2$ or $\dfrac{b^2}{4a^2}$ to each side. ──→ | $x^2 + \dfrac{b}{a}x + \dfrac{b^2}{4a^2} = -\dfrac{c}{a} + \dfrac{b^2}{4a^2}$ |

| 4 | Factor the left side and write the simplest name for the right side. ───→ | $\left(x + \dfrac{b}{2a}\right)^2 = \dfrac{b^2 - 4ac}{4a^2}$ |

5. Write the equivalent compound *or* sentence. ────────→

$$x + \frac{b}{2a} = \frac{\sqrt{b^2 - 4ac}}{2a}$$

$$or \quad x + \frac{b}{2a} = \frac{-\sqrt{b^2 - 4ac}}{2a}$$

> This Example develops the Quadratic Formula. Go through the steps carefully with students.

6. Find the truth numbers. ───────→

$$x = \frac{-b}{2a} + \frac{\sqrt{b^2 - 4ac}}{2a}$$

$$or \quad x = \frac{-b}{2a} - \frac{\sqrt{b^2 - 4ac}}{2a}$$

7. Simplify. ────────────→

$$x = \frac{-b + \sqrt{b^2 - 4ac}}{2a}$$

$$or \quad x = \frac{-b - \sqrt{b^2 - 4ac}}{2a}$$

Solution set: $\left\{ \dfrac{-b + \sqrt{b^2 - 4ac}}{2a}, \dfrac{-b - \sqrt{b^2 - 4ac}}{2a} \right\}$

Quadratic Formula

Any quadratic equation of the form $ax^2 + bx + c = 0$ is equivalent to the following compound sentence:

$$x = \frac{-b + \sqrt{b^2 - 4ac}}{2a} \quad or \quad x = \frac{-b - \sqrt{b^2 - 4ac}}{2a}$$

example 2

Solve $6x^2 - x - 1 = 0$ by the quadratic formula.

Solution:

1. Write the values of a, b, and c. $\longrightarrow$ $a = 6$ $\quad$ $b = -1$ $\quad$ $c = -1$

2. Substitute these values in the two equations of the quadratic formula. Then simplify.

$$x = \frac{-b + \sqrt{b^2 - 4ac}}{2a}$$

$$= \frac{-(-1) + \sqrt{(-1)^2 - 4(6)(-1)}}{2(6)}$$

$$= \frac{1 + \sqrt{1 + 24}}{12}$$

$$= \frac{1 + \sqrt{25}}{12}$$

$$= \frac{1 + 5}{12} = \frac{1}{2}$$

$$x = \frac{-b - \sqrt{b^2 - 4ac}}{2a}$$

$$= \frac{1 - \sqrt{25}}{12}$$

$$= \frac{1 - 5}{12}$$

$$= \frac{-4}{12}$$

$$= -\frac{1}{3}$$

Solution set: $\left\{\frac{1}{2}, -\frac{1}{3}\right\}$

example 3

Solve $2x^2 - x = 5$.

Solution:

1. Subtract 5 from each side. $\longrightarrow$ $2x^2 - x - 5 = 0$ ◀ *In the form* $ax^2 + bx + c = 0$

2. Write the values of a, b, and c. $\longrightarrow$ $a = 2$ $\quad$ $b = -1$ $\quad$ $c = -5$

3. Substitute these values in the two equations of the quadratic formula. Then simplify.

$$x = \frac{-b + \sqrt{b^2 - 4ac}}{2a}$$

$$= \frac{-(-1) + \sqrt{(-1)^2 - 4(2)(-5)}}{2(2)}$$

$$= \frac{1 + \sqrt{1 + 40}}{4}$$

$$= \frac{1 + \sqrt{41}}{4}$$

$$x = \frac{-b - \sqrt{b^2 - 4ac}}{2a}$$

$$= \frac{-(-1) - \sqrt{(-1)^2 - 4(2)(-5)}}{2(2)}$$

$$= \frac{1 - \sqrt{1 + 40}}{4}$$

$$= \frac{1 - \sqrt{41}}{4}$$

Solution set: $\left\{\frac{1 + \sqrt{41}}{4}, \frac{1 - \sqrt{41}}{4}\right\}$

The Table of Square Roots on page 198 can be used to approximate the solutions of Example 3.

$$\frac{1}{4} + \frac{\sqrt{41}}{4} \approx 0.25 + \frac{6.4}{4}$$

$$\frac{1}{4} - \frac{\sqrt{41}}{4} \approx 0.25 - \frac{6.4}{4}$$

You can also write in the following forms in order to approximate by use of a calculator.

$$\approx 0.25 + 1.6$$

$$\approx 0.25 - 1.6$$ $(\sqrt{41} + 1) \div 4$ and $(\sqrt{41} - 1) \div 4$

$$\approx 1.9$$

$$\approx -1.35 \text{ or } -1.4$$

The solutions of $2x^2 - x = 5$ are approximately 1.9 and -1.4.

CLASSROOM EXERCISES

Compare each equation to $ax^2 + bx + c = 0$. Then write the values of a, b, and c for each equation. (Examples 2 and 3)

3. $a = 1, b = 5, c = 0$

1. $x^2 + 3x - 2 = 0$ $a = 1, b = 3, c = -2$ **2.** $-2x^2 - x + 5 = 0$ $a = -2, b = -1,$ **3.** $x^2 + 5x = 0$
                                         $c = 5$

4. $4 - x^2 - x = 0$ $a = -1, b = -1,$ **5.** $x^2 = -3x - 5$ $a = 1, b = 3, c = 5$ **6.** $3x^2 - 1 = 5x$
                $c = 4$

6. $a = 3, b = -5, c = -1$

WRITTEN EXERCISES

See the Teacher's Manual for the suggested assignments.

Goal: To solve quadratic equations by the quadratic formula
Sample Problem: Solve $3x^2 - 8x + 5$.   **Answer:** $\{1, \frac{5}{3}\}$

Solve by the quadratic formula. (Examples 1–3)

1. $x^2 + 5x - 6 = 0$ $-6, 1$ **2.** $x^2 + 3x - 10 = 0$ $-5, 2$ **3.** $x^2 + 6x - 7 = 0$
                                                                       $-7, 1$

4. $x^2 + 2x - 8 = 0$ $-4, 2$ **5.** $x^2 - 7x + 10 = 0$ $2, 5$ **6.** $x^2 - 7x + 12 = 0$ $3, 4$

7. $x^2 = 4x + 12$ $-2, 6$ **8.** $x^2 = 2x + 15$ $-3, 5$ **9.** $-x^2 + 6x - 9 = 0$ 3

10. $-x^2 + 10x - 25 = 0$ 5 **11.** $6x^2 + x - 2 = 0$ $-\frac{2}{3}, \frac{1}{2}$ **12.** $4x^2 + 12x + 5 = 0$ $-\frac{5}{2}, -\frac{1}{2}$

13. $x^2 - 3 = 0$ $\sqrt{3}, -\sqrt{3}$ **14.** $x^2 - 5 = 0$ $\sqrt{5}, -\sqrt{5}$ **15.** $x^2 - 6x = 0$ $0, 6$

16. $x^2 + 9x = 0$ $-9, 0$ **17.** $3x - 5x^2 + 1 = 0$ **18.** $5x^2 + 7x - 10 = 0$
                                        $\frac{3 + \sqrt{29}}{10}, \frac{3 - \sqrt{29}}{10}$ $\frac{-7 + \sqrt{249}}{10}, \frac{-7 - \sqrt{249}}{10}$

Solve by the quadratic formula. Approximate to one decimal place.

19. $x^2 + 2x - 1 = 0$ $0.4, -2.4$ **20.** $x^2 + 4x + 1 = 0$ $-0.3, -3.7$ **21.** $2x^2 - 3x - 1 = 0$ $1.8, -0.3$

22. $-3x^2 + 6x - 2 = 0$ $1.6, 0.4$ **23.** $2x^2 - 6x + 3 = 0$ $2.4, 0.6$ **24.** $-5x^2 + x + 1 = 0$ $0.6, -0.4$

REVIEW CAPSULE FOR SECTION 18.6

Find the value of $b^2 - 4ac$. (Section 3.6)

1. $a = -2; b = -5; c = 1$ 33 **2.** $a = 4; b = 3; c = 5$ -71 **3.** $a = 1; b = 6; c = -2$ 44

18.6 The Discriminant

OBJECTIVE: To compute the value of $b^2 - 4ac$ for a quadratic equation and identify the solutions as Rational, Irrational, or Not Real

In using the quadratic formula, you find the value of the expression $b^2 - 4ac$.

> The expression $b^2 - 4ac$ is called the **discriminant.**

The value of the discriminant describes the kinds of numbers that belong to the solution set of a quadratic equation. It tells whether they are <u>rational</u> or <u>irrational</u> numbers.

P-1 **What are the solutions of $x^2 + x - 12 = 0$?**   −4, 3

P-2 **What are the values of a, b, and c in $x^2 + x - 12 = 0$?**
$a = 1, b = 1, c = -12$

P-3 **What is the value of the discriminant, $b^2 - 4ac$?**   49

P-4 **What kind of number is $\sqrt{49}$, rational or irrational?** Rational

Solution set: $\{-4, 3\}$ $b^2 - 4ac = 49$ ◀ **Perfect square**

The solutions are rational numbers because the value of the discriminant is a perfect square.

P-5 **What are the solutions of $x^2 - 5 = 0$?** $\sqrt{5}, -\sqrt{5}$

P-6 **What are the values of a, b, and c in $x^2 - 5 = 0$?** $a = 1, b = 0, c = -5$

P-7 **What is the value of the discriminant?**   20

P-8 **What kind of number is $\sqrt{20}$, rational or irrational?**   Irrational

Solution set: $\{\sqrt{5}, -\sqrt{5}\}$ $b^2 - 4ac = 20$ ◀ **Not a perfect square**

Since the value of the discriminant is not a perfect square, the solutions are irrational.

P-9 What are the solutions of $x^2 - 4x + 4 = 0$? 2

P-10 What are the values of *a*, *b*, and *c* in $x^2 - 4x + 4 = 0$? $a = 1, b = -4, c = 4$

P-11 What is the value of the discriminant? 0

Solution set: {2} $b^2 - 4ac = 0$ ◄ *Perfect square*

Since the value of the discriminant is 0, the solutions are rational <u>and</u> equal.

P-12 What are the solutions of $x^2 + 4 = 0$? There are no real solutions.

P-13 What are the values of *a*, *b*, and *c* in $x^2 + 4 = 0$? $a = 1, b = 0, c = 4$

P-14 What is the value of the discriminant? -16

P-15 What kind of number is $\sqrt{-16}$, real or not real? Not real

Solution set: No real numbers $b^2 - 4ac = -16$ ◄ *The value of the discriminant is negative.*

There are no real solutions because the value of the discriminant is a negative number.

P-16 What word or expression describes the solutions of each equation, <u>R</u>ational, <u>I</u>rrational, or <u>N</u>ot Real?

a. $8x^2 - 2x - 1 = 0$ **b.** $x^2 - x - 1 = 0$ Irrational
      Rational
c. $x^2 - 2x + 4 = 0$ **d.** $x^2 - 16x + 64 = 0$ Rational
      Not Real

Value of the discriminant and the solution set of $ax^2 + bx + c = 0$:

1. If $b^2 - 4ac$ is 0 or a perfect-square counting number, the solutions are rational.
2. If $b^2 - 4ac$ is positive and not a perfect square, the solutions are irrational.
3. If $b^2 - 4ac = 0$, the solution set contains one number. The solution is rational.
4. If $b^2 - 4ac$ is negative, no real solutions exist.

CLASSROOM EXERCISES

Write Rational or Irrational to describe the solutions for each equation having the given value of its discriminant. (P-4, P-8, P-11)

1. 25 Rational
2. 36 Rational
3. 0 Rational
4. 12 Irrational
5. 17 Irrational

6. Rational
6. 1

7. 100 Rational
8. 4 Rational
9. 5 Irrational
10. 22 Irrational
11. 9 Rational
12. 32

12. Irrational

Write the value of $b^2 - 4ac$ for each equation. (P-3, P-7, P-11, P-14)

13. $x^2 + x - 2 = 0$ 9
14. $x^2 + 2x + 1 = 0$ 0
15. $x^2 - 3x + 2 = 0$ 1

16. $x^2 - 5x + 5 = 0$ 5
17. $x^2 + 16 = 0$ −64
18. $x^2 - 7 = 0$ 28

19. $2x^2 - 3x - 1 = 0$ 17
20. $5x^2 + 5x + 1 = 0$ 5
21. $x^2 - x + 1 = 0$ −3

WRITTEN EXERCISES

See the Teacher's Manual for the suggested assignments.

Goal: To describe the solutions of quadratic equations by use of the discriminant

Sample Problems: a. $2x^2 - 7x + 1 = 0$ **b.** $x^2 - 8x + 16 = 0$

Answers: a. Irrational   **b.** One rational solution

Compute the value of $b^2 - 4ac$ for each equation. Then write Rational, Irrational, or Not Real for the solutions. (P-1 through P-16)

1. $x^2 - x - 6 = 0$ 25; Rational
2. $x^2 + 4x - 5 = 0$ 36; Rational
3. $-x^2 + 2x + 8 = 0$
3. 36; Rational

4. $-x^2 + 8x - 12 = 0$ 16; Rational
5. $2x^2 - x - 2 = 0$ 17; Irrational
6. $3x^2 + 3x - 1 = 0$
6. 21; Irrational

7. $-x^2 + 4x - 4 = 0$ 0; Rational
8. $-x^2 + 10x - 25 = 0$ 0; Rational
9. $x^2 - 7 = 0$
9. 28; Irrational

10. $x^2 - 13 = 0$ 52; Irrational
11. $x^2 + 25 = 0$ −100; Not real
12. $2x^2 + x + 6 = 0$
12. −47; Not real

13. $2x^2 = 3 - 5x$ 49; Rational
14. $3x^2 = 9x - 5$ 21; Irrational
15. $x^2 = 10x$
15. 100; Rational

16. $3x^2 = 12x$ 144; Rational
17. $5x^2 - 2x = 0$ 4; Rational
18. $3x - 2x^2 = 0$
18. 9; Rational

19. $x^2 - 2x + 7 = 0$ −24; Not real
20. $3x^2 - 2x + 8 = 0$ −92; Not real
21. $6x^2 - 9x + 3 = 0$
21. 9; Rational

22. $10x^2 - 11x + 3 = 0$ 1; Rational
23. $-5x^2 + 11x + 1 = 0$ 141; Irrational
24. $-8x^2 - 9x + 2 = 0$
24. 145; Irrational

25. $9x^2 = 5$ 180; Irrational
26. $3x^2 - 10 = 0$ 120; Irrational
27. $-x^2 - x + 1 = 0$
27. 5; Irrational

REVIEW CAPSULE FOR SECTION 18.7

Write each equation in the form $ax^2 + bx + c = 0$. (Section 18.2)

1. $x(x - 4) = 78$ $x^2 - 4x - 78 = 0$
2. $x(2x + 5) = 102$ $2x^2 + 5x - 102 = 0$
3. $x(3x - 1) - x^2 = 128$
     $2x^2 - x - 128 = 0$

18.7 Problem Solving with Quadratic Equations

OBJECTIVE: To solve a word problem that can be described by a quadratic equation

example 1
The length of a rectangle is 3 centimeters more than its width. The area is 18 square centimeters. Find the length and width.

Solution: Let x = the width.
Then $x + 3$ = the length.

The formula for computing the area of a rectangle is $A = lw$.

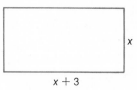

x

$x + 3$

☐1 Write the equation. ⟶ $(x + 3)x = 18$

◀ Product of length and width equals area.

☐2 Distributive Property ⟶ $x^2 + 3x = 18$

☐3 Subtract 18 from each side. ⟶ $x^2 + 3x - 18 = 0$

The number -6 is a solution of the equation but is not part of the solution to the problem.

☐4 Factor. ⟶ $(x + 6)(x - 3) = 0$

☐5 Factors of Zero Property ⟶ $x + 6 = 0$ or $x - 3 = 0$

◀ The measure must be positive.

☐6 Solve for x. ⟶ $x = -6$ $x = 3$

Width = 3 centimeters; Length = 6 centimeters

example 2
The product of two consecutive integers is 72. What are the integers?

Solution: Let n = the smaller integer. Then $n + 1$ = the greater integer.

☐1 Write an equation. ⟶ $n(n + 1) = 72$

☐2 Distributive Property ⟶ $n^2 + n = 72$

☐3 Subtract 72 from each side. ⟶ $n^2 + n - 72 = 0$

☐4 Factor. ⟶ $(n + 9)(n - 8) = 0$

☐5 Factors of Zero Property ⟶ $n + 9 = 0$ or $n - 8 = 0$

☐6 Solve for n. ⟶ $n = -9$ $n = 8$

Smaller Integer	Greater Integer
-9	-8
8	9

◀ There are two answers: 1. -9 and -8; 2. 8 and 9.

example 3

The area of a rectangle less the area of a square equals 15 square meters. The width of the rectangle equals the length of each side of the square. The length of the rectangle is 2 meters more than twice the width. Find the width and length of the rectangle.

Solution: Let x = the width of the rectangle.
Let x = the length of each side of the square.
Then $2x + 2$ = the length of the rectangle.

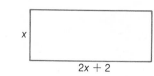

$$x(2x + 2) - x^2 = 15$$
$$2x^2 + 2x - x^2 = 15$$
$$x^2 + 2x - 15 = 0$$
$$(x + 5)(x - 3) = 0$$
$$x = -5 \quad or \quad x = 3$$

◄ **The width cannot be negative.**

Width = 3 meters; Length = 8 meters

CLASSROOM EXERCISES

Write an equation for each problem. Let n represent the smaller number.
(Examples 1 and 2)

1. The product of two consecutive integers is 210. $n(n + 1) = 210$

2. The product of two consecutive even integers is 48. $n(n + 2) = 48$

3. One integer is three more than another integer. Their product is 108. $n(n + 3) = 108$

4. One number is 15 less than another number. Their product is -36. $n(n + 15) = -36$

5. The length of a rectangle is 5 units greater than the width. The area is 24 square units. $n(n + 5) = 24$

6. The length of a rectangle is three units more than twice the width. The area is 65 square units. $n(2n + 3) = 65$

7. One number is three times as great as another number. The square of the smaller number is 18 less than the square of the greater number. $n^2 = 9n^2 - 18$

8. One number is three more than another number. The square of the smaller number is 51 more than the square of the greater number. $n^2 = (n + 3)^2 + 51$

WRITTEN EXERCISES

Goal: To use quadratic equations to solve problems

Sample Problem: The sum of two numbers is −13 and their product is 40. Find the numbers.

Answer: Equation: $x^2 + 13x + 40 = 0$
The numbers are −5 and −8.

Solve each problem. (Examples 1−3)

1. The width of a rectangle is 2 units less than the length. If the area is 80 square units, what are the length and width? **length: 10, width: 8**

2. The length of a rectangle is 5 units more than the width. If the area is 50 square units, what are the length and width? **length: 10, width: 5**

3. The product of two consecutive integers is 30. Find two pairs of such integers. **5 and 6; −6 and −5**

4. The product of two consecutive integers is 56. Find two pairs of such integers. **7 and 8; −8 and −7**

5. One integer is 13 less than another integer. Their product is −40. Find all possible pairs of such integers. **−8 and 5; −5 and 8**

6. The sum of two integers is 8, and their product is −20. Find the integers. **−2 and 10**

7. A square hole is cut in a rectangular plate as shown in the figure. The width of the rectangle is twice the length of each side of the square hole. The length of the rectangle is 13 units. Find the width of the rectangle if the area of the plate after the square hole is cut is 105 square units. **10 units**

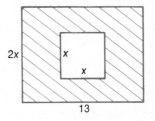

8. A rectangular plate has a rectangular piece cut from one corner as shown in the figure. The area after the rectangular piece is cut out is 40 square units. Use the information given in the figure to find the length and width of the original rectangular plate. **length: 8, width: 6**

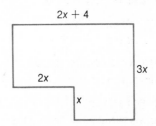

Career

Industrial Production Technician

Technicians in industrial production assist production engineers in planning the efficient use of labor, machines, and materials. An important goal is to keep the amount of raw materials to a minimum. For example, a food processor wants containers that provide the desired capacity but with dimensions that require the least amount of material (surface area). The formula below gives S, the surface area of a cylindrical container in square centimeters.

$$S = \frac{(3.14r^3 + c)2}{r}$$

c = capacity in milliliters
r = radius in centimeters

EXAMPLE: Find, to the nearest whole number, the value of r that will require a minimum amount of material for a cylindrical can with a capacity of 354 milliliters.

SOLUTION: $S = \dfrac{(3.14r^3 + 354)2}{r}$

Use a calculator to complete the table shown at the right.

r	3.0	3.5	4.0	4.5
S	?	?	?	?

By calculator: When $r = 3.0$, $S = (3^3 \times 3.14 + 354) \times 2 \div 3$.

Solve also for r = 3.5, 4.0 and 4.5.

$$\boxed{3}\ \boxed{\times}\ \boxed{=}\ \boxed{=}\ \boxed{\times}\ \boxed{3}\ \boxed{.}\ \boxed{1}\ \boxed{4}$$

$$\boxed{+}\ \boxed{3}\ \boxed{5}\ \boxed{4}\ \boxed{\times}\ \boxed{2}\ \boxed{\div}\ \boxed{3}\ \boxed{=}\qquad 292.52$$

In the table, the smallest value for S is 277.5. The corresponding value of r is about **4 centimeters**.

r	3.0	3.5	4.0	4.5
S	292.5	279.2	277.5	284.5

EXERCISES

1. In the Example, show that 3.8 is the value of r to the nearest *tenth*. (HINT: Find the values of S for $r = 3.7$, 3.8, and 3.9)

   1. See below.

2. In the Example, the formula for the height of the can is $h = \dfrac{c}{3.14r^2}$. Find, using $r = 3.8$, the value of h that requires a minimum amount of material.

   $h = 7.8$ cm

1.

r	3.7	3.8	3.9
s	277.3	277.0	277.1

S is smallest when $r = 3.8$.

Career

CHAPTER SUMMARY

NOTE: You may wish to administer a quiz covering sections 18.4 through 18.7. See page M-45 of the Teacher's Manual for the suggested quiz.

IMPORTANT TERMS

Quadratic equation *(p. 450)*

Zeros of a function *(p. 450)*

Completing the square *(p. 460)*

Quadratic formula *(p. 463)*

Discriminant *(p. 466)*

IMPORTANT IDEAS

1. The solutions of a quadratic equation of the form $ax^2 + bx + c = 0$ are the same as the zeros of the function $y = ax^2 + bx + c$.

2. *Factors of Zero Property:* If a and b are real numbers and $ab = 0$, then $a = 0$ or $b = 0$.

3. Any quadratic equation of the form $(x + r)^2 = s$ in which r and s are rational numbers, $s \geq 0$, is equivalent to "$x + r = \sqrt{s}$ or $x + r = -\sqrt{s}$."

4. It is possible to write any quadratic equation in a form that makes the left side a trinomial square.

5. *Steps for solving $ax^2 + bx + c = 0$ by completing the square:*
   a. Add $-c$ to each side.
   b. Multiply each side by $\frac{1}{a}$.
   c. Compute $\left(\frac{1}{2} \cdot \frac{b}{a}\right)$.
   d. Compute $\left(\frac{1}{2} \cdot \frac{b}{a}\right)^2$.
   e. Add $\left(\frac{1}{2} \cdot \frac{b}{a}\right)^2$ to each side.
   f. Factor the left side.
   g. Write the equivalent compound *or* sentence.
   h. Solve.

6. *Quadratic Formula:* Any quadratic equation of the form $ax^2 + bx + c = 0$ is equivalent to the following compound sentence:
$$x = \frac{-b + \sqrt{b^2 - 4ac}}{2a} \text{ or } x = \frac{-b - \sqrt{b^2 - 4ac}}{2a}$$

7. *Value of the discriminant and the solution set of $ax^2 + bx + c = 0$*
   a. If $b^2 - 4ac$ is 0 or a perfect-square counting number, the solutions are rational.
   b. If $b^2 - 4ac$ is positive and not a perfect square, the solutions are irrational.
   c. If $b^2 - 4ac$ equals 0, the solution set contains one number. The solution is rational.
   d. If $b^2 - 4ac$ is negative, no real solutions exist.

CHAPTER REVIEW

NOTE: The Teacher's Resource Book contains two forms of each Chapter Test.

SECTION 18.1

Change each equation to the form $ax^2 + bx + c = 0$.

1. $x^2 + 5x = 2$ $x^2 + 5x - 2 = 0$

2. $x^2 = 3 - 2x$ $x^2 + 2x - 3 = 0$

Graph $y = x^2 - 1$. Refer to this graph to estimate the solutions of each equation.

3. $x^2 - 1 = 2$ −1.7, 1.7

4. $x^2 - 1 = 0$ −1, 1

SECTION 18.2

Solve by using the Factors of Zero Property.

5. $x^2 - 9x - 10 = 0$ −1, 10

6. $x^2 = -21 + 10x$ 3, 7

7. $2x^2 + 10x = 0$ 0, −5

SECTION 18.3

Write the solutions of each equation.

8. $x^2 = 256$ 16, −16

9. $x^2 = 361$ 19, −19

10. $(x - 6)^2 = 64$ −2, 14

SECTION 18.4

Solve by completing the square.

11. $x^2 - 8x - 20 = 0$ −2, 10

12. $x^2 + 4x - 32 = 0$ −8, 4

13. $4x^2 - x - 3 = 0$

$-\frac{3}{4}, 1$

SECTION 18.5

Solve by the quadratic formula.

14. $8x^2 - 6x + 1 = 0$ $\frac{1}{4}, \frac{1}{2}$

15. $6x^2 - x - 1 = 0$ $-\frac{1}{3}, \frac{1}{2}$

16. $x^2 + 5x + 7 = 0$

No real number

SECTION 18.6

Compute the value of $b^2 - 4ac$ for each equation. Then write <u>Rational</u> or <u>Irrational</u> for the solutions.

17. $x^2 - 4x + 4 = 0$ 0; Rational

18. $x^2 + 5x - 14 = 0$ 81; Rational

19. $-3x^2 + 4x + 5 = 0$

76; Irrational

SECTION 18.7

Solve each problem. Show your work.

20. One number is 3 greater than another number. Their product is 10. What are the two pairs of numbers that satisfy these conditions? 2 and 5; −5 and −2

21. The sum of two numbers is 10, and their product is 16. What are the numbers? 2 and 8

CUMULATIVE REVIEW: CHAPTERS 13–18

3. Shirts: x; ties: y; $y = x + 1$; $15x + 6y = 90$; Ans: 5 ties, 4 shirts
4. Hardbacks: x; paperbacks: y; $y = x + 5$; $4.25x + 2.50y = 59.75$; Ans: 7 hardbacks, 12 paperbacks
5. Ten's digit: x; one's digit: y; $x + y = 13$; $2y = x - 1$; Ans: 94
6. Ten's digit: x; one's digit: y; $x + y = 10$; $12x = 3y$; Ans: 28

For each problem (a) select two variables for the unknown numbers, (b) write two equations, and (c) solve. (Sections 13.1–13.5)

1. Three times the smaller of two numbers is decreased by 5. The result is   See above.
the greater number. The sum of the numbers is 27. Find the numbers.

2. Twice the greater of two numbers is three less than the smaller number.
The sum of the two numbers is -39. Find the two numbers.   See above.

3. Mr. Harvey bought some shirts on sale for $15.00 each and some ties for
$6.00 each. He bought one more tie than shirts, and the total cost was
$90.00. Find the number of each item he purchased.   See above.

4. Beverly bought some books at a used book sale held annually for
charities. She bought 5 more paperbacks than hardbacks at a total cost
of $59.75. The paperbacks cost $2.50 each and the hardbacks cost $4.25
each. How many of each did she buy?   See above.

5. The sum of the digits of a two-digit number is 13. Twice the one's digit is
one less than the ten's digit. Write the two-digit number.   See above.

6. The sum of the digits of a two-digit number is 10. Twelve times the ten's
digit equals three times the one's digit. Write the two-digit number.   See above.

7. A plane averages 775 kilometers per hour flying with a tailwind. Its speed
is 725 kilometers per hour flying against the wind. Find the plane's speed
in still air and the speed of the wind.   See above.

8. A motor boat travels at a speed of 46 kilometers per hour downstream in
a river. Its speed is reduced to 34 kilometers per hour going upstream.
Find the speed of the boat in still water and the speed of the current.

9. A 2% acid solution is mixed with a $4\frac{1}{2}$% acid solution. How many grams
of each solution are used to obtain 110 grams of a 3% solution?

10. A 5% salt solution is mixed with 220 grams of a $7\frac{1}{2}$% salt solution. The
mixtures is a 6% salt solution. Find the amount of the 5% solution and
the 6% solution in grams.

Write the number or numbers that cannot be in the domain of each variable.
(Section 14.1)

11. $\dfrac{5}{3x}$ 0

12. $\dfrac{x + 3}{x}$ 0

13. $\dfrac{x - 5}{2x + 3}$ $-\dfrac{3}{2}$

14. $\dfrac{3x + 1}{(x - 2)(x + 5)}$

2, -5

Simplify. No divisor equals zero. (Section 14.2)

15. $\dfrac{x(x - 3)}{5(x - 3)}$ $\dfrac{x}{5}$

16. $\dfrac{(x - 2)(x + 1)}{(x + 3)(x - 2)}$ $\dfrac{x + 1}{x + 3}$

17. $\dfrac{2x + 14}{x^2 + 7x}$ $\dfrac{2}{x}$

18. $\dfrac{x + 5}{x^2 - 25}$ $\dfrac{1}{x - 5}$

Multiply and simplify. (Sections 14.3–14.5)

19. $\dfrac{3}{5x} \cdot \dfrac{10x}{9}$ $\frac{2}{3}$

20. $-\dfrac{5xy}{9} \cdot \dfrac{12}{15y^2}$ $-\frac{4x}{9y}$

21. $\dfrac{x}{x-3} \cdot \dfrac{2(x-3)}{5x}$ $\frac{2}{5}$

22. $\dfrac{(x+1)(x-4)}{2x(x+2)} \cdot \dfrac{6(x+2)}{3(x-4)}$ $\frac{x+1}{x}$

23. $\dfrac{2x^2-2x}{3x-9} \cdot \dfrac{6x+6}{x^2-1}$ $\frac{4x}{x-3}$

24. $\dfrac{x^2-x-2}{4x} \cdot \dfrac{4x+8}{x^2-4}$ $\frac{x+1}{x}$

Divide and simplify. (Section 14.6)

25. $\dfrac{y}{7} \div \dfrac{2y^2}{21}$ $\frac{3}{2y}$

26. $\dfrac{2x-1}{x+3} \div \dfrac{2x-1}{5}$ $\frac{5}{x+3}$

27. $\dfrac{x(x+5)}{x-3} \div (x+5)$ $\frac{x}{x-3}$

Simplify. (Section 14.7)

28. $\dfrac{2x+10}{3x-15} \div \dfrac{4}{x^2-25}$ $\frac{(x+5)^2}{6}$

29. $\dfrac{x+1}{x^2-2x-3} \div \dfrac{15x^2}{5x-15}$ $\frac{1}{3x^2}$

30. $\dfrac{\frac{2}{3}+\frac{x}{2}}{\frac{5x}{6}}$ $\frac{4+3x}{5x}$

Add or subtract. Simplify where necessary. (Sections 15.1 and 15.2)

31. $\dfrac{9}{x} - \dfrac{7}{x}$ $\frac{2}{x}$

32. $\dfrac{12y}{y+2} - \dfrac{11y}{y+2}$ $\frac{y}{y+2}$

33. $\dfrac{5x}{2x-3} + \dfrac{7x}{2x-3}$ $\frac{12x}{2x-3}$

34. $\dfrac{8}{x-y} + \dfrac{2x+7}{x-y}$ $\frac{2x+15}{x-y}$

35. $\dfrac{3x-1}{x+4} + \dfrac{x+8}{x+4}$ $\frac{4x+7}{x+4}$

36. $\dfrac{2t+3}{5t-7} - \dfrac{t-5}{5t-7}$ $\frac{t+8}{5t-7}$

Find each LCM. (Section 15.3)

37. $4x^2y$; $6xy^2$ $12x^2y^2$

38. $9rs^2$; $6st$ $18rs^2t$

39. x^2-9; x^2-6x+9 $(x-3)^2(x+3)$

40. $6y^2-3y$; $2y^2+y-1$ $3y(2y-1)(y+1)$

Add or subtract. (Sections 15.4–15.6)

41. $\dfrac{4}{3x^2} - \dfrac{5}{6x}$ $\frac{8-5x}{6x^2}$

42. $\dfrac{5}{12st} + \dfrac{3}{8t^2}$ $\frac{10t+9s}{24st^2}$

43. $\dfrac{2}{x} + \dfrac{x+5}{x+3}$ $\frac{x^2+7x+6}{x(x+3)}$

44. $\dfrac{4}{x-1} - \dfrac{3}{x+2}$ $\frac{x+11}{(x-1)(x+2)}$

45. $\dfrac{3}{2x-6} - \dfrac{1}{3x-9}$ $\frac{7}{6(x-3)}$

46. $\dfrac{3}{x^2-4} + \dfrac{5}{2x-4}$ $\frac{5x+16}{2(x+2)(x-2)}$

Solve and check each equation. (Section 15.7)

47. $\dfrac{2}{3x} = \dfrac{1}{3}$ $x=2$

48. $\dfrac{5}{x-7} = 3$ $x=8\frac{2}{3}$

49. $\dfrac{1}{x-2} - \dfrac{2}{x} = \dfrac{3}{x-2}$ $x=1$

Write the slope-intercept form of each inequality. (Section 16.1)

50. $4x - y + 3 < 0$ $y > 4x+3$

51. $2x - y > 8$ $y < 2x-8$

52. $-2x + 2y + 5 \geq 0$ $y \geq x - \frac{5}{2}$

Graph each inequality. (Sections 16.2–16.3)

53. $y > -\frac{1}{2}x + 1$

53. The region above the line with equation $y = -\frac{1}{2}x + 1$

54. $y < -2x - 1$

54. The region to the left of the line with equations $y = 2x - 1$

55. $y \leq x - 2$

55. The region below the line with equation $y = x - 2$

56. $y \geq \frac{1}{3}x + 1$

56. The region above the line with equation $y = \frac{1}{3}x + 1$

In Ex. 57-59, each graph is a region with two straight lines as its boundaries.
The quadrants that contain the region are indicated as are the equations of the boundaries.

Graph each linear system. (Section 16.4)

57. $\begin{cases} y \le -x + 1 \\ y \le 2x + 3 \end{cases}$ Quadrants: All; Boundaries: Below $y = -x + 1$, right of $y = 2x + 3$; Boundaries are included.

58. $\begin{cases} y \ge x + 2 \\ y > 1 \end{cases}$ Quadrants: I, II; Boundaries: Above $y = 1$, left of $y = x + 2$; Boundary $y = 1$ not included.

59. $\begin{cases} y > -\frac{3}{2}x + 1 \\ y < \frac{2}{3}x - 2 \end{cases}$ See below.

Graph each linear system. (Section 16.5)

In Ex. 60-20, each graph is a region with three straight lines as its boundaries.

60. $\begin{cases} y \le -x + 2 \\ y \ge \frac{1}{2}x - 1 \\ y \ge -2 \end{cases}$ Quadrants: All; Left of $y = -x + 2$, above $y = \frac{1}{2}x - 1$, above $y = -2$; Boundaries are included.

61. $\begin{cases} y \le -x + 2 \\ x \ge 1 \\ y \ge -1 \end{cases}$ Quadrants: All; Below $y = -x + 2$, right of $x = 1$, above $y = -1$; Boundaries are included.

62. $\begin{cases} y \le x \\ y \le x + 2 \\ y \le 3 \end{cases}$ See below.

Write three ordered pairs of each function. Let the x values equal −2, 0, and 3. (Section 17.1)

63. $\{(x, y) : y = -x^2 + x - 3\}$ $(-2, 9), (0, -3), (3, -9)$

64. $\{(x, y) : y = 2x^2 - x - 1\}$ $(-2, 9), (0, -1), (3, 14)$

Graph each function. (Section 17.2)

For Ex. 65 and 66; the lowest point of graph (parabola) is given. Then two other points are given.

65. $\{(x, y) : y = x^2 + 1\}$
Lowest point: $(0, 1)$; $(1, 2), (-1, 2)$

66. $\{(x, y) : y = x^2 + 2x - 3\}$
Lowest point: $(-1, -4)$; $(0, -3), (-2, -3)$

Complete each table. Then graph the two functions in the same coordinate plane. (Section 17.3)

In Ex. 67 and 68, each graph is a parabola that opens upward or downward as indicated.

67. $y = \frac{1}{2}x^2$
Upward at $(0, 0)$

x	y
−2	? 2
−1	? $\frac{1}{2}$
0	? 0
1	? $\frac{1}{2}$
2	? 2

$y = x^2$
(Upward at $(0, 0)$)

x	y
−2	? 4
−1	? 1
0	? 0
1	? 1
2	? 4

68. $y = -\frac{3}{2}x^2$
Downward at $(0, 0)$

x	y
−2	? −6
−1	? $-\frac{3}{2}$
0	? 0
1	? $-\frac{3}{2}$
2	? −6

$y = -\frac{3}{2}x^2 + 2$
Downward at $(0, 2)$

x	y
−2	? −4
−1	? $\frac{1}{2}$
0	? 2
1	? $\frac{1}{2}$
2	? −4

Write the number of units and the direction the graph of the first function can be moved to obtain the graph of the second function. (Section 17.4)

69. $y = 2x^2$ 3 units right
$y = 2(x - 3)^2$

70. $y = -3x^2$ 1 unit left
$y = -3(x + 1)^2$

71. $y = -5x^2$
$y = -5(x + 2)^2$
2 units left

Write an equation for a function for which the graph can be obtained as described in each exercise. (Section 17.5)

72. The graph of $-3x^2$ is moved 2 units to the right and 5 units upward. $y = -3(x - 2)^2 + 5$

73. The graph of $\frac{5}{2}x^2$ is moved 1 unit to the left and 6 units upward. $y = \frac{5}{2}(x + 1)^2 + 6$

74. The graph of $2x^2$ is moved 3 units to the left and 4 units downward. $y = 2(x + 3)^2 - 4$

59. Quadrants: I and IV; Boundaries: Right of $y = \frac{3}{2}x + 1$, below $y = \frac{2}{3}x - 2$; Boundaries are not included.

62. Quadrants: I, III, IV; Boundaries: Right of $y = x$, right of $y = x + 2$, below $y = 3$; Boundaries are included.

Change each polynomial to the form $(x - h)^2 + k$. (Section 17.6)

75. $x^2 + 2x - 5$ $\quad (x - (-1))^2 - 6$ **76.** $x^2 - 4x + 3$ $\quad (x - 2)^2 - 1$ **77.** $x^2 - 6x - 5$ $\quad (x - 3)^2 - 14$

Write the coordinates of the vertex of each graph. (Section 17.7)

78. $y = -(x + 7)^2 - 5$ $\;(-7, -5)$ **79.** $y = 2(x - 2)^2 + 1$ $\;(2, 1)$ **80.** $y = \frac{1}{3}(x - \frac{1}{2})^2 + \frac{5}{2}$ $\;(\frac{1}{2}, \frac{5}{2})$

Graph $y = x^2 + 2x - 5$. Refer to this graph to estimate the solutions of each equation. (Section 18.1)

81. $x^2 + 2x - 5 = 3$ Solutions: $-4, 2$ **82.** $x^2 + 2x - 5 = 0$ **83.** $x^2 + 2x - 5 = -2$

Solutions: $-3.5, 1.5$ Solutions: $-3, 1$

Solve by using the Factors of Zero Property. (Section 18.2)

84. $x^2 + 10x = 0$ $\;-10, 0$ **85.** $x^2 - 5x = 0$ $\;0, 5$ **86.** $2x^2 = 2x$ $\;0, 1$

87. $x^2 - x - 12 = 0$ $\;-3, 4$ **88.** $x^2 + 3x - 10 = 0$ $\;-5, 2$ **89.** $2x^2 - 9x - 5 = 0$ $\;-\frac{1}{2}, 5$

Solve. (Section 18.3)

90. $(x - 2)^2 = 64$ $\;-6, 10$ **91.** $(x + 5)^2 = 100$ $\;-15, 5$ **92.** $x^2 - 5x + \frac{25}{4} = 0$ $\;\frac{5}{2}$

Solve by completing the square. (Section 18.4)

93. $x^2 - 4x - 3 = 0$ $\;2 + \sqrt{7}, 2 - \sqrt{7}$ **94.** $x^2 + 2x - 7 = 0$ $\;-1 + 2\sqrt{2}, -1 - 2\sqrt{2}$ **95.** $x^2 - 5x - \frac{3}{4} = 0$ $\;\frac{5}{2} + \sqrt{7}, \frac{5}{2} - \sqrt{7}$

Solve by the quadratic formula. (Section 18.5)

96. $4x^2 + 4x - 3 = 0$ $\;-1\frac{1}{2}, \frac{1}{2}$ **97.** $3x^2 + 8x - 3 = 0$ $\;-3, \frac{1}{3}$ **98.** $2x^2 - 4x - 1 = 0$ $\;\frac{2 + \sqrt{6}}{2}, \frac{2 - \sqrt{6}}{2}$

Compute the value of $b^2 - 4ac$ for each equation. Then write Rational *or* Irrational *for the solutions. (Section 18.6)*

99. $3x^2 = 5 - x$ $\;61;$ Irrational   **100.** $6x^2 - 7x = 5$ $\;169;$ Rational   **101.** $3x^2 = 10$ $\;120;$ Irrational

Solve each problem. Show your work. (Section 18.7)

102. The product of two consecutive integers is 42. Find two pairs of such integers. 6 and 7; -7 and -6

103. The product of two consecutive odd integers is 35. Find two pairs of such integers. 5 and 7; -7 and -5

A-1 Computer Programming Statements

This section can be studied any time after Chapter 3 has been studied.

A computer is given instructions in a step-by-step form called a **computer program.**

The language used for the computer programs in this book is called BASIC which stands for Beginner's All Purpose Symbolic Instruction Code.

In Program 1, the numbers 1∅, 2∅, 3∅, 4∅, and 5∅ are **line numbers.** The symbol ∅ is used to distinguish zero from the letter "O". The letters A1, A2, and S are <u>variables</u>.

The value printed for S is 8.7.

Program 1

```
1∅  LET A1 = 3.1
2∅  LET A2 = 5.6
3∅  LET S = A1 + A2
4∅  PRINT S
5∅  END
```

Definition

A **variable** in BASIC is a single capital letter or a capital letter followed by one of the digits zero through nine.

A, B, K,
A2, X5, Y∅

There are several versions of the BASIC language with slight differences in rules for writing programs. The rules presented in this book apply to most versions of BASIC.

Rules

Line Number Rules in BASIC

1. Each line of a program has a line number.

2. Line numbers are positive integers.

3. The END statement has the greatest line number in the program.

In lines 5, 1∅, and 15 of Program 2, the number 3 and the expressions B + 5 and A + 1 are called <u>arithmetic expressions.</u>

The equations B = 3, A = B + 5, and A = A + 1 are <u>arithmetic statements.</u>

Program 2

```
 5  LET B = 3
1∅  LET A = B + 5
15  LET A = A + 1
2∅  PRINT A
25  END
```

Definition

Each single numeral or expression on the <u>right</u> of an equality symbol in BASIC is an **arithmetic expression.**

| Definition | An **arithmetic statement** in BASIC is an equation that has one variable on the left and an arithmetic expression on the right. | A2 = B − 1
 A = A + 1 |

In BASIC arithmetic statements, the equality symbol, =, has a meaning different from the meaning in algebra.

| Definition | The = symbol in a BASIC arithmetic statement means "replace the value of the variable on the left by the value of the numeral or expression shown on the right." |

In Program 2, A = B + 5 means "replace the current value of A by the value of B + 5." The statement A = A + 1 means "replace the current value of A by the value of A + 1."

The value assigned to A in line 1∅ of Program 2 is 8. The value assigned to A in line 15 is 9 because the expression A + 1 equals 9. The value of A printed by line 2∅ is 9.

The BASIC statement A = A + 1 differs from an equation in algebra. In algebra there is no value of A that will make A = A + 1 true.

EXERCISES

The answers to all exercises of this section can be found on page 537 of the student's book.

Write _Yes_ or _No_ to show whether each symbol is a BASIC _variable._

1. K
2. Y∅
3. AB
4. S9
5. R + S
6. X1∅
7. ∅
8. E∅
9. J6
10. 6F
11. K1
12. XX
13. T5
14. 15
15. R1∅∅

Write _Yes_ or _No_ to tell whether each sentence is an acceptable arithmetic statement in BASIC.

16. T2 = R + S − 3
17. W = W + Y
18. A + B = C
19. X = 5.2
20. T8 = T9 + T1∅
21. X = X + 1
22. L∅ = L∅ + 5
23. 2X = Y + 5
24. Y1 − Y2 = Y3
25. −23 = A5
26. B = W + ∅.8
27. K9 = K8 − 3

Refer to the program at the right for Exercises 28-31.

28. What value is assigned to R in line 4∅?
29. What value is assigned to S in line 5∅?
30. What value is assigned to A in line 6∅?
31. What value is assigned to B in line 7∅?

```
1∅   LET A = 6
2∅   LET B = 5
3∅   LET C = 1∅
4∅   LET R = A + B
5∅   LET S = B − C
6∅   LET A = A + R
7∅   LET B = B − S
8∅   PRINT R, S, A, B
9∅   END
```

Write the value assigned to each variable in Exercises 32-41.
Refer to the program at the right.

```
10   LET S0 = 1
20   LET S1 = 1
30   LET S2 = S0 + S1
40   LET S3 = S1 + S2
50   LET S4 = S2 + S3
60   LET S5 = S3 + S4
70   LET S6 = S4 + S5
80   LET S7 = S5 + S6
90   LET S8 = S6 + S7
100  LET S9 = S7 + S8
110  PRINT S0, S1, S2, S3, S4
120  PRINT S5, S6, S7, S8, S9
130  END
```

32. S2 in line 30
33. S3 in line 40
34. S4 in line 50
35. S5 in line 60
36. S6 in line 70
37. S7 in line 80
38. S8 in line 90
39. S9 in line 100
40. Write all the values printed in line 110.
41. Write all the values printed in line 120.

Refer to Programs 1 and 2 on page 479 for Exercises 42-45.

42. Write a program that will compute the sum S of two numbers represented by A and B. Print the two numbers and the sum.

43. Write a program that will compute the sum S1 of two numbers represented by R and S. Print the two numbers and the sum.

44. Write a program that will compute a negative difference D between two numbers represented by E and F. Let F be the greater number. Print the difference.

45. Write a program that will compute a positive difference Y between two negative numbers represented by P and Q. Let Q be the greater number. Print the difference.

A-2   Computer Programming Operations

This section can be studied any time after Chapter 3 has been studied.

Here are the symbols for arithmetic operations in the BASIC language. "Exponentiate" means "raise to a power."

Operation	Symbol
Add	+
Subtract	−
Multiply	*
Divide	/
Exponentiate	↑

The last three operations are illustrated below.

Operation	Arithmetic Expression	Value
Multiplication	3 * 4	12
Division	1Ø/2	5
Exponentiation	3↑2	9

In BASIC, **exponentiation** (raising to a power) is done first. Multiplication and division are performed next from left to right and then addition and subtraction from left to right.

EXAMPLE 1   Write the value of −15 + 5 * 11 − 4 ↑ 2/8.

Solution:

1. Exponentiate. ⟶ −15 + 5 * 11 − 4 ↑ 2/8 = −15 + 5 * 11 − 16/8
2. Multiply and divide. ⟶ = −15 + 55 − 2
3. Add and subtract. ⟶ = 38

Parentheses are used in BASIC but not as multiplication symbols. The operations inside parentheses are performed first as shown in the expressions below.

a. (5 + 3) * 2 = 16   b. (8 − 2)/3 = 2   c. (2 * 3) ↑ 2 = 36

Expression **a** above would <u>not</u> be correct in BASIC if written as (5 + 3)2. The multiplication symbol * is necessary.

It is often necessary to use <u>nested parentheses</u> in BASIC.

$$(2 * (X − 3))/4$$

The innermost parentheses are around X − 3. These are called **nested parentheses**. To find the value, perform the operations with the innermost parentheses first.

EXAMPLE 2   Write the value of (2 * (X − 3))/4 if X equals 7.

    Solution: (2 * (X − 3))/4 = (2 * (7 − 3))/4

                             = (2 * 4)/4

                             = 8/4 = 2

EXERCISES   The answers to all exercises of this section can be found on page 538 of the student's book.

Write the value of each BASIC *arithmetic expression.*

1. 2 + 3 * 4   **2.** 5 − 8/2   **3.** 1.4 * 3 ↑ 2
4. 2.3 * 2 ↑ 3   **5.** 12.1 + 8.4/3   **6.** 5.6 + 12.5/5

7. $(4 - 1) * 5$ 8. $8 - (7 - 2)$ 9. $10/(7 - 9)$

10. $12/2 * 8$ 11. $5.6 - 2.2 * 3$ 12. $2.7 - 1.3 * 4$

13. $6.2/2 * 6$

14. $8.1 * 2/3$

15. $(2 - 10) * 2/4$ 16. $(5 - 19)/7 * 3$

17. $((7.2 + 0.9) * 2)/3$ 18. $34.5/(12.8 - (3.1 + 4.7))$

Write the value assigned to X *if* A = 2, B = 3, C = 5.

19. $X = (A + B) * C$ 20. $X = (2 * B) \uparrow A$ 21. $X = (B - C)/A$

22. $X = (C - (A + B))$ 23. $X = A * B \uparrow 2/3$ 24. $X = A * (B \uparrow 2/3)$

25. $X = (A + 2) * (B + 3)$ 26. $X = 12/(A - (B + C))$

Write each expression as a BASIC *language arithmetic expression.*

27. $2Y$ 28. $27A$ 29. R^3 30. B^4 31. $A(B + C)$

32. $(R + S)T$ 33. $XY \div 2$ 34. $A \div BC$ 35. $2X^3$ 36. $5W^2$

37. ABC^2 38. $10XY^3$ 39. $(X + Y)^5$ 40. $(A - B)^6$ 41. $A + 2(B - C)^2$

Refer to the program at the right. Write the value assigned to the given variable in each statement in Exercises 42-47.

```
10  LET A = 2.4
20  LET B = 0.9
30  LET C = (A + B) * 2
40  LET D = A + B ↑ 2
50  LET X = (B - (A + C))/3
60  LET Y = (C - 0.21) ↑ 2
70  LET W = A * B/3
80  LET R = A/0.8 * B
90  PRINT X, Y, W, R
100  END
```

42. C in statement 30

43. D in statement 40

44. X in statement 50

45. Y in statement 60

46. W in statement 70

47. R in statement 80

Write programs as described.

48. Write a BASIC program to compute the perimeter of a rectangle. Use the formula below. Let $\ell = 5.6$ decimeters and $w = 4.3$ decimeters.

$$P = 2(\ell + w)$$

49. Write a BASIC program to compute the area of a triangle. Use the formula below. Let $b = 12.3$ centimeters and $h = 6$ centimeters.

$$A = \frac{bh}{2}$$

A–3 READ and DATA Statements

This section
can be studied
any time after
Chapter 4
has been
studied.

Program 1 uses three new statements
called READ, DATA, and GO TO
statements.

The word LET is unnecessary
in some forms of BASIC. It is
omitted in statement 3Ø.

Program 1

```
10  READ L, W
20  DATA 10, 6, 15.2, 13.5
30  P = 2 * (L + W)
40  PRINT P
50  GO TO 10
60  END
```

The READ statement instructs the computer to look for values in a
DATA statement that are to be assigned to variables of the READ
statement.

The first value shown in the DATA statement is assigned to L. The
second value is assigned to W. Then a value is computed for P.

The statement in line 5Ø instructs the computer to go back to line 1Ø.
Again, values are read for L and W. The next value for L is 15.2, and
the next value for W is 13.5.

There are no more values for L and W.
The computer will print the values
of P and a message
OUT OF DATA IN LINE 1Ø
as shown at the right.

```
32
57.4
OUT OF DATA IN LINE 10
```

Flow charts are often used to
plan how to write computer
programs. The flow chart at
the right is a plan for Program 2.

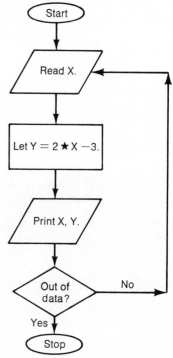

Program 2
```
10  READ X
20  DATA −5, −3, −1, 0, 1, 3, 5
30  Y = 2 * X − 3
40  PRINT X, Y
50  GO TO 10
60  END
```

Statement 2Ø provides 7 values for X.
After −13 is computed for Y,
statement 5Ø instructs the computer
to "read" another value for X.

	The results of the program	−5	−13
	are printed as shown at	−3	−9
	the right.	−1	−5
		0	−3
		1	−1
		3	3
		5	7

OUT OF DATA IN LINE 10

EXERCISES

The answers to all exercises of this section can be found on page 538 of the student's book.

Write the values assigned to X.

1.
```
10  READ Y
20  DATA 2, 3
30  X = 5 * Y
```

2.
```
10  READ R
20  DATA 1.3, 2.6
30  X = 0.5 + R
```

3.
```
10  READ E, F
20  DATA 10, 3, 13, 17
30  X = E − F
```

4.
```
10  READ A, B
20  DATA 2, 4, 10, 15
30  X = A + B
```

5.
```
10  READ R, S
20  DATA 12, 3, 5, 7
30  X = R − S * 3
```

6.
```
10  READ A
20  DATA 2, 3, 4
30  X = 5 * A ↑ 2
```

Write all the values that will be printed by each PRINT statement.

7.
```
10  READ A
20  DATA −3, −1, 2, 5
30  X = A ↑ 2
40  PRINT X
50  GO TO 10
60  END
```

8.
```
10  READ B
20  DATA −2, −1, 2, 3
30  X = B ↑ 3
40  PRINT X
50  GO TO 10
60  END
```

9.
```
10  READ R, S
20  DATA 5.1, 2.6, 0.8, 0.9
30  W = 2 * (R + S)
40  PRINT W
50  GO TO 10
60  END
```

10.
```
10  READ C, D
20  DATA 12.4, 3.9, 4.6, 5.9
30  Y = (C − D) * 3
40  PRINT Y
50  GO TO 10
60  END
```

11.
```
10  READ Y2, Y1, X2, X1
20  DATA 5, 2, −3, 4, −3, 4, 1, −3
30  DATA 0, −5, −3, 7
40  A = (Y2 − Y1)/(X2 − X1)
50  PRINT A
60  GO TO 10
70  END
```

12.
```
10  READ R1, R2
20  DATA 10, 5, 7, 15
30  DATA 4.2, 8.3
40  R = R1 * R2/(R1 + R2)
50  PRINT R
60  GO TO 10
70  END
```

13. Write a BASIC program with READ and DATA statements that will compute two values for A in the formula A = L * W. List the values for A.

14. Write a BASIC program with READ and DATA statements that will compute the circumferences of three circles with diameters having lengths 12 millimeters, 0.56 centimeters, and 2.85 decimeters. Let π = 3.14.

A–4 IF Statements

This section can be studied any time after Chapter 5 has been studied.

Program 1 has an IF-THEN statement in line 4Ø.

Statement 4Ø instructs the computer to go back to line 2Ø when the value of N is less than 11. When the value of N is 11 or greater, the computer will go to line 5Ø and stop the program. The set of steps that are repeated over and over is called a **loop**.

Program 1

```
1Ø  LET N = 1
2Ø  PRINT N;
3Ø  LET N = N + 1
4Ø  IF N < 11 THEN 2Ø
5Ø  END
```

The table at the right will help you see how the values for N are computed by Program 1.

The first value assigned to N is 1. Then N is replaced by 1 in N + 1 to give a new value for N which is 2. A new value for N + 1 is found by replacing N by 2, and so on.

You can see that the value of N increases by 1 each time the computer runs through a loop of the program.

N		N + 1
1	→	2
2	→	3
3	→	4
4	→	5
5	→	6
6	→	7
7	→	8
8	→	9
9	→	1Ø
1Ø	→	11

The semicolon in line 2Ø causes the values of N to be printed horizontally. The results would be printed as shown below.

```
1   2   3   4   5   6   7   8   9   1Ø
DONE
```

The table below shows symbols that are used with IF-THEN statements. The "=" symbol has the same meaning as in algebra. You know that its meaning is different in LET statements.

Symbol in BASIC	Meaning	Symbol in Algebra
=	"is equal to"	=
< >	"is not equal to"	≠
>	"is greater than"	>
<	"is less than"	<
> =	"is greater than or equal to"	≥
< =	"is less than or equal to"	≤

EXAMPLE: Write all values of Y that would be printed in Program 2.

Solution:

Program 2

```
10  LET X = 4
20  LET Y = X ↑ 2 + 1
30  PRINT Y;
40  LET X = X − 1
50  IF X >= −4 THEN 20
60  END
```

1. Compute the first value for Y in line 20.

   Y = X ↑ 2 + 1 when X = 4.

   $Y = 4^2 + 1$ or **17**

2. Compute the next value for X in line 40.

   X − 1 when X = 4

   4 − 1 = **3**

3. Continue finding each value of Y and the next value for X.

4. Determine what value of X will cause the program to end. In line 50 the computer will not go back to line 20 if X >= −4. This is true when X = −5.

   All the values of Y will be printed as shown below.

   17   10   5   2   1   2   5   10   17

EXERCISES

The answers to all exercises of this section can be found on page 538 of the student's book.

Write all the values of N that would be printed for each program.

1.
```
10  LET N = −1
20  PRINT N
30  LET N = N − 2
40  IF N > −12 THEN 20
50  END
```

2.
```
10  LET N = 15
20  PRINT N
30  LET N = N − 3
40  IF N > −10 THEN 20
50  END
```

3.
```
10  LET N = 1
20  PRINT N
30  LET N = 2 * N − 3
40  IF N > −50 THEN 20
50  END
```

4.
```
10  LET N = 1
20  PRINT N
30  LET N = 5 − 3 * N
40  IF N < 50 THEN 20
50  END
```

Write all values of Y that would be printed for each program.

5.
```
10  LET X = −3
20  LET Y = 4 * X − 5
30  PRINT Y;
40  LET X = X + 1
50  IF X <= 3 THEN 20
60  END
```

6.
```
10  LET X = 6
20  LET Y = 2 − 2 * X
30  PRINT Y;
40  LET X = X − 2
50  IF X >= −6 THEN 20
60  END
```

7.
```
10  READ X
20  DATA −3, 0, 2, −1
30  LET Y = 1 − X ↑ 2
40  IF Y <= 0 THEN 10
50  PRINT Y;
60  GO TO 10
70  END
```

8.
```
10  READ X
20  DATA −2, 4, 0, −3
30  LET Y = X ↑ 2 − 10
40  IF Y >= 0 THEN 10
50  PRINT Y
60  GO TO 10
70  END
```

9. Write a program to count 10, 9, 8, · · ·, 0 and print each value. Make sure the computer stops after printing 0.

10. Write a program to count by twos starting with −6 and ending with −22: −6, −8, −10, · · ·, −22. Make sure the computer stops after printing −22.

11. Write a program to print the sequence 1, 3, 7, 15, 31, 63. The first three statements are given at the right.

```
10  N = 1
20  PRINT N
30  N = 2 * N + 1
```

12. Write a program to print the sequence −1, −3, −7, −15, −31, −63. The first three statements are given.

```
10  N = −1
20  PRINT N
30  N = 2 * N − 1
```

A–5   FOR and NEXT Statements

This section can be studied any time after Chapter 6 has been studied.

Two statements called FOR and NEXT statements are used in this program. Statement 10 of the program assigns −2, −1, 0, 1, and 2 as values of X in that order.

```
10  FOR X = −2 TO 2
20  LET Y = X ↑ 2 − 3
30  PRINT X; Y
40  NEXT X
50  END
```

Statement 30 causes both the X and Y values to be printed. The results are shown at the right.

−2	1
−1	−2
0	−3
1	−2
2	1

DONE

In the program above, the value of the variable was increased by 1 for each loop. The statement below causes the value of X to increase by 0.5 for each loop.

```
10  FOR X = 1 TO 3 STEP .5
```

EXAMPLE:

Write a program with FOR and NEXT statements that will compute and print values of y for the function, $\{(x, y) : y = 10 − x^2\}$. The domain is $\{5, 3, 1, −1, −3, −5\}$.

Solution:
```
10  FOR X = 5 TO −5 STEP −2
20  LET Y = 10 − X ↑ 2
30  PRINT Y;
40  NEXT X
50  END
```

The results of the program are shown at the right.

−15	1	9	9	1	−15

DONE

The answers to all exercises of this section can be found on page 538 of the student's book.

Write the values of Y that would be printed for each program.

1.
```
1Ø  FOR X = -3 TO Ø
2Ø  Y = 3 * X + 3
3Ø  PRINT Y
4Ø  NEXT X
5Ø  END
```

2.
```
1Ø  FOR X = 1 TO 3
2Ø  Y = 2 * X - 1
3Ø  PRINT Y
4Ø  NEXT X
5Ø  END
```

Write the values of A that would be printed for each program.

3.
```
1Ø  FOR A = 2.4 TO 3 STEP .1
2Ø  PRINT A
3Ø  NEXT A
4Ø  END
```

4.
```
1Ø  FOR A = Ø TO -4 STEP -.5
2Ø  PRINT A
3Ø  NEXT A
4Ø  END
```

Write all the values of N that would be printed for each program.

5.
```
1Ø  FOR A = 1 TO 5
2Ø  N = A ↑ 2
3Ø  PRINT N
4Ø  NEXT A
5Ø  END
```

6.
```
1Ø  FOR A = -2 TO 2
2Ø  N = A ↑ 2
3Ø  PRINT N
4Ø  NEXT A
5Ø  END
```

7.
```
1Ø  FOR A = -2 TO 2
2Ø  N = 2 * A ↑ 2 - 2 * A
3Ø  PRINT N
4Ø  NEXT A
5Ø  END
```

8.
```
1Ø  FOR A = 1 TO 5
2Ø  N = -3 * A ↑ 2 + A - .5
3Ø  PRINT N
4Ø  NEXT A
5Ø  END
```

9.
```
1Ø  FOR A = -5 TO Ø
2Ø  N = -A ↑ 2 - A
3Ø  PRINT N
4Ø  NEXT A
5Ø  END
```

10.
```
1Ø  FOR A = -3 TO Ø
2Ø  N = -A ↑ 3 - A
3Ø  PRINT N
4Ø  NEXT A
5Ø  END
```

11.
```
1Ø  FOR A = 1 TO 2 STEP .2
2Ø  N = A ↑ 2 - 1
3Ø  PRINT N
4Ø  NEXT A
5Ø  END
```

12.
```
1Ø  FOR A = Ø TO -3 STEP -.5
2Ø  N = -A ↑ 2
3Ø  PRINT N
4Ø  NEXT A
5Ø  END
```

Write a program to print values of y for each given function. Use FOR and NEXT statements. The domain is -3, -2, -1, 0, 1, 2, 3 .

13. $\{(x, y) : y = 2x + 5\}$

14. $\{(x, y) : y = 3x - 4\}$

15. $\{(x, y) : y = x^2 - 2x + 1\}$

16. $\{(x, y) : y = -x^2 + 5x - 2\}$

17. $\{(x, y) : y = (x - 2)(x + 3)\}$

18. $\{(x, y) : y = (x + 1)(x - 5)\}$

Glossary

The following definitions and statements reflect the usage of terms in this textbook.

Absolute Value The *absolute value* of a positive number equals the number. The *absolute value* of a negative number equals the opposite of the number. The *absolute value* of 0 equals 0. (Page 2)

Algebraic Expression An *algebraic expression* is an expression with one or more variables. (Page 19)

Axis of a Parabola A vertical line that contains the vertex of a parabola is called the *axis of the parabola*. (Page 443)

Base See **Power**.

Binomial A *binomial* is a polynomial of two terms. (Page 211)

Coefficient In a monomial of the form ax^n, the number represented by a is the *coefficient* or *numerical coefficient*. (Page 206)

Completing the Square Writing a quadratic equation in a form that makes the left side a trinomial square is called *completing the square*. (Page 460)

Constant Term In a polynomial, a term with no variables is called the *constant term*. (Page 218)

Cube Root A *cube root* of a number is one of its three equal factors. (Page 184)

Degree of a Monomial The *degree of a monomial* in one variable is determined by the exponent of the variable. (Page 237)

Degree of a Polynomial The *degree of a polynomial* is the highest degree of the monomials of the polynomial. (Page 237)

Determinant A *determinant* is a square array of the form $\begin{vmatrix} a & b \\ c & d \end{vmatrix}$ in which a, b, c, and d are real numbers. (Page 307)

Determinant of a System of Equations The *determinant of a system of equations* is a determinant that is formed with the coefficients of the variables as elements. (Page 308)

Difference of Two Squares A binomial such as $x^2 - 16$ is called a *difference of two squares*. The first term and the absolute value of the constant term are perfect squares. (Page 248)

Domain The set of replacements for a variable is the *domain*. (Page 100)

Domain of a Relation The *domain of a relation* is the set of x values of its ordered pairs. (Page 134)

Equation An *equation* is a sentence that contains the equality symbol "=". (Page 52)

Equivalent Equations *Equivalent equations* have the same solution. (Page 52)

Exponent See **Power**.

Expression An *expression* includes at least one of the operations of addition, subtraction, multiplication, or division. (Page 17)

Fourth Root A *fourth root* of a number is one of its four equal factors. (Page 184)

Function A *function* is a relation in which no two ordered pairs have the same x value. (Page 134)

Greatest Common Factor The *greatest common factor* of two or more counting numbers is the greatest number that is a factor of all the numbers. (Page 235)

Integers   The set of *integers* consists of the set of whole numbers and their opposites. (Page 26)

Intersection of Two Sets   The *intersection of two sets* is the set of elements that the sets have in common. (Page 411)

Irrational Number   An *irrational number* is a number that cannot be expressed as a quotient of two integers. (Page 27)

Least Common Multiple (LCM)   The *least common multiple (LCM)* of two or more counting numbers is the smallest counting number that is divisible by the given numbers. (Page 378)

Like Radicals   Radicals such as $6\sqrt{2}$ and $5\sqrt{2}$ are called *like radicals*. They have equal radicands. (Page 191)

Like Terms   *Like terms* have exactly the same variables and the same powers of these variables. (Page 45)

Linear Function   A function that has the points of its graph lying in a non-vertical straight line is a *linear function*. (Page 263)

Monomial of One Variable   A *monomial of one variable* over { rational numbers } is an expression of the form ax^n in which a is any rational number and n is any nonnegative integer. (Page 206)

Numerical Coefficient   See **Coefficient**.

Origin   The point 0 where the X axis and the Y axis meet is called the *origin*. (Page 124)

Parallel Lines   *Parallel lines* are two lines in the same plane that do not have a common point. (Page 276)

Perfect Square   Positive numbers such as 1, 4, 9, 16, 25, and 36 are *perfect squares*, because each is the square of a counting number. (Page 27)

Perimeter   The *perimeter* of a geometric figure such as a triangle, square, or rectangle is the sum of the lengths of its sides. (Page 83)

Polynomial   A *polynomial* is a monomial or the sum of two or more monomials. (Page 211)

Power   An expression such as $(-2)^3$ is called a *power*. The 3 is the *exponent* and the -2 is the *base*. (Page 19)

Prime Factorization   The *prime factorization* of a number is the number expressed as a product of its prime-number factors. (Page 179)

Prime Number   A *prime number* is a counting number greater than 1 that has exactly two counting-number factors, 1 and the number itself. (Page 178)

Quadrants   The four regions of the coordinate plane are called *quadrants*. (Page 127)

Quadratic Equation   A *quadratic equation* is an equation of the form $ax^2 + bx + c = 0$, $(a \neq 0)$. (Page 450)

Quadratic Function   A *quadratic function* is a function described by the rule $y = ax^2 + bx + c$, in which a, b, and c are rational numbers with $a \neq 0$. (Page 422)

Quadratic Polynomials   Second degree polynomials are called *quadratic polynomials*. (Page 237)

Range of a Relation   The *range of a relation* is the set of y values of its ordered pairs. (Page 134)

Ratio   A quotient of two numbers is called a *ratio*. (Page 271)

Rational Expression   A *rational expression* is one that can be written as the quotient of two polynomials. (Page 346)

Rational Number   A *rational number* is a number that can be expressed as a quotient of two integers, in which the denominator is not zero. (Page 26)

Real Numbers   The set of *real numbers* contains all the rational numbers and all the irrational numbers. (Page 27)

Reciprocals　Two numbers are *reciprocals* of each other if their product is 1.　(Page 14)

Relation　A *relation* is a set of ordered pairs. (Page 130)

Repeating Decimal　A *repeating decimal* has a digit or sequence of digits that is infinitely repeated.　(Page 26)

Root of an Equation　See **Solution of an Equation.**

Scientific Notation　*Scientific notation* is a numeral of the form $N \times 10^a$, in which a is an integer and N is a rational number such that $1 \leq N < 10$.　(Page 170)

Slope　In the rule for the linear function $y = ax + b$, a represents the *slope* of its graph. (Page 268)

Square Root　A *square root* is one of two equal factors of a number.　(Page 178)

Solution of an Equation　The *solution* or *root of an equation* is a number that makes the equation true.　(Page 52)

Solution Set of a Linear Equation　The *solution set of a linear equation* is the set of ordered pairs (x, y) that makes the equation true.　(Page 293)

Solution Set of a System of Two Equations　The *solution set of a system of two equations* is the set of ordered pairs that makes both equations true.　(Page 296)

Terms　The monomials that form a polynomial are called its *terms*.　(Page 211)

Trinomial　A *trinomial* is a polynomial of three terms.　(Page 211)

Trinomial Square　A trinomial that has two equal binomial factors is called a *trinomial square*. (Page 251)

Union of Two Sets　The *union of two sets* is the set of elements in either one of the two sets or in both of them.　(Page 406)

Variable　A *variable* is a letter such as x that represents one or more numbers.　(Page 19)

Vertex of a Parabola　The *vertex of a parabola* that is a graph of a quadratic function is either the lowest point or the highest point of the graph. (Page 442)

Whole Numbers　The set of *whole numbers* consists of zero and the counting numbers.　(Page 26)

X Intercept　The x value of a point common to the X axis and a straight line is called the X *intercept* of the line.　(Page 279)

Y Intercept　The y value of the point that a line has in common with the Y axis is the Y *intercept*. (Page 265)

Zeros of a Function　The *zeros of a function* are the values of x which makes the value of the function 0. (Page 450)

Index

Absolute value, 2
Acceleration due to gravity, 445
Addition
  Associative Property of, **30**
  Commutative Property of, **30**
  method of solving systems of
    equations, 304
  of polynomials, 215
  of radicals, 191
  of rational expressions, **389**
  Property for Equations, **52**
  Property for Inequalities, **107**
  Property of Opposites, **30**
  Property of Zero, **30**
Air Conditioning Technician, 144
Algebraic expression, **19**
Altitude of a plane, 229
Amperage, 368
Applications,
  average speed, 68
  careers, 47, 96, 144, 201-202,
    257-258, 313, 368, 417-418,
    472
  circumference of a circle, 283
  compound interest, 119
  conditions to equations, 78-82
  cruising range of a car, 93
  digit problems, 327-330
  discount, 88
  distance/rate/time, 68, 92-93,
    173, 332-336
  distance to the horizon, 229
  fuel tank capacity, 93
  gravity, 445
  latitude and longitude, 285
  list price, 88
  longitude and time zones, 341
  mileage, 93
  mixture problems, 337-340
  money problems, 323-326
  number problems, 320-322
  objects in free fall, 141, 150,
    331, 445
  per cent, 88
  perimeter, 68, **83**
  of quadratic equations,
    469-471
  rate, 68
  rate of discount, 88
  rate of work, 395-396
  sale price, 88
  saving energy and money, 22

  simple interest, 283
  space technology, 173
  temperature, 22, 282, 284
  time, 68
  unit·price, 70
  using functions, 141
  words to equations, 74-77
Arithmetic mean, **47**
Arithmetic statement (BASIC),
  479, **480**
Associative Property
  of Addition, **30**
  of Multiplication, **34**
Average, **47**
Axis of a parabola, **443**

Base, 19
BASIC, Computer programming
  in, 479-489
Binomial(s), **211**
British Thermal Units (BTU's),
  144

Calculator Exercises
  adding or subtracting fractions,
    384
  checking equations, 61
  checking inequalities, 110, 410
  checking a system of equations,
    303
  continued fractions, 358
  evaluating fractions, 162
  evaluating polynomials, 214
  evaluating powers, 21
  evaluating radicals, 190
  finding an average
    (Statistician), 47
  formula for finding a sum, 247
  least value of a quadratic
    function, 435
  magic squares, 133
  objects in free fall, 331
  paper caper, 275
  radicals within radicals, 459
  using formulas, 82
Careers
  Air Conditioning Technician,
    144
  Electrician, 368
  Engineering Technician, 96
  Industrial Production
    Technician, 472

  Life Scientist, 257-258
  Meteorologist, 201-202
  Pharmacist, 313
  Production Planner, 417-418
  Statistician, 47
Celsius, 201 ff.
Centigram, 339
Centimeter, 68 ff.
  square, 469
Coefficient, **206**
  leading, **244**
Combining like terms, **45**
Common monomial factor, 234
Commutative Property
  of Addition, **30**
  of Multiplication, **34**
Comparison Property, **104**
Completing the square, **461**
Complex fractions, 365-366
Compound interest, 119
Computer program, **479**
Continued fractions, 358
Cooling capacity, 144
Coordinate of a point, **124**
Counting number, **26**
Cruising range, 93
Cube root, **184**
Customary measures (see inch,
  mile, pound, etc.)

DATA statement (BASIC), 484
Decigram, 337
Decimals, repeating and non-
  repeating, 26-27
Degree of a polynomial, **237**
Denominator, rationalizing a, **195**
Determinant, **307**
  element of a, **307**
  of a system, **308**
Difference of two squares, **248**
Difference Rule for Rational
  Expressions, **372**
Digit, 26
  problems, 327
Discount, **88**
Discriminant, **466**
Distance problems, 332
Distance to the horizon, 229
Distributive Property, **42**
Division
  of polynomials, 222
  of positive and negative

numbers, 14, **15**
  of rational expressions, 362
  Property for Equations, **56**
  Property for Inequalities, **114**
Domain, **100**
  of a relation, **134**

Electrician, 368
Element of a determinant, **307**
Empty set, 112
END statement (BASIC), 479
Engineering Technician, 96
Equation(s), **52**
  Addition Property for, **52**
  checking, 61
  Division Property for, **56**
  equivalent, **52**
  linear, **290**
  Multiplication Property for, **55**
  quadratic, 450
  root of, **52**
  solution of, **52**
  standard form of a linear, **290**
  Subtraction Property for, **53**
  systems of, **296**
  with rational expressions, **393**
Equator, 285
Equivalent
  equations, **52**
  inequalities, 107
Exponent(s), **19**
  negative, **159**
  Property of Negative, **159**
  Property of a Zero, **156**
Exponentiation, in BASIC, **482**
Expression, **17**
  algebraic, 19
  arithmetic, in BASIC, **479**
  evaluating an, 19
  rational, **346**

Factor(s), 234
  common, 42
  common monomial, **234**
  greatest common, **235**
  of Zero Property, **453**
Factoring, 42
  combined types, 254
  common monomial, 235
  difference of two squares, **249**
  perfect trinomial squares, 252
  quadratic trinomials, 240
Fahrenheit, 22 ff.
Flow chart, **484**

Foot, 69 ff.
  square, 144
  cubic, 78
FOR and NEXT statements
  (BASIC), 488
Formula(s), **130**
  for changing Celsius degrees
    to Fahrenheit degrees, 282
  for changing Celsius degrees
    to Kelvin degrees, 284
  for circumference of a circle,
    283
  for compound interest at 12%
    compounded daily, 119
  for cruising range of a car, 93
  for distance/rate/time, **68**, 92,
    173, 332-336
  for distance to the horizon,
    229
  for distance traveled by an
    object in free fall, 141, 150,
    331, 445
  for finding a sum, 247
  for greatest safe load, 96
  for output current and
    voltage, 368
  for perimeter of a rectangle,
    68
  for finding sale price, 88
  for simple interest, 283
  for unit price, 70
  for the weight of a person
    on Mars, 140
  for wind chill temperature,
    202
  problem solving with, 68, 92
  quadratic, **463**
  using, 82
Fourth root, **184**
Fraction(s)
  adding or subtracting, 384
  complex, 365
Fuel tank capacity, 93
Function(s), **134**
  graph of, 135, 262
  linear, **263**
  quadratic, **422**
  zeros of a, **450**

Gallon, 75 ff.
GO TO statement (BASIC), 484
Gram, 313 ff.

IF statement (BASIC), 486

Inch, 69 ff.
  square, 96
Industrial Production Technician,
  472
Inequality(ies), 100
  Addition Property for, **107**
  checking, 110, 303, 410
  Division Property for, **114**
  graphing, 404, 406
  graphing systems of, 411, 415
  in two variables, 400
  Multiplication Property for,
    113
  problem solving with, 116
  slope-intercept form of, **401**
  Subtraction Property for, **108**
  systems of three or more, 415
Integer(s), **26**
Interest, compound, 119
Intersection of two sets, **411**
Irrational number, **27**, 181

Kilogram, 70 ff.
Kilometer, 69 ff.

Latitude and Longitude, 285
Leading coefficient, **244**
Least common multiple, **378**
  of polynomials, **379-380**
Life Scientist, 257-258
Like radicals, **191**
Like terms, **45**
  in equations, 62
Line(s)
  parallel, **276**
  slope of a, **268**
Line numbers (BASIC), 479
Linear
  equation, **290**
  function, 262-263
  inequality, 400
  system, 411
Linear equation, **290**
  graph of a, 293
  solution set of a, **293**
  standard form of, **290**
Linear inequalities, **400**
  graphing, **404**
  slope-intercept form of, **401**
List price, **88**
Liter, 81 ff.
Longitude and time zones, 341
Loop (BASIC), 486

Magic Squares, 133
Meteorologist, 201-202
Meter, 69 ff.
  square, 81
  cubic, 338
Metric measures
  of area, 81, 469
  of capacity, 81, 338
  of length, 68, 69
  of mass, 70, 76, 337, 338, 339
  of volume, 338
  See also Meter, Kilometer,
    Gram, Kilogram, etc.
Mileage, 93
Milligram, 338
Milliliter, 313 ff.
Millimeter, 69 ff.
Mixture problems, 337
Molecular weight, 313
Money problems, 323
Monomial, **206**, 237
  as a common factor, **234**
Multiplication
  Associative Property of, **34**
  Commutative Property of, **34**
  of polynomials, 218
  of positive and negative
    numbers, 10, **11**, 38
  of rational expressions, 352
  Property for Equations, **55**
  Property for Inequalities, **113**
  Property of One, **34**
  Property of Reciprocals, **34**
Multiplication/Addition method,
  305

Negative
  exponents, **159**
  numbers, 2, 4, 10, 15
Nested parentheses (BASIC), 482
Number problems, 320
Numerical coefficient, **206**

Objects in free fall, 141, 150,
  331, 445
Opposite(s), 2
  Order Property of, **104**
Order
  of operations, 21
  Property of Opposites, **104**
  Transitive Property of, **105**
Ordered pair, **124**
Origin, **124**
Ounce, 70

OUT OF DATA line (BASIC),
  484

Parabola, 425
  axis of a, **443**
  vertex of a, **442**
Parallel lines, **276**
Per cent
  problem solving using, 88
Perfect square, 179
Perimeter(s)
  of a geometric figure, **83**
  of a rectangle, **68**, 83
  problem solving with, 68, 83
Pharmacist, 313
Point, coordinates of a, **124**
Polynomial(s), **211**
  degree of a, **237**
  evaluating, 214
  operations with, 215, 218,
    222
  prime, **234**
  quadratic, **237**
Positive number, 2, 10, 15
Pound, 140 ff.
Power(s), **19**
  Product Property of, **153**
  Property of the Power of a,
    166
  Quotient Property of, **155**
Prime
  factorization, 178, **179**
  meridian, **285**
  number, **178**
  polynomial, **234**
PRINT statement (BASIC), 479
Problem Solving (see Applications)
Product
  Property of Powers, **153**
  Property of the Power of a,
    163
  Property of Radicals, **182**
Product Rule for Rational
  Expressions, 349
Production Planner, 417-418
Programming, linear, 415
Property(ies)
  Addition, for Equations, **52**
  Addition, for Inequalities, **107**
  Addition, of Opposites, **30**
  Addition, of Zero, **30**
  Associative, of Addition, **30**
  Associative, of Multiplication,
    34

Commutative, of Addition, **30**
Commutative, of Multiplication,
  34
Comparison, **104**
Distributive, **42**
Division, for Equations, **56**
Division, for Inequalities, **114**
Factors of Zero, **453**
Multiplication, for Equations,
  55
Multiplication, for Inequalities,
  113
Multiplication, of One, **34**
Multiplication, of Reciprocals,
  34
of a Zero Exponent, **156**
of Negative Exponents, **159**
of the Opposite of a
  Difference, **356**
of the Power of a Power, **166**
of the Power of a Product, **163**
of the Power of a Quotient,
  164
Order, of Opposites, **104**
Product, of Powers, **153**
Product, of Radicals, **182**
Quotient, of Powers, **155**
Quotient, of Radicals, **194**
Special, of Real Numbers, **38**
Subtraction, for Equations, **53**
Subtraction, for Inequalities,
  108
Transitive, of Order, **105**
Proportion, direct and indirect,
  368

Quadrant, **127**
Quadratic
  equation, **450**
  formula, **463**
  function, **422**
    graph of, **425**
    least value of, 435
  polynomial, **237**
    standard form of, **440**
  trinomial, **237**
Quotient
  Property of Powers, **155**
  Property of the Power of a,
    164
  Property of Radicals, **194**
Quotient Rule for Rational
  Expressions, 362

Radical(s)
evaluating, 190
like, **191**
Product Property of, **182**
Quotient Property of, **194**
simplest form of, 188
symbol, 178
within radicals, 459
Radicand, **184**
Range
cruising, **93**
of a relation, **134**
Rate of discount, **88**
Rate of work, **395**
Ratio, **271**
Rational expression(s), **346**
adding and subtracting, **389**
dividing, 362
equations with, **393**
multiplying, 352
Product Rule for, **349**
Quotient Rule for, **362**
simplifying, 349, 350
Sum and Difference Rules for, **372**
Rational number, **26**, 181
Rationalizing a denominator, **195**
READ statement (BASIC), 484
Real number(s), **27**
Special Properties of, **38**
Reciprocal(s), **14**
finding, 14
Multiplication Property of, **34**
Regular price, **88**
Relation, **130**
domain and range of a, **134**
graph of a, 130
Repeating decimal, **26**
Root(s)
cube and fourth, **184**
of an equation, 52
square, **178**
Table of Square, 198

Sale price, 88
Saving Energy and Money, 22
Scientific notation, **170**
Set description, **130**
Simplifying rational expressions, **350**
Slope(s), **268**
formula, **271**
positive and negative, 269
slope-intercept form, **268**
Solution of an equation, **52**
Solution set, **100**
of a linear equation, **293**
of a linear inequality, **400**
of a system of two equations, **296**
Solving inequalities, 111
Space Technology, 173
Square(s), 178, 179
completing the, **461**
difference of two, 248
Table of, 198
trinomial, **251**
Square root(s), **178**
Table of, 198
Standard form
of a linear equation, **290**
of a quadratic polynomial, **440**
Statistician, 47
Substitution method of solving systems of equations, 300, **302**
Subtraction
of polynomials, 215
of positive and negative numbers, **8**
of rational expressions, 389
Property for Equations, **53**
Property for Inequalities, **108**
System(s) of equations, 296
determinant form of, **307**
solution set of, **296**
solving by addition method, **304**

solving by determinants, 310
solving by multiplication/addition method, **305**
solving by substitution method, 300, **302**

Table of Squares and Square Roots, 198
Term(s), **211**
constant, **218**
like, **45**
Terminating decimal, 27
Transitive Property of Order, **105**
Trinomial, **211**
quadratic, **237**
square, **251**

Union of two sets, 406
Unit price, **70**

Variable(s), 19
in BASIC, **479**
Vertex
of a parabola, **442**
of a triangle, 415
Vertical line, equation of, 280
Voltage, 368

Whole number, 26
Wind chill temperature, 201
Word problems
(see Applications)

X axis, 124
X intercept, **279**

Y axis, 124
Y intercept, **265**
Yard, 69 ff.

Zeros of a function, 450
Zone description, 341

Answers to Selected Exercises

The answers to the odd-numbered problems in the *Classroom Exercises*, *Written Exercises*, *Mid-Chapter Reviews*, *Chapter Reviews*, *Cumulative Reviews*, *Careers*, *Special Topic Applications* and *Calculator Exercises* are given on the following pages.

The answers are provided for all of the problems in the *Review Capsules*, *Pivotal Exercises* (**P-1, P-2**, etc.), and *Appendix*.

CHAPTER 1   OPERATIONS ON NUMBERS

Page 3   Classroom Exercises   1. 25   **3.** 0.001   **5.** $\frac{2}{3}$ **7.** $-8\frac{7}{8}$ **9.** -8.5 **11.** 9   **13.** 0   **15.** $\frac{4}{5}$
17. 0.053   **19.** $\frac{1}{4}$ **21.** -0.01 **23.** -2.5 **25.** $-2\frac{1}{2}$ **27.** 12   **29.** -5

Page 3   Written Exercises   1. -23 **3.** 0.12   **5.** 0   **7.** $-\frac{3}{5}$ **9.** $5\frac{6}{7}$ **11.** 18   **13.** 227   **15.** $\frac{7}{8}$ **17.** $5\frac{1}{8}$
19. 0.083   **21.** 2.73   **23.** 23   **25.** -6.8 **27.** 12   **29.** 23   **31.** -13 **33.** 13

Pages 5-6   P-1   a. -9 **b.** $-2\frac{1}{2}$ **c.** -4.7 **P-2   a.** 2   **b.** $1\frac{1}{2}$ **c.** 2.6   **P-3   a.** -3 **b.** $-\frac{2}{3}$ **c.** -7.4

Page 6   Classroom Exercises   1. b   **3.** d   **5.** -40 **7.** -6 **9.** -0.7 **11.** 16   **13.** 3.4   **15.** $\frac{1}{5}$ **17.** -6
19. -3.3 **21.** $-7\frac{1}{2}$ **23.** 0   **25.** 0

Page 7   Written Exercises   1. -42 **3.** -106 **5.** -0.08 **7.** 8   **9.** 4.7   **11.** 0.13   **13.** -25 **15.** -32
17. -8.9 **19.** 0   **21.** 0   **23.** 0   **25.** -10 **27.** 16   **29.** -45.5 **31.** 0   **33.** -6.97 **35.** 0   **37.** 12
39. -22 **41.** -47 **43.** 12.5   **45.** $-10\frac{7}{8}$

Page 7   Review Capsule for Section 1.3   1. a. 4   **b.** 4 Both a and b are the same.   **2. a.** 4   **b.** 4 Both a and b are the same.   **3. a.** 7   **b.** 7 Both a and b are the same.   **4. a.** 10   **b.** 10 Both a and b are the same.
5. a. 21   **b.** 21 Both a and b are the same.   **6. a.** 0   **b.** 0 Both a and b are the same.

Page 8   P-1 10, 0.8, -37, 0   **P-2   a.** 18   **b.** 20   **c.** -25 **d.** 4.2

Pages 8-9   Classroom Exercises   1. $20 + (-15)$ **3.** $0 + (-12)$ **5.** $(-12) + (-6)$ **7.** $-20 + 18$ **9.** $5 + 23$
11. $-\frac{1}{4} + (-8)$ **13.** -4 **15.** -23 **17.** -34 **19.** -10 **21.** 16   **23.** -14

Page 9   Written Exercises   1. 4   **3.** 6   **5.** -5 **7.** -9 **9.** -22 **11.** -10.8 **13.** -24.7 **15.** $-\frac{5}{8}$ **17.** 31
19. 32   **21.** 2   **23.** 42   **25.** 8.3   **27.** 0.11   **29.** -13 **31.** -18 **33.** 8   **35.** 4.4   **37.** $-\frac{1}{7}$ **39.** 1.3
41. 25   **43.** 8   **45.** 16

Page 9   Review Capsule for Section 1.4   1. 30   **2.** 5.2   **3.** 9   **4.** $\frac{1}{3}$ **5.** 2.25   **6.** 0.56   **7.** 1.44   **8.** 0

Pages 10-11   P-1 0   **P-2** $-8, -16, -24$ **P-3   a.** -42 **b.** -4.8 **c.** 0   **d.** -1 **P-4** 6, 12, 18
P-5   a. 45   **b.** $\frac{6}{5}$ **c.** 0.26   **d.** 3

Page 11   Classroom Exercises   1. -36 **3.** -96 **5.** -3 **7.** 0   **9.** -25 **11.** -2.1 **13.** 77   **15.** 150

17. 6   19. 6   21. 1   23. 1

Page 12   Written Exercises   1. −70   3. 0   5. −66   7. −12   9. −10   11. $-\frac{4}{15}$ 13. −20.4   15. −8.36   17. 72   19. 1   21. 87   23. 3200   25. 1   27. 99   29. −432   31. 198   33. −3600   35. 0   37. 1.56   39. $-\frac{8}{15}$ 41. 30   43. 96   45. 0   47. 6.   49. 60   51. −20

Page 13   Mid-Chapter Review   1. −17   3. $\frac{1}{2}$ 5. 0.06   7. 0   9. 2.5   11. −17   13. 10   15. −33   17. $-4\frac{1}{2}$ 19. −26   21. 11 + (−7)   23. 12.1 + 7.9   25. −13   27. 8   29. 5.9   31. −52   33. −3   35. 0   37. 45

Page 13   Review Capsule for Section 1.5   1. $\frac{3}{2}$ 2. $\frac{12}{1}$ 3. $\frac{8}{5}$ 4. $\frac{7}{3}$ 5. $\frac{22}{7}$ 6. 1   7. 1   8. 1   9. 1   10. 3   11. 3   12. 3   13. $\frac{3}{4}$

Pages 14-15   P-1   a. $\frac{10}{3}$ b. $-\frac{1}{3}$ c. $\frac{3}{4}$ d. 1   e. −1   **P-2**   a. 64   b. $\frac{1}{9}$ c. 0   **P-3**   a. $-1\frac{19}{27}$ b. $15\frac{3}{7}$ c. −0.3

Pages 15-16   Classroom Exercises   1. −8 × 4   3. 28 × $(-\frac{1}{7})$ 5. 175   7. 3   9. −0.5   11. $-\frac{2}{3}$ 13. −36   15. −0.7

Page 16   Written Exercises   1. 24   3. 3   5. $10\frac{2}{3}$ 7. $\frac{1}{6}$ 9. −0.9   11. $-10\frac{2}{3}$ 13. −3   15. −9   17. 0   19. −11   21. −0.9   23. −10   25. −4   27. −5   29. 52   31. 0   33. 41   35. $-\frac{1}{3}$ 37. 81   39. −10   41. 10   43. 33   45. 39

Page 16   Review Capsule for Section 1.6   1. 14   2. 2   3. 4. −216   5. 106   6. 2

Page 17   P-1   a. Correct   b. Incorrect   c. Correct   d. Incorrect

Page 18   Classroom Exercises   1. 16   3. 0   5. 5   7. 12   9. 43   11. 12   13. −11   15. −16

Page 18   Written Exercises   1. 9   3. −12   5. −0.5   7. 13   9. 4   11. −60   13. 9   15. −90   17. −14   19. −35   21. 20   23. 5.7   25. 9   27. −22   29. 9   31. 14   33. −2   35. 6.7

Page 18   Review Capsule for Section 1.7   1. 8   2. 0.064   3. $\frac{8}{27}$ 4. 9   5. −1   6. −64

Pages 19-20   P-1   a. 12   b. 2   c. $-7\frac{1}{2}$ **P-2**   a. 4   b. −4   c. 33

Page 20   Classroom Exercises   1. 36   3. 125   5. −64   7. −4   9. 8   11. −16   13. −110   15. 11   17. −23   19. 18   21. −17   23. 30   25. 25   27. −10   29. 0

Pages 20-21   Written Exercises   1. 121   3. 1000   5. −343   7. 54   9. 37   11. −18   13. 18   15. 13   17. 60   19. 8   21. −2   23. 0   25. −84   27. 30   29. 83   31. 300   33. 190   35. 60   37. −790   39. 256   41. −216   43. 13   45. $-\frac{3}{8}$ 47. 26   49. $-112\frac{1}{2}$ 51. −55   53. −35   55. $-\frac{16}{7}$ 57. 0   59. $\frac{1}{5}$

Page 21   Calculator Exercises   1. 49   2. 729   3. 625   4. 194,481   5. 117,649   6. −64

Page 22 Special Topic Application 1. $56 more 3. $196 more 5. $273 more 7. $99 more
9. $66 more

Page 23 Chapter Review 1. 1.5 3. $\frac{3}{8}$ 5. 0 7. 2.6 9. 35 11. −3 13. 4 15. 11 17. −14
19. −13.5 21. $6\frac{1}{2}$ 23. $-13\frac{7}{8}$ 25. 42 + (−68), −26 27. −53 + 26, −27 29. 42.9 + 18.5, 61.4
31. 75 + 13, 88 33. −204 35. 450 37. −9 39. −8.4 41. 10.08 43. −12 45. 16 47. $-\frac{1}{18}$
49. $1\frac{1}{3}$ 51. −9 53. 23 55. 28 57. −8 59. 5 61. 12 63. −9 65. −48 67. 1 69. −21

CHAPTER 2 REAL NUMBERS

Page 26 P-1 a. 2 b. −6 c. 0 d. −213

Page 28 Classroom Exercises 1. $\frac{7}{2}, \frac{14}{4}$ 3. $\frac{0}{1}, \frac{0}{3}$ 5. $\frac{-2}{8}, \frac{-4}{16}$ 7. $\frac{-5}{1}, \frac{-10}{2}$ 9. 0.5000. . .
11. 0.571428571428. . . 13. −.375000. . . 15. Rational 17. Rational 19. $\{28, 17\}$ 21. $\{-1.8, -124,$
$-\frac{22}{7}\}$ 23. $\{28, -1.8, 3\frac{1}{4}, -124, 17-\frac{22}{7}, 5.436436...\}$

Page 28 Written Exercises 1. $\frac{-14}{16}, \frac{-28}{32}$ 3. $\frac{35}{8}, \frac{70}{16}$ 5. $\frac{-183}{100}, \frac{-366}{200}$ 7. $\frac{20}{1}, \frac{40}{2}$ 9. $\frac{-3}{1}, \frac{-6}{2}$
11. −24.000. . . 13. 0.6363. . . 15. 0.4285714285714. . . 17. Rational 19. Irrational 21. Rational
23. Rational 25. Irrational 27. Irrational 29. $\{\frac{10}{2}, -2, 4.7, 0, -1\frac{3}{4}, \frac{7}{8}, 19, -\frac{17}{4}, -6, -0.9\}$
31. $\{-2, -1\frac{3}{4}, -\frac{17}{4}, -6, -0.9\}$ 33. $\{\pi\}$ 35. a, b, c, e, f 37. c, e 39. c, e 41. c, e 43. d, e
45. a, b, c, e, f

Page 29 Review Capsule for Section 2.2 1. 6 + (−4) 2. 7 + (−6) 3. 15 + (−8) 4. 4 + (−9) 5. 5 + (−12)
6. 23 + (−19) 7. 14 + (−18) 8. 2 + (−25) 9. 17 10. 17 11. $\frac{1}{16}$ 12. $-\frac{19}{60}$ 13. 1.1 14. 1.2
15. −9 16. −9 17. $-\frac{1}{9}$ 18. $4\frac{1}{6}$ 19. −7.1 20. −5.1 21. 2 22. 3 23. $\frac{1}{12}$ 24. $\frac{37}{60}$ 25. −1.8
26. −0.9 27. 1 28. −5 29. $\frac{11}{12}$ 30. $\frac{1}{12}$ 31. −2.6 32. 10.7

Page 31 P-1 a. 8.2, Commutative Property for Addition b. 6, Associative Property for Addition
P-2 a. 9 b. $-\frac{7}{8}$ c. $\frac{5}{6}+y$ d. $b-0.8$

Pages 31-32 Classroom Exercises 1. 0 3. $4\frac{1}{3}$ 5. −0.7 7. 0 9. 0.6 11. $3\frac{1}{2}$ 13. 0 15. 0 17. 3
19. 2.1 + x 21. $4\frac{1}{6}-a$ 23. x + y − 6 25. 5.1 − a − b

Pages 32-33 Written Exercises 1. 0, Addition Property of Opposites 3. 7, Commutative Property of
Addition 5. −8, Addition Property of Opposites 7. 2.5 9. $1\frac{1}{2}$ 11. 5 13. 1.7 15. −a − 0.3
17. p + 1 19. 2 − u 21. f − 4.4 23. −17 + k − b 25. $d-2\frac{1}{8}-f$ 27. a − 0.05 − b 29. r − g − 30
31. $-3\frac{3}{4}$ 33. $a-b-5\frac{5}{8}$ 35. −82 + q 37. $c-d-11\frac{1}{2}$ 39. 39 41. 10.6 43. −256 45. $1\frac{5}{8}$

47. 143   49. $-m - n - p + 5\frac{1}{4}$ 51. $8.91 + a - c$

Page 33   Review Capsule for Section 2.3   1. -30 2. 45   3. $-\frac{1}{4}$ 4. $\frac{6}{25}$ 5. -2.48 6. 7.02   7. -70
8. 88   9. $\frac{5}{8}$ 10. -4.8 11. 4.94   12. 36.04   13. $\frac{1}{5}$ 14. $\frac{5}{2}$ 15. $-\frac{1}{4}$ 16. 3   17. $-\frac{8}{3}$ 18. $\frac{1}{10}$ 19. 1
20. $-\frac{12}{1}$ 21. $-\frac{1}{13}$ 22. $\frac{1}{11}$ 23. -1 24. $\frac{5}{8}$

Page 35   P-1   a. 8.1, Commutative Property of Multiplication   b. 7, Associative Property of Multiplication
c. $-\frac{1}{9}$, Multiplication Property of Reciprocals   **P-2**   a. -9.6 b. 48n   c. 100pq

Pages 35-36   Classroom Exercises   1. 1   3. 62   5. 1   7. 17.8   9. 3.04   11. 16   13. 54   15. $\frac{4}{5}$ 17. $\frac{1}{2}$
19. 570   21. -12 23. 20   25. $-0.8yz$ 27. $-120mn$ 29. $-1.08bh$

Page 36   Written Exercises   1. $-\frac{5}{7}$, Multiplication Property of 1   3. 8, Associative Property of Multiplication
5. $-\frac{1}{2}$, Commutative Property of Multiplication   7. 40   9. 36   11. 0.42pq   13. 288m   15. $-27t$
17. $-5.4mp$ 19. 225xy   21. $1\frac{3}{10}$ 23. -7.98 25. 1   27. $-xyz$ 29. $-16trs$

Page 37   Mid-Chapter Review   1. $\frac{-10}{12}, \frac{-15}{18}$ 3. $\frac{14}{5}, \frac{28}{10}$ 5. $\frac{35}{10}, \frac{70}{20}$ 7. 0.444...   9. 0.7272...
11. 5.25000...   13. Rational   15. Rational   17. Rational   19. Rational   21. $\sqrt{36}$ 23. $\frac{2}{3}, -\sqrt{5}, -1\frac{2}{7}$,
$\sqrt{36}, -9.3$ 25. $-15.5 - a + b$ 27. $-6\frac{1}{2}$ 29. $r - s - 4\frac{3}{8}$ 31. $y + z - 4$ 33. 36   35. -120
37. $-1600k$ 39. $-8.82ay$ 41. $-24pf$

Page 37   Review Capsule for Section 2.4   1. $-12xy^2$ 2. $35a^2b^2$ 3. $3p^2qr$ 4. $-2mn^2s$
5. $x - 8$ 6. $-t - 1$ 7. $6.5f^2gt^2$ 8. $w - 16$ 9. $-22 + p$

Pages 38-39   P-1   a. $-x - 2$ b. $-4 + t$ c. $-\sqrt{2}$ d. mk   **P-2**   a. $\frac{-5k}{7}$ b. 1   c. 1   d. -1

Page 40   Classroom Exercises   1. $a - b$ 3. $x + y$ 5. $-x - y$ 7. $x - 2 - y + a$ 9. $a - 6 + b$ 11. $-4h$
13. $-2xy$ 15. $-3x^2y$ 17. $-2a^2c^2$ 19. $-\frac{1}{2}y^2z^2$ 21. $-16m^2n^2$ 23. 1   25. $-\frac{9}{f}$ 27. -1 29. 1

Page 40   Written Exercises   1. ac   3. $-f$ 5. $-4d$ 7. $-m - n$ 9. $2a - 11 - b$ 11. 16cd   13. $-4q$
15. $-9a^2$ 17. $6x^2y^2$ 19. $\frac{4}{3}a^2b^2$ 21. $-1.56r^2s^2$ 23. $\frac{-2 - y}{x}$ 25. 1   27. $-\frac{3}{p}$ 29. 1   31. 1
33. 7fg   35. 1   37. $-0.78r^2$ 39. $\frac{2}{15}x^2y$ 41. $-3 - r + 3s$ 43. $-\frac{3b}{t}$ 45. -1 47. $-195 - 3a^2 - 5b^2$
49. -1 51. $-1.5xy + 54rstx + 40w^2x^2$

Page 41   Review Capsule for Section 2.5   1. $14a + 16$ 2. $21 + 24x$ 3. $-10 - 30b$ 4. $-8y - 32$
5. $12pq - 8p$ 6. $-\frac{1}{2}xy - 8x^2y$ 7. Yes   8. No   9. Yes   10. No   11. No   12. Yes

Pages 42-43   P-1   a. $-15a + 10$ b. $-3m - 2$ c. $6rs - 15r$ **P-2**   a. 3x   b. 4c   c. $-7t$ **P-3**   a. $6(y + 4)$
b. $2n(5m - 2)$ c. $3x(5x - 1)$ d. $-3v(3 + w)$

Page 43   Classroom Exercises   1. $10p + 10q$ 3. $2k - 6$ 5. $8r + 8s$ 7. $-3m^2 + m$ 9. $8(m + n)$
11. $2(3x + 5y)$ 13. $5(x - y)$ 15. $t(4m - 9n)$ 17. $-3(a + b)$ 19. $-r(6r + 1)$

Page 44 Written Exercises 1. $10a + 10b$ 3. $-3x - 6$ 5. $7r - 56$ 7. $24p + 16$ 9. $4r^2 + 12r$
11. $-2y^2 + 12y$ 13. $24t^2 - 20ut$ 15. $-2t^2 + 3t$ 17. $5(a + b)$ 19. $4(r + 5s)$ 21. $2k(m + 2n)$
23. $pq(p + q)$ 25. $3(r - s)$ 27. $8(x - 1)$ 29. $8x(k - 2y)$ 31. $13x(x - 2y^2)$ 33. $-7b(2a + 1)$
35. $3x(-x + 2)$ 37. $xy(-2 + 5)$ or $3xy$ 39. $-2(5a + b)$ 41. $7a + 7b - 7c$ 43. $-32kp - 24kq + 16kr$
45. $-r^3s + 2r^2s^2 - 3rs^3$ 47. $5(a - 3b + 2c)$ 49. $3x(2x^2 + x - 6)$ 51. $6(5r - 6x - 23)$

Page 44 Review Capsule for Section 2.6 1. 7 2. -10 3. -6 4. -13 5. -6 6. 5 7. -20 8. 5

Page 45 P-1 a. Like b. Unlike c. Unlike

Page 46 Classroom Exercises 1. $11y$ 3. $2x$ 5. $2ab$ 7. 0 9. $12z$ 11. $8x - 1$ 13. -7 15. $-2t + 5$
17. $a^2 - a + 5$ 19. $2x^2 + 1$ 21. $\frac{1}{9}a^2 + 2\frac{1}{2}a + \frac{1}{2}$ 23. $5.7m + 2.1m^2 + n$ 25. $-66p^2 - p - 73$

Page 46 Written Exercises 1. $20y$ 3. $19t$ 5. $-17x$ 7. $-2t^2$ 9. $7z^2$ 11. $6a - 6$ 13. $-0.2t^2 + 2t$
15. $-3g - 3.4$ 17. $\frac{17}{20}a - 1\frac{1}{2}b$ 19. $-2a^2 - 5a - 18$ 21. $3.3t^2 + 2.8t + 0.3$ 23. $\frac{11}{24}r^2 - \frac{8}{15}s^2 + \frac{1}{3}$
25. $-50f^2 - 17f - 45$ 27. $0.5t$ 29. $ab^2 - 2a^2b + ab - a^2b^2$ 31. $8v^2 + 10w^2 - 4w$ 33. $75a^2 + 25$
35. $-4\frac{1}{3}x^2 - \frac{1}{4}x + \frac{1}{5}$

Page 47 Career 1. 86.7 3. 19

Pages 49-50 Chapter Review 1. $\frac{-26}{32}, \frac{-39}{48}$ 3. $\frac{31}{8}, \frac{62}{16}$ 5. $\frac{-37}{1}, \frac{-74}{2}$ 7. $-21.000\ldots$ 9. $-0.333\ldots$
11. $4.5000\ldots$ 13. $13\frac{1}{2}, -5, 0, 4.1, 13, -\sqrt{9}, \frac{5}{8}, -0.5$ 15. $13\frac{1}{2}, 4.1, 13, \frac{5}{8}, \pi$ 17. $-5, 0, 13, -\sqrt{9}$ 19. -5
21. -8.9 23. $f - d - \frac{3}{4}$ 25. $-28 + r - s$ 27. 84 29. -240 31. -17 33. 12 35. $288x$ 37. $49c$
39. $-s + 5$ 41. $-5a + 3b - c$ 43. $m - n - a - b$ 45. $4st$ 47. $-3x^2$ 49. $100a^2b^2c$ 51. 1 53. $-\frac{5}{s}$
55. -1 57. $-8b - 72$ 59. $15 - 18t$ 61. $-6r^2 + 15r$ 63. $-2\frac{1}{4}t^2 - 3t$ 65. $10(t - w)$ 67. $2(x + 3y)$
69. $3x(2x + 1)$ 71. $-3(4x + y)$ 73. $-3k$ 75. $-2.3n - 3.2$ 77. $2r^2s - 3s^2$

CHAPTER 3 EQUATIONS

Pages 52-53 P-1 a. True b. True c. True **P-2** a. $y = -1$ b. $x = 29$ c. $t = 0$ d. $k = 22$
P-3 a. $n = -1$ b. $k = 1$ c. $x = 0$

Page 53 Classroom Exercises 1. -12 3. -8 5. $+13.7$ 7. $+\frac{5}{2}$ 9. -23 11. $y = 5$ 13. $q = 26$
15. $b = 4$ 17. $h = -2\frac{5}{6}$ 19. $y = 17$ 21. $c = -17$

Page 54 Written Exercises 1. $x = 33$ 3. $z = 12$ 5. $b = -4\frac{1}{4}$ 7. $d = 38$ 9. $f = 24$ 11. $g = 1$ 13. $j = 17$
15. $n = -24$ 17. $x = -1$ 19. $b = 4.8$ 21. $k = 2$ 23. $y = -1\frac{1}{5}$ 25. $x = -33$ 27. $b = 10.1$ 29. $d = -3\frac{1}{4}$
31. $f = 8.8$ 33. $x = -3\frac{1}{2}$ 35. $k = 12.8$ 37. $p = 1.3$ 39. $z = -62$ 41. $b = 33.4$

Page 54 Review Capsule for Section 3.2 1. 1 2. 1 3. 1 4. 1 5. 1 6. 1 7. 1 8. 1 9. 1 10. 1
11. 1 12. 1 13. 9 14. -7.02 15. $-7\frac{1}{2}$ 16. 117 17. $2\frac{5}{8}$ 18. -988 19. 464 20. -102.5

21. 8   22. $\frac{1}{4}$ 23. 15   24. −52   25. $-25\frac{5}{6}$ 26. 0.4   27. −2.5   28. −0.05

Pages 55-56   **P-1** a. True   b. True   c. True   **P-2** a. b = −36   b. x = −100   c. n = 1   d. b = 256
P-3 a. y = 0.1   b. x = −3   c. n = 1   d. t = −3   **P-4** a. 2   b. $-\frac{4}{3}$ c. $-\frac{3}{5}$ d. $\frac{5}{4}$

Page 57 **Classroom Exercises**   1. Multiply by 12.   3. Divide by 14.   5. Divide by −8.9.   7. Multiply by $-\frac{3}{2}$.
9. j = 28   11. z = 140   13. r = −4.8   15. t = 81   17. t = −6   19. a = −0.3   21. k = −16   23. k = 36

Page 57 **Written Exercises**   1. x = −65   3. y = −100   5. x = −116.2   7. t = 60   9. v = 184   11. x = −83.2
13. s = −33   15. r = −0.544   17. a = −7   19. d = −8   21. x = −10.2   23. x = −9   25. x = $8\frac{3}{4}$
27. r = 0   29. z = −88   31. k = 75   33. w = −30   35. m = 48   37. x = −35   39. p = 56   41. x = −2
43. x = −240.5

Page 58 **Review Capsule for Section 3.3**   1. 5n   2. 3r   3. b   4. t   5. x   6. y

Pages 58-59   **P-1** a. t = 7   b. k = 8   c. r = −4   **P-2** a. b = −7   b. s = 25   c. d = 60

Page 59 **Classroom Exercises**   1. Subtract 5.   3. Add 5.6.   5. Subtract 3.   7. Subtract 5.   9. Add 6.
11. Subtract 6.5.   13. Yes   15. No   17. No   19. Yes   21. No

Page 60 **Written Exercises**   1. x = 7   3. b = −13   5. c = −22   7. e = −19   9. y = −8   11. y = $-3\frac{3}{4}$
13. x = −56   15. x = −9.6   17. a = 150   19. x = −5.5   21. h = −300   23. g = $1\frac{1}{2}$ 25. z = −7.2
27. c = 15   29. x = −1.55   31. j = 33   33. b = 50   35. r = −24   37. x = $25\frac{2}{3}$ 39. x = $10\frac{1}{2}$ 41. k = $\frac{5}{6}$
43. d = $30\frac{1}{2}$ 45. h = $\frac{7}{12}$ 47. z = −4   49. v = $\frac{5}{3}$ 51. c = −14

Page 61 **Mid-Chapter Review**   1. b = −12   3. y = 4.5   5. t = 150   7. a = −3   9. z = $-3\frac{1}{3}$ 11. x = 13
13. y = 7   15. t = −15   17. j = 12

Page 61 **Calculator Exercises**   1. 4.2 is correct (see Example 1, p. 58).   3. −5 is correct.

Page 61 **Review Capsule for Section 3.4**   1. 3n + 3   2. 2.7t   3. $-2\frac{1}{2}k - \frac{1}{2}$ 4. 14m − 20   5. 30 − 5x
6. 45 + 30n   7. −8k + 48   8. 60 + 36x   9. $\frac{1}{2}y + \frac{3}{4}$

Page 62 **P-1** a. m = 3   b. k = −7   **P-2** a. y = −1   b. r = 5

Page 63 **Classroom Exercises**   1. 4y + 6 = 13   3. −5r + 8 = 17   5. −9.7 = 3.1m − 4.8   7. −2x + 3 = 19
9. $-2\frac{1}{4}n - 5 = 1\frac{1}{4}$ 11. 12x − 3 + 6 = 10; 12x + 3 = 10   13. −5 = 5t − 3 + 3t; −5 = 8t − 3   15. $\frac{1}{3} - 2q + 10$
$+ \frac{1}{4}q = 6; -1\frac{3}{4}q + 10\frac{1}{3} = 6$ 17. $\frac{3}{4}x - \frac{3}{2} + 6x + \frac{1}{2} = -11; 6\frac{3}{4}x - 1 = -11$ 19. −6 = 12 − 8t + 5t − 20; −6
= −8 − 3t   21. 7   23. −11   25. −3

Page 64 **Written Exercises**   1. x = 7   3. z = −0.4   5. x = −8   7. b = 7   9. x = −12   11. f = 14
13. k = $-5\frac{5}{6}$ 15. m = −38   17. n = −1   19. x = $-\frac{1}{9}$ 21. h = 11   23. d = −5.1   25. e = 3.8

27. $t = 35\frac{1}{2}$ 29. $y = 2\frac{1}{2}$ 31. $z = 9$ 33. $y = -4$

Page 64   Review Capsule for Section 3.5   1. $33\}$ $15\}$ 2. $-4\}$ $-4\}$ 3. $17.5\}$ $17.5\}$ 4. $16\}$ $16\}$ 5. $6\frac{3}{4}\}$ $6\frac{3}{4}\}$ 6. $-18\}$ $-18\}$

Pages 65-66   P-1   a. $t = -2$ b. $j = -4$ **P-2**   a. $p = -14$ b. $f = 1\frac{1}{3}$ **P-3**   a. $y = 1\frac{1}{2}$ b. $g = -4$

Page 66   Classroom Exercises   1. $x - 2 = 5$; $-2 = -x + 5$ 3. $8 + 4a = 6$; $8 = -4a + 6$ 5. $-3d - 6 = 12$; $-6 = 12 + 3d$ 7. $5p + 2 = 6$ 9. $-8 = 4z + 5$ 11. $10.8 = 9.2 + 10.5j$

Page 67   Written Exercises   1. $x = 17$ 3. $a = 13$ 5. $c = -12$ 7. $k = -6\frac{2}{3}$ 9. $x = 7$ 11. $z = -4\frac{1}{2}$
13. $p = -21\frac{1}{4}$ 15. $t = -0.8$ 17. $x = -14\frac{1}{2}$ 19. $y = -11\frac{2}{3}$ 21. $n = 3\frac{3}{4}$ 23. $y = -\frac{5}{9}$ 25. $y = -8\frac{1}{2}$
27. $q = 1\frac{12}{13}$ 29. $k = -2\frac{2}{3}$ 31. $d = -6$ 33. $r = \frac{17}{18}$ 35. $p = -5$ 37. $d = \frac{1}{4}$ 39. $g = -2$

Page 68   Classroom Exercises   1. $t = 3$ hr   3. 70 ft per second   5. $\ell = 45$ kilometers

Page 69   Written Exercises   1. 300,000 km per sec.   3. 2.3 seconds   5. 0.7m

Page 70   Special Topic Application   1. 397-gram bottle; 0.22 cents per gram; 907-gram bottle; 0.18 cents per gram; Better buy: the 907-gram bottle for \$1.63   3. 12-ounce cheese: 9.2 cents per ounce; 16-ounce cheese: 8.9 cents per ounce; Better buy: the 16-ounce cheese for \$1.42   5. Flank steak: about 49 cents per serving; Ground meat: about 43 cents per serving; Better buy: The ground meat

Page 71   Chapter Review   1. $x = -7$ 3. $b = 19$ 5. $f = -42$ 7. 30.3   9. $k = -9$ 11. $m = -112$
13. $t = 36$ 15. $y = -8.3$ 17. $z = 11\frac{1}{4}$ 19. $m = -10$ 21. $x = 7\frac{1}{3}$ 23. $v = -57.6$ 25. $x = 11$ 27. $y = 5$
29. $t = -21.5$ 31. $p = \frac{2}{7}$ 33. $h = -7$ 35. $y = 9.5$ 37. $t = \frac{4}{3}$ 39. $g = 15$ 41. 19.2 meters per second
43. 83.9 inches

CHAPTER 4   PROBLEM SOLVING: ONE VARIABLE

Pages 75-76   Classroom Exercises   1. $n + 12$ 3. $\frac{n}{8}$ 5. $1800n$ 7. $\frac{1200}{n}$ 9. $26 - n$ (For Ex. 11-20, variables may vary.)   11. Let n = low temperature, $n + 27 = 50$, $n = 23°$ 13. Let p = total number of points, $\frac{p}{20} = 18$, $p = 360$ 15. Let n = number of passengers, $104 = n + 11$, $n = 93$ 17. Let r = average amount of rainfall. $r - 9.4 = 69.3$, $r = 78.7$ cm   19. Let s = this year's sales. $3s = 372,000$, $s = \$124,000$

Pages 76-77   Written Exercises   (For Ex. 1-18, variables may vary.)   1. $2t$ 3. $V + 25,000$ 5. $m - 15.8$
7. $\frac{b}{28}$ 9. $A - 512$ 11. Let c = total cost, $\frac{c}{24} = 86$, $c = \$2064$ 13. Let ℓ = length of rectangle, $14.2 = \ell$
$- 5.8$, $\ell = 20$ m   15. Let h = high temperature for the day. $-5.3 = h - 7.9$, $h = 2.6°$ 17. Let a = amount of sale. $0.06a = 33.60$, $a = \$560$ 19. ℓ 21. n 23. o 25. k

Page 77   Review Capsule for Section 4.2   1. $x = 27$ 2. $y = 4$ 3. $w = 5.4$ 4. $r = 5.8$ 5. $k = 13$
6. $t = 83.2$

Page 79 Classroom Exercises 1. Let p = the number of first class seats. p + 186 + p = 234 3. Let p = number of miles driven in May, p − 775 = number of miles driven in June. p + p − 775 = 3521 5. Let p = cost of labor, then p + 3.58 = cost of parts. p + p + 3.58 = 75.62 7. Let p = rainfall in May, $2p − 4\frac{3}{5}$ = amount of rainfall in June, $p + 2p − 4\frac{3}{5} = 14\frac{9}{10}$ 9. Let p = amount she earned first year, then 2p − 5000 = amount she earned second year. p + 2p − 5000 = 93,000 11. Let p = the number of true/false questions, 3p − 7 = the number of multiple choice questions. p + 3p − 7 = 105

Pages 80-82 Written Exercises (For Ex. 1-18, variables may vary.) 1. Let v = the number of visiting runners, then v + 448 = the number of local runners. v + v + 448 = 3640, v = 1596, v + 448 = 2044 3. Let w = the number of women, then w − 5 = the number of men. w + w − 5 = 35, w = 20, w − 5 = 15 5. Let s = value of sculptures, then s + 350,000 = value of the paintings. s + s + 350,000 = 1,260,000, s = $455,000, s + 350,000 = $805,000 7. Let c = capacity of smaller car, then 2c + 2.3 = capacity of larger car. c + 2c + 2.3 = 140.9, c = 46.2 L, 2c + 2.3 = 94.7 L 9. Let r = number of reserved seats, then 2r − 1000 = no. of general admissions. r + 2r − 1000 = 12,500, r = 4500, 2r − 1000 = 8,000 11. Let c = amount of cargo space, then 5c + 5 = amount of passenger space. c + 5c + 5 = 131, c = 21 ft³, 5c + 5 = 110 ft³ 13. Let h = number of hours worked the first week, then $h + 2\frac{3}{4}$ = number of hours worked in second week. $h + h + 2\frac{3}{4} = 45\frac{3}{4}$, $h = 21\frac{1}{2}$, $h + 2\frac{3}{4} = 24\frac{1}{4}$ 15. Let f = no. of foreign coins, then 3f − 26 = no. of U. S. coins. 3f − 26 + f = 998, f = 256, 3f − 26 = 742 17. Let f = amount entered first day, then f + 12 = amount entered on second day. f + f + 12 = 256; f = 122, f + 12 = 134

Page 82 Calculator Exercises 1. 52.38 cm 3. 615.6 km

Page 82 Review Capsule for Section 4.3 1. t = 26 2. w = 61.5 3. n = 4.2 4. $p = 3\frac{1}{4}$ 5. x = 6.8 6. r = 10.3 7. d; 4d 8. 7d; 2d 9. 5d, 4d, 2d 10. 37d, 9d, 4d

Page 83 P-1 a. 23 in b. 24 m c. 24 cm

Pages 84-85 Classroom Exercises 1. Let m = length, m − 10 = width; 2m + 2(m − 10) = 140 3. Let m = width, m + 16 = length. 2m + 2(m + 16) = 102 5. Let m = length of second leg, 2m = first leg, m + 2m + 17 = 50 7. Let sides be 3m, 4m, and 5m; 3m + 4m + 5m = 38.4 9. Let 6m = width, 13m = length; 2(6m) + 2(13m) = 228 11. Let 5m = one side, 9m = other side. 34.3 + 5m + 9m = 70.7

Pages 85-86 Written Exercises (For Ex. 1-14, variables may vary.) 1. Let h = height, h + 6 = length. 2h + 2(h + 6) = 84, h = 18 ft, h + 6 = 24 ft 3. Let s = shorter side, s + 1.7 = longer side, 8.5 + s + s + 1.7 = 51.2, s = 20.5 m, s + 1.7 = 22.2 m 5. Let sides be 5x, 12x, and 13x. 5x + 12x + 13x = 204, x = 6.8, 5x = 34 m, 12x = 81.6 m, 13x = 88.4 m 7. Let 4x, 7x, and 9x be the lengths of the legs. 4x + 7x + 9x = 684, x = 34.2, 4x = 136.8 km, 7x = 239.4 km, 9x = 307.8 km 9. Let w = width, 2w − 4 = length; 2w + 2(2w − 4) = 148, w = 26 ft, 2w − 4 = 48 ft 11. Let h = height, $h + 2\frac{1}{2}$ = width. $2h + 2(h + 2\frac{1}{2}) = 44$, $h = 9\frac{3}{4}$ in, $h + 2\frac{1}{2} = 12\frac{1}{4}$ in 13. Let cable length = 18x, tower height = 11x. 18x + 11x + 35.6 = 108.1, x = 2.5, 18x = 45, 11x = 27.5 m

Page 87 Mid-Chapter Review (For Ex. 1-10, variables may vary.) 1. Let v = number of visitors last year. 356,000 = v + 45,000, v = 311,000 3. Let c = charge for local calls. 2c = 38.50, c = $19.25 5. Let b = number of boys, then b + 7 = number of girls. b + b + 7 = 45, b = 19, b + 7 = 26 7. Let c = number of cars the second hour, then c − 2900 = number of cars the first hour. c + c − 2900 = 24,500; c = 13,700, c − 2900 = 10,800 9. Let w = width, then 2w + 6.2 = length. 2(w) + 2(2w + 6.2) = 106.6, w = 15.7 m, 2w + 6.2 = 37.6 m

Page 87 Review Capsule for Section 4.4 1. \$115.2   2. \$7   3. 139   4. \$11.98   5. 42   6. 42.5
7. \$33.75   8. 305.

Page 90 Classroom Exercises 1. \$128   3. \$3.80   5. Let p = list price. 0.35p = 31.50   7. Let p = list price,
then 0.12p = discount. p − 0.12p = 396
9.

	Batting Average	Times at Bat	Number of Hits
Last Season	30%	t	0.30t
This Season	28%	(t + 15)	0.28(t + 15)

$$0.30t + 3 = 0.28(t + 15)$$

Page 91 Written Exercises (For Ex. 1-7, variables may vary.)   1. Let p = list price, 0.20p = discount.
0.20p = 115, p = \$575   3. Let p = list price, 0.20p = discount. p − 0.20p = 48, p = \$60, 0.20p = \$12
5. Let g = number who tried out for girls team, g + 4 = number for boys team. 0.75g = 0.60(g + 4), g = 16,
g + 4 = 20   7. Let t = number of tickets sold. 0.65t = number at \$8, 0.35t = number at \$10, 0.65t = 0.35t
+ 960, t = 3200

Page 91 Review Capsule for Section 4.5 1. 2070 mi   2. 419.2 mi   3. 62.9 mi   4. 287 km

Page 94 Classroom Exercises 1. Rate returning x − 6, 6(x) = 6.4(x − 6)   3. Fuel tank capacity of car B
= x − 2. 10x = 12(x − 2) − 112

Page 95 Written Exercises
1.

	r	t	d
Going	x + 15	$2\frac{4}{5}$	$2\frac{4}{5}(x + 15)$
Returning	x	4	4x

$(x + 15)2\frac{4}{5} = 4x,$

$x = 35,$

$x + 15 = 50$ mi/hr going

3.

	r	t	d
Going	x	1	x
Returning	x − 7	$1\frac{1}{4}$	$1\frac{1}{4}(x − 7)$

$x = 1\frac{1}{4}(x − 7),$

$x = 35$ mi/hr,

$x − 7 = 28$ mi/hr

5.

	Fuel Capacity	Mileage	Range
Car A	x	5	5x
Car B	x − 35	8.5	8.5(x − 35)

$5x = 8.5(x − 35),$

$x = 85$ L,

$x − 35 = 50$ L

7.

	r	t	d
Going	r	4	4r
Returning	r − 10	5	5(r − 10)

$4r = 5(r − 10),$

$r = 50$ mi/hr,

$r − 10 = 40$ mi/hr

Page 96 Career 1. 3560 pounds   3. 21,360 pounds   5. 4786.67 pounds

Page 97 Chapter Review 1. Let d = total distance traveled. d − 25.6 = 278.3, d = 303.9 km   3. Let b = total
score. $\frac{b}{5}$ = 168, b = 840   5. Let n = number of non-fiction books, n + 82 = number of fiction books. n + n
+ 82 = 372, n = 145, n + 82 = 227   7. Let f = number of miles father drove, then 2f + 100 = number of miles
Alice drove. f + 2f + 100 = 1150, f = 350 mi, 2f + 100 = 800 mi   9. Let w = width, w + 11.8 = length.
2(w) + 2(w + 11.8) = 80, w = 14.1 m, w + 11.8 = 25.9 m   11. Let length = 7x, width = 3x. 2(7x) + 2(3x) = 166,

x = 8.3, 7x = 58.1 mm, 3x = 24.9 mm   **13.** Let p = list price, .4p = discount, p − .4p = 274.50, p = $457.50
15. Let x = number of games each played. 0.90(x) = 0.85(x) + 1, x = 20
17.

	r	t	d
Going	x	4.25	4.25x
Returning	x + 5	4	4(x + 5)

4.25 x = 4(x + 5),
x = 80 km/hr,
x + 5 = 85 km/hr

CHAPTER 5 PROPERTIES OF ORDER

Pages 100-101 **P-1** To show that all integers less than 2 are truth numbers   **P-2** 2 is equal to 2.   **P-3** 3 is not equal to 2.   **P-4** To show that 3 is a truth number of $x \leq 3$ **P-5** a. $\{x : x \geq 3\frac{1}{2}\}$; b. $\{x : x < -2\frac{1}{2}\}$; Assume {real numbers} as the domain.

Page 102 **Classroom Exercises** **1.** $\{x : x \geq -1\}$; {integers}   **3.** $\{x : x < 2\frac{1}{2}\}$; {real numbers}   **5.** 0, 4, 9
7. $-\pi, 0, 3.9$ **9.** $-5, 3\frac{1}{4}, 8\frac{1}{3}$

Page 102 **Written Exercises** **1.** $\{-2, -1, 0, 1\}$ **3.** $\{x : x \leq 0\}$; {integers}   **5.** $\{x : x > -2\}$
7. $\{x : x \leq -1\}$ **9.** $\{x : x \geq -1\frac{1}{2}\}$ **11.** On a number line, the points 2, 3, 4, 5, etc.   **13.** On a number line, the points $-3, -4, -5, -6$, etc.   **15.** On a number line, all points to the left of, and not including, $-\frac{3}{4}$.
17. On a number line, all points to the right of, and including, 2.7.   **19.** $\{0, 1, 2\}$ **21.** $\{0, 1, 2, 3, 4, 5\}$
23. $\{9\}$ **25.** $\{0, 1, 2, 3, 4, 5, 6, 7, 8, 9\}$ **27.** $\{0, 1, 2, \cdots, 9\}$ **29.** No   **31.** No

Page 103 **Review Capsule for Section 5.2** **1.** $\frac{5}{10} > \frac{3}{10}$ **2.** $\frac{3}{4} > \frac{1}{4}$ **3.** $\frac{2}{5} > -\frac{3}{5}$ **4.** $\frac{7}{8} > \frac{6}{8}$ **5.** $-\frac{4}{10} > -\frac{5}{10}$
6. $-\frac{3}{8} > -\frac{5}{8}$ **7.** $\frac{5}{6} > \frac{4}{6}$ **8.** $-\frac{1}{3} > -\frac{2}{3}$

Pages 104-105 **P-1** $a > b$ **P-2** $a < b$ **P-3** a. $6 > -y, -y < 6$ b. $-t < 1\frac{3}{4}, 1\frac{3}{4} > -t$ c. $-s < r, r > -s$
P-4 $r < 1.8$ **P-5** $1.8 < t$ **P-6** $r < t$ **P-7** $x < y$ **P-8** If $a > b$ and $b > c$, then $a > c$.

Page 105 **Classroom Exercises** For Ex. 1-7, only one of two possible inequalities is given for each pair.
1. $-5 < 2$ **3.** $-12 < -9$ **5.** $1.3 > 1.03$ **7.** $\frac{3}{4} > \frac{3}{8}$ **9.** $a > c$ **11.** No

Page 106 **Written Exercises** **1.** $-1.7 < 1.6$ **3.** $-1\frac{7}{8} < -1\frac{3}{4}$ **5.** $\frac{5}{13} < \frac{5}{12}$ **7.** $-\frac{13}{16} < -\frac{12}{17}$ **9.** $-3 > b$
11. $a > \frac{1}{2}$ **13.** $a + b > -2$ **15.** $b < -a$ **17.** True **19.** False **21.** False **23.** True **25.** $y < x$
27. $x < y$ **29.** $y < x$ **31.** $x < y$

Page 106 **Review Capsule for Section 5.3** **1.** $t = 135$ **2.** $x = -15$ **3.** $y = 13$ **4.** $w = 7.9$ **5.** $t = -6.1$
6. $r = 1\frac{5}{8}$ **7.** $d = -\frac{5}{6}$ **8.** $p = 3.86$ **9.** $s = -0.53$

Page 107 **P-1** $5 + (-2) = 3$ **P-2** $-1 < x - 2$ **P-3** 2 **P-4** $x > 1$

Pages 108-109 **Classroom Exercises** **1.** Subtract 5   **3.** Subtract 7   **5.** Add 0.8   **7.** $\{x : x < 11\}$
9. $\{a : a < 2\}$ **11.** $\{w : w < 4\}$ **13.** $\{r : r < 4\}$ **15.** $\{x : x > -8\}$ **17.** $\{x : x < 8\}$

Page 109 Written Exercises 1. No **3.** Yes **5.** No **7.** Yes **9.** No **11.** $\{y : y > -5\}$ **13.** $\{t : t < -7\}$
15. $\left\{x : x < -1\frac{1}{2}\right\}$ **17.** $\{q : q < -3.1\}$ **19.** $\left\{w : w > 2\frac{3}{8}\right\}$ **21.** $\{y : y > 7.9\}$ **23.** $\{x : x > -1\}$
25. $\{a : a > 7\}$ **27.** $\{p : p \geq -5\}$ **29.** $\{x : x \leq 4\}$ **31.** $\{a : a \geq -4\}$ **33.** $\{r : r \geq 5\}$

Page 110 Mid-Chapter Review 1. On a number line, all points to the right of, and not including, -4. **3.** On a number line, the points 4, 3, 2, 1, 0, -1, etc. **5.** On a number line, the numbers 6, 5, 4, 3, 2, 1, 0. **7.** $a < b$
9. $b < a$ **11.** $b < a$ **13.** $\{t : t < 5\}$ **15.** $\{x : x > -1.2\}$ **17.** $\left\{r : r < -\frac{1}{4}\right\}$

Page 110 Calculator Exercises 1. Since $21.01 < 21.20$, 13 is a solution. **3.** Since $4.2 < 4.8$, 11.9 is a solution.

Page 110 Review Capsule for Section 5.4 1. $n = 1\frac{4}{5}$ **2.** $t = 2\frac{2}{3}$ **3.** $w = -7$ **4.** $y = -10$ **5.** $p = 1\frac{2}{3}$
6. $m = 5$

Page 112 Classroom Exercises 1. $-3 < x + 2$ **3.** $a - 2 < -7$ **5.** $-y + \frac{1}{2} > -12\frac{1}{4}$ **7.** $3w - 5 - 2w < 2w + 12 - 2w$ **9.** $3\frac{1}{2}x - 2 - 2\frac{1}{2}x > 2\frac{1}{2}x + 10 - 2\frac{1}{2}x$ **11.** $0.6m - 0.7 + 0.4m < -0.4m + 0.2 + 0.4m$ **13.** $-3x + 6 < -5 - 2x$ **15.** $5 - x < -2x + 6 - 2$ **17.** $5y - 2 - 3y < 3y - 4$ **19.** $a - 5 < a + 2$ **21.** $5x - 5 < 2x - 6 + 3x$

Page 112 Written Exercises 1. $\{x : x > -5\}$ **3.** $\{a : a < -5\}$ **5.** $\left\{y : y < 12\frac{3}{4}\right\}$ **7.** $\{w : w < 17\}$
9. $\{x : x > 12\}$ **11.** $\{m : m < 0.9\}$ **13.** $\{x : x > 11\}$ **15.** $\{x : x < -1\}$ **17.** $\{y : y > 2\}$ **19.** $\{$reals$\}$
21. $\{\ \}$, or $\emptyset$

Page 112 Review Capsule for Section 5.5 1. $x = 36$ **2.** $n = -84$ **3.** $t = 60$ **4.** $r = -16$ **5.** $w = -5.6$
6. $p = -5\frac{1}{2}$ **7.** $q = 4\frac{1}{5}$ **8.** $s = -26$

Pages 113-114 P-1 **a.** $-2 < 3$ **b.** $-1 > -5$ **c.** $\frac{3}{2} > -4$ **d.** $-6 < 0$ **P-2** Each side becomes zero.
P-3 $>$ **P-4 a.** 2 **b.** -3 **c.** $\frac{5}{4}$ **d.** $-\frac{3}{2}$ **P-5** Dividing by 3: **a.** $x < 3$ **b.** $-2x > 2$ **c.** $4x < -1$
d. $-5x < \frac{1}{3}$ Dividing by -3: **a.** $-x > -3$ **b.** $2x < -2$ **c.** $-4x > 1$ **d.** $5x > -\frac{1}{3}$

Pages 114-115 Classroom Exercises 1. $5x > 10$ **3.** $10a > 50$ **5.** $-3y < -6$ **7.** $r > -6$ **9.** Divide by 2.
11. Multiply by $-\frac{2}{3}$. **13.** $>$ **15.** $<$

Page 115 Written Exercises 1. $\{y : y < 5\}$ **3.** $\{t : t > -20\}$ **5.** $\{r : r > -3\}$ **7.** $\{x : x > -2\}$
9. $\{w : w < -6\}$ **11.** $\{x : x < 6\}$ **13.** $\{q : q < -9\}$ **15.** $\left\{x : x < -\frac{11}{3}\right\}$ **17.** $\{n : n < -10\}$
19. $\{x : x > -3\}$

Page 115 Review Capsule for Section 5.6 1. $x = 2$ **2.** $n = -4$ **3.** $t = -7\frac{1}{2}$ **4.** $t = -4\frac{1}{2}$ **5.** $p = 1$
6. $r = -\frac{1}{3}$ **7.** $y = 1\frac{9}{13}$ **8.** $m = 2\frac{8}{9}$

Pages 116-117 P-1 The order of an inequality is unchanged if each side is multiplied by a positive number.
P-2 Each side is multiplied by a negative number. **P-3** -3 is the reciprocal of $-\frac{1}{3}$, the coefficient of x.
P-4 $\{$real numbers$\}$; ϕ or the empty set

Pages 117-118 Classroom Exercises 1. $2x > 2$ 3. $\frac{1}{2}x < -4$ 5. $-15 < -5x$ 7. $2x + 2 < -3$ 9. $-6 > x$ $+4$ 11. $x > -2$ 13. $x > -10$ 15. $x > -2$ 17. ϕ

Page 118 Written Exercises 1. $\{x : x < \frac{8}{3}\}$ 3. $\{x : x < -\frac{13}{2}\}$ 5. $\{y : y > 8\}$ 7. $\{b : b > \frac{7}{2}\}$ 9. $\{m : m < -2\}$ 11. $\{x : x > -\frac{1}{5}\}$ 13. $\{q : q > 6\}$ 15. $\{x : x > 0\}$ 17. ϕ 19. $\{$ real numbers $\}$ 21. $\{x : x < -1\}$ 23. 0 or 1

Page 119 Special Topic Application 1. \$4.35 3. \$213.40 5. \$224.59 7. \$15,177.18

Pages 120-122 Chapter Review 1. $\{-3, -2, -1, 0\}$ 3. $\{x : x < 1\frac{1}{2}\}$ 5. On a number line, the points 4, 3, 2, 1, 0 7. On a number line, all points to the right of, and not including, -3. 9. All points to the left of, and not including, 4. 11. $-r > 12$ 13. $-a < 3$ 15. $x < 4.2$ 17. $1 < x$ 19. $a < b$ 21. True 23. No 25. No 27. Yes 29. $\{x : x < 1\}$ 31. $\{x : x < -2\}$ 33. $\{x : x < -9.7\}$ 35. $x < -8$ 37. $x > 11$ 39. $x < 7\frac{1}{2}$ 41. $x < -5$ 43. $x < 4$ 45. $x > 1.6$ 47. $x > 10\frac{1}{3}$ 49. ϕ

CHAPTER 6 RELATIONS AND FUNCTIONS

Pages 124-125 P-1 Right; Left **P-2** Up; Down **P-3** $3; -2$ **P-4** They do not have the same location. **P-5** The first number is x. **P-6** The first coordinate, 5, is positive. **P-7** The second coordinate, 3, is positive. **P-8** Start at 0, and move left 2 units along the X axis; -2 **P-9** Down 4 units parallel to the Y axis; -4 **P-10** $(-2, -4)$

Pages 125-126 Classroom Exercises 1. right 3, down 2 3. left 3, up 7 5. right 7, down 1 7. right 8, up 3 9. left 3, down 3 11. $(2, 1)$ 13. $(-3, -1)$ 15. $(3, -2)$ 17. $(2, -3)$ 19. $(-4, -3)$

Page 126 Written Exercises For Ex. 1-11, the moves described locate the given points. Always start at origin. 1. Move 1 unit right and 4 units up. 3. left 5, up 3 5. right 6, down 1 7. left 4, down 1 9. left 4, down 4 11. right 3, up 3 13. $(-5, -1)$ 15. $(-2, 3)$ 17. $(-4, -2)$ 19. $(4, 3)$ 21. $(-1, 1)$ 23. $(-2, -1)$

Page 126 Review Capsule for Section 6.2 1. -4 and -3 2. 5 and 6 3. -1 and 0 4. -4 and -3 5. -4 and -3 6. -2 and -1

Pages 127-128 P-1 x negative, y negative; x positive, y negative **P-2** Start at 0 and move $2\frac{1}{2}$ units left. **P-3** Move $3\frac{1}{4}$ units up parallel to the Y axis. **P-4** $(0, 0); (-3, -4)$

Page 129 Classroom Exercises 1. II 3. I 5. On the Y axis, 5 units down from the origin. 7. On the X axis, $5\frac{1}{2}$ units to the left of the origin.

Page 129 Written Exercises For Ex. 1-19, each point may be located on a graph by the directions following each coordinate pair. Always start at $(0, 0)$, the point of origin. Note in Ex. 9, 11, and 15 there is only one move to locate each point. 1. right $4\frac{1}{2}$ units, up 3 units 3. left 2, down $4\frac{1}{2}$ 5. left $2\frac{3}{4}$, up $4\frac{1}{4}$ 7. left 3.5, up 2.2 9. up 4 11. left $3\frac{1}{2}$ 13. left 6, down 2 15. down 2 17. left 1, up 2 19. left 7, up 2 21. parallelogram

Page 129 **Review Capsule for Section 6.3** 1. $y = 1\frac{1}{4}$ 2. $y = 2.75$ 3. $y = -30$ 4. $y = 2.1$

Page 130 **P-1** (2, 1), (0, 1), (−2, 1), (2, −1), (0, −1), (2, −1) **P-2** −5, −3, −1, 1, 3

Pages 131-132 **Classroom Exercises** For Ex. 1-5, the answers are read thus, "The set of ordered pairs (x, y) such that 1. y equals x 3. y equals x squared 5. y equals x squared plus two x plus 1 7. (1, 1), (−1, −1) 9. (1, 1), (−1, 1) 11. (1, 4), (−1, 0) 13. (−3, 3), (0, 0), (2, 2) 15. (−1, 2), (0, 1), (1, 0)

Page 132 **Written Exercises** 1. $\{(1, 0), (2, 1), (3, 2), (4, 3)\}$ 3. $\{(1, 1), (2, 4), (3, 9), (4, 16)\}$ 5. $\{(1, 1), (2, 2), (3, 3), (4, 4)\}$ 7. $\{(1, 1), (2, \sqrt{2}), (3, \sqrt{3}), (4, 2)\}$ 9. $\{(1, 1), (2, 1), (3, 1), (4, 1)\}$ 11. $\{(1, 1), (2, 3), (3, 7), (4, 13)\}$ For Ex. 13-15, each consists of 4 points. To locate each point, start at origin. Move in the stated direction the stated number of units. 13. (1 right, 2 up), (1 right, 3 up), (3 left, 5 up), (3 left, $4\frac{1}{2}$ down) 15. (Note: $\pi \approx 3.14$); (origin), (up π), (down π), (right π) Each graph consists of 4 points. Ordered pairs are given. 17. (−1, 0), (0, 1), (1, 2), (2, 3) 19. (−1, −6), (0, −7), (1, −6), (2, −3) 21. (−1, 1), (0, 0), (1, 1), (2, 2) 23. (−1, 1), (0, 1), (1, 1), (2, 1) 25. (−1, 3), (0, 1), (1, 1), (2, 3)

Page 133 **Mid-Chapter Review** 1. (−4, −2) 3. (−2, 0) 5. (0, 3) 7. (−5, 3) For Ex. 9-13, each point may be located on a graph by the directions following each coordinate pair. Always start at (0, 0), the point of origin. 9. right 2 units, down 1 unit 11. left 3, up 5 13. left 2.5, down 3.5 15. $\{(-2, 4), (-1, 3), (0, 2), (1, 3), (2, 4)\}$

Page 133 **Calculator Exercises** 1. 1.2 3. 1.4 5. 1.3 7. 1.1

Page 133 **Review Capsule for Section 6.4** 1. A(−2, 1), B(−2, −1), C(−4, 2), D(−4, −2) 2. A(−2, 3), B(2, 3), C(−1, 0), D(1, 0) 3. A(−3, −2), B(−1, −3), C(2, 1), D(2, −1)

Pages 134-135 **P-1** −1, 0, 4, −3; 3, −2, 0 **P-2** Two x values are equal in A; No two x values are equal in B. **P-3** Show that no two x values of relation T are equal. **P-4** P and S **P-5** Yes; A vertical line will have only one point in common with the graph.

Page 136 **Classroom Exercises** 1. Domain: $\{3, -5, 4, 0\}$; Range: $\{7, 2, -1, 0\}$ 3. Domain: $\{3, \sqrt{2}, \pi, \frac{1}{3}\}$; Range: $\{8, -1, -2\}$ 5. Domain: $\{2, 3, 4, 5\}$; Range: $\{3, 4, 5, 6\}$ 7. Domain: $\{1, -1, 0, \frac{1}{2}, -\frac{1}{2}\}$; Range: $\{1, 0, \frac{1}{2}\}$ 9. Yes 11. Yes 13. Yes 15. Yes

Pages 136-137 **Written Exercises** 1. D = $\{5, -3, -1, 1\}$; R = $\{10, 2, 0, -3\}$ 3. D = $\{\frac{1}{2}, -1, -\frac{1}{2}, 2\}$; R = $\{2, \frac{1}{2}, -1\}$ 5. D = $\{-1, -2, \pi, 0\}$; R = $\{\sqrt{2}, \sqrt{3}, -1, -\pi\}$ 7. D = $\{0, 1, 1.5, -1, -\pi\}$; R = $\{0, 1, -1\}$ 9. D = $\{0, \frac{1}{2}, 1, 1\frac{1}{2}, -\frac{1}{2}, -1\}$; R = $\{0, 1, -1\}$ 11. Yes 13. Yes 15. No 17. No. Apply the vertical line test to each graph. If the line has more than one point in common with a graph, the graph is not a function. 19. Yes 21. No 23. Yes 25. No

Page 137 **Review Capsule for Section 6.5** 1. $\{(-2, 2), (1, 1), (7, -1)\}$ 2. $\{(-2, -2), (1, 1), (0, 2)\}$ 3. $\{(-3, 3), (-2, 2), (1, 1), (0, 0)\}$ 4. $\{(-2, -2), (0, 0)\}$ 5. $\{(-2, -2), (0, 0)\}$ 6. $\{(0, 0)\}$

Pages 138-139 **P-1** −3 **P-2** $\{y : y \geq -1\}$ **P-3** $\frac{5}{4}$

Pages 139-140 Classroom Exercises 1.

x	0	−1	1	−2	2
y	0	−2	2	−4	4

3. The vertical line does not cross the graph at more than one point. **5.** {real numbers} **7.** 0 **9.** $\{x : -1 \leq x < 3\}$ **11.** $1\frac{1}{2}$

Page 140 Written Exercises The graph is either a line, two lines, or a curve (parabola). Points on the graph are given. **1.** Line; (0, 0), (2, −4) **3.** Line; (0, 1), (2, −1) **5.** Two line (inverted V); (0, 0), (−2, −2), (2, −2) **7.** Two lines (V-shaped), (−2, 1), (−1, 0), (0, 1), (2, 3) **9.** Line parallel to the x axis; (0, −3), (2, −3)
11. Curve; (−2, −2), (−1, 1), (0, 2), (1, 1), (2, −2) **13.** Curve; (−2, 4), (−1, $1\frac{1}{2}$), (0, 0), (1, $-\frac{1}{2}$), (2, 0) **15.** Curve; (−2, −6), (−1, −2), (0, 0), (1, 0), (2, −2)

Page 140 Review Capsule for Section 6.6 1. 46 pounds **2.** 71.2 pounds **3.** 36.8 pounds **4.** 84 pounds **5.** 53.2 pounds

Pages 141-142 P-1 4.9; 19.6 **P-2** 15 m **P-3** c.

Page 142 Classroom Exercises 1. 4 seconds **3.** 14.7 m **5.** 10 seconds **7.** Distance fallen between second and third seconds (24.5 m) is less than distance fallen between fourth and fifth seconds, 44.1 meters.

Page 143 Written Exercises 1. 1812.5 m **3.** 3 seconds **5.** 10 cents **7.** 10 cents **9.** 30 cents: any amount over 60 g up to and including 90 g; 40 cents: any amount over 90 g up to and including 120 g **11.** 27 m **13.** 58 m **15.** 75 km/hr

Page 144 Career 1. 8000 BTU's **3.** 6000 BTU's **5.** 3500 BTU's

Pages 145-146 Chapter Review Each point will be located by moving in the stated direction the stated number of units. **1.** left 3, up 2 **3.** left 3, down 4 **5.** right 3, down 3 **7.** down 4 Each point in Ex. 9-15 will be located by moving in the stated direction the stated number of units. **9.** right 2, down $3\frac{1}{2}$ **11.** right $2\frac{1}{4}$, up $1\frac{3}{4}$ **13.** up 3 **15.** left $2\frac{1}{2}$, down $3\frac{1}{2}$ For Ex. 17-21, each graph consists of four points, for which the roster lists ordered pairs. **17.** {(−1, −8), (0, −5), (2, 1), (3, 4)} **19.** {(−1, 0), (0, −1), (2, 3), (3, 8)}
21. {(−1, 2), (0, 1), (2, 1), (3, 2)} **23.** D = $\left\{-\frac{1}{2}, 2, 4\right\}$; R = {0, 6, −3} **25.** D = {−3, 0, −2}; R = $\left\{\frac{1}{2}, -5, 0, -4\right\}$ **27.** Yes **29.** No **31.** The graph is a line through the points (0, −3), (1, −2), (2, 1), (3, 0).
33. Two lines (V-shaped) through (−2, 0), (0, −2), (2, 0).

Pages 147-150 Cumulative Review for Chapters 1-6 1. 29 **3.** 14 **5.** −4 **7.** −43 **9.** −35 **11.** −3.1
13. 65 **15.** −3.84 **17.** −4 **19.** 15 **21.** 27 **23.** 50 **25.** 48 **27.** −2 **29.** Rational **31.** Irrational
33. −22 **35.** −3.4 + x − y **37.** 72 **39.** −36xy **41.** 4x − y + 3 **43.** 30r²s **45.** −6r² + 15r
47. 6x(x − 4) **49.** 4s − 6t **51.** x = −14 **53.** x = −42 **55.** x = 13 **57.** x = −44.4 **59.** x = 13
61. x = −24 **63.** x = $-\frac{13}{2}$ **65.** x = $\frac{39}{4}$ **67.** x = 7 **69.** x = $-\frac{16}{5}$ **71.** 160 meters **73.** 15.95 − c = 6.23;
c = $9.72 **75.** 214.7 = x + 23.4; x = 191.3 kilometers **77.** Let x = the number of persons enrolled in advanced classes. Then 2x − 18 = the number enrolled in beginning classes; x + 2x − 18 = 477; There are 165 persons in advanced classes and 312 in beginning classes. **79.** Let x = the amount of purchase without the discount; 1204.32 = 0.96x; x = $1254.50 **81.** Graph consists of points 0, 1, 2, 3, 4, and 5. **83.** t < −9
85. x < −7 **87.** x > 4 **89.** x < −20 **91.** x < −7 **93.** (−1, 2) **95.** (2, 2) **97.** left 4, down 3
99. down $3\frac{1}{2}$ **101.** Contains: (−2, −3), (−1, 0), (0, 1), (1, 0) **103.** Yes **105.** No **107.** Contains:
(−2, −4), (2, −2) **109.** 49,000 cm

CHAPTER 7 POWERS

Pages 152-153 **P-1** a. $2 \circ 2 \circ 2 \circ 2$ b. $x \cdot x \circ x$ c. $y \circ y \circ y \cdot y \circ y$ d. $4 \circ 4 \cdot 4$ e. $z \circ z$ **P-2** 5
P-3 $(-3) \circ (-3)$; $(-3) \circ (-3) \circ (-3) \circ (-3)$ **P-4** $a + b$ times **P-5** a. $(-1.9)^5$ b. $(\frac{1}{2})^7$ c. t^9
P-6 a. $t^6 + t^5$ b. $3k^5 - 2k^4 + 3k^3$ **P-7** -4.8

Pages 153-154 **Classroom Exercises** 1. 2^5 3. $(-5)^6$ 5. $(\frac{1}{2})^5$ 7. k^{22} 9. 7^6 11. 2^{x+3} 13. $x = 10$
15. $x = 3$ 17. $x = 27$

Page 154 **Written Exercises** 1. 12^{10} 3. 5^4 5. $(3.2)^{12}$ 7. $(-15)^9$ 9. $(-6)^{11}$ 11. $(-\frac{2}{3})^8$ 13. a^7
15. r^{8+t} 17. a^{11} 19. 5^{2+m} 21. $y^3 + y^4$ 23. $x^9 + x^7$ 25. $2^5 - 2^7$ 27. $n^4 - n^3 + n^2$ 29. $x = 11$
31. $x = 5$ 33. $x = 3$ 35. $x = \pi$

Page 154 **Review Capsule for Section 7.2** 1. True 2. True 3. False 4. False

Pages 155-156 **P-1** $x \circ x \circ x \circ x \circ x$; $x \circ x \circ x$ **P-2** a. 17^3 b. $(1.8)^5$ c. m^7 **P-3** 113^0 **P-4** 1
P-5 1 **P-6** a. 2 b. 0 c. 1

Page 157 **Classroom Exercises** 1. 3^3 3. $(-3)^4$ 5. a^2 7. 2^3 9. $(\frac{1}{2})^7$ 11. $(-5)^{t-4}$ 13. False
15. False 17. True 19. 1 21. 1 23. 1 25. 1

Pages 157-158 **Written Exercises** 1. 10^2 3. $(\frac{1}{2})^1$, or $\frac{1}{2}$ 5. x^4 7. 2^3 9. $(0.6)^1$, or 0.6 11. π^3
13. True 15. False 17. False 19. True 21. True 23. $x = 5$ 25. $x = 10$ 27. $x = 5$ 29. $x = 4$
31. $x = 1$ 33. $y = 1$ 35. $a = 0$ 37. $x = 0$ 39. $p = $ any nonzero real number 41. -1 43. 5 45. -1

Page 158 **Review Capsule for Section 7.3** 1. -2 2. 5 3. -4 4. -10 5. 5

Pages 159-160 **P-1** a. $\frac{1}{r^3}$ b. $\frac{1}{m^6}$ c. $\frac{1}{3^2}$ or $\frac{1}{9}$ d. $\frac{1}{16}$ e. $\frac{1}{1000}$ **P-2** Add the exponents. Keep the same
base. **P-3** a. 17^{-1} b. $(1.2)^4$ c. r^{-3} **P-4** Subtract the exponents. Keep the same base. **P-5** a. 5^2
b. 3.7^{-3} c. y^2 d. x^5 e. r^{-4}

Page 161 **Classroom Exercises** 1. 5^{-10} 3. $(5.2)^{-2}$ 5. r^{-8} 7. x^7 9. 2^2

Page 161 **Written Exercises** 1. $\frac{1}{r^4}$ 3. $\frac{2}{y^5}$ 5. $\frac{1}{4^2}$ or $\frac{1}{16}$ 7. $\frac{1}{(-3)^3}$ or $-\frac{1}{27}$ 9. $\frac{a}{b^3}$ 11. 2^5 or 32 13. a^{-3}
15. 2 17. a^2 19. $x^{-5}; \frac{1}{x^5}$ 21. $n^{-1}; \frac{1}{n}$ 23. r^3 25. t^3 27. $p^{-2}; \frac{1}{p^2}$ 29. 10^4 31. $y^{-2}; \frac{1}{y^2}$ 33. r^0; 1

Page 162 **Mid-Chapter Review** 1. 12^{x+y} 3. $(-6)^{14}$ 5. $(-0.9)^4$ 7. r^{10} 9. 21^2 11. $(\frac{3}{4})^3$ 13. 1
15. 0 17. $\frac{1}{(0.6)^3}$ or $\frac{1}{0.216}$ 19. $\frac{1}{w^6}$ 21. $\frac{1}{12^2}$ or $\frac{1}{144}$ 23. $\frac{1}{m^3}$

Page 162 **Calculator Exercises** 1. 0.0009766 3. 0.0003925 5. 6.1096817 7. 0.0000485

Page 162 **Review Capsule for Section 7.4** 1. $8w^3$ 2. $-27t^3$ 3. $-0.001r^3$ 4. $\frac{p^4}{625}$

Pages 163-164 **P-1** 2 **P-2** 8 **P-3** a. $x^2 y^2$ b. $9a^2$ c. $8r^3$ d. $9r^2$ **P-4** $r^{-3}s^{-3}$ **P-5** a. $\frac{9}{t^2}$ b. $\frac{p^4}{q^4}$
c. $\frac{8r^3}{s^3}$ d. $\frac{1}{r^4}$

Page 165 Classroom Exercises 1. $4a^2$ **3.** $\frac{1}{4}y^2$ **5.** $25n^2$ **7.** $4b^2$ **9.** $0.25a^2$ **11.** $-8r^3$ **13.** x^2y^2
15. a^4b^4 **17.** $\frac{9}{x^2}$ **19.** $\frac{m^5}{n^5}$ **21.** $\frac{x^2}{y^2}$ **23.** $\frac{-8}{x^3}$

Page 165 Written Exercises 1. $27r^3$ **3.** $4a^2$ **5.** $-27p^3$ **7.** a^2b^2 **9.** $-r^3s^3$ **11.** $4x^2y^2$ **13.** $9p^2q^2$
15. $-8a^3b^3$ **17.** $\frac{8}{x^3}$ **19.** $-\frac{a^3}{8}$ **21.** $\frac{x^2}{y^2}$ **23.** $\frac{1}{4y^2}$ **25.** $\frac{1}{p^3q^3}$ **27.** $-\frac{1}{3t}$ **29.** $\frac{27a^3}{b^3}$

Page 165 Review Capsule for Section 7.5 1. m^{12} **2.** $(-3)^6$ **3.** t^{-9} **4.** $(2a)^{-6}$ **5.** g^{-20} **6.** $(-0.5)^6$

Pages 166-168 P-1 $(x^2)(x^2)(x^2)$ **P-2** $2 \cdot 3 = 6$ **P-3** $(-4)(-3) = 12$ **P-4** a. m^{15} b. k^8 c. t^{-4}
P-5 a. 512 b. $\frac{1}{2048}$ c. $\frac{1}{1024}$ d. m^5

Page 168 Classroom Exercises 1. 3^6 **3.** $\frac{1}{a^3}$ **5.** y^6 **7.** $(0.5)^8$ **9.** $(-3)^{24}$ **11.** $\frac{1}{t^6}$ **13.** $\frac{q^4}{9}$ **15.** $\frac{1}{x^2}$
17. $\frac{1}{r^6s^9}$ **19.** $\frac{1}{x^6y^9}$ **21.** 1 **23.** $\frac{s^8}{m^4}$

Page 169 Written Exercises 1. a^8 **3.** $\frac{1}{y^{10}}$ **5.** $\frac{1}{m^5}$ **7.** $\frac{1}{t^4}$ **9.** $9r^6$ **11.** $8a^6b^3$ **13.** $32x^5y^{10}$ **15.** $\frac{x^{15}}{32}$
17. $\frac{32a^{10}b^{15}}{c^{105}}$ **19.** $-8t^9$ **21.** $\frac{1}{8x^3y^6}$ **23.** $\frac{m^2}{4n^3}$ **25.** $\frac{64r^2}{s^6}$ **27.** $\frac{-y^5}{32x^{10}z^{15}}$ **29.** $0.0000128m^{28}n^{35}$
31. t^{12} **33.** $\frac{s^9}{8r^6}$ **35.** $\frac{a^6b^9}{64}$ **37.** $-\frac{n^9}{27x^9}$ **39.** $\frac{1}{25m^4n^6r^6}$

Page 169 Review Capsule for Section 7.6 1. a. 1.5678 b. 156.78 **2.** a. 826.605027 b. 82660.5027
3. a. 48278.3 b. $4,827,830$ **4.** a. $5,280,000$ b. $528,000,000$ **5.** a. 67.5928 b. 0.675928
6. a. 502.65 b. 5.0265 **7.** a. 0.000018 b. 0.00000018 **8.** a. $16,000$ b. 160

Pages 170-171 P-1 a. $N = 5.8, a = 3$ b. $N = 3.76, a = -1$ c. $N = 1.0059, a = -6$ **P-2** The exponent
shows how many places to "move" the decimal point.

Page 172 Classroom Exercises 1. 300 **3.** 7030 **5.** 46.2 **7.** $50,001$ **9.** 5.3×10^2 **11.** 4.86×10^1
13. 7.6×10^4 **15.** 4.83×10^{-4}

Page 172 Written Exercises 1. 4200 **3.** 0.00029 **5.** $86,200$ **7.** 0.100726 **9.** $7,280,000$
11. 0.00005607 **13.** 9.2×10^{-3} **15.** 2.705×10^3 **17.** 1.734×10^{-2} **19.** 2.7×10^7 **21.** 2.75×10^{-5}
23. 2×10^6 **25.** $12,800,000$ meters **27.** $9,450,000,000,000$

Page 173 Special Topic Application 1. $t = 490$ sec **3.** $t \approx 4$ hr

Pages 174-176 Chapter Review 1. 27^9 **3.** r^7 **5.** t^9 **7.** 19^5 **9.** $(2.7)^2$ **11.** $(\sqrt{7})^3$ **13.** 1 **15.** 1
17. -1 **19.** $\frac{1}{t^{10}}$ **21.** $\frac{5}{x^2}$ **23.** $\frac{q}{p^2}$ **25.** $k^{-2}; \frac{1}{k^2}$ **27.** $m^{-5}; \frac{1}{m^5}$ **29.** $p^{-5}; \frac{1}{p^5}$ **31.** $16t^2$ **33.** $-32r^5$
35. $\frac{25}{p^2}$ **37.** $\frac{1}{16m^2}$ **39.** $\frac{1}{y^3}$ **41.** $\frac{1}{g^{10}}$ **43.** $\frac{27m^6n^9}{p^3}$ **45.** $\frac{x^6}{64y^3z^{12}}$ **47.** $31,870$ **49.** 0.005279
51. 8000.02 **53.** 5.219×10^{-3} **55.** 5.12×10^8 **57.** 3.1536×10^7

CHAPTER 8 ROOTS

Page 178 **P-1** 6; −6 **P-2** 0 **P-3** There are no two equal factors of −16. **P-4** a. 49 b. $\frac{1}{4}$ c. 0.09 d. 400 e. $\frac{9}{16}$ **P-5** a. −7 b. $\frac{1}{2}$ c. −0.3 d. 100 **P-6** 1, 3, 5, and 15 are factors of 15.

Page 180 Classroom Exercises 1. 100 3. 144 5. $\frac{1}{9}$ 7. 0.16 9. $\frac{25}{4}$ 11. 3 13. 0 15. 10 17. $-\frac{1}{4}$ 19. −0.1 21. 3 • 7 23. 2 • 2 • 2 25. 2 • 13 27. 7 • 7 29. 3 • 13 31. 3 • 3 • 5

Page 180 Written Exercises 1. 11 3. −10 5. $\frac{2}{5}$ 7. $-\frac{1}{3}$ 9. 0.9 11. 10 13. 12 15. 50 17. 5 • 13 19. 2 • 3 • 3 21. 2 • 3 • 3 • 3 23. 2 • 2 • 2 • 3 • 5 25. 2 • 3 • 3 • 11 27. 22 29. 28 31. 44 33. 56 35. 76 37. 72 39. 95 41. 62

Pages 181-182 **P-1** a. Irrational b. Rational c. Irrational d. Rational **P-2** a. 29 b. $\frac{1}{4}$ c. 1029 **P-3** a. $\sqrt{35}$ b. $\sqrt{66}$ c. 6

Page 183 Classroom Exercises 1. $\sqrt{10}$ 3. 8 5. 10 7. $\sqrt{2}$ 9. $\frac{1}{3}$ 11. 0 13. 20 15. −2

Page 183 Written Exercises 1. 13 3. $13\frac{3}{8}$ 5. 54 7. 6 9. $\sqrt{51}$ 11. $-\sqrt{10}$ 13. $\sqrt{30}$ 15. $\sqrt{5}$ 17. $\frac{1}{2}$ 19. 4 21. 6 23. $\sqrt{30}$ 25. 10 27. x = 6 29. x = $\sqrt{14}$ 31. x = 6 or x = −6 33. x = $\sqrt{14}$ or x = $-\sqrt{14}$

Page 183 Review Capsule for Section 8.3 1. 125 2. 216 3. 343 4. 512 5. 729 6. 625 7. 1296 8. 2401

Pages 184-185 **P-1** a. 7 b. −9 c. 5 d. −13 **P-2** a. 2 b. 6 c. 5 d. 4

Pages 185-186 Classroom Exercises 1. 2 3. −5 5. 4 7. 25 9. 11 11. 36 13. 10 15. 14 17. 30 19. $3\sqrt{5}$ 21. $6\sqrt{2}$ 23. 3 25. 2 27. 9 29. $2\sqrt[3]{7}$ 31. 55

Page 186 Written Exercises 1. 6 3. 38 5. $6\sqrt{3}$ 7. $35\sqrt{35}$ 9. $4\sqrt{6}$ 11. $12\sqrt{10}$ 13. $6\sqrt{5}$ 15. $10\sqrt{21}$ 17. $2\sqrt{2}$ 19. $3\sqrt{3}$ 21. $2\sqrt{6}$ 23. $2\sqrt{10}$ 25. $-4\sqrt{3}$ 27. $2\sqrt{30}$ 29. $4\sqrt{6}$ 31. 3 33. 2 35. $3\sqrt[3]{3}$ 37. $2\sqrt[4]{9}$ 39. $5\sqrt[3]{10}$ 41. $5\sqrt[4]{2}$ 43. −10 45. $-2\sqrt[3]{7}$

Page 186 Review Capsule for Section 8.4 1. $3\sqrt{2}$ 2. $5\sqrt{15}$ 3. $2\sqrt{10}$ 4. $21\sqrt{3}$ 5. $10\sqrt{10}$ 6. $3\sqrt{42}$

Pages 187-188 **P-1** a. 10 b. $\frac{1}{2}$ c. $\sqrt{17}$ d. $\frac{2}{3}$ **P-2** A negative number cannot have a real number as a square root. **P-3** a. a^3 b. x^4 c. b^6 d. y^{14} **P-4** a; x^2; y^3 **P-5** a. No b. Yes c. Yes d. No

Pages 188-189 Classroom Exercises 1. a 3. ab 5. xy^2 7. 3y 9. 5n 11. $3x^3$ 13. $x^2\sqrt{x}$ 15. $2a\sqrt{2a}$ 17. $xy\sqrt{2x}$ 19. $x\sqrt{6}$ 21. rt 23. x^4 25. $2k^2$

Page 189 Written Exercises 1. 6y 3. yz^3 5. $x^2\sqrt{x}$ 7. $2\sqrt{x}$ 9. $4y\sqrt{y}$ 11. $2x\sqrt{2}$ 13. $2a^2\sqrt{2a}$ 15. $2\sqrt{3ab}$ 17. $7ab\sqrt{ab}$ 19. $2ab\sqrt{6b}$ 21. $5r^2s^3\sqrt{3r}$ 23. $2rst^2\sqrt{5st}$ 25. x^4 27. $x^4\sqrt[3]{x}$ 29. $3xy^2$ 31. $2b\sqrt[3]{2a^2}$ 33. $3mn^2\sqrt[3]{2m^2n^2}$ 35. $2r^2s^3\sqrt[3]{4rs}$ 37. x^2 39. $2\sqrt{x}$ 41. $2x^2$ 43. $x\sqrt[3]{12}$ 45. $3a^2$ 47. $4b^3$

Page 190 Mid-Chapter Review 1. 221 3. 1925 5. 27 7. 36 9. 48 11. 21 13. $-\sqrt{14}$ 15. 5 17. $\sqrt{210}$ 19. $7\sqrt{10}$ 21. $10\sqrt{7}$ 23. $9\sqrt{5}$ 25. $3\sqrt[3]{4}$ 27. $3\sqrt[4]{2}$ 29. $7m^3n$ 31. $3r^2s^2\sqrt{3s}$ 33. $6ab^2c^3\sqrt{3abc}$ 35. $3p^2q^2\sqrt[3]{2p}$

Page 190 Calculator Exercises 1. 8 3. 6.5574385 5. 2

Page 190 Review Capsule for Section 8.5 1. 17m 2. 2.7t 3. 77k 4. −0.3w

Pages 191-192 P-1 a. $(7+a)x$ b. $(t-r)y$ c. $(11+3)m$ or $14m$ **P-2** $11\sqrt{2}$ **P-3** a. $5\sqrt{5}$ b. $7\sqrt{3}$ c. $-3\sqrt{10}$ **P-4** 2, 2, and 3 **P-5** $\sqrt{3}$; $\sqrt{15}$ **P-6** $2 \cdot 2 \cdot 2$; $2 \cdot 5 \cdot 5$

Pages 192-193 Classroom Exercises 1. $7\sqrt{3}$ 3. $4\sqrt{2}$ 5. $12\sqrt{10}$ 7. $3\sqrt{2}$ 9. $-2\sqrt{11}$ 11. $5\sqrt{x}$ 13. $\frac{1}{2}\sqrt{a}$ 15. $10\sqrt{m}$ 17. 5

Page 193 Written Exercises 1. $15\sqrt{3}$ 3. $4\sqrt{2}$ 5. $-3\sqrt{3}$ 7. $4\sqrt{2}$ 9. $2\sqrt{11}$ 11. $\sqrt{5}+\sqrt{15}$ 13. $\sqrt{19}-\sqrt{3}$ 15. $12\sqrt{x}$ 17. $-5\sqrt{t}$ 19. $2\sqrt{s}$ 21. $11\sqrt{2}$ 23. 0 25. $5\sqrt{3}$ 27. $7\sqrt{5}$ 29. $11\sqrt{2}$ 31. $5\sqrt{7a}$ 33. $4\sqrt{2r}$ 35. $12\sqrt{y}$ 37. $7\sqrt{3}$ 39. $\sqrt{7}$ 41. 0

Page 193 Review Capsule for Section 8.6 1. 6 2. $5x^2$ 3. $13x$ 4. $\frac{1}{3}x^2$

Pages 194-195 P-1 $\frac{2}{3}; \frac{2}{3}$ **P-2** a. $\frac{n}{3}$ b. $\frac{\sqrt{2}}{x}$ c. $\frac{r\sqrt{r}}{4}$ d. $\frac{8}{a}$ **P-3** a. $\frac{\sqrt{5}}{\sqrt{5}}$ b. $\frac{\sqrt{2n}}{\sqrt{2n}}$ c. $\frac{\sqrt{12s}}{\sqrt{12s}}$ or $\frac{\sqrt{3s}}{\sqrt{3s}}$ d. $\frac{\sqrt{x}}{\sqrt{x}}$

Page 196 Classroom Exercises 1. $\frac{1}{2}$ 3. $\frac{3}{5}$ 5. $\frac{4}{5}$ 7. 2 9. 2 11. 2

Page 196 Written Exercises 1. $\frac{x}{4}$ 3. $\frac{7}{a}$ 5. $\frac{y^2}{10}$ 7. $\frac{\sqrt{2}}{x}$ 9. $\frac{2\sqrt{3}}{a}$ 11. 5 13. 6 15. 7 17. 5 19. x 21. $\frac{2}{y}$ 23. $\frac{b}{a}$ 25. $\sqrt{5}$ 27. $\sqrt{6}$ 29. $\sqrt{11}$ 31. $\frac{\sqrt{15}}{5}$ 33. $\frac{a\sqrt{b}}{b}$ 35. $\frac{\sqrt{15st}}{5t}$

Page 196 Review Capsule for Section 8.7 1. $2 \cdot 2 \cdot 2 \cdot 3 \cdot 7$ 2. $2 \cdot 2 \cdot 3 \cdot 3 \cdot 5$ 3. $2 \cdot 2 \cdot 61$ 4. $2 \cdot 2 \cdot 2 \cdot 2 \cdot 3 \cdot 3$ 5. $3 \cdot 3 \cdot 23$ 6. $2 \cdot 3 \cdot 3 \cdot 13$

Pages 197-199 P-1 a. 784 b. 5776 c. 676 **P-2** a. 28 b. −78 c. 27 **P-3** a. 5.099 b. 8.832 c. −5.292 **P-4** $2 \cdot 2 \cdot 2 \cdot 2 \cdot 2 \cdot 5$ **P-5** $2 \cdot 3 \cdot 5 \cdot 7$

Page 200 Classroom Exercises 1. 841 3. 8649 5. 72 7. −88 9. 6.164 11. 8.832 13. 9.487 15. −12.247 17. 93 19. 59

Page 200 Written Exercises 1. 12.962 3. 15.620 5. 14.388 7. 16.585 9. 21.634 11. 0.866 13. 0.816 15. 0.936, or 0.935 17. 0.958 19. 0.306 21. 12.69 23. 12.45 25. 13.68 27. 8.66 29. 1.87 31. 3.57

Page 202 Career 1. 1.3° C (Table: 1.1° C) 3. −31.4° C (Table: −31.7° C)

Pages 203-204 Chapter Review 1. −7 3. 0.6 5. 23 7. $-\sqrt{33}$ 9. 6 11. $6\sqrt{3}$ 13. $2\sqrt{13}$ 15. $3\sqrt{11}$ 17. $2\sqrt[3]{3}$ 19. r^3 21. $3x^2\sqrt{x}$ 23. $2ab^2\sqrt{7ab}$ 25. $2mn\sqrt[3]{2n}$ 27. $10\sqrt{13}$ 29. $9\sqrt{3}$

31. $-7\sqrt{6}$ 33. $\dfrac{\sqrt{2}}{4}$ 35. $\dfrac{2\sqrt{5}}{t}$ 37. $\dfrac{\sqrt{70}}{10}$ 39. $\dfrac{x\sqrt{6xy}}{2y}$ 41. 12.369   43. 0.829   45. 0.842

CHAPTER 9   POLYNOMIALS

Page 206   P-1 a. $a = 3.7, n = 2$ b. $a = -1, n = 1$ c. $a = -15, n = 0$ **P-2** $n = -2$, which is a negative number.
P-3 a. $\dfrac{1}{3}$ b. 1   c. -1 d. $-\dfrac{1}{5}$

Page 207   Classroom Exercises   1. Yes   3. No   5. Yes   7. 2   9. $-7\dfrac{1}{2}$ 11. $3\dfrac{2}{3}$

Page 207   Written Exercises   1. Yes   3. Yes   5. No   7. Yes   9. No   11. Yes   13. No   15. No   17. 5
19. $\dfrac{3}{5}$ 21. 1.8   23. -1 25. $\dfrac{3}{5}$ 27. $\dfrac{3}{5}$ 29. -3 31. 24   33. -8.3

Page 207   Review Capsule for Section 9.2   1. m^6 2. t^8 3. r^{10} 4. y^{12} 5. w^4 6. q^3 7. n^4 8. a^5

Pages 208-209   P-1 a. x^7 b. y^{11} c. r^6 **P-2** 10   **P-3** r^2s^3 **P-4** a. x^3 b. y^3 c. r

Pages 209-210   Classroom Exercises   1. $20y^3$ 3. $-42x^5$ 5. $-8x^3y^2$ 7. $-6x^3y$ 9. $24x^4y^3$ 11. $9x^2$
13. $-2b^4$ 15. $-9s^4t$ 17. $-8p^2qr$

Page 210   Written Exercises   1. $72m^5$ 3. $-96r^3t^5$ 5. $5p^4q^5$ 7. $-24t^4$ 9. $21m^3n^4$ 11. $-27a^4b^6$
13. $-1.52r^2s^3t^4$ 15. $8.4u^3x^3y^3z^3$ 17. $-4k^3$ 19. $4y^2$ 21. $-0.6m^6n^2$ 23. $29abc^2$ 25. $-3\dfrac{1}{7}x^8y^6z^4$
27. $\dfrac{4}{15}m^9n^2q^2$

Page 210   Review Capsule for Section 9.3   1. $x^2 + (-2x)$ 2. $2n^3 + (-5)$ 3. $4y^2 + (-y)$ 4. $3a^4 + (-5a)$
5. $(-5t^3) + (-4t)$

Page 211   P-1 $2x^2$, $(-9x)$, and $\dfrac{1}{4}$ **P-2** a. and d.; b. and c.

Pages 212-213   Classroom Exercises   1. Yes   3. Yes   5. Yes   7. No   9. No   11. Yes   13. Yes   15. Yes
17. $5x^2 - 2x + 3$ 19. $3x^3 + 12$ 21. $5x^2y - 5$ 23. $x^{12} + 5x^8 - 3x^5 - 3x^2$

Page 213   Written Exercises   1. Yes   3. No   5. No   7. Yes   9. Yes   11. $3x^2 - 4x + 7$ 13. $x^5 + 4x^3$
$- 3x^2 + 5x - 1$ 15. $3x^2 - 9x + 8$ 17. $3x^3y + 5x^2y^2 + xy^3 - 5$ 19. $m^3 - 2m^2n + 5mn - 10$
21. $-0.5x^4 - 1.9x^2 + 2.4x$ 23. -23 25. -15 27. 32   29. 49   31. $x^2 - 3x - 5$ 33. $x^2 + x + 12$

Page 214   Mid-Chapter Review   1. 32   3. 8   5. $-6r^3t$ 7. $-5s$ 9. $-3x^2 + 6x + 12$ 11. $0.2x^3 - 3.2x^2$
$+ 2.8x - 1.4$ 13. 20   15. -180

Page 214   Calculator Exercises   1. 67,349   3. 1472

Page 214   Review Capsule for Section 9.4   1. $-3x^2 + 2x$ 2. $-3x^3 - 4x$ 3. $-6x^2 + 4x + 12$ 4. $-5x + 7$
5. $x^2 + 3x - 5$

Pages 215-216 **P-1** a. $x^2 - x + 3$ b. $2x^2 + 4x - 5$ **P-2** a. $2x^2 + 4x + 3$ b. $x^3 - 2x^2 + 5x - 1$
P-3 a. $4x^3$ b. $-2x^2$ c. $-x$ d. 8

Page 216 **Classroom Exercises** 1. $7x - 7$ 3. $-2x^2 - 5x - 1$ 5. $2x^2 + 4x + 1$ 7. $3x^2 + 3x - 3$
9. $-x^2 - 4x$

Page 217 **Written Exercises** 1. $11x^2 - 2x - 8$ 3. $1.5x^2 + 2.9x + 0.8$ 5. $-2x^3 - 4x^2 - 3x + 9$ 7. $-2x^2$
$+ 6x - 18$ 9. $3x^3 - 5x^2 - 3x + 2$ 11. $4x^2 - 7x + 15$ 13. $-3x^3 + 5x^2 - 3x + 7$ 15. $2.1x^2 + 4.4x$
$+ 6.7$ 17. $7x^3 - 7x^2 - 4x - 9$

Page 217 **Review Capsule for Section 9.5** 1. $-6x^2 + 10x$ 2. $-20x^2 + 10x$ 3. $-40x^2 + 12x$ 4. $-6x - 4$

Pages 218-219 **P-1** a. $-2x^2$ b. $-15x$ c. 12   **P-2** a. 5   b. -12 c. 9   **P-3** a. $2x^2 + 9x + 4$
b. $6x^2 + 5x - 6$

Page 220 **Classroom Exercises** 1. $x^2 + 3x + 2$ 3. $x^2 + 2x - 3$ 5. $x^2 - 6x + 8$ 7. $x^2 + 3x - 40$
9. $2x^2 + 5x + 2$ 11. $4x^2 - 11x - 3$ 13. $2x^2 + 5x$ 15. $x^3 - 4x^2 + 7x - 6$ 17. $6x^3 + 9x^2 - 10x - 15$

Pages 220-221 **Written Exercises** 1. $x^2 + 8x + 15$ 3. $x^2 - 2x - 8$ 5. $x^2 - 8x + 15$ 7. $x^2 + 2x - 35$
9. $2x^2 + 13x + 15$ 11. $3x^2 + 11x - 4$ 13. $5x^2 - 17x + 6$ 15. $8x^2 - 2x - 15$ 17. $x^3 - 6x^2 + 11x - 12$
19. $2x^3 + 13x^2 + 11x - 20$ 21. $x^3 + 6x^2 - 5x - 30$ 23. $6x^3 - 13x^2 + 27x - 14$ 25. $-20x^3 - 17x^2$
$- 6x - 20$ 27. $12x^4 - 6x^3 - 8x^2 + 20x - 8$ 29. $-10x^4 + 17x^3 + 20x^2 + 12x - 30$ 31. $8x^4 - 10x^3$
$- 4x^2 + 13x - 10$ 33. $6x^4 + 7x^3 - 29x^2 + 18x - 8$ 35. $-20x^4 - 17x^3 + 10x^2 - 24x - 30$
37. $-2x^5 - 3x^4 + 3x^3 - 10x^2 + 21x - 9$

Page 221 **Review Capsule for Section 9.6** 1. $-4x + 2$ 2. $-2x - 4$ 3. $8x - 3$ 4. $2x^2 + 8$

Pages 222-223 **P-1** $6x^2; 4x; 2$ **P-2** $2x^2; -x$

Pages 223-224 **Classroom Exercises** 1. $-5x^2$ 3. $3x^2 - 5$ 5. $x + 5$ 7. $3x + 2$

Page 224 **Written Exercises** 1. $2x + 3$ 3. $3 - 2xy$ 5. $3x + 4$ 7. $5x - 6$ 9. $3x - 4$ 11. $x^2 - 3x + 2$
13. $2x^2 - 3x + 1$ 15. $x - 5$ 17. $x^2 + 3$ 19. $2x^2 - 5x + 10$ 21. $x^2 + 2x + 4$ 23. $x^3 + 3x^2 + 9x + 27$

Page 224 **Review Capsule for Section 9.7** 1. $10x^2 + 25x$ 2. $12x^3 - 6x$ 3. $-12x^3 - 20x$ 4. $-12x^2$
$- 3x$ 5. $x^4 + x^3 - x^2$ 6. $2x^4 - x^3 + x^2$ 7. $2x^4 - 2x^3 - 2x^2$

Pages 225-226 **P-1** $3x$ **P-2** It is not in the form ax^n, with a real and n a non-negative integer.
P-3 $-8x^3 + 10x^2 - 12x - 19$ **P-4** $2x^2$

Page 227 **Classroom Exercises** Note: In the answers for Ex. 1-5, Q stands for quotient and R stands for
remainder. 1. Q: $x - 5$; R: 3   3. Q: $2x + 2$; R: -1 5. Q: $x + 1$; R: $-2x + 2$ 7. $10x^2 - 15x$; $6x - 9$
9. $x^3 - 3x$; $2x^2 - 6$; $2x + 11$

Pages 227-228 **Written Exercises** 1. $2x - 5 + \dfrac{3}{x + 4}$ 3. $2x + 7 - \dfrac{4}{2x - 3}$ 5. $3x + 4 - \dfrac{5}{5x - 6}$ 7. $5x - 6$
$- \dfrac{10}{2x + 5}$ 9. $6x - 5 + \dfrac{x}{2x^2 - 1}$ 11. $x^2 - 3x + 6 - \dfrac{8x - 8}{x^2 + x - 1}$ 13. $x - 5 - \dfrac{6}{x^2 + 8x + 2}$ 15. $x^2 + 2x$
$- 3 + \dfrac{24}{2x^2 + 9x + 4}$ 17. $x^2 - y^2 - \dfrac{y^3}{x + y}$ 19. $x^2 - 2x + 4 - \dfrac{16}{x + 2}$ 21. $x^2 - 2xy + y^2 + \dfrac{y^3}{2x - 3y}$

23. $4x^2 + 2x + 1$ 25. $a + 6$ 27. $x^2 - 5x + 29 - \dfrac{148}{x + 5}$ 29. $3a + 4$ 31. $4a^2 + 9a + 3$ 33. $x^2 - xy + y^2$
35. $x - y$ 37. $x^3 + x^2 + x + 1$

Page 229 Special Topic Application   1. 138 km   3. 226 km   5. 391 km   7. 124 km

Pages 230-232 Chapter Review   1. Yes   3. No   5. -32 7. -12.8 9. $21t^6$ 11. $2a^4b^5$ 13. $-12t^2$
15. $\dfrac{1}{6}x^9y^2z^2$ 17. $\dfrac{13}{4}x^2y^4$ 19. No   21. No   23. $7x^2 + 3x - 16$ 25. $-3x^3 - x^2 + 12x + 5$ 27. $4x^2$
$- 7x - 17$ 29. $5x^3 + 2x^2 - 11x - 5$ 31. $6x^2 - 7x - 5$ 33. $x^4 - 5x^3 - 2x^2 - 2x + 12$ 35. $2x^2 + x$
$- 21$ 37. $20x^2 + 17x - 10$ 39. $6x^4 - 23x^3 + 7x^2 + 10x - 35$ 41. $x + 7$ 43. $x^2 - 3x + 4$ 45. $-2x + 5$
$+ \dfrac{5}{4x + 11}$ 47. $x^2 - x - 3 - \dfrac{2}{x^2 + 3}$

CHAPTER 10 FACTORING POLYNOMIALS

Pages 234-235 P-1 $2x(2x - 3)$ **P-2** $4x^2$

Page 236 Classroom Exercises   1. Yes   3. No   5. No   7. Yes   9. $2(2x + 1)$ 11. $5(x + 3)$
13. $2(x^2 + 5)$ 15. $-3(x - 2)$ 17. $5x(x^2 - 2)$ 19. $8(3 - x^2)$

Page 236 Written Exercises   1. $4(x - 1)$ 3. $5(x + 2)$ 5. $x(2x + 3)$ 7. $-3x(x - 3)$ 9. $4x^2(2x - 3)$
11. $6x(2x^2 - 3)$ 13. $x(x^2 - 2x + 3)$ 15. $2x(x^3 - 2x - 5)$ 17. $-5x(x + 2)$ 19. $4x^2(2x^3 - 3x + 5)$
21. $5(x^4 - 7x^2 - 2)$ 23. Prime polynomial

Page 236 Review Capsule for Section 10.2   1. $x^2 + 2x + 2x + 2 \cdot 2$ 2. $x^2 + 4x + 2x + 4 \cdot 2$ 3. $x^2 + 7x$
$+ 3x + 7 \cdot 3$ 4. $x^2 + 3x + 2x + 3 \cdot 2$ 5. $x^2 + 11x + 1x + 11 \cdot 1$ 6. $x^2 + 5x + 4x + 5 \cdot 4$

Pages 237-238 P-1 a. Second   b. First   c. Zero   d. Eighth   **P-2** a. First   b. Third   c. Fourth
P-3 a. $(x + 7)$ and $(x + 3)$ b. $(x + 2)$ and $(x + 10)$ **P-4** 5; 2; 10   **P-5** 9 and 4

Page 238 Classroom Exercises   1. Second   3. First   5. Fifth   7. $(x + 4), (x + 3)$ 9. $(x + 3), (x + 5)$
11. $(x + 5), (x + 4)$ 13. $(x + 4), (x + 8)$

Page 239 Written Exercises   1. $(x + 3)(x + 4)$ 3. $(x + 5)(x + 3)$ 5. $(x + 4)(x + 5)$ 7. $(x + 8)(x + 4)$
9. $(x + 3)(x + 11)$ 11. $(x + 5)(x + 2)$ 13. $(x + 3)(x + 2)$ 15. $(x + 7)(x + 3)$ 17. $(x + 13)(x + 2)$
19. $(x + 10)(x + 3)$ 21. $(x + 7)(x + 4)$ 23. $(x + 12)(x + 11)$ 25. $(x + 15)(x + 10)$ 27. $(x + 13)(x + 16)$

Page 239 Review Capsule for Section 10.3   1. $(x - 2)(x + 5)$ 2. $(x + 2)(x - 3)$ 3. $(x - 4)(x - 6)$
4. $(x - 2)(x - 10)$ 5. $(x - 5)(x - 5)$ 6. $(x - 9)(x - 9)$

Pages 240-242 P-1 10; 16   **P-2** $r + s$ **P-3** rs **P-4** $-7; 12$ **P-5** $-1; -20$ **P-6** 5; 10

Page 242 Classroom Exercises   1. 3, 2   3. 6, 3   5. None   7. 4, -2 9. 2, 4   11. None   13. $x^2 + 4x$
$+ 3x + 12$ 15. $x^2 + 5x + 3x + 15$ 17. $x^2 - 3x - 2x + 6$ 19. $x^2 + 5x - x - 5$ 21. $x^2 + 6x - x - 6$
23. $x^2 + 7x - x - 7$

Page 243 Written Exercises   1. 7; 12   3. 14; 33   5. 4; -32 7. $-8; -48$ 9. $-17; 72$ 11. $-3; 2$
13. $x^2 + 12x + x + 12$ 15. $x^2 + 5x + 6x + 30$ 17. $x^2 - 5x - 3x + 15$ 19. $x^2 - 8x - 3x + 24$

21. $x^2 - 8x + 5x - 40$ 23. $x^2 + 7x - 3x - 21$ 25. $x^2 - 12x + 3x - 36$ 27. $x^2 - 6x - x + 6$
29. $x^2 - 14x + 3x - 42$ 31. $(x + 1)(x + 1)$ 33. $(x + 5)(x + 7)$ 35. $(x - 4)(x - 3)$
37. $(x - 6)(x - 5)$ 39. $(x - 4)(x + 3)$ 41. $(x - 6)(x + 5)$ 43. $(x + 6)(x - 5)$ 45. $(x - 7)(x - 2)$
47. $(x + 7)(x - 2)$ 49. $(x - 9)(x - 4)$ 51. $(x - 5)(x + 3)$ 53. $(x + 17)(x + 2)$ 55. $(x - 24)(x + 2)$
57. $(x + 2)(x + 1)$ 59. $(x - 8)(x + 7)$

Page 244 P-1 a. 5   b. 1   c. −1

Page 246 Classroom Exercises 1. $r + s = 3; rs = 2$ 3. $r + s = 10; rs = 9$ 5. $r + s = 11; rs = 18$ 7. $r + s = 11;$
$rs = 18$ 9. $r + s = 17; rs = 30$ 11. $r + s = -1; rs = -6$ 13. $r + s = -5; rs = -50$ 15. $r + s = -7; rs = -30$
17. $r + s = -17; rs = 72$

Page 246 Written Exercises 1. $2x^2 - 3x + 1$ 3. $3x^2 + x - 2$ 5. $(2x + 1)(x + 1)$ 7. $(3x + 1)(x + 3)$
9. $(3x + 2)(x + 3)$ 11. $(3x + 1)(2x + 3)$ 13. $(3x + 1)(2x + 5)$ 15. $(3x + 2)(x - 1)$ 17. $(2x + 5)(x - 5)$
19. $(5x + 1)(3x - 2)$ 21. $(2x - 3)(x - 2)$ 23. $(4x - 1)(2x - 3)$ 25. $(2x - 1)(x + 3)$ 27. $(5x - 2)$
$(3x + 4)$ 29. $(9x + 7)(2x + 1)$ 31. $(12x + 3)(x - 3)$ or $3(4x + 1)(x - 3)$ 33. $(8x + 3)(x + 4)$

Page 247 Mid-Chapter Review 1. $4x(3x - 1)$ 3. $3x(x^2 + 3x - 5)$ 5. $2xy(x + 3)$ 7. $5x^2y(x - 2 + 5y)$
9. $(x + 7)(x + 5)$ 11. $(x + 10)(x + 5)$ 13. $(x + 8)(x - 5)$ 15. $(x - 11)(x + 8)$ 17. $(x + 12)(x - 6)$
19. $(x - 11)(x - 9)$ 21. $(2x - 3)(x + 2)$ 23. $(5x - 2)(4x + 1)$

Page 247 Calculator Exercises 1. 21   3. 210   5. 4095   7. 500500

Page 247 Review Capsule for Section 10.5 1. $(x - 12)(x + 12)$ 2. $(x - 2y)(x + 2y)$ 3. $(2x - 3)(2x + 3)$

Pages 248-249 P-1 a. and c.   **P-2** $(x + a)(x - a)$ **P-3** 11   **P-4** a. x^3 b. r^4 c. t^6

Pages 249-250 Classroom Exercises 1. $(a + 1)(a - 1)$ 3. $(p + 3)(p - 3)$ 5. $(x + 5)(x - 5)$ 7. $(t + 7)$
$(t - 7)$ 9. $(b + 9)(b - 9)$ 11. $(p + q)(p - q)$ 13. $(2x + y)(2x - y)$ 15. $(x^2 + 5)(x^2 - 5)$

Page 250 Written Exercises 1. $x^2 - 64$ 3. $x^2 - 121$ 5. $4x^2 - y^2$ 7. $x^2y^2 - 9$ 9. $25x^2 - 9$
11. $x^4 - 4$ 13. $(a + 5)(a - 5)$ 15. $(2x + 1)(2x - 1)$ 17. $(3a + 4)(3a - 4)$ 19. $(x^2 + 2)(x^2 - 2)$
21. $(2x^2 + 3)(2x^2 - 3)$ 23. $(2x + y)(2x - y)$ 25. $(ab + 1)(ab - 1)$ 27. $(4t + 9)(4t - 9)$ 29. $(xy + r)$
$(xy - r)$ 31. $(4xy^2 + 3)(4xy^2 - 3)$ 33. $(x^3 + 2)(x^3 - 2)$ 35. $(x^5 + y^4)(x^5 - y^4)$ 37. 224   39. 165
41. 396   43. 884   45. 1591   47. 3599

Page 250 Review Capsule for Section 10.6 1. $x^2 + 12x + 36$ 2. $x^2 - 6x + 9$ 3. $4x^2 - 20x + 25$
4. $20x^2 + 9x + 1$ 5. $4x^2 + 28x + 49$ 6. $x^2 - 2xy + y^2$ 7. $9x^2 + 12x + 4$ 8. $25x^2 - 10x + 1$

Pages 251-252 P-1 3; 9; 9   **P-2** The value of b is negative.   **P-3** a. $4x^2 + 20x + 25$ b. $x^2 - 14x + 49$
c. $9x^2 - 6x + 1$ **P-4** a. $(x + 1)(x + 1)$ b. $(x - 6)(x - 6)$ c. $(3x - 4)(3x - 4)$

Page 252 Classroom Exercises 1. Yes   3. Yes   5. Yes   7. No   9. No   11. No   13. $(x + 2)(x + 2)$
15. $(x - 3)(x - 3)$ 17. $(x + 8)(x + 8)$ 19. $(x - 12)(x - 12)$ 21. $(2x + 1)(2x + 1)$

Page 253 Written Exercises 1. No   3. Yes   5. No   7. No   9. No   11. Yes   13. $x^2 - 10x + 25$
15. $x^2 + 14x + 49$ 17. $4x^2 + 12x + 9$ 19. $25x^2 - 10x + 1$ 21. $16x^2 + 40x + 25$ 23. $4x^2 - 4x + 1$
25. $(6x - 1)(6x - 1)$ 27. $(5x + 2)(5x + 2)$ 29. $(3x - 4)(3x - 4)$ 31. $(7x + 10)(7x + 10)$
33. $(7x - 1)(7x - 1)$ 35. $(x + 2y)(x + 2y)$ 37. $(2x + 3y)(2x + 3y)$ 39. $(xy - 8)(xy - 8)$
41. $(3xy + 7)(3xy + 7)$

Page 253   Review Capsule for Section 10.7   1. B   **2.** D   **3.** A   **4.** C

Page 254   P-1 2   **P-2** 3

Pages 255-256   Classroom Exercises   1. 4; $(x^2 - 3)$ **3.** 4; $(x^2 - 5x + 7)$ **5.** 5; $(3x^2 - x - 5)$ **7.** y;
$(x^2 y - 3x + 5)$ **9.** -4; $(x^2 + 5)$ **11.** 3b; $(a^2 b - 3a + 2)$ **13.** 3y; $(x^2 - 10x + 25)$

Page 256   Written Exercises   1. $2(y + 3)(y - 3)$ **3.** $2(x + 2)(x + 2)$ **5.** $3(x + 7)(x + 3)$ **7.** $4(x - 6)(x - 4)$
9. $5(x - 5)(x + 4)$ **11.** $(2y + 3)(2y - 3)$ **13.** $a(x + 2)(x + 2)$ **15.** $2(3x + 1)(x - 2)$ **17.** $4(3x - 1)(x - 3)$
19. $-3(x^2 + 4)$ **21.** $a(2x + 3)(2x - 3)$ **23.** $y(x - 5)(x - 5)$ **25.** $3(x + 5)(x - 5)$ **27.** $2(4 - d)(4 - d)$
29. $3(x - 4)(x + 2)$ **31.** $2(1 + 8x)(1 - 8x)$ **33.** $a(b - 5)(b + 4)$ **35.** $3(2a - 1)(4a - 3)$ **37.** $(2ab + c)$
$(2ab + c)$ **39.** $2(4xy^2 + 3t)(4xy^2 - 3t)$ **41.** $2(5x - 2)(3x - 1)$ **43.** $2x^2 y^2 (5y - 6xy^2 + 9)$

Page 258   Career   1. 64 hybrid tall; 64 pure short   **3.** 64 pure tall; 64 hybrid tall   **5.** 14 pure rough coats;
28 hybrid rough coats; 14 pure smooth coats   **7.** 28 pure rough coats; 28 hybrid rough coats

Pages 259-260   Chapter Review   1. $2x(2x - 5)$ **3.** $6ab(3a + 5ab - 7)$ **5.** $abc(ac^2 - b + abc)$ **7.** $(x + 7)$
$(x + 3)$ **9.** $(x + 5)(x + 10)$ **11.** $(x + 7)(x + 3)$ **13.** $(x + 6)(x - 3)$ **15.** $(x - 6)(x - 3)$ **17.** Prime
19. $(2x - 3)(x + 1)$ **21.** $(4x - 1)(x + 2)$ **23.** $(3x - 5)(x + 1)$ **25.** $(3a + 4b)(3a - 4b)$ **27.** $(rs + xy)$
$(rs - xy)$ **29.** $(x^2 + 13)(x^2 - 13)$ **31.** Yes   **33.** No   **35.** No   **37.** $(x - 4)(x - 4)$ **39.** $(2x - 3)(2x - 3)$
41. $(x - 2y)(x - 2y)$ **43.** $5(x + 2)(x - 2)$ **45.** $3(x - 2)(x - 2)$ **47.** $3(x^2 - 4x + 32)$

CHAPTER 11   LINEAR EQUATIONS

Pages 262-263   P-1 $(3, 5)$, $(-4, -9)$, etc.   **P-2** Substitute 3 for x and 5 for y in $y = 2x - 1$.   **P-3** a: -1,
b: $\frac{1}{2}$; a: $\frac{2}{3}$, b: $-\frac{1}{4}$; a: -3, b: 10   **P-4** Functions a. and b.

Pages 263-264   Classroom Exercises   1.

x	-2	-1	0	2
y	-6	-3	0	6

3.

x	-5	-2	0	3
y	-49	-19	1	31

5. a: -3; b: 7
7. a: -1; b: -3 **9.** a: -7; b: 0   **11.** a: -0.5; b: 3.8

Page 264   Written Exercises   Four points are given.   1. $(3, 0)$, $(0, 3)$, $(1, 2)$, $(-2, 5)$ **3.** $(0, -1)$, $(1, 2)$, $(2, 5)$,
$(-1, -4)$ **5.** $(-1, -2)$, $(2, 4)$, $(0, 0)$, $(3, 6)$ **7.** $(-3, -2)$, $(1, -2)$, $(0, -2)$, $(2, -2)$ **9.** $(-1, -2)$, $(3, 0)$,
$(5, 1)$, $(-3, -3)$ **11.** Yes   **13.** Yes   **15.** Yes   **17.** Yes   **19.** No

Page 264   Review Capsule for Section 11.2   1. $y = -3$ **2.** $y = \frac{3}{4}$ **3.** $y = -10$ **4.** $y = 0$ **5.** $y = 1.3$
6. $y = 0.6$ **7.** $y = \sqrt{3}$ **8.** $y = 5$

Pages 265-266   P-1 In each the value of b is 2.   **P-2** $(0, 2)$ **P-3** x value: 0; y values: 1(A), -3(B), 3(C),
-1(D)   **P-4** a. $\frac{5}{2}$ or $2\frac{1}{2}$ b. 4

Pages 266-267   Classroom Exercises   1. 1   **3.** $\frac{1}{2}$ **5.** $1\frac{1}{2}$ **7.** $\frac{1}{2}$ **9.** $-\frac{1}{3}$ **11.** -1 **13.** 0   **15.** 6

Page 267   Written Exercises   1. 7   **3.** $\frac{7}{2}$ **5.** $-\frac{5}{3}$ **7.** 0.3   **9.** 6   **11.** 0   Ex. 13-21 -- Two points are
given.   **13.** $(0, 1)$, $(-1, 0)$ **15.** $(0, -3)$, $(-2, 1)$ **17.** $(0, 5)$, $(4, 7)$ **19.** $(0, 0)$, $(2, -6)$ **21.** $(0, \frac{3}{2})$, $(5, 4)$

Page 267 Review Capsule for Section 11.3 In each exercise, two points are given. 1. (0, 5), (2, 6) 2. (0, 3), (2, 4) 3. (0, 1), (6, 4) 4. (0, 0), (4, 2) 5. (0, −3), (−4, −5) 6. (0, −5), (−2, −6)

Pages 268-269 P-1 2 **P-2** a **P-3** In all four the value of b is −1. **P-4** a. Slope: $-\frac{3}{4}$, Y intercept: −2 b. Slope: 5, Y intercept: $-\frac{1}{2}$ c. Slope: $-\frac{3}{2}$, Y intercept: $\frac{5}{2}$ **P-5** I, II, and IV **P-6** I and III; II and IV

Pages 269-270 Classroom Exercises 1. Slope: 3; Y intercept: 2 3. Slope: 1; Y intercept: 5 5. Slope: $\frac{1}{3}$; Y intercept: −6 7. y = 5x + 3 9. y = −1x + 0 or y = −x 11. y = 3x + 10

Page 270 Written Exercises 1. 1 3. $-\frac{1}{2}$ 5. 2 7. −3 9. $-\frac{1}{2}$ 11. −4 13. y = −x + 5 15. $y = -\frac{1}{3}x - 3$ 17. y = −x 19. I, III 21. II, IV 23. II, IV 25. I, III 27. II, IV 29. I, III

Page 270 Review Capsule for Section 11.4 1. $-\frac{3}{5}$ 2. $-\frac{3}{2}$ 3. 5 4. $\frac{5}{8}$ 5. $\frac{2}{3}$

Page 271 P-1 $\frac{3}{2}$ **P-2** Vertical motion: 3; Horizontal motion: 2 **P-3** 6 units; 4 units

Page 273 Classroom Exercises 1. $\frac{3}{5}$ 3. $\frac{3}{2}$ 5. $-\frac{1}{3}$ 7. −1 9. $\frac{1}{2}$ 11. −1 13. 2 15. $-\frac{1}{2}$ 17. 2

Pages 273-274 Written Exercises 1. 1 3. 0 5. $-\frac{3}{4}$ 7. $-\frac{7}{6}$ 9. −1 11. 0 13. $-\frac{3}{4}$ 15. $-\frac{3}{2}$ 17. y = x + 5 19. $y = \frac{9}{4}x - 3$ 21. $y = \frac{8}{5}x$ 23. y = −6 25. y = − x + 5 27. $y = \frac{2}{3}x + 6$ In Ex. 29-33, a second point is given that can be found using the given slope. The line can be drawn using the two points. 29. (1, 3) 31. (6, −6) 33. (0, 3)

Page 275 Mid-Chapter Review For Exercises 1-5, 4 points are given. 1. (0, −3), (1, −2), (2, −1), (3, 0) 3. (−2, 5), (−1, 3), (0, 1), (1, −1) 5. (−2, −3), (0, −2), (2, −1), (4, 0) For Exercises 7 and 9, the Y intercept and 2 ordered pairs are given. 7. Y intercept: 3; (−1, 4), (1, 2). 9. Y intercept: $\frac{5}{2}$; (1, 2), (3, 1) 11. $y = -\frac{1}{4}x - 1$ 13. −1 15. 0

Page 275 Calculator Exercises 1. About 98 inches 3. About 27,000,000 miles

Pages 276-277 P-1 They appear to be parallel. **P-2** a. and c. **P-3** 0

Pages 277-278 Classroom Exercises 1. Yes 3. Yes 5. y = 4x + 3 7. $y = \frac{3}{2}x + 10$ 9. y = −5.3x + 0.6

Page 278 Written Exercises In Ex. 1-5, each graph is a pair of parallel lines. Two points are given for each line. 1. (0, 3), (1, 1); (0, −1), (−1, 1) 3. (0, −2), (4, 4); (0, 1), (−2, −2) 5. (0, 3), (4, 8); (0, 0), (4, 5) In Ex. 7-9, the graph is a set of three parallel lines. Two points are given for each line. 7. (0, −3), (2, 1); (0, 3), (−2, −1); (0, 0), (2, 4) 9. (0, 3), (−2, 1); (0, −3), (2, −1); (0, 0), (3, 3) The graphs of Ex. 11 and 13 are horizontal lines. One point is given for each line. 11. (0, 5) 13. (0, $\frac{3}{2}$) 15. The graph of y = 2x − 2 and y = 2x + 3 is a pair of parallel lines. Similarly for y = −3x − 5 and y = −3x + 4.

Page 278 Review Capsule for Section 11.6 1. x = −2 2. x = 2 3. x = 12 4. $x = \frac{3}{4}$

Pages 279-280 P-1 (−4, 0) **P-2** a. 5 b. $-\frac{1}{2}$ c. −4 **P-3** {−2} **P-4** There is more than one y value for the x value, −2.

Page 281 Classroom Exercises 1. −3 3. 1 5. −2 7. $\frac{5}{2}$ 9. −5 11. 1 13. $4\frac{1}{2}$ 15. x = −5 17. x = −1 19. $x = 2\frac{1}{2}$

Page 281 Written Exercises 1. −6 3. 3 5. −2 7. 3 9. 4 11. −4 In Ex. 13-19, each graph is a straight line. Two ordered pairs are given for each line, one using the X intercept, the other using the Y inter-cept. 13. (2, 0), (0, −4) 15. (6, 0), (0, −3) 17. (−3, 0), (0, 6) 19. $(\frac{5}{2}, 0)$, (0, −5) In Ex. 21 and 23, the graphs are vertical lines. One point is given for each line. 21. (5, 0) 23. $(2\frac{1}{2}, 0)$

Page 281 Review Capsule for Section 11.7 1. slope = 2; Y intercept = 3 2. slope = 1.8; Y intercept = 32 3. slope = π; Y intercept = 0 4. slope = 1; Y intercept = 273 5. slope = 2.5; Y intercept = 3

Pages 282-283 P-1 95; −40 **P-2** Approximately 17 **P-3** 1.6 **P-4** $10 **P-5** 20 cm

Pages 283-284 Classroom Exercises 1. 38° C 3. −7° C 5. −29° C 7. 6 m 9. 7 m

Page 284 Written Exercises 1. See Ex. 2 on p. 269 (y = 2x). This graph is similar except that only the portion in the first quadrant is drawn. 3. The graph is a portion of a line and contains the points (−273, 0) and (0, 273). The graph is in Quadrants One and Two only. 5. 68° F 7. 104° F 9. −22° F 11. 18 km/hr 13. 54 km/hr 15. 113° F 17. 72.5° F

Page 285 Special Topic Application 1. Dallas, Texas 3. Toledo, Ohio 5. Paris, France 7. Tokyo, Japan

Pages 286-288 Chapter Review 1. No 3. Yes 5. The graph is a straight line. The coordinates of four points are given. (−1, 3), (0, 1), (1, −1), (2, −3) 7. −10 9. 3.8 11. y = 4x − 1 13. y = −2.8x + 2.9 15. II, IV 17. I, III 19. $-\frac{1}{2}$ 21. 0.8 23. −2 25. −3 27. y = 2x − 2 29. y = $\frac{3}{4}$x − $\frac{5}{2}$ 31. The lines are parallel; two points are given. (0, −2), (4, 0); (0, 3), (4, 5); (0, 0), (4, 2) The graphs of Ex. 33 and 35 are horizontal lines. One point is given. 33. (0, −3) 35. (0, 3.5) 37. $-2\frac{1}{2}$ 39. 8 In Ex. 41 and 43, each graph is a straight line. Two ordered pairs are given for each, one using the X intercept, the other, the Y intercept. 41. (0, 1), (−1, 0) 43. (0, −6), (2, 0) In Ex. 45 and 47, the graphs are vertical lines. One point is given for each line. 45. (−1, 0) 47. $(\frac{7}{2}, 0)$ 49. 19.6 m 51. 12.6 m

CHAPTER 12 SYSTEMS OF LINEAR EQUATIONS

Pages 290-291 P-1 b. **P-2** a. y = −x + 2 b. y = 2x − 5 c. y = 4x − 10

Page 291 Classroom Exercises 1. Yes 3. Yes 5. No 7. No 9. No 11. No In Ex. 13-21, another answer can be given. For example, −x − y + 5 = 0 is the other answer to Ex. 13. 13. x + y − 5 = 0 15. 3x − y − 1 = 0 17. 3x − 2y + 7 = 0 19. 12x − y + 15 = 0 21. x − y = 0 23. y = 2x + 1 25. y = 3x + 2 27. y = x + 5 29. y = $-\frac{1}{2}$x + 3

Page 292 Written Exercises In Ex. 1-17, another answer can be written. For example, −3x + y + 5 = 0 is the other answer to Ex. 1. 1. 3x − y − 5 = 0 3. 2x + 3y − 10 = 0 5. 3x − y − 3 = 0 7. 4x − 3y − 12 = 0 9. x − 6y + 3 = 0 11. 3x − 2y − 6 = 0 13. 2x + 6y + 5 = 0 15. 3x + 3y + 2 = 0 17. 4x + y = 0 19. y = −x + 2 21. y = −3x + 5 23. y = $-\frac{1}{2}$x + $\frac{3}{2}$ 25. y = $\frac{5}{2}$x + $\frac{1}{2}$ 27. y = 2x − 3 29. y = $\frac{3}{2}$x + $\frac{5}{2}$ 31. y = $\frac{1}{5}$x + $\frac{2}{5}$ 33. y = 2x + 6 35. y = $-\frac{5}{7}$x 37. y = $\frac{3}{2}$x + 9 39. y = 2x − 4 41. y = $\frac{3}{4}$x + 9

Page 292 Review Capsule for Section 12.2 1. $y = -1$ 2. $y = 1$ 3. $y = -5\frac{1}{2}$ 4. $y = 3\frac{2}{3}$ 5. $y = -\frac{3}{4}$
6. $y = 1\frac{1}{2}$

Pages 293-294 P-1 The Y intercept; The X intercept **P-2** $(3, -2)$

Page 295 Classroom Exercises 1.

x	0	2	4
y	2	0	-2

3.

x	-2	0	2
y	-1	0	1

5.

x	0	5	2
y	-5	0	-3

7.

x	0	5	-4
y	$-\frac{5}{3}$	0	-3

Page 295 Written Exercises In Ex. 1-8, each graph is a straight line. Three ordered pairs from Classroom Exercises 12.2 are shown for each exercise. 1. $(0, 2), (2, 0), (4, -2)$ 3. $(-2, -1), (0, 0), (2, 1)$ 5. $(0, -5)$, $(5, 0), (2, -3)$ 7. $(0, -\frac{5}{3}), (5, 0), (-4, -3)$ In Ex. 9-17, each graph is a straight line. Two points are given for each line. 9. $(1, -1), (3, 2)$ 11. $(-2, -3), (2, -2)$ 13. $(0, 0), (5, 4)$ 15. $(-1, 0), (2, -3)$ 17. $(0, -6), (2, 0)$

Page 295 Review Capsule for Section 12.3 1. $(-1, 2)$ 2. $(-1, 1)$ 3. $(-3, 14)$

Page 296 P-1 $(-3, -2)$

Page 298 Classroom Exercises 1. No 3. Yes 5. No 7. Yes 9. Yes 11. $\{(-2, 1)\}$ 13. $\{(-1\frac{1}{2}, 2)\}$

Page 299 Written Exercises In Ex. 1-21, each graph is a pair of straight lines. The solution set is given for each exercise. 1. $\{(1, 3)\}$ 3. $\{(-1, 4)\}$ 5. $\{(-3, 4)\}$ 7. ϕ 9. $\{(5, -2)\}$ 11. $\{(0, 0)\}$ 13. $\{(0, 0)\}$ 15. $\{(1, -3)\}$ 17. $\{(1, 5)\}$ 19. $\{(-1, -\frac{3}{2})\}$ 21. $\{(\frac{16}{3}, \frac{2}{3})\}$

Page 299 Review Capsule for Section 12.4 1. $x = 9$ 2. $x = -2\frac{2}{3}$ 3. $x = -2$ 4. $x = 1$ 5. $y = 1$
6. $y = -\frac{1}{12}$

Page 301 P-1 $2x - 3$ **P-2** $\frac{1}{2}y + 2$

Page 302 Classroom Exercises In Ex. 1-9, other answers can also be given. 1. $x = 2y + 3$ 3. $x = 1 - 3y$
5. $x = 3 - 3y$ 7. $x + (2x - 3) - 5 = 0$ 9. $-2(3y + 1) + 5y - 2 = 0$

Page 302 Written Exercises 1. $\{(6, 2)\}$ 3. $\{(14, 10)\}$ 5. $\{(10, 6)\}$ 7. ϕ 9. $\{(3, -4)\}$ 11. $\{(0, -2)\}$

Page 303 Mid-Chapter Review 1. $2x + z - 11 = 0$ 3. $5x + 2y + 13 = 0$ 5. This graph is a straight line. The coordinates of two points are given. $(0, -4), (2, 2)$ 7. In Ex. 7-11, each graph is a pair of straight lines. The solution set is given for each exercise. 7. $\{(-2, -3)\}$ 9. $\{(2, -2)\}$ 11. $\{(4, -1)\}$

Page 303 Calculator Exercises 1. No 3. Yes 5. No

Page 303 Review Capsule for Section 12.5 1. $-6x + 2y = -28; 6x + 12y = 42$ 2. $-4x - 6y = -44; 15x + 6y$ $= 108$ 3. $-6x + 4y + 16 = 0; -6x + 9y + 36 = 0$ Opposite coefficients for x: Ex. 1; Opposite coefficients for y: Ex. 2; Neither: Ex. 3

Page 305 **P-1** Multiply each side of eq. 1 by: (a.) 3; (b.) −1; (c.) −7 **P-2** a. Multiply each side of equation 1 by 5 and each side of equation 2 by 8. b. Multiply each side of equation 1 by 4 and each side of equation 2 by 3. c. Multiply each side of equation 1 by 3 and each side of equation 2 by −2.

Page 306 **Classroom Exercises** 1. $2x = -4$ 3. $3x + 6 = 0$ 5. $-4x = -8$ 7. Multiply equation 1 by 2. 9. Multiply equation 2 by −2. 11. Multiply equation 1 by 3 and equation 2 by 4.

Page 306 **Written Exercises** 1. $\left\{\left(\frac{24}{5}, \frac{12}{5}\right)\right\}$ 3. $\{(0, 2)\}$ 5. $\left\{\left(\frac{1}{2}, 4\right)\right\}$ 7. $\{(2, -3)\}$ 9. $\left\{\left(\frac{9}{7}, -\frac{10}{7}\right)\right\}$ 11. $\{(0, 0)\}$ 13. $\{(0, 0)\}$ 15. $\{(2, -2)\}$ 17. $\left\{\left(1, -\frac{1}{3}\right)\right\}$

Pages 307-308 **P-1** First row: $\pi, -2$; Second column: $-2, -\sqrt{3}$ **P-2** a. −15 b. 0 c. 2 **P-3** a. $2p - 3q$ b. $-5x$ c. $s^2 + t^2$ **P-4** In the determinant form the left hand side has only an x term and a y term.

Page 309 **Classroom Exercises** 1. 2 3. 13 5. −3 7. 17 9. 7 11. −13 13. −48 15. 0 17. 6 19. −3

Page 309 **Written Exercises** 1. −28 3. 0 5. −2 7. 4 9. 0 11. −223 13. $\begin{vmatrix} 2 & -1 \\ 1 & -3 \end{vmatrix}; -5$ 15. $\begin{vmatrix} -2 & 5 \\ 1 & -3 \end{vmatrix}; 1$ 17. $\begin{vmatrix} 2 & -1 \\ 5 & -1 \end{vmatrix}; 3$ 19. $\begin{vmatrix} 5 & 3 \\ -3 & 1 \end{vmatrix}; 14$ 21. $\begin{vmatrix} 4 & 5 \\ 5 & 6 \end{vmatrix}; -1$

Page 310 **P-1** 13; −9; 7

Page 312 **Classroom Exercises** 1. $x = \dfrac{\begin{vmatrix} 2 & -1 \\ -1 & 2 \end{vmatrix}}{\begin{vmatrix} 3 & -1 \\ 1 & 2 \end{vmatrix}}, y = \dfrac{\begin{vmatrix} 3 & 2 \\ 1 & -1 \end{vmatrix}}{\begin{vmatrix} 3 & -1 \\ 1 & 2 \end{vmatrix}}$ 3. $x = \dfrac{\begin{vmatrix} 1.5 & -0.5 \\ -2.5 & 1.5 \end{vmatrix}}{\begin{vmatrix} 0.5 & -0.5 \\ -1.5 & 1.5 \end{vmatrix}}, y = \dfrac{\begin{vmatrix} 0.5 & 1.5 \\ -1.5 & -2.5 \end{vmatrix}}{\begin{vmatrix} 0.5 & -0.5 \\ -1.5 & 1.5 \end{vmatrix}}$

Page 312 **Written Exercises** 1. $\{(5, 1)\}$ 3. $\{(-2, 1)\}$ 5. $\left\{\left(-\frac{3}{23}, -\frac{42}{23}\right)\right\}$ 7. $\left\{\left(\frac{7}{4}, \frac{9}{4}\right)\right\}$ 9. $\left\{\left(0, \frac{1}{2}\right)\right\}$ 11. Yes 13. Yes 15. No

Page 313 **Career** 1. 29.6 grams 3. 0.5 grams

Pages 314-315 **Chapter Review** 1. $2x + 3y - 5 = 0$ 3. $2x + 6y - 3 = 0$ 5. $y = -3x + 7$ 7. $y = 8x - 15$ In Ex. 9-13, each graph is a straight line. The coordinates of two points are given for each line. 9. (0, 3), (2, −1) 11. (−1, 0), (4, 1) 13. (0, −2), (3, 0) In Ex. 15 and 17, each graph is a pair of straight lines. The solution set is given for each exercise. 15. $\{(-3, 2)\}$ 17. $\{(1, 2)\}$ 19. $\{(-3, 3)\}$ 21. $\{(2, -1)\}$ 23. $\{(2, -1)\}$ 25. $\{(2, 5)\}$ 27. 41 29. −1 31. $\{(1, -1)\}$ 33. $\left\{\left(\frac{53}{11}, -\frac{19}{11}\right)\right\}$

Pages 316-318 **Cumulative Review: Chapters 7-12** 1. 8^5 3. r^8 5. $(13)^4$ 7. 3^{-3} 9. p^{-7} 11. $49t^2$ 13. $-\dfrac{27}{x^3}$ 15. $\dfrac{8}{t^6}$ 17. $\dfrac{16a^4 b^{12}}{c^8}$ 19. 58,000 21. 0.4005 23. −13 25. 20 27. $-\sqrt{15}$ 29. 35 31. $2\sqrt{14}$ 33. $2\sqrt[3]{4}$ 35. $2t\sqrt{5t}$ 37. y^5 39. $6\sqrt{7}$ 41. $-2\sqrt{2}$ 43. $\dfrac{3}{a}$ 45. $\dfrac{\sqrt{6}}{3}$ 47. 14.424 49. 1.528 51. Yes 53. No 55. $-60x^3 y^4$ 57. $-5x^2$ 59. 11 61. $-x^2 + 4x + 3$ 63. $-x^3 + 5x^2$ $- 4x + 11$ 65. $12x^2 - 11x - 15$ 67. $2x^3 + 7x^2 - 11x + 20$ 69. $x^2 - 5$ 71. $-2x + 5 - \dfrac{4}{5x + 2}$ 73. $2(2x^2 - x + 6)$ 75. $x^2 + 3x + 6x + 18; (x + 3)(x + 6)$ 77. $(x - 5)(x + 3)$ 79. $(2x - 3)(x + 3)$ 81. $(3x + 5)(3x - 5)$ 83. $(3x - 5)(3x - 5)$ 85. $2x(3x + 2)(2x - 1)$ 87. (0, −3), (4, −1) 89. −5

91. $-\frac{2}{3}$ 93. -1 95. $y = -2x + 5$ 97. 2 99. $(0, 0), (3, 4.8)$ 101. $(0, 460), (200, 660)$ 103. $y = 2x$ $+\frac{1}{2}$ 105. $(0, 2), (4, 4)$ 107. $\{(3, 2)\}$ 109. $\{(-3, 5)\}$ 111. $\left\{(\frac{17}{2}, 7)\right\}$ 113. $\left\{(-\frac{1}{7}, -\frac{6}{7})\right\}$

CHAPTER 13 PROBLEM SOLVING: TWO VARIABLES

Page 321 Classroom Exercises 1. First number: x; second number: y; $x + y = 25$ 3. Jerry's age: x; Mary's age: y; $x + y = 25$ 5. Ken's age: x; mother's age: y; $x + 29 = y$ 7. Width: x; length: y; $x + y = 51$ 9. First number: x; second number: y; $2x + 3y = 19$

Page 322 Written Exercises 1. Larger: x; smaller: y; $x + y = 28$; $x - y = 3$; Answer: $15\frac{1}{2}, 12\frac{1}{2}$ 3. First: x; second: y; $x + y = -12$; $x - y = 42$; Answer: 15, -27 5. Smaller: x; greater: y; $2x + 2 = y$; $3x + 2y = 39$; Answer: 5, 12 7. Length: x; width: y; $x = 8 + y$; $2x + 2y = 34$; Answer: $4\frac{1}{2}, 12\frac{1}{2}$ 9. Ann's age: x; John's age: y; $y + 7 = x$; $x + y = 45$; Answer: 26, 19

Page 322 Review Capsule for Section 13.2 1. 5n 2. 100t 3. 5w 4. 12y 5. 850k 6. 75n

Page 325 Classroom Exercises 1. $44x + 39y = 337$ 3. $9x + 4.5y = 58.5$ 5. $x + 5y = 235$ 7. $15x + 25y = 420$ 9. $x + y = 60$; $5x + 10y = 650$ 11. $x + y = 55$; $325x + 135y = 11415$ 13. $x + y = 20$; $2.4x + 3.2y = 54.40$

Page 326 Written Exercises 1. $2.89 records: x; $1.95 records: y; $x + y = 9$; $289x + 195y = 2037$; Answer: 3 at $2.89, 6 at $1.95 3. Orange juice: x; cocoa: y; $y = x + 20$; $20x + 15y = 1140$; Answer: Orange juice: 24, cocoa: 44 5. Tomatoes: x; beans: y; $x + y = 50$; $35x + 45y = 2030$; Answer: 22 cans of tomatoes, 28 cans of beans 7. Fives: x; tens: y; $x + y = 86$; $5x + 10y = 675$; Answer: 37 fives, 49 tens

Page 326 Review Capsule for Section 13.3 1. a. 82 b. 16 2. a. 59 b. 45 3. a. 20 b. 0 4. a. 67 b. 42

Page 327 P-1 Ten's digits: 3, 9, 1, 7, 1; one's digits: 5, 0, 4, 8, 1 **P-2** Because xy represents the product of the digits, not the number

Page 329 Classroom Exercises 1. $x + y = 12$ 3. $y = x - 5$ 5. $5x = 7y$ 7. $x + y = 2x - 1$ 9. $y - x = -8$

Page 330 Written Exercises 1. $y = x - 2$; $x + y = 12$; Ans: 75 3. $x = 2y$; $x = y + 4$; Ans: 84 5. $x + y = 15$; $2x = 3y - 5$; Ans: 87 7. $y = x + 1$; $10x + y = 8y + 2$; Ans: 34 9. $x - y = -4$; $10x + y = 2(x + y) + 3$; Ans: 15 11. $x + y = 5$; $10y + x = 9 + (10x + y)$; Ans: 23

Page 331 Mid-Chapter Review 1. Larger: x; Smaller: y; $x + y = -12$; $x - y = 3$; Answer: $-4\frac{1}{2}, -7\frac{1}{2}$ 3. x: $5.95 products; y: $8.50 products; $x + y = 287$; $595x + 850y = 212330$; Answer: 124 at $5.95, 163 at $8.50 5. x: ten's digit; y: one's digit; $10x + y = 4y - 7$; $y = 4x + 1$; Answer: 29

Page 331 Calculator Exercises 1. 16 feet 3. 144 feet 5. 400 feet 7. 784 feet 9. 1296 feet

Page 331 Review Capsule for Section 13.4 1. 2350 miles 2. 560 kilometers 3. 1050 meters 4. 27,360 feet

Pages 333-335 Classroom Exercises 1. 20x 3. 10(x + y) 5. x − 5 7. y + x 9. With the wind: x + y = 300; Against the wind: x − y = 250 11. 18(x − y) = 5000; 15(x + y) = 5000

Pages 335-336 Written Exercises 1. Speed in still water: x; speed of current: y; x − y = 8; x + y = 10; Ans: speed in still water: 9 km/hr, speed of current: 1 km/hr 3. x + y = 5; 70x + 7y = 224; Ans: 3 hours by bus; 2 hours hiking 5. x + 20 = y; 10x + 5y = 1300; Ans: eastbound train: 80 km/hr, westbound train: 100 km/hr

Page 336 Review Capsule for Section 13.5 1. x = 48 2. x = 100 3. x = 150 4. x = 450

Page 337 P-1 20 grams

Pages 338-339 Classroom Exercises 1. Orange juice: 200 mℓ; water: 600 mℓ 3. Sugar: 100 g; water: 400 g 5. Oxygen: 100 m³; nitrogen: 400 m³ 7. 8 9. 0.06y 11. 120 13. 15; 485 15. 40; 30

Pages 339-340 Written Exercises 1. 9 g 3. 5% 5. 220 + x 7. x + y = 300; 0.06x + 0.03y = 0.04(300) 9. Grams of 4% solution: x; grams of 8% solution: y; x + y = 400; 0.04x + 0.08y = 0.05(400); Ans: 4% solution: 300 g, 8% solution: 100 g 11. x + 48 = y; 0.12x + 0.20(48) = 0.15y; Ans: 12% solution: 80 g, 15% solution: 128 g

Page 341 Career 1. ZD: −3; 9:05 P.M. 3. ZD: +8; 10:05 A.M. 5. ZD: −5; 11:05 P.M. 7. ZD: +4; 2:05 P.M. 9. ZD: −1; 7:05 P.M.

Pages 342-344 Chapter Review 1. Greater: x; smaller: y; x + y = 17; x = y + 33; Ans: 25 and −8 3. Length: x; width: y; x = 2y − 3; 2x + 2y = 24; Ans: width: 5 m, length: 7 m 5. Adult tickets: x; student tickets: y; x + y = 204; 1.25x + 0.75y = 215; Ans: 124 adult tickets, 80 student tickets 7. Ten's digit: x; one's digit: y; x = 3y; x + y = 12; Ans: 93 9. Ten's digit: x; one's digit: y; 10x + y = 9y; x + y = 9; Ans: 45 11. 3x + 2y = 1000; x = 6y; Ans: plane: 300 km/hr, jeep: 50 km/hr 13. Grams of 12% salt solution: x; grams of 20% salt solution: y; x + y = 800; 0.12x + 0.20y = 0.17(800); Ans: 12% solution: 300 g, 20% solution: 500 g

CHAPTER 14 PRODUCTS AND QUOTIENTS OF RATIONAL EXPRESSIONS

Page 346 P-1 $\dfrac{x^2 + x - 1}{1}$ **P-2** a. Yes b. Yes c. No d. Yes e. No f. Yes

Page 347 Classroom Exercises 1. Yes 3. No 5. Yes 7. Yes 9. 0 11. 3 13. $\dfrac{1}{2}$ 15. 1, −1

Page 348 Written Exercises 1. Yes 3. Yes 5. Yes 7. No 9. No 11. Yes 13. $-\dfrac{5}{2}$ 15. $\dfrac{4}{3}$ 17. $\dfrac{4}{3}$ 19. 0 21. 0 23. 10 25. 0 27. 2, −2 29. $\dfrac{1}{3}$ 31. 1, −7

Page 348 Review Capsule for Section 14.2 1. 2 · 3 · 3 · x · x · x 2. 2 · 2 · 3 · a · b · b 3. (x + 5)(x − 5) 4. (c + 9)(c − 9) 5. x(x + 7) 6. (a + b)(a − b) 7. (x − 3)(x − 3) 8. 3b(a + b) 9. 3a(a + 2b) 10. a(5a − b) 11. (x + 2)(x + 2) 12. (x − y)(x + y)

Page 350 P-1 x + 2, x − 2; x + 3, x − 2

Page 351 Classroom Exercises 1. $\dfrac{1}{3}$ 3. $\dfrac{1}{x}$ 5. $\dfrac{3}{x}$ 7. $\dfrac{x + 2}{x + 3}$ 9. $\dfrac{1}{x}$

Page 351   Written Exercises   1. $\dfrac{x}{2}$ 3. $\dfrac{3}{7x}$ 5. $\dfrac{x}{5}$ 7. $\dfrac{2}{3}$ 9. $\dfrac{x+2}{x+5}$ 11. $\dfrac{4x-4}{3x+9}$ 13. $\dfrac{3}{5}$ 15. $\dfrac{x+3}{x+5}$
17. $\dfrac{1}{x-3}$ 19. $\dfrac{x+4}{x}$ 21. $\dfrac{x}{x-2}$ 23. $\dfrac{x}{x-2}$ 25. $\dfrac{2x}{5y}$ 27. $\dfrac{a+b}{c}$ 29. $\dfrac{a-b}{3}$ 31. $\dfrac{5a-b}{3a+6b}$

Page 351   Review Capsule for Section 14.3   1. $2 \cdot 2 \cdot 3 \cdot x \cdot x \cdot y \cdot y \cdot y$ 2. $2 \cdot 2 \cdot 5 \cdot r \cdot r \cdot r \cdot s \cdot t \cdot t$
3. $2 \cdot 3 \cdot 3 \cdot a \cdot a \cdot b \cdot b \cdot b \cdot c \cdot c \cdot c$ 4. $2 \cdot 2 \cdot 3 \cdot 3 \cdot p \cdot p \cdot p \cdot p \cdot p \cdot q \cdot q \cdot r \cdot r \cdot r$

Pages 352-353   P-1 a. 8   b. $\dfrac{4}{5}$ c. $1\dfrac{3}{4}$ d. $\dfrac{1}{20}$ **P-2** x^2 and 20 have no common factors.

Pages 353-354   Classroom Exercises   1. $\dfrac{2}{5}$ 3. 1   5. $\dfrac{2x}{3y}$ 7. $\dfrac{5}{6}$ 9. $\dfrac{3}{5a}$ 11. $\dfrac{2}{5}$ 13. $\dfrac{1}{15}$ 15. 6ab
17. $-\dfrac{x}{3y}$ 19. 1

Page 354   Written Exercises   1. $\dfrac{5}{24}$ 3. $\dfrac{5y}{3x}$ 5. $\dfrac{3}{5}$ 7. $\dfrac{14}{15}$ 9. 2x   11. $\dfrac{20y}{x}$ 13. $-\dfrac{21b^2}{5a}$ 15. $\dfrac{25xy}{4}$
17. $6a^2bc$ 19. 1   21. $\dfrac{33a^2c}{50}$ 23. $-\dfrac{3ab}{2}$

Page 354   Review Capsule for Section 14.4   1. x^2-x 2. $3x-15$ 3. x^2-x-6 4. $x^2-10x+25$
5. $2a^2+3ab+b^2$ 6. $2a^2-ab-b^2$ 7. $-x+2$ 8. $-2+a$

Pages 355-356   P-1 $-a+b$ **P-2** a. $2-x$ b. $t-5$ c. $m-r$ **P-3** $2-x$ **P-4** $x^2+3x+2; 3x-9$

Page 357   Classroom Exercises   1. $\dfrac{2}{3}$ 3. $\dfrac{x^2+4x+3}{x^2+6x+8}$ 5. 1   7. $\dfrac{1}{x+2}$ 9. $-\dfrac{5}{6}$ 11. 1   13. $\dfrac{x+1}{x}$ 15. $-\dfrac{2}{3}$

Page 357   Written Exercises   1. $\dfrac{11}{12}$ 3. $-\dfrac{14}{15}$ 5. $\dfrac{x-3}{x-1}$ 7. $\dfrac{x-3}{2y}$ 9. $x-3$ 11. $\dfrac{2}{x+2}$ 13. $\dfrac{x^2-5x+6}{x^2+5x+6}$
15. $-\dfrac{5}{x}$ 17. 1   19. $-\dfrac{1}{3}$ 21. $\dfrac{x}{x+3}$

Page 358   Mid-Chapter Review   1. $-\dfrac{7}{5}$ 3. $\dfrac{9}{5}$ 5. $\dfrac{x}{2y}$ 7. $\dfrac{x+6}{2x}$ 9. $\dfrac{4}{15}$ 11. $-\dfrac{25rs}{6t^2}$ 13. $\dfrac{6}{5}$ 15. $2r-3$

Page 358   Calculator Exercises   1. 0.6521739   3. 0.6034483

Page 358   Review Capsule for Section 14.5   1. $(x+1)(x-3)$ 2. $(x-3)(x-2)$ 3. $(2x-1)(x+3)$
4. $(2x+3)(2x-1)$

Pages 359-360   P-1 $x, x+2; x+2, x-2$ **P-2** a. $2x-1, x+1$ b. $x+6, x-6$ c. $2x^2, 3x-2$
P-3 $x-5, x+2; x+3, x-3; x+2, x+2$

Page 361   Classroom Exercises   1. $\dfrac{x-2}{x+4}$ 3. $\dfrac{x+5}{x+2}$ 5. $\dfrac{x-1}{2}$ 7. $\dfrac{5x^2}{x^3-x^2-9x+9}$ 9. $\dfrac{x+1}{x}$

Page 361   Written Exercises   1. $\dfrac{x+2}{x}$ 3. $\dfrac{5x+10}{3}$ 5. $\dfrac{5x^2+10x}{x^2-25}$ 7. $\dfrac{x+1}{5}$ 9. $\dfrac{x+4}{4}$ 11. $\dfrac{-3x+6}{2}$
13. $\dfrac{3}{2x^2+9x-5}$ 15. $\dfrac{2x^3-6x^2+12x-8}{3x-1}$

Page 361   Review Capsule for Section 14.6   1. $\dfrac{x-3}{2}$ 2. $\dfrac{2x}{3x-1}$ 3. $x+4$ 4. $\dfrac{2x-5}{4x+3}$

Pages 362-363   P-1 a. $\dfrac{x-3}{x+2} \cdot \dfrac{x-2}{x}$ b. $\dfrac{3x}{5} \cdot \dfrac{9x}{4}$ c. $\dfrac{2x^2}{5} \cdot \dfrac{1}{x+1}$ **P-2** $\dfrac{x-2}{x} \cdot \dfrac{5}{x-2}$ **P-3** $\dfrac{4(r-3)}{9pq}$

Pages 363-364 Classroom Exercises 1. $\dfrac{2}{3} \cdot \dfrac{6}{5}$ **3.** $\dfrac{2x}{6} \cdot \dfrac{3}{x}$ **5.** $\dfrac{2}{x-2} \cdot \dfrac{5}{x}$ **7.** $\dfrac{x-7}{5x} \cdot \dfrac{4}{x+1}$ **9.** $\dfrac{1}{x+2} \cdot \dfrac{1}{x-3}$
11. $\dfrac{x+1}{x} \cdot \dfrac{2x}{x-10}$ **13.** $\dfrac{x+8}{x-5} \cdot \dfrac{x-10}{x+2}$

Page 364 Written Exercises 1. $\dfrac{2}{3}$ **3.** 6 **5.** $\dfrac{3a}{5}$ **7.** $\dfrac{1}{2}$ **9.** $\dfrac{2xy}{3}$ **11.** $\dfrac{5}{2xy}$ **13.** $\dfrac{x-5}{5}$ **15.** $\dfrac{2x^2+4}{x^2}$
17. $\dfrac{1}{2x+10}$ **19.** $\dfrac{x^4+6x^2+9}{3}$ **21.** $\dfrac{5x}{2}$ **23.** $\dfrac{2x^2+4x+2}{3x^2-6x+3}$

Page 364 Review Capsule for Section 14.7 1. 42 **2.** 104 **3.** 30 **4.** 120

Page 365 P-1 $\dfrac{1}{x^2-25}$

Pages 366-367 Classroom Exercises 1. $2, x-3$ **3.** $x, 3x-1$ **5.** $x+2, x-2$ **7.** $4, x-4$ **9.** $3, x-7$
11. $x, x-7$ **13.** $2x, x-5$ **15.** $x+4, x-4$ **17.** $3x, x-5$ **19.** $5x, x+3$

Page 367 Written Exercises 1. $\dfrac{2}{5x^2+15x}$ **3.** $\dfrac{1}{2}$ **5.** $\dfrac{x-5}{2}$ **7.** $\dfrac{x^2-5x+6}{x^2+5x+6}$ **9.** $\dfrac{x^2+10x+24}{3x^4-21x^3-18x^2+216x}$
11. $\dfrac{xy-y^2}{2}$ **13.** $\dfrac{2}{7}$ **15.** $\dfrac{5a+18}{12}$ **17.** $\dfrac{3a+6b}{10a+5b}$ **19.** 1 **21.** $-\dfrac{5}{x+3}$

Page 368 Career 1. 2300 volts **3.** 1.625 amperes

Page 369-370 Chapter Review 1. Yes **3.** No **5.** -3 **7.** $\dfrac{1}{2}$ **9.** $\dfrac{5x}{6}$ **11.** $\dfrac{1}{3}$ **13.** $\dfrac{2}{x}$ **15.** $\dfrac{2xy}{3ab^2}$
17. $\dfrac{1}{ax-a^2}$ **19.** $\dfrac{x^2-2x}{7}$ **21.** $-\dfrac{5}{6}$ **23.** $\dfrac{x+1}{x+2}$ **25.** 1 **27.** $-\dfrac{10x}{3a}$ **29.** $\dfrac{2x-4}{x^2+2x}$ **31.** $\dfrac{2x^2+8}{3x}$
33. $\dfrac{13a}{25}$ **35.** $\dfrac{10a-12b}{5a+3b}$

CHAPTER 15 SUMS AND DIFFERENCES OF RATIONAL EXPRESSIONS

Page 372 P-1 $\dfrac{5}{7}; -\dfrac{1}{2}$ **P-2 a.** $\dfrac{9}{x}$ **b.** $\dfrac{7}{a}$ **c.** $\dfrac{x}{y}$ **P-3** 3

Pages 373-374 Classroom Exercises 1. $\dfrac{3}{5}$ **3.** $\dfrac{1}{6}$ **5.** $\dfrac{3}{x}$ **7.** $\dfrac{7}{3x}$ **9.** $\dfrac{11}{x+1}$ **11.** $\dfrac{3x}{x+3}$ **13.** $-\dfrac{4a}{a+1}$
15. $\dfrac{2x+3y}{x+y}$ **17.** $\dfrac{3x}{11}$ **19.** $\dfrac{2x+5}{y+1}$

Page 374 Written Exercises 1. $\dfrac{11}{13}$ **3.** $-\dfrac{5}{17}$ **5.** $\dfrac{16}{a}$ **7.** $-\dfrac{5}{y}$ **9.** $\dfrac{12}{x+3}$ **11.** $-\dfrac{1}{a-3}$ **13.** $\dfrac{7x}{x+2}$
15. $-\dfrac{4a}{a+1}$ **17.** $\dfrac{a+b}{2a+b}$ **19.** $\dfrac{3r-5s}{r-2s}$ **21.** $-\dfrac{4y}{19}$ **23.** $-\dfrac{2x}{3y}$ **25.** $-\dfrac{4}{9t}$

Page 374 Review Capsule for Section 15.2 1. $x-3$ **2.** $-t+6$ **3.** $4m-16$ **4.** r^2-4r-2
5. $3n^2+2n-12$ **6.** $-2s^2+2s-3$

Page 375 P-1 Their values cannot be the same. **P-2** The numerator and denominator have no common factors.

Page 376 Classroom Exercises 1. $\dfrac{x+5}{x+2}$ **3.** $\dfrac{3y+3}{y+3}$ **5.** $\dfrac{4b+1}{b+2}$ **7.** 1 **9.** $\dfrac{2x+5}{x-3}$ **11.** $\dfrac{2x+2}{x+y}$

Page 377 Written Exercises 1. $\dfrac{2x+5}{x+y}$ **3.** $\dfrac{6r-1}{r+s}$ **5.** $\dfrac{4x-7}{x+2}$ **7.** $\dfrac{4a-5}{a+b}$ **9.** 1 **11.** 2 **13.** x **15.** 3a
17. x − 4 **19.** y − 4 **21.** 4 **23.** $-\dfrac{6}{x+5}$

Page 377 Review Capsule for Section 15.3 1. 2, 2, 2, 3, x, x, x, y, y **2.** 2, 2, 2, 7, r, r, s, s, s, t, t, t
3. 2, 2, (m − 3), (m + 3) **4.** (x − 5), (x − 1) **5.** 3, 2, (x + 4), (x − 3)
6. 2, 2, (a + 2), (a − 2), (a − 2), (a + 1)

Page 379 P-1 (x − y)(x + y)3xy

Page 380 Classroom Exercises 1. 3 · 7 **3.** 2 · 3 · x · x · y **5.** 2 · 3 · 5 · abc **7.** (x − 3)(x − 5)
9. (a + b)(a − b) **11.** 3(a − b) **13.** (2x − y)(x + 2y) **15.** 3 · 5xy **17.** 3 · 5(a + b)(a − b)

Page 380 Written Exercises 1. 30 **3.** 12x²y **5.** 60a²b **7.** (x − 3)(x + 3) **9.** 3(x − y)(x + y)
11. 6b(b + 5)(b − 6) **13.** x²(x − 5)(x + 5) **15.** 5(x + 2)² **17.** (x − 4)²(x + 2) **19.** (x − 2)(x − 3)(x + 3)
21. 2(2x − 3y)(2x + 3y) **23.** (2x − 3)(x + 1)(3x + 2) **25.** 5(3x − 2)(2x − 1)(2x + 1)

Pages 381-382 P-1 Multiplying by these numbers gives the LCM, 6x, as the denominator for both fractions.
P-2 40x²y **P-3** There is no common factor. **P-4** $\dfrac{5r}{1}$

Pages 382-383 Classroom Exercises 1. $\dfrac{x}{x}$ **3.** $\dfrac{2}{2}$ **5.** $\dfrac{2x}{2x}$ **7.** $\dfrac{3s}{3s}$ **9.** $\dfrac{3ab}{3ab}$; 6ab **11.** 3a; 10xy **13.** $\dfrac{3x}{3x}$; 45x²
15. $\dfrac{2y}{2y};\dfrac{3x}{3x}$; 4y; 4y + 15x

Page 383 Written Exercises 1. $\dfrac{29}{35}$ **3.** $\dfrac{5b+7a}{ab}$ **5.** $-\dfrac{7}{2x}$ **7.** $\dfrac{7}{10x}$ **9.** $\dfrac{15b-5a}{12ab}$ **11.** $\dfrac{2b+3a}{a^2b^2}$
13. $\dfrac{15b^2-a^2}{6a^2b^2}$ **15.** $\dfrac{2a^2+3b^2}{abc}$ **17.** $\dfrac{2+15a^3b}{3a^2b}$ **19.** $\dfrac{40c^2d-3d}{8c}$ **21.** $\dfrac{35}{6x}$ **23.** $\dfrac{6+4b-15b^2}{6ab^2}$
25. $\dfrac{az+by+cx}{xyz}$

Page 384 Mid-Chapter Review 1. $-\dfrac{4}{t}$ **3.** $\dfrac{8m}{m+8}$ **5.** $\dfrac{3(a-1)}{a+1}$ **7.** m − 2 **9.** 6t(t + 3)(t − 3)
11. $\dfrac{2b-15a}{5ab}$ **13.** $\dfrac{c^2+2d^2}{6cd}$

Page 384 Calculator Exercises 1. 1.25 **3.** 1.3194444 **5.** 1.4583333

Page 384 Review Capsule for Section 15.5 1. $\dfrac{x-2}{x-1}$ **2.** $\dfrac{5x}{x-3}$ **3.** $\dfrac{2(x+1)}{(x-4)}$ **4.** $\dfrac{2x}{3}$

Page 386 P-1 $\dfrac{x+4}{x+4};\dfrac{x-1}{x-1}$

Pages 386-387 Classroom Exercises 1. x(x + 1) **3.** (x + 5)(x − 3) **5.** r(r + 4) **7.** (2x − 1)(x + 3)
9. x(x − 1) **11.** $\dfrac{a+3}{a+3}$; 3a + 9 **13.** $\dfrac{y-2}{y-2}$; 2y − 4 **15.** $\dfrac{x-2}{x-2}$; x² − 3x + 2 **17.** $\dfrac{x-2}{x-2}$; x² + 3x − 10

Page 387 Written Exercises 1. $\dfrac{3x+2}{x(x+1)}$ **3.** $\dfrac{2a+8}{a(a+2)}$ **5.** $\dfrac{x^2+2x+25}{(x+5)(x-3)}$ **7.** $\dfrac{a^2-2a+10}{a(a-5)}$ **9.** $\dfrac{a^2+b^2}{(a+b)(a-b)}$
11. $\dfrac{a^2+6a-7}{(a-3)(a+2)}$ **13.** $\dfrac{-7x+14}{(2x-1)(x+3)}$ **15.** $\dfrac{2(x^2+2x-5)}{(x-1)(x-2)}$ **17.** $\dfrac{-4b+1}{(b-1)(b-2)}$ **19.** $\dfrac{6x+1}{x(x-1)}$

Page 387 Review Capsule for Section 15.6 1. 6(2x − 1) **2.** 5(x + 3)(x − 3) **3.** x(x − 2)(x + 5)

Pages 388-389 P-1 2(x + 2); 3(x + 2) **P-2** There are no common factors. **P-3** x, x + 1 **P-4** x + 1, x + 2
P-5 x(x + 1)(x + 2)

Page 390 Classroom Exercises 1. $x(x-1)(x+1)$ 3. $(x+3)^2(x-2)$ 5. $(y+2)(y-3)(y+1)$
7. $2(x+1)(x-2)^2$ 9. $2, x-3$ 11. $4, x+3$ 13. $x+2, x-1$ 15. $a+5, a-2$

Pages 390-391 Written Exercises

1. $\dfrac{3}{2x+2} + \dfrac{1}{x^2-1} = \dfrac{3}{2(x+1)} + \dfrac{1}{(x-1)(x+1)}$

$\qquad = \dfrac{3}{2(x+1)}\left(\dfrac{x-1}{x-1}\right) + \dfrac{1}{(x-1)(x+1)}\left(\dfrac{2}{2}\right)$

$\qquad = \dfrac{3(x-1)}{2(x+1)(x-1)} + \dfrac{1(2)}{2(x+1)(x-1)} = \dfrac{3x-1}{2(x+1)(x-1)}$

3. $\dfrac{1}{x^2+x-6} - \dfrac{2}{x^2-2x} = \dfrac{1}{(x-2)(x+3)} - \dfrac{2}{x(x-2)}$

$\qquad = \dfrac{1}{(x-2)(x+3)}\left(\dfrac{x}{x}\right) - \dfrac{2}{x(x-2)}\left(\dfrac{x+3}{x+3}\right)$

$\qquad = \dfrac{1(x)}{x(x+3)(x-2)} - \dfrac{2(x+3)}{x(x+3)(x-2)}$

$\qquad = \dfrac{-x-6}{x(x+3)(x-2)}$

5. $\dfrac{4x-6}{6(x-3)(x-1)}$ or $\dfrac{2x-3}{3(x-3)(x-1)}$ 7. $\dfrac{x-7}{(x+2)(x-1)(x-3)}$ 9. $\dfrac{7x+5}{10(x-5)(x+5)}$ 11. $\dfrac{x^2+4x-2}{2(x-2)(x+2)}$

13. $\dfrac{-2a-49}{(a-3)(a+2)(a-7)}$ 15. $\dfrac{2(x^2+x-3)}{(x+1)(x-1)(x+3)}$ 17. $\dfrac{-a^2+5a+4}{(2a+1)(a-3)(a-1)}$

Page 391 Review Capsule for Section 15.7 1. $9r$ 2. $t(t-1)$ 3. $4(q+2)$

Page 393 P-1 $3x(x+2)$

Page 394 Classroom Exercises 1. $0, 3$ 3. $0, -1$ 5. $-\dfrac{1}{2}$ 7. $4(x-3)$ 9. $2x(5x-1)$ 11. $2x(x+3)$

Page 394 Written Exercises 1. $\{4\}$ 3. $\{0\}$ 5. $\{16\}$ 7. ϕ 9. $\{15\}$ 11. $\{-8\}$ 13. $\left\{-\dfrac{3}{4}\right\}$ 15. $\left\{\dfrac{2}{5}\right\}$
17. $\left\{-\dfrac{1}{4}\right\}$ 19. $\{0\}$

Page 396 Special Topic Application 1. 12 hours 3. 440 hours

Pages 397-398 Chapter Review 1. $\dfrac{8}{3x}$ 3. $\dfrac{a}{a+5}$ 5. 1 7. $\dfrac{2(a+2)}{5a-1}$ 9. 2 11. $6x(x-2)$ 13. $y^2(y-2)$
$(y-3)$ 15. $2(y+2)(y-2)$ 17. $\dfrac{5}{6a}$ 19. $\dfrac{9y-10x}{12xy}$ 21. $\dfrac{a^2+ab+a-b}{(a+b)(a-b)}$ 23. $\dfrac{4a^2-23a+3}{(a+7)(a-3)}$
25. $\dfrac{2x^2-2x-7}{(x+1)(x+2)}$ 27. $\dfrac{3x-2}{3(x+2)}$ 29. $\dfrac{-9x+16}{(2x+3)(2x-3)}$ 31. $\dfrac{5x^2-4x+3}{x(x-1)(x-1)(x+1)}$ 33. $\left\{\dfrac{11}{3}\right\}$
35. $\left\{-\dfrac{15}{2}\right\}$ 37. ϕ

CHAPTER 16 SYSTEMS OF INEQUALITIES

Pages 400-401 P-1 Many answers are possible. $\left(2, -1\dfrac{1}{2}\right)$ is one answer.

Pages 401-402 Classroom Exercises In Ex. 1-7, many other answers are possible. 1. $(-2, -3), \left(0, \dfrac{1}{2}\right), (2, -3)$
3. $(-3, 4), \left(0, \dfrac{1}{2}\right), (1, 0)$ 5. $(-2, 1), \left(0, -\dfrac{1}{3}\right), (2, -3)$ 7. $(-2, 4), (1, 4), \left(2, 4\dfrac{1}{2}\right)$ 9. $y < 2x+1$
11. $y \le 3x+2$ 13. $y < -x-10$

Page 402 **Written Exercises** In Ex. 1-11, many other answers are possible. 1. $(-1, -3)$, $(0, -2)$, $(1, 1)$, $(2, 1)$, $(3, 4)$ 3. $(-2, 7)$, $(-1, 5)$, $(0, 2)$, $(1, -1)$, $(3, -8)$ 5. $(-2, -5)$, $(-1, -4)$, $(0, -6)$, $(1, -3)$, $(4, -2)$ 7. $(-3, 2)$, $(-1, -1)$, $(0, -1)$, $(2, -3)$, $(3, 2)$ 9. $(-2, -18)$, $(-1, -6)$, $(0, 2)$, $(1, 12)$, $(2, 25)$ 11. $(-3, 0)$, $(0, 2)$, $(1, 3)$, $(3, 4)$, $(4, 10)$ 13. $y > 3x + 5$ 15. $y \le -4x + 6$ 17. $y > x + 3$ 19. $y > 3x - 15$ 21. $y \ge -\frac{2}{3}x + 2$ 23. $y > 2x - \frac{5}{2}$ 25. $y \ge \frac{1}{2}x + \frac{3}{14}$ 27. $y < -\frac{5}{3}x + \frac{1}{3}$

Page 402 **Review Capsule for Section 16.2** For Ex. 1-8, each graph is a straight line. Two points are given for each. 1. $(0, 2)$; $(1, 1)$ 2. $(0, -1)$; $(2, 3)$ 3. $(0, -3)$; $(2, 0)$ 4. $(0, 2)$; $(4, 7)$ 5. $(0, \frac{3}{2})$; $(1, 2)$ 6. $(0, -1)$; $(-2, 5)$ 7. $(0, -2)$; $(2, -2)$ 8. $(-3, 0)$; $(-3, 4)$

Page 403 **P-1** The region in which $y > 2x - 1$. The line $y = 2x - 1$. The region in which $y < 2x - 1$.

Page 405 **Classroom Exercises** 1. Yes 3. No 5. Yes 7. No 9. $y > -x$ 11. $y < -\frac{1}{3}x - 1$

Page 405 **Written Exercises** In Written Exercises 1-17, each graph is a region that does not include its linear boundary. The location of the region with respect to the boundary is indicated for each exercise. 1. The region is at the right of the boundary. 3. right of the boundary 5. right of the boundary 7. right of the boundary 9. above the boundary 11. left of the boundary 13. left of the boundary 15. left of the boundary 17. left of the boundary

Page 405 **Review Capsule for Section 16.3** 1. $y \le 2$ 2. $y \le x - 5$ 3. $y \ge 2x$ 4. $y \ge \frac{1}{2} - 3x$ 5. $y \le -x + 1$ 6. $y \ge 2 - x$

Page 406 **P-1** -2.9, 12, 473, etc. **P-2** -3 **P-3** -3, -2.7, 5, etc. **P-4** $(-2, 4)$, $(-1, 3)$, $(0, 2)$, $(1, 1)$, etc.; $(-2, 3)$, $(-1, 2)$, $(0, 1)$, $(1, 0)$, etc.

Page 408 **Classroom Exercises** 1. Yes 3. Yes 5. Yes 7. Yes 9. Yes 11. $y \ge -x$ 13. $y \le \frac{1}{2}x + 1$

Page 409 **Written Exercises** In Written Exercises 1-17, each graph is a region that has a straight line as its only boundary. The boundary is included in the graphs of Ex. 1-15 but not in the graphs of Ex. 17. The location of the region with respect to its boundary is indicated for each exercise. 1. The region is at the right of the boundary. 3. right of boundary 5. right of boundary 7. right of boundary 9. right of boundary 11. right of boundary 13. above boundary 15. left of boundary 17. right of boundary 19. $y \le x + 1$ 21. $y \ge -2x - 2$ 23. $y \le -\frac{1}{3}x + 1$

Page 410 **Mid-Chapter Review** 1. $y < -5x + 2$ 3. $y < \frac{3}{2}x + \frac{5}{2}$ 5. $y < \frac{4}{3}x - \frac{1}{2}$ In Exercises 7-12, each graph is a region that does not include its linear boundary. The location of the region with respect to the boundary is indicated for each exercise. 7. The region is at the left of the boundary. 9. right of the boundary 11. left of the boundary In Exercises 13-18, each graph is a region that has a straight line as its only boundary. The boundary is included in each of the graphs. 13. The region is at the left of the boundary. 15. right of the boundary 17. right of the boundary

Page 410 **Calculator Exercises** 1. Yes 2. Yes 3. Yes

Page 410 **Review Capsule for Section 16.4** 1. $(-2, 3)$, $(-4, 3)$ 2. $(0, -1)$, $(3, 5)$ 3. $(2, -4)$ 4. $(-4, 3)$

Page 411 P-1 3.8, 2, −7, etc. P-2 −1.9, 0, 13, etc. P-3 −1.9, 0, 2, 3.8, etc..

Page 414 Classroom Exercises 1. IV 3. II 5. $\begin{cases} y < x \\ y > -x \end{cases}$ 7. $\begin{cases} y \leq x \\ y \geq -x \end{cases}$

Page 414 Written Exercises In Written Exercises 1-11, each graph is a region with two straight lines as its boundaries. The quadrants that contain the region are indicated, as are the equations of the boundaries.
1. Quadrants: III, IV; Boundaries: Left: $y = x + 1$, Right: $y = -x - 1$; Boundaries not in the graph.
3. Quadrants: I, II, and III; Boundaries: Right: $y = 2x + 1$, Below: $y = -x + 2$; Right boundary in the graph. Below boundary not in the graph. 5. Quadrants: II, III; Boundaries: Above: $x + 2y = 4$, Below: $x - 2y = -4$. Left boundary in the graph. 7. The portion of the line $x - 3y = 3$ that is in Quadrant III and on the Y axis. 9. Quadrants: II and III; Boundaries: Right: $x = -1$, Below: $y = 2$; Right boundary not in the graph. Below boundary in the graph. 11. Quadrants: I, III, and IV; Boundaries: Left: $x = -1$, Below: $y = 3x$; Below boundary in the graph. Left boundary not in the graph.

Page 414 Review Capsule for Section 16.5 1. Yes 2. No 3. Yes 4. No

Page 416 Classroom Exercises 1. B 3. No graph.

Page 416 Written Exercises In Ex. 1-7, the name of the polygon formed by the linear system is given. The coordinates of the vertices of each polygon are also given. 1. Triangle; Vertices: (0, 0), (0, 5), (5, 0)
3. Triangle; Vertices: (2, 2), (−3, 2), (2, −3) 5. Rectangle; Vertices: (−3, 1), (2, 1), (−3, −3), (2, −3)
7. Trapezoid; Vertices: (0, 2), (2, 2), (−4, −2), (6, −2) 9. Maximum value: 24, when $x = 6$ and $y = 0$; Minimum value: 0, when $x = 0$ and $y = 0$ 11. Maximum value: $\frac{2}{3}$, when $x = 0$ and $y = 2$; Minimum value: −2, when $x = 3$ and $y = 0$.

Page 417-418 Career 1. Plant A should produce 7200 calculators and Plant B should produce 3000 calculators. The cost would be $13,410.00.

Pages 419-420 Chapter Review In Ex. 1 and 3, many other answers are possible. 1. (−2, 2), (−1, 2), (0, −2) (1, −4), (2, −4) 3. (−2, −4), (−1, −3), (0, 0), (1, 2), (2, 6) 5. $y \geq 3x - 2$ 7. $y > \frac{1}{3}x + \frac{5}{3}$ In Ex. 9-13, each graph is a region that does not include its linear boundary. The location of the region with respect to the boundary is indicated for each exercise. 9. The region is above the boundary. 11. The region is to the left of the boundary. 13. The region is below the boundary. In Ex. 15-19, each graph is a region that includes its linear boundary. The location of the region with respect to the boundary is indicated for each exercise.
15. The region is above the boundary. 17. The region is above the boundary. 19. The region is above the boundary. In Ex. 21-25, each graph is a region with two straight lines as it boundaries. The quadrants that contain the region are indicated as are the equations of the boundaries. 21. Quadrants: II, III, and IV; Boundaries: Below: $y = -x - 1$, Below: $y = \frac{1}{2}x + 2$; Boundaries not in the graph. 23. Quadrants: II; Boundaries: Left: $x + y = 2$, Right: $2x + y = -3$; Left boundary not in the graph. Right boundary in the graph. 25. Quadrants: I, II, III, IV; Boundaries: Above: $y = -3$, Right: $x = 2$; Above boundary in the graph. Right boundary not in the graph. In Ex. 27-29, the name of the polygon formed by the linear system is given. The coordinates of the vertices of each polygon are given. 27. Triangle; Vertices: (0, 0), (0, 3), (3, 0)
29. Rectangle; Vertices: (−1, −2), (−1, 4), (7, −2), (7, 4) 31. Maximum value: 15, when $x = 5$ and $y = 0$; Minimum value: −15, when $x = -5$ and $y = 0$.

CHAPTER 17 QUADRATIC FUNCTIONS

Page 422 P-1 a. and d.

Page 423 Classroom Exercises 1. Yes 3. No 5. No 7. No 9. No 11. Yes 13. Yes 15. No

Page 424 Written Exercises 1. No 3. Yes 5. No 7. Yes 9. No 11. Yes 13. $(-3, -9)$, $(-1, -1)$, $(2, -4)$ 15. $(-3, 4)$, $(-1, 0)$, $(2, 9)$ 17. $(-3, 6)$, $(-1, -2)$, $(2, 1)$ 19. $(-3, -9)$, $(-1, 1)$, $(2, -14)$ 21. $7; -3; 12$ 23. $16; 4; 1$ 25. $-3; -3; 12$

Page 424 Review Capsule for Section 17.2

1.
x	-2	-1	0	1	2
y	1	-2	-3	-2	1

2.
x	-2	-1	0	1	2
y	-2	1	2	1	-2

3.
x	-2	-1	0	1	2
y	4	$1\frac{1}{2}$	0	$-\frac{1}{2}$	0

Page 425 P-1 a. $-1\frac{3}{4}$ b. $2\frac{1}{4}$ c. $-3\frac{3}{4}$ **P-2** $\{y : y \geq -4\}$

Pages 426-427 Classroom Exercises

1.
x	y
-2	4
-1	1
0	0
1	1
2	4

3.
x	y
-2	6
-1	3
0	2
1	3
2	6

5.
x	y
-2	6
-1	1
0	0
1	3
2	10

7. 2 9. $2\frac{1}{4}$ 11. 0, 2 13. $\frac{1}{2}, 1\frac{1}{2}$

Page 427 Written Exercises In Ex. 1-5, each parabola turns at a high point (maximum), or low point (minimum). This point is given for each exercise. 1. Turns at $(0, 1)$; low point 3. Turns at $(1, 4)$; high point 5. Turns at $(1, 2)$; low point In Ex. 7-11, the high or low point and three points on the parabola are given. 7. $(-1, -1)$; $(0, -2)$; $(1, -1)$ Turns at $(0, -2)$; low point 9. $(-1, 0)$; $(-\frac{1}{2}, \frac{1}{4})$; $(0, 0)$ Turns at $(-\frac{1}{2}, \frac{1}{4})$; high point 11. $(2, 2)$; $(3, 1)$; $(4, 2)$ Turns at $(3, 1)$; low point

Page 427 Review Capsule for Section 17.3 1. $a = -1, b = 2, c = -5$ 2. $a = 2, b = -3, c = 1$ 3. $a = \frac{1}{2}, b = -3, c = 7$ 4. $a = -4, b = 0, c = -1$

Pages 428-429 P-1 1. $a = -\frac{5}{2}, b = 0, c = 0$ 2. $a = 3, b = -4, c = -1$ 3. $a = 1, b = 3, c = 0$ **P-2** $y = \frac{1}{2}x^2$; $y = x^2$; $y = 2x^2$ **P-3** $y = -\frac{1}{2}x^2$; $y = -x^2$; $y = -2x^2$

Pages 429-430 Classroom Exercises 1. The point with coordinates $(0, 0)$ 3. Downward 5. $\{y : y \geq 0\}$ 7. downward 9. downward 11. $y = 3x^2$ 13. $y = 0.09x^2$

Pages 430-431 Written Exercises In Ex. 1-9, the graphs are all parabolas which open upward or downward.

1.
x	y	opens
-2	4	upward
-1	1	at
0	0	(0, 0)
1	1	
2	4	

x	y	opens
-4	4	upward
-2	1	at
0	0	(0, 0)
2	1	
4	4	

3.
x	y	opens
-3	$-\frac{9}{2}$	downward
-2	-2	at
0	0	(0, 0)
2	-2	
3	$-\frac{9}{2}$	

x	y	opens
-2	-6	downward
-1	$-\frac{3}{2}$	at
0	0	(0, 0)
1	$-\frac{3}{2}$	
2	-6	

5.

x	y	opens
-2	-8	downward
-1	-2	at
0	0	(0, 0)
1	-2	
2	-8	

x	y	opens
-2	6	upward
-1	$\frac{3}{2}$	at
0	0	(0, 0)
1	$\frac{3}{2}$	
2	6	

7.

x	y	opens
-2	2	upward
-1	$\frac{1}{2}$	at
0	0	(0, 0)
1	$\frac{1}{2}$	
2	2	

x	y	opens
-2	0	upward
-1	$-\frac{3}{2}$	at
0	-2	(0, -2)
1	$-\frac{3}{2}$	
2	0	

9.

x	y	opens
-4	-12	downward
-2	-3	at
0	0	(0, 0)
2	-3	
4	-12	

x	y	opens
-4	-11	downward
-2	-2	at
0	1	(0, 1)
2	-2	
4	-11	

In Ex. 11 and 13, the parabolas open at the origin to the right or to the left of the Y axis.

11.

x	y	opens
1	1	to the
1	-1	right
0	0	
4	2	
4	-2	

13.

x	y	opens
2	1	to the
2	-1	right
0	0	
8	2	
8	-2	

Page 431 Review Capsule for Section 17.4 1. $x^2 - 4x + 4$ 2. $x^2 + 6x + 9$ 3. $x^2 - 10x + 25$ 4. $x^2 + 12x + 36$ 5. $x^2 + 4.2x + 4.41$ 6. $x^2 - 5.4x + 7.29$

Page 432 P-1 $a = \frac{1}{2}, b = -2, c = 2$

Page 434 Classroom Exercises 1. 2 units right   3. 1 unit right   5. 2 units left   7. 10 units left   9. 7 units right   11. 6 units left

Page 434 Written Exercises 1. 5 units right   3. 8 units left   5. $3\frac{1}{2}$ units left   7. 2.7 units right   9. Second parabola is 2 units to left of first.   11. Second parabola is 3 units to right of first.   13. Second parabola is $\frac{3}{2}$ units to left of first.   15. Second parabola is 2 units to right of first.   17. Second parabola is 1 unit to left of first.

Page 435 Mid-Chapter Review 1. $f(-2) = 4$; $f(-1) = 2\frac{1}{2}$; $f(0) = 0$; $f(1) = -3\frac{1}{2}$; $f(2) = -8$ 3. $f(-2) = -1$; $f(-1) = -3$; $f(0) = -3$; $f(1) = -1$; $f(2) = 3$ In Ex. 5, the high point and three points on the parabola are given.   5. $(-1, 1\frac{1}{2})$; $(0, 2)$; $(1, 1\frac{1}{2})$ Turns at $(0, 2)$; high point.   In Ex. 7-11, the graphs are all parabolas which open upward or downward.

7.

x	y	opens
-4	12	upward
-2	3	at
0	0	(0, 0)
2	3	
4	12	

x	y	opens
-4	-12	downward
-2	-3	at
0	0	(0, 0)
2	-3	
4	12	

9.

x	y	opens
-2	8	upward
-1	2	at
0	0	(0, 0)
1	2	
2	8	

x	y	opens
-2	2	upward
-1	$\frac{1}{2}$	at
0	0	(0, 0)
1	$\frac{1}{2}$	
2	2	

11.

x	y
−2	−10
−1	−4
0	−2
1	−4
2	−10

opens downward at (0, −2)

x	y
−2	3
−1	$1\frac{1}{2}$
0	1
1	$1\frac{1}{2}$
2	3

opens upward at (0, 1)

13. 5 units to the right

15. 4 units to the left

Page 435 Calculator Exercises 1. 75 3. −149.36531

Page 435 Review Capsule for Section 17.5 1. $g(-2) = 9$; $g(0) = 3$; $g(2) = 1$ 2. $g(-2) = -5$; $g(0) = -5$; $g(2) = -21$

Pages 436-438 P-1 Quadratic **P-2** 2 units up **P-3** Move 3 units right and 2 units up. **P-4** 3 units down **P-5** Move 4 units left and 3 units down. **P-6** If h is positive, it is to the right. If h is negative, it is to the left. **P-7** If k is positive, it is above. If k is negative, it is below.

Page 438 Classroom Exercises 1. Yes 3. No 5. Yes 7. a 9. k 11. 5 units right, 2 units down 13. 2 units left, 3 units down 15. 1 unit left, 1 unit down

Page 439 Written Exercises In Ex. 1-7, the relationship between the first and second parabola is given.
1. Moves 3 units up, 2 units right. 3. Moves 2 units up, 3 units left. 5. Moves 3 units down, 1 unit left.
7. Moves $2\frac{1}{2}$ units up, $3\frac{1}{2}$ units right. 9. $y = 2(x - 3)^2$ 11. $y = \frac{1}{2}(x + 2)^2 + 5$ 13. $y = \frac{1}{3}(x + 1)^2 - 5$
15. $y = -(x - 3)^2 - 2$ 17. $y = 3x^2 - 5$

Page 439 Review Capsule for Section 17.6 1. 4; $(x - 2)(x - 2)$ 2. 9; $(x + 3)(x + 3)$ 3. $\frac{1}{4}$; $(x + \frac{1}{2})(x + \frac{1}{2})$
4. $\frac{9}{4}$; $(x - \frac{3}{2})(x - \frac{3}{2})$ 5. 25; $(x + 5)(x + 5)$ 6. 81; $(x + 9)(x + 9)$ 7. $\frac{25}{4}$; $(x - \frac{5}{2})(x - \frac{5}{2})$ 8. $\frac{49}{4}$; $(x - \frac{7}{2})(x - \frac{7}{2})$

Page 440 P-1 a. $a = -1, h = -3, k = -\frac{3}{4}$ b. $a = \frac{3}{2}, h = \frac{1}{4}, k = \frac{5}{4}$

Page 441 Classroom Exercises 1. $(x + 1)^2$ 3. $(x - 3)^2$ 5. $(x + \frac{1}{2})^2$ 7. $(x - \frac{5}{2})^2$

Page 441 Written Exercises 1. $x^2 - 6x + 11$ 3. $2x^2 - 4x - 5$ 5. $3x^2 + 12x + 15$ 7. $\frac{1}{2}x^2 - 2x + 8$
9. $(x - (-1))^2 + 2$ 11. $(x - 2)^2 - 3$ 13. $(x - (-3))^2 - 14$ 15. $(x - 5)^2 - 26$ 17. $(x - \frac{1}{2})^2 + \frac{19}{4}$
19. $(x - (-\frac{3}{2}))^2 - \frac{25}{4}$

Page 441 Review Capsule for Section 17.7 1. $a = 3$; $h = 2$; $k = 1$ 2. $a = 4$; $h = 5$; $k = -2$ 3. $a = \frac{1}{2}$; $h = -\frac{3}{2}$; $k = -5$

Pages 442-443 P-1 Lowest point **P-2** $\frac{1}{2}$; 2; 3 **P-3** a. $(\frac{1}{2}, \frac{5}{2})$ b. $(-3, -7)$ **P-4** $x = 2$ **P-5** a. $h = 5$ b. $h = -3$ c. $h = \frac{1}{4}$ d. $h = -\frac{4}{3}$ **P-6** $(-3, -2)$

Pages 443-444 Classroom Exercises 1. $(5, 2)$ 3. $(-2, 6)$ 5. $(0, 0)$ 7. $(\frac{1}{2}, \frac{3}{4})$ 9. $(5, 0)$ 11. $x = -1$
13. $x = \frac{1}{2}$ 15. $x = 0$ 17. $x = 0$

Page 444 Written Exercises 1. $(1, 10)$ 3. $(7, -2)$ 5. $(-2, 3)$ 7. $(-1, -8)$ 9. $(\frac{1}{2}, -\frac{2}{3})$ 11. $x = 5$ 13. $x = 3$ 15. $x = -1$ 17. $x = \frac{1}{3}$ 19. $x = -\frac{7}{2}$ 21. $x = -\frac{1}{10}$

Page 445 Special Topic Application 1. $s = 1102.5$ meters   3. 314 meters

Pages 446-448 Chapter Review 1. No   3. $-5; -1; -11$ 5. Turns at $(0, -1)$; low point $(-1, 0)$; $(0, -1)$; $(1, 0)$ 7. Turns at $(1, \frac{1}{2})$; high point $(0, 0)$; $(1, \frac{1}{2})$; $(2, 0)$ 9. Turns at $(-1, -4)$; low point $(-2, -3)$; $(-1, -4)$; $(0, -3)$ In Ex. 11 and 13, three points are given for each parabola and the point at which it opens.
11. $(-1, -\frac{1}{2})$; $(0, 0)$; $(1, -\frac{1}{2})$. $(-1, -2)$; $(0, 0)$; $(1, -2)$; both downward at $(0, 0)$ 13. $(-1, \frac{5}{2})$; $(0, 0)$; $(1, \frac{5}{2})$; upward at $(0, 0)$. $(-1, -\frac{5}{2})$; $(0, 0)$; $(1, -\frac{5}{2})$; downward at $(0, 0)$.   15. $(\frac{1}{2}, -1)$; $(0, 0)$; $(\frac{1}{2}, 1)$ Turns right at $(0, 0)$.
17. $(-1, -1)$; $(0, 0)$; $(-1, 1)$ Turns left at $(0, 0)$ 19. 3 units left   21. $\frac{5}{2}$ units right   In Ex. 23 and 25, the relationship between the first and second parabola is given.   23. Moves 2 units down, 3 units right.   25. Moves 3 units up, 1 unit left.   27. $y = -10(x + 5)^2$ 29. $y = \frac{5}{2}(x - 2)^2 - 3$ 31. $x^2 + 2x - 4$ 33. $-3x^2 + 12x - 11$
35. $\frac{1}{2}x^2 + 4x$ 37. $(x - 3)^2 - 7$ 39. $(x - (-\frac{3}{2}))^2 - \frac{5}{2}$ 41. $(x - 1)^2 - \frac{1}{2}$ 43. $(10, 5)$ 45. $(6, 0)$ 47. $x = 2$
49. $x = -\frac{9}{2}$

CHAPTER 18 QUADRATIC EQUATIONS

Page 450 P-1 $-1, 2$

Pages 451-452 Classroom Exercises 1. $x^2 - 2x - 3 = 0$ 3. $3x^2 - 5x + 6 = 0$ 5. $x^2 + 2x + 4 = 0$ 7. 1, 3
9. 0, 4   11. 2

Page 452 Written Exercises 1. $x^2 - 5x + 3 = 0$ 3. $2x^2 - 5x + 10 = 0$ 5. $x^2 - 9 = 0$ 7. $-3, 1$ 9. -3.4, 1.4   11. No real truth numbers.   13. No real truth numbers.   15. 2   17. 0.6, 3.4

Page 452 Review Capsule for Section 18.2 1. $(x - 6)(x + 2)$ 2. $(x - 5)(x - 2)$ 3. $(x - 6)(x + 4)$
4. $(x + 8)(x - 7)$ 5. $(2x - 1)(x + 4)$ 6. $(3x - 2)(x - 1)$ 7. $(7 + x)(1 - x)$ 8. $(9x - 2)(x - 7)$

Page 453 P-1 $-5; 2$

Page 455 Classroom Exercises 1. $\{3, -5\}$ 3. $\{6, -6\}$ 5. $\{-4, -7\}$ 7. $\{\frac{1}{2}, -5\}$ 9. $\{-\frac{3}{2}, -1\}$

Page 455 Written Exercises 1. $\{0, -3\}$ 3. $\{5, -5\}$ 5. $\{0, 10\}$ 7. $\{10, -10\}$ 9. $\{-5, 1\}$ 11. $\{-4, 1\}$
13. $\{-4\}$ 15. $\{2\}$ 17. $\{2, 6\}$ 19. $\{3, 8\}$ 21. $\{-9\}$ 23. $\{-8, 9\}$ 25. $\{-3, \frac{1}{3}\}$ 27. $\{-\frac{2}{3}, \frac{1}{2}\}$
29. $\{-\frac{4}{3}, \frac{1}{4}\}$ 31. $\{-\frac{5}{4}, \frac{1}{2}\}$ 33. $\{-\frac{5}{2}, 9\}$ 35. $\{-1, \frac{3}{4}\}$

Pages 456-457 P-1 a. 4, -4 b. 7, -7 c. 10, -10 **P-2** -5 **P-3** 1; 16; 16; 16

Pages 457-458 Classroom Exercises 1. $\{1, -1\}$ 3. $\{11, -11\}$ 5. $x - 6 = 6$ or $x - 6 = -6$ 7. $x - \frac{1}{2} = 4$
or $x - \frac{1}{2} = -4$ 9. 4; 2; No   11. 25; 25; Yes   13. $\frac{9}{4}; \frac{3}{4};$ No   15. $x + 10, x + 10$ 17. $x - \frac{1}{4}, x - \frac{1}{4}$
19. $x - \frac{3}{2}, x - \frac{3}{2}$

Page 458 Written Exercises 1. 3, −3 3. 13, −13 5. $\sqrt{7}, -\sqrt{7}$ 7. $5\sqrt{3}, -5\sqrt{3}$ 9. $x - 5 = 6$ or $x - 5$ $= -6$ 11. $x + 6 = 5$ or $x + 6 = -5$ 13. $x + \frac{1}{2} = \frac{1}{2}$ or $x + \frac{1}{2} = -\frac{1}{2}$ 15. −12, 10 17. $\{3 + \sqrt{5}, 3 - \sqrt{5}\}$ 19. $\{0, 1\}$ 21. $\left\{-\frac{2}{3} + \frac{\sqrt{5}}{3}, -\frac{2}{3} - \frac{\sqrt{5}}{3}\right\}$ 23. $\{-4\}$ 25. $\{5\}$ 27. $\left\{\frac{1}{4}\right\}$ 29. $\left\{\frac{2}{5}\right\}$ 31. 25 33. 16 35. 3

Page 459 Mid-Chapter Review 1. −4, 1 3. 1.4, −4.4 5. 0.6, −3.6 7. $\frac{1}{2}$, −5 9. $-\frac{1}{3}$, 1 11. $-\frac{1}{3}, -\frac{1}{2}$ 13. −9, 15 15. −1, 2 17. −2, −8

Page 459 Calculator Exercises 1. 2.5572611 3. 3.7002175 5. 2.8314161 7. 10.512436

Page 459 Review Capsule for Section 18.4 1. $x^2 - 6x = -3$ 2. $x^2 + 5x = 4$ 3. $x^2 - 4x = -10$ 4. $2x^2 - x = -3$ 5. $2x^2 - 4x = -5$ 6. $2x^2 + 3x = 10$

Page 462 Classroom Exercises 1. 4 3. 1 5. $\frac{1}{4}$ 7. $\frac{1}{36}$ 9. $\frac{\sqrt{3}}{2}, -\frac{\sqrt{3}}{2}$ 11. $\frac{\sqrt{5}}{2}, -\frac{\sqrt{5}}{2}$ 13. $\frac{1}{2} + \frac{\sqrt{3}}{2},$ $\frac{1}{2} - \frac{\sqrt{3}}{2}$ 15. $x + 9, x + 9$ 17. $x + \frac{3}{2}, x + \frac{3}{2}$ 19. $x - \frac{1}{5}, x - \frac{1}{5}$

Page 462 Written Exercises 1. $\{-3, 5\}$ 3. $\{-5, 1\}$ 5. $\{-3, 2\}$ 7. $\left\{-1 + \sqrt{6}, -1 - \sqrt{6}\right\}$ 9. ϕ 11. $\left\{3 + \sqrt{14}, 3 - \sqrt{14}\right\}$ 13. $\left\{-4 + \sqrt{3}, -4 - \sqrt{3}\right\}$ 15. $\left\{\frac{3}{2} + \frac{\sqrt{13}}{2}, \frac{3}{2} - \frac{\sqrt{13}}{2}\right\}$ 17. $\left\{-\frac{3}{2} + \frac{\sqrt{29}}{2},\right.$ $\left.-\frac{3}{2} - \frac{\sqrt{29}}{2}\right\}$ 19. $\left\{-\frac{1}{5} + \frac{\sqrt{6}}{5}, -\frac{1}{5} - \frac{\sqrt{6}}{5}\right\}$ 21. $\left\{-\frac{3}{2}, 1\right\}$ 23. $\left\{-\frac{1}{3}, 2\right\}$ 25. $\left\{1 + \frac{\sqrt{3}}{3}, 1 - \frac{\sqrt{3}}{3}\right\}$ 27. $\left\{\frac{1}{4} + \frac{\sqrt{41}}{4}, \frac{1}{4} - \frac{\sqrt{41}}{4}\right\}$

Page 462 Review Capsule for Section 18.5 1. $\frac{5}{2}$; −1 2. 2; −4 3. $\frac{2 + \sqrt{6}}{4}, \frac{2 - \sqrt{6}}{4}$

Page 465 Classroom Exercises 1. $a = 1, b = 3, c = -2$ 3. $a = 1, b = 5, c = 0$ 5. $a = 1, b = 3, c = 5$

Page 465 Written Exercises 1. $\{-6, 1\}$ 3. $\{-7, 1\}$ 5. $\{2, 5\}$ 7. $\{-2, 6\}$ 9. $\{3\}$ 11. $\left\{-\frac{2}{3}, \frac{1}{2}\right\}$ 13. $\left\{\sqrt{3}, -\sqrt{3}\right\}$ 15. $\{0, 6\}$ 17. $\left\{\frac{3 + \sqrt{29}}{10}, \frac{3 - \sqrt{29}}{10}\right\}$ 19. $\{0.4, -2.4\}$ 21. $\{1.8, -0.3\}$ 23. $\{2.4, 0.6\}$

Page 465 Review Capsule for Section 18.6 1. 33 2. −71 3. 44

Pages 466-467 P-1 −4, 3 **P-2** $a = 1, b = 1, c = -12$ **P-3** 49 **P-4** Rational **P-5** $\sqrt{5}, -\sqrt{5}$ **P-6** $a = 1,$ $b = 0, c = -5$ **P-7** 20 **P-8** Irrational **P-9** 2 **P-10** $a = 1, b = -4, c = 4$ **P-11** 0 **P-12** There are no real truth numbers. **P-13** $a = 1, b = 0, c = 4$ **P-14** −16 **P-15** Not real **P-16** a. Rational b. Irrational c. Not real d. Rational

Page 468 Classroom Exercises 1. Rational 3. Rational 5. Irrational 7. Rational 9. Irrational 11. Rational 13. 9 15. 1 17. −64 19. 17 21. −3

Page 468 Written Exercises 1. 25; Rational 3. 36; Rational 5. 17; Irrational 7. 0; Rational 9. 28; Irrational 11. −100; Not real 13. 49; Rational 15. 100; Rational 17. 4; Rational 19. −24; Not real 21. 9; Rational 23. 141; Irrational 25. 180; Irrational 27. 5; Irrational

Page 468 Review Capsule for Section 18.7 1. $x^2 - 4x - 78 = 0$ 2. $2x^2 + 5x - 102 = 0$ 3. $2x^2 - x - 128 = 0$

Page 470 Classroom Exercises 1. $n(n + 1) = 210$ 3. $n(n + 3) = 108$ 5. $n(n + 5) = 24$ 7. $n^2 = 9n^2 - 18$

Page 471 Written Exercises 1. Length: 10, Width: 8   3. 5 and 6, −6 and −5   5. −8 and 5; −5 and 8
7. 10 units

Page 472 Career   1. When r = 3.7, S = 277.3. When r = 3.8, S = 277.0. When r = 3.9, S = 277.1. Thus, to the
nearest tenth, 3.8 is the value of r corresponding to the smallest value of S.

Pages 473-474 Chapter Review 1. $x^2 + 5x − 2 = 0$ 3. −1.7, 1.7   5. −1, 10   7. 0, −5   9. 19, −19
11. −2, 10   13. $−\frac{3}{4}, 1$ 15. $−\frac{1}{3}, \frac{1}{2}$ 17. 0; Rational   19. 76; Irrational   21. 2 and 8

Cumulative Review: Chapters 13-18   1. 8 and 19   3. 4 shirts and 5 ties   5. 94   7. 750 km/hr in still air;
25 km/hr speed of wind   9. 66 gm of 2% acid; 44 gm of $4\frac{1}{2}$%   11. 0   13. $−\frac{3}{2}$ 15. $\frac{x}{5}$ 17. $\frac{2}{5}$ 19. $\frac{2}{3}$
21. $\frac{2}{5}$ 23. $\frac{4x}{x−3}$ 25. $\frac{3}{2y}$ 27. $\frac{x}{x−3}$ 29. $\frac{1}{3x^2}$ 31. $\frac{2}{x}$ 33. $\frac{12x}{2x−3}$ 35. $\frac{4x+7}{x+4}$ 37. $12x^2y^2$
39. $(x − 3)^2(x + 3)$ 41. $\frac{8 −.5x}{6x^2}$ 43. $\frac{x^2 + 7x + 6}{x(x + 3)}$ 45. $\frac{7}{6(x − 3)}$ 47. x = 2   49. x = 1   51. $y < 2x − 8$
In Ex. 53-56, the graph is a region with a straight line as its boundary.   53. Above $y = −\frac{1}{2}x + 1$; Boundary is
not included.   55. Below y = x − 2; Boundary is included.   In Ex. 57-59, each graph is a region with two
straight lines as its boundaries. The quadrants that contain the region are indicated as are the equations of the
boundaries.   57. Quadrants I, II, III, IV; Boundaries: Below y = −x + 1; Right of y = 2x + 3; Boundaries are
included.   59. Quadrants: I and IV; Boundaries: Right of $y = \frac{3}{2}x + 1$, Below $y = \frac{2}{3}x − 2$; Boundaries are not
included.   In Ex. 60-63, each graph is a region with three straight lines as its boundaries.   61. Quadrants: I,
II, III, IV; Below y = −x + 2; Right of x = 1; Above y = −1; Boundaries are included.   63. (−2, 9), (0, −3),
(3, −9)   For Ex. 65, the lowest point of the graph is given. Then two other points are given.
65. Lowest point: (0, 1); (1, 2), (−1, 2)   In Ex. 67, the graph is a parabola which opens upward
as indicated.

67.

x	y	Upward
−2	2	at
−1	$\frac{1}{2}$	(0, 0)
0	0	
1	$\frac{1}{2}$	
2	2	

x	y	Upward
−2	4	at
−1	1	(0, 0)
0	0	
1	1	
2	4	

69. 3 units right   71. 2 units left   73. $y = \frac{5}{2}(x + 1)^2 + 6$
75. $(x − (−1))^2 − 6$ 77. $(x − 3)^2 − 14$ 79. (2, 1)
81. −4, 2   83. −3, 1   85. 0, 5   87. −3, 4
89. $5, −\frac{1}{2}$ 91. −15, 5   93. $2 + \sqrt{7}, 2 − \sqrt{7}$
95. $\frac{5}{2} + \sqrt{7}, \frac{5}{2} − \sqrt{7}$ 97. $−3, \frac{1}{3}$ 99. 61; Irrational
101. 120; Irrational   103. 5 and 7; −7 and −5

APPENDIX

Page 480 Exercises 1. Yes   2. Yes   3. No   4. Yes   5. No   6. No   7. No   8. Yes   9. Yes   10. No
11. Yes   12. No   13. Yes   14. No   15. No   16. Yes   17. Yes   18. No   19. Yes   20. No   21. Yes
22. Yes   23. No   24. No   25. No   26. Yes   27. Yes   28. 11   29. −5   30. 17   31. 10   32. 2
33. 3   34. 5   35. 8   36. 13   37. 21   38. 34   39. 55   40. 1, 1, 2, 3, 5   41. 8, 13, 21, 34, 55   For
Exercises 42-45, blanks are given in place of the many number combinations that may be supplied by the
students.

42. 10 LET A = ___
20 LET B = ___
30 LET S = A + B
40 PRINT A, B, S
50 END

43. 10 LET R = ___
20 LET S = ___
30 LET S1 = R + S
40 PRINT R, S, S1
50 END

44. 10 LET E = ___
20 LET F = ___
30 LET D = E − F
40 PRINT D
50 END

45. 5 LET P = ___
10 LET Q = ___
15 LET Y = Q − P
20 PRINT Y
25 END

Page 482 **Exercises** 1. 14 2. 1 3. 12.6 4. 18.4 5. 14.9 6. 8.1 7. 15 8. 3 9. −5 10. 48
11. −1.0 12. −2.5 13. 18.6 14. 5.4 15. −4 16. −6 17. 5.4 18. 6.9 19. 25 20. 36 21. −1
22. 0 23. 6 24. 6 25. 24 26. −2 27. 2 * Y 28. 27 * A 29. R ↑ 3 30. B ↑ 4 31. A * (B + C)
32. (R + S) * T 33. X * Y/2 34. A/B * C 35. 2 * X ↑ 3 36. 5 * W ↑ 2 37. A * B * C ↑ 2
38. 1Ø * X * Y ↑ 3 39. (X + Y) ↑ 5 40. (A − B) ↑ 6 41. A + 2 * (B − C) ↑ 2 42. 6.6 43. 3.21
44. −2.7 45. 40.8321 46. 0.72 47. 2.7 48.

```
1Ø LET L = 5.6
2Ø LET W = 4.3
3Ø LET P = 2 *(L + W)
4Ø PRINT P
5Ø END
```

49.

```
1Ø LET B = 12.3
2Ø LET H = 6
3Ø LET A = B * H/2
4Ø PRINT A
5Ø END
```

Page 485 **Exercises** 1. 10, 15 2. 1.8, 3.1 3. 7, −4 4. 6, 25 5. 3, −16 6. 20, 45, 80 7. 9, 1, 4, 25
8. −8, −1, 8, 27 9. 15.4, 3.4 10. 25.5, −3.9 11. −0.428571, −1.75, −0.5 12. 3.33333, 4.77272,
2.7888 13. 15, 7 14.

```
1Ø READ D
2Ø DATA 12, Ø.56, 2.85
3Ø C = 3.14 * D
4Ø PRINT C
5Ø GO TO 1Ø
6Ø END
```

Page 487 **Exercises** 1. −1, −3, −5, −7, −9, −11 2. 15, 12, 9, 6, 3, Ø, −3, −6, −9 3. 1, −1, −5, −13, −29
4. 1, 2, −1, 8, −19 5. −17, −13, −9, −5, −1, 3, 7 6. −1Ø, −6, −2, 2, 6, 1Ø, 14 7. 1 8. −6, −1Ø, −1
9.
```
1Ø LET X = 1Ø
2Ø PRINT X
3Ø LET X = X − 1
4Ø IF X >= Ø THEN 2Ø
5Ø END
```
10.
```
1Ø LET N = −6
2Ø PRINT N
3Ø LET N = N − 2
4Ø IF N >= −22 THEN 2Ø
5Ø END
```
11.
```
4Ø IF N <= 63 THEN 2Ø
5Ø END
```
12.
```
4Ø IF N >= −63 THEN 2Ø
5Ø END
```

Page 489 **Exercises** 1. −6, −3, Ø, 3 2. 1, 3, 5 3. 2.4, 2.5, 2.6, 2.7, 2.8, 2.9, 3 4. Ø, −Ø.5, −1, −1.5, −2,
−2.5, −3, −3.5, −4 5. 1, 4, 9, 16, 25 6. 4, 1, Ø, 1, 4 7. 12, 4, Ø, Ø, 4 8. −2.5, −1Ø.5, −24.5, −44.5,
−7Ø.5 9. −2Ø, −12, −6, −2, Ø, Ø 10. 3Ø, 1Ø, 2, Ø 11. Ø, Ø.44, Ø.96, 1.56, 2.24, 3 12. Ø, −Ø.25, −1,
−2.25, −4, −6.25, −9
13.
```
1Ø FOR X = −3 TO 3
2Ø LET X = 2 * X + 5
3Ø PRINT Y
4Ø NEXT X
5Ø END
```
The programs for Exercises 14-18 are identical to the
program for Exercise 13 except for line 2Ø. Line 2Ø
is given.

14. 2Ø LET Y = 3 * X − 4 15. 2Ø LET Y = X ↑ 2 − 2 * X + 1 16. 2Ø LET Y = −X ↑ 2 + 5 * X − 2
17. 2Ø LET Y = (X − 2) *(X + 3) 18. 2Ø LET Y = (X + 1) * (X − 5)

B 2
C 3
D 4
E 5
F 6
G 7
H 8
I 9
J 0